Text, Reader, Critic

Introducing Contexts and Interpretations

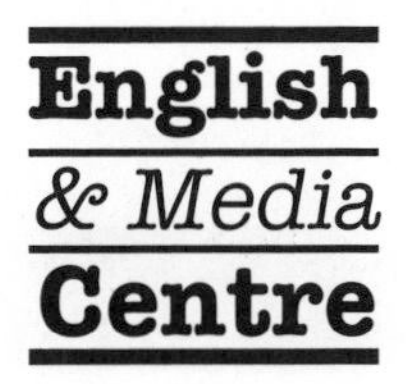

English
& Media
Centre

Written by: Jane Ogborn and Lucy Webster with Barbara Bleiman

Edited by: Barbara Bleiman and Lucy Webster
Editorial assistance: Lisa Hallgarten
Design: Eamonn England
Additional design: Fran Stowell
Cover: Blaise Thompson

Printed by: Redwood Books
Published by: The English & Media Centre, 18 Compton Terrace, London N1 2UN
© 2000
ISBN: 0907016 69 3

Thanks to: Richard Exton and the ILEA Summer School programme; Richard Jacobs;
Jenny Stevens and Tim Seward for additional material. Jane Miller and Peter
Buckroyd for their helpful comments and support.

Acknowledgements

Thanks to: David Higham Associates for an extract from *In Search of Our Mother's Gardens* by Alice Walker (Women's Press); The Estate of Angela Carter c/o Rogers, Coleridge & White Ltd, 20 Powis Mews, London W11 1JN for an extract from 'Charlotte Bronte: Jane Eyre' from *Expletives Deleted* by Angela Carter; Faber and Faber for 'Everything that Rises Must Converge' from *The Complete Stories of Flannery O'Connor*, an extract from 'Strugnells Sonnets' from *Making Cocoa for Kingsley Amis* by Wendy Cope, an extract from *Killing Time* by Simon Armitage and *Request Stop* by Harold Pinter; Macmillan for an extract from *The Silent Woman* by Janet Malcolm; Oxford University Press for extracts from *Faultlines: Cultural Materialism and the Politics of Dissident Reading* by Alan Sinfield, 1992; Penguin Books for an extract from *Bitter Fame: A Life of Sylvia Plath* by Anne Stevenson (©Anne Stevenson, 1989); Peterloo Poets for 'The Donkey' by U.A. Fanthorpe; PFD on behalf of Ronald Hayman for an extract from *The Death and Life of Sylvia Plath* (Minerva); Philip Allan Updates for extracts from 'English in Crisis' by Terry Eagleton from *The English Review;* The Random House group for: 'Cat in The Rain' from *The Short Stories of Ernest Hemingway,* Jonathon Cape, and extracts from *The Common Pursuit* by F.R. Leavis (Hogarth Press); *Culture and Imperialism* by Edward Said (Chatto & Windus); *Why Read the Classics* by Italo Calvino, and *Small World* by David Lodge (Secker and Warburg); Simon & Schuster for 'Embroidery' from *The Golden Apples of the Sun* by Ray Bradbury; Taylor & Francis/Routledge for an extract from *A Beginners' Guide to Critical Reading: an anthology of Literary Texts* by Richard Jacobs; an extract from *The Self-Conceived* by Helène Moglen (Norton); *The Guardian* for several extracts and articles; *The Times Literary Supplement*; *The Financial Times; The London Review of Books.* Every effort has been made to trace and acknowledge copyright but if any accidental infringment has been made we would welcome information to redress the situation.

Contents

Introduction

Section 1 – short activities

Section 2 – extended activities

Appendices

Teachers' notes   118

Website

Additional resources to complement the resources in the pack can be found in the Teaching Materials section of the English and Media Centre website (www.englishandmedia.co.uk)

Unit 8:   Extracts from *Why Read the Classics?* by Italo Calvino (TRCunit8.doc)
Unit 11:   An extract from *The Self Conceived* by Hélène Moglen (TRCunit11.doc)
Unit 13:   An interview with Matthew Bourne, director of Adventure in Motion Pictures on his all male adaptation of *Swan Lake* (TRCunit13.doc).

Introduction

EMC Advanced Literature Series

EMC Advanced Literature Series is a resource for A Level English Literature (and elements of Language and Literature). It is designed to meet the requirements of the new AS/A2 specifications for 2000 in challenging, innovative and practical ways. Each publication includes:

- texts for study, both literary texts and extracts from literary criticism
- student activities
- teachers' notes, with additional guidance, support and suggestions for extension activities and other useful sources of ideas and information.

Text, Reader, Critic

This publication focuses particularly on the changed emphases implied by the requirement for assessment of the students' ability to:

- respond with knowledge and understanding to literary texts of different types and periods (AO2i)
- explore and comment on relationships and comparisons between literary texts (AO2ii)
- articulate independent opinions and judgements, informed by different interpretations of literary texts by other readers (AO4)
- show understanding of the contexts in which literary texts are written and understood (AO5i)
- evaluate the significance of cultural, historical and other contextual influences upon literary texts and study (AO5ii).

Despite these shifts towards a greater emphasis on contextual issues and different interpretations, the text remains central. A Level students are still expected to focus primarily on the texts set for study in each module, and to:

- read closely and carefully
- get to know the text really well
- get below the surface and between the lines
- interpret and make meanings
- see patterns – big ones and small ones
- make links with other things they have read
- be alert to ways writers choose to use language.

Personal responses, critical readings

This priority is reflected in the approaches and materials used in the pack. It is not intended to be a course in 'Literary Theory'. The texts and related activities have been chosen to support the students' development of a genuine personal response to texts, by introducing 'different interpretations by other readers' which go beyond the sharing of responses within the peer group. The texts and activities provide students with plenty of opportunities to develop close reading skills.

Earlier activities are shorter, introducing students to some of the key ideas relevant to the study of literature at A level:

- the role of the reader
- what readers bring to texts – their knowledge, understanding and implicit or explicit assumptions which they make
- how readers are constructed, by gender, race, class, education and politics
- how readers are positioned, by the text and by its contexts, and by other readers
- the nature of the text.

The ideas explored in Section 2 are more challenging and are therefore more appropriate for A2 students. The activities offer practical, accessible and enjoyable ways of experimenting with different readings, drawing on a variety of theoretical positions. Many of these longer units require students to assimilate, compare and analyse a range of texts and are particularly appropriate for helping students develop the skills demanded by the synoptic papers – both those with unseen texts and those with pre-release and previously studied material.

Different texts will invite different critical approaches. For this reason it is not likely to be helpful to A Level students for teachers to interpret AO4 as an *instruction* to 'teach critics', if by that they understand 'named writers about literature'. AO4 makes it clear that the student's responsibility is to develop her or his own viewpoints about texts, making use of other readers' views to do so. Increasing the students' awareness of how texts can be read differently will be of more use to them than a limited amount of reading of single critics, no matter how distinguished.

The activities, therefore, aim to extend students' abilities to consider and evaluate critically different readings and approaches. In line with all five Assessment Objectives, the pack focuses on an exploration of the text and the relations between writer, text, reader and context. All readers and critics base their readings on these variables, choosing to emphasise particular elements, depending on their view of 'literature' or the theoretical position they favour.

Using the pack

The pack uses different critical approaches, from the 'pure' practical criticism of I.A. Richards to the eclectic methods of modern readers who adopt and adapt the ideas of the post-colonialists, the feminists, psychoanalysts and so on. It does not attempt to consider all the different sub-divisions of recent critical theory – nor even all the major positions of the twentieth century. Theories about narrative for example have not been included; these are considered in the introductory section to *The Modern Novel* (EMC Advanced Literature Series).

The Critical timeline in Appendix 3 (page 113) provides an overview of this critical history, while Appendix 4 (page 117) suggests how this relates to the growth of English as a university and school subject. The intention is not to suggest that the history of criticism is one of unproblematic progress and development. However, the proliferation of different readings and approaches is presented as something to be welcomed. Critical theories such as feminism and post-colonialism, for example, have challenged the assumptions implicit in the work of white, predominantly male readers like Leavis. At the end of the twentieth century one of the positive developments has been the dissolving of the boundaries between critical positions: critics construct a personal framework for reading texts from a whole range of critical theories.

Student activity sheets, which incorporate short pieces of criticism, introduce each unit. Primary texts follow the activities. Students will need access to *Othello* Act 1 scene 3 for Unit 18 and copies of Ted Hughes's poem 'The Rabbit Catcher' and Sylvia Plath's 'The Rabbit Catcher' for Unit 20. The Teachers' Notes outline: the purpose and aim of the unit; practical information about the organisation of the activities; ideas for discussion and some suggestions for extension work. The notes also highlight units which could be used as preparation for the synoptic papers or as a starting point for coursework assignments. For those attempting the A Level extension papers or going on to study English at university, the activities offer an unthreatening introduction to critical theory. Students wanting to investigate theory further could start with some of the books suggested in the reading list in Appendix 2 (page 111).

Section 1
Short Activities

What readers bring to texts

This activity gives you opportunities
● to explore your own reading of a short story
● to think about how this reading is shaped
● to compare your reading with the readings of other people in the class.

Exploring a response to a story
Your teacher will give you four pieces of information about a story you are going to read.

1) The title
2) The first section
3) The author
4) More about the author.

● At each stage, as you learn something new about the story, jot down your response to the following questions:
 – am I going to like this?
 – why?
 – why not?

● Now read the rest of the story, pausing after the places listed below to answer the questions:
 – do I like this story?
 – why?
 – why not?

 i) 'you don't remember faces so much as hands and what they did.'
 ii) They all stared intently at the beautiful scene with the flaw in it.
 iii) 'Nobody knows what it might do when it comes.'
 iv) The woman sighed finally and began to relax.
 v) The end.

Your experiences as a reader
● Look back at your own responses and consider critically the factors which influenced, informed and shaped your response.

 Some possible factors are suggested here:
 i) your experience of reading other short stories (typical patterns of tension and so on)
 ii) your knowledge of the type of stories Ray Bradbury writes
 iii) the context of the story (for example, the time and place in which it is set)
 iv) the context of your reading
 v) your understanding of the ways writers direct the response of the reader
 vi) your experience of how to interpret the associations of words and the significance of metaphors and so on.

Sharing your response
● Share your responses with another person in the class. Make a note of the similarities and differences in your responses. Look particularly at the way you began to piece together your response to the story as a whole, and the way this changed and developed.

- You all read the same words on the page, in the same situation. What do the differences and similarities in the responses suggest about the process of reading and interpretation? You should think about:
  - the reader
  - the writer
  - the text
  - the context (the situation in which you read the story).

- Choose a couple of points where agreement between you is particularly strong. What directed and shaped your responses in these instances? Were the same factors an influence? Could this aspect of the story be interpreted differently? If you think it could, why and by whom? If not, why not?

- Do the same for a couple of points where there is disagreement between you.

Whole class discussion

- Prepare to report back your discoveries to the rest of the class.

- As a class, sum up what you have learned about the reading process. Come up with a list of all the different factors which affect an individual's response to a text. Some of the things you might include are suggested here:
  - knowledge of the genre
  - information about the author
  - an awareness of the historical period.

'Embroidery' by Ray Bradbury

The dark porch air in the late afternoon was full of needle flashes, like a movement of gathered silver insects in the light. The three women's mouths twitched over their work. Their bodies lay back and then imperceptibly forward, so that the rocking chairs tilted and murmured. Each woman looked to her own hands, as if quite suddenly she had found her heart beating there.

'What time is it?'

'Ten minutes to five.'

Got to get up in a minute and shell those peas for dinner.'

'But –' said one of them.

'Oh yes, I forgot. How foolish of me ...' The first woman paused, put down her embroidery and needle, and looked through the open porch door, through the warm interior of the quiet house, to the silent kitchen. There upon the table, seeming more like symbols of domesticity than anything she had ever seen in her life, lay the mound of fresh-washed peas in their neat, resilient jackets, waiting for her fingers to bring them into the world.

'Go hull them if it'll make you feel good,' said the second woman.

'No,' said the first. 'I won't. I just won't.'

The third woman sighed. She embroidered a rose, a leaf, a daisy on a green field. The embroidery needle rose and vanished.

The second woman was working on the finest, most delicate piece of embroidery of them all, deftly poking, finding, and returning the quick needle upon innumerable journeys. Her quick black glance was on each motion. A flower, a man, a road, a sun, a house; the scene grew under hand, a miniature beauty, perfect in every threaded detail.

'It seems at times like this that it's always your hands you turn to,' she said, and the others nodded enough to make the rockers rock again.

'I believe,' said the first lady, 'that our souls are in our hands. For we do *everything* to the world with our hands. Sometimes I think we don't use our hands half enough; it's certain we don't use our heads.'

They all peered more intently at what their hands were doing.

'Yes,' said the third lady, 'when you look back on a whole lifetime, it seems you don't remember faces so much as hands and what they did.'

They recounted to themselves the lids they had lifted, the doors they had opened and shut, the flowers they had picked, the dinners they had made, all with slow or quick fingers, as was their manner or custom. Looking back, you saw a flurry of hands, like a magician's dream, doors popping wide, taps turned, brooms wielded, children spanked. The flutter of pink hands was the only sound; the rest was a dream without voices.

'No supper to fix tonight or tomorrow night or the next night after that,' said the third lady.

'No windows to open or shut.'

'No coal to shovel in the basement furnace next winter.'

'No papers to clip cooking articles out of.'

And suddenly they were crying. The tears rolled softly down their faces and fell into the material upon which their fingers twitched.

'This won't help things,' said the first lady at last, putting the back of her thumb to each under-eyelid. She looked at her thumb and it was wet.

'Now look what I've done!' cried the second lady exasperated. The others stopped and peered over. The second lady held out her embroidery. There was the scene, perfect except that while the embroidered yellow sun shone down upon the embroidered green field, and the embroidered brown road curved toward an embroidered pink house, the man standing on the road had something wrong with his face.

'I'll just have to rip out the whole pattern, practically, to fix it right,' said the second lady.

'What a shame.' They all stared intently at the beautiful scene with the flaw in it.

The second lady began to pick away at the thread with her little deft scissors flashing. The pattern came out thread by thread. She pulled and yanked, almost viciously. The man's face was gone. She continued to seize at the threads.

'What are you *doing*?' asked the other woman.

They leaned and saw what she had done.

The man was gone from the road. She had taken him out entirely.

They said nothing but returned to their own tasks.

'What time is it?' asked someone.

'Five minutes to five.'

'Is it supposed to happen at five o'clock?'

'Yes.'

'And they're not sure what it'll do to anything, really, when it happens?'

'No, not sure.'

'Why didn't we stop them before it got this far and this big?'

'It's twice as big as ever before. No, ten times, maybe a thousand.'

'This isn't like the first one or the dozen later ones. This is different. Nobody knows what it might do when it comes.'

They waited on the porch in the smell of roses and cut grass.

'What time is it now?'

'One minute to five.'

The needles flashed silver fire. They swam like a tiny school of metal fish in the darkening summer air.

Far away a mosquito sound. Then something like a tremor of drums. The three women cocked their heads, listening.

'We won't hear anything, will we?'

'They say not.'

'Perhaps we're foolish. Perhaps we'll go right on, after five o'clock, shelling peas, opening doors, stirring soups, washing dishes, making lunches, peeling oranges ...'

'My, how we'll laugh to think we were frightened by an old experiment!' They smiled a moment at each other.

'It's five o'clock.'

At these words, hushed, they all busied themselves. Their fingers darted. Their faces were turned down to the motions they made. They made frantic patterns. They made lilacs and grass and trees and houses and rivers in the embroidered cloth. They said nothing, but you could hear their breath in the silent porch air.

Thirty seconds passed.

The second woman sighed finally and began to relax.

'I think I just *will* go shell those peas for supper,' she said. 'I ...'

But she hadn't time even to lift her head. Somewhere, at the side of her vision, she saw the world brighten and catch fire. She kept her head down, for she knew what it was. She didn't look up, nor did the others, and in the last instant their fingers were flying; they didn't glance about to see what was happening to the country, the town, this house, or even this porch. They were only staring down at the design in their flickering hands.

The second woman watched an embroidered flower go. She tried to embroider it back in, but it went, and then the road vanished, and the blades of grass. She watched a fire, in slow motion almost, catch upon the embroidered house and unshingle it, and pull each threaded leaf from the small green tree in the hoop, and she saw the sun itself pulled apart in the design. Then the fire caught upon the moving point of the needle while still it flashed; she watched the fire come along her fingers and arms and body, untwisting the yarn of her being so painstakingly that she could see it in all its devilish beauty, yanking out the pattern from the material at hand. What it was doing to the other women or the furniture or the elm tree in the yard, she never knew. For now, yes, now! it was plucking at the white embroidery of her flesh, the pink thread of her cheeks, and at last it found her heart, a soft red rose sewn with fire, and it burned the fresh, embroidered petals away, one by delicate one ...

What is the context of a text?

The aims of this unit are
- to extend your understanding of the different contexts which may throw light on a text, taking this beyond 'historical background'
- to look at the context in which 'texts are written and understood', for example: matters of genre; language; textual production
- to consider the way in which the text is received
- to look at a text in relation to the writer's entire works.

Yesterday's news
- Working in pairs or small groups, jot down some of the songs, television programmes and trends which you associate particularly with the late twentieth and early twenty-first century. A few examples are given here to get you started:
  - Ali G
  - *The Simpsons*
  - Dreamcast
  - *The Royle Family*.

- Choose one of these and annotate it with some of the references, jokes and so on which you think will need explaining in 10, 20 or 50 years time.

A first reading
- On your own, read and jot down your response to the poem 'Killing Time.'

A poem for a particular time
This is an extract from a longer poem by Simon Armitage, written when he was poet in residence with the New Millennium Experience Company.

- Re-read the poem and make a note of how you respond to the poem now that you know when, and for what purpose, it was written. Some things you might consider are suggested here:
  - it is about events set in a particular time
  - it was commissioned (a poem written to order)
  - it is a public poem
  - it is an extract from a longer poem.

- In pairs or small groups, talk about the way your response to the poem and your understanding of it altered.

Understanding the references
The poem is set at a particular time and place in the late twentieth century. It uses an event more normally recounted in newspaper stories to explore life, beliefs and attitudes in twentieth century Britain. This means that readers in the future may need to do some research before they can fully understand what it is about.

- Imagine you are editing the poem for a reader in the year 2050. Work in pairs and highlight the parts of the poem which you think will need explaining. What knowledge does it assume the reader will have?

- Are there any references in the poem which puzzle you or which you don't understand? If there are, stop and consider why this might be.

- Still working in pairs, write the footnotes which you think a reader in 2050 will need.

The contexts of the poem
- Working in small groups, compare the footnotes you have written and spend a few minutes talking about what different people think will need contextualising in the future.

- Use the details collected to try to classify the contexts of this text. Illustrate each one with an example from the poem.

Context	Example	Notes
Historical/political		
Generic (literary conventions)		
Linguistic		
Cultural		
Social/shared values		

- As a class talk about the ways in which the experience of reading a text alters in the following situations:
  - reading a text without knowing the context (political, social and cultural) in which a text is written
  - reading a text when the references are familiar – 'natural'
  - reading a text in conjunction with footnotes.

Writing for the moment
- Write your own section of a poem in the style of Simon Armitage's 'Killing Time'. Focus it on one of the following:
  - an area of life you feel you are an expert on, for example, club culture
  - a current cultural trend, for example, fashion or music
  - what's happening in a soap you watch
  - the week's big news stories and how they are reported.

- Use your poem to explore or comment more generally on life at the beginning of the twenty-first century.

From *Killing Time* – Simon Armitage

Meanwhile, hot air rises.
And the two men held for twenty-one days in living conditions
      decidedly worse
than those in most high security prisons
       are not the victims
of some hard-line, oppressive regime, or political refugees,
     or eco-warriors
digging in on the side of rare toads and ancient trees,
      or dumbstruck hostages,
or Western tourists kidnapped by gun-toting terrorists,
      or moon-eyed murderers
on death row, or self-captivated Turner Prize exhibitionists,
      but balloonists, actually,
jet-streaming the globe, riding the one, continuous corner
      of the world's orb.
In a picnic basket swinging from a bunsen burner
      suspended beneath
a tuppeny rain-hood filled with nothing but ether,
      Messrs Piccard and Jones
hitched a ride on a current of air and lapped the equator
      in less time than it takes the moon
to go through its snowball-cycle of freezing and thawing.
      Think of all the mental energy
and tax dollars pumped into that Stealth bomber thing
      with its invisible paint
and silent engines and non-reflective angles;
      all that fuss
when all along we could have sided with the angels.
      All we have to do,
apparently, is catch the breeze and hold our breath,
      strike a match
and watch the planet going round and round beneath.

Alternative ways of interpreting a text

The exercise encourages you
- to produce as many different readings of a text as possible
- to consider the usefulness of different kinds of contextual information
- to learn to discriminate between relevant and irrelevant additional information.

Reading 'Request Stop'

- Read 'Request Stop' all the way through, to yourself. Annotate it to show your thoughts about the following:
  - where you would expect to come across 'Request Stop'
  - the genre it belongs to
  - the characters
  - what it is about.

- Get into small groups and compare your first ideas.

- Use your ideas as the starting point for doing a workshop performance of 'Request Stop'.

- As you work on your performance, record your initial discussions, including the ideas you decide not to follow up, the disagreements and the reasons for pursuing certain interpretations. If possible, use a tape recorder to do this.

Performing 'Request Stop'

- Take it in turns to perform your version of 'Request Stop' to the rest of the class.

- As you watch the different performances, make a note of what each group has chosen to emphasise.

Alternative interpretations

- As a whole class talk about the different ways people of the same age and in the same situation interpreted this short text. Talk about the factors which influenced and shaped your interpretations, for example:
  - the writer's instructions (stage directions)
  - the language (the choice of words used by the characters)
  - your knowledge of dramatic conventions
  - your knowledge of the time in which it was written
  - your knowledge of contemporary social factors (asylum seekers, care in the community).

- How many other ways of performing this text can you now suggest?

'Request Stop' by Harold Pinter

[*A queue at a Request Bus Stop. A* WOMAN *at the head, with a* SMALL MAN *in a raincoat next to her, two other* WOMEN *and a* MAN.]

WOMAN [*to* SMALL MAN]: I beg your pardon, what did you say?

Pause.

All I asked you was if I could get a bus from here to Shepherds Bush.

Pause.

Nobody asked you to start making insinuations.

Pause.

Who do you think you are?

Pause.

Huh. I know your sort, I know your type. Don't worry, I know all about people like you.

Pause.

We can all tell where you come from. They're putting your sort inside every day of the week.

Pause.

All I've got to do, is report you, and you'd be standing in the dock in next to no time. One of my best friends is a plain clothes detective.

Pause.

I know all about it. Standing there as if butter wouldn't melt in your mouth. Meet you in a dark alley it'd be ... another story. [*To the others, who stare into space.*] You heard what this man said to me. All I asked him was if I could get a bus from here to Shepherds Bush. [*To him.*] I've got witnesses, don't you worry about that.

Pause.

Impertinence.

Pause.

Ask a man a civil question he treats you like a threepenny bit. [*To him.*] I've got better things to do, my lad, I can assure you. I'm not going to stand here and be insulted on a public highway. Anyone can tell you're I foreigner. I was born just around the corner. Anyone can tell you're just up from the country for a bit of a lark. I know your sort.

Pause.

She goes to a LADY.

Excuse me lady. I'm thinking of taking this man up to the magistrate's court, you heard him make that crack, would you like to be a witness?

The LADY *steps into she road.*

LADY: Taxi ...

She disappears.

WOMAN: We know what sort she is. [*Back to position.*] I was the first in this queue.

Pause.

Born just round the corner. Born and bred. These people from the country haven't the faintest idea of how to behave. Peruvians. You're bloody lucky I don't put you on a charge.
You ask a straightforward question –

The others suddenly thrust out their arms at a passing bus. They run off left after it. The WOMAN, *alone, clicks her teeth and mutters. A man walks from the right to the stop, and waits. She looks at him out of the corner of her eye. At length she speaks shyly, hesitantly, with a slight smile.*

Excuse me. Do you know if I can get a bus from here ... to Marble Arch?

How the context of the reading affects interpretations

This activity suggests that
- the meaning of a text is not fixed
- the meaning a reader makes of a text is affected by many contextual factors, including the way in which it is encountered.

Reading two poems

You will be working in pairs on either page 17 or pages 18 and 19.

- Working in pairs, quickly read poem A. Spend no more than five minutes talking about your response to the poem and what you understand it to be about.

- Next, turn to poem B. This is the poem you will be focusing on and you should spend some time reading, annotating and talking about the form, language, structure and themes. You could begin by looking closely at the title and jotting down the expectations it raises.

- On your own, or in pairs, draft a paragraph summing up what you think poem B is about and your reasons for thinking this.

- Compare your ideas about poem B with one or two more pairs who have been working on the same sheet.

Comparing responses

- Join up with another pair who have been working on the other sheet.

- Take it in turns to read and talk through your interpretation of poem B on your sheet. As you listen, make a note of anything which surprises you.

- Compare your responses to poem B. Highlight the differences in your interpretations and use these to explore in more detail what influenced and shaped your reading of the poem. Some ideas to get you started are suggested below:
  - the title of the poem
  - the effect of reading poem B *after* reading poem A.

- Prepare to feed back what you have learned to the rest of the class.

Whole class discussion

- Listen to each group's feedback. Draw together some conclusions about the ways in which an individual's reading of a text is shaped, particularly the relationship between the contexts in which you read, and your interpretations of the text.

Poem A
What the Donkey Saw

Poem B
Nativity

No room in the inn, of course,
And not that much in the stable,
What with the shepherds, Magi, Mary,
Joseph, the heavenly host –
Not to mention the baby
Using our manger as a cot.
You couldn't have squeezed another cherub in
For love or money.

Still, in spite of the overcrowding,
I did my best to make them feel wanted.
I could see the baby and I
Would be going places together.

U.A. Fanthorpe

After two thousand years
The star burned out
The kings froze in history
The angels froze in the bible
The mysteries in tinsel.
When the shepherds heard voices
They knew it was only the wind.

Out of that arctic legend
Only one escaped
On the high horse of power:
Riding the centuries down
His drumming hooves have harried
All others off the roads.
Now he assumes his hour –

And everything that is
Must crawl beneath
The Herod-coloured sky.
He is the lord of all.

His guards lean on the gates
The road is barred
The bullrushes cut down:
Around the derelict fable
His soldiers tighten their net
And now they beat
Hard on the stable door.

Where through the only gate
No magistrate may guard
His enemy leaps in.
He lies in a hollow of straw
Deserted by kings and gods
With only the cows and the sheep
Too silly to get out.

In despite of Herod's curfew
Light stirs in the city.
Because it is pitiful
Pity runs to the child:
Help breaks down the door
Because it has cried for help:
The poor press back the guards.

Bringing whatever is needed
Because it is in need
Because the seed must grow
And the child is the seed.

Poem A
Your Attention Please

YOUR ATTENTION PLEASE –
The polar DEW has just warned that
A nuclear rocket strike of
At least one thousand megatons
Had been launched by the enemy
Directly at our major cities
This announcement will take
Two and a quarter minutes to make,
You therefore have a further
Eight and a quarter minutes
To comply with the shelter
Requirements published in the Civil
Defence Code – section Atomic Attack.
A specially shortened Mass
Will be broadcast at the end
Of this announcement –
Protestant and Jewish services
Will begin simultaneously –
Select your wavelength immediately
According to instructions
In the Defence Code. Do not
Take well-loved pets (including birds)
Into your shelter – they will consume
Fresh air. Leave the old and bed-
Ridden, you can do nothing for them.
Remember to press the sealing
Switch when everyone is in
The shelter. Set the radiation
Aerial, turn on the geiger barometer.
Turn off your Television now.
Turn off your radio immediately
The services end. At the same time

Secure explosion plugs in the ears
Of each member of your family. Take
Down your plasma flasks. Give your children
The pill marked one and two
In the C.D. green container, then put
Them to bed. Do not break
The inside airlock seals until
The radiation All Clear shows
(Watch for the cuckoo in your
Perspex panel), or your District
Touring Doctor rings your bell.
If before this your air becomes
Exhausted or if any of your family
Is critically injured, administer
The capsule marked 'Vally Forge'
(Red pocket in No 1 Survival Kit)
For painless death. (Catholics
Will have been instructed by their priests
What to do in this eventuality.)
This announcement is ending, Our President
Has already given orders for
Massive retaliation – it will be
Decisive. Some of us may die.
Remember, statistically
It is not likely to be you.
All flags are flying fully dressed
On Government buildings – the sun is shining.
Death is the least we have to fear.
We are all in the hands of God,
Whatever happens by His will.
Now go quickly to your shelters.

Peter Porter

Poem B
A Poem for CND

After two thousand years
The star burned out
The kings froze in history
The angels froze in the bible
The mysteries in tinsel.
When the shepherds heard voices
They knew it was only the wind.

Out of that arctic legend
Only one escaped
On the high horse of power:
Riding the centuries down
His drumming hooves have harried
All others off the roads.
Now he assumes his hour –

And everything that is
Must crawl beneath
The Herod-coloured sky.
He is the lord of all.

His guards lean on the gates
The road is barred
The bullrushes cut down:
Around the derelict fable
His soldiers tighten their net
And now they beat
Hard on the stable door.

Where through the only gate
No magistrate may guard
His enemy leaps in.
He lies in a hollow of straw
Deserted by kings and gods
With only the cows and the sheep
Too silly to get out.

In despite of Herod's curfew
Light stirs in the city.
Because it is pitiful
Pity runs to the child:
Help breaks down the door
Because it has cried for help:
The poor press back the guards.

Bringing whatever is needed
Because it is in need
Because the seed must grow
And the child is the seed.

The social and cultural contexts of language

The aim of this unit is
● to help you focus on the knowledge you bring to texts, particularly your understanding of the social and cultural contexts of the language of literary texts.

The little Renault already looked sculpted out of snow, and the key would not turn in the door lock. She freed it with a patent squirt imported from Finland, and hastily discontinued, called Superpiss. Charles had given it to her for a joke, suggesting she used it as a visual aid to introduce Saussurean linguistics to first year undergraduates, holding the tube aloft to demonstrate that what is onomatopoeia in one language community may be obscenity in another.

Nice Work by David Lodge

When we talk, listen and write in our first language it is easy to forget just how complicated this language is. We take for granted many of the rules and conventions. This unit highlights some of the ways in which particular words are given additional significance by both individual readers and societies. As a result the word, and its visual representation, comes to mean more than what it stands for – or signifies – on a literal level.

The activities give you the chance to consider a well known poem from the point of view of a reader who is unfamiliar with the social and cultural contexts of the English language. For this reader to fully appreciate the poem you may need to find an explanation for things which, as a student of English Literature, you have become used to taking for granted. For example, in love poetry 'rose' does not refer (only) to the flower, but is often used as a metaphor for the experience of being in love.

The Alien Robot

Imagine a robot from an alien planet lands on earth. The robot has been programmed to understand the following:
– the way the English language works grammatically in ordinary speech and writing
– the dictionary definition of words, including the words humans use to describe emotions, for example 'love'
– the fact that language is used to communicate instructions, explanations and descriptions
– that language exists in written and spoken form.

However, the robot has no experience or understanding of the following:
– gender differences (in the robot's world there is no such thing as he or she)
– language used in a non-literal way (for example, metaphor and symbolism)
– words which have more than one meaning
– the use of language for anything other than communicating basic instructions, explanations and descriptions
– poetry or literature.

During his visit the alien robot comes across 'Sonnet 18' by William Shakespeare, printed on page 21.

A robotic response
- Read the poem a couple of times, underlining anything you think would be a problem for the robot. Annotate a few of these with your ideas to show why the robot would find it difficult.

- As a class, spend a few minutes sharing your first ideas.

Questioning the poem
- Working in pairs or small groups, take responsibility for looking more closely at one of the aspects of language about which the robot has no understanding (gender, non-literal language and so on). Write five questions the robot would need answering before it could understand the poem.

- Using what you know about the conventions of the language and its social and cultural contexts, try and provide your answers to the robot's questions.

- Prepare a short account of your discoveries to present to the rest of the class.

Whole class discussion
- Listen to the poem being read out loud, followed by the groups' presentations.

- As a class, sum up what you have learned about the significance of the social and cultural contexts of language.

Sonnet 18

Shall I compare thee to a summer's day?
Thou art more lovely and more temperate.
Rough winds do shake the darling buds of May,
And summer's lease hath all too short a date:
Sometime too hot the eye of heaven shines,
And often is his gold complexion dimm'd;
And every fair from fair sometime declines,
By chance or nature's changing course untrimm'd;
But thy eternal summer shall not fade,
Nor lose possession of that fair thou ow'st,
Nor shall Death brag thou wand'rest in his shade,
When in eternal lines to time thou grow'st.
   So long as men can breathe or eyes can see,
   So long lives this, and this gives life to thee.

Positioning the reader – socially, culturally, politically

The aims of this unit are
- to involve you in thinking about the meaning and significance of a single image – in this case the Union Jack – when seen from different perspectives
- to introduce the idea that individual attitudes and opinions are shaped by the social, political and cultural contexts within which the reader is operating.

Reading signs

- Look at the image printed on page 24. Make a note of everything you associate with this image.

- Compare your list with the person next to you. Look over your own list and tick the associations which reflect your personal response to this image – what does the Union Jack mean to you? Try and work out why it has these meanings for you. What does this say about you? What does it say about your attitude towards the beliefs, values, country and so on which are associated with the image of the Union Jack?

One image, multiple meanings

The people listed below represent social groups likely to have different responses to the image of the Union Jack.

- In pairs, take responsibility for considering the image from the point of view of one or two of these groups. In role, prepare a short speech explaining what this image means to you.

- an officer in the Ist World War in 1914
- an officer in the 1st World War in 1917
- a National Front supporter
- a war veteran
- a member of the IRA
- the managing director of the British Tourist Board

- a football supporter – English
- a football supporter – any other nationality
- a second generation immigrant
- an Englishman/woman
- a Scotsman/woman
- an asylum seeker.

- Listen to the different responses and as a class make a note of all the factors influencing the way in which particular people respond to the same image.

- Talk about the significance of a single image or text having such a wide variety of meanings.

A question of place?

Images (and texts) not only alter their meaning according to the position from which they are 'read' and interpreted, but also according to *where* they are placed.

- As a class, brainstorm as many places you can think of where you might see the Union Jack today.

- What meanings would it have if displayed in the following places:
- on a coffin
- on a plastic carrier bag

- on the cover of a punk album
- in one or two of the places on your list.

● You should think about the reason the flag is being used in this context – what is its significance? What message is being communicated through the relationship between the image and the context in which it is placed?

Shifting meanings

● Collect some more examples of symbols and images, the significance of which we take for granted. Use the example given below to get you started.

White dresses have, in Christian cultures come to be associated with purity, innocence and weddings. In many other cultures white dresses are worn at funerals. The significance of the white dress is not shared by the whole world. The meaning of the 'text' of the white dress is placed on it by the 'reader', in this case the different social and cultural groups.

● Working on your own or in pairs, write a short paragraph summing up what you have learned about the unstable, multiple meanings of texts. What are the implications for reading literature? Use the ideas suggested here to get you started:
  - the meaning of a text is not just contained within it
  - the author/producer of a text has no control over the way it is subsequently interpreted.

The Union Jack

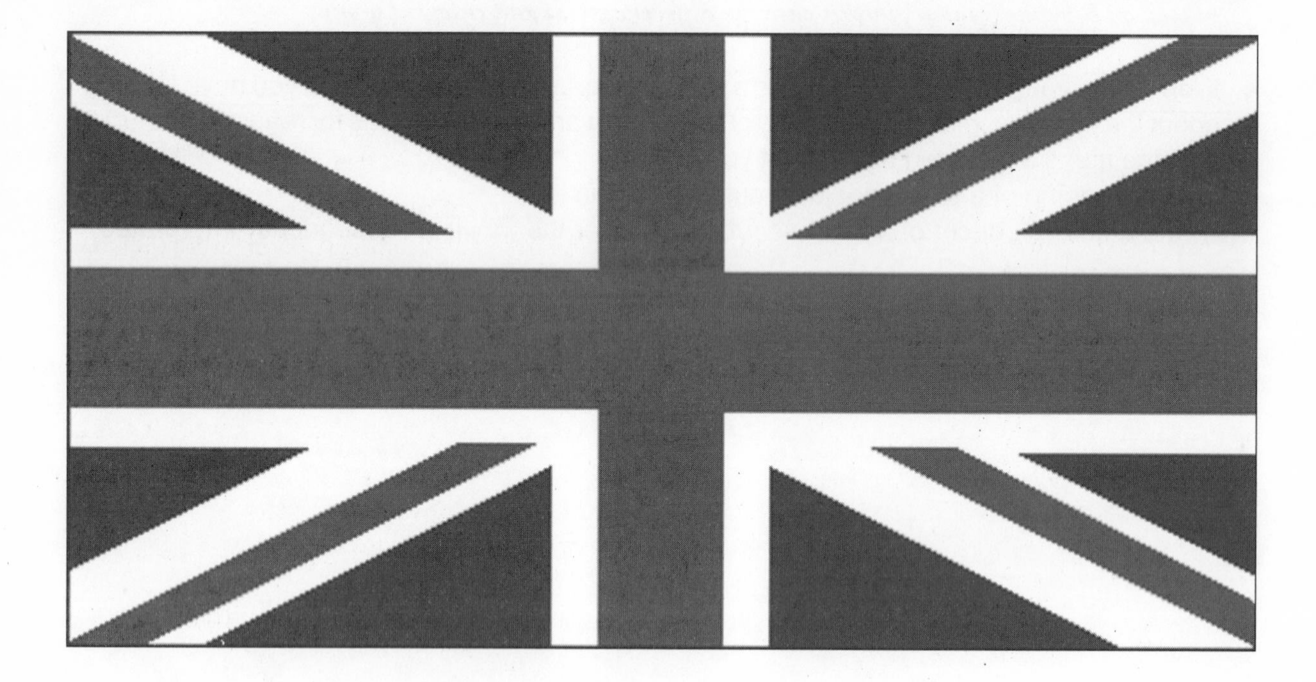

Text, Reader, Critic   © English & Media Centre 2000

Reading at a moment in time

The aim of this role play is
- to explore the impact the poetry of World War 1 had at the time it was published
- make you think about the difference between these responses and your personal readings
- to consider the role literature has played in shaping twenty-first century attitudes to war.

The 1914 Poem of the Year: a role play

Much poetry was written about the outbreak of the First World War, and newspapers were keen to print it. The purpose of this role play is to choose the 1914 Poem of the Year. Each newspaper is to submit its own Poem of the Year to an independent panel representing various sections of the population. The panel then chooses the overall Poem of the Year.

Reading the poems

- On your own read the four poems and make a brief note of your response as a reader at the beginning of the twenty-first century. In a different coloured pen make a note of how you think people would have responded to each poem when it was printed in a newspaper in 1914.

- Read these brief descriptions of the writer, the period and the poem. Working in pairs or small groups, try matching each description to a poem.

Jessie Pope's 'The Call'
- written by a thirty-three year old professional writer who threw herself into the work of raising troops and morale through verses published in the Tory press
- Owen's 'Dulce et Decorum Est' was originally addressed to her
- this strand of stirring patriotic writing took many forms; war was frequently presented as chivalric or as a sport played for honour and glory by young men.

Rupert Brooke's 'Peace'
- from a collection of sonnets entitled Sonnets of 1914
- crystallised a perceived youthful enthusiasm for the War
- was used for propaganda purposes, especially as Brooke died early in the hostilities
- his work is frequently presented as idealistic jingoism untainted by experience.

Teresa Hooley's 'A War Film'
- her use of free, imagist verse was regarded as 'avant garde'
- the intensely personal tone of 'A War Film' would have been perceived by many as a breach of poetic decorum
- although much poetry by women dwelt on the fact that the young soldiers were mothers' sons, boyfriends and husbands, it was often with a sense of glory in the sacrifice that women were making in letting them go.

Ewart Alan Mackintosh's 'Recruiting'
- written by a twenty-one year old Oxford classical scholar with political ambitions
- Mackintosh had not joined up when he wrote the poem, but his eligibility for military service already set him apart from the easy sloganising of those who stayed at home
- his later poetry expresses, as that of many officers did, a deep and painful love for the men who died under his command.

- Share your ideas in whole class discussion and talk about the way in which you came to your decisions.

Who printed the poem?
The papers which printed the poems are all listed here with a brief description of their politics and ideologies.

The Mail: Tory in its sympathies; fiercely patriotic.

The Times: the 'heavyweight' newspaper for opinion formers; tended to take the Liberal government line.

The Nation: claimed to keep its options open; prided itself that it represented conflicting points of view.

The Observer: a 'thinking' person's newspaper.

- Working in groups, try and decide which newspaper printed each poem. One person in each group should take responsibility for recording the main points of your discussion and the reasons behind your final decision.

- In class discussion share your decisions and the reasons behind them. Focus particularly on any poems about which there is disagreement or doubt.

Organise yourselves into five groups, representing the four newspapers and an independent judging panel.

The independent panel
The panel consists of:
– a young man of recruitable age
– a well known writer
– a parent
– a civilian above recruitable age with a small business.

- As members of the independent panel your task is to work out the criteria you will use to choose the Poem of the Year. You must do this in role, bearing in mind that it is 1914 and Britain is at war.

The newspaper teams
- As members of the editorial team which originally printed the poem your task is to prepare a speech arguing the case for its being chosen as Poem of the Year. This can include criticism of other entries.

Making the case
- In your newspaper groups take it in turns to present your case to the independent panel. Begin your presentation with a reading of the poem.

- Members of the panel discuss the presentations in public. When you have made your choice announce it to the newspaper groups and explain the reason behind your decision.

Debriefing

● In pairs or small groups, use what you have discovered in this unit to help you draw up as full a list as possible of the different factors influencing the way you respond to a particular poem. A few examples are suggested here to get you thinking:
  – the political situation
  – social attitudes (towards the country, the idea of war, the role of poetry and so on)
  – personal views on current affairs.

● For each factor you identify, write a sentence explaining how it shaped your reading of the war poems first in role as a newspaper editor in 1914, and then as a young adult nearly a century later.

● As a class, use what you have learned from this unit to talk about the following statement.

There is no such thing as a truly personal response to a poem. All readings are shaped by the beliefs, attitudes and events taking place in the society of the time.

Poem 2

I saw,
With a catch of the breath and the heart's uplifting,
Sorrow and pride,
  The 'week's great draw' –
The Mons Retreat;
The 'Old Contemptibles' who fought, and died,
The horror and the anguish and the glory.

As in a dream,
Still hearing machine-guns rattle and shells scream,
I came out into the street.

When the day was done,
My little son
Wondered at bath-time why I kissed him so,
Naked upon my knee.
How could he know
The sudden terror that assaulted me? ...

The body I had borne
Nine moons beneath my heart,
A part of me ...
If, someday,
It should be taken away
To War. Tortured. Torn.
Slain.
Rotting in No Man's Land, out in the rain –
My little son ...
Yet all those men had mothers, every one.

How should he know
Why I kissed and kissed and kissed him, crooning
his name?
He thought that I was daft.
He thought it was a game,
And laughed, and laughed.

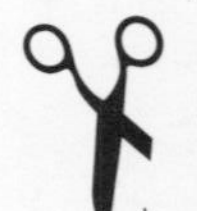

Poem 1

Now, God be thanked Who has matched us with His hour,
  And caught our youth, and wakened us from sleeping,
With hand made sure, clear eye, and sharpened power,
  To turn, as swimmers into cleanness leaping,
Glad from a world grown old and cold and weary,
  Leave the sick hearts that honour could not move,
And half-men, and their dirty songs and dreary,
  And all the little emptiness of love!

Oh! we, who have known shame, we have found
  release there,
Where there's no ill, no grief, but sleep has mending.
  Naught broken save this body, lost but breath;
Nothing to shake the laughing heart's long peace there
  But only agony, and that has ending;
And the worst friend and enemy is but Death.

Text, Reader, Critic   © English & Media Centre 2000

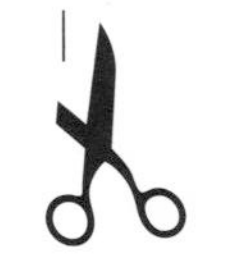

Poem 4

Who's for the trench –
    Are you, my laddie?
Who'll follow French –
    Will you, my laddie?
Who's fretting to begin,
Who's going out to win?
And who wants to save his skin –
    Do you, my laddie?

Who's for the khaki suit –
    Are you, my laddie?
Who longs to charge and shoot –
    Do you, my laddie?
Who's keen on getting fit,
Who means to show his grit,
And who'd rather wait a bit –
    Would you, my laddie?

Who'll earn the Empire's thanks –
    Will you, my laddie?
Who'll swell the victor's ranks –
    Will you, my laddie?
When that procession comes,
Banners and rolling drums –
Who'll stand and bite his thumbs –
    Will you, my laddie?

Poem 3

'Lads, you're wanted, go and help,'
On the railway carriage wall
Stuck the poster, and I thought
Of the hands that penned the call.

Fat civilians wishing they
'Could go and fight the Hun.'
Can't you see them thanking God
That they're over forty-one?

Girls with feathers, vulgar songs –
Washy verse on England's need –
God – and don't we damned well know
How the message ought to read.

'Lads, you're wanted!' over there,'
Shiver in the morning dew,
More poor devils like yourselves
Waiting to be killed by you.

Go and help to swell the names
In the casualty lists.
Help to make a column's stuff
For the blasted journalists.

Help to keep them nice and safe
From the wicked German foe.
Don't let him come over here!
'Lads, you're wanted – out you go,'

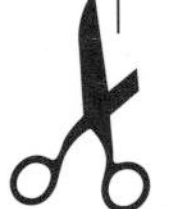

Literature and the canon

The aim of this unit is to get you to think and talk about what you are doing when you study literature at A Level. In what ways it is different from just 'reading'?

What is Literature?

This section asks you to consider the questions listed here.

– What is 'Literature'?
– What can it do for you ?
– Why are you studying it?

● In no more than 30 or 40 words try to write down what you understand by the word 'Literature'.

● Write down three or more reasons why people read in general. Now write down three or more reasons why people read 'Literature'.

● Share your ideas in whole class discussion. Talk about the assumptions lying behind your ideas.

● Look carefully at the following statements about literature. What answers do they suggest to the questions, 'What is Literature?' and 'Why do people read it?'.

● How do their opinions and attitudes compare with yours?

When treating upon that glorious and inexhaustible subject, the Literature of our country – I shall esteem it my duty to inculcate lessons of virtue, through the medium of the masters of our language.'
Professor Thomas Dale, 1928

'It helps to shape the personality, refine the sensibility, sharpen the critical intelligence.'
Bullock Report, 1974

'Literature ... is any kind of writing which for some reason or another somebody values highly.'
Terry Eagleton, 1983

'the civilising experience of contact with great literature and [its] universality.'
Newbold Report, 1967

● Make a list of the books you have read over the last six months. Sort them into 'Literature' and other kinds of reading.

● In pairs or small groups, compare your lists and talk about how you decided which category each book should go in.

So what is English Literature?

Terry Eagleton is a Marxist critic and a writer about literary theory who teaches at Oxford University.
● Read the following extract from his article 'English in Crisis'.

One of the traditional rationales for studying literature was, to put it crudely, that it made you a finer sort of person. This case suffered a severe setback when it was discovered that Nazi concentration camp commandants used to while away their leisure hours reading Goethe. Another rationale was that the study of literature introduced you to the truest, most timeless values of humanity. Casting a quick eye through the annals of English literature, this case is perhaps a bit hard to swallow. Most of the agreed major writers of literature, for example, have been thoroughly imbued with the prejudices of their age, elitist, sexist, frequently reactionary in outlook, illiberal in opinion. Of the agreed major authors of twentieth-century English literature, two (Pound and Yeats) fellow-travelled with fascism, while others (Eliot, Lawrence) displayed extreme right-wing, pseudo-fascistic sentiments. Wordsworth wrote in praise of capital punishment, Edmund Spenser advocated the oppression of the Irish people, Joseph Conrad detested popular democracy, George Eliot feared the radical working class, Alexander Pope sneered at women and Shakespeare is unlikely to have been over enthusiastic about Jews. One wonders whether this is really the kind of stuff any decent liberal should place in the hands of an impressionable Young Person. Perhaps all of this can be dismissed as superficial political comment, remote from the 'transcendental' nature of great literature; but politics, at the deepest level, means the values by which whole communities live, and if literature is as much a social product as washing powder and automobiles then such considerations can hardly be irrelevant to it. Throughout the history of the English people, a great many individuals other than Spenser, Pope and Conrad have produced an enormous amount of literature; but since they were peasants, women, Chartist activists or foreigners scribbling away in some British colony, their work was not regarded as 'timeless' or 'disinterested' enough to qualify for an entry ticket into the canon of Great Authors.

One of the permanent embarrassments of studying literature is that nobody has ever been able to come up with an adequate definition of what exactly it is. The dividing lines between 'literary' works and other forms of writing are notoriously blurred and unstable. Cardinal Newman is (perhaps) literature, but Charles Darwin is not; some execrable poetry in a 'high' mode belongs to the canon, but some superb contemporary science fiction in a more popular mode does not. *East Enders* is not literature, but quite a few turgid minor seventeenth-century dramas are. The poet, John Cooper Clarke, who can pack a fair-sized hall any night of the week, is not really literature, whereas a more respectable poet who would be lucky to pack a broom cupboard will be graced with the title. There is, in fact, no such thing as literature: literature is just the kind of writing which the cultural and academic establishments decide is literary. And those decisions can vary a good deal from age to age and society to society.

So, indeed, can the issue of what form of writing is considered *valuable*. The custodians of English literature seem to believe that there are certain literary works which just are, unquestionably and for all time, of major distinction; but one glance at the mixed fortunes of such works throughout the history of literary judgement should be enough to dissuade us of any such delusion. Many an eighteenth-century critic thought Shakespeare rather vulgar, and many a writer we now value highly was denigrated or ignored in his or her day. The grounds on which we judge literary works to be good, bad or indifferent may shift from time to time and place to place. If a future age can simply find nothing relevant to itself in Shakespeare – if his work has come to appear desperately alien to their own preoccupations – then Shakespeare will have ceased to be valuable. And there is no reason to assume, dogmatically, that this would inevitably be a bad thing.

On a traditional, critical view, literary works are the creative expression of the unique experience of certain highly gifted individuals, embodying the fundamental truths of humanity. For much contemporary critical theory, almost every phrase in this formulation is deeply suspect. There is, for example, a good deal of heated controversy these days over what we mean by an 'author' in the first place. Who is the author of *Nightmare on Elm Street*, and does it matter? 'Many things', wrote a famous French poet, 'go into the creation of a literary work other than an author'. Is it adequate to see literature as an 'expression' of the individual, and does it necessarily incarnate fundamental truths? Do all great works of literature 'transcend' their specific time and place, or are they not rather deeply rooted in the history which surrounds them?

From 'English in Crisis' by Terry Eagleton

● Read the article for a second time, highlighting any points which you find useful in clarifying and developing your own answers to the questions:
– what is Literature?
– why do people study it?

Who decides what is Literature?
In the first paragraph Eagleton refers to 'the custodians of English Literature', 'agreed major authors of twentieth century English literature' and 'the canon of Great Authors'.
Straightaway a number of questions need answering:
– who are these custodians?
– who 'agrees' about major authors?
– what is a 'canon'?

● To begin to answer these questions, look at the books set for examination at AS/A2 level and the following extracts from the National Curriculum for England and Wales.

Examples of major playwrights
William Congreve, Oliver Goldsmith, Christopher Marlowe, Sean O'Casey, Harold Pinter, J B Priestley, Peter Shaffer, G B Shaw, R B Sheridan, Oscar Wilde.

List of major writers published before 1914
Jane Austen, Charlotte Brontë, Emily Brontë, John Bunyan, Wilkie Collins, Joseph Conrad, Daniel Defoe, Charles Dickens, Arthur Conan Doyle, George Eliot, Henry Fielding, Elizabeth Gaskell, Thomas Hardy, Henry James, Mary Shelley, Robert Louis Stevenson, Jonathan Swift, Anthony Trollope, H G Wells.

Examples of fiction by major writers after 1914
E M Forster, William Golding, Graham Greene, Aldous Huxley, James Joyce, D H Lawrence, Katherine Mansfield, George Orwell, Muriel Spark, William Trevor, Evelyn Waugh.

List of major poets published before 1914
Matthew Arnold, Elizabeth Barrett Browning, William Blake, Emily Brontë, Robert Browning, Robert Burns, Lord Byron, Geoffrey Chaucer, John Clare, Samuel Taylor Coleridge, John Donne, John Dryden, Thomas Gray, George Herbert, Robert Herrick, Gerard Manley Hopkins, John Keats, Andrew Marvell, John Milton, Alexander Pope, Christina Rossetti, William Shakespeare (sonnets), Percy Bysshe Shelley, Edmund Spenser, Alfred Lord Tennyson, Henry Vaughan, William Wordsworth, Sir Thomas Wyatt.

Examples of major poets after 1914
W H Auden, Gillian Clarke, Keith Douglas, T S Eliot, U A Fanthorpe, Thomas Hardy, Seamus Heaney, Ted Hughes, Elizabeth Jennings, Philip Larkin, Wilfred Owen, Sylvia Plath, Stevie Smith, Edward Thomas, R S Thomas, W B Yeats.

Examples of recent and contemporary drama, fiction and poetry
Drama: Alan Ayckbourn, Samuel Beckett, Alan Bennett, Robert Bolt, Brian Friel, Willis Hall, David Hare, Willie Russell, R C Sherriff, Arnold Wesker.
Fiction: J G Ballard, Berlie Doherty, Susan Hill, Laurie Lee, Joan Lingard, Bill Naughton, Alan Sillitoe, Mildred Taylor, Robert Westall.
Poetry: Simon Armitage, James Berry, Douglas Dunn, Liz Lochhead, Adrian Mitchell, Edwin Muir, Grace Nichols, Jo Shapcott.

Examples of drama, fiction and poetry by major writers from different cultures and traditions
Drama: Athol Fugard, Arthur Miller, Wole Soyinka, Tennessee Williams.
Fiction: Chinua Achebe, Maya Angelou, Willa Cather, Anita Desai, Nadine Gordimer, Ernest Hemingway, H H Richardson, Doris Lessing, R K Narayan, John Steinbeck, Ngugi wa Thiong'o.
Poetry: E K Brathwaite, Emily Dickinson, Robert Frost, Robert Lowell, Les Murray, Rabindranath Tagore, Derek Walcott.

Examples of non-fiction and non-literary texts
Personal record and viewpoints on society: Peter Ackroyd, James Baldwin, John Berger, James Boswell, Vera Brittain, Lord Byron, William Cobbett, Gerald Durrell, Robert Graves, Samuel Johnson, Laurie Lee, Samuel Pepys, Flora Thompson, Beatrice Webb, Dorothy Wordsworth.
Travel writing: Jan Morris, Freya Stark, Laurens Van Der Post.
Reportage: James Cameron, Winston Churchill, Alistair Cooke, Dilys Powell.
The natural world: David Attenborough, Rachel Carson, Charles Darwin, Steve Jones.

- Working in groups talk about the lists. Use the questions suggested here as a focus for your discussion.

  - Who compiled these lists?
  - What overlaps can you find?
  - How many of the listed writers have you heard of?
  - How many have you read?
  - Have any writers you personally consider to be important been left out?

Constructing the canon

The following extract is taken from Terry Eagleton's book *Literary Theory*.

- Read the extract and, working as a class, work out the main points of Eagleton's argument and discuss whether you agree with it.

...the so called 'literary canon', the unquestioned 'great tradition' of the 'national literature', has to be recognised as a construct, fashioned by particular people for particular reasons at a certain time. There is no such thing as a literary work or tradition which is valuable in itself, regardless of what anyone might have said or come to say about it. 'Value' is a transitive term: it means whatever is valued by certain people in specific situations, according to particular criteria and in the light of given purposes'

Terry Eagleton, *Literary Theory* , 1983

- Who do you think 'fashioned' the National Curriculum 'construct' ? For what purposes?

The lists of major writers and poets published before 1914 represent the Department for Education and Employment's version of the canon of English Literature. Originally the word 'canon' referred to religious texts and church law, but in the context of literature it has come to mean: the body of texts and writers traditionally regarded as 'great' and thus possessing special authority.

An alternative canon

The status and authority of the 'canon' is constantly under attack, challenged by people who disagree with the writers included and excluded. Your own lists of 'missing' writers will have highlighted some of the reasons why the idea of a single canon is contentious.

- As a group, produce an alternative canon of between 10 and 20 texts which you think students should study in Years 12 and 13. What are your criteria for choosing these texts? What is the balance between the 'literary' texts and the others? How does this compare with the balance in your lists of set texts?

Trying out critical positions – reading a short story

The work in this unit
- is based on an intriguing and challenging short story
- demonstrates the ways in which one story can be read in, from different critical positions
- encourages you to become aware of the position you are reading from, why you chose to approach the text in this way and the implications of this.

A first reading
- Read the story, and make a note of your first reactions to it. Don't worry if some of these are negative.

- Re-read the story and write down three to five questions which you would like to ask the writer about it. One question might be about the title. What do you think it means? What connections does it have with the story and its characters? Put your questions aside for later.

- In small groups or as a class share your first responses to the story. Using what you have learned so far about the process of reading, spend a few minutes thinking about reasons you might find it difficult to get to grips with the story.

- In your group, discuss the statements listed below, referring closely to the story to support your views, and also to raise counter arguments.

  Julian's mother is racist.
  Julian is cruel to his mother.
  The author is racist.
  The title has very little to do with the story.
  The author writes well about what she knows, but the story is unbalanced.
  It is a tragic story.
  It is a comic story.
  It is a satirical story.

Exploring patterns
- In pairs work through the text highlighting in different colours any words, images or ideas which are to do with things rising or falling, up or down.

- Record your findings in a chart like the one shown below.

Up/rising	Comment	Down/falling	Comment

- Join up with another pair and talk about your findings. Write down the insights this exercise has given you into the themes, characters and message of the story. It doesn't matter how tentative these are.

- In whole class discussion, share what you have discovered about the story.

- Look back at your questions and consider which, if any, you are now able to tackle.

Reading from critical positions

- Work in pairs for this activity. Your teacher will give you a card outlining the interests of particular types of critics, for example feminist critics, or those who are interested in literature as something beautiful rather than relevant, or critics interested in language and so on. Read your card carefully and talk together about what the critics on your card are interested in.

- In role as the critic described on your card re-read 'Everything that Rises Must Converge' and prepare a short presentation on your interpretation of the text. To illustrate your reading you should include an analysis of key quotations.

- Listen to the presentations and, as a class talk about the different points foregrounded and passed over by critics reading from these specific positions. Which positions have most in common with each other? Which positions seem most at odds with each other? Why do you think this is?

- With which critical position – or combination of positions – are you most in sympathy/?

An alternative reading

- Consider these extracts from 'Beyond the Peacock', an essay by Alice Walker about her response to Flannery O'Connor. How would you describe the critical position or positions she adopts in this reading? What do you find interesting or unusual about the way Alice Walker chooses to write literary criticism?

- In what ways does this response by 'another reader' inform your own opinion and judgement of 'Everything that Rises Must Converge'?

A contextual reading

- What does it add to your reading of the story to know that:
  - Flannery O'Connor was a Catholic, who believed firmly in divine grace, the possibility of salvation through moments of epiphany or revelation
  - that she was interested in the theories of a Jesuit mystic called Teillard de Chardin, who believed that the universe is in a continuous process of upward convergence towards 'point Omega', the ultimate, mysterious 'Great Presence'. Love is the force that brings convergence, while selfishness, racism, ignorance and elitism drag the world down, away from 'Point Omega'.

Your own reading

- Use all the work you have done on the different readings of 'Everything that Rises Must Converge' to write your own response to the story.

'Everything that rises must converge' by Flannery O'Connor

Her doctor had told Julian's mother that she must lose twenty pounds on account of her blood pressure, so on Wednesday nights Julian had to take her downtown on the bus for a reducing class at the Y. The reducing class was designed for working girls over fifty, who weighed from 165 to 200 pounds. His mother was one of the slimmer ones, but she said ladies did not tell their age or weight. She would not ride the buses by herself at night since they had been integrated, and because the reducing class was one of her few pleasures, necessary for her health, and *free*, she said Julian could at least put himself out to take her, considering all she did for him. Julian did not like to consider all she did for him, but every Wednesday night he braced himself and took her.

She was almost ready to go, standing before the hall mirror, putting on her hat, while he, his hands behind him, appeared pinned to the door frame, waiting like Saint Sebastian for the arrows to begin piercing him. The hat was new and had cost her seven dollars and a half. She kept saying, 'Maybe I shouldn't have paid that for it. No, I shouldn't have. I'll take it off and return it tomorrow. I shouldn't have bought it.'

Julian raised his eyes to heaven. 'Yes, you should have bought it,' he said. 'Put it on and let's go.' It was a hideous hat. A purple velvet flap came down on one side of it and stood up on the other; the rest of it was green and looked like a cushion with the stuffing out. He decided it was less comical than jaunty and pathetic. Everything that gave her pleasure was small and depressed him.

She lifted the hat one more time and set it down slowly on top of her head. Two wings of gray hair protruded on either side of her florid face, but her eyes, sky-blue, were as innocent and untouched by experience as they must have been when she was ten. Were it not that she was a widow who had struggled fiercely to feed and clothe and put him through school and who was supporting him still, 'until he got on his feet,' she might have been a little girl that he had to take to town.

'It's all right, it's all right,' he said. 'Let's go.' He opened the door himself and started down the walk to get her going. The sky was a dying violet and the houses stood out darkly against it, bulbous liver-colored monstrosities of a uniform ugliness though no two were alike. Since this had been a fashionable neighborhood forty years ago, his mother persisted in thinking they did well to have an apartment in it. Each house had a narrow collar of dirt around it in which sat, usually, a grubby child. Julian walked with his hands in his pockets, his head down and thrust forward and his eyes glazed with the determination to make himself completely numb during the time he would be sacrificed to her pleasure.

The door closed and he turned to find the dumpy figure, surmounted by the atrocious hat, coming toward him. 'Well,' she said, 'you only live once and paying a little more for it, I at least won't meet myself coming and going.'

'Some day I'll start making money,' Julian said gloomily – he knew he never would – 'and you can have one of those jokes whenever you take the fit.' But first they would move. He visualized a place where the nearest neighbors would be three miles away on either side.

'I think you're doing fine,' she said, drawing on her gloves. 'You've only been out of school a year. Rome wasn't built in a day.'

She was one of the few members of the Y reducing class who arrived in hat and gloves and who had a son who had been to college. 'It takes time,' she said, 'and the world is in such a mess. This hat looked better on me than any of the others, though when she brought it out I said, 'Take that thing back. I wouldn't have it on my head,' and she said, 'Now wait till you see it on,' and when she put it on me, I said, We-ull,' and she said, 'If you ask me, that hat does something for you and you do something for the hat, and besides,' she said, 'with that hat, you won't meet yourself coming and going.''

Julian thought he could have stood his lot better if she had been selfish, if she had been an old hag who drank and screamed at him. He walked along, saturated in depression, as if in the midst of his martyrdom he had lost his faith. Catching sight of his long, hopeless, irritated face, she stopped suddenly with a grief-stricken look, and pulled back on his arm. 'Wait on me,' she said. 'I'm going back to the house and take this thing off and tomorrow I'm going to return it. I was out of my head. I can pay the gas bill with that seven-fifty.'

He caught her arm in a vicious grip. 'You are not going to take it back,' he said. 'I like it.'

'Well,' she said, 'I don't think I ought ...'

'Shut up and enjoy it,' he muttered, more depressed than ever.

'With the world in the mess it's in,' she said, 'it's a wonder we can enjoy anything. I tell you, the bottom rail is on the top.'

Julian sighed.

'Of course,' she said, 'if you know who you are, you can go anywhere.' She said this every time he took her to the reducing class. 'Most of them in it are not our kind of people,' she said, 'but I can be gracious to anybody. I know who I am.'

'They don't give a damn for your graciousness,' Julian said savagely. 'Knowing who you are is good for one generation only. You haven't the foggiest idea where you stand now or who you are.'

She stopped and allowed her eyes to flash at him. 'I most certainly do know who I am,' she said, 'and if you don't know who you are, I'm ashamed of you.'

'Oh hell,' Julian said.

'Your great-grandfather was a former governor of this state,' she said. 'Your grandfather was a prosperous landowner. Your grandmother was a Godhigh.'

'Will you look around you,' he said tensely, 'and see where you are now?' and he swept his arm jerkily out to indicate the neighborhood, which the growing darkness at least made less dingy.

'You remain what you are,' she said. 'Your great-grandfather had a plantation and two hundred slaves.'

'There are no more slaves,' he said irritably.

'They were better off when they were,' she said. He groaned to see that she was off on that topic. She rolled onto it every few days like a train on an open track. He knew every stop, every junction, every swamp along the way, and knew the exact point at which her conclusion would roll majestically into the station: 'It's ridiculous. It's simply not realistic. They should rise, yes, but on their own side of the fence.'

'Let's skip it,' Julian said.

'The ones I feel sorry for,' she said, 'are the ones that are half white. They're tragic.'

'Will you skip it?'

'Suppose we were half white. We would certainly have mixed feelings.'

'I have mixed feelings now,' he groaned.

'Well let's talk about something pleasant,' she said. 'I remember going to Granpa's when I was a little girl. Then the house had double stairways that went up to what was really the second floor – all the cooking was done on the first. I used to like to stay down in the kitchen on account of the way the walls smelled. I would sit with my nose pressed against the plaster and take deep breaths. Actually the place belonged to the Godhighs but your grandfather Chestny paid the mortgage and saved it for them. They were in reduced circumstances,' she said, 'but reduced or not, they never forgot who they were.'

'Doubtless that decayed mansion reminded them,' Julian muttered. He never spoke of it without contempt or thought of it without longing. He had seen it once when he was a child before it had been sold. The double stairways had rotted and been torn down. Negroes were living in it. But it remained in his mind as his mother had known it. It appeared in his dreams regularly. He would stand on the wide porch, listening to the rustle of oak leaves, then wander through the high-ceilinged hall into the parlor that opened onto it and gaze at the worn rugs and faded draperies. It occurred to him that it was he, not she, who could have appreciated it. He preferred its threadbare elegance to anything he could name and it was because of it that all the neighborhoods they had lived in had been a torment to him – whereas she had hardly known the difference. She called her insensitivity 'being adjustable.'

'And I remember the old darky who was my nurse, Caroline. There was no better person in the world. I've always had a great respect for my colored friends,' she said. 'I'd do anything in the world for them and they'd ...'

'Will you for God's sake get off that subject?' Julian said. When he got on a bus by himself, he made it a point to sit down beside a Negro, in reparation as it were for his mother's sins.

'You're mighty touchy tonight,' she said. 'Do you feel all right?'

'Yes I feel all right,' he said. 'Now lay off.'

She pursed her lips. 'Well, you certainly are in a vile humor,' she observed. 'I just won't speak to you at all.'

They had reached the bus stop. There was no bus in sight and Julian, his hands still jammed in his pockets and his head thrust forward, scowled down the empty street. The frustration of having to wait on the bus as well as ride on it began to creep up his neck like a hot hand. The presence of his mother was borne in upon him as she gave a pained sigh. He looked at her bleakly. She was holding herself very erect under the preposterous hat, wearing it like a banner of her imaginary dignity. There was in him an evil urge to break her spirit. He suddenly unloosened his tie and pulled it off and put it in his pocket.

She stiffened. 'Why must you look like *that* when you take me to town?' she said. 'Why must you deliberately embarrass me?'

'If you'll never learn where you are,' he said, 'you can at least learn where I am.'

'You look like a – thug,' she said.

'Then I must be one,' he murmured.

'I'll just go home,' she said. 'I will not bother you. If

you can't do a little thing like that for me ...'

Rolling his eyes upward, he put his tie back on. 'Restored to my class,' he muttered. He thrust his face toward her and hissed, 'True culture is in the mind, the *mind,'* he said, and tapped his head, 'the mind.'

'It's in the heart,' she said, 'and in how you do things and how you do things is because of who you *are.'*

'Nobody in the damn bus cares who you are.'

'I care who I am,' she said icily.

The lighted bus appeared on top of the next hill and as it approached, they moved out into the street to meet it. He put his hand under her elbow and hoisted her up on the creaking step. She entered with a little smile, as if she were going into a drawing room where everyone had been waiting for her. While he put in the tokens, she sat down on one of the broad front seats for three which faced the aisle. A thin woman with protruding teeth and long yellow hair was sitting on the end of it. His mother moved up beside her and left room for Julian beside herself. He sat down and looked at the floor across the aisle where a pair of thin feet in red and white canvas sandals were planted.

His mother immediately began a general conversation meant to attract anyone who felt like talking. 'Can it get any hotter?' she said and removed from her purse a folding fan, black with a Japanese scene on it, which she began to flutter before her.

'I reckon it might could,' the woman with the protruding teeth said, 'but I know for a fact my apartment couldn't get no hotter.'

'It must get the afternoon sun,' his mother said. She sat forward and looked up and down the bus. It was half filled. Everybody was white. 'I see we have the bus to ourselves,' she said. Julian cringed.

'For a change,' said the woman across the aisle, the owner of the red and white canvas sandals. 'I come on one the other day and they were thick as fleas – up front and all through.'

'The world is in a mess everywhere,' his mother said 'I don't know how we've let it get in this fix.'

'What gets my goat is all those boys from good families stealing automobile tires,' the woman with the protruding teeth said. 'I told my boy, I said you may not be rich but you been raised right and if I ever catch you in any such mess, they can send you on to the reformatory. Be exactly where you belong.'

'Training tells,' his mother said. 'Is your boy in high school?'

'Ninth grade,' the woman said.

'My son just finished college last year. He wants to write but he's selling typewriters until he gets started,' his mother said.

The woman leaned forward and peered at Julian. He threw her such a malevolent look that she subsided

against the seat. On the floor across the aisle there was an abandoned newspaper. He got up and got it and opened it out in front of him. His mother discreetly continued the conversation in a lower tone but the woman across the aisle said in a loud voice, 'Well that's nice. Selling typewriters is close to writing. He can go right from one to the other.'

'I tell him,' his mother said, 'that Rome wasn't built in a day.'

Behind the newspaper Julian was withdrawing into the inner compartment of his mind where he spent most of his time. This was a kind of mental bubble in which he established himself when he could not bear to be a part of what was going on around him. From it he could see out and judge but in it he was safe from any kind of penetration from without. It was the only place where he felt free of the general idiocy of his fellows. His mother had never entered it but from it he could see her with absolute clarity.

The old lady was clever enough and he thought that if she had started from any of the right premises, more might have been expected of her. She lived according to the laws of her own fantasy world, outside of which he had never seen her set foot. The law of it was to sacrifice herself for him after she had first created the necessity to do so by making a mess of things. If he had permitted her sacrifices, it was only because her lack of foresight had made them necessary. All of her life had been a struggle to act like a Chestny without the Chestny goods, and to give him everything she thought a Chestny ought to have; but since, said she, it was fun to struggle, why complain? And when you had won, as she had won, what fun to look back on the hard times! He could not forgive her that she had enjoyed the struggle and that she thought *she* had won.

What she meant when she said she had won was that she had brought him up successfully and had sent him to college and that he had turned out so well – good looking (her teeth had gone unfilled so that his could be straightened), intelligent (he realized he was too intelligent to be a success), and with a future ahead of him (there was of course no future ahead of him). She excused his gloominess on the grounds that he was still growing up and his radical ideas on his lack of practical experience. She said he didn't yet know a thing about 'life,' that he hadn't even entered the real world – when already he was as disenchanted with it as a man of fifty.

The further irony of all this was that in spite of her, he had turned out so well. In spite of going to only a third-rate college, he had, on his own initiative, come out with a first-rate education; in spite of growing up dominated by a small mind, he had ended up with a large one; in spite of all her foolish views, he was free of prejudice and unafraid to face facts. Most miraculous of all, instead of being blinded by love for her as she was for him, he had cut himself emotionally free of her and could see her with complete objectivity. He was not dominated by his mother.

The bus stopped with a sudden jerk and shook him from his meditation. A woman from the back lurched forward with little steps and barely escaped falling in his newspaper as she righted herself. She got off and a large Negro got on. Julian kept his paper lowered to watch. It gave him a certain satisfaction to see injustice in daily operation. It confirmed his view that with a few exceptions there was no one worth knowing within a radius of three hundred miles. The Negro was well dressed and carried a briefcase. He looked around and then sat down on the other end of the seat where the woman with the red and white canvas sandals was sitting. He immediately unfolded a newspaper and obscured himself behind it. Julian's mother's elbow at once prodded insistently into his ribs. 'Now you see why I won't ride on these buses by myself,' she whispered.

The woman with the red and white canvas sandals had risen at the same time the Negro sat down and had gone further back in the bus and taken the seat of the woman who had got off. His mother leaned forward and cast her an approving look.

Julian rose, crossed the aisle, and sat down in the place of the woman with the canvas sandals. From this position, he looked serenely across at his mother. Her face had turned an angry red. He stared at her, making his eyes the eyes of a stranger. He felt his tension suddenly lift as if he had openly declared war on her.

He would have liked to get in conversation with the Negro and to talk with him about art or politics or any subject that would be above the comprehension of those around them, but the man remained entrenched behind his paper. He was either ignoring the change of seating or had never noticed it. There was no way for Julian to convey his sympathy.

His mother kept her eyes fixed reproachfully on his face. The woman with the protruding teeth was looking at him avidly as if he were a type of monster new to her.

'Do you have a light?' he asked the Negro.

Without looking away from his paper, the man reached in his pocket and handed him a packet of matches.

'Thanks,' Julian said. For a moment he held the matches foolishly. A NO SMOKING sign looked down upon him from over the door. This alone would not have deterred him; he had no cigarettes. He had quit smoking some months before because he could not afford it. 'Sorry,' he muttered and handed back the matches. The Negro lowered the paper and gave him an annoyed look. He took the matches and raised the paper again.

His mother continued to gaze at him but she did not take advantage of his momentary discomfort. Her eyes retained their battered look. Her face seemed to be unnaturally red, as if her blood pressure had risen. Julian allowed no glimmer of sympathy to show on his face. Having got the advantage, he wanted desperately to keep it and carry it through. He would have liked to teach her a lesson that would last her a while, but there seemed no way to continue the point. The Negro refused to come out from behind his paper.

Julian folded his arms and looked stolidly before him, facing her but as if he did not see her, as if he had ceased to recognize her existence. He visualized a scene in which, the bus having reached their stop, he would remain in his seat and when she said, 'Aren't you going to get off?' he would look at her as at a stranger who had rashly addressed him. The corner they got off on was usually deserted, but it was well lighted and it would not hurt her to walk by herself the four blocks to the Y. He decided to wait until the time came and then decide whether or not he would let her get off by herself. He would have to be at the Y at ten to bring her back, but he could leave her wondering if he was going to show up. There was no reason for her to think she could always depend on him.

He retired again into the high-ceilinged room sparsely settled with large pieces of antique furniture. His soul expanded momentarily but then he became aware of his mother across from him and the vision shriveled. He studied her coldly. Her feet in little pumps dangled like a child's and did not quite reach the floor. She was training on him an exaggerated look of reproach. He felt completely detached from her. At that moment he could with pleasure have slapped her as he would have slapped a particularly obnoxious child in his charge.

He began to imagine various unlikely ways by which he could teach her a lesson. He might make friends with some distinguished Negro professor or lawyer and bring him home to spend the evening. He would be entirely justified but her blood pressure would rise to 300. He could not push her to the extent of making her have a stroke, and moreover, he had never been successful at making any Negro friends. He had tried to strike up an acquaintance on the bus with some of the better types, with ones that looked like professors or ministers or lawyers. One morning he had sat down next to a distinguished-looking dark brown man who had answered his questions with a sonorous solemnity but who had turned out to be an undertaker. Another day he had sat down beside a cigar-smoking Negro with a diamond ring on his finger, but after a few stilted pleasantries, the Negro had rung the buzzer and risen, slipping two lottery tickets into Julian's hand as he climbed over him to leave.

He imagined his mother lying desperately ill and his being able to secure only a Negro doctor for her. He toyed with that idea for a few minutes and then dropped it for a momentary vision of himself participating as a sympathizer in a sit-in demonstration. This was possible but he did not linger with it. Instead, he approached the ultimate horror. He brought home a beautiful suspiciously Negroid woman. Prepare yourself, he said. There is nothing you can do about it. This is the woman I've chosen. She's intelligent, dignified, even good, and she's suffered and she hasn't thought it *fun*. Now persecute us, go ahead and persecute us. Drive her out of here, but remember, you're driving me too. His eyes were narrowed and through the indignation he had generated, he saw his mother across the aisle, purple-faced, shrunken to the dwarf-like proportions of her moral nature, sitting like a mummy beneath the ridiculous banner of her hat.

He was tilted out of his fantasy again as the bus stopped. The door opened with a sucking hiss and out of the dark a large, gaily dressed, sullen-looking colored woman got on with a little boy. The child, who might have been four, had on a short plaid suit and a Tyrolean hat with a blue feather in it. Julian hoped that he would sit down beside him and that the woman would push in beside his mother. He could think of no better arrangement.

As she waited for her tokens, the woman was surveying the seating possibilities – he hoped with the idea of sitting where she was least wanted. There was something familiar-looking about her but Julian could not place what it was. She was a giant of a woman. Her face was set not only to meet opposition but to seek it out. The downward tilt of her large lower lip was like a warning sign: DON'T TAMPER WITH ME. Her bulging figure was encased in a green crepe dress and her feet overflowed in red shoes. She had on a hideous hat. A purple velvet flap came down on one side of it and stood up on the other; the rest of it was green and looked like a cushion with the stuffing out. She carried a mammoth red pocketbook that bulged throughout as if it were stuffed with rocks.

To Julian's disappointment, the little boy climbed up on the empty seat beside his mother. His mother lumped all children, black and white, into the common category, 'cute,' and she thought little Negroes were on the whole cuter than little white children. She smiled at the little boy as he climbed on the seat.

Meanwhile the woman was bearing down upon the empty seat beside Julian. To his annoyance, she squeezed herself into it. He saw his mother's face change as the woman settled herself next to him and he realized with satisfaction that this was more objectionable to her than it was to him. Her face seemed almost gray and

there was a look of dull recognition in her eyes, as if suddenly she had sickened at some awful confrontation. Julian saw that it was because she and the woman had, in a sense, swapped sons. Though his mother would not realize the symbolic significance of this, she would feel it. His amusement showed plainly on his face.

The woman next to him muttered something unintelligible to herself. He was conscious of a kind of bristling next to him, a muted growling like that of an angry cat. He could not see anything but the red pocketbook upright on the bulging green thighs. He visualized the woman as she had stood waiting for her tokens – the ponderous figure, rising from the red shoes upward over the solid hips, the mammoth bosom, the haughty face, to the green and purple hat.

His eyes widened.

The vision of the two hats, identical, broke upon him with the radiance of a brilliant sunrise. His face was suddenly lit with joy. He could not believe that Fate had thrust upon his mother such a lesson. He gave a loud chuckle so that she would look at him and see that he saw. She turned her eyes on him slowly. The blue in them seemed to have turned a bruised purple. For a moment he had an uncomfortable sense of her innocence, but it lasted only a second before principle rescued him. Justice entitled him to laugh. His grin hardened until it said to her as plainly as if he were saying aloud: Your punishment exactly fits your pettiness. This should teach you a permanent lesson.

Her eyes shifted to the woman. She seemed unable to bear looking at him and to find the woman preferable. He became conscious again of the bristling presence at his side. The woman was rumbling like a volcano about to become active. His mother's mouth began to twitch slightly at one corner. With a sinking heart, he saw incipient signs of recovery on her face and realized that this was going to strike her suddenly as funny and was going to be no lesson at all. She kept her eyes on the woman and an amused smile came over her face as if the woman were a monkey that had stolen her hat. The little Negro was looking up at her with large fascinated eyes. He had been trying to attract her attention for some time.

'Carver!' the woman said suddenly. 'Come heah!'

When he saw that the spotlight was on him at last, Carver drew his feet up and turned himself toward Julian's mother and giggled.

'Carver!' the woman said. 'You heah me? Come heah!'

Carver slid down from the seat but remained squatting with his back against the base of it, his head turned slyly around toward Julian's mother, who was smiling at him. The woman reached a hand across the aisle and snatched him to her. He righted himself and hung backwards on her knees, grinning at Julian's mother. 'Isn't he cute?' Julian's mother said to the woman with the protruding teeth.

'I reckon he is,' the woman said without conviction.

The Negress yanked him upright but he eased out of her grip and shot across the aisle and scrambled, giggling wildly, onto the seat beside his love.

'I think he likes me,' Julian's mother said, and smiled at the woman. It was the smile she used when she was being particularly gracious to an inferior. Julian saw everything lost. The lesson had rolled off her like rain on a roof.

The woman stood up and yanked the little boy off the seat as if she were snatching him from contagion. Julian could feel the rage in her at having no weapon like his mother's smile. She gave the child a sharp slap across his leg. He howled once and then thrust his head into her stomach and kicked his feet against her shins. 'Be-have,' she said vehemently.

The bus stopped and the Negro who had been reading the newspaper got off. The woman moved over and set the little boy down with a thump between herself and Julian. She held him firmly by the knee. In a moment he put his hands in front of his face and peeped at Julian's mother through his fingers.

'I see yoooooooo!' she said and put her hand in front of her face and peeped at him.

The woman slapped his hand down. 'Quit yo' foolishness,' she said, 'before I knock the living Jesus out of you!'

Julian was thankful that the next stop was theirs. He reached up and pulled the cord. The woman reached up and pulled it at the same time. Oh my God, he thought. He had the terrible intuition that when they got off the bus together, his mother would open her purse and give the little boy a nickel. The gesture would be as natural to her as breathing. The bus stopped and the woman got up and lunged to the front, dragging the child, who wished to stay on, after her. Julian and his mother got up and followed. As they neared the door, Julian tried to relieve her of her pocketbook.

'No,' she murmured, 'I want to give the little boy a nickel.'

'No!' Julian hissed. 'No!'

She smiled down at the child and opened her bag. The bus door opened and the woman picked him up by the arm and descended with him, hanging at her hip. Once in the street she set him down and shook him.

Julian's mother had to close her purse while she got down the bus step but as soon as her feet were on the ground, she opened it again and began to rummage inside. 'I can't find but a penny, she whispered, 'but it looks like a new one.

'Don't do it!' Julian said fiercely between his teeth. There was a streetlight on the corner and she hurried to get under it so that she could better see into her pocketbook. The woman was heading off rapidly down the street with the child still hanging backward on her hand.

'Oh little boy!' Julian's mother called and took a few quick steps and caught up with them just beyond the lamp-post. 'Here's a bright new penny for you,' and she held out the coin, which shone bronze in the dim light.

The huge woman turned and for a moment stood, her shoulders lifted and her face frozen with frustrated rage, and stared at Julian's mother. Then all at once she seemed to explode like a piece of machinery that had been given one ounce of pressure too much. Julian saw the black fist swing out with the red pocketbook. He shut his eyes and cringed as he heard the woman shout, 'He don't take nobody's pennies!' When he opened his eyes, the woman was disappearing down the street with the little boy staring wide-eyed over her shoulder. Julian's mother was sitting on the sidewalk.

'I told you not to do that,' Julian said angrily. 'I told you not to do that!'

He stood over her for a minute, gritting his teeth. Her legs were stretched out in front of her and her hat was on her lap. He squatted down and looked her in the face. It was totally expressionless. 'You got exactly what you deserved,' he said. 'Now get up.'

He picked up her pocketbook and put what had fallen out back in it. He picked the hat up off her lap. The penny caught his eye on the sidewalk and he picked that up and let it drop before her eyes into the purse. Then he stood up and leaned over and held his hands out to pull her up. She remained immobile. He sighed. Rising above them on either side were black apartment buildings, marked with irregular rectangles of light. At the end of the block a man came out of a door and walked off in the opposite direction. 'All right,' he said, 'suppose somebody happens by and wants to know why you're sitting on the sidewalk?'

She took the hand and, breathing hard, pulled heavily up on it and then stood for a moment, swaying slightly as if the spots of light in the darkness were circling around her. Her eyes, shadowed and confused, finally settled on his face. He did not try to conceal his irritation. 'I hope this teaches you a lesson,' he said. She leaned forward and her eyes raked his face. She seemed trying to determine his identity. Then, as if she found nothing familiar about him, she started off with a headlong movement in the wrong direction.

'Aren't you going on to the Y?' he asked.

'Home,' she muttered.

'Well, are we walking?'

For answer she kept going. Julian followed along, his hands behind him. He saw no reason to let the lesson she had had go without backing it up with an explanation of its meaning. She might as well be made to understand what had happened to her. 'Don't think that was just an uppity Negro woman,' he said. 'That was the whole colored race which will no longer take your condescending pennies. That was your black double. She can wear the same hat as you, and to be sure,' he added gratuitously (because he thought it was funny), 'it looked better on her than it did on you. What all this means,' he said, 'is that the old world is gone. The old manners are obsolete and your graciousness is not worth a damn.' He thought bitterly of the house that had been lost for him. 'You aren't who you think you are,' he said.

She continued to plow ahead, paying no attention to him. Her hair had come undone on one side. She dropped her pocketbook and took no notice. He stooped and picked it up and handed it to her but she did not take it.

'You needn't act as if the world had come to an end,' he said, 'because it hasn't. From now on you've got to live in a new world and face a few realities for a change. Buck up,' he said, 'it won't kill you.'

She was breathing fast.

'Let's wait on the bus,' he said.

'Home,' she said thickly.

'I hate to see you behave like this,' he said. 'Just like a child. I should be able to expect more of you.' He decided to stop where he was and make her stop and wait for a bus. 'I'm not going any farther,' he said, stopping. 'We're going on the bus.'

She continued to go on as if she had not heard him. He took a few steps and caught her arm and stopped her. He looked into her face and caught his breath. He was looking into a face he had never seen before. 'Tell Grandpa to come get me,' she said.

He stared, stricken.

'Tell Caroline to come get me,' she said.

Stunned, he let her go and she lurched forward again, walking as if one leg were shorter than the other. A tide of darkness seemed to be sweeping her from him. 'Mother!' he cried. 'Darling, sweetheart, wait!' Crumpling, she fell to the pavement. He dashed forward and fell at her side, crying, 'Mamma, Mamma!' He turned her over. Her face was fiercely distorted. One eye, large and staring, moved slightly to the left as if it had become unmoored. The other remained fixed on him, raked his face again, found nothing and closed.

'Wait here, wait here!' he cried and jumped up and began to run for help toward a cluster of lights he saw in the distance ahead of him. 'Help, help!' he shouted, but his voice was thin, scarcely a thread of sound. The lights drifted farther away the faster he ran and his feet moved numbly as if they carried him nowhere. The tide of darkness seemed to sweep him back to her, postponing from moment to moment his entry into the world of guilt and sorrow.

Beyond the Peacock:
The Reconstruction of Flannery O'Connor

It was after a poetry reading I gave at a recently desegregated college in Georgia that someone mentioned that in 1952 Flannery O'Connor and I had lived within minutes of each other on the same Eatonton-to-Milledgeville road. I was eight years old in 1952 (she would have been 28) and we moved away from Milledgeville after less than a year. Still, since I have loved her work for many years, the coincidence of our having lived near each other intrigued me, and started me thinking of her again.

As a college student in the sixties I read her books endlessly, scarcely conscious of the difference between her racial and economic background and my own, but put them away in anger when I discovered that, while I was reading O'Connor – Southern, Catholic, and white – there were other women writers – some Southern, some religious, all black – I had not been allowed to know. For several years, while I searched for, found, and studied black women writers, I deliberately shut O'Connor out, feeling almost ashamed that she had reached me first. And yet, even when I no longer read her, I missed her, and realized that though the rest of America might not mind, having endured it so long, I would never be satisfied with a segregated literature. I would have to read Zora Hurston *and* Flannery O'Connor, Nella Larsen *and* Carson McCullers, Jean Toomer *and* William Faulkner, before I could begin to feel *well* read at all.

I thought it might be worthwhile, in 1974, to visit the two houses, Flannery O'Connor's and mine, to see what could be learned twenty-two years after we moved away and ten years after her death. It seemed right to go to my old house first – to set the priorities of vision, so to speak – and then to her house, to see, at the very least, whether her peacocks would still be around. To this bit of nostalgic exploration I invited my mother, who, curious about peacocks and abandoned houses, if not about literature and writers, accepted.

In her shiny new car, which at sixty-one she has learned to drive, we cruised down the wooded Georgia highway to revisit our past.

...

'O'Connor wrote a story once called 'Everything That Rises Must Converge.'

'What?'

'Everything that goes up comes together, meets, becomes one thing. Briefly, the story is this: an old white woman in her fifties -'

'That's not old! I'm older than that, and I'm not old!'

'Sorry. This middle-aged woman gets on a bus with her son, who likes to think he is a Southern liberal . . . he looks for a black person to sit next to. This horrifies his mother, who, though not old, has old ways. She is wearing a very hideous, very expensive hat, which is purple and green.'

'Purple and *green?*'

'Very expensive. *Smart.* Bought at the best store in town. She says, 'With a hat like this, I won't meet myself coming and going.' But in fact, soon a large black woman, whom O'Connor describes as looking something like a gorilla, gets on the bus with a little boy, and she is wearing this same green-and-purple hat. Well, our not-so-young white lady is horrified, out*done*.'

'*I bet* she was. Black folks have money to buy foolish things with too, now.'

'O'Connor's point exactly! Everything that rises, must converge.'

'Well, the green-and-purple-hats people will have to converge without me.'

'O'Connor thought that the South, as it became more 'progressive', would become just like the North. Culturally bland, physically ravished, and, where the people are concerned, well, you wouldn't be able to tell one racial group from another. Everybody would want the same things, like the same things, and everybody would be reduced to wearing, symbolically, the same green-and-purple hats.'

'And do you think this is happening?'

'I do. But that is not the whole point of the story. The white woman, in an attempt to save her pride, chooses to treat the incident of the identical hats as a case of monkey-see, monkey-do. She assumes she is not the monkey, of course. She ignores the idiotic-looking black woman and begins instead to flirt with the woman's son, who is small and black and *cute*. She fails to notice that the black woman is glowering at her. When they all get off the bus she offers the little boy a 'bright new penny.' And the child's mother knocks the hell out of her with her pocketbook.'

'I bet she carried a large one.'

'Large, and full of hard objects.'

'Then what happened? Didn't you say the white woman's son was with her?'

'He had tried to warn his mother. 'These new Negroes are not like the old,' he told her. But she never listened. He thought be hated his mother until he saw her on the ground, then he felt sorry for her. But when he tried to help her, she didn't know him. She'd retreated in her mind to a historical time more congenial to her desires. 'Tell Grandpapa to come get me,' she says. Then she totters off, alone, into the night.'

'Poor *thing*,' my mother says sympathetically of this horrid woman, in a total identification that is *so* Southern and *so* black.

'That's what her son felt, too, and *that* is how you know it is a Flannery O'Connor story. The son has been changed by his mother's experience. He understands that, though she is a woman who has tried to live in the past, she is also a pathetic creature and so is he. But it is too late to tell her about this because she is stone crazy.'

'What did the black woman do after she knocked the white woman down and walked away?'

'O'Connor chose not to say, and that is why, although this good story, it is, to me, only half a story. *You* might know the other half ...'

'Well, I'm not a writer, but there *was* an old white woman I once wanted to strike ...' she begins.

'Exactly,' I say.

I discovered O'Connor when I was in college in the North and took a course in Southern writers and the South. The perfection of her writing was so dazzling I never noticed that no black Southern writers were taught. The other writers we studied – Faulkner, McCullers, Welty – seemed obsessed with a racial past that would not let them go. They seemed to beg the question of their characters' humanity on every page. O'Connor's characters – whose humanity if not their sanity is taken for granted, and who are miserable, ugly, narrow-minded, atheistic, and of intense racial smugness and arrogance, with not a graceful, pretty one anywhere who is not, at the same time, a joke – shocked and delighted me.

It was for her description of Southern white women that I appreciated her work at first, because when she set her pen to them not a whiff of magnolia hovered in the air (and the tree itself might never have been planted), and yes, I could say, yes, these white folks without the magnolia (who are indifferent to the tree's existence), and these black folks without melons and superior racial patience, these are like Southerners that I know.

She was for me the first great modern writer from the South, and was, in any case, the only one I had read who wrote such sly, demythifying sentences about white women as: 'The woman would be more or less pretty – yellow hair, fat ankles, muddy-colored eyes.'

Her white male characters do not fare any better – all of them misfits, thieves, deformed madmen, idiot children, illiterates, and murderers, and her black characters, male and female, appear equally shallow, demented, and absurd. That she retained a certain distance (only, however, in her later, mature work) from the inner workings of her black characters seems to me all to her credit, since, by deliberately limiting her treatment of them to cover their observable demeanor and actions, she leaves them free, in the reader's imagination, to inhabit another landscape, another life, than the one she creates for them. This is a kind of grace many writers do not have when dealing with representatives of an oppressed people within a story, and their insistence on knowing everything, on being God, in fact, has burdened us with more stereotypes than we can ever hope to shed.

Andalusia is a large white house at the top of a hill with a view of a lake from its screened-in front porch. It is neatly kept, and there are, indeed, peacocks strutting about in the sun. Behind it there is an unpainted house where black people must have lived. It was, then, the typical middle-to-upper-class arrangement: white folks up front, the 'help,' in a far shabbier house, within calling distance from the back door. Although an acquaintance of O'Connor's has told me no one lives there now – but that a caretaker looks after things – I go up to the porch and knock. It is not an entirely empty or symbolic gesture: I have come to this vacant house to learn something about myself in relation to Flannery O'Connor, and will learn it whether anyone is home or not.

What I feel at the moment of knocking is fury that someone is paid to take care of her house, though no one lives in it, and that her house still, in fact, stands, while mine – which of course we never owned anyway – is slowly rotting into dust. Her house becomes – in an instant – the symbol of my own disinheritance, and for that instant I hate her guts. All that she has meant to me is diminished, though her diminishment within me is against my will.

In Faulkner's backyard there is also an unpainted shack and a black caretaker still lives there, a quiet, somber man who, when asked about Faulkner's legendary 'sense of humor' replied that, as far as he knew, 'Mr. Bill never joked.' For years, while reading Faulkner, this image of the quiet man in the backyard shack stretched itself across the page.

Standing there knocking on Flannery O'Connor's

door, I do not think of her illness, her magnificent work in spite of it; I think: it all comes back to houses. To how people live. There are rich people who own houses to live in and poor people who do not. And this is wrong. Literary separatism, fashionable now among blacks as it has always been among whites, is easier to practice than to change a fact like this. I think: I would level this country with the sweep of my hand, if I could.

'Nobody can change the past,' says my mother.

'Which is why revolutions exist,' I reply.

My bitterness comes from a deeper source than my knowledge of the difference, historically, race has made in the lives of white and black artists. The fact that in Mississippi no one even remembers where Richard Wright lived, while Faulkner's house is maintained by a black caretaker is painful, but not unbearable. What comes close to being unbearable is that I know how damaging to my own psyche such injustice is. In an unjust society the soul of the sensitive person is in danger of deformity from just such weights as this. For a long time I will feel Faulkner's house, O'Connor's house, crushing me. To fight back will require a certain amount of energy, energy better used doing something else.

We walk about quietly, listening to the soft sweep of the peacocks' tails as they move across the yard. I notice how completely O'Connor, in her fiction, has described just this view of the rounded hills, the tree line, black against the sky, the dirt road that runs from the front yard down to the highway. I remind myself of her courage and of how much – in her art – she has helped me to see. She destroyed the last vestiges of sentimentalism in white Southern writing; she caused white women to look ridiculous on pedestals, and she approached her black characters as a mature artist – with unusual restraint and humility. She also cast spells and worked magic with the written word. The magic, the wit, and the mystery of Flannery O'Connor I know I will always love, I also know the meaning of the expression. 'Take what you can use and let the rest rot.' If ever there was an expression designed to protect the health of the spirit, this is it.

Critical position cards

GREAT AUTHORS

I prefer to read literature written by great artists whose work has stood the test of time. Even a minor work by a great author has value. What is important is to read the text closely, without being distracted by questions about the writer's life, or too much concern with the conditions in which the work was produced. The writer's art is what the reader should be able to see clearly.
This text interests me because …
I dislike this text because …

GENRE THEORY

I believe that all literature can be classified into various types, or forms e.g. tragedy, comedy, romance, thriller, epic, lyric etc. I look for ways in which the text relates to the conventions of its genre. You can only really make sense of a text when you recognise the tradition to which it belongs.
This text interests me because …
I dislike this text because …

MORAL

For me, literature is nothing unless it teaches its readers something, and helps them to become better people. All good literature is basically moral and uplifting. It is important to consider the themes in the text, to understand its moral purpose.
This text interests me because …
I dislike this text because …

READER-RESPONSE THEORY

I believe that the text needs to have a reader before it can mean anything. I work on constructing meanings from the text, filling in the gaps, making connections and predictions, and seeing how far these expectations of it are confirmed or disappointed. I think that the 'mistakes' a reader makes when predicting what will happen in a text are an important part of the meaning.
This text interests me because …
I dislike this text because …

STRUCTURALISM/POST-STRUCTURALISM

I am not interested so much in when a text was written, or who it was written by, or even what it is about. I believe that we use language, not simply to describe the world, but to construct it. Therefore, in literature, I am most interested in how the text is constructed: its form, its overall structure and the patterns of language in it, especially pairs of opposites. Texts from popular culture, societies, belief systems are all structures which can be explored and analysed like a literary text. Some critics who, like me, were interested in patterns and structures became more interested in the gaps, silences and absences in texts. They became known as post-structuralists.
This text interests me because …
I dislike this text because …

PSYCHOANALYTIC

Because of my interest in the unconscious, I pay most attention to what is glossed over or 'repressed'. I want to look beyond the obvious surface meaning to what the text is 'really' about. I also look for representations of psychological states or phases in literature, and am more interested in the emotional conflicts between the characters or groups in a text than in its wider context.
This text interests me because …
I dislike this text because …

FEMINIST

I believe that 'feminine' and 'masculine' are ideas constructed by our culture, and it is important to be aware of this when reading texts from periods and cultures different from our own. I prefer to read literature written by women, which explores women's experience of the world. I am interested in how women are represented in texts written by men, and how these texts display the power relations between the sexes.

This text interests me because …

I dislike this text because …

MARXIST

I read literature to understand the class struggle at various times and in various places, and to explore the causes of conflict between the privileged and the working class. I think it is important to relate a text to the social context of its author and the historical contexts in which it was written and is read.

This text interests me because …

I dislike this text because …

RACE/POST-COLONIAL

The literature I prefer to read is often outside the white Anglo-Saxon tradition. I began by being interested in texts which explore the black struggle against injustice and oppression. I am aware of the negative portrayals of black people, and their absence generally, in white literature. I have become more interested in challenging the claims made by traditional critics that great literature has timeless and universal significance. I am aware when Eurocentric attitudes are taken for granted, and I look in the text for cultural, regional, social and national differences in outlook and experiences. I am interested in the way colonial countries and people are represented in texts by Western writers. I also explore the ways in which post-colonial writers write about their own identity and experiences.

This text interests me because …

I dislike this text because …

CULTURAL MATERIALIST/NEW HISTORICIST

I read historical and other relevant texts, alongside the literary ones, in order to see more clearly the context in which the literature was produced, and to recover its history. I am interested in pre-twentieth century texts, often those written in the Renaissance, for example Shakespeare. I look at the ways these texts have been packaged and consumed in the present day. However, I also analyse the text closely, in order to question previous ways in which the text has been read. The word 'cultural' in my label means that I consider all forms of culture, popular as well as high culture, to be relevant; 'materialist' means that I believe that it is impossible for any form of culture to be independent of economic and political systems.

This text interests me because …

I dislike this text because …

Section 2
Extended Activities

Reading critically

The extract from *Small World* by David Lodge offers
● an amusing take on the whole world of 'different interpretations' and 'other readers'
● a useful, serious summary of the main approaches to reading texts.

Before you tackle any of the units in section 2, consolidate what you have learned already by reading the extract from David Lodge's comic and satirical novel *Small World*. *Small World* is set in the world of academic conferences. It is the sequel to *Changing Places*, in which Philip Swallow, the English academic, and Morris Zapp, the American Professor, first appear. The extract on page 50 describes the lectures given by the characters, summarising their views on the process of reading and the relations between reader, writer, text and context.

A conference of critics
● Enjoy reading the extract from the novel. If possible, work in groups and read it out loud.

● Re-read it and, working in pairs, highlight the different critical theories, using the critical position cards to help you identify the different approaches used by the characters: Philip Swallow; Morris Zapp; von Turpitz; Fulvia Morgana and Michael Tardieu. Make up an extra character, to express one other critical position you think is interesting or important. Which approach do you find most convincing?

A critical role play
Imagine the characters in David Lodge's novel meet to discuss one of your set texts. What would each have to say about it? What would they emphasise? What would they ignore or play down? How would they try and convince the other readers that their reading is right?

● In pairs take responsibility for working on one of the characters. Prepare a short statement outlining his or her reading of the text. Use the extract from the novel and the critical position cards to help you.

● Take it in turns to read the statements and carry on the critical discussion, in role.

From *Small World* by David Lodge

An immense audience was gathered in the Grand Ballroom to hear the forum on 'The Function of Criticism'. There must have been well over a thousand people sitting on the rows of gilt-painted, plush-upholstered chairs, and hundreds more standing at the back and along the sides of the vast, chandelier-hung room.

A roar of conversation rose to the gold and white ceiling, until Arthur Kingfisher, lean, dark-eyed, hook-nosed, white-maned, silenced the crowd with a tap of his pencil on his microphone. He introduced the speakers. Philip Swallow, who, Persse noted with surprise, had shaved off his beard, and seemed to regret it, fingering his weak chin with nervous fingers like an amputee groping for a missing limb; Michael Tardieu, pouchy and wrinkled, in a scaly brown leather jacket that was like some extrusion of his own skin; von Turpitz, scowling under his skullcap of pale, limp hair, dressed in a dark business suit and starched shirt; Fulvia Morgana, sensational in black velvet dungarees worn over a long-sleeved tee-shirt of silver lamé, her fiery hair lifted from her haughty brow by a black velvet sweatband studded with pearls; Morris Zapp, in his grossly checked sports jacket and roll-neck sweater, chewing a fat cigar.

Philip Swallow was the first to speak. He said the function of criticism was to assist in the function of literature itself, which Dr. Johnson had famously defined as enabling us better to enjoy life, or better to endure it. The great writers were men and women of exceptional wisdom, insight, and understanding. Their novels, plays and poems were inexhaustible reservoirs of values, ideas, images, which, when properly understood and appreciated, allowed us to live more fully, more finely, more intensely. But literary conventions changed, history changed, language changed, and these treasures too easily became locked away in libraries, covered with dust, neglected and forgotten. It was the job of the critic to unlock the drawers, blow away the dust, bring out the treasures into the light of day. Of course, he needed certain specialist kills to do this: a knowledge of history, a knowledge of philology[1], of generic convention and textual editing. But above all he needed enthusiasm, the love of books. It was by the demonstration of this enthusiasm in action that the critic forged a bridge between the great writers and the general reader.

Michael Tardieu said that the function of criticism was not to add new interpretations or appreciations of *Hamlet* or *Le Misanthrope* or *Madame Bovary* or *Wuthering Heights* to the hundreds that already existed in print or to the thousands that had been uttered in classrooms and lecture theatres, but to uncover the fundamental laws that enabled such works to be produced and understood. If literary criticism was supposed to be knowledge, it could not be founded on interpretation, since interpretation was endless, subjective, unverifiable and unfalsifiable. What was permanent, reliable, accessible to scientific study, once we ignored the distracting surface of actual texts, were the deep structural principles and binary oppositions that underlay all texts that had ever been written and that ever would be written.

Seigfried von Turpitz said that, while he sympathized with the scientific spirit in which his French colleague approached the difficult question of defining the essential function of criticism, he was obliged to point out that the attempt to derive such a definition from the formal properties of the literary art-object as such was doomed to failure, since such art-objects enjoyed only an as it were virtual existence until they were realized in the mind of a reader. (When he reached the word 'reader' he thumped the table with his black-gloved fist.)

Fulviana Morgan said the function of criticism was to wage undying war on the very concept of 'literature' itself, which was nothing more than an instrument of bourgeois hegemony, a fetishistic reification of the so-called aesthetic values erected and maintained through an elitist educational system in order to conceal the brutal facts of class oppression under industrial capitalism.

Morris Zapp said more or less what he had said at the Rummidge conference.

What Morris Zapp said at the earlier conference was:

'You see before you,' he began, ' a man who once believed in the possibility of interpretation. That is, I thought that the goal of reading was to establish the meaning of texts. I used to be a Jane Austen man. I think I can say in all modesty I was *the* Jane Austen man. I wrote five books on Jane Austen, every one of which was trying to establish what the novels meant, –

---

[1]Philology: The study of literature and of disciplines relevant to literature or to language used in literature

and, naturally, to prove that no one had properly understood what they meant before. Then I began a commentary on the works of Jane Austen, the aim of which was to be utterly exhaustive, to examine the novels from every conceivable angle – historical, biographical, rhetorical, mythical, structural, Freudian, Jungian, Marxist, existentialist, Christian, allegorical, ethical, phenomenological, archetypal, you name it. So that when each commentary was written, there would be *nothing further to say* about the novel in question.

'Of course I never diminished it. The project was not so much Utopian as self defeating. By that I don't just mean that if successful it would have eventually put us all out of business. I mean that it couldn't succeed because it isn't possible, and it isn't possible because of the nature of language itself, in which meaning is constantly being transferred from one signifier to another and can never be absolutely possessed.

'To understand a message is to decode it. Language is a code. *But every decoding is another encoding.* If you say something to me I check that I have understood your message by saying it back to you in my own words, that is, different words from the ones you used, for if I repeat your own words exactly you will doubt whether I have really understood you. But if I use *my* words it follows that I have changed *your* meaning, however slightly; and even if I were, deviantly, to indicate my comprehension by repeating back to you your own unaltered words, that is no guarantee that I have duplicated your meaning in my head, because I bring a different experience of language, literature, and non-verbal reality to those words, therefore they mean something different to me from what they mean to you. And if you think I have not understood the meaning of your message, you do not simply repeat it in the same words, you try to explain it in different words, different from the ones you used originally; but then the *it* is no longer the *it* you started with. And for that matter you are not the *you* that you started with. Time has moved on since you opened your mouth to speak, the molecules in your body have changed, what you

intended to say has been superseded by what you did say, and that has already become part of your personal history, imperfectly remembered. Conversation is like playing tennis with a ball made of Krazy Putty that keeps coming back over the net in a different shape.

'Reading, of course, is different from conversation. It is more passive in the sense that we can't interact with the text, we can't affect the development of the text by our own words, since the text's words are already given. That is what perhaps encourages the quest for interpretation. If the words are fixed once and for all, on the page, may not their meaning be fixed also? Not so, because the same axiom, *every decoding is another encoding*, applies to literary criticism even more stringently than it does to ordinary spoken discourse. In ordinary spoken discourse, the endless cycle of encoding-decoding-encoding may be terminated by an action, as when for instance I say, 'The door is open,' and you say, 'Do you mean you would like me to shut it?' and I say, 'If you don't mind,' and you shut the door – we may be satisfied that at a certain level my meaning has been understood. But if the literary text says, 'The door was open,' I cannot ask the text what it means by saying that the door was open, I can only speculate about the significance of that door – opened by what agency, leading to what discovery, mystery, goal? The tennis analogy will not do for the activity of reading – it is not a to-and-fro process, but an endless, tantalising leading on,

After a graphic comparison of reading with striptease, Zapp concludes:

'To read is to surrender oneself to an endless displacement of curiosity and desire from one sentence to another, from one action to another, from one level of the text to another. The text unveils itself before us, but never allows itself to be possessed; and instead of striving to possess it we should take pleasure in its teasing.'

Readings through time

In this unit you will
- explore further the idea that different readings of the same text are possible
- explore the suggestion that any interpretation reflects the interests and concerns of the critic and of the society in which they are reading
- discover how different interpretations by other readers can help you consider your own response from a critical position.

The extracts, written between 1847 and 1992, focus on 'other readers'' opinions of, and judgements on Charlotte Brontë's novel, *Jane Eyre*.

Who are these readers?

Assessment Objective 4 of the AS and A2 syllabus states that: 'Candidates will be assessed on their ability to articulate independent opinions and judgements, informed by different interpretations of literary texts by other readers.'

- Working on your own spend a few minutes thinking about what this statement means and its relevance for the way you read. As you note down your ideas, think back to any work you may have done in section 1, particularly on the stories by Ray Bradbury and Flannery O'Connor.

  - Who are these 'other readers'?
  - What are these 'different interpretations'?
  - How can interpretations by these 'other readers' help you develop your own 'opinions'.

- Share your ideas with the rest of the class.

Independent voices, informed readings

- Read through the extracts, annotating each one to show what seems to you to be the reader's opinions and judgements. What is each one most interested in?

- Next, working in small groups, take responsibility for looking more closely at one of the extracts. Use the prompts to help you focus your analysis and discussion of this reading.

  - What does the reader seem to be expecting from a novel?
  - What does he or she like and dislike about *Jane Eyre*? Why?
  - Which aspects of the novel is the reader concentrating their attention on, for example plot, character, structure and so on?
  - In what ways, if at all, has this reader been informed by the interpretations and judgements of other readers?

- Prepare to feedback your discoveries to the whole class.

Changing interests and different approaches

The different interpretations of *Jane Eyre* suggest that each reader is not only informed by other individual readings but is also influenced by the context in which their reading is constructed. Some of these wider influences are suggested here:

- changes in the style of literary texts
- changes in criticism
- more general shifts and developments in society (for example, attitudes towards the role of women, class, race and literature itself).

● As a class, talk about the ways in which critical attention seems to have shifted between 1847 and 1992.

- What were the nineteenth century critics most interested in?
- What are the late twentieth century critics (Williams and Carter) interested in?
- In what ways have the critical methods of these readers altered over time? Use the 'Critical position' cards to help you explore the positions from which each of the critics is reading.

The Spectator (6 November 1847)

A story which contains nothing beyond itself is a very narrow representation of human life. *Jane Eyre* is this, if we admit it to be true; but its truth is not probable in the principal incidents, and still less in the manner in which the characters influence the incidents so as to produce conduct. There is a low tone of behaviour (rather than of morality) in the book; and, what is worse than all, neither the heroine nor hero attracts sympathy. The reader cannot see anything loveable in Mr Rochester, nor why he should be so deeply in love with Jane Eyre; so that we have intense emotion without cause. The book, however, displays considerable skill in the plan, and great power, but rather shown in the writing than the matter; and this vigour sustains a species of interest to the last.

Although minute and somewhat sordid, the first act of the fiction is the most truthful; especially the scenes at the philanthropic school.

The Quarterly Review Elizabeth Eastlake Rigby (December, 1848)

Still we say again this is a very remarkable book. We are painfully alive to the moral, religious, and literary deficiencies of the picture, and such passages of beauty and power as we have quoted cannot redeem it, but it is impossible not to be spellbound with the freedom of the touch. It would be mere hackneyed courtesy to call it 'fine writing'. It bears no impress of being written at all, but is poured out rather in the heat and hurry of an instinct, which flows ungovernably on to its object, indifferent by what means it reaches it, and unconscious too. As regards the author's chief object, however, it is a failure – that, namely, of making a plain, odd woman, destitute of all the conventional features of feminine attraction, interesting in our sight. We deny that he had succeeded in this. Jane Eyre, in spite of some grand things about her, is a being totally uncongenial to our feelings from beginning to end. We acknowledge her firmness – we respect her determination – we feel for her struggles; but for all that, and setting aside higher considerations, the impression she leaves on our mind is that of a decidedly vulgar-minded woman – one whom we should not care for as an acquaintance, whom we should not seek as a friend, whom we should not desire for a relation, and whom we should scrupulously avoid for a governess.

Early Victorian Novelists Lord David Cecil (1934)

Her heroines do not try to disentangle the chaos of their consciousness, they do not analyse their emotions or motives. Indeed, they do not analyse anything. They only feel very strongly about everything. And the sole purpose of their torrential autobiographies is to express their feelings. *Jane Eyre, Villette, The Professor,* the best parts of *Shirley,* are not exercises of the mind, but cries of the heart; not a deliberate self-diagnosis, but an involuntary self-revelation.

Further, they are all revelations of the same self. It might be thought that since they are about different people her books had different imaginative ranges. But they have not; and inevitably. You can learn about the external life of many different sorts of people by observation: but no amount of observation can teach you about the inner life of anyone but yourself. All subjective novelists write about themselves. Nor was Charlotte Brontë an exception. Fundamentally, her principal characters are all the same person; and that is Charlotte Brontë. Her range is confined, not only to a direct expression of an individual's emotions and impressions, but to a direct expression of Charlotte Brontë's emotions and impressions. In this, her final limitation, we come indeed to the distinguishing fact of her character as a novelist. The world she creates is the world of her own inner life; she is her own subject.

She does not pause to consider probability either. Charlotte Brontë's incapacity to make a book coherent as a whole is only equalled by her incapacity to construct a plausible machinery of action for its component parts. Her plots are not dull; but they have every other defect that a plot could have; they are at once conventional, confusing and unlikely.

Her books – and this is true of no other English novelist of comparable merit – are, but for the continued presence of certain figures, incoherent. Nor is this because they are like *Pickwick,* a succession of adventures only connected by a hero. No, each is a drama: but not one drama. Charlotte Brontë will embark on a dramatic action and then, when it is half finished, without warning abandon it for another, equally dramatic, but without bearing on what has come before or will follow after. The first quarter of *Jane Eyre* is about Jane's life as a child; the next half is devoted to her relation with Rochester: in the last quarter of the book, St John Rivers appears, and the rest of the book, except for the final chapters, is concerned with her relation to him.

The English Novel Walter Allen (1954)

It is perhaps the index of Charlotte's achievement, however, that she needs to be read in adolescence; come to her work after that and a considerable act of imagination is called for before she can be read with sympathy.

Fundamental to all her novels is the pupil-master relationship, which is her rationalization, based on her own limited experience of life outside Haworth, of one of the commonest sexual dreams of women: the desire to be mastered, but to be mastered by a man so lofty in his scorn for women as to make the very fact of being mastered a powerful adjunct to the woman's self-esteem. It is a fantasy with obvious affinities with the Cinderella story: the man stoops down, as it were, from a great height. But it goes a step beyond the Cinderella story in sophistication. The woman triumphs not merely because she compels the proud man to stoop. Phyllis Bentley has argued that *Jane Eyre* is much more than 'a mere "escape" romance' because Jane does not 'enjoy a complete, unreal triumph'; she is left with a half-blind husband. It would indeed be absurd to condemn *Jane Eyre* as a novel of escape, yet that Rochester should be half blind and almost helpless at the end is the sign of the uncompromising nature of Charlotte Brontë's fantasy: the proud man is struck in his pride by Nemesis. When he is helpless it is the woman's turn to stoop; Rochester's mutilation is the symbol of Jane's triumph in the battle of the sexes.

The English Novel Raymond Williams (1970)

Jane Eyre is first-person in a quite radical way where *Wuthering Heights* is multipersonal: an effect of experience before ever it is a method. The connecting power of Charlotte Brontë's fiction is in just this first-person capacity to compose an intimate relationship with the reader: from the easy friendly beginning – 'I was glad of it, I never liked long walks' – to the final and secret sharing – 'I kept these things then, and pondered them in my heart': things the reader knows but the others – the other characters, the outside world – do not.

'Reader, I married him.' But that address to the reader, that capital public address, is a late pulling-away as the story fades into retrospect, into the given account. While the experience lasts, the 'I' of the novel and the subjective position – the only available position – of the reader are on a much closer bearing. What matters throughout is this private confidence, this mode of confession: the account given as if in a private letter, in private talk; the account given to a journal, a private journal, and then the act of writing includes – as it were involuntarily, yet it is very deliberate and conscious art – the awareness of the friend, the close one, the unknown but in this way intimate reader: the reader *as* the writer, while the urgent voice lasts.

Given the action of *Jane Eyre,* which is in every sense dramatic, there is a pull, all the same, between action and consciousness.

Expletives Deleted Angela Carter (1992)

In 1847, a young woman of genius, vexed at publishers' rejections of *The Professor,* the first novel she had completed, on the grounds that it 'lacked colour' and was too short, sat down to give the reading public exactly what she had been told they wanted – something 'wild, wonderful and thrilling', in three volumes. Rarely, if ever, has such a strategy proved so successful. The young woman's name was Charlotte Brontë and the novel she produced, *Jane Eyre,* is still, after a century and a half, 'wild, wonderful and thrilling'. It remains the most durable of melodramas, angry, sexy, a little crazy, a perennial bestseller – one of the oddest novels ever written, a delirious romance replete with elements of pure fairytale, given its extraordinary edge by the emotional intelligence of the writer and the exceptional sophistication of her heart.

Charlotte Brontë lived during one of the greatest periods of social change in English history. In all her novels, she is attempting to describe a way of living that had never existed before and had come into being with the unprecedented social and economic upheavals of England in the early industrial revolution. Jane Eyre herself is the prototype Charlotte Brontë heroine – a woman on her own for whose behaviour there are no guidelines. This woman is not only capable of earning her own living but also must and needs to do so; for her, therefore, love is a means of existential definition, an exploration of the potentials of her self, rather than the means of induction into the contingent existence of the married woman, as it had been for the previous heroines of the bourgeois novel.

I don't think for one moment that Charlotte Brontë knew she was doing this, precisely. When she wrote *Jane Eyre,* she thought she was writing a love story; but in order for Charlotte Brontë, with her precise configuration of class background and personal history, to write a love story, she had, first of all, to perform an analysis of the operation of erotic attraction upon a young woman who is not rich nor beautiful but, all the same, due to her background and education, free to choose what she does with her life.

The clarity and strength of Charlotte Brontë's perception of her heroine's struggle for love is extraordinary. Yet, of all the great novels in the world, *Jane Eyre* veers the closest towards trash. Elizabeth Rigby, writing in the *Quarterly Review,* 1848, makes the exact point that the novel combines 'such genuine power with such horrid taste'. She went on, a touch petulantly. 'the popularity of *Jane Eyre* is a proof how deeply the love of the illegitimate romance is implanted in our nature.' In order to do something new, in order to describe a way of being that had no existing language to describe it, Charlotte Brontë reverted, to a large extent, to pre-bourgeois forms. *Jane Eyre* is the classic formulation of the romance narrative, with its mysteries of parentage, lost relatives miraculously recovered, stolen letters, betrayal, deceit – and it fuses elements of two ancient fairytales, *Bluebeard,* specifically referred to in the text when Thornfield Hall is compared to Bluebeard's castle, and *Beauty and the Beast,* plus a titillating hint of *Cinderella.* The archaic sub-literary forms of romance and fairytale are so close to dreaming they lend themselves readily to psychoanalytic interpretation. Episodes such as that in which Rochester's mad wife rips apart the veil he has bought Jane to wear at his second, bigamous wedding have the delirium of dream language. As a result, *Jane Eyre* is a peculiarly unsettling blend of penetrating psychological realism, of violent and intuitive feminism, of a surprisingly firm sociological grasp, and of the utterly non-realistic apparatus of psycho-sexual fantasy – irresistible passion, madness, violent death, dream, telepathic communication.

Will the real poem please stand up? Wyatt's 'They flee from me'

The aim of the activity is to raise some questions about
- the way we decide whether a text is genuine
- the role played by writers, editors and readers in creating the meaning of a text.

This sequence of activities on Wyatt's poem 'They flee from me' was researched and devised by Richard Jacobs (Collyer's College, Horsham; visiting lecturer at the University of Brighton), whose *A Beginners' Guide to Critical Reading: an Anthology of Literary Texts* is forthcoming from Routledge (April 2001). This provides in one volume a stimulating collection of texts from 1530-1980 and accompanying commentaries exploring the inter-relations between texts and contexts and illustrating contemporary critical approaches to literary study.

- Working on your own, read the two poems. Highlight the main differences between the two and make a note of which one you prefer and why.

- Share your ideas with the rest of the class and listen to what other people have to say.

The genuine article?
Printed below are a number of statements.
- Consider each one in turn, ticking those you agree with or think might be possible.

- The two poems should be treated as completely different poems.
- They are two versions of the same poem.
- Only one can be the 'real' poem.
- Both could be genuine.
- It is irrelevant which poem is genuine.
- It is impossible to tell which poem is the genuine one.
- The relationship between the poems is central to understanding their significance.

- If you were told that only one of the poems were genuine, which one would you choose. Why?

- Either in pairs or as a class, take responsibility for arguing for the status of one of the poems printed here.

- Listen to each case and take a vote on which you think is the 'original' or 'genuine' poem.

Commentary
- Read Richard Jacobs's commentary on the two poems, ticking any points you agree with.

- As a class, talk about your response to the following:
- the issues raised by the two poems and the commentary (for example, authorship, the role of the editor and reader, the concept of a 'genuine' text)
- the criteria we use to determine the value of poetry.

A critical commentary on Wyatt's 'They Flee from Me'

The two poems date from the early 16th century, more than fifty years before Shakespeare wrote his best-known plays. It is/they are apparently by Sir Thomas Wyatt, one of Henry VIIIth's courtiers and diplomats. It is thought Wyatt might have seriously displeased the king by getting entangled with Anne Boleyn. In the poem/s a man is reflecting on the fact that women, and one in particular, seem to be 'forsaking' him, to use the word in the poem and in the title to one of them. The spelling has been modernised.

The sexiness of the second verse, the dress coming off and the 'small' [slender] arms catching the man who thought it was his place to do the catching, may be the first thing to strike you, and reasonably enough. Bodies are often eroticized in Renaissance literature but this is particularly beguiling. Then you might wonder about the image in the first verse: what are the women, in this man's life, compared to in this verse, and what do we make of it? Readers often think the comparison is to birds but what if 'heart' is a pun on 'hart' [male deer], and indeed 'dear' on 'deer'? Issues of tame and wild, in the sexual politics of the poem, become even more pointed when we think of those deer kept in royal parks, somehow both aloof and vulnerable, stalked and stalking.

For who is stalking or indeed seducing whom here? The speaker may have assumed that the power was his and, in the light of his experience with one particular woman, seems to need to express a response appropriate to the changed circumstances of the new sexual politics. But isn't his response rather different in the two versions? If you read them again, perhaps aloud, and then highlight or list the differences, even the tiny and apparently trivial ones, what are you led to suspect? How might this help us reconstruct some sort of explanation for the two versions?

Readers, once they've heard the two versions a few times, nearly always prefer (A). It's smoother, more 'poem-like'. The differences, with one exception, mean that many lines are a little longer, with the resulting rhythmical smoothening effect. More to the point, the speaker has evidently been treated 'unkindly' and not 'kindly', and is likely to feel that the newfangled fashion of women choosing to seduce and then leave men is 'bitter' to him rather than 'strange'. The final gesture of

repeating the seducing woman's 'how like you this?' in turning to the reader (by implication male) for confirmation of the speaker's vindictive feelings has a nice ironic force as he turns her own words against her now. The end of (B) – 'I would fain know' [I'd like to know] – seems oddly muted in comparison.

The impression of a smoother rhythm in (A) is no accident. You may have noticed that (A) is in regular iambic pentameter. In contrast (B) sounds more halting and more like speech. So, taken together, the rhythmical differences and the emotional dramatic differences point towards (A) being the 'real poem' and (B) being – what? A draft? A careless copy? A stolen or poorly remembered version? The first page of the *Penguin Book of English Verse*, a best-selling collection continuously in print since 1956 when it first appeared, authenticates this impression of (A), for there it is in unmodernised form on page 1, complete with a jaunty title, the first poem in Penguin's great march of English poetry.

But Wyatt wrote (B). A man called Tottel concocted (A) in 1557 and what he did, or so it seems, was to think to himself that Wyatt was trying to write iambic pentameter and that he couldn't do it, poor chap. Tottel also seems to have thought that Wyatt had shirked his duty when expressing the appropriate male responses to these women throwing their weight about. So Tottel added those pretty fatuous extra words, shifted the order around a bit for more smoothing, thus reducing the swish-swish effect of the gown falling from her shoulders, beefed up the bitterness and the public-attention-getting voice of the ending, and added the flag-waving title.

Wyatt's muted irony in 'kindly' and the suggestive notes of old-world courtesy in 'through my gentleness' (where the word, as in Chaucer, evokes the codes of gentility appropriate to being a gentleman) and in 'I have leave to go of her goodness' sit rather awkwardly with the confident aggression in Tottel's last lines where the voice is coarser, over-certain, more male. The title is coming out of the same confidence. ('Enjoyed' there presumably means 'sexually had his way with', but the *Oxford English Dictionary* inexplicably only allows this meaning from the 1590s). And as part of the same process of alteration the rhythm loses its halting, bemused diffidence. The rhythm becomes regular and predictable; the emotion loses its sense of muted, painful uncertainty. A difficult moment in the long history of male-female sexual relations meets with a difficult moment in the long history of English poetic metre. It's a twinned moment of anxiety, resolved in a doubly unfortunate way by an editor, not a poet.

And Tottel had his way: 'Wyatt's' poem was published, which it wasn't in his lifetime, his manuscript versions languished in libraries, and the *Penguin Book of English Verse*, which could have chosen Wyatt's manuscript version but instead began with Tottel's influential collection, continues to perpetuate this imposition of metrical and male sexual orthodoxy on a delicate, moving poem.

The point about the altered metre and rhythm, the imposition of the pentameter, needs a little more elaboration. What was Wyatt writing if not pentameters? Scholars and editors disagree about what they think Wyatt was trying to do. For example, is the final '-ed' at the end of verbs sounded or not? However, they seem to agree that the oppressively orthodox reign of the iambic pentameter was not yet established in the sort of power that it later exercised over poets. So it is a moment of uncertain power for this poetic form as much as for male-female power-relations. My guess, hearing (B) in my head, is that the poem shows the influence of a much more ancient form of organising the English poetic line: the Anglo-Saxon technique of lines in two halves, with each containing two stressed syllables which could come anywhere in the half-line. This is known as an 'accentual' rather than a 'syllabic' technique. Try sounding it this way. It's more like conversation; it feels right for the halting, uncertain voice. It also feels more folky, more earthy and earthed, as if the rhythm is obscurely appealing to old authorities in the sexual dilemma, in these difficult modern times of women exercising power.

A related example of this kind of echo of Anglo-Saxon verse comes at the end of *King Lear*. Kent is going off to die, presumably of a broken heart after the death of his loved king. There are two early 17th century texts of the play and editors disagree about which is Shakespeare's 'real' version. In one Kent says 'I have a journey, sir, shortly to go;/My master calls and I must not say no' where the second line is the predicted pentameter; in the other he says 'I have a journey, sir, shortly to go; /My master calls me, I must not say no'. The effect there is of something like a spell, an old rite, with a bare, spare simplicity, as if prehistoric, like the play. Wyatt's 'They flee from me' (B) seems to need to connect with something of this spare, earthy ordinariness, but charged like a spell. Whatever it is,

Tottel steamrolls over it, raising the volume and playing to the gallery.

But here is a note of scepticism. What if someone, tomorrow, proves that Wyatt wanted (A) more than (B), that it was he who gave Tottel a revised and 'improved' version, and that it's a mere accident that the earlier version escaped the wastepaper basket? Certainly the new orthodoxy about *King Lear* is that Shakespeare himself revised the text and could then have been responsible, such is the logic, for changing from 'calls me, I...' to 'calls and I...'. What if Wyatt asked Tottel to improve his poem? Or if someone proves that he was happy, even though he didn't officially authorise it, with the outcome? Is there a danger in making too much about the idea of the 'original'? Aren't all texts, let alone versions of texts, equally unstable entities? Tomorrow I might find in my cellar an earlier version of 'They flee from me' which is closer to (A) than to (B). Or Wyatt's ghost might tell me in a seance that he's had a good look at all the versions around and – got a pencil? –he'd like to dictate to me his final stab at the thing before retiring for ever.

The poem, perhaps because the Penguin Book placed it (or Tottel) on its first page, has enjoyed an enormous currency, rather more than any other pre-17th century lyric poem. Rumour has it that T.S.Eliot was the guiding influence behind the editor's choice for the Penguin anthology. Perhaps there was some logic in Eliot, a poet and critic not exactly in the vanguard of liberal attitudes towards women, preferring the Tottel.

Anyway, in whatever version it is known, this is among the nation's favourite love poems, if polls of such things can be believed. And versions continue to proliferate. An A level examination board recently asked its candidates to compare a parody by Gavin Ewart with a poem purporting to be the Wyatt but which turned out to be a bizarre stitching together of bits of Tottel and bits of Wyatt. It also shifted the emphasis of the last line so that it read: '*How like you this?*' - what hath she now deserved?' which changes Tottel's speaker's question to the reader into an incredulously sarcastic mocking of what the woman said to him (which this version also italicized). That turns up the volume and the aggression yet further, a strange note for the examiners to want to strike, unless the intention was to goad students into a response. So rewrite the poem. But, then, why not? All texts are randomised collections of words, most editions of *King Lear* are a stitching together of bits from the two early printings, and these days, with downloading, editing, cutting and pasting at our fingertips, why not randomise or customise further? So why not? But why?

Richard Jacobs

The lover showeth how he is forsaken of such as he sometime enjoyed

No title

They flee from me, that sometime did me seek
With naked foot stalking within my chamber.
Once have I seen them gentle, tame, and meek,
That now are wild, and do not once remember
That sometime they have put themselves in danger,
To take bread at my hand, and now they range,
Busily seeking in continual change.

Thanked be fortune, it hath been otherwise
Twenty times better: but once especiall,
In thin array, after a pleasant guise,
When her loose gown did from her shoulders fall,
And she me caught in her arms long and small,
And therewithal, so sweetly did me kiss,
And softly sayd: 'Dear heart, how like you this?'

It was no dream: for I lay broad awaking.
But all is turned now through my gentleness,
Into a bitter fashion of forsaking:
And I have leave to go of her goodness,
And she also to use newfangleness.
But, since that I unkindly so am served:
How like you this, what hath she now deserved?

They flee from me, that sometime did me seek
With naked foot stalking in my chamber.
I have seen them gentle, tame, and meek
That now are wild, and do not remember
That sometime they put tbemself in danger
To take bread at my hand; and now they range,
Busily seeking with a continual change.

Thanked he fortune it hath been otherwise
Twenty times better, but once in special,
In thin array after a pleasant guise
When her loose gown from her shoulders did fall,
And she me caught in her arms long and small,
Therewithal sweetly did me kiss,
And softly said, 'Dear heart, how like you this?'

It was no dream: I lay broad waking.
But all is turned through my gentleness
Into a strange fashion of forsaking,
And I have leave to go of her goodness,
And she also to use newfangleness.
But since that I so kindly am served,
I would fain know what she hath deserved.

Textual relations

The aims of this activity are
- to extend your understanding of what is meant by 'different interpretations ... by other readers'
- to highlight the influence of past texts on each writer
- to pose the question, can our reading of a twentieth century text influence our interpretation and therefore the meaning of an earlier one?

The influence of past texts
- Read the following statement and in pairs talk about what you think it means.

No text can be absolutely original. All works of literature, music, art and so on contain echoes of, and references to, earlier texts.

A text may echo or refer to an earlier work. The echoes and references may be in the genre the writer has chosen, or the way in which he or she follows or breaks its conventions. It may be in aspects of language, or of form. In some cases, the allusions and the similarity in form or language may be unconscious. In many instances, however, the relationship with the earlier text is deliberate and openly acknowledged. In such cases the meaning of the later text depends, in part, on the reader's familiarity with the text it alludes to or plays against. This relationship between texts is known as 'intertextuality'.

- Before going any further, think about the implications of 'intertextuality' for readers and the way they approach texts. For example, does it matter if the reader has no knowledge of other texts in the same genre? Can a parody of an earlier text be appreciated by someone who has never read the original? Think about these issues in relation to other subjects, for example, popular music. Can the Fugees' song 'I'll be watching you', a version of Sting's 'Every breath you take' be appreciated without a knowledge of the original? Do Oasis assume their fans are familiar with the work of the Beatles?

Reading 'Strugnell's sonnet'
You will be given a poem by Wendy Cope, written in the voice of Strugnell, an imaginary poet.

- Read the poem and make a note of your response. You should think about:
- her purpose
- who the poem is addressed to (if anyone)
- the tone of the poem
- its effect.

The poem is a sonnet.
- How important do you think it is to know about the conventions and history of the sonnet to appreciate the poem. What might this knowledge add to your reading? What might it take away?

- Share your ideas about the poem and the significance of its form with the rest of the class.

Reading 'Sonnet 55'

● Read the poem and make a note of your response. You should think about:
- Shakespeare's purpose in writing
- who the poem is addressed to (if anyone)
- the tone of the poem
- its effect
- anything else which interests you about this sonnet and your reading of it.

Re-reading Strugnell

● Go back and re-read Cope's poem 'Strugnell's sonnet' and make a note of your response now you have read 'Sonnet 55'. How does this knowledge of the earlier poem affect your reading? Does this make your first response invalid?

● List the similarities and differences between the two poems. How has Cope used Shakespeare's sonnet? How has she changed it and to what effect? Some ideas are given below to start you thinking.

- Both sonnets follow the same structure, but Cope's poem ends on an anti-climax
- Cope's language echoes Shakespeare's. However, his language is elevated, whereas hers is mundane.

Re-writing the past

In the activity you have just completed, you read the later poem first. Your knowledge of the twentieth century poem, written by a woman in the voice of an imagined poet must, in some way, have affected your response to the 'original'.

● Does this mean a later poem can alter the meaning of an earlier one? And if it does, what does this suggest about the relationship between writer, text, readers and context?

Writing a parody

● Have a go at writing a parody of another poem, perhaps one that you are studying elsewhere in the course.

● Exchange poems and, working in pairs, try out some of the activities in this unit on the original poem and your parody.

'Strugnell's sonnet'

'Sonnet 55'
(published 1609)

Not only marble, but the plastic toys
From cornflake packets will outlive this rhyme:
I can't immortalise you, love – our joys
Will lie unnoticed in the vault of time.
When Mrs Thatcher has been cast in bronze
And her administration is a page
In some O Level text-book, when the dons
Have analysed the story of our age,
When travel firms sell tours of outer space
And aeroplanes take off without a sound
And Tulse Hill has become a trendy place
And Upper Norwood's on the underground
  Your beauty and my name will be forgotten –
  My love is true, but all my verse is rotten.

Nor marble nor the gilded monuments
Of princes shall outlive this powerful rhyme.
But you shall shine more bright in these contents
Than unswept stone besmeared with sluttish time.
When wasteful war shall statues overturn,
And broils root out the work of masonry,
Nor Mars his sword nor war's quick fire shall burn
The living record of your memory.
'Gainst death and all oblivious enmity
Shall you pace forth; your praise shall still find room
Even in the eyes of all posterity
That wear this world out to the ending doom.
  So, till the judgment that yourself arise,
  You live in this, and dwell in lovers' eyes.

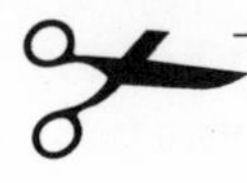

Adam and Eve – re-reading as a feminist

This unit aims
- to highlight the importance of looking at the perspective from which a story is told, particularly in terms of gender
- to show that there is never only one interpretation of an event or 'story'
- to suggest that, in many cases the stories which are given a voice reflect the interests of the people who have the most power in the society.

The story of Adam and Eve
- As a whole class, share everything you know about the story of Adam and Eve. Some things you should consider are suggested here:
- what happens
- who is involved
- what you know about the characters
- the point of view from which the story is told
- the themes, message or moral of the story
- the places you could read this story
- the ways in which the story is used or referred to today.

The beginning of it all
The key passages from Genesis, the first book of the Old Testament, are re-printed on page 68.

- Read the story as it is told here and jot down your first response.

- Working in pairs, spend a few minutes comparing your ideas about the story with the version told here.

- Read the story for a second time, this time concentrating on the way the Old Testament version presents the woman and her relationship with Adam.

Reading Milton reading the Bible
The extracts printed on page 69 are taken from Milton's epic poem *Paradise Lost*. This section of the poem also tells the story of Adam and Eve. In the first extract Adam is describing Eve.

- Read the first extract and in no more than five key words, make a note of your impression of Eve. Compare your choices with another person and talk about how you developed this impression.

- Read the poem for a second time, highlighting:
- the words used to describe Eve
- the words used to convey Adam's feelings about her.
  How is she presented?

- What do the word choices suggest about Adam's (and Milton's) attitude towards her?

- Compare the words Milton uses to depict Eve with those used in *Genesis*. What difference do the word choices make?

Milton's Eve and the Fall

In the second extract from the poem, Milton describes how Eve reacts to the serpent's attempt to tempt her to eat the apple, the forbidden fruit from the tree which will give knowledge of good and evil.

- Read the extract, annotating it to show how Eve is presented here and Milton's attitude towards her. Pull out short quotations to illustrate your interpretation of the poem.

- Use a chart like the one shown here to help you compare the ways in which the Old Testament and Milton tell the story of Adam and Eve. Don't worry about the final column for the time being.

	Old Testament	Milton extract 1	Milton extract 2	Trible's challenge/ commentary
Presentation of Eve				
How is this impression created (e.g direct comment, metaphor, word choices, point of view)				
Representation of the Fall (Who is responsible? What are the consequences?)				
Point of view				
Tone				
Overall impression				
Intended reader				

- As a class talk about the similarities and differences between the account of the 'Fall' in the Old Testament and the story as told by Milton.

Back to the beginning: a radical re-reading

The Old Testament and Milton tell the story of Adam and Eve from a male perspective. This 'masculinist' reading is evident both in the descriptions of Eve and in what the narrative voice chooses to focus on.

- Go back over the two versions of the story, noting down any points where there seems to be a gap, a contradiction or a statement which, in your opinion, is not justified. Write the questions you would like each text to answer.

- Use the two texts, your discussion work and your own annotations to re-tell this story from the perspective of Eve.

- Spend some time listening to these different readings of this story and talk about the difference this shift in perspective makes to your interpretation of the story.

The challenge of feminism

In her book *Treasures Old and New: Biblical Theology and the Challenge of Feminism*, Phyllis Trible returns to the original Hebrew text to construct a reading of this story from a feminist perspective.

- To help you grasp Trible's argument, read through the questions listed here. Use them to help you sort out the argument and its implications for the way the story of Adam and Eve is (re-)read and (re-)written. Once you have got to grips with her reading of the story, fill in the fifth column of the chart.

- What is Phyllis Trible's interpretation of the text?
- What challenges does it offer to the Christian reading included here in the Authorized version of the Old Testament?
- How does it differ from Milton's, and from the way the story is usually interpreted?
- What is her attitude towards Eve? How does she see her?
- How does she construct her alternative interpretation? What methods does she use?
- How convincing do you find this re-reading of the story?

Genesis, chapter two vs. 21-25

And the Lord God caused a deep sleep to fall upon Adam and he slept: and he took one of his ribs, and closed up the flesh instead thereof;

And the rib, which the Lord God had taken from man, made he a woman, and brought her unto the man.

And Adam said, This is now bone of my bones, and flesh of my flesh: she shall be called Woman, because she was taken out of Man.

Therefore shall a man leave his father and mother, and shall cleave unto his wife: and they shall be one flesh.

And they were both naked, the man and his wife, and were not ashamed.

Genesis, chapter three vs. 6 and 11-13

And when the woman saw that the tree was good for food, and that it was pleasant to the eyes, and a tree to be desired to make one wise, she took of the fruit thereof and did eat, and gave also unto her husband with her, and he did eat.

[They then realise they are naked, and that they have done wrong, and try to hide from God:]

And he [God] said, Who told thee thou wast naked? Hast thou eaten of the tree, whereof I commanded thee that thou shouldst not eat?

And the man said : The woman whom thou gavest to be with me, she gave me of the tree and I did eat.

And the Lord God said unto the woman, What is this that thou hast done?

And the woman said, The serpent beguiled me and I did eat.

Paradise Lost

Mine eyes he closed, but open left the cell
Of fancy, my internal sight; by which,
Abstract as in a trance, methought I saw,
Though sleeping, where I lay, and saw the Shape
Still glorious before whom awake I stood;
Who, stooping, opened my left side, and took
From thence a rib, with cordial spirits warm,
And life-blood streaming fresh; wide was the wound,
But suddenly with flesh filled up and healed.
The rib he formed and fashioned with his hands;
Under his forming hands a creature grew,
Man-like, but different sex, so lovely fair
That what seemed fair in all the world seemed now
Mean, or in her summed up, in her contained
And in her looks, which from that time infused
Sweetness into my heart unfelt before,
And into all things from her air inspired
The spirit of love and amorous delight.
She disappeared, and left me dark; I waked
To find her, or for ever to deplore
Her loss, and other pleasures all abjure:
When, out of hope, behold her not far off,
Such as I saw her in my dream, adorned
With what all Earth and Heaven could bestow
To make her amiable. On she came,
Led by her Heavenly Maker, though unseen
And guided by his voice, nor uninformed
Of nuptial sanctity and marriage rites.
Grace was in all her steps, heaven in her eye,
In every gesture dignity and love.
I, overjoyed, could not forbear aloud:–
'This turn hath made amends; thou hast fulfilled
Thy words, Creator bounteous and benign,
Giver of all things fair – but fairest this
Of all thy gifts! – nor enviest. I now see
Bone of my bone, flesh of my flesh, my Self
Before me. Woman is her name, of Man
Extracted; for this cause he shall forgo
Father and mother, and to his wife adhere,
And they shall be one flesh, one heart, one soul.'

Extract 1 Book VIII lines 459-499

'Goddess humane, reach, then, and freely taste!'
He [Satan]ended; and his words, replete with guile,
Into her heart too easy entrance won.
Fixed on the fruit she gazed, which to behold
Might tempt alone; and in her ears the sound
Yet rung of his persuasive words, impregned
With reason, to her seeming, and with truth.
Meanwhile the hour of noon drew on, and waked
An eager appetite, raised by the smell
So savoury of that fruit, which with desire,
Inclinable now grown to touch or taste,
Solicited her longing eye;

Extract 2 Book IX lines 732-743

John Milton

From *Treasures Old and New: Biblical Theology and the Challenge of Feminism* by Phyllis Trible

Throughout the ages theologians have used this most familiar of all texts, the story of the Garden in Genesis 2-3, to legitimate patriarchy as the will of God. So powerful has been this interpretation that it has burrowed its way into the collective psyche of the Western world. Among major contentions appear the following: man is created first and woman last; this order of creation makes her subordinate to him; she derives from his side; she becomes his helper, his assistant, not his equal; she seduces him into disobedience; she is cursed and then punished by being explicitly subjected to the rule of her husband.

Over against this misogynous reading feminism sets a counter exegesis. It begins with the making of a pun, the forming of *hà-'àdàm* dust from *hà-'àdàmâ*. The definite article *hà-* preceding the common noun - *'àdàm* indicates the generic rather than the particular. The pun resulting from linkage with the corresponding word *hà- 'àdàmâ* becomes in English 'the human from the humus'. Other than references to dust and nostrils, the description of the human remains sparse. Most importantly, it is not sexually identified as the male or 'the first man'. Man the male enters the story only with the advent of woman the female. And that happens at the end of chapter 2. By divine surgery the one human from the humus becomes two, female and male, in the sexually explicit vocabulary *'issa'* and *'is'*. These two are bone of bones and flesh of flesh, the language of mutuality and equality. Thus Yhwh God does not create the primal woman second to the primal man.

Moreover, she is not his 'helper', his subordinate, his assistant, his inferior. Overwhelmingly in scripture the Hebrew word *'ézer'*, traditionally translated 'helper', describes God as the superior one who creates and saves Israel. (So if we have trouble with this word, it is not the trouble we thought we had.) In the Garden story the phrase accompanying *'ézer'*, namely 'fit for' or 'corresponding to', (*kenegdô*) tempers the connotation of superiority to specify mutuality and companionship.

The woman called Eve is not 'Adam's rib'. That rib or side (which belongs anyway to the sexually undifferentiated first creature) constitutes but raw material requiring further divine activity. God takes the material and 'builds it into woman'. The Hebrew verb build (bnh) indicates considerable labour to produce solid and lasting results. It constructs towns, towers, altars, and fortifications. Hence, the primal woman appears as no weak, dainty, ephemeral creature. Instead, she is the culmination of the story, fulfilling humanity in sexuality. Though equal in creation with the man, she becomes elevated in emphasis by the design of the narrative. 'Therefore, a man leaves his father and his mother and cleaves to his woman and they become one flesh' (Gen. 2.24). In this description only the man has parental identity; the woman stands alone. Her independence as a human creature remains intact.

In Genesis 3 the serpent addresses the woman with plural verb forms, thereby rendering her spokesperson for the human couple (hardly the pattern of patriarchal culture). 'Did God say, 'You shall not eat of any fruit ...?'' he asked. To answer his question, the woman states the case for obedience even more strongly than did God. She maintains, 'From the fruit of the tree that is in the midst of the Garden, God said, 'You shall not eat from it and you shall not touch it, lest you die'' (Gen. 3.2-3). This quotation embellishes the divine words with the phrase, 'you shall not touch it'. The woman's interpretive skills emerge. Her understanding guarantees obedience. If the tree is not touched, then its fruit cannot be eaten. Thus she builds 'a fence around Torah', a procedure that her rabbinical successors have developed fully to protect the law of God and ensure obedience. Speaking with clarity and authority, Eve is theologian, ethicist, hermeneut, rabbi, and preacher. By contrast, the man *who was with her* (a telling phrase that many translations over centuries have omitted) appears mindless and mute. His one act is belly-oriented: 'and he ate' (Gen. 3.6).

Disobedience shatters the created mutuality of the sexes. The man betrays the woman and blames God for putting her in the Garden. In the ensuing judgments, God's words to the woman require careful exegesis. 'Your desire is for your man but he rules over you (Gen. 3.16). Contrary to conventional interpretation, these words do not proclaim male dominance and female subordination as the will of God.

They do not characterize creation nor prescribe human relationships. Instead, they describe life after disobedience, with patriarchy as one of its manifestations. Disobedience leads to expulsion from the Garden.

Overall, the story of the Garden shows us who we are, creatures of mutuality and equality, and who we have become, creatures of oppression. And so it opens possibilities for change, for a return to our true creaturehood under God. In other words, the story calls upon female and male to repent. A feminist biblical theology seeks a redemptive appropriation of this story.

Psychoanalytic criticism – what the text didn't say

> The aim of this unit is to give you the opportunity to read the poetry of Emily Dickinson from the perspective of a psychoanalytic critic.

Introducing psychoanalysis

Critics who read texts from different theoretical positions have always been willing to borrow techniques and approaches from other academic disciplines, for example:

- Marxist critics use ideas and frameworks which were developed originally within the sphere of politics
- the methods used by structuralists are based on the work of the linguist, Saussure
- social anthropology, post-colonial studies and the women's movement have all been mined for new ways of reading and interpreting texts.

Many of these theoretical positions focus on aspects of the text which traditional readings have ignored or marginalised, for example the role of women or the working class. They highlight the gaps and contradictions in a text, what gets left unspoken and the puzzles which are left unresolved. This interest is partly because we are now more aware that, throughout history and the history of literary studies, the people who held political power also decided which stories should be told. The activities on *Othello* and *Mansfield Park* on pages 75, 81 and 85 of this pack explore this idea further.

The influence of Freud

Exploring the gaps in the text and considering the significance of absences owes a great deal to psychoanalysis and the theories developed by Freud (1856-1939). These ideas were later adapted and extended by the French psychoanalyst, Jacques Lacan (1902-1981). He was particularly interested in the similarities between the way the unconscious and language systems work. Where Freud was most interested in the relationship between the conscious and unconscious mind, Lacan concentrated on the unconscious itself, arguing that it is 'the kernel of our being'.

Many of Freud's ideas and the terms he used have become part of everyday conversation, for example: the unconscious, repression, symbol and the Oedipus complex.

- As a class, share anything you already know about Freud and his theories.

Psychoanalysis and the literary critic

Critics who read from a psychoanalytic position suggest that the aims and methods of psychoanalysis and literary criticism are very similar. The two lists included on page 72 show some of the main ideas of psychoanalysis and the characteristics of language and literature.

- Read through the two sets of statements and, in small groups, highlight any connections between the two disciplines.

Language and literature

- Texts and critical interpretations foreground particular values, beliefs and stories and marginalise others.
- Linguists argue that our ideas about the world are created by, rather than reflected through language.
- Words replace or stand in for the thing itself.
- The relationship between a word (known as the signifier) and the thing it refers to (the signified) is not natural. It is arbitrary and is maintained only by convention.
- Literary texts use concrete images and symbols to represent abstract meanings, feelings and so on.
- Literary texts avoid saying things explicitly.
- Metaphors compress several things into one verbal image.
- In metonymy the part stands for the whole and all it represents, for example crown stands for monarchy.

Psychoanalysis

- The *unconscious mind* has a strong influence on the way we behave.
- People *repress* and 'forget' feelings, conflicts and desires, pushing these into the unconscious.
- The repressed material (which the subject may be worried by or ashamed of) is *sublimated* or elevated into something believed to be more acceptable, for example sexual feelings may be expressed as religious passion.
- A trivial memory may be a *screen* or a cover-up for a more important memory which the subject cannot acknowledge consciously.
- In dreams, concrete images represent abstract feelings, desires and real events. Single dream images may represent or *condense* a number of real people, desires and so on.
- In dreams a real person or event may be *displaced* or represented by something else.
- The unconscious reveals itself through language, for example in word associations, puns, slips, allusions and so on.
- As soon as individuals are able to speak of themselves as 'I' they become divided. The word 'I' represents or is a substitute for the actual 'I' who does the thinking and speaking.

Psychoanalytic criticism

Psychoanalytic criticism developed as a result of literary critics identifying similarities between the aims and methods of the two disciplines. Readers who use psychoanalytic theories to read texts focus their interpretation on the following:
- the difference between what a literary work is about on the surface and what, on a first reading, remains hidden (unconscious). They argue that this is what the text is really about.
- the unconscious motives of the author and characters – what remains unsaid or unacknowledged
- the gaps and contradictions in the text
- the individual rather than the society in which the work was written or is set and read.

This means they do the following:
- reject the traditional ways of interpreting character
- reject the idea that literature can ever be realistic or reflect the real world
- concentrate on novels which draw attention to themselves as works of literature and 'play' with literary devices and conventions
- are particularly interested in the text's exploration of 'identity'
- explore the unstable relationship between a word (the signifier) and the thing (the signified).

Reading Emily Dickinson

- Once you are familiar with some of the interests and methods of the psychoanalytic critic, have a go at reading the selection of poems by Emily Dickinson, paying attention to the meanings foregrounded by this approach.

- Working in pairs or small groups take responsibility for looking closely at one of the poems.

- Annotate the poem to show your reading.

- Feed back your psychoanalytic reading of the poem and, as a class, talk about how helpful you found this approach in responding to the poem. Which aspects of the poem does *this* reading ignore or repress?

670

One need not be a Chamber – to be Haunted –
One need not be a House –
The Brain has Corridors – surpassing
Material Place –

Far safer, of a Midnight Meeting
External Ghost
Than its interior Confronting –
That Cooler Host.

Far safer, through an Abbey gallop,
The Stones a'chase –
Than Unarmed, one's a'self encounter –
In lonesome Place –

Ourself behind ourself, concealed –
Should startle most –
Assassin hid in our Apartment
Be Horror's least.

The Body – borrows a Revolver –
He bolts the Door –
O'erlooking a superior spectre –
Or More –

280

I felt a Funeral, in my Brain,
And Mourners to and fro
Kept treading – and treading – till it seemed
That Sense was breaking through –

And when they all were seated,
A Service, like a Drum –
Kept beating – beating – till I thought
My Mind was going numb –

And then I heard them lift a Box
And creak across my Soul
With those same Boots of Lead, again,
Then Space – began to toll,

As all the Heavens were a Bell,
And Being, but an Ear,
And I, and Silence, some strange Race
Wrecked, solitary, here –

And then a Plank in Reason, broke,
And I dropped down, and down –
And hit a World, at every plunge,
And Finished knowing – then –

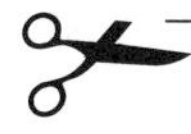

512

The Soul has Bandaged moments –
When too appalled to stir –
She feels some ghastly Fright come up
And stop to look at her –

Salute her – with long fingers –
Caress her freezing hair –
Sip, Goblin, from the very lips
The Lover – hovered – o'er –
Unworthy, that a thought so mean
Accost a Theme – so – fair

The Soul has moments of Escape –
When bursting all the doors –
She dances like a Bomb, abroad,
And swings upon the Hours,

As do the Bee – delirious borne –
Long Dungeoned from his Rose –
Touch liberty – then know no more,
But Noon, and Paradise –

The Soul's retaken moments –
When, Felon led along,
With shackles on the plumed feet,
And staples, in the Song,

The Horror welcomes her, again,
These, are not brayed of Tongue –

754

My Life had stood – a Loaded Gun –
In Corners – till a Day
The Owner passed – identified –
And carried Me away –

And now We roam in Sovereign Woods –
And now We hunt the Doe –
And every time I speak for Him –
The Mountains straight reply –

And do I smile, such cordial light
Upon the Valley glow –
It is as a Vesuvian face
Had let its pleasure through –

And when at Night – Our good Day done –
I guard My Master's Head –
'Tis better than the Eider-Duck's
Deep Pillow – to have shared –

To foe of His – I'm deadly foe –
None stir the second time –
On whom I lay a Yellow Eye –
Or an emphatic thumb –

Though I than He – may longer live
He longer must – than I –
For I have burt the power to kill,
Without – the power to die –

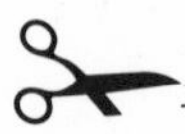

1072

Title divine – is mine!
The Wife – without the Sign!
Acute Degree – conferred on me –
Empress of Calvary!
Royal – all but the Crown!
Betrothed – without the swoon
God sends us Women –
When you – hold – Garnet to Garnet –
Gold – to Gold –
Born – Bridalled – Shrouded –
In a Day –
Tri Victory
'My Husband' – women say –
Stroking the Melody –
Is *this* – the way?

Adapting classic texts

The unit explores the term 'different interpretations' in relation to film adaptations.

Adaptations
Film and television adaptations of novels and plays can be divided into two groups: 'versions' and 're-workings'.

'Versions'
Here the director aims to reproduce the text in a visual medium, without re-interpreting it. Claims are made for the authenticity of the representation. The accounts of the filming of classic novels such as the BBC's version of *Pride and Prejudice* emphasise the amount of time spent in making sure the period detail is accurate. Although minor characters and small sections of the written text may be omitted, and characters cast inappropriately, viewers who know the original are unlikely to find much to argue with. A version is unlikely to provoke controversy or heated discussion about either the adaptation or the original text.

'Re-workings'
In the case of re-workings, the director interprets the text, producing a particular 'reading' of it. The aim is to bring out aspects of the original in new and unexpected ways. Re-workings play off the audience's knowledge of the original text in order to stimulate argument and debate. Like literary critics, these directors argue that there is no such thing as a 'natural' or 'right' reading of a text. Each time the text is read or filmed a new version is created. These critics argue that anyone who claims to have produced an adaptation which is faithful to the written text, which does not highlight or 'foreground' particular issues or attempt to be 'relevant' to a modern audience, simply does not understand that an adaptation is in itself an interpretation.

- Working in pairs spend a few minutes talking about the issues raised by the whole process of adapting novels and plays for the screen. Jot down your opinions about a) the possibility of producing a version which is 'faithful' to the written text and b) the extent to which directors should feel free to 're-work' the text to create their own interpretation. Illustrate your ideas with examples from any film, TV or stage adaptations with which you are familiar.

- Share your ideas as a class.

Texts for our times
Directors who 're-work' classic texts often claim that it is an interpretation 'for our times.'

- As a class, brainstorm what you think directors mean by this. In what ways can a classic text be 'for our times'? How can a novel written in the nineteenth century, for example, be filmed in a way which reflects twenty-first century values, interests and perceptions?

- What aspects of a pre-twentieth century novel do you think are likely to prove most interesting and problematic to a director attempting to re-work a classic text? Use the examples given here to get you started:
  - the presentation of women
  - shifts in what is considered normal or appropriate behaviour.

Adaptations which offer a new interpretation of the text tell us as much about the society in which they are produced as about the society in which the original story was written and is set. The differences between Laurence Olivier's and Kenneth Branagh's presentation of patriotism in their film adaptations of *Henry V* reflect the social and political contexts in which each film was made.

Filming *Mansfield Park* – a radical re-reading

In recent years the popularity of 'period drama' has led to a number of 'versions' of Jane Austen's most engaging and accessible novels, for example *Sense and Sensibility*, *Emma* and *Pride and Prejudice*. There have also been several film treatments which would claim to be 'adaptations', for example, *Clueless*, a radical re-working of *Emma*. In Spring 2000 a new and controversial film adaptation of *Mansfield Park* re-opened the debate about the relationship between author, text and reader – whether this reader is a film director, a literary critic or a student.

> This activity explores the act of 'reading' and 'interpreting' from two different angles
> - the way in which Patricia Rozema, the director of *Mansfield Park*, interpreted and re-worked the novel
> - the ways in which different reviewers read and respond to this new interpetation.

The response of the reviewers

A selection of reviews of the film are printed on pages 78–80.

- In pairs take responsibility for looking in detail at two or three of these reviews. Use the reviews to identify the main changes Patricia Rozema made to *Mansfield Park*.

- Join up with another pair who have concentrated on a different review and share what you have discovered about Patricia Rozema's interpretation of the novel.

- Make a note of your own views of this adaptation.

- Re-read the reviews, this time focusing on the different responses provoked by the adaptation. In pairs or small groups talk about what the reviews, whether positive or negative, have in common.

The 'universal' classic – 'not for an age, but for all time'

- Look back at the unfavourable reviews of Patricia Rozema's *Mansfield Park*. What do these reviewers – and the people they quote – object to? Conversely, what arguments are put forward by the reviewers who welcome her reading of the text?

- Summarise the two positions in your own words.

Section 1, Unit 8 looks critically at the concepts of the 'canon', examining the unspoken assumptions lying behind this construct. According to a long held view about 'Literature', novels, poems or plays included in the canon must be timeless, of universal significance and relevant to all time. More recent critical theories challenge this position and the assumptions on which it is based. Although the different theories focus on particular aspects of the text, they all argue that the stories which have been presented as universal are in fact those which confirm the interests of the people with the power. Rather than being of universal significance, the texts which feature in the canon represent a very partial view of experience – predominantly white, male and Western. This is the focus of Alan Sinfield's discussion of *Othello* on pages 87–89.

Role playing the debate – a critical confrontation
- The two sides of the debate are represented by the quotations re-printed below.

'It is a greater service to Austen to produce a vital work relevant to a modern audience than a piece of archaeology.'

'It is much better to leave a classic text alone.'

- Working in pairs or small groups, use what you have learned so far to prepare a short statement in defence of one of these positions. Your teacher will tell you which one to work on.

- Stage the debate.

Re-reading history: today's values, yesterday's texts
One of the most controversial aspects of Patricia Rozema's reading of *Mansfield Park* was her decision to foreground a particularly difficult and troubling aspect of the story: the fact that Sir Thomas Bertram's wealth depends on the slave trade. Although it is not a central concern in the novel, there *is* textual evidence for her interpretation. So why did it provoke such heated debate?

In the novel the source of the Bertram's wealth is accepted without question. As a result, the whole issue of slavery and colonial exploitation is marginalised, pushed into the background. There are three reactions to this.
1. Readers who believe that the classics are 'universal' argue that Jane Austen's novels exist outside the sphere of politics.
2. Some readers maintain that it is wrong to interpret texts from other cultures and historical periods according to the political and social values of our own time, whether these be about race, gender or class. Similar responses are prompted by the use of psychoanalytic methods to read texts written before Freud developed his theories of the unconscious.
3. A third group of readers and critics argue that these issues existed long before the theories and arguments were explicitly outlined. Like Patricia Rozema, these readers argue that the things which are not mentioned in a text are as significant as those which are. Unexplained gaps, silences and contradictions are all seen as interesting areas for exploration. By bringing the issue of race into the foreground, Rozema problematises the accepted values of the text and the society in which it is set. Jane Austen's brief and undeveloped references to wider social and political issues are not seen as evidence of a lack of interest; rather they are seen as drawing attention to a troubling aspect of the dominant society.

- Look back at the reviews of *Mansfield Park* and the notes you made on these. Identify a quotation to illustrate the three positions outlined here.

- On your own spend a few minutes thinking about the position with which you have most sympathy.

- Share your thoughts in class discussion and talk about the arguments for and against each position. What are the implications of each for the ways in which readers approach texts?

Review 1

Patricia Rozema takes some diabolical liberties with her perversely experimentalist, and frankly preposterous, reading of *Mansfield Park* ... In taking on the dullest, most emotionally reticent of Austen's novels, Rozema has the challenge of working with the most boring and priggish hero and heroine in English Literature ... Furthermore, Rozema has to deal with Austen's enigmatic hints about slavery and Mansfield Park's master Sir Thomas Bertram's plantation in Antigua. She amplifies the genteel minuet of courtship in Austen's world into a raunchy, fully-fledged sex scene, and a little light gay flirting between Fanny and Mary Crawford. And, in line with post-Edward Said orthodoxy in reading *Mansfield Park*, Austen's poor, narrow shoulders have to bear the weight of twenty-first century analysis and guilt. Rozema makes Fanny fully and explicitly aware of the source of Mansfield Park's wealth – but how, having made her aware, can our heroine do nothing without seeming complicit with slave ownership? Rozema's solution is to suggest that slavery is equivalent to a woman's position in marriage: a fallacious cop-out. It's very silly and PC ...

The Guardian, 31.03.00

Review 2

[The following quotations were included in a film review in *The Times*, 16.11.99.]

'It is much better to leave classic texts alone. Unfortunately, people will always try to sensationalise things to line their own pockets. There is a lot of passion in Jane Austen's texts, but it is under the surface.'

Susan McCarton, honorary secretary of the Jane Austen Society

'There is a shot of Henry and Maria partly naked and clearly making love. It is tastefully done and not pornographic. This is a faithful adaptation that is true to the spirit of the novel. It has some contemporary spin to the spirit of the novel.' ...

David Thompson, head of BBC Film

'It is a greater service to Austen to produce a vital work relevant to a modern audience than a 'piece of archaeology'. At the end of the day, this is not a Jane Austen movie, it is a Patricia Rozema movie. I know how arrogant that sounds, but it is a different piece of art.'

Patricia Rozema, Director of *Mansfield Park*

Review 3

[Rozema's adaptation aims] to expose bits of the period's unspoken moral or political infrastructure.
So Sir Thomas Bertram ... is given a strong script bollocking for his slave-colony interests in Antigua, a subject of complete neutrality to Austen. In addition Sir T's eldest son is found with a book of Caribbean porn drawings. Lady B takes opium ...
As one character says (though Rozema obviously didn't), 'This is 1806, for heaven's sake!' Sex may have been invented but political correctness hadn't. So we squirm at attitudinising like 'We all live off the profits'...
It's a shame, since elsewhere this is a sly, well-acted movie whose fair stab at re-eroticising Austen deserved better than having to co-exist with seizures of political precognition.

Financial Times, 30.03.00

Review 4

What she has done is to present ... a challenging, experimental look at its historical dimension. ... Rozema amplifies the novel's playful dance of courtship into something more explicitly sexual: Henry Crawford and Maria are discovered in flagrante and the sisterly intimacies of Fanny and Mary Crawford are given a little homoerotic spin.

With slavery, we have something more difficult. Since Edward Said's writings on the subject, every wised-up Jane Austen fan knows that her decorous drawing room world was at least partly financed by the evil of slavery.

Rozema is quite justified in drawing out the realities of Sir Thomas's plantation in the Indies. Her problem is that, if we are not thoroughly to despise the heroes and heroines, they must have abolitionist sentiments put in their mouths – and that is simply not convincing. Moreover, the implied compassionate equation of slavery with a wife's servitude in marriage is quite a stretch.

P. Bradshaw

Review 5

Mansfield Park, the dullest of Jane Austen's novels, has metamorphosed on screen into a Regency bonkbuster crackling with barely suppressed lesbianism.
...

Aficionados are also hot under their bonnets about how Fanny's uncle, Sir Thomas Bertram ... apppears haunted that his wealth is rooted in the slave trade.

'There is no mention of West Indies slavery in *Mansfield Park*,' says Dennis [an Austen expert]. 'Jane Austen scrupulously avoided large social issues to focus on individuals and it is hard to understand how a filmmaker can make that change with integrity.'

The Guardian, 16.11.99

Review 6

Rozema's *Mansfield Park* is a stunning revisionist reading of Austen's darkest novel. Adaptations cannot replicate the novel on which they are based, and Rozema's movie, more of an intervention than an adaptation, departs radically and frequently. Despite paying lip-service to civility, Janeites tend to be the grumpiest of fans, and many have taken umbrage at Rozema's deviations. More than simple purism is at issue here: Austen's own narrative method makes us feel so uniquely privileged in our closeness to her that we readily believe that no one could possibly understand or visualize a character as perfectly as we alone can, and in all decency – *decency,* mind you – should not even try. For true believers, adaptations will not only disappoint but scandalize. Yet Rozema's 'unfaithfulness' obliges us to think responsibly about what we want a director to be faithful to.

Instead of the frail self-denying, inhibited girl of the novel, Rozema's Fanny Price is sturdy, energetic, and self-possessed. ... I found the innovation ingenious and rewarding, conducing towards the last thing we expect from Austeniana nowadays, alas: freshness and surprise. Here, Fanny retreats to her room not to struggle with feelings of injury, but to engage in the sweetest revenge, writing well. ...

But this spirited heroine with a flair for comedy encounters a history of England that is not funny. Small wonder no one has been standing in line to film *Mansfield Park:* the earnest clergyman, the dignified father, the vivacious young lady, the dashing young man, even the good girl are all benighted, and their country house tainted. To discover why, we must address what some read Austen to avoid: politics. In a haunting early scene, torn from her family to be treated as a semi-menial among affluent relations, Fanny hears a wailing song from a ship off the coast. 'Black cargo', the coachman says. The comforts of Fanny's new home, we learn, come from slave labour on plantations owned by Fanny's uncle, Sir Thomas. Drawing on Austen's attachment to abolitionist writers, Rozema doesn't glamorize the country estate, and this is one of her most transgressive moves. ... [Mansfield Park] looks cold, at times scarcely furnished, and in disrepair, corrupted by the moral crime on which it subsists and on which account it cannot thrive. In a climactic scene of Rozema's invention, Fanny discovers sketches depicting the torture and rape of Sir Thomas's slaves. These are not the pretty pictures we associate with Austen, and because of them the movie almost got an R-rating – a mind-boggling yet satisfying thought. But Austen, and most writers at the time, would have concurred in the moral if not the manner: Sir Thomas's misrule abroad sullies his authority and leads to moral turpitude at home. ... Austen's Mansfield Park is a seductive place, and [Rozema's] Sir Thomas believes in his own show of benevolence. Sir Thomas, depraved by unchecked power, makes no attempt even to appear right-thinking. ...

Times Literary Suppplement, 31.12.99

Post-colonialism and *Mansfield Park*

> This unit explores in more detail the possibility of reading a nineteenth century novel from the perspective of a post-colonial society.

Patricia Rozema's reading of *Mansfield Park* owes much to the work of the critic, Edward Said. Several of the film reviewers (on pages 78–80) refer to his influential and innovative work on the novel.

Reading Edward Said

Said sees the brief and unexplored allusions to places like Australia, in *Great Expectations*, and Antigua, in *Mansfield Park*, as significant absences in the texts. He argues that these allusions deserve the attention of modern readers. This is the focus of post colonial criticism. The extracts on page 82–83 are taken from his book *Culture and Imperialism*.

- Read through the extracts quickly to get the general gist of the argument. In your own words jot down what you understand to be the main points of his argument.

- Talk about your reading of this critical position with one or two other people in your class.

- In pairs re-read the argument. This time highlight the points which give you most insight into the interests of critics who read from a post-colonial perspective. Do they use any of the techniques which are characteristic of other critical positions you have come across (for example, the interest psychoanalytic critics have in uncovering the contradictions in the text)?

- Feed back what you have learned in a whole class discussion.

Post-colonial critics

The points listed here summarise the main interests of post-colonial critics.
- Tick the ones demonstrated by Said's analysis of *Mansfield Park* and pull out a quotation to illustrate each point you have ticked.

> **Post-colonial critics:**
> - reject the idea that the 'canon' represents universal experiences and values
> - challenge the assumption that the 'canon' is representative of the whole story of history
> - show that these texts offer a very partial picture of experience
> - explore and demonstrate the inability of the canonical texts to empathise with other cultures
> - argue that when included in these texts, cultures other than the dominant one are represented in a stereotypical way, for example as either barbarian or exotic (See Sinfield's cultural materialist reading of *Othello* on pages 87–89 for an illustration of this.)
> - explore the way these 'other' cultures have been represented in literature
> - argue that literature is often evasive, silent and contradictory in relation to colonisation
> - claim that the voices of the other cultures are silenced or marginalised
> - argue that in many texts the truth about colonisation (for example, slavery) is repressed
> - foreground cultural difference and diversity.

A post-colonial reading

- Working in pairs or as a class, have a go at reading the extract from *The Last of the Mohicans* on page 84 from the perspective of a post-colonial critic. Begin by highlighting the sections you think a post-colonialist would focus on. Do you think it is legitimate (and illuminating) to read colonial or pre-colonial texts from this perspective?

From *Culture and Imperialism* by Edward Said

A great deal of recent criticism has concentrated on narrative fiction, yet very little attention has been paid to its position in the history and world of empire. Readers of this book will quickly discover that narrative is crucial to my argument here, my basic point being that stories are at the heart of what explorers and novelists say about strange regions of the world; they also become the method colonised people use to assert their own identity and the existence of their own history.

The novels ... I consider here [*Great Expectations* and links with Australia, and *Mansfield Park* and links with the Caribbean] I analyse because first of all I find them estimable and admirable works of art and learning, in which I and many other readers take pleasure and from which we derive profit. Second, the challenge is to connect them not only with that pleasure and profit but also with the imperial process of which they were manifestly and unconcealedly a part; rather than condemning or ignoring their participation in what was an unquestioned reality in their societies, I suggest that what we learn about this hitherto ignored aspect actually and truly *enhances* our reading and understanding of them.

(Intro p xiii)

[In the twentieth century] we have become so accustomed to thinking of the novel's plot and structure as constituted mainly by temporality that we have overlooked the function of space, geography and location ... Like many other novels, *Mansfield Park* is very precisely about a series of both small and large dislocations and relocations in space that occur before, at the end of the novel, Fanny Price, the niece, becomes the spiritual mistress of Mansfield Park. And that place is located by Austen at the centre of an arc of interests and concerns spanning the hemisphere, two major seas, and four continents.

What sustains this life [at Mansfield Park] is the Bertram estate in Antigua, which is not doing well. Austen takes pains to show us two apparently disparate but actually convergent processes: the growth of Fanny's importance to the Bertrams' economy, including Antigua, and Fanny's own steadfastness in the face of numerous challenges, threats and surprises. In both, Austen's imagination works with a steel-like rigour through a mode that we might call geographical and spatial clarification. Fanny's ignorance when she arrives at Mansfield as a frightened ten year old is signified by her inability 'to put the map of Europe together', and for much of the first half of the novel the action is concerned with a whole range of issues whose common denominator, misused or misunderstood, is space; not only is Sir Thomas in Antigua to make things better there and at home, but at Mansfield Park, Fanny, Edmund and her Aunt Norris negotiate where she is to live, read and work, where fires are to be lit; the friends and cousins concern themselves with the improvement of estates, and the importance of chapels (i.e. religious authority) to domesticity is envisioned and debated.

[Austen narrates the reestablishment of Sir Thomas' rule over Mansfield Park immediately after his unexpected return from Antigua.]

Not only is this a Crusoe setting things in order: it is also the early Protestant eliminating all traces of frivolous behaviour. There is nothing in *Mansfield Park* that would contradict us, however, were we to assume that Sir Thomas does exactly the same things – on a larger scale – in his Antigua plantations. ... Austen here synchronises domestic with international authority, making it plain that the values associated with such higher things as ordination, law and propriety must be grounded firmly in actual rule over and possession of territory. She sees clearly that to hold and rule Mansfield Park is to hold and rule an imperial estate in close, not to say inevitable association with it. What assures the domestic tranquillity and attractive harmony of one is the productivity and regulated discipline of the other.

Since Austen refers to and uses Antigua as she does in *Mansfield Park*, there needs to be commensurate effort on the part of her readers to try to understand *what* she referred to, why she gave it the importance she did, and why indeed she made the choice, for she might have done something different to establish Sir Thomas' wealth. ... Sir Thomas' property in the Caribbean would have had to be a sugar plantation maintained by slave labour (not abolished until the 1830s): these are not dead historical facts, but, as Austen certainly knew, evident historical realities.

Interpreting Jane Austen depends on *who* does the interpreting, *when* it is done, and no less important, from *where* it is done. If with feminists, with great cultural critics sensitive to history and class like Raymond Williams, with cultural and stylistic interpreters, we have been sensitised to the issues their interests raise, we should now proceed to regard the geographical division of the world ... as not neutral (any more than class and gender are neutral) but as politically charged, beseeching the attention and elucidation its considerable proportions require.

I think of such a reading as completing or complementing others, not discounting or displacing them.

All the evidence says that even the most routine aspects of holding slaves on a West Indian sugar plantation were cruel stuff. And everything we know about Austen and her values is at odds with the cruelty of slavery. Fanny Price reminds her cousin that after asking Sir Thomas about the slave trade, 'There was such a dead silence' as to suggest that one world could not be connected with the other since there is simply no common language for both. That is true. .... In order more accurately to read works like *Mansfield Park*, we have to see them in the main as resisting or avoiding that other setting (i.e. the world of trade, economics, dependent races and territories, the rise, decline and fall of the British Empire, and the emergence of a post colonial consciousness) which their formal inclusiveness, historical honesty, and prophetic suggestiveness cannot completely hide. In time there would no longer be a dead silence when slavery was spoken of, and the subject became central to a new understanding of what Europe was.

It would be silly to expect Jane Austen to treat slavery with anything like the passion of an abolitionist or a newly liberated slave. Yet what I have called the rhetoric of blame, so often now employed by minority or disadvantaged voices, attacks her, and others like her, retrospectively, for being white, privileged, insensitive, complicit. Yes, Austen belonged to a slave-owning society, but do we therefore jettison her novels as so many trivial exercises in aesthetic frumpery? Not at all, I would argue, if we take seriously our intellectual and interpretative vocation to make connections, to deal with as much of the evidence as possible, fully and actually, to read what is there or not there, above all, to see complementarity and interdependence instead of isolated, venerated or formalised experience that excludes and forbids the hybridising intrusions of human history.

From *The Last of the Mohicans*

He turned to the silent, still, upright and rigid form of the Indian runner who had born to the camp the unwelcome tidings of the preceding evening. Although in a state of perfect repose, and apparently disregarding, with characteristic stoicism, the excitement and bustle around him, there was a sullen fierceness mingled with the quiet of the savage that was likely to arrest the attention of much more experienced eyes than those which now scanned him in unconcealed amazement. The native bore the tomahawk and knife of his tribe; and yet his appearance was not altogether that of a warrior. On the contrary, there was an air of neglect about his person, like that which might have proceeded from great, and recent exertion, which he had not yet found leisure to repair. The colours of the war paint had blended in dark confusion about his fierce countenance, and rendered his swarthy lineaments still more savage and repulsive than if art had attempted an effect which had been thus produced by chance. His eye alone which glistened like a fiery star amid lowering clouds, was to be seen in its state of native wildness.

As the searching yet wary glance of the one met the wondering look of the other, a low sound of gentle voices announced the approach of those whose presence was alone wanted to enable the cavalcade to move, and a young man in the dress of an officer conducted to their steed two ladies, who, as it was apparent by their dresses, were prepared to encounter the fatigues of a journey in the woods. One, and she was the most juvenile in appearance, though both were young, permitted glimpses of her dazzling complexion, fair golden hair and bright blue eyes, to be caught as she artlessly suffered the morning air to blow aside the green veil which descended low from her beaver [hat]. There was nothing more bright nor delicate than the bloom on her cheek, nor more cheering than the animated smile which she bestowed on the youth as he assisted her into the saddle. The other, who appeared to share equally in the attentions of the young officer, concealed her charms with a care fitted to the experience of four or five additional years. It could be seen, however, that her person was rather fuller and more mature than that of her companion.

No sooner were these ladies seated than their attendant sprang lightly into the saddle of the war horse, when the whole three bowed to Webb, who in courtesy awaited their parting on the threshold of his cabin, and turning their horses' heads they proceeded at a slow amble, followed by their train towards the northern entrance of the encampment. The Indian runner glided by and led the way along the military road in front. The veil of the older lady opened its fold momentarily and betrayed an indescribable look of pity, admiration and horror as her dark eyes followed the easy motions of the savage. The tresses of this lady were shining and black like the plumage of a raven. Her complexion was not brown but it appeared rather charged with the colour of rich blood that seemed ready to burst its bounds. And yet there was neither coarseness nor want of shadowing in a countenance that was exquisitely regular and dignified and surpassingly beautiful. She smiled, as if in pity at her momentary forgetfulness, discovering by the act a row of teeth that would have shamed the purest ivory.

Meanwhile, the younger lady inquired of the young officer who rode by her side:
'Are such spectres as that Indian frequent in the woods, Heyward; or is this sight a special entertainment ordered on behalf of Cora and myself?'

James Fenimore Cooper
(1826)

Readings of *Othello* – evaluating the critics

The aims of the case study on *Othello* are to
- give you the opportunity to explore three different approaches to reading and interpreting any Shakespeare play
- show how reading from a historical perspective reveals things about a text which a traditional reading does not recognise.

As you read the arguments, analysis and judgements of the critics and work through the activities, try to think critically about the methods each one uses.

A.C Bradley's lecture on *Othello*

As a critic of Shakespeare, Bradley was mainly concerned with the characters in the plays, often writing about them as if they were real people with lives outside the boundaries of the text. He has had considerable influence on the way Shakespeare's plays are read.

- Read the short extract printed here and in class discussion talk about the approach Bradley uses and the conclusions he reaches. How do you respond to this type of criticism? For example, do you find it persuasive? If so, is this because it is closely argued or because it is the common sense view?

Of Shakespeare's characters, Falstaff, Hamlet, Iago and Cleopatra (I name them in the order of their births) are probably the most wonderful. Of these, again, Hamlet and Iago, whose births come nearest together, are perhaps the most subtle. And if Iago had been a person as attractive as Hamlet as many thousands of pages might have been written about him, containing as much criticism good and bad. As it is, the majority of interpretations of his character are inadequate not only to Shakespeare's conception but, I believe, to the impressions of most readers of taste who are bewildered by analysis. ...

One must constantly remember not to believe a syllable that Iago utters on any subject, including himself, until one has tested his statement by comparing it with other statements of his own or other people, and by considering whether he had in the particular circumstances any reason for telling a lie or for telling the truth. The implicit confidence which his acquaintances placed in his integrity has descended to most of his critics; and this, re-inforcing the comical habit of quoting as Shakespeare's own statement everything said by his characters, has been a fruitful source of misinterpretation,

F. R. Leavis's *Common Pursuit* – Leavis reading Bradley

In the essay printed here, F.R Leavis, another influential critic, attacks Bradley's interpretation of the play, and asserts his own in its place. Early in the essay Leavis calls Bradley's methods 'completely wrong headed' and ' a very potent and mischievous influence'.

- Skim read the passage and, in pairs talk about your first response both to the ideas outlined in it and the critical approach adopted by Leavis. You should also think about:
- the tone of the passage (for example, tentative, open, confident and so on)
- the style in which it is written
- Leavis's relationship with the reader
- the assumptions Leavis makes about his intended reader.

According to the version of *Othello* elaborated by Bradley the tragedy is the undoing of the noble Moor by the devilish cunning of Iago. Othello we are to see as a nearly faultless hero whose strength and virtue are turned against him. Othello and Desdemona, so far as their fate depended on their characters and untampered-with mutual relations, had every ground for expecting the happiness that romantic courtship had promised. It was external evil, the malice of the demi-devil, that turned a happy story of romantic love – of romantic lovers who were qualified to live happily ever after, so to speak – into a tragedy. This – it is the traditional version of *Othello* and has, moreover, the support of Coleridge – is to sentimentalize Shakespeare's tragedy and to displace its centre.

Here is Bradley:

'Turning from the hero and the heroine to the third principal character we observe (what has often been pointed out) that the action and catastrophe of *Othello* depend largely on intrigue. We must not say more than this. We must not call the play a tragedy of intrigue as distinguished from a tragedy of character.'

And we must not suppose that Bradley sees what is in front of him. The character he is thinking of isn't Othello's. 'Iago's plot', he goes on, 'is Iago's character in action'.

In fact the play (we need hardly stop short of saying) is Iago's character in action. Bradley adds, it is true, that Iago's plot 'is built on his knowledge of Othello's character, and could not otherwise have succeeded'. But Iago's knowledge of Othello's character amounts pretty much to Bradley's knowledge of it (except, of course, that Iago cannot realize Othello's nobility quite to the full): Othello is purely noble, strong, generous, and trusting, and as tragic hero is, however formidable and destructive in his agonies, merely a victim – the

victim of Iago's devilish 'intellectual superiority' (which is 'so great that we watch its advance fascinated and appalled'). It is all in order, then, that Iago should get one of the two lectures that Bradley gives to the play, Othello sharing the other with Desdemona. And it is all in the tradition; from Coleridge down, Iago – his motivation or his motivelessness – has commonly been, in commentaries on the play, the main focus of attention.

The plain fact that has to be asserted in the face of this sustained and sanctioned perversity is that in Shakespeare's tragedy of *Othello* Othello is the chief personage – the chief personage in such a sense that the tragedy may fairly be said to be Othello's character in action. Iago is subordinate and merely ancillary. He is not much more than a necessary piece of dramatic mechanism – that at any rate is a fit reply to the view of Othello as necessary material and provocation for a display of Iago's fiendish intellectual superiority. Iago, of course, is sufficiently convincing as a person; he could not perform his dramatic function otherwise. But something has gone wrong when we make him interesting in this kind of way:

'His fate – which is himself – has completely mastered him: so that, in the later scenes, where the improbability of the entire success of a design built on so many different falsehoods forces itself on the reader, Iago appears for moments not as a consummate schemer, but as a man absolutely infatuated and delivered over to certain destruction.'

We ought not, in reading those scenes, to be paying so much attention to the intrinsic personal qualities of Iago as to attribute to him tragic interest of that kind.

From 'Diabolic Intellect and the Noble Hero : or the sentimentalist's *Othello*' – F.R. Leavis in *The Common Pursuit*

- Read the passage again, this time annotating it to show the following:
- Bradley's views about the play, and the characters of Othello and Iago (as reported by Leavis)
- Leavis's judgements of these views
- Leavis's own reading of the text
- what you learn about the play and the characters.

Analysing Leavis

- How persuasive do you find Leavis's attack on Bradley's interpretation? Spend a few minutes considering the techniques Leavis uses to convince the reader that his approach to the play is 'correct' – the only one possible. Some of the features and techniques which you should look out for are suggested here:
- phrases like 'In fact' and 'The plain fact is'
- the pronouns 'our' and 'we'
- verbs like 'should'
- the use of quotation
- close analysis of the language
- references to other readers.

● Do you find Leavis's critical approach helpful in clarifying your own views about the characters? If so, why? If not, why not?

Exploring the cultural context – the power and the story

In the passages included in this section, the critic Alan Sinfield, discusses *Othello* from the critical position known as cultural materialism. This is one of the critical theories which developed as a challenge to the approach advocated by Leavis. The 'Leavisites' had, for many years been accepted as the 'normal' and 'right' way to read literature. Sinfield places his analysis of the text within the wider social, political and cultural context in which it was written and performed. He explores the representation of character and motive in relation to the following:

– the culture in which the play is set
– the stories which characters in the play tell
– the significance of these stories
– the reasons certain stories and not others are believed.

He suggests that racism and sexism are not just aspects of Iago's individual personality, but are fundamental to the structure of the play. Later in the essay, Sinfield uses his close analysis of *Othello* as a focus for exploring the ways in which power is controlled in society. He develops his ideas about why certain stories are believed by questioning the concept of 'common sense'. In common with many cultural materialist critics he then uses his discoveries about society to provide further insights into the literary text.

Telling tales – the significance of the story

● On your own and then in small groups, read through Act 1 Scene 3 of *Othello*. Talk about what seems to be happening in this scene. Read the scene for a second time, this time focusing on the different stories which are told or referred to by the different characters. Use a table like the one shown here to record your discoveries.

Story	Who tells the story?	How is the story received?	Reasons for this reception?

● Feed back your ideas to the rest of the class.

● Read Sinfield's discussion of the significance of storytelling in *Othello*, printed here as Extract 1. As you read highlight the main ideas. Compare his ideas about the stories with your own. How convincing do you find his analysis? Are there any aspects of his interpretation or the methods he uses which you would like to challenge him about?

Extract 1

Stephen Greenblatt has remarked how Othello's identity depends upon a constant performance of his 'story'; when in difficulty, his immediate move is to rehearse his nobility and service to the state. Actually, all the characters in *Othello* are telling stories, and to convince others even more than themselves. At the start, Iago and Roderigo are concocting a story – a sexist and racist story about how Desdemona is in 'the gross clasps of a lascivious Moor' (1.1.126). Brabantio believes this story and repeats it to the Senate, but Othello contests it with his 'tale':

'I will a round unvarnish'd tale deliver,
Of my whole course of love'.   (1.3.90-1.),
The tale is – that Othello told a story. Brabantio 'Still question'd me the story of my life' ' (1 .3. 29) and this story attracted Desdemona. She asked to hear it through, observing,

 'if I had a friend that lov'd her,
I should but teach him how to tell my story,
And that would woo her.'   (1.3.163-5)

So the action advances through a contest of stories, and *the conditions of plausibility* are therefore crucial – they determine which stories will be believed. Brabantio's case is that Othello must have enchanted Desdemona –anything else is implausible:

'She is abus'd, stol'n from me and corrupted,
By spells and medicines, bought of mountebanks,
For nature so preposterously to err,
(Being not deficient, blind, or lame of sense,)
Sans witchcraft could not.'   (1.3.60-4)

To Brabantio, for Desdemona to love Othello would be preposterous, an error of nature. To make this case, he depends on the plausibility, to the Senate, of the notion that Blacks are inferior outsiders. This, evidently, is a good move. Even characters who want to support Othello's story accept that he is superficially inappropriate as a husband for Desdemona. She says as much herself when she declares, 'I saw Othello's visage in his mind' (1.3.252): this means, he may look like a black man but really he is very nice. And the Duke finally tells Brabantio: 'Your son-in-law is far more fair than black' (1.3.290) meaning, Othello doesn't have many of those unpleasant characteristics that we all know belong to Blacks, he is really quite like a white man.

With the conditions of plausibility so stacked against him, two main strategies are available to Othello, and he uses both. One is to appear very calm and responsible – as the Venetians imagine themselves to be. But also, and shrewdly, he uses the racist idea of himself as exotic: he says he has experienced 'hair-breadth scapes', redemption from slavery, hills 'whose heads touch heaven', cannibals, anthropophagi, 'and men whose heads/Do grow beneath their shoulders' (l.3.l29-5). These adventures are of course implausible – but not when attributed to an exotic. ...

However, this is not, of course, the end of the story. Iago repeats his racist and sexist tale to Othello, and persuades him of its credibility:

'I know our country disposition well ...
She did deceive her father, marrying you ...
Not to affect many proposed matches,
Of her own clime, complexion, and degree,
Whereto we see in all things nature tends ...'

Othello is persuaded of his inferiority and of Desdemona's inconstancy, and he proceeds to act as if they were true. 'Haply, for I am black', he muses (3.3.267), and begins to take the role of the 'erring barbarian' (1.3.356-7) that he is alleged to be. ... It is very difficult not to be influenced by a story, even about yourself, when everyone else is insisting upon it. So in the last lines of the play, when he wants to reassert himself, Othello 'recognizes' himself as what Venetian culture has really believed him to be: an ignorant, barbaric outsider – like, he says, the 'base Indian' who threw away a pearl. ...

As Peter Stallybrass has observed, Iago is convincing not because he is 'superhumanly ingenious but, to the contrary, because his is the voice of 'common sense', the ceaseless repetition of the always-already 'known' the culturally 'given'.' The racism and sexism in the play should not be traced just to Iago's character, therefore, or to his arbitrary devilishness, but to the Venetian culture that sets the conditions of plausibility.

From 'Cultural Materialism, Othello, and the Politics of Plausibility' in *Faultlines: Cultural Materialism and the Politics of Dissident Reading* Alan Sinfield

The power of 'common sense'

● Before reading Extract 2, remind yourself of the activity on the meaning/s of the Union Jack in Section 1 Unit 6. As a class talk about your discoveries, particularly:
– the different readings of this 'text'
– the ways in which readers are constructed by their social, political and cultural context.

● Read through Sinfield's theory of 'scripting', highlighting the main points. In small groups, or as a class, summarise his argument in three or four bullet points.

● Have a go at putting Sinfield's ideas into practice by exploring the power relations in the play you are studying. Who has the power ('scripts') and who do they exercise it over (who is 'scripted')?

Extract 2

The strength of ideology derives from the way it gets to be common sense; 'it goes without saying'. For its production is not an external process, stories are not outside ourselves, something we just hear or read about. Ideology makes sense for us – of us – because it is already proceeding when we arrive in the world and we come to consciousness in its terms. As the world shapes itself around and through us, certain interpretations of experience strike us as plausible: they fit with what we have experienced already, and are confirmed by others around us.

Ideology is produced everywhere and all the time in the social order, but some institutions – by definition, those that usually corroborate the prevailing power arrangements – are vastly more powerful than others. The stories they endorse are more difficult to challenge, even to disbelieve. ... At the same time I would not want to lose a traditional sense [that] ... the most effective stories are given specific scope and direction by powerful men. They authorize scripts, we may say, that the other characters resist only with difficulty. ...

The state is the most powerful scriptor; it is best placed to enforce its story. In *Othello,* the Duke offers Brabantio, for use against Desdemona's alleged enchanter, 'the bloody book of law' (I. 3. 67-70): the ruling elite have written this, and they decree who shall apply it. At the end of the play, Othello tries to control the story that will survive him – 'When you shall these unlucky deeds relate,/Speak of them as they are... (5.2.342-3). However, the very last lines are spoken by Lodovico, the Venetian nobleman and representative of the Senate: 'Myself will straight aboard, and to the state/This heavy act with heavy heart relate.' The state and the ruling elite will tell Othello's story in the way they choose.

From 'Cultural Materialism, Othello, and the Politics of Plausibility' in *Faultlines: Cultural Materialism and the Politics of Dissident Reading* **Alan Sinfield**

Comparing the critics

- To help you compare the approaches adopted by the different readers included in this unit complete a chart like the one on page 90. Use these questions to help you think critically about the methods each critic uses.

- Does the critic start with an exploration of the play and develop an interpretation based on this reading?
- Does the critic start with a theory, idea or interpretation and use the play in support of this?
- Does the critic look outside the text, and if so where? Or does he or she focus solely on the text itself?

The critics' debate

Imagine the three critics had the chance to defend their critical practices. What would they say? How would each one convince the others that his/her approach is relevant, illuminating, rigorous, accessible, interesting and so on?

● Choose one scene from a Shakespeare play you are studying. Try to write 2-3 paragraphs adopting the different approaches of the three critics, for example treating the characters as real people or investigating who is in control of the 'story'.

	Bradley	Leavis	Sinfield
Critical methods			
Insights gained			
Challenges			

Three readings of Hemingway's 'Cat in the Rain'

The aim of this unit is to introduce you in a practical way to the approach and methods of a structuralist reader.

Reading the story

The complete text of 'Cat in the Rain' by Ernest Hemingway is printed on pages 98-99.

- Working on your own quickly read through the story and jot down your first impressions of what it is about.

- Read the story for a second time, making a note of what seem to you to be its key features. Some of the things you should pay attention to are suggested here:
- what happens
- the characters and their relationships
- the tone of the passage
- the way the story is told (for example, the 'narrative voice', the perspective from which the story is told, the balance between dialogue, description and comment, the choice of words and so on).

Summarising the story

- Use your notes to write a 30 word summary of the story. This must be in continuous prose, not notes, and must accurately reflect your interpretation of the story. You might find it helpful to draft a longer summary first.

- In pairs, compare your summaries and talk about their similarities and differences. What do the summaries reveal about your readings of the story?

- Join up with another pair and take it in turns to read out your summaries. As you listen, tick any aspects of your summary shared by the other versions. Highlight anything which you have included but which the other people in your group have left out.

The perfect summary

- Working in your group, use your individual summaries to construct a 30 word version which you are all happy to accept. Make a brief note of anything which you found it difficult to come to an agreement about.

- Take it in turns to feed back the main points of your group work to the rest of the class. Talk about what you think this story is 'about', as opposed to 'what happens in it'.

- Make a note of any problems of interpretation you have come across while reading, summarising and talking about this story. Are there any points which you are still arguing about, or where you personally have a different opinion from the rest of the class? If there are, don't give in – defend your reading!

'Cat in the Rain'– a realist text?

'Cat in the Rain' is traditionally interpreted as an example of a 'realist' text. A 'realist' text presents its subject matter as a direct reflection of the world, seeing and describing things as they are. It hides the fact that, like all representations of the world, whether in writing, painting or speech, it must also be an interpretation. It does not draw attention to the way it is written.

● Skim read the story again, picking out four or five places where Hemingway seems to you to be 'seeing and describing things as they are' – i.e. writing a 'realist' text. Compare your choices with the person next to you and spend a few minutes talking about why these examples illustrate the features of a realist text.

Challenging the realist reading

Critical theories, such as feminism, structuralism and psychoanalytic criticism have challenged the assumptions on which realist texts depend. These theories argue that all texts offer a particular interpretation of the world and that readers should not accept the so-called 'realist' text at face value.

In the series of extracts in this unit, the critic David Lodge considers three different readings of the story, one of which is his own.

Carlos Baker – one critical interpretation

● Read Carlos Baker's overview of his interpretation of the story, printed here and jot down the main points he makes.

'Cat in the Rain', another story taken in part from the woman's point of view, presents a corner of the female world in which the male is only tangentially involved. It was written at Rapallo in May, 1923.

From the window of a hotel room where her husband is reading and she is fidgeting, a young wife sees a cat outside in the rain. When she goes to get it, the animal (which somehow stands in her mind for comfortable bourgeois domesticity) has disappeared. This fact is very close to tragic because of the cat's association in her mind with many other things she longs for: long hair she can do in a knot at the back of her neck; a candle-lighted dining table where her own silver gleams; the season of spring and nice weather; and of course, some new clothes. But when she puts these wishes into words, her husband mildly advises her to shut up and find something to read. 'Anyway', says the young wife, 'I want a cat. I want a cat. I want a cat now. If I can't have long hair or any fun, I can have a cat.' The poor girl is the referee in a face-off between the actual and the possible. The actual is made of rain, boredom, a preoccupied husband, and irrational yearnings. The possible is made of silver, spring, fun, a new coiffure, and new dresses. Between the actual and the possible, stands the cat. It is finally sent up to her by the kindly old inn-keeper, whose sympathetic deference is greater than that of the young husband.

● Look again at your original notes on the story and, using different coloured pens, annotate the extract to show the following:
– anything about Baker's reading you want to challenge
– anything you agree with
– statements which make you re-consider your own reading.

David Lodge comments on Baker's interpretation

David Lodge goes on to comment on this interpretation, unpicking the assumptions on which it is based.

● Read this commentary and, with a partner, spend a few minutes talking about how Lodge's critique affects your response to both the story and Baker.

There are several things to quibble with in this account of the story. Most important perhaps is Baker's assumption that the cat sent up by the hotel keeper at the end is the same as the one that the wife saw from her window. This assumption is consistent with Baker's sympathy with the wife as a character, implied by his reference to her as 'the poor girl' and his description of the disappearance of the cat as 'very close to tragic'. The appearance of the maid with a cat is the main reversal in the narrative. If it is indeed the cat she went to look for, then the reversal is a happy one for her, and confirms her sense that the hotel keeper appreciated her as a woman more than her husband. ...

The description of the tortoise-shell cat as 'big', however, suggests that it is not the one to which the wife referred by the diminutive term 'kitty', and which she envisaged stroking on her lap. We might infer that the padrone, trying to humour a client, sends up the first cat he can lay hands on, which is in fact quite inappropriate to the wife's needs. This would make the reversal an ironic one at the wife's expense, emphasising the social and cultural abyss that separates her from the padrone, and revealing her quasi-erotic response to his professional attentiveness as a delusion.

John Hagopian – a second critical interpretation

● Read Lodge's summary of Hagopian's interpretation of 'Cat in the Rain'. Annotate it to show your opinion of this reading.

John V. Hagopian gives a very different reading of this story. It is, he says, about 'a crisis in the marriage ... involving the lack of fertility, which is symbolically foreshadowed by the public garden (fertility) dominated by the war monument (death)' in the first paragraph. Hagopian's reading of the story hinges on the identification of the cat as a symbol of a wanted child, and of the man in the rubber cape (lines 52-3) as a symbol of contraception:

'As [the wife] looks out into the wet empty square, she sees a man in a rubber cape crossing to the café in the rain . . . The rubber cape is a protection from rain, and rain is a fundamental necessity for fertility and fertility is precisely what is lacking in the American wife's marriage. An even more precise interpretation is possible but perhaps not necessary here.'

What Hagopian is presumably hinting at is that 'rubber' is an American colloquialism for contraceptive sheath, and that the wife notices the man in the rubber cape because of the subconscious association – a piece of classic Freudian 'symbolism'. It is an ingenious interpretation and all the more persuasive because there seems to be no very obvious reason for introducing the man in the cape into the story. Admittedly, the cape does signify, by contrast, the wife's lack of protection from the rain, thus emphasising the padrone's thoughtfulness in sending the maid with the umbrella. But if we accept Hagopian's reading then the umbrella itself, opening with almost comical opportuneness and effortlessness behind her, becomes a symbol of how the wife's way of life comes between her and a vital, fertile relationship with reality. Her later demands for new clothes, a new hairstyle, a candle-lit dining-table are, according to Hagopian, expressions of a desire that never reaches full consciousness, for 'motherhood, a home with a family, an end to the strictly companionate marriage with George.' And the cat, he says, is by this stage in the story 'an obvious symbol for a child'.

Unlike Baker, Hagopian sees the final reversal in the story as ironic:

'The girl's symbolic wish is grotesquely fulfilled in painfully realistic terms. It is George, not the padrone, by whom the wife wants to be fulfilled, but the padrone has sent up the maid with a big tortoise-shell cat, a huge creature that swings down against her body. It is not clear whether this is exactly the same cat as the one the wife had seen from the window – probably not; in any case, it will most certainly not do. The girl is willing to settle for a child-surrogate, but the big tortoise-shell cat obviously cannot serve that purpose.'

● Share your first thoughts. How persuasive do you find the overall conclusions reached through Hagopian's reading? How do you react to the interpretation of the 'cape' and 'cat' as symbols of the woman's repressed desires?

● As a class, talk about the main differences between Baker's and Hagopian's interpretations. What aspects of each reading do you find plausible, even convincing? What is your reaction to encountering two such contradictory readings of the same story?

Lodge's reading – a structuralist's view

Lodge goes on to construct his own reading, using the critical practices of the structuralist.

The main ideas of structuralist criticism

- Things (including words and literary texts) can only be understood in relation to their wider context and the larger structures of which they are a part (for example, an individual novel should only be seen in relation to the whole genre of the novel).
- The meanings we give to words are arbitrary, for example there is no natural relationship between the word 'cat' and the animal it refers to.
- Words are only defined by what they are not, for example 'man' is defined by not being 'woman', 'rich' is defined by not being 'poor'.
- Language doesn't reflect or record the world, it creates it. The words we choose to name things reveal a lot about our opinions, beliefs and view of the world in which we live.

What structuralist critics do

- Structuralists use these techniques to analyse any cultural structure, for example fashion trends, not just literary texts.
- Rather than focusing on the content of a literary text, structuralists are interested in looking first for any parallels, echoes, reflections, repetitions, contrasts and patterns.
- Rlthough structuralist critics are interested in the underlying patterns outside the text, the readings are based on a close analysis of language choices and narrative techniques of the text itself. This is exemplified by Lodge exploring the significance of Hemingway's use of the definite or indefinite article ('a cat' or 'the cat') and the difference this makes to the meaning of the story.
- The structuralist explores the significance of the patterns, contrasts and so on within the context of larger structures, for example the genre or the society.
- The structuralist's interpretation of the text is based on the significance of these patterns.
- Post-structuralists doubt whether any structures remain the same long enough for patterns to be identified and so focus instead on the gaps and silences in a text.

Lodge focuses his own analysis of the story on the following:
- the ambiguity of the ending
- the gap between the plot, the characters and the actual point of the story
- the ways in which Hemingway creates a multi-layered text without any obvious use of imagery or metaphors.

The tools he uses for his analysis are those of the structuralist and post-structuralist. He examines:
- the narrative structure, particularly the shifting point of view
- the structures below the surface of the text
- the significance of the patterns in the story, particularly oppositions.

Shifting points of view

● Read Lodge's analysis of the points of view in the story and the significance of the ending and talk about your response to this reading.

The ambiguity of the ending is crucial. By refusing to resolve the issue of whether the wife gets the cat she wants, the implied author indicates that this is not the point of the story.

There are several reasons why this ending is ambiguous. One, obviously, is that the story ends where it does, for if it continued for another line or two, or moment or two, it would become apparent from the wife's response whether the cat was the one she had seen from the window, whether she is pleased or disconcerted by it being brought to her, and so on. In other respects there is nothing especially striking about the story's treatment of time, though we may admire the smooth transition in the first paragraph from summary of a state of affairs obtaining over a period of days or weeks to the state of affairs obtaining on a particular afternoon, and the subtle condensation of durational time in the final scene between husband and wife, marked by changes in the light outside the window. The order of events is strictly chronological. The story tends towards reiteration rather than summary, telling *n* times what happened *n* times or *n* times what happened once rather than telling once what happened *n* times. This is important because it reinforces the definition of the characters according to a very limited repertoire of gestures. Thus the wife is frequently described as looking out of the window, the husband as reading, the manager as bowing (and the weather as raining).

The story of the quest for the cat involves four characters, and in theory could be narrated from four points of view, each quite distinct and different in import. The story we have is written from the point of view of the American couple rather than that of the Italian hotel staff, and from the wife's point of view rather than the husband's. We must distinguish here between voice and perspective. The story is narrated throughout by an authorial voice which refers to the characters in the third person and uses the past tense. This is the standard mode of authorial narration and by convention the narrator is authoritative, reliable and, within the fictional world of the discourse, omniscient. The authorial voice in this story, however, renounces the privilege of authorial omniscience in two ways, firstly by abstaining from any comment or judgment or explanation of motive regarding the behaviour of the characters, and secondly by restricting itself to the perspective of only two of the characters, and for part of the story to the perspective of only one. By this I mean that the narrator describes nothing that is not seen by either husband or wife or both. Yet it is not quite true to say that the narrator has no independent angle of vision: he has. As in a film, we sometimes see the wife from the husband's angle, and the husband sometimes from the wife's angle, but much of the time we see them both from some independent, impersonal angle.

The first paragraph adopts the common perspective of the American couple, making no distinction between them. With the first sentence of the second paragraph, 'The American wife stood at the window looking out', the narrative adopts her perspective but without totally identifying with it. Note the difference between *'her*

husband in line 27, which closely identifies the narration with her perspective, and 'the husband' in line 30, 'the wife' in line 33 which subtly reasserts the independence of the authorial voice. From this point onwards, however, for the next fifty lines the narration identifies itself closely with the wife's perspective, following her out of the room and downstairs into the lobby, and reporting what she thinks as well as what she sees.

The sequence of sentences beginning 'She liked' (line 42) affect us as being a transcription rather than a description of her thoughts because they could be transposed into monologue (first person/present tense) without any illogicality or stylistic awkwardness. Sentences in free indirect speech, 'The cat would be round to the right. Perhaps she could go along under the eaves' (lines 47) and 'Of course, the hotel-keeper had sent her' (line 52), mark the maximum degree of identification of the narration with the wife's point of view. When she returns to the room the narration separates itself from her again. There is a lot of direct speech from now on, no report of the wife's thoughts, and occasionally the narration seems to adopt the husband's perspective alone, e.g. 'George looked up and saw the back of her neck, clipped close like a boy's' (line 93) and – very importantly:

'Someone knocked on the door.

'Avanti,' George said. He looked up from his book.

In the doorway stood the maid. She held a big tortoiseshell cat.'

We can now fully understand why the ending of the story is so ambiguous: it is primarily because the narration adopts the husband's perspective at this crucial point. Since he did not rise from the bed to look out of the window at the cat sheltering from the rain, he has no way of knowing whether the cat brought by the maid is the same one – hence the non-committal indefinite article, 'a big tortoise-shell cat'. If, however, the wife's perspective had been adopted at this point and the text had read:

"Avanti,' the wife said. She turned round from the window.

In the doorway stood the maid. She held a big tortoise-shell cat ...'

then it would be clear that this was not the cat the wife had wanted to bring in from the rain (in which case the definite article would be used). It is significant that in the title of the story, there is no article before 'Cat', thus giving no support to either interpretation of the ending.

A closer look at paragraph one of 'Cat in the Rain'

Lodge makes the following points about Hemingway's style of writing and what this means for a reader:

– his stories are deceptively simple
– it is a mistake to look for a 'single clue' to the meaning of his stories
– Hemingway was not interested in providing clear motives for what happens in the story (which is what a realist text does)
– he creates depths of meaning in his story without using rhetorical techniques such as similes and metaphors
– he achieves the depths of meaning by using words which, as well as as having a literal (or denotative) meaning have other implications and associations (connotations).

Lodge's reading of the whole story is based on the close analysis of the first paragraph, re-printed for you here.

● Read the opening paragraph and pull out one or two literal statements. Talk briefly about any other associations they may have and what insight, if any, they give you into the story.

There were only two Americans stopping at the hotel. They did not know any of the people they passed on the stairs on their way to and from their room. Their room was on the second floor facing the sea. It also faced the public garden and the war monument. There were big palms and green benches in the public garden. In the good weather there was always an artist with his easel. Artists liked the way the palms grew and the bright colors of the hotels facing the gardens and the sea. Italians came from a long way-off to look up at the war monument. It was made of bronze and glistened in the rain. It was raining. The rain dripped from the palm trees. Water stood in pools on the gravel paths. The sea broke in a long line in the rain and slipped back down the beach to come up and break again in a long line in the rain. The motor cars were gone from the square by the war monument. Across the square in the doorway of the café a waiter stood looking out at the empty square.

● Read the opening paragraph for a final time, highlighting any pairs of oppositions which you notice and record these in a chart like the one shown below. Add a comment suggesting what the significance of the oppositions might be. Can you see them repeated or developed throughout the rest of the story?

Opposition	Significance	Relation to rest of story

David Lodge's own analysis of paragraph one

● Now read Lodge's analysis of this paragraph. As you read compare his analysis with your own and reflect critically on the insight his reading gives you into the story.

'There were only two Americans stopping at the hotel.' Americans opposed to other nationalities: index of cultural isolation.

'They did not know any of the people they passed on the stairs on their way to and from their room.' Index of social isolation and mutual dependence – vulnerability to breakdown in relationship.

'Their room was on the second floor facing the sea.' Culture faces nature.

'It also faced the public garden and the war monument.' Culture paired with nature (public: garden) and opposed to nature (monument: garden). Pleasure (garden) opposed to pain (war).

'There were big palms and green benches in the public garden.' Culture and nature integrated. Benches same colour as vegetation.

'In the good weather there was always an artist with his easel. Artists liked the way the palms grew and the bright colors of the hotels facing the gardens and the sea.' Culture and nature happily fused. Image of euphoria.

'Italians came from a long way off to look up at the

war monument.' Euphoria qualified. War monument attracts the living but commemorates the dead. Looking associated with absence (of the dead). 'Italian' opposed to 'American'.

'It was made of bronze and glistened in the rain.' Inert mineral (bronze) opposed to organic vegetable (palm). Rain opposed to good weather. Euphoria recedes.

'It was raining. Rain dripped from the palm trees.' Euphoria recedes further. Weather uninviting.

'Water stood in pools on the gravel paths.' Image of stagnation.

'The sea broke in a long line in the rain and slipped back down the beach to come up and break again in a long line in the rain.' Excess of wetness. Monotony. Ennui.

'The motor cars were gone from the square by the war monument. Across the square in the doorway of the café a waiter stood looking out at the square.' Images of absence, loss, ennui.

The first paragraph, then, establishes the thematic core of the story through oppositions between nature and culture, joy and ennui. Joy is associated with a harmonious union of culture and nature, ennui is the result of some dissociation or discontinuity between culture and nature. The wife, looking out of the window at a scene made joyless by the rain, sees a cat with whose discomfort she emotionally identifies. Her husband, though offering to fetch it, implies his indifference to her emotional needs by not actually moving. The husband is reading, a 'cultural' use of the eyes. The wife is looking, a 'natural' use of the eyes. Her looking, through the window, expresses a need for communion. His reading of a book is a substitute for communion, and a classic remedy for ennui. It is worth noticing that he is reading on the bed – a place made for sleeping and making love; and the perversity of this behaviour is symbolised by the fact that he is lying on the bed the wrong way round. As the story continues, the contrast between looking and reading, both activities expressing the loss or failure of love, becomes more insistent. Denied the kitty, a 'natural' object (opposed to book) which she could have petted as a substitute for being petted, the wife looks in the mirror, pining for a more natural feminine self. Then she looks out of the window again, while her husband, who has not shifted his position (his immobility opposed to the padrone's punctilious bowing), reads on and impatiently recommends her to 'get something to read'.

One text, many readings
David Lodge begins his essay by saying:

Is it possible, or useful, to bring the whole battery of modern formalism and structuralism to bear upon a single text, and what is gained by so doing? Does it enrich our reading by uncovering depths and nuances of meaning we might not otherwise have brought to consciousness, help us to solve problems of interpretation and to correct misreadings? Or does it merely encourage a pointless and self-indulgent academicism, by which the same information is shuffled from one set of categories to another, from one jargon to another, without any real advance in appreciation or understanding?

At another point he claims 'it seems to me, the structuralist notion of language as a system of differences and of meaning as the product of structural oppositions can genuinely help settle a point of interpretation.'

● As a class consider the two positions put forward here. What is your opinion and why?

● Look back at your summary and notes on the meaning of 'Cat in the Rain'. Compare this with your ideas now, after reading and debating the story from different critical perspectives. Has your own reading of it changed? If so, how? Have you, for example, incorporated the interpretations and conclusions from different readings? Or have you been persuaded by one in particular?

● Write a short piece, explaining how your own reading of 'Cat in the Rain' has been confirmed, modified or changed by the discussions you have had with other people, and the alternative interpretations you have read.

'Cat in the Rain' by Ernest Hemingway

There were only two Americans stopping at the hotel. They did not know any of the people they passed on the stairs on their way to and from their room. Their room was on the second floor facing the sea. It also faced the public garden and the war monument. There were big palms and green benches in the public garden. In the good weather there was always an artist with his easel. Artists liked the way the palms grew and the bright colors of the hotels facing the gardens and the sea.

10 Italians came from a long way off to look up at the war monument. It was made of bronze and glistened in the rain. It was raining. The rain dripped from the palm trees. Water stood in pools on the gravel paths. The sea broke in a long line in the rain and slipped back down the beach to come up and break again in a long line in the rain. The motor cars were gone from the square by the war monument. Across the square in the doorway of the café a waiter stood looking out at the empty square.

20 The American wife stood at the window looking out. Outside right under their window a cat was crouched under one of the dripping green tables. The cat was trying to make herself so compact that she would not be dripped on.

'I'm going down and get that kitty,' the American wife said.

'I'll do it,' her husband offered from the bed.

'No, I'll get it. The poor kitty out trying to keep dry under a table.'

30 The husband went on reading, lying propped up with the two pillows at the foot of the bed.

'Don't get wet,' he said.

The wife went downstairs and the hotel owner stood up and bowed to her as she passed the office. His desk was at the far end of the office. He was an old man and very tall.

'Il piove,[1]' the wife said. She liked the hotel-keeper.

'Si, Si, Signora, brutto tempo[2]. It is very bad weather.'

He stood behind his desk in the far end of the dim 40 room. The wife liked him. She liked the deadly serious way he received any complaints. She liked his dignity. She liked the way he wanted to serve her. She liked the way he felt about being a hotel-keeper. She liked his old, heavy face and big hands.

Liking him she opened the door and looked out. It was raining harder. A man in a rubber cape was crossing the empty square to the café. The cat would be around to the right. Perhaps she could go along under the eaves. As she stood in the doorway an umbrella opened behind her. It was the maid who looked after their room.   50

'You must not get wet,' she smiled, speaking Italian. Of course, the hotel-keeper had sent her.

With the maid holding the umbrella over her, she walked along the gravel path until she was under their window. The table was there, washed bright green in the rain, but the cat was gone. She was suddenly disappointed. The maid looked up at her.

'Ha perduto qualque cosa, Signora?'[3]

'There was a cat,' said the American girl.   60

'A cat?'

'Si, il gatto.'

'A cat?' the maid laughed. 'A cat in the rain?'

'Yes, –' she said, 'under the table.' Then, 'Oh, I wanted it so much. I wanted a kitty.'

When she talked English the maid's face tightened.

'Come, Signora,' she said. 'We must get back inside. You will be wet.'

'I suppose so,' said the American girl.

They went back along the gravel path and passed in the door. The maid stayed outside to close the umbrella. As the American girl passed the office, the padrone 70 bowed from his desk. Something felt very small and tight inside the girl. The padrone made her feel very small and at the same time really important. She had a momentary feeling of being of supreme importance. She went on up the stairs. She opened the door of the room. George was on the bed, reading.

'Did you get the cat?' he asked, putting the book down.

'It was gone.'

'Wonder where it went to,' he said, resting his eyes 80 from reading.

She sat down on the bed.

'I wanted it so much,' she said. 'I don't know why I wanted it so much. I wanted that poor kitty. It isn't any fun to be a poor kitty out in the rain.'

---

[1] 'It's raining.'

[2] 'Yes, yes, Madam, awful weather'

[3] 'Have you lost something, Madam?'

George was reading again.

She went over and sat in front of the mirror of the dressing table looking at herself with the hand glass. She studied her profile, first one side and then the other.

90 Then she studied the back of her head and her neck.

'Don't you think it would be a good idea if I let my hair grow out?' she asked, looking at her profile again.

George looked up and saw the back of her neck, clipped close like a boy's.

'I like it the way it is.'

'I get so tired of it,' she said. 'I get so tired of looking like a boy.'

George shifted his position in the bed. He hadn't looked away from her since she started to speak.

100 'You look pretty darn nice,' he said.

She laid the mirror down on the dresser and went over to the window and looked out. It was getting dark.

'I want to pull my hair back tight and smooth and make a big knot at the back that I can feel,' she said. 'I want to have a kitty to sit on my lap and purr when I stroke her.'

'Yeah?' George said from the bed.

'And I want to eat at a table with my own silver and I want candles. And I want it to be spring and I want to brush my hair out in front of a mirror and I want a kitty 110 and I want some new clothes.'

'Oh, shut up and get something to read,' George said. He was reading again.

His wife was looking out of the window. It was quite dark now and still raining in the palm trees.

'Anyway, I want a cat,' she said, 'I want a cat. I want a cat now. If I can't have long hair or any fun, I can have a cat.'

George was not listening. He was reading his book. 120 His wife looked out of the window where the light had come on in the square.

Someone knocked at the door.

'Avanti,' George said. He looked up from his book.

In the doorway stood the maid. She held a big tortoise-shell cat pressed tight against her and swung down against her body.

'Excuse me,' she said, 'the padrone asked me to bring this for the Signora.'

Re-reading the life – the text, the critic, the writer and her lover

The aim of the unit is to explore the possibilities and dangers of interpreting literature on the basis of knowledge of the writer's life.

For this unit you will need to have a copy of the two poems entitled 'The Rabbit Catcher', provided by your teacher.

Reading 'The Rabbit Catcher'

- On your own, read the poem 'The Rabbit Catcher' several times.

- In as much detail as you can, make notes on your impression of this poem and what you think it might be about. Be prepared to explain the development of your reading.

- Feed back your ideas to the rest of the class and talk about the similarities and differences in the interpretations produced by a 'closed' reading of the poem (i.e one in which you do not bring external knowledge to bear on your reading).

- What other information do you think might illuminate your reading of the poem? For example, what do you think would be added to your understanding of the poem by the following information: the identity, gender and background of the poet; further writings by the same person; other readings of this poem?

Beyond the poem

This poem, 'The Rabbit Catcher', was written by Sylvia Plath.

- Share what you know about her life and work. You should pool everything you know, whether or not you know the information to be accurate or suspect it may just be speculation.

- Does this information alter the way you approach the poem? Does the knowledge you now have lead you to see additional meanings and significances in Plath's choice of words and images?

Many readers have read the work of Sylvia Plath in terms of her life. This conflating of the life and their work can be both illuminating and distorting.

The 'story' of Sylvia Plath's life is tragic and intriguing. The basic details of her life and death are well documented: a bright and creative girl who attempted suicide, studied at Harvard and Cambridge, married the poet Ted Hughes and committed suicide soon after the marriage collapsed. It is also well known that Ted Hughes and his sister Olwyn maintained tight control over Plath's work after her death, and over what was written about her life. The decision not to grant permission for the poems to be included in this resource pack exemplifies this attitude. Until shortly before his death in 1998, Hughes refused to tell his version of their relationship or to reveal his emotional response to Plath's death. This silence led to much biographical and critical speculation. The 'facts' seem to provide insights into the poetry, while the poems are often read as a commentary on a private life which is at once public knowledge and shrouded in mystery.

A biographical reading

The texts printed here are extracts from two biographies of Sylvia Plath. Both explore the poem 'The Rabbit Catcher.'

- Read both extracts.

- Work in pairs, each person taking responsibility for analysing in detail one of these extracts.

- Highlight any interpretations based on the close analysis of the language.
- In a different colour, highlight anything which suggests that the poem is being read as a commentary on the life.
- Try to identify any other critical approaches used (for example, psychoanalytic criticism or feminism).

- Go through your analysis of the extract with your partner and note down your discoveries.

- Compare these readings of the poem with your own. What are the main points of similarity and difference? What is your response to this type of reading (for example, do you find it interesting, illuminating, intriguing, far-fetched and so on)?

Extract 1

Developing a theme which was stated only briefly in 'Zoo Keeper's Wife', one of the April poems, 'Pheasant', and 'The Rabbit Catcher', which is dated 21 May, protest against Hughes's predatoriness towards animals and birds. Feeling privileged to be visited by the majestic pheasant which was pacing through the uncut grass by the elm on the hill, she pleads with him not to kill it. In the first draft of the poem about the rabbit catcher, his young wife dreams of a marriage which will give her enough freedom to become herself. In the event, she has too little, but it's the man who gets angry, threatening to do whatever he feels like doing. In the final version the speaker finds herself in a hostile landscape. Tasting the malignity of the gorse, she associates its yellow flowers with candles and extreme unction. The inescapable snares are zeros, closing on nothing. This image is reminiscent of the sly world's hinges which shut against the mussel hunter at Rock Harbour. In the first draft of 'The Rabbit Hunter' the husband's hands muffle the wife like gloves; in the final draft she identifies more subtly with his victims. Looking at his blunt hands as they encircle a tea-mug, she tells herself how excited he is by the little deaths which wait for him like sweethearts, and she compares the marriage with a snare. There are tight wires between them, and she's being killed by the constriction as a ring-like mind slides shut on her.

As the poems show, death was again beckoning seductively ...

The Death and Life of Sylvia Plath Ronald Hayman

Extract 2

'The Rabbit Catcher' – which, unlike 'Event,' Ted did not see for some time – is another case of Sylvia's adapting immediate experience to her self-destructive perspective. In her journal entry for May 14, 1953, three months before her first suicide attempt, she had written: 'I want to love somebody because I want to be loved. In a rabbit fear I may hurl myself under the wheels of the car because the lights terrify me, and under the dark blind death of the wheels I will be safe.' In 'The Rabbit Catcher,' which is partly a cry for help, partly one of blind terror, and partly an act of emotional blackmail, the poet almost wills the worst to happen. It originated during a walk she and Ted had taken some months before. Coming upon a line of snares along a cliff top, Sylvia had wildly rushed around tearing them up. As a countryman, Ted Hughes was sympathetic to the simple economics of village life and saw nothing admirable in Sylvia's harming the rabbit catcher's livelihood. It was one of the small incidents, after they came to Devon, that made Ted realize how different their attitudes toward country life were. To Sylvia the snares were not only cruel; they were terrifying symbols of an inevitable yet irresistible finality:

'There was only one place to get to.
Simmering, perfumed,
The paths narrowed into the hollow.
And the snares almost effaced themselves –
Zeros, shutting on nothing.'

The last stanza refers directly to her marriage:

'And we, too, had a relationship
Tight wires between us,
Pegs too deep to uproot, and a mind like a ring
Sliding shut on some quick thing,
The constriction killing me also.'

The relationship is curiously set in the past, and its ending is compared to the noose of a rabbit trap that kills her.

Yet nothing had happened to harm her marriage other than her upsurge of jealousy. The shrill pain of 'The Rabbit Catcher' is true only of her own magnified inner terrors and consequent fury. In these two poems, moreover, she avoids mention of her own behavior, unless the 'groove of old faults, deep and bitter' includes recognition of this side of things. Her concept of marriage was absolute and all-demanding. It was perfect or it was nothing. As a mother and a 'good wife' she was owed total allegiance. And her marriage had to be unlike any other: she seemed unable to conceive even of its 'going through a bad patch' to continue with better understanding. And as all self-criticism for the part she played in the rift was absent, what 'better understanding' could there ever be?

Bitter Fame Anne Stevenson

Avoiding a biographical reading

The danger with the biographical approach, attractive as it may be, is that readers may think that they can discover the truth about the life from the poetry. This is what the critic Jacqueline Rose tries to avoid. Her book, *The Haunting of Sylvia Plath,* is not a biography, but an attempt to use psychoanalytic criticism to analyse and illuminate the poetry. Her treatments of the poems are interpretations, not parts of a case study on the life. In the case of Plath's poem 'The Rabbit Catcher', her analysis was one which Hughes found it impossible to accept, in part because he thought Rose's interpretation *was* biographical.

Extract 3 recounts a meeting, between Janet Malcolm, a biographer of Sylvia Plath's and Jacqueline Rose, during which the two women discussed Rose's reading of the poem and Hughes's response to it. It is written by Janet Malcolm.

● Read extract 3 quickly to get the gist of it.

● Read the extract for a second time and make a note of the main points of the reading. How does Rose justify her interpretation?

● As a class, talk about how Rose's interpretation of Plath and the methods she uses to construct this reading differ from those of Stevenson and Hayman.

Extract 3

Although Rose is a critic of distinction and originality, in the eyes of the Hugheses she was just another member of the pack of Ted Hughes's tormentors and pursuers, and they fought the publication of *The Haunting of Sylvia Plath* with their usual clumsy fierceness.

In accordance with post-structuralist theory, Rose argues for suspension of all certainty about what happened, and thus of judgment and blame. 'I'm not *ever* interested in what happened between Plath and Hughes,' she told me. 'My position is that you're left with a tangle of competing viewpoints, and if you try to make sense of it you'll go wrong one way or another. You have to live with the anxiety that such uncertainty generates. It's not helpful to resolve it too fast.' In her book Rose says of *Bitter Fame,* 'One of the strangest effects of reading this book, especially if you have read the unedited letters and journals, is that it precisely becomes impossible to know whom to believe.' (In fact, it is *only* if you have read the letters and journals – or have been in other ways alerted to the controversial character of the Plath-Hughes narrative – that *Bitter Fame* seems strange. The lay reader, who knows only what the biographer tells him, reads it, as he reads every other biography, in a state of bovine equanimity.) Rose continues her argument:

'Like the child caught up in a hideous divorce case between its parents, the writing of the life of Sylvia Plath, both by herself and by those who knew her, forces you – and makes it impossible for you – to take sides. Whom to believe, how to know, what is the truth of the case? ...'

What Rose leaves out of account is the psychological impossibility of a writer's not taking sides. ... Rose's book is fuelled by a bracing hostility toward Ted and Olwyn Hughes. It derives its verve and forward thrust from the cool certainty with which (in the name of 'uncertainty' and 'anxiety') she presents her case against the Hugheses. In the 'Archive' chapter, her accusations against Hughes for his 'editing, controlling, and censoring' reach an apogee of harshness.

Rose is the libber in whom the Hugheses finally met their match, who could not be contemptuously dismissed, who was a serious and worthy opponent. In *The Haunting of Sylvia Plath* she speaks for the dead poet and against Hughes in a way no other writer has done. ...

The Haunting of Sylvia Plath is a brilliant achievement. The framework of deconstructive, psychoanalytic, and feminist ideology on which Rose has mounted her polemic against the Hugheses gives the work a high intellectual shimmer. ...

Jacqueline Rose went on to speak of 'another area of trouble with the estate,' which she said she found 'at least as interesting.' This area was a chapter of Rose's book called 'No Fantasy Without Protest,' whose centerpiece is a reading of Plath's poem 'The Rabbit Catcher.' Ted Hughes had taken violent exception to this reading and had asked Rose to remove it. [S]he was utterly unprepared for his objections to the 'Rabbit Catcher' reading, which said nothing critical of him, and, in fact, took issue with the conventional feminist reading of the poem as a parable of the domination of men over women – the snares the narrator encounters on a walk in the country being seen as the trap that conventional marriage is for women – and as a direct commentary on Plath's own marriage. Rose offers an alternative reading, which finds in the poem's arresting, enigmatic imagery a fantasy of androgyny. Although no commentator had ever found this fantasy before – it is doubtful whether Plath herself would have been aware of it – Rose's reading does not seem very remarkable in today's climate of acceptance of both enacted and imagined homosexuality; the bisexual component of human sexuality is a commonplace of post-Freudian thought. But for Hughes – perhaps for the whole pre-Freudian English nation – the idea of unstable sexual identity was unacceptable, and Rose's suggestion that Plath even thought about such things as lesbian sex (never mind doing them) struck Hughes as abhorrent beyond imagination. I speak for Hughes so confidently because he made his views public in a letter written in response to a letter by Rose and published in the *TLS* on April 10, 1992. In his letter Hughes movingly, if bafflingly, told of his concern about the injurious effect that Rose's reading of 'The Rabbit Catcher' would have on his children (now in their thirties). 'Professor Rose distorts, reinvents etc Sylvia Plath's 'sexual identity' with an abandon I could hardly believe – presenting her in a role that I vividly felt to be humiliating to Sylvia Plath's children,' he wrote, and he went on:
'... I did not see how Ms Rose could fail to have full and instant knowledge of the peculiar kind of suffering such a moment induces – the little dull blow of something like despair, the helpless rage and shame for their mother, the little poisoning of life, the bitter but quite useless fury against the person who shot this barbed arrow into them just to amuse herself.'

In her 'No Fantasy Without Protest' chapter Rose writes of this opening:
'For the sexuality that it writes cannot be held to a single place – it spreads, blinds, unreels like the oil in the sea. Most crudely, that wind blowing, that gagging, calls up the image of oral sex and then immediately turns it around, gagging the speaker with her own blown hair, her hair in her mouth, her tasting the gorse (Whose body – male or female – is this? Who – man or woman – is tasting whom?), even while 'black spikes' and 'candles' work to hold the more obvious distribution of gender roles in their place. For Freud, such fantasies, such points of uncertainty, are the regular unconscious subtexts – for all of us – of the more straightforward reading, the more obvious narratives of stable sexual identity which we write.'
At her tea table, Rose continued, 'In my communications to Hughes I said – and I say this over and over again in my book – 'Look, I'm in no sense speaking of Plath's lived sexual identity in the world, about which I know nothing. I'm only discussing fantasy.' But he says that the distinction is not viable, because the fantasy concerns very intimate aspects of their life. It's true, it is intimate and it is private. But if you cannot talk about fantasy in a discussion of the literary writings of Sylvia Plath, then you cannot talk about Sylvia Plath. Because that's what she writes about. About the psyche and about inner images. Wonderful inner images of difficulty and pain – images which implicate us all, I think. I don't accept the reading that says they demonstrate her pathology. I'm not interested in the question of whether she was pathological or not. I don't think one knows, and I think you can only make statements like 'She was pathological' if you are absolutely sure of your own sanity, which I consider a morally unacceptable position.'
... 'The passage about what literary critics do to the living and the dead is an argument against the right to do criticism,' Rose said. 'This line about how critics reinvent the living - 'They extend over the living that licence to say whatever they please, to ransack their psyches and reinvent them however they please.' It implies two things. First, that I am saying I have *the* truth about the Hugheses' lives – which I never say I do - and, second, that they themselves possess it, and any interpretation beyond theirs is a violation of that singular truth. [I]n the end he leaves no room for literary criticism. Which may be what Ted Hughes wants to say. Which is a very interesting thing to say. But it also means there's no room for reading, rereading, interpretation, and discussion of meanings in our culture. The implications of this are really quite extraordinary.'

The Silent Woman, **Janet Malcolm**

Is Rose's reading biographical?

While Rose maintains that her criticism of Plath's poetry has nothing to do with the 'life lived', Malcolm suggests that, like all readings, Jacqueline Rose's interpretation is biased, and is therefore to some extent biographical.

- Do you agree that no reading can be neutral or wholly detached from the critic's knowledge of the biography?

The story according to Ted Hughes

- Read 'The Rabbit Catcher' by Ted Hughes and jot down your reaction to it as a poem.

- In pairs or small groups share your ideas about the text.

- Given your knowledge of Plath's poetic account of this incident and the controversy surrounding the different biographical interpretations of it, talk about the following:
- whether it is possible to evaluate the text on its poetic merits alone
- whether an innocent reading of this poem is possible (Would it be possible if only Plath's poem, *not* the biographical material was known?)
- whether this poem means that you now need to reconsider the biographical readings of Plath's poem
- what Hughes's poem suggests about the value of biographical readings.

Re-reading Plath

- Without looking at your earlier notes, read Plath's 'The Rabbit Catcher' again. Spend a few minutes writing about your response.

You have now jotted down your response to Plath's poem at three different stages:
- with no knowledge of the author or the context in which the poem was written and has been received
- with biographical information
- in relation to Hughes's poem of the same name.

- Compare all three readings. How has the new information affected your reading? For example, it might:
- cause you to re-think your interpretation of the poem
- cause you to re-think your interpretation of the character of Sylvia Plath and her relationship with Ted Hughes
- add new layers of meaning
- confuse you.

Reviews of *Birthday Letters*

Ted Hughes's poem 'The Rabbit Catcher' is taken from *Birthday Letters*. The publication of *Birthday Letters* in 1998 re-ignited the whole debate about the relationship between writers' lives, their work and the rights of the critic to interpret both.

- In pairs or small groups take responsibility for looking closely at one or two of the reviews. Read and talk about the way the reviewers discuss the work, the lives and the whole controversy. Annotate the review to show the following:
- places where the emphasis is on textual analysis
- biographical facts
- biographical speculation
- background to the ongoing story of Plath and Hughes in the media and in the books written about them.

- Use your annotations to try and answer the questions suggested here.

- What is the balance between textual analysis and biographical information?

- Is the biographical information used to illuminate the text or vice versa?
- What other contexts are used to illuminate the poems (for example, Plath's poetry; earlier textual and biographical readings; the social and political context; a knowledge of psychology or the development of feminism)?
- Which, if any, of these contexts do you think illuminate the text?

● Take it in turns to report back your readings of the reviews to the whole class.

The significance of the Ted and Sylvia story
The conflicting interpretations, the rows about who has a right to the work, let alone the life, the conflating of the work with its author all consolidate many of the issues and debates about the connections between writer, text and reader. Some of these are listed below.

● Read through the list and, in the light of the work you have done in this unit, talk about how your own thoughts on the connections between writer, reader and text have changed and developed.

- The social, political and cultural background of the writer and the reader contribute to the meaning of any text.
- Knowing about the relationships between texts influences a reader's interpretation.
- Readers are the real writers producing a new version of the text with each reading.
- The writer has no authority over the meanings attributed to their work.
- Psychoanalytical and biographical readings can contribute to, or distort to your appreciation of the poems.

Review 1

Ever since Sylvia Plath's death in 1963, there has been an argument as to who was responsible, whose fault it was – Plath's or Ted Hughes's – that she died. On the face of it, *Birthday Letters,* Hughes's extraordinary poetic sequence to Plath, might be seen as another stage of that quarrel. Or else, and far more productively, these poems might serve to bring that futile process of recrimination – of accusation and counter-accusation – to its end.

... These poems are not, however, a defence, an argument in Hughes's own service as they will no doubt be accused of being, or, as many have been suggesting over the past weeks, a reply – at last – to his critics, to those who have accused him of hardheartedness, and worse, in relation to Plath. To read them in these last terms seems to me to do Hughes no favours, and in fact weakens their peculiar quality and deprives them of a large measure of their force.

These poems offer their readers an account of a failure. Written after – and some, clearly long after – Plath's death, they circle round a missing centre, trying to find a reason for why she took her own life. If they are at times assertive and confident – knowing, even – they are just as often questioning and unsure (the number of question marks in the poems actually outstrips the number of poems in the book). These poems gather strength as they lose their conviction. The question – why did he fail her? – comes through finally much more loudly than the question to which, at moments, Hughes seems to offer some kind of an answer– why Sylvia Plath was bound, long before he ventured half-blind onto the scene, to die.

On first reading, there does seem to be a narrative of explanation that can be lifted out of these poems: that Sylvia Plath was doomed by the eight-year-old girl inside her who failed to grieve a father who died too soon; that her whole project – 'trajectory perfect as if through ether' – was to get back to that father in his grave (whereas Hughes had 'no more purpose in me than my own dog which I did not have'). This leaves Hughes no option but to go seeking for them both: 'a big shock to meet me face to face in the dark adit where I have come looking for your daughter' (this, one of the only two poems not addressed to Plath, comes near the end, as if Hughes was left with no other place to go). According to this story, from very early on, Plath was heading inexorably to her death, and Hughes was a helpless bystander. If Hughes's earlier poetry often reads as a tribute to a nature in excess of his own mastery, this would then be the first time that such a force at which he also marvels so utterly defeats him.

But precisely because what Hughes is writing about is a form of energy with a strength and will of its own, no attempt – if indeed this is the attempt – to hand it over to Plath alone, to her distressed and haunted selfhood as he sees it, can work. Lines like these, often cited over the past two weeks, are almost too easy to lift out of the poems: 'auditioned for the male lead in your drama', 'I was a fly outside on the window pane/of my own domestic drama', 'Your life was a liner I voyaged in', 'Inside your Bell Jar/I was like a mannikin in your eyeball'. But they only tell half, if indeed that much, of the story. For every one of these seeming explanations we get another which makes it impossible to see this tragedy as Plath's fate, as her doing, alone. Something of cosmic proportions 'billions of years in anonymous matter', enters the house searching for a place to land: 'Who's here? That's the question: 'Who's here?' In this poetic journey – whose pronoun is no longer 'you' but 'we' – they are in it together: 'we caught each other and fell in a heap', 'fate assembled us', 'the myth we sleepwalked into'; 'we had no idea what we were seeing'. Try working out, for example, whose is the blackness in these lines:

'I folded
Black wings round you, wings of the blackness
That enclosed me, rocking me, infantile,
And enclosed you with me.'

Even if you read this as Hughes as protector, this is hardly self-exculpation. Ironically, the more he convinces us that this was his role, so the felt dimensions of his own failing become that much more brutally clear. One of the most striking things about these poems, especially on second reading, is how engaged, active, participating, Hughes is as protagonist of this tale: 'I was focused,/So locked into you, so brilliantly.' And just how much, indeed, he accuses himself:

'I brought you to Devon. I brought you into my dreamland.
I sleepwalked you into my land of totems.'

(This poem is called 'Error'). He hews her a writing table out of coffin elm; when she smashes his table top, it is he who exhorts that energy into poetic words: "Marvellous!' I shouted, 'Go on. Smash it into kindling.

That's the stuff you're keeping out of your poems!", only to ask what he has done: 'Deep in the cave of your ear/The goblin snapped his fingers. So what had I given him?' In what is bound to be one of the most controversial poems, 'The Rabbit Catcher', which comes like many of these poems in reply to Plath's of the same name, Hughes lays out the violent terms of their difference:

'I saw
The sanctity of a trapline desecrated.
You saw blunt fingers, blood in the cuticles,'

But then he asks:

'Had you caught something in me,
Nocturnal and unknown to me? Or was it
Your doomed self, your tortured, crying,
Suffocating self?'

It is as if these poems at once enter the fray and call a halt: 'Let the blame hit the olive trees.' This is poetry, as 'a combustion of the stuff of judgement'.

Nothing has ever evoked Plath like this; the way these poems summon her ('real, warm, lucent'), celebrate her ('a great bird, you surged in the plumage of your excitement') is, above all else, what overpowers. But they do also present the reader with some puzzles. One is their view of Plath's own poetry. In Hughes's previous writings, he has seemed to date the birth of her best creativity from 'Poem for a Birthday', the long sequence which she wrote in 1959 (this, I had assumed, was one of the meanings hidden in the title of *Birthday Letters*). But in this collection, Plath's poetry seems to be sprung from a bad and dangerous place. In more than one poem, something not quite Plath, something wreaking havoc, brings the words - 'like entrails' (used twice) - onto the page:

'Who caught all
That teeming population, every one,
To hang their tortured eyes and tongues up
In your poems?'

If this is true, then her readers are dupes. All they have is 'the empty mask' of her genie; or gloves from which 'the hands have vanished'. Or worse, they are the guilty party to the crime:

'In the wilderness
Between the locusts and the honey
They demanded it. Oh, no problem
If that's all you want,
You said, and you gave it.'

And this is not to speak of the image, in the penultimate poem addressed to his children, of those who have written about Plath's work:

'Let them
Jerk their tail-stumps, bristle and vomit
Over their symposia.'

The appearance of *Birthday Letters* has been used to produce a caricature of feminism as always pitying Plath and blaming Hughes as a man with no heart to speak of. As if there was not also another strand to feminism, one which has precisely learnt from Plath the uselessness of this opposition, admiring her for her brave and agile capacity to berate both the world and herself. It seems pointless and invasive to speculate on why Ted Hughes has chosen to publish these poems today. But there is a question that can be put. If these poems have been published they cannot be addressed to Plath or their children alone. They must be calling for a response. Of understanding? Of sympathy? Why then does Hughes once again represent with such unremitting anger those who have responded to Plath's writing, or who have been inspired by what she wrote to write words of their own? Perhaps the success of *Birthday Letters* could also help to bring this battle to an end. So that the continuing love of Sylvia Plath, by those who have only her words to go on, might no longer be seen as the death of her.

Jacqueline Rose, *The Observer*, 1.2.98

Review 2

These are poems of astonishing tragic power, a force intensified for the reader by their sudden appearance. *Birthday Letters* is a shock. Which is highly appropriate, given how full of shocks the book is itself.

Some of those shocks are both literal and metaphorical at once, perhaps most poignantly in 'Tender Places': 'Your temples, where the hair crowded in,/Were the tender places', the poem begins, as might any love poem. Then the shock; 'Once to check/ I dropped a file across the electrodes of a twelve-volt battery – it exploded /Like a grenade.'

This juxtaposition jolts us into a fierce (and tender) poem about the terrible ordeals of electro-convulsive therapy Plath endured following her failed suicide attempt. What is so moving about this poem, and about the collection, is the passionate empathy Hughes reveals with his wife's scars and sufferings. He loved her and he felt for her, and the intensity of that love will no doubt come as a surprise to many who have taken Hughes's awkward silence for a hardened heart.

As 'Tender Places' indicates, the first difficulty presented by *Birthday Letters* is how to read it. As a collection of poems? As a biographical document? To pretend that it's possible, or even desirable, to read the sequence as pure poetry (whatever that might be) excised from its troubled context, is delusional – and unfair to Hughes's achievement. On the other hand, it would be equally damaging if *Birthday Letters* were to suffer the same fate as that frequently imposed on Sylvia Plath's work, which so often has been milked for the crassest of biographical arguments, as though it were circumstantial evidence in a murder trial.

Given the bitter battles fought over Plath's poems for what they 'really' mean, what's so intriguing about *Birthday Letters* is the way in which the poems specifically foreground interpretations and repeatedly suggest how fluid it can be. ...

This becomes vividly apparent in 'The Rabbit Catcher', itself a response to Plath's own poem of the same title. (Much of *Birthday Letters* enters a dialogue with Plath's work, as was the case when both poets were alive, their poems infecting each other's.) Where Hughes here scorns his wife for seeing 'baby-eyed/ Strangled innocents', versus his 'sacred/Ancient customs', in Plath's poem the rabbit catcher is more troubling than a murderer of sentiment: 'How they awaited him, those little deaths!/ They waited like sweethearts. They excited him', she writes, characteristically and dangerously investing her imagery with the language of sexuality and power.

Sarah Maguire, *The Guardian*, 22.1.98

Review 3

It has always been possible, and been thought instructive (despite Plath's warning that 'we write poems that are as distinct and different as our fingerprints themselves must be'), to read the two poets' works off against each other, to search for tell-tale marks of one on the other ... but these new poems offer fresh opportunities for rereading, counter-reading and misreading of an entirely different order.

Up until now readers of the poetry have been unwelcome spectators of the relationship – peering over Hughes's shoulder, furiously reading between the lines of the poems with one eye, squinting at Plath's private journals and letters with the other, straining to hear the buzz of tittle tattle and rumour. In *Birthday Letters* Hughes shrugs off his irritation with the peepers and spies and turns round to face us. This is no snatched glimpse at a private correspondence; if anything, it's more like a mail-shot, or a press release: coming out of the blue and serialised in the cut-price *Times*, it is explicit, unapologetic and unashamed. These are public poems ... indignant, accusatory, evangelical. ... In publishing these poems Hughes is addressing not some obscure partner in an obscure partnership, but the great mass of his own and Plath's readers. There is to be no mystification or flim-flam: we know who he's writing about, and what he's writing about. He wants us to hear his side of the story.

Ian Sansom, *London Review of Books*, 19.2.98

Appendices

Reading critics

Don't be bullied by critics! You are a critic too. Remember critical texts are secondary texts – they could not exist without the poem, novel, or play. Use their different readings to develop independent and informed readings.

1. You don't have to read the whole book – don't even try!

2. Use the Index. Follow up only the references to the text or topic you are working on.

3. If it's a book of essays by several different people, read the editor's introductory chapter first. It will give you an overview of the critical position of the whole book, and it also usually gives you a summary of what each essay is about. Then home in on the ones that sound most useful.

4. Keep a note of where you take any useful quotations from:
   name of writer
   title of essay or book
   page number of quotation
   name of whole text
   name of editor or author
   publisher
   date of publication
   Make sure you acknowledge the quotation by quoting the writer's name and the essay or book you found it in when you use the quotation.
   N.B. www.amazon.com is NOT enough!

5. Read the critics after you have read the text and thought about it yourself. Reading critics first is NOT a short cut to your own 'opinions and judgements' (AO4). The critics' ideas will make a lot more sense if you have some familiarity with the text they are writing about. They might make you change your mind – they might just make you more sure of your own ideas. If you read them first you won't know what to think.

6. Read the introduction to your set books, if they have them. But do it after you've read the text. They ought to print them at the back of the book! Try to find editions with recent introductions by critics, who may also be writers if you're lucky. AS Byatt's introduction to the Vintage paperback edition (1999) of *The Bell* by Iris Murdoch, is a good example.

7. Use the Critical Position cards to help you identify the approach(es) the critic is making use of.

8. Read the criticism critically. Does the critic have a particular purpose (for example, to challenge previously accepted readings)? If they do, do they make this purpose clear or is it kept hidden from the reader?

9. Consider which other readings are excluded by the particular position adopted by the critic. What 'different interpretations' would you offer as a challenge to this reading.

10. If you quote critics in essays, or use their ideas directly, acknowledge this fact and comment on how useful you found their readings. If you choose to quote, select very short extracts that highlight the key idea you want to comment on. Attribute quotations using the approach suggested in point 4.

Reading list

General

Books and journals written for students

Beginning Theory Peter Barry (Manchester University Press)
A straightforward explanation of major literary theories with clear demonstrations of how each one works in practice. Encourages readers to think critically about what the theory reveals and conceals about a text and to recognise that no way of reading can be neutral or disinterested. Thought-provoking open questions and guidance on how to apply the theories.

Doing English Robert Eaglestone (Routledge)
A critical discussion of the assumptions lying behind the development of 'English Literature' as an academic subject. Aims to bridge the gap between school and university English, introducing students to the arguments surrounding 'literary theory' and alternative ways of reading. It does not go into detail about individual theories. A direct style, questions at the start of each short chapter and bullet points summarising key points at the end make this a very accessible book for students.

Literary Terms: a practical glossary Brian Moon (English & Media Centre)
Full definitions of key terms and theories. Questions and activities support students getting to grips with the ideas and how these can be applied in practice.

The English Studies Book Rob Pope (Routledge)
A comprehensive handbook and anthology which includes discussion of English Literature and its development; its relationship with other disciplines; the principles and ideologies behind key literary theories; practical demonstrations of how to use the theories to read texts and activities encouraging students to question both texts and the way they and others read.

The English Review (Phillip Allan Publishers)
A must for stimulating reading, as a reference, as a source of sample essays and for examples of good, engaging critical writing.

emagazine
Short articles on subjects of interest to advanced level students, often by writers and critics.

Texts referred to in the publication

Expletives Deleted Angela Carter (Vintage)
Discussions of classic texts from the perspective of a feminist. Includes some psychoanalytic criticism. The style is informal and easy to read, not academic.

The Death and Life of Sylvia Plath Ronald Hayman (Minerva)
A central text in the controversial readings of Plath's poetry. Adopts a biographical approach.

The Silent Woman Janet Malcolm (Picador)
A central text in the controversial readings of Plath's poetry. Analysis of the 'Sylvia Plath industry' and the critical readings of her life and work.

The Haunting of Sylvia Plath Jacqueline Rose (Virago)
A central text in the controversial readings of Plath's poetry. Psychoanalytic readings of the poetry from the point of view of a feminist.

Bitter Fame Anne Stevenson (Penguin)
A central text in the controversial readings of Plath's poetry. Adopts a biographical approach.

The Common Pursuit and *The Great Tradition* F.R. Leavis (Hogarth Press)
Classic examples of the Liberal Humanist, 'non-theoretical' approach to reading and criticism.

A Beginners' Guide to Critical Reading: an anthology of literary terms Richard Jacobs (Routledge)
An anthology of texts with accessible and engaging commentaries by Jacobs.

Encourages the reader to see the text and context as inter-related and to introduce different ways of approaching literary texts. A good resource for teachers and enthusiastic students.

'Analysis and Interpretation of the Realist Text: A pluralistic approach to Ernest Hemingway's Cat in the Rain' in *Poetics Today, Volume 1:4* David Lodge
Critical discussion of earlier readings of Hemingway and Lodge's own structuralist reading of the text. Challenging, but in extract form a good demonstration of what the theory means in practice.

The Self-Conceived Helène Moglen (Norton)
Psychoanalytic readings of the Brontes from a feminist perspective.

Culture and Imperialism Edward Said (Chatto and Windus)
A seminal work in the development of post-colonialism as a literary theory.

'Cultural Materialism, Othello and the Politics of Plausibility' in *Faultlines: Cultural Materialism and the Politics of Dissident Reading* Alan Sinfield (Oxford University Press)
Practical demonstration of the principles and interests of the cultural materialist and historicist critic.

In Search of Our Mother's Gardens Alice Walker (The Women's Press)
Personal engagements with literature from the perspective of a black feminist novelist.

The English Novel from Dickens to Lawrence Raymond Williams (Oxford University Press)
Key Marxist and cultural critic explores the novel.

Other interesting critical texts

An Introduction to Literary Theory Terry Eagleton (Basil Blackwell Ltd)
Key introductory text to major theories of the late twentieth century. Written from a Marxist perspective. As theory goes, relatively accessible.

The Art of Fiction David Lodge (Penguin)
Very short, informal essays on key aspects of the novel. Discussion is based round one or two key extracts. Useful both as starting points for discussion and as models of exploratory criticism.

Modern Criticism and Theory David Lodge with Nigel Wood (Longman)
An anthology of key texts from the major theorists of the late twentieth century. The texts themselves are challenging but the introductions by the editors are lucid and concise.

Ways of Reading Marian Montgomery, Alan Durant, Nigel Fabb, Tom Furniss & Sarah Mills (Routledge)
Accessible explanations and clearly developed activities on tricky aspects of 'reading' and criticism, for example, point of view. Uses a wide range of extracts including media texts.

Imagining Characters A.S. Byatt and Ignês Sodré (Vintage)
Written in the form of conversations. Byatt, a novelist and Sodré, a psychoanalyst discuss six female writers. It includes a conversation about *Mansfield Park*.

Why Read the Classics? Italo Calvino (Jonathon Cape)
Calvino wrestles with the question of what literature is and what makes it worthwhile.

Radical Tragedy Jonathon Dollimore (Manchester University Press)
Cultural materialist readings of Shakespeare and his contemporaries.

Henry V, War Criminal John Sutherland (Oxford University Press)
A quirky look at some of the unresolved questions and contradictions in Shakespeare. Follows the same approach as 'Was Heathcliff a Murderer' and 'Can Jane Eyre Be Happy?'

A Literature of their Own Elaine Showalter (Virago)
Key text in the development of feminist criticism.

'Shakespeare and Feminist Criticism' by Ann Thompson in *The Shakespeare Myth* ed. Graham Holderness (Manchester University Press)
Includes 'Shakespeare and Feminist Criticism' by Ann Thompson, a feminist reading of Shakespeare using the methods of cultural materialists. Suitable as a model of how students might approach their own set text.

A critical time line

Period	Critic	Text	Big Idea
Ancient Greece	Aristotle 384-322 BC	*Poetics*	Definition of tragedy & comedy; tragedy is regarded as the superior genre.
Renaissance	Sir Philip Sidney 1554-1586	*Apology for Poetry* pub. 1595	The creative role of the artist; the nature and value of poetry.
C17 Neo-classical	John Dryden 1631-1700	*Essay on Dramatic Poesy* 1668	Principles of drama, comparing Shakespeare's treatments of tragedy and comedy with classical 'rules'.
C18 Augustan age	Dr Johnson 1709-1784	*Lives of the Poets* 1779-1781	Biographies and criticisms of contemporary and recent writers; reflects the tastes of his time; (biased against the Metaphysicals).
C19 Romantics	William Wordsworth 1770-1850	Preface to *Lyrical Ballads* 1800	Reacts against style of C18 poetry; redefines poetry and poetic language as the ordinary language of man.
	Samuel Taylor Coleridge 1772-1834	*Biographia Literaria* 1817	Mixture of autobiography, philosophy & literary criticism; takes a psychological approach to creativity 100 years before Freud.
	Percy Bysshe Shelley 1792-1822	*Defence of Poetry* 1821 (pub. 1840)	Political importance of poetry & poets: 'the unacknowledged legislators of mankind'.
	William Hazlitt 1778-1830	*Characters of Shakespeare's Plays* 1817-1818 *Lectures on the English Poets* 1818-1819	Essayist, political commentator & critic; shrewd, vigorous, personal responses.
Victorians	Matthew Arnold 1822-1888	*Essays in Criticism* 1865 & 1888 *Culture & Anarchy* 1869	Sees culture and education as defence against industrialisation; sees poetry as substitute for religion; believes great works can be 'touchstones' of literary excellence by which to judge others.
	Henry James 1843-1916	essays on the art of fiction 1865 – 1914	As a novelist, more concerned with the nature of literature: structure of texts, effects on readers, literary language
C20 Practical criticism (now often referred to as 'Liberal humanists')	F.R.Leavis 1895-1978	*Revaluation* 1936 *The Common Pursuit* 1952 *The Great Tradition* 1948	Close reading of texts; identification of limited number of great texts worthy of study; emphasis on the moral value of literature.

Period	Critic	Text	Big Idea
	I.A. Richards 1893-1979	*Principles of Literary Criticism* 1924	Colleague of Leavis; interested in linguistics & psychology as well as literature.
Challenging the 'Liberal humanists'			
Early C20 Russian Formalists	Roman Jakobson 1896-1982		Form & technique; verbal devices - the 'literariness' of literary language; how it makes everyday experience 'strange'.
1930s & 1940s New Criticism	Cleanth Brooks 1906- W.K. Wimsatt (USA) 1907-75 William Empson (UK) 1906-84		Influenced by Leavis & Richards. Interested in poems as unified aesthetic objects, rather than in their authors or their historical contexts.
1950s, 1960s and 1970s Semiotics			The study of signs and sign systems; avoids cultural and philosophical comment about the significance of these signs.
Structuralism	Levi Strauss; 1908- Roland Barthes; 1915-80 Jacques Lacan 1901-81	Based on the theories of Ferdinand de Saussure (French) 1857-1913	Theories of language (its structures and functions); distinguishes between 'language' (the universal human phenomenon of speech), 'a language' (e.g. English, French, Chinese) and 'speech' (language in use). Language is a system of signs - there is no essential link between the word and the thing we agree it stands for e.g. dog, chien, hund. No word can be defined in isolation from other words e.g. male/female, dark/light. Our world is constructed by language, not simply described by it. Structuralists look for ways of showing the underlying organisation of texts, their structures and patterns. They interpret texts in relation to the larger structures of society. Any social or cultural structure can be interpreted as a text.
1960s Marxist	Raymond Williams 1921-1987	*Culture & Society 1780-1950* 1958 *Drama from Ibsen to Brecht* 1962 *The Country & the City* 1973	One of the founders of cultural studies; challenges accepted ways of writing about drama & dramatic forms; sees writing as political activity; close links with cultural materialism.
Post structuralism	Roland Barthes (French) 1915-1980		Many structuralists realised that describing a complete system was not possible as this is

Period	Critic	Text	Big Idea
	Jacques Derrida (French) 1930- Michel Foucault (French) 1926-1984		always changing. These critics became known as post-structuralists. They do not believe that texts conform to constant underlying structures, arguing that meanings are shifting and unstable, dependant on social and cultural contexts. They suggest that in trying to identify patterns, many structuralists had misunderstood the very nature of the 'text'. The most radical form of post-structuralism is deconstruction.
Deconstruction	Jacques Derrida 1930-		Derrida's work upset many people because, by treating the whole world as a text which could be taken apart or de-constructed he challenged many of the ways we organise societies. He showed that structuring thought and society according to oppositions in which one is regarded as superior is not natural, but a construction.
Beyond structuralism and post-structuralism			
1970s Psychoanalytic	Jacques Lacan (French) 1901-1981		This form of literary criticism is based on the work of Sigmund Freud (1856-1939). These critics are interested in the subconscious, childhood, experience, memory, dreams and symbols. Feminist critics like Jacqueline Rose use and adapt some of the ideas of the psychoanalysts.
Reader-response	Wolfgang Iser (Germany) 1926- Stanley Fish (USA) 1938-		These critics emphasise the importance of the reader who interprets the text and interacts with it to make meaning. Mistaken interpretations and the corrections we make are an important part of the meaning.
Feminist	Elaine Showalter 1941- Jacqueline Rose	*The Haunting of Sylvia Plath* 1992	Deconstructs the opposition man/woman. Some feminists champion women's rights and writing by women. Others focus on the presentation of women by male writers.

Period	Critic	Text	Big Idea
Cultural materialist	Alan Sinfield	*Political Shakespeare* (ed. with Jonathon Dollimore) 1994	These critics read historical and other relevant texts alongside the literary ones, in order to see the context in which the literature was produced more clearly, and to recover its history. Most interested in pre-20th century texts, often those written in the Renaissance, for example, Shakespeare. They explore the ways these texts have been packaged and consumed in the present day. However, they also analyse the text closely, in order to question previous ways in which the text has been read. They consider all forms of culture, popular as well as high culture, to be relevant and argue that it is impossible for any form of culture to be independent of economic and political systems.
New Historicist	Steven Greenblatt	*Learning to Curse: Essays in Early Modern Culture* *Essays in Renaissance Self-fashioning Shakespearean Negotiations* 1990	These critics read literary and non literary texts together. They concentrate on the context in which the text was originally produced. Many New Historicists explore whether Renaissance literature criticises the political and religious institutions or whether in the end they uphold the status quo.
Post-Colonial	Edward Said 1935-	*Culture & Imperialism* 1993	These critics challenge the claims made by traditional critics that great literature has timeless and universal significance. They are aware when Eurocentric attitudes are taken for granted, and looks in the text for cultural, regional, social and national differences in outlook and experiences. They are interested in the way colonial countries and people are represented in texts by Western writers. They also explores the ways in which post-colonial writers write about their own identity and experiences.

'English Literature': the historical context

In conjunction with the critical time-line, this brief overview of 'English Literature' sets your AS and A2 level studies in the context of the subject's historical development.

Literary theory is not a completely modern phenomenon. It has a long history. For example, if, when you discuss *Macbeth* you talk about the idea that there is a fatal weakness in Macbeth which causes him to listen to the witches and act on what they seem to promise him, and you decide that this weakness or 'flaw' is what brings about his death, you are using a theory about what makes a tragedy which originated in Ancient Greece. It was the theory of Aristotle (384-322 BC), a pupil of Plato and tutor to Alexander the Great. His study of literature, and the conclusions he came to, have had a great influence on European writers ever since. Again, if when you read a play by Arthur Miller you discuss whether or not the main character can really be called a hero, because he is only a salesman, or a longshoreman, or the boss of a factory, you are also working with Aristotle's literary theory about the nature of the tragic hero.

English Literature did not exist as a subject considered worth studying at university level until about 1840, when it was introduced at King's College, London. Oxford resisted it until 1894, and Cambridge until 1911. Up to the end of the nineteenth century, theories about literature did exist, but instead of being developed by academics and critics, they most often came from writers themselves. The writers, most often poets, considered what had been written before them, reacting against it and trying to express what they felt they were trying to do in their own work. Literary criticism came from reviewers, commenting on the literature of the day. They might describe and summarise, focus on the writer's biography, or reputation, and they often expressed the assumptions which they personally brought to their reading. Modern literary theory in England could be said to begin in the 1860s with Matthew Arnold, a school inspector and poet, and his views about the relationship between literature and contemporary society. He believed that works of literature generally acknowledged as 'great' could be used by readers as 'touchstones' in their attempts to make judgements. These ideas lead almost directly to F.R. Leavis, and his ideas about the great tradition of a limited number of great authors. At the same time as Arnold was publishing his views, a parallel strand of thinking about literature as art, about how it is structured and how it achieves its effects, was being developed by writers like Henry James.

The Critical Positions cards introduce some ways of approaching texts developed during the second half of the twentieth century. The Time Line gives a general overview of the early thinking about texts and their relation to the later critical theories.

All critics and readers are involved with the relationship between the text, the writer, the reader and the context of both writing and reading. You might find it useful to think of any literary theory as always focusing on these same four variables, no matter when the critical theory was developed, the particular position it takes in relation to the text, or which country the writer comes from. Different theoretical positions represent the choices critics make about the ways in which these variables are combined and emphasised.

Notes for Teachers

Assessment Objectives

The activities in *Text, Reader, Critic* all address the Assessment Objectives for AS and A2 level:

AO1   communicate clearly the knowledge, understanding and insight appropriate to literary study, using appropriate terminology and accurate and coherent written expression

AO2i   respond with knowledge and understanding to literary texts of different types and periods

AO2ii   respond with knowledge and understanding to literary texts of different types and periods, exploring and commenting on relationships and comparisons between literary texts

AO3   show detailed understanding of the ways in which writers' choices of form, structure and language shape meaning

AO4   articulate independent opinions and judgements, informed by different interpretations of literary texts by other readers

AO5i   show understanding of the contexts in which literary texts are written and understood

AO5ii   evaluate the significance of cultural, historical and other contextual influences on literary texts and study.

Unit 1:
What readers bring to texts

The aim of this activity is to give students the opportunity to explore their own readings and how these are shaped, and to compare these with the readings of other people in the class.

Organising the activity – *before reading*
Before students read the whole story, give them the following pieces of information at staged intervals. At each stage students note down their response.
1. The title: 'Embroidery'.
2. The opening section (printed below).

> The dark porch air in the late afternoon was full of needle flashes, like a movement of gathered silver insects in the light. The three women's mouths twitched over their work. Their bodies lay back and then imperceptibly forward, so that the rocking chairs tilted and murmured. Each woman looked to her own hands, as if quite suddenly she had found her heart beating there.
>> "What time is it?"
>> "Ten minutes to five."
>> "Got to get up in a minute and shell those peas for dinner."

3. The author is a man.
4. The author is a man who writes science fiction.

Discussion may focus on the following areas:
– The students' changing responses to the story (the difference it made to their interpretation of the story to learn about its contexts, for example that it was written by a male science fiction writer)
– what this changing response suggests about the ways individuals and groups of readers approach texts (for example, the extent to which any reading is shaped by the knowledge and assumptions the reader brings to the text)
– where the meaning of a text lies (i.e. not just in the words on the page but in the way the reader responds to them)
– whether or not it is interesting or important to make explicit the influences shaping a response
– how readers come to any sort of shared reading
– the idea that individual readers belong to a 'Community of readers' who share certain experiences and assumptions about a text.

You may want to go on to talk about other aspects of the story, for example its relationship to other examples of science fiction or to use it to introduce the features and conventions of the 'short story'.

Unit 2:
What is the context of a text?

The aim of this unit is to extend students' understanding of the variety of different contexts which may throw light on a text, taking this beyond 'historical background'. The activity looks at the context in which 'texts are written and understood', for example: matters of genre; language; textual production; the way in which the text is received; and its place in a writer's entire works.

Organising the activity
The students should be given the poem extract and asked to respond to it without the information about the circumstances in which it was produced.

The discussion should establish the range of contexts which can be used for thinking about any text and may focus on the following:
— in what ways, if at all, the poem could be appreciated without this contextual knowledge, for example from an aesthetic point of view (and what sorts of knowledge this might require)
— the levels of meaning added to a single poem through a knowledge of its contexts
— the difference it makes to read the poem when this contextual material is made explicit rather than assumed
— the relationship between the origins of the poem (in a news item) and its metaphorical significance (as a comment on contemporary life).
It is possible that some students will already need help contextualising the poem; this could form the basis of further discussion work.

You may want to go on to consider the extract in relation to the following:
— textual information: e.g. the formal constraints placed on the writer and the significance of the date and manner of publication Commissioned by the New Millennium Experience Company in 1999, the poem had to consist of 1000 lines
— the film *Killing Time*, also written by Simon Armitage and broadcast on Channel 4 on New Year's Day, 2000
— biographical information about the author
— the rest of 'Killing Time': to contextualise a part within the whole poem, and see its relationship in terms of form and content
— more poems by Armitage
— other 'occasional' poems where the immediate context is particularly significant, for example, Shelley's 'England 1819'.

Unit 3:
Alternative ways of interpreting a text

The aim of this exercise is to encourage students to produce as many different readings of the text beyond the literal as possible. Also to consider the usefulness of different kinds of contextual information, and learn to discriminate between relevant and irrelevant additional information.

Organising the activity
Follow the instructions on the student activity sheet.

Discussion may focus on the following:
—· the different interpretations of 'Request Stop' generated by the groups (for example: communication; being British; surrealism; loneliness) and how these were formed
— what the interpretation reveals about the text and the reader
— whether a text can support any number of readings
— whether some texts are more open than others to alternative interpretations
— whether contextual knowledge 'closes' some of these interpretations. If so, does this make these readings wrong?
— the way in which the act of performance contributes to and crystallises interpretation.

You may want to extend the discussion further to consider the themes, tone, and genre in more detail. The following activities offer some ways you might do this.

— Introduce the connection between genre and interpretation by telling the group that the text is published in Pinter's *Collected Plays*, where it is labelled as a review sketch. Is it a play, or a sketch? What's the difference? What other kinds of performance does it remind you of? TV comedy? Films?
— Refer back to the exercise on the contexts of 'Killing Time', and develop this into discussion of what kinds of contextual information are useful in interpreting a particular text. For example, how much use would a map of the London bus routes be?
— Explore the difference it makes to read the sketch alongside another Pinter piece, extracts from works by other playwrights writing at the same time or some biographical information about Pinter's position in British theatre in the twentieth century.

Unit 4:
How the context of the reading affects interpretation

The aim of this activity is to suggest that the meaning of a text is not fixed; what the reader makes of it is affected by many contextual factors, including the way in which it is encountered.

Organising the activity

The main focus of the discussion should be on the poem on the right hand side of page 17 or on the poem on page 19, depending on which group they are in. (It's the same poem – different title.) It is important not to let the students know initially that the right hand poems are different. Let them find this out for themselves once they move into their second discussion group.

Discussion may focus on the following:
- the way in which the *immediate* context in which the poem is read provokes particular expectations
- how these expectations, the way the poem is presented and its connections with other texts influence the reader's interpretation.

You could go on to ask students to:
- think up another title for the 'Nativity'/'Poem for CND' piece
- find a further poem to pair with 'Nativity'
- do a similar pairing of a poem or song of their own choice.

Unit 5:
The social and cultural contexts of language

The aim of this activity is to make students focus on the knowledge they bring to texts, particularly their understanding of the social and cultural contexts of the language of literary texts.

Organising the activity

Follow the instructions on the student sheet. Use any difficulties students have with these texts as part of the exercise.

Discussion may focus on the following:
- whether the interpretations we place on words, images and so on are natural or inevitable or whether they are culturally determined (Ask the students how an Icelander would respond to the central metaphor of the 'Summer's day'.)
- the extent to which students already feel 'alien-ated' from the poem held up as representative of the culture in which they are living and reading
- the language of literary language which has been absorbed into the culture

- whether it is useful to make texts strange in this way.

You could use this activity as a way of making explicit the difficulties students experience when encountering unfamiliar texts. Conversely, when analysing familiar texts, use the activity to help students gain a degree of critical distance.

Unit 6:
Positioning the reader – socially, culturally, politically

The Union Jack exercise demonstrates the critical theory which sees the meaning of a text – whether visual or verbal – as shifting and unstable. The exercise involves students in thinking about the meaning and significance of this image when seen from different perspectives, Students are introduced to the idea that individual attitudes and opinions are shaped, in part, by the social, political and cultural contexts within which the reader is operating.

Organising the activity

Follow the instructions on the student sheet. Discussion may focus on the following:
- the extent to which the meaning and significance of a word is imposed by individuals, groups and societies
- whether any of these meanings are natural or innate
- the relationship between a 'text' and political and cultural beliefs
- the consequences of reading a text in a particular way.

You may want to go on to think about other images and 'texts' which have meanings imposed on them by different cultures or appropriated by particular groups, for example, the red rose. Ask students to consider whether this happens in all societies and cultures.

Unit 7:
Reading at a moment in time

The aim of this role play is to engage students imaginatively in an exploration of the contemporary impact of poems written at the beginning of World War 1. Students are also expected to reflect on the difference between these responses and their personal readings, and to consider the role literature has played in shaping twenty-first century attitudes to war.

The unit is particularly appropriate for students who have done some work on the literature from, or about World War 1, for example the poetry of Wilfred Owen, *Regeneration* or *Birdsong* and for those preparing for the synoptic paper for AQA (A).

Organising the activity
The poems which appear without titles on the student sheet are identified here.
Poem 1:   'Peace' by Rupert Brooke
Poem 2:   'A War Film' by Teresa Hooley
Poem 3:   'Recruiting' by Ewart Alan Mackintosh
Poem 4:   'The Call' by Jessie Pope.

Discussion may focus on the following:
– the ways the social and political context in which a poem is read, as well as produced, alters its effect
– how far what the reader brings to a text is a product of prevailing social trends as much as personal opinions
– the ways in which the literature of the period has shaped a shared reading of both the texts and the events of World War 1.

You may want to go on to give students a selection of more recent war poetry, for example, Carol Ann Duffy's 'War Photographer' (the Gulf War) and Tony Harrison's 'Three Poems from Bosnia' and ask them to consider the extent to which these poems are also products of a specific time. You could also consider the poems in relation to the contextual material on World War 1 included in *The Modern Novel* (EMC Advanced Literature Series).

Unit 8:
Literature and the canon

The aim of this unit is to stimulate discussion about what students are doing when they study literature at A Level in what ways it is different from just 'reading'. The extract from Terry Eagleton shows how the ideas of critics can be used as springboards for students' own ideas. As with the earlier exercises, the aim is to increase their conscious awareness of aspects of their work in English which they may have been taking for granted.

Organising the activity
Follow the instructions on the student sheet. Students will need access to the list of books set for examination at AS/A2 level by the Awarding Body you are studying.

Discussion may focus on the following:
– the students' own views of English Literature, the canon and the classics
– whether the idea of a canon is useful
– whether 'English' is a subject like maths
– what should be studied

– the challenges to the accepted view of what English is.

Further opinions on the canon and 'classics' can be found in *Why Read the Classics?* by Italo Calvino and *The Test of Time*. An extract from Calvino's essay can be found on the English and Media website (www.englishandmedia.co.uk). You may want to ask students to explore their ideas of Literature in relation to a selection of Bestseller lists and to compare the texts on these with those included in the National Curriculum or chosen for examination at post 16. This activity would be particularly interesting for students studying texts which are also bestsellers, for example, *Captain Corelli's Mandolin* or *Snow Falling on Cedars*. Another possibility would be to consider the historical context of English Literature (Appendix 4 on page 117) in the light of Eagleton's comments.

Unit 9:
Trying out critical positions: reading a short story

The aim of this unit is to offer students an intriguing and challenging short story. It demonstrates the ways in which one story can be read from different theoretical positions. It is not intended to suggest that one reading is better than another, but to explore the different aspects of a text foregrounded by a particular approach. The activities encourage students to become aware of the position they are reading from, why they chose to approach the text in this way and the implications of this. Alice Walker's reading shows students how she combines insights gained from different critical positions to produce a personal but informed response. She reads as a woman, as a black American, as someone interested in her own shifting interpretation. Her reading is based on the exploration of both the text and context.

It may be possible to use the work in this unit as a starting point for internal assessment.

Organising the activity
The sequence of activities assumes that students will find the story difficult at first; that approaching it through an exploration of plot and character may not take them very far and that they will need to re-read it several times. The Critical Position cards offer students different ways into a challenging text. Students should keep a record of the ways their response develops as they accumulate more information and encounter 'different interpretations by other readers'. The Critical Position cards which are *most* helpful for this activity are:

- Great authors
- Moral
- Structuralist
- Reader-response
- Feminist
- Marxist
- Race/Post-colonial.

Before using the Critical Position cards with a text, it would be worthwhile spending some time discussing the attitudes and assumptions lying behind the views expressed on the card. Arguing with the assumptions made and offering alternative arguments will help students see that any position is inevitably partial.

Extracts from Hermione Lee's introduction to 'Everything that Rises Must Converge', paraphrased in the final activity are included in these notes.

Discussion may focus on the following:
- the aspects of the text which are foregrounded or marginalised by the critical positions, and whether or not these are mutually exclusive
- whether an exploration of the readings produced by different critical positions is a useful way of developing students' own approach to interpretation
- the way in which Alice Walker's criticism exemplifies a reading which remains resolutely independent and personal while still being informed by a range of critical theories.

You could go on to repeat the activity using extracts from set texts to allow students to reinforce their appreciation of what these different readings offer and what they preclude. The cards are also recommended for use with many of the later, more extended activities, for example Unit 10 'Reading critically' and Unit 11 'Readings through time' (Jane Eyre).

You may want to use the following extracts from Hermione Lee to stimulate students' thinking both about the title and about the usefulness or otherwise of using biographical information as a way in to textual interpretations.

> O'Connor's admiration for Teilhard de Chardin, a palaeontologist, Jesuit and mystic, is expressed in the title, which is taken from his theory in *The Phenomenon of Man* that the universe is in a continuous process of upward convergence towards 'point Omega', the ultimate, mysterious central 'Great Presence'. Love is the agent of convergence; egoism, elitism, racism and ignorance are retrograde, dragging the world 'backwards towards plurality and into matter.'
>
> Evidently Julian, despising his mother's

> absurd family pride, pleased with his own rational liberalism, looking out at the South from 'the inner compartment of his mind where he spent most of his time' is a long way from 'point Omega'. The principle of convergence seems to be satirised by Julian's mother's insensitive comments on her 'coloured friends' ('They should rise, yes. But on their own side of the fence') and by the ridiculous coincidence of the identical hats worn by the white and the black mother on the integrated bus. O'Connor casts a bleak, caustic eye on race relations in the South, and is not interested in voicing outrage or sympathy. Nevertheless the story does effect an unexpected and alarming 'spiritual renovation'. Julian is catapulted into the purgatorial world 'of guilt and sorrow' and Teihard de Chardin's proposition is proved by the action of grace upon distorted, negative, retrograde materials.
>
> **Hermione Lee**

Critical Position cards

For A level students the cards represent simplified versions of the different ways of thinking about literature which lie behind much criticism written during the twentieth century. The Critical Time Line (Appendix 3) provides a chronological overview of the history of theory and the relations between the different positions. It shows how each theory has grown out of or in opposition to an earlier position. The cards demonstrate the ways in which readers can move between a number of different positions in constructing their own interpretations.

Teachers and students who are particularly engaged by critical theory may want to devise cards for some of other theories which are beginning to emerge, for example Masculinist and Queer readings. As Deconstruction does not aim to produce an interpretation of a text, but rather to show the impossibility of such an interpretation, it has not been included as a Critical Position card. The bibliography in Appendix 2 suggests books which offer an accessible, but more comprehensive introduction to critical theory.

The Critical Position cards fall into the following three groups:

Traditional: Great Authors and Moral

Taken as a group, the Great Authors and Moral cards represent the liberal humanist position in the tradition of Leavis. It is characterised by close textual analysis of the work of a selected group of writers and a belief that 'educated' readers will all recognise the same merits in a literary work. Unlike later critics, Leavis did not articulate his critical framework, implying that his approach was the 'natural' and 'common sense' way of reading literature. The continued influence of this position is seen in the list of prescribed authors in the National Curriculum and the selection of many set books at A level. His influence remains strong in English teaching, particularly in the tradition of using 'practical criticism' as a test of students' abilities as readers. Some of the strengths and weaknesses of his approach may be seen in the extracts from Leavis's essay on *Othello*, on page 87.

Structuralism/Post-structuralism; Genre theory and Reader-response

These cards represent some theoretical positions which rocked the academic establishment in the 1960s and 70s. They represent a significant break with the 'traditional' methods of Leavis and his followers. All theories which have developed and evolved since owe something to the work of the structuralists and to those who subsequently challenged and extended these ideas. The theories and methods are based on new thinking about language and communication developed during the early years of the twentieth century, for example the work of the linguist Saussure.

Modern critics: Marxists, Feminists, Psychoanalytists; Cultural materialists, New historicists and Post colonial critics

This final group share certain assumptions about the world and the place of interpretation of texts within it. They represent the theoretical positions which come from the cross fertilisation of literary studies with disciplines such as women's studies, and cultural and political studies. They exemplify the way in which readers can move between a number of different positions in constructing their own interpretations.

Preparing for Section 2

The short activities in Section 1 encourage students to become more aware of what they are doing when they read a text and talk about what it means. They demonstrate some of the ideas about writers, texts and readers which have been significant in critical writings during the second half of the twentieth century, for example:
- reading – and, more importantly, re-reading is an active process of interpretation
- texts do not have simple fixed meanings
- the context in which a text is produced and in which it is received / read affects the interpretation of it
- readers read from positions determined by their own gender, race, class and also by the social and cultural context in which they live
- texts do not have single fixed 'right' meanings; some people think they don't 'mean' anything at all until the reader reads and

makes meaning out of them
- all readers bring a lot of knowledge to new texts, learned from all the other reading they have done – about genres, about literary conventions, and about how different kinds of texts work
- readers come to texts with expectations and assumptions, created in them by their reading and by the society in which they live
- the 'author' does not have control of the text once it has been written and is read and re-read by other people. Each new reading of the text is also a re-writing of it.

Before students tackle the more extended investigations into 'different readings' in Section 2, they might find it helpful to consider explicitly these ideas about the relationship between reader, writer and text. Working in small groups, students could look in detail at several of these summary statements and try to attach these to the activities they have already done in Section 1.

Students could re-visit some of the units from Section 1 and consider them from the perspective of the different Critical Position cards, for example, use the Structuralist card to interpret 'Killing Time'.

The Critical Position cards can be used with any of the units in Section 2 to focus the different interpretations or as an extension activity. The cards are used in the activities in Units 10 ('Reading critically') and 11 ('Reading through time').

The more extended units in Section 2 are based on groups of connected texts and would make an ideal preparation for the Synoptic Papers, particularly for AQA A and B.

Unit 10: Reading critically

The extract from *Small World* by David Lodge offers both an amusing take on the whole world of 'different interpretations' and 'other readers' and a useful, serious summary of the main approaches encountered in Section 1.

Organising the activity
Follow the instructions on the student sheet.

Discussion may focus on the following:
- whether or not critical theories offer a useful framework for reading a text
- the purpose of critical interpretation
- the insights offered by the different critical positions.

You may want to extend the role play to consider some of the other texts in Section 1, set texts or 'non-literary texts' of their own choosing.

Unit 11:
Readings through time

The aim of the activities on critical writings on *Jane Eyre* is to show how critics bring different sets of assumptions to a text. The extracts suggest that any interpretation reflects the interests and concerns of the critic and of the society in which they are reading.

Organising the activity

To do this activity, it may actually be better if students have not read *Jane Eyre*! However, if the class have read or studied the novel, ask each person to write a few short statements summarising their response before they tackle the activities on the interpretations of 'other readers'. After the activities ask students to talk about how these other interpetations may cause them to re-think their own reading, if at all.

Discussion may focus on the following:
– shifts in critical interest between the text's first publication and the end of the twentieth century
– the changing methods and styles of critical interpretation
– what each critic's reading adds to the student's own reading
– whether it is possible to select from these readings to develop an informed, personal reading
– whether it is important to know about the earlier readings in order to appreciate the later ones.

You may want to go on to do a similar activity on a selection of criticism around a text being studied for examination. Students who are studying *Jane Eyre* or who are keen to follow up the feminist and psychoanalytic readings in Angela Carter's essay may be interested in the extract from *The Self Conceived* by Helène Moglen included on the English and Media Centre website (www.englishandmedia.co.uk).

Unit 12:
Will the real poem please stand up? Wyatt's 'They flee from me'

The aim of the activity is to raise some questions about the way we determine the authenticity of a text and to explore the role played by writers, editors and readers in creating its meaning.

Organising the activity

Follow the instructions on the student sheet.

Discussion may focus on the following:
– the influence of earlier, often unacknowledged interpretations and editing in shaping our responses
– what the controversy suggests about the authority of the author.

Unit 13:
Textual relations

The aim of this activity is to extend the definition of 'different interpretations ... by other readers'. The argument that each reading of a text is also a re-writing is made explicit in the discussion of Wendy Cope's reading of Shakespeare's 'Sonnet 55'. It highlights the influence of past texts on each writer and poses the question, can our reading of a twentieth century text influence our interpretation and therefore the meaning – of an earlier one?

Organising the activity

Follow the instructions on the student sheet.

Discussion may focus on the following:
– the extent to which any text is original
– whether readings are enhanced or distorted by knowledge of earlier texts
– whether a reader can appreciate a text without knowledge of the texts to which it alludes explicitly or implicitly.

You may want to go on to use the pairs of texts suggested here as the basis of a coursework essay. Where a pairing includes at least one prose text, these texts could also form a useful focus for the Textual transformation paper in the Language/Literature specification from AQA (B).

Odyssey/Omeros: Derek Walcott
King Lear/ A Thousand Acres: Jane Smiley
The Tempest/Indigo: Marina Warner
Jane Eyre/Wide Sargasso Sea: Jean Rhys
Great Expectations/Jack Maggs: Peter Carey
Coral Island/Lord of the Flies: William Golding
North & South/Nice Work: David Lodge
Grimms' Tales/The Bloody Chamber: Angela Carter
Hamlet/Rosencranz and Guildenstern are Dead: Tom Stoppard
Dogg's Hamlet/Cahoot's Macbeth: Tom Stoppard
Hamlet/The Marowitz Hamlet: Charles Marowitz
Dr Faustus/The Tragical History of Dr Faustus: Charles Marowitz
Mrs Dalloway/The Hours: Michael Cunningham
The Wasteland/The Graphic Wasteland: Martin Rowson.

Unit 14:
Adam and Eve –
re-reading as a feminist

This unit highlights the importance of paying attention to the perspective from which a story is told, particularly in terms of gender. Its aim is to show how each decision a writer makes results in one story being privileged and another version being silenced – there is never only one interpretation of an event or 'story'. The sequence of activities suggests that in many cases the stories which are given a voice reflect the dominant structures in a society.

Organising the activity

The unit begins with an exploration of different visual representations of the 'Fall', giving students an opportunity to consider the ways in which this story has been interpreted in different periods and from different perspectives. This is followed by the version of the 'Fall' told in Genesis and Milton's reading and re-writing of the story. It concludes with a feminist re-reading/re-writing of the story.

Discussion may focus on the following:
– the way readers take for granted the authority of canonical texts
– the way readers have taken for granted the male perspective
– the insights offered by feminist readings
– the role of linguistic analysis in literary interpretation
– the connections between alternative interpretations of different types of texts.

You may want to go on to get students to produce their own re-writing of a text to highlight the story which is repressed in the original. Carol Ann Duffy's collection *The World's Wife* and U.A. Fanthorpe's *Only Here for the Bier* are entertaining and illuminating models of how this might be done.

Reading Shakespeare as a feminist

The activities suggested here, give students the chance to read the Shakespeare play they are studying from the perspective of a feminist critic. Which aspects of the play are foregrounded and which are pushed to the margins?

- Choose scenes in which one of the female characters appears:
  – without the hero
  – with other women
  – alone.

- Use the questions suggested below to explore the way the character is represented.
  – How are they presented in these different situations?
  – What aspects of their characters does Shakespeare bring out in these scenes?
  – How does he do this (for example, through the imagery, the woman's behaviour, what she does or does not say, what others do or do not say about her)?
  – How do you react to the women in each case? Does your own gender make a difference to the way you read the female character?

- Now choose a scene where the same woman appears with the hero. Look at the woman through the hero's eyes.
  – What sort of woman does he see?
  – Is this the whole picture? What else do you know about her?

- Look at the woman/the women through the eyes of the other men in the play.
  – What sort of woman/women do they see?
  – Is this the same as, or different from what the hero sees?

- Use the same activities to explore the role and representation of women in one or two more texts. For example, try them with a modern play or novel written by a man. Then do the same for one written by a woman. What do you discover about the ways in which gender differences have been represented in literature in different periods? To what extent do you think your reading is affected by your own gender and the context in which you are constructing these readings?

Unit 15:
Psychoanalytic criticism –
what the text didn't say

The aim of this unit is to give students the opportunity to consider actively the ways in which psychoanalysis and literary interpretation each take from the other discipline. It uses poetry by Emily Dickinson to demonstrate what it actually means to read a text from this perspective.

Organising the activity

Follow the instructions on the student sheet. As students tend to be particularly interested in psychoanalytic readings, this unit comes with a health warning! It is worth spending some time considering whether, if adopted wholesale, psychoanalytic criticism can distract from, rather than illuminate, the text. The work on Jacqueline Rose's critical reading of Sylvia Plath (Unit 20) could form the focus for a discussion on the strengths and weaknesses of psychoanalytic criticism.

Discussion may focus on the following:
– the insights gained from applying the ideas of the psychoanalysts to literature

- the possibility that psychoanalytic criticism takes the reader away from the text or results in a distorted reading
- what psychoanalysis reveals about the process of interpretation
- the suggestion that a text, like a mind, can repress or sublimate unacceptable emotions or ideas
- links between psychoanalytical criticism and other modern critical theories which explore gaps and silences (for example, feminism and post-colonialism).

You may want to go on to experiment with a psychoanalytic reading of a set text. Is it possible? Does it illuminate particular aspects of the text or make the reader re-think his or her interpretation? *Frankenstein, Wuthering Heights*, the poetry of Sylvia Plath and Shakespeare all lend themselves to being explored from this perspective. Angela Carter's reading of *Jane Eyre* on page 56 provides an interesting example of how this critical theory can be applied in practice. Alternatively, you could go on to consider the other ways of reading Emily Dickinson.

Unit 16:
Adapting classic texts –
Mansfield Park

The unit explores intertextuality and 'different interpretations' in relation to film adaptations. It uses Patricia Rozema's controversial adaptation of *Mansfield Park* and the critical responses to it as a case study. The adaptation is seen as one reading or interpretation of the novel, while the reviewers reveal that the process of interpretation is layered. Visual texts are shown to be as open to different readings as printed ones.

Organising the activity
Follow the instructions on the student sheet. Students do not need to have read the book or seen the film.

Discussion may focus on the following:
- whether Rozema's reading of *Mansfield Park* has produced a new, and therefore re-written version of the original text
- what the conflicting reviews reveal about the process of interpretation (the role that the reviewer's beliefs and assumptions about the original text play in shaping a response to an adaptation)
- the authority of the author versus the authority of the reader
- whether we can ever know the intention of the author
- connections with Unit 12 (Will the real text please stand up?).

You may want to go on to consider more classic texts which have been adapted in a variety of media, for example the all male version of *Swan Lake* produced by Adventures in Motion Pictures. An interview with Matthew Bourne, the director, is included on the English and Media Centre website (www.englishandmedia.co.uk).

Unit 17:
Post-colonialism and
Mansfield Park

This unit builds on the critical responses to Rozema's reading of the novel and her representation in the film of slavery as the origins of the Bertram's wealth. Extracts from Edward Said's ground breaking interpretation of *Mansfield Park* introduce students to the concerns and practices of the post-colonialist reader.

Organising the activity
Follow the instructions on the student sheet.

Discussion may focus on the following:
- whether it is valid to interpret a colonial or pre-colonial text in the light of post-colonial understandings and attitudes
- what a post-colonial perspective suggests about the connections between interpretation and the beliefs and behaviour of society
- whether the author's intentions should be a consideration in our interpretation of a text.

Students who are interested in post-colonialism may want to go on to read some works by post-colonial writers, for example Eavan Boland, Salman Rushdie, Zadie Smith.

Unit 18:
Readings of *Othello* –
evaluating the critics

The aim of the case study on *Othello* is to demonstrate how reading from a specific critical position, in this case the historical perspective of the cultural materialist, foregrounds aspects of the play which the conventional emphasis on plot, character and theme marginalises or does not recognise. Once again, both the extracts from critical writing and the activities emphasise the importance of analysing the primary text in detail.

Organising the activity
Follow the instructions on the student sheet.

Students will need access to a copy of Act 1 Scene 3 of the play.

The traditional reading
A.C. Bradley and F.R. Leavis both represent the 'traditional' approach, commenting on character in the play. The extract from Leavis is a typically assertive and dismissive response to Bradley's interpretation.

A cultural materialist reading
Alan Sinfield reads the play from the position of the cultural materialist. He places the play and Shakespeare's presentation of Othello in its cultural and historical context. He challenges the assumption that the evil, the racism and sexism in the play is located specifically in the character of Iago. His interpretation is grounded in his political awareness about dominant ideologies in society and their reflections in contemporary texts.

A feminist reading
Discussion may focus on the following:
- what insights the methods of Leavis and Bradley offer
- how more recent theories build on or react against these critics
- the methods and insights of the cultural materialists (for example, the use of other texts and materials, contemporary with the literary text)
- the connections between a cultural materialist reading and some of the ideas about text, context and reader introduced in Section 1 (for example, Units 6 and 7).

You may want to go on to repeat the activities in relation to critical material about, and alternative interpretations of any other Shakespeare play being studied.
As an extension activity you could offer students John Sutherland's eclectic and quirky reading of the play published in *Henry V, War Criminal*. He focuses on textual problems or inconsistencies which readers or audiences may brush aside. He discusses these problems in relation to his knowledge of historical and cultural contexts, using close reading and interrogation of the text to give weight to his analysis. Students could compare his approach with other critical positions which also explore contradictions and gaps, for example post-colonialism and psychoanalysis. Another possibility would be to compare his treatment of the characters as real people with the approach of Bradley and Leavis.

Unit 19:
Three readings of Hemingway's 'Cat in the Rain'

The aim of this unit is to introduce students in a practical way to the approach and methods of a structuralist reader. The emphasis on close reading highlights the connection between the 'new' theories and more traditional methods. David Lodge's reading of the story provides not only a model of a critical method, but offers a more sceptical perspective on the process of criticism.

Organising the activity
It is a substantial unit of work, requiring approximately three hours to complete fully. If short of time you could miss out the readings by Baker and Hagopian and instead focus only on the introductory activities (page 91) and David Lodge's structuralist reading (page 94-97).

Students will need to be familiar with the following terms:

Denotative/denotation: the basic, primary meaning of a word or a phrase.

Connotative/ connotation: the range of associations and implications which the same word carries.

Metonymy: using something associated with the subject to stand for the subject itself. For example, referring to 'the Crown' but meaning 'the king'.

Synecdoche: very much the same device. Using a part (A sail! A sail!) to stand for the whole (There's a ship!).

Discussion may focus on the following:
- the way all critical readings foreground some aspects of a story and suppress others
- the difference between what happens in a story and what it is about
- the importance of paying close attention to the text
- the importance of paying attention to the point of view from which the story is told and/or events seen
- the implications of accepting 'realist' texts as reflections of the world
- the way in which a personal response can be informed and clarified by 'different interpretations … by other readers'
- the use of a critical method to criticise the interpretations of other readers.

You may want to go on to apply the structuralist framework to one of the other texts in the pack, for example the short story *Embroidery* (page 9).

Unit 20:
Re-reading the life –
the text, the critic, the writer, and her lover

Unfortunately, the estates of Ted Hughes and Sylvia Plath refused to grant permission for the poems to be re-printed in the pack. You will need to provide students with copies of 'The Rabbit Catcher' by Ted Hughes (in *Birthday Letters*, Faber and Faber) and 'The Rabbit Catcher' by Sylvia Plath (in *Collected Poems*, Faber and Faber).

The aim of the unit is to explore the possibilities and dangers of biographical interpretations in relation to the work of Sylvia Plath and Ted Hughes. It focuses on the analysis of Plath's 'The Rabbit Catcher' and its companion poem in Hughes's *Birthday Letters*.

Organising the activity
Follow the instructions on the student sheet.

The work on Plath and Hughes pulls together many of the issues about texts, contexts and reading explored in earlier units. It raises questions about the following:
- the uses of biographical material to interpret a text
- the possibility that biographical readings distract from, rather than illuminate a text
- who has authority over the meaning of a text
- the contexts in which a text was written and is understood
- the need to re-read texts in the light of new contextual information
- the difficulty of approaching a well-known text free from pre-conceived interpretations
- the difficulty of appreciating a text without knowledge of the other texts it relates to (is it possible to appreciate Hughes's poem without knowing Plath's?).

ROAD ATLAS EU

Contents

	Distance map and chart
ii – iii	Map symbols
iv	International road signs and travel web links
v	Key to map pages
vi – xvii	Route planning maps 1:4 654 000
2 – 181	Road maps 1:1 000 000
182 – 187	Road maps 1:750 000
188 – 191	Index to place names 1:750 000
192 – 207	City through-route maps
192	Amsterdam, Athina, Barcelona, Belfast
193	Beograd, Berlin, Bern, Birmingham
194	Bonn, Bordeaux, Bratislava, Brussel/Bruxelles
195	București, Budapest, Cardiff, Chișinau
196	Dublin, Edinburgh, Firenze, Frankfurt
197	Glasgow, Göteborg, Den Haag, Hamburg
198	Helsinki, İstanbul, København, Köln
199	Leipzig, Lisboa, Ljubljana, London
200	Lyon, Madrid, Manchester, Marseille
201	Milano, München, Napoli, Oslo
202	Palermo, Paris, Podgorica, Praha
203	Rīga, Roma, Rotterdam, Sankt Peterburg
204	Sarajevo, Sevilla, Skopje, Sofiya
205	Stockholm, Strasbourg, Tallinn, Torino
206	Toulouse, Valencia, Venezia, Vilnius
207	Warszawa, Wien, Zagreb, Zürich
208 – 211	City street plans
208	Amsterdam, Athina, Berlin, Bern
209	Brussel/Bruxelles, Dublin, Helsinki, København
210	Lisboa, London, Madrid, Oslo
211	Paris, Roma, Stockholm, Wien
212 – 272	Index to place names 1:1 000 000
	Driving information and web links

Country identifier

A	Austria		
AL	Albania		
AND	Andorra	Andorre	Andorra
B	Belgium	Belgique	Belgien
BG	Bulgaria	Bulgarie	Bulgarien
BIH	Bosnia and Herzegovina	Bosnie-et-Herzégovine	Bosnien und Herzegowina
BY	Belarus	Bélarus	Belarus
CH	Switzerland	Suisse	Schweiz
CY	Cyprus	Chypre	Zypern
CZ	Czech Republic	République tchèque	Tschechische Republik
D	Germany	Allemagne	Deutschland
DK	Denmark	Danemark	Dänemark
DZ	Algeria	Algérie	Algerien
E	Spain	Espagne	Spanien
EST	Estonia	Estonie	Estland
F	France	France	Frankreich
FIN	Finland	Finlande	Finnland
FL	Liechtenstein	Liechtenstein	Liechtenstein
FO	Faroe Islands	Iles Féroé	Färöer-Inseln
GB	United Kingdom GB & NI	Grande-Bretagne	Grossbritannien
GBA	Alderney	Alderney	Alderney
GBG	Guernsey	Guernsey	Guernsey
GBJ	Jersey	Jersey	Jersey
GBM	Isle of Man	île de Man	Insel Man
GBZ	Gibraltar	Gibraltar	Gibraltar
GR	Greece	Grèce	Griechenland
H	Hungary	Hongrie	Ungarn
HR	Croatia	Croatie	Kroatien
I	Italy	Italie	Italien
IRL	Ireland	Irlande	Irland
IS	Iceland	Islande	Island
L	Luxembourg	Luxembourg	Luxemburg
LT	Lithuania	Lituanie	Litauen
LV	Latvia	Lettonie	Lettland
M	Malta	Malte	Malta
MA	Morocco	Maroc	Marokko
MC	Monaco	Monaco	Monaco
MD	Moldova	Moldavie	Moldawien
MK	Macedonia (F.Y.R.O.M.)	Ancienne République yougoslave de Macédoine	Ehemalige jugoslawische Republik Mazedonien
MNE	Montenegro	Monténégro	Montenegro
N	Norway	Norvège	Norwegen
NL	Netherlands	Pays-Bas	Niederlande
P	Portugal	Portugal	Portugal
PL	Poland	Pologne	Polen
RKS	Kosovo	Kosovo	Kosovo
RO	Romania	Roumanie	Rumänien
RSM	San Marino	Saint-Marin	San Marino
RUS	Russia	Russie	Russland
S	Sweden	Suède	Schweden
SK	Slovakia	République slovaque	Slowakei
SLO	Slovenia	Slovénie	Slowenien
SRB	Serbia	Sérbie	Serbien
TN	Tunisia	Tunisie	Tunisien
TR	Turkey	Turquie	Türkei
UA	Ukraine	Ukraine	Ukraine

Published by Collins
An imprint of HarperCollins Publishers
Westerhill Road
Bishopbriggs
Glasgow G64 2QT
www.harpercollins.co.uk

First published 2004

New edition 2015

A catalogue record for this book is available from the British Library

ISBN 978-0-00-814637-5

10 9 8 7 6 5 4 3 2 1

Printed in China by RR Donnelley APS

All mapping in this atlas is generated from Collins Bartholomew digital databases.
Collins Bartholomew, the UK's leading independent geographical information supplier, can provide a digital, custom, and premium mapping service to a variety of markets.
For further information:
Tel: +44 (0)141 306 3752
e-mail: collinsbartholomew@harpercollins.co.uk
or visit our website at: www.collinsbartholomew.com

If you would like to comment on any aspect of this book, please contact us at the above address or online.
e-mail: collinsmaps@harpercollins.co.uk

facebook.com/collinsmaps @collinsmaps

Map symbols

Road maps	Carte routière	Strassenkarten
E55 Euro route number	Route européenne	Europastrasse
A13 Motorway	Autoroute	Autobahn
Motorway – toll	Autoroute à péage	Gebührenpflichtige Autobahn
Motorway – toll (vignette)	Autoroute à péage (vignette)	Gebührenpflichtige Autobahn (Vignette)
Motorway junction – full access	Echangeur d'autoroute avec accès libre	Autobahnauffahrt mit vollem Zugang
Motorway junction – restricted access	Echangeur d'autoroute avec accès limité	Autobahnauffahrt mit beschränktem Zugang
Motorway services	Aire de service sur autoroute	Autobahnservicestelle
309 Main road – dual carriageway	Route principale à chaussées séparées	Hauptstrasse – Zweispurig
Main road – single carriageway	Route principale à une seule chaussée	Hauptstrasse – Einspurig
516 Secondary road – dual carriageway	Route secondaire à chaussées séparées	Zweispurige Nebenstrasse
Secondary road – single carriageway	Route secondaire à seule chaussée	Einspurige Nebenstrasse
Other road	Autre route	Andere Strasse
Motorway tunnel	Autoroute tunnel	Autobahntunnel
Main road tunnel	Route principale tunnel	Hauptstrassetunnel
Motorway/road under construction	Autoroute/route en construction	Autobahn/Strasse im Bau
Road toll	Route à péage	Gebührenpflichtige Strasse
Distance marker / Distances in kilometres / Distances in miles (UK only) 16 10	Marquage des distances / Distances en kilomètres / Distances en miles (GB)	Distanz-Markierung / Distanzen in Kilometern / Distanzen in Meilen (GB)
Steep hill	Colline abrupte	Steile Strasse
2587 Mountain pass (height in metres)	Col (Altitude en mètres)	Pass (Höhe in Metern)
Scenic route	Parcours pittoresque	Landschaftlich schöne Strecke
International airport	Aéroport international	Internationaler Flughafen
Car transport by rail	Transport des autos par voie ferrée	Autotransport per Bahn
Railway	Chemin de fer	Eisenbahn
Tunnel	Tunnel	Tunnel
Funicular railway	Funiculaire	Seilbahn
Rotterdam Car ferry	Bac pour autos	Autofähre
2587 Summit (height in metres)	Sommet (Altitude en mètres)	Berg (Höhe in Metern)
Volcano	Volcan	Vulkan
Canal	Canal	Kanal
International boundary	Frontière d'Etat	Landesgrenze
Disputed International boundary	Frontière litigieuse	Umstrittene Staatsgrenze
GB Country abbreviation	Abréviation du pays	Regionsgrenze
Urban area	Zone urbaine	Stadtgebiet
28 Adjoining page indicator	Indication de la page contigüe	Randhinweis auf Folgekarte
National Park	Parc national	Nationalpark

1:1 000 000

1 centimetre to 10 kilometres   0 10 20 30 40 50 60 70 80 km   1 inch to 16 miles
0 10 20 30 40 50 miles

City maps and plans	Plans de ville	Stadtpläne
★ Place of interest	Site d'intérêt	Sehenswerter Ort
Railway station	Gare	Bahnhof
Parkland	Espace vert	Parkland
Woodland	Espace boisé	Waldland
General place of interest	Site d'intérêt général	Sehenswerter Ort
Academic/Municipal building	Établissement scolaire/installations municipales	Akademisches/Öffentliches Gebäude
Place of worship	Lieu de culte	Andachtsstätte
Transport location	Infrastructure de transport	Verkehrsanbindung

Places of interest

🏛	Museum and Art Gallery	Musée / Gallerie d'art	Museum / Kunstgalerie
	Castle	Château	Burg / Schloss
	Historic building	Monument historique	historisches Gebäude
	Historic site	Site historique	historische Stätte
m	Monument	Monument	Denkmal
	Religious site	Site religieux	religiöse Stätte
	Aquarium / Sea life centre	Aquarium / Parc Marin	Aquarium
	Arboretum	Arboretum	Arboretum, Baumschule
	Botanic garden (National)	Jardin botanique national	botanischer Garten
★	Natural place of interest (other site)	Réserve naturelle	landschaftlich interessanter Ort
	Zoo / Safari park / Wildlife park	Parc Safari / Réserve sauvage / Zoo	Safaripark / Wildreservat / Zoo
★	Other site	Autres sites	Touristenattraktion
	Theme park	Parc à thème	Freizeitpark
◆	World Heritage site	Patrimoine Mondial	Weltkulturerbe
	Athletics stadium (International)	Stade international d'athlétisme	internationales Leichtathletik Stadion
⚽	Football stadium (Major)	Stade de football	Fußballstadion
	Golf course (International)	Parcours de golf international	internationaler Golfplatz
	Grand Prix circuit (Formula 1) / Motor racing venue / MotoGP circuit	Circuit auto-moto	Autodrom
	Rugby ground (International - Six Nations)	Stade de rugby	internationales Rugbystadion
	International sports venue	Autre manifestation sportive	internationale Sportanlage
	Tennis venue	Court de tennis	Tennis
Valcotos ⊛	Winter sports resort	Sports d'hiver	Wintersport

Be aware!

★ On the spot fines for motoring offences are common in many European countries, including France, Spain, and Italy. For each fine an official receipt should be issued.

★ Speed camera detectors are illegal in many European countries whether in use or not. You should ensure that they are removed from your vehicle. In France you are liable to a prison sentence, a fine, and confiscation of the device and your vehicle. GPS/satellite navigation systems which show speed camera locations are illegal.

★ In Austria, Bulgaria, Czech Republic, Hungary, Romania, Slovakia, Slovenia and Switzerland, all vehicles using motorways and expressways must display a motorway vignette. Failure to do so will result in a heavy on-the-spot fine. Vignettes are available at major border crossing points and major petrol stations.

★ Dipped headlights are compulsory when using road tunnels in Austria, Switzerland and Germany.

★ Penalties for speeding or drink-driving in many European countries are often more severe than in the UK, e.g. in France traffic offences are subject to on-the-spot fines, where it is also compulsory to carry a breathalyser kit, and recommended to carry two.

★ In many European countries you must drive with dipped headlights at all times. In France it is mandatory to do so in poor visibility only, but is recommended at all times.

★ In Denmark you must indicate when changing lanes on a motorway.

★ In Spain you must carry two red warning triangles to be placed in front and behind the vehicle in the event of accident or breakdown.

★ In many European countries, as in the UK and Ireland, the use of mobile phones while driving is not permitted unless 'hands-free'.

★ Fluorescent waistcoats and warning triangles should be carried inside the car and not in the boot.

★ In Austria, Bosnia-Herzegovina, Czech Republic, Estonia, Finland, Germany, Iceland, Latvia, Lithuania, Norway, Slovenia and Sweden, cars must have winter tyres fitted between December and March.

★ Some European cities have introduced an environmental zone for vehicle emission levels. This is usually accompanied by a charge to drive into the designated central zone.

International road signs and travel web links

Informative signs

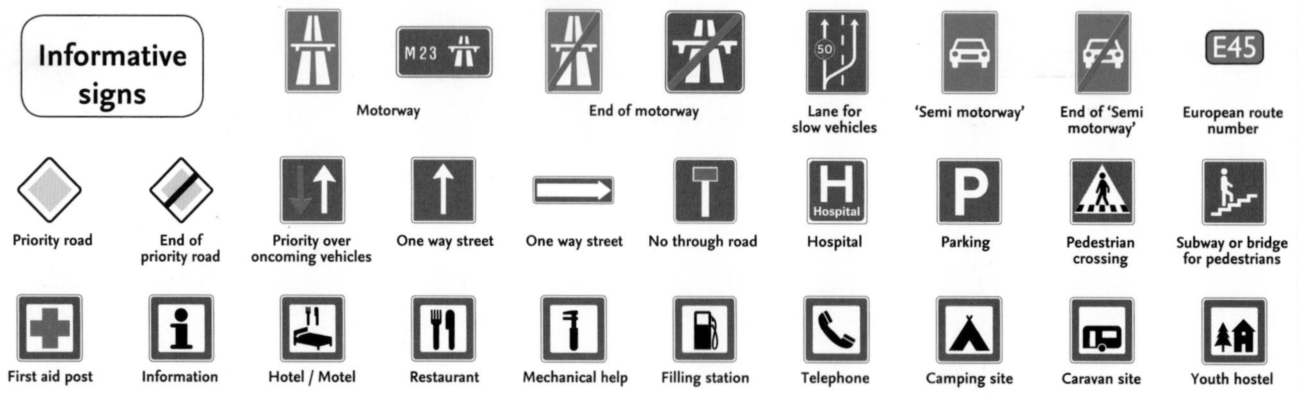
Motorway
End of motorway
Lane for slow vehicles
'Semi motorway'
End of 'Semi motorway'
European route number
Priority road
End of priority road
Priority over oncoming vehicles
One way street
One way street
No through road
Hospital
Parking
Pedestrian crossing
Subway or bridge for pedestrians
First aid post
Information
Hotel / Motel
Restaurant
Mechanical help
Filling station
Telephone
Camping site
Caravan site
Youth hostel

Warning signs

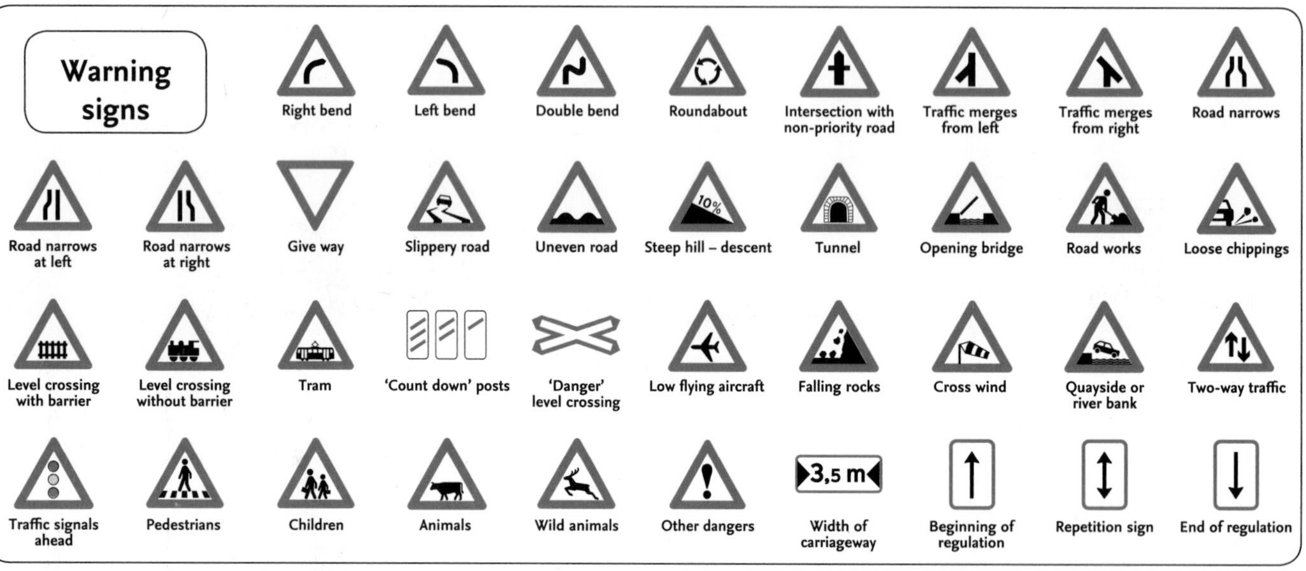
Right bend
Left bend
Double bend
Roundabout
Intersection with non-priority road
Traffic merges from left
Traffic merges from right
Road narrows
Road narrows at left
Road narrows at right
Give way
Slippery road
Uneven road
Steep hill – descent
Tunnel
Opening bridge
Road works
Loose chippings
Level crossing with barrier
Level crossing without barrier
Tram
'Count down' posts
'Danger' level crossing
Low flying aircraft
Falling rocks
Cross wind
Quayside or river bank
Two-way traffic
Traffic signals ahead
Pedestrians
Children
Animals
Wild animals
Other dangers
Width of carriageway
Beginning of regulation
Repetition sign
End of regulation

Regulative signs

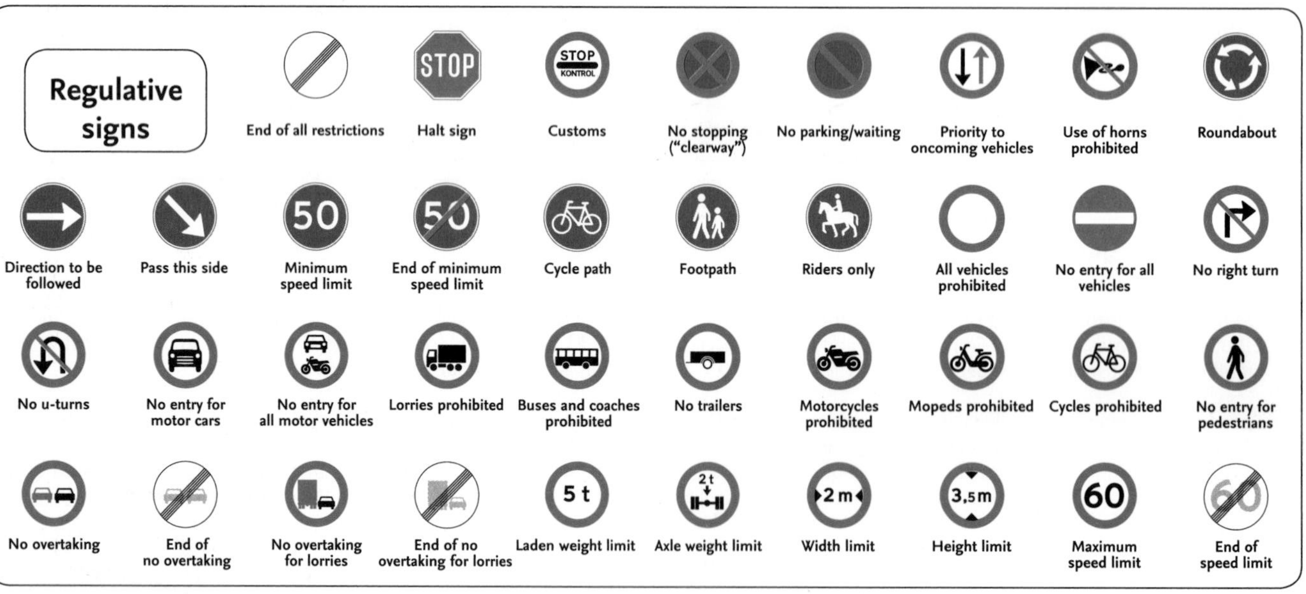
End of all restrictions
Halt sign
Customs
No stopping ("clearway")
No parking/waiting
Priority to oncoming vehicles
Use of horns prohibited
Roundabout
Direction to be followed
Pass this side
Minimum speed limit
End of minimum speed limit
Cycle path
Footpath
Riders only
All vehicles prohibited
No entry for all vehicles
No right turn
No u-turns
No entry for motor cars
No entry for all motor vehicles
Lorries prohibited
Buses and coaches prohibited
No trailers
Motorcycles prohibited
Mopeds prohibited
Cycles prohibited
No entry for pedestrians
No overtaking
End of no overtaking
No overtaking for lorries
End of no overtaking for lorries
Laden weight limit
Axle weight limit
Width limit
Height limit
Maximum speed limit
End of speed limit

Travel & route planning

Driving information www.drive-alive.co.uk
The AA www.theaa.com
The RAC www.rac.co.uk
ViaMichelin www.viamichelin.com
Bing Maps www.bing.com/maps/
Motorail information www.railsavers.com
Ferry information www.aferry.com
Eurotunnel information www.eurotunnel.com/uk/home/

General information

UK Foreign & Commonwealth Office www.gov.uk/government/organisations/foreign-commonwealth-office
Country profiles www.cia.gov/library/publications/the-world-factbook/index.html
World Heritage sites http://whc.unesco.org/en/list
World time wwp.greenwichmeantime.com
Weather information www.metoffice.gov.uk

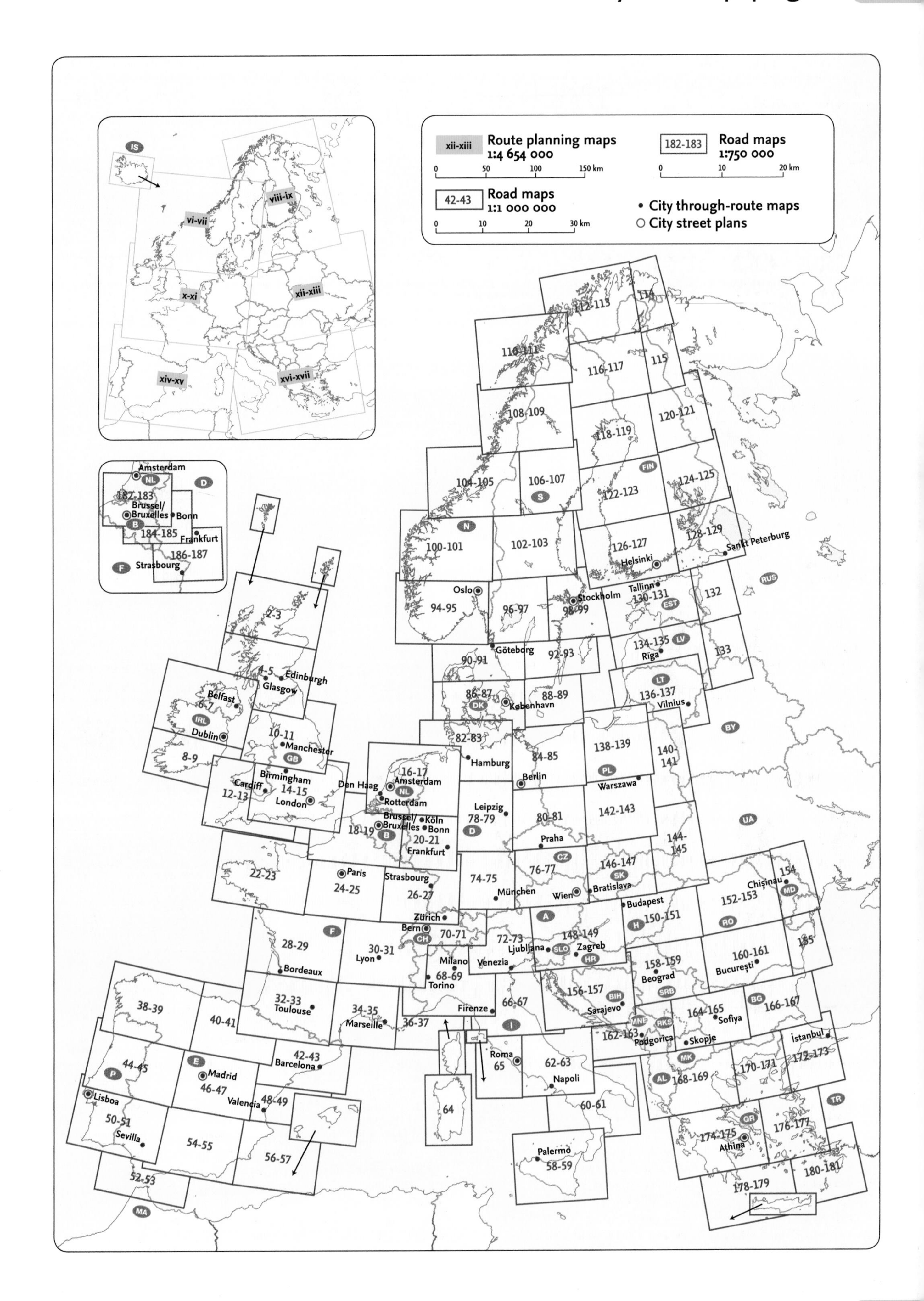
Route planning maps 1:4 654 000
Road maps 1:750 000
Road maps 1:1 000 000
City through-route maps
City street plans

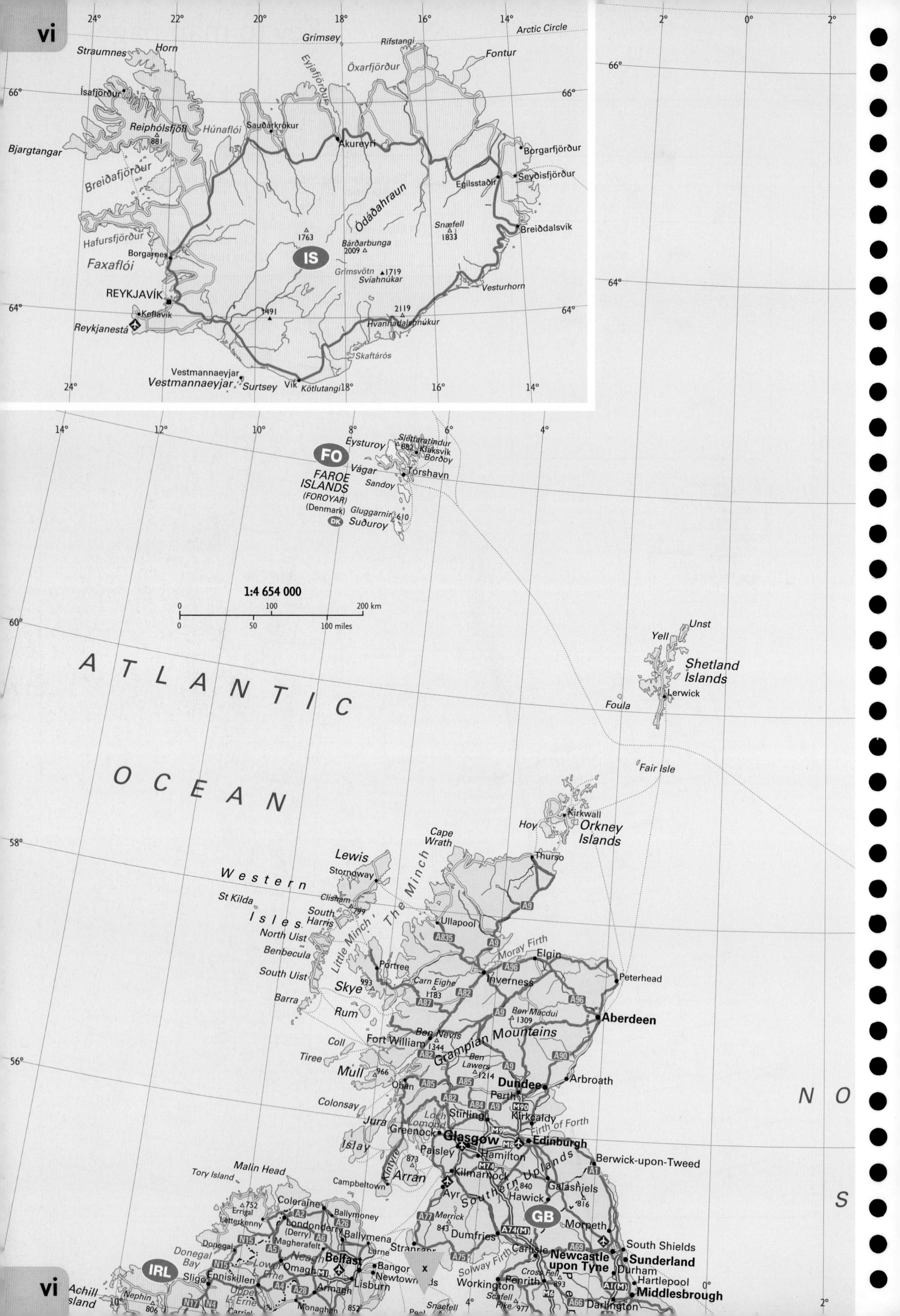

Arctic Circle
Grímsey
Rifstangi
Straumnes
Horn
Fontur
Öxarfjörður
Eyjafjörður
Ísafjörður
Sauðárkrókur
Reipholsfjöll
881
Húnaflói
Akureyri
Bjargtangar
Borgarfjörður
Breiðafjörður
Egilsstaðir
Seyðisfjörður
Ódáðahraun
Snæfell
1833
1763
Breiðdalsvík
Hafursfjörður
Bárðarbunga
2009
Borgarnes
IS
Faxaflói
Grímsvötn
1719
Sviahnúkar
REYKJAVÍK
Vesturhorn
Keflavík
1491
2119
Hvannadalshnúkur
Reykjanestá
Skaftárós
Vestmannaeyjar
Vestmannaeyjar
Surtsey
Vík
Kötlutangi
Eysturoy
Slættaratindur
882
Klaksvík
Borðoy
FO
Vágar
Tórshavn
FAROE ISLANDS
(FOROYAR)
(Denmark)
Sandoy
Gluggarnir
610
DK
Suðuroy
1:4 654 000
0
100
200 km
0
50
100 miles
ATLANTIC
OCEAN
Unst
Yell
Shetland Islands
Lerwick
Foula
Fair Isle
Kirkwall
Hoy
Orkney Islands
Cape Wrath
Thurso
Lewis
Stornoway
Western Isles
The Minch
Little Minch
St Kilda
Clisham
799
South Harris
North Uist
Benbecula
South Uist
Ullapool
A835
A9
Moray Firth
Elgin
A96
Portree
Peterhead
Inverness
Carn Eighe
1183
Skye
993
A82
A87
Barra
Rum
A9
Ben Macdui
1309
A96
Aberdeen
Ben Nevis
1344
Coll
Fort William
Grampian Mountains
A82
A90
Tiree
Ben Lawers
1214
Mull
966
Oban
A85
A85
Dundee
Arbroath
Perth
A82
A84
A9
M90
Colonsay
Jura
Loch Lomond
Stirling
Kirkcaldy
Firth of Forth
Greenock
Glasgow
M8
Edinburgh
Islay
Paisley
Hamilton
Berwick-upon-Tweed
Malin Head
873
M74
Tory Island
Kintyre
Arran
Kilmarnock
840
Southern Uplands
Galashiels
Campbeltown
Ayr
Hawick
816
752
Errigal
Letterkenny
Coleraine
A2
Ballymoney
A26
Londonderry
(Derry)
A6
Ballymena
Merrick
843
A77
Dumfries
A74(M)
GB
Morpeth
Magherafelt
Donegal
N15
A5
Larne
Stranraer
A75
Solway Firth
Carlisle
A69
South Shields
Newcastle upon Tyne
Sunderland
Donegal Bay
IRL
Lough Neagh
Belfast
M1
Bangor
Newtownards
Durham
Sligo
Enniskillen
Omagh
Lower Lough Erne
Upper Lough Erne
Lisburn
Workington
Penrith
Cross Fell
893
Hartlepool
A1(M)
Armagh
A4
A28
M6
Middlesbrough
Achill Island
Nephin
806
N17
N4
Monaghan
852
Snaefell
Scafell Pike
977
A66
Darlington
NOS

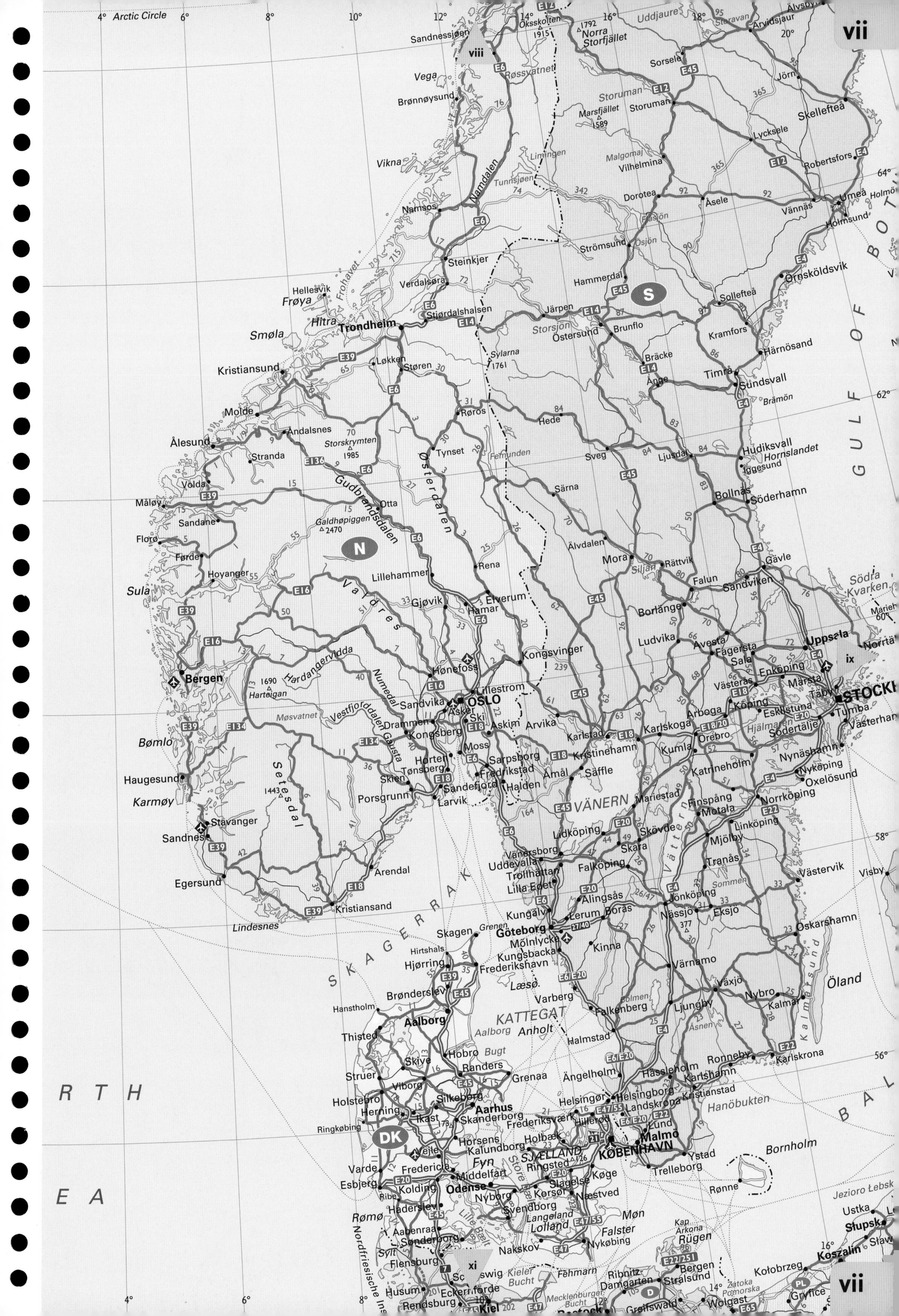
vii
Arctic Circle
Sandnessjøen
viii
Vega
Brønnøysund
Oksskolten
Norra Storfjället
Uddjaure
Storavan
Arvidsjaur
Sorsele
Røssvatnet
Storuman
Marsfjället
Jörn
Skellefteå
Lycksele
Robertsfors
Limingen
Malgomaj
Vilhelmina
Vikna
Namdalen
Tunnsjøen
Dorotea
Åsele
Vännäs
Umeå
Holmsund
Namsos
Strömsund
Steinkjer
Frohavet
Verdalsøra
Hammerdal
Örnsköldsvik
Hellesvik
Frøya
Hitra
Smøla
Trondheim
Stjørdalshalsen
Järpen
Storsjön
Östersund
Brunflo
Sollefteå
Kramfors
Härnösand
Kristiansund
Løkken
Støren
Sylarna
Bräcke
Ånge
Timrå
Sundsvall
Brämön
Molde
Røros
Hede
Åndalsnes
Ålesund
Storskrymten
Stranda
Tynset
Femunden
Sveg
Ljusdal
Hudiksvall
Hornslandet
Iggesund
Volda
Gudbrandsdalen
Østerdalen
Särna
Måløy
Otta
Sandane
Bollnäs
Söderhamn
Galdhøpiggen
Florø
Førde
Älvdalen
Mora
Siljan
Rättvik
Gävle
Hoyanger
Lillehammer
Rena
Falun
Sandviken
Sula
Valdres
Gjøvik
Elverum
Hamar
Borlänge
Ludvika
Avesta
Fagersta
Sala
Uppsala
Bergen
Hardangervidda
Numedal
Hønefoss
Kongsvinger
Hårteigan
Lillestrom
OSLO
Sandvika
Asker
Ski
Askim
Arvika
Västerås
Enköping
Märsta
Täby
STOCKHOLM
Møsvatnet
Vestfjorddalen
Drammen
Kongsberg
Karlstad
Karlskoga
Arboga
Köping
Eskilstuna
Södertälje
Bømlo
Gausta
Moss
Horten
Sarpsborg
Kristinehamn
Örebro
Kumla
Hjälmaren
Nynäshamn
Setesdal
Tønsberg
Skien
Fredrikstad
Halden
Sandefjord
Åmål
Säffle
Katrineholm
Nyköping
Oxelösund
Haugesund
Karmøy
Porsgrunn
Larvik
VÄNERN
Mariestad
Finspång
Motala
Norrköping
Stavanger
Sandnes
Lidköping
Skövde
Linköping
Vättern
Mjölby
Vänersborg
Skara
Uddevalla
Trollhättan
Falköping
Tranås
Västervik
Visby
Egersund
Arendal
Lilla Edet
Alingsås
Jönköping
Eksjö
Kristiansand
Kungälv
Lerum
Borås
Nässjö
Oskarshamn
Lindesnes
SKAGERRAK
Skagen
Grenen
Göteborg
Mölnlycke
Kinna
Hirtshals
Hjørring
Kungsbacka
Frederikshavn
Värnamo
Læsø
Varberg
Brønderslev
Växjö
Nybro
Öland
Kalmar
Kalmarsund
Hanstholm
Falkenberg
Ljungby
Aalborg
KATTEGAT
Anholt
Thisted
Halmstad
Hobro
Skive
Randers
Ronneby
Karlskrona
Struer
Grenaa
Ängelholm
Hässleholm
Karlshamn
Viborg
Holstebro
Herning
Silkeborg
Aarhus
Helsingør
Helsingborg
Landskrona
Kristianstad
Hanöbukten
Ikast
Skanderborg
Frederiksværk
Hillerød
Lund
Ringkøbing
DK
Horsens
Holbæk
Malmö
KØBENHAVN
Bornholm
Vejle
Kalundborg
SJÆLLAND
Ystad
Fredericia
Fyn
Ringsted
Trelleborg
Varde
Middelfart
Esbjerg
Kolding
Odense
Slagelse
Køge
Rønne
Ribe
Nyborg
Korsør
Næstved
Haderslev
Svendborg
Langeland
Møn
Rømø
Aabenraa
Lolland
Falster
Sønderborg
Nakskov
Nykøbing
Rügen
Sylt
Flensburg
Fehmarn
Bergen
Stralsund
Kołobrzeg
Koszalin
Ustka
Słupsk
Jezioro Łebsko
Husum
Eckernförde
Kieler Bucht
Ribnitz-Damgarten
Zatoka Pomorska
Gryfice
Rendsburg
Kiel
Mecklenburger Bucht
Greifswald
Wolgast
PL
D
xi
ix
N
S
GULF OF BOTHNIA
Södra Kvarken
NORTH SEA
BALTIC
vii

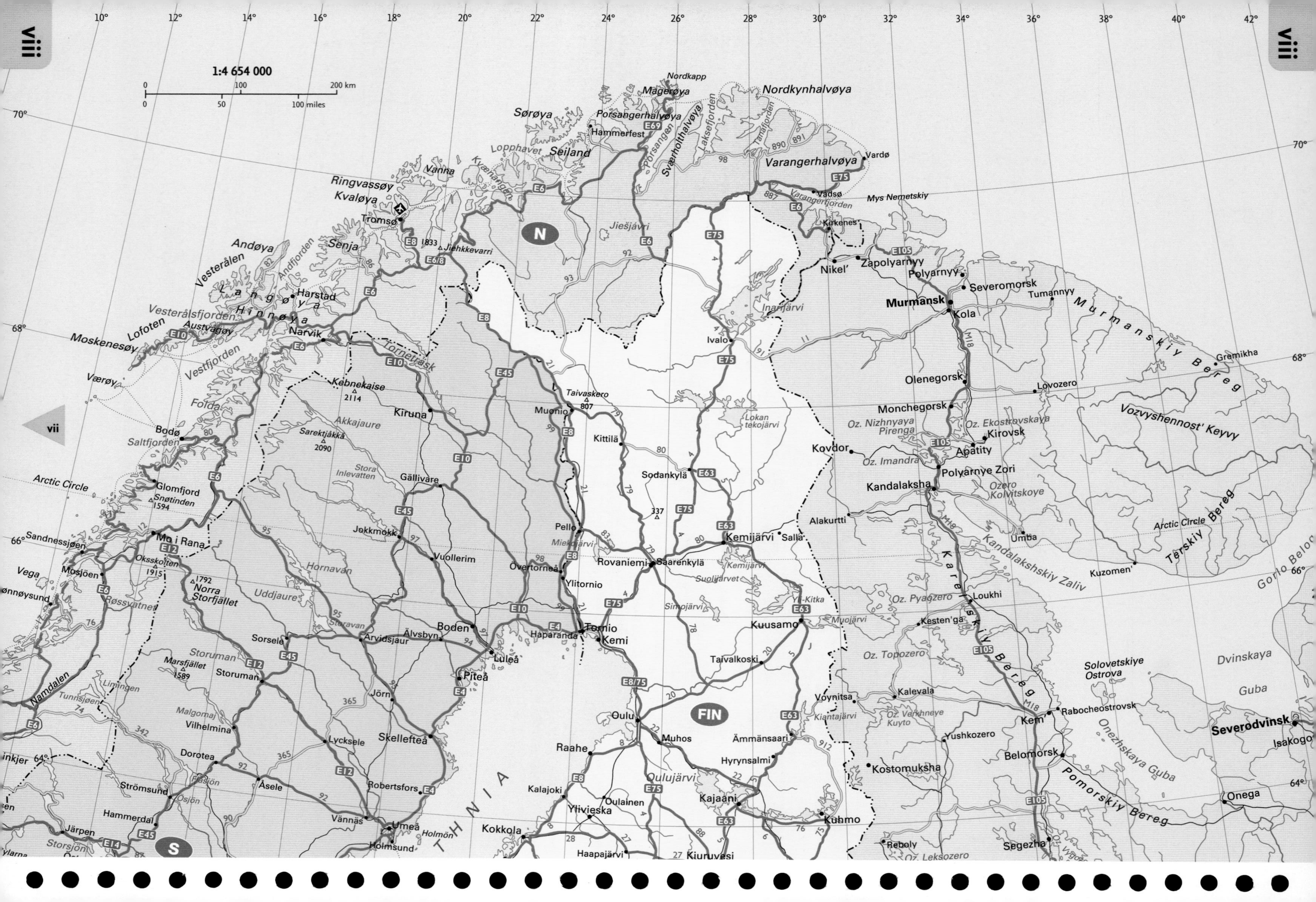
1:4 654 000
0 100 200 km
0 50 100 miles
10° 12° 14° 16° 18° 20° 22° 24° 26° 28° 30° 32° 34° 36° 38° 40° 42°
70° 68° 66° 64°
N
FIN
S
Nordkapp
Magerøya
Nordkynhalvøya
Sørøya
Porsangerhalvøya
Hammerfest
Porsangen
Sværholthalvøya
Laksefjorden
Tanafjorden
Loppahavet
Seiland
Varangerhalvøya
Vardø
Vadsø
Varangerfjorden
Mys Nemetskiy
Kirkenes
Vanna
Kvænangen
Ringvassøy
Kvaløya
Tromsø
Jiešjávri
Andøya
Senja
1833 Jiehkkevarri
Vesterålen
Andfjorden
Harstad
Langøya
Hinnøya
Vesterålsfjorden
Lofoten
Austvågøy
Narvik
Moskenesøy
Vestfjorden
Værøy
Folda
Bodø
Saltfjorden
Torneträsk
Kebnekaise 2114
Kiruna
Akkajaure
Sarektjåkkå 2090
Stora Inlevatten
Gällivare
Arctic Circle
Glomfjord
Snøtinden 1594
Jokkmokk
Vuollerim
Sandnessjøen
Mo i Rana
Okstindan 1915
Vega
Mosjöen
1792 Norra Storfjället
Hornavan
Uddjaure
Røssvatnet
Brønnøysund
Storavan
Arvidsjaur
Älvsbyn
Boden
Luleå
Piteå
Sorsele
Storuman
Marsfjället 1589
Namdalen
Limingen
Tunnsjøen
Jörn
Malgomaj
Vilhelmina
Lycksele
Skellefteå
Dorotea
Åsele
Robertsfors
Strömsund
Flåsjön
Osjön
Hammerdal
Vännäs
Umeå
Holmön
Holmsund
Järpen
Storsjön
THNIA
Muonio
Taivaskero 807
Kittilä
Sodankylä
337
Pello
Miekojärvi
Övertorneå
Ylitornio
Rovaniemi
Saarenkylä
Kemijärvi
Salla
Suolijärvet
Simojärvi
Haparanda
Tornio
Kemi
Kuusamo
Yli-Kitka
Taivalkoski
Oulu
Muhos
Raahe
Ämmänsaari
Hyrynsalmi
Oulujärvi
Kalajoki
Oulainen
Ylivieska
Kajaani
Kokkola
Haapajärvi
Kiuruvesi
Kuhmo
Ivalo
Inarijärvi
Lokan tekojärvi
Nikel'
Zapolyarnyy
Polyarnyy
Severomorsk
Murmansk
Kola
Tumannyy
Murmanskiy Bereg
Gremikha
Olenegorsk
Lovozero
Monchegorsk
Oz. Nizhnyaya Pirenga
Oz. Ekostrovskaya
Kirovsk
Apatity
Kovdor
Oz. Imandra
Polyarnye Zori
Kandalaksha
Ozero Kolvitskoye
Vozvyshennost' Keyvy
Alakurtti
Umba
Arctic Circle
Terskiy Bereg
Kandalakshskiy Zaliv
Kuzomen'
Gorlo Belogo
Oz. Pyaozero
Loukhi
Kesten'ga
Muojärvi
Karel'skiy Bereg
Oz. Topozero
Solovetskiye Ostrova
Dvinskaya Guba
Voynitsa
Kalevala
Kiantajärvi
Oz. Verkhneye Kuyto
Kem'
Rabocheostrovsk
Severodvinsk
Isakogorka
Yushkozero
Belomorsk
Onezhskaya Guba
Kostomuksha
Pomorskiy Bereg
Onega
Reboly
Oz. Leksozero
Segezha
vii

viii

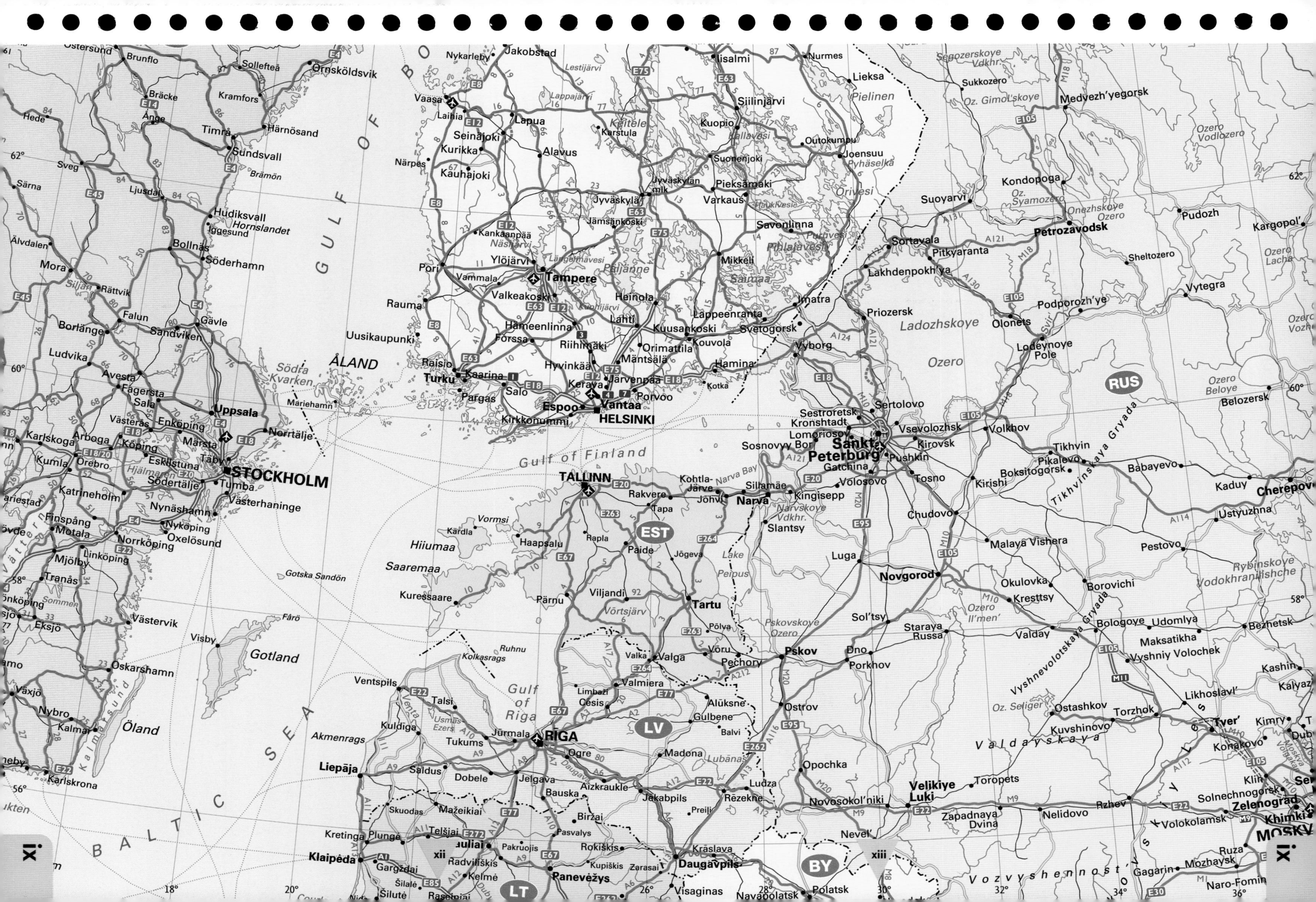
GULF OF BOTHNIA
BALTIC SEA
Gulf of Finland
Gulf of Riga
RUS
EST
LV
LT
BY
ÅLAND
Gotland
Öland
Saaremaa
Hiiumaa
Ladozhskoye Ozero
Onezhskoye Ozero
Lake Peipus
Ozero Il'men'
Ozero Beloye
Rybinskoye Vodokhranilishche
Tikhvinskaya Gryada
Valdayskaya Vozvyshennost'
STOCKHOLM
HELSINKI
TALLINN
RIGA
Sankt-Peterburg
Uppsala
Västerås
Örebro
Norrköping
Linköping
Södertälje
Nyköping
Gävle
Falun
Borlänge
Sundsvall
Härnösand
Örnsköldsvik
Östersund
Hudiksvall
Söderhamn
Bollnäs
Mora
Karlskrona
Kalmar
Växjö
Västervik
Oskarshamn
Visby
Norrtälje
Mariehamn
Turku
Tampere
Pori
Rauma
Vaasa
Seinäjoki
Jyväskylä
Lahti
Espoo
Vantaa
Porvoo
Kotka
Hamina
Kouvola
Lappeenranta
Imatra
Mikkeli
Savonlinna
Kuopio
Joensuu
Varkaus
Iisalmi
Jakobstad
Hämeenlinna
Salo
Vyborg
Priozersk
Sortavala
Petrozavodsk
Kondopoga
Medvezh'yegorsk
Pudozh
Kargopol'
Vytegra
Belozersk
Cherepovets
Tikhvin
Volkhov
Kirishi
Novgorod
Pskov
Luga
Narva
Kingisepp
Tartu
Pärnu
Viljandi
Rakvere
Kohtla-Järve
Haapsalu
Kuressaare
Valga
Võru
Daugavpils
Jelgava
Liepāja
Ventspils
Jūrmala
Valmiera
Cēsis
Rēzekne
Jēkabpils
Klaipėda
Panevėžys
Velikiye Luki
Toropets
Rzhev
Tver'
Torzhok
Vyshniy Volochek
Bologoye
Valday
Staraya Russa
Borovichi
Ostashkov
Nelidovo
Zelenograd
Volokolamsk
Mozhaysk
Ruza
Klin
Kimry
Kashin
Kalyazin
Bezhetsk
Nevel'
Polatsk
Navapolatsk
Ostrov
Opochka
Porkhov
Dno
Sol'tsy
Chudovo
Gatchina
Kronshtadt
Sosnovyy Bor
Svetogorsk

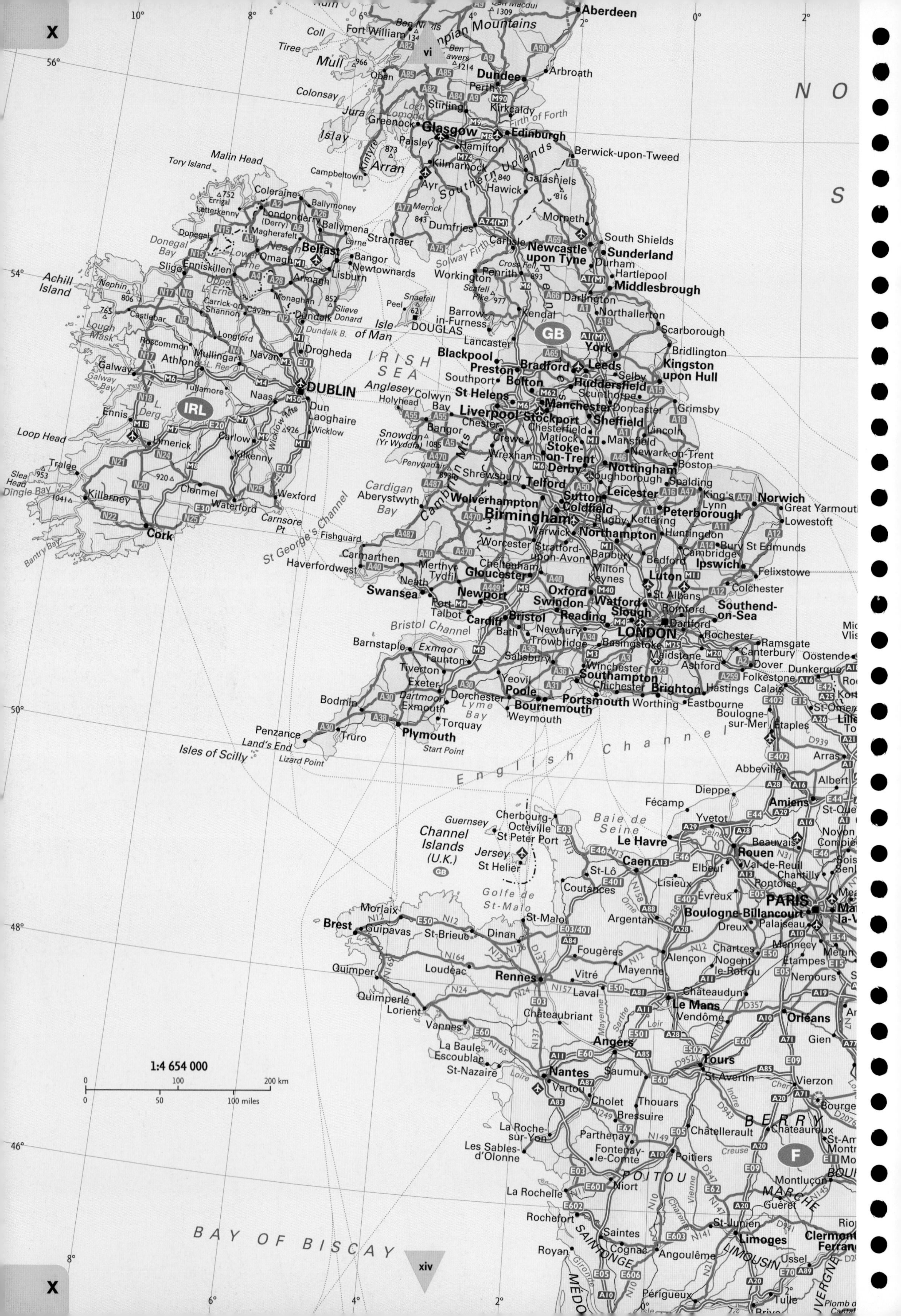
Aberdeen
Grampian Mountains
Fort William
Ben Nevis
Coll
Tiree
Mull
Oban
Dundee
Arbroath
Perth
Colonsay
Stirling
Kirkcaldy
Jura
Greenock
Loch Lomond
Firth of Forth
Glasgow
Edinburgh
Islay
Paisley
Hamilton
Kintyre
Arran
Kilmarnock
Southern Uplands
Berwick-upon-Tweed
Malin Head
Tory Island
Campbeltown
Ayr
Galashiels
Hawick
Coleraine
Errigal
Letterkenny
Ballymoney
Londonderry (Derry)
Magherafelt
Ballymena
Larne
Merrick
Dumfries
Morpeth
Donegal
Donegal Bay
Lough Neagh
Belfast
Stranraer
Carlisle
Newcastle upon Tyne
South Shields
Sunderland
Sligo
Enniskillen
Omagh
Bangor
Newtownards
Lisburn
Armagh
Solway Firth
Cross Fell
Durham
Hartlepool
Middlesbrough
Achill Island
Nephin
Upper Lough Erne
Monaghan
Workington
Penrith
Scafell Pike
Darlington
Carrick-on-Shannon
Cavan
Slieve Donard
Snaefell
Peel
Barrow-in-Furness
Kendal
Northallerton
Castlebar
Lough Mask
Dundalk
Dundalk B.
Isle of Man
DOUGLAS
GB
Scarborough
Longford
Roscommon
Lancaster
York
Bridlington
Drogheda
IRISH SEA
Blackpool
Preston
Bradford
Leeds
Kingston upon Hull
Galway
Athlone
Mullingar
L. Ree
Navan
Southport
Bolton
Selby
Galway Bay
Tullamore
DUBLIN
Anglesey
Colwyn Bay
St Helens
Huddersfield
Scunthorpe
Grimsby
Naas
Holyhead
Manchester
Doncaster
Ennis
L. Derg
IRL
Dun Laoghaire
Wicklow Mts
Wicklow
Liverpool
Stockport
Sheffield
Lincoln
Loop Head
Limerick
Carlow
Bangor
Chester
Chesterfield
Matlock
Mansfield
Snowdon (Yr Wyddfa)
Crewe
Newark-on-Trent
Kilkenny
Wrexham
Stoke-on-Trent
Tralee
Slea Head
Dingle Bay
Penygadair
Derby
Nottingham
Boston
Shrewsbury
Loughborough
Spalding
Clonmel
Cardigan Bay
Aberystwyth
Telford
Leicester
King's Lynn
Norwich
Great Yarmouth
Killarney
Wexford
Waterford
Cambrian Mts
Wolverhampton
Sutton Coldfield
Lowestoft
Birmingham
Rugby
Kettering
Peterborough
Carnsore Pt
Cork
St George's Channel
Fishguard
Warwick
Northampton
Huntingdon
Bantry Bay
Worcester
Stratford-upon-Avon
Cambridge
Bury St Edmunds
Carmarthen
Banbury
Bedford
Ipswich
Haverfordwest
Merthyr Tydfil
Cheltenham
Milton Keynes
Felixstowe
Gloucester
Luton
Neath
Oxford
St Albans
Colchester
Swansea
Newport
Swindon
Watford
Southend-on-Sea
Port Talbot
Cardiff
Bristol
Reading
Slough
Romford
Bristol Channel
Bath
Newbury
LONDON
Dartford
Barnstaple
Exmoor
Trowbridge
Basingstoke
Rochester
Ramsgate
Taunton
Salisbury
Maidstone
Canterbury
Tiverton
Winchester
Ashford
Dover
Oostende
Exeter
Yeovil
Southampton
Folkestone
Dunkerque
Dartmoor
Dorchester
Chichester
Brighton
Hastings
Calais
Bodmin
Poole
Portsmouth
Worthing
Eastbourne
Exmouth
Lyme Bay
Bournemouth
Boulogne-sur-Mer
Torquay
Weymouth
Étaples
Penzance
Truro
Plymouth
Land's End
Start Point
Isles of Scilly
Lizard Point
English Channel
Arras
Abbeville
Albert
Dieppe
Amiens
Fécamp
Guernsey
Cherbourg-Octeville
Baie de Seine
Yvetot
Channel Islands (U.K.)
St Peter Port
Le Havre
Beauvais
Noyon
Jersey
St Helier
Rouen
Caen
Elbeuf
Val-de-Reuil
Chantilly
St-Lô
Lisieux
Pontoise
Coutances
Golfe de St-Malo
Évreux
PARIS
Morlaix
Argentan
Boulogne-Billancourt
Brest
Guipavas
St-Brieuc
Dinan
St-Malo
Dreux
Palaiseau
Fougères
Alençon
Chartres
Mennecy
Melun
Nogent-le-Rotrou
Étampes
Quimper
Loudéac
Rennes
Vitré
Mayenne
Nemours
Quimperlé
Laval
Châteaudun
Lorient
Châteaubriant
Le Mans
Vendôme
Orléans
Vannes
Loir
Gien
Angers
La Baule-Escoublac
Tours
St-Nazaire
Nantes
Saumur
St-Avertin
Vierzon
Vertou
Loire
Cholet
Thouars
Indre
Cher
Bourges
Bressuire
BERRY
La Roche-sur-Yon
Parthenay
Châtellerault
Châteauroux
Les Sables-d'Olonne
Fontenay-le-Comte
Poitiers
Creuse
F
POITOU
Niort
Montluçon
La Rochelle
MARCHE
Guéret
Rochefort
Vienne
Charente
SAINTONGE
Saintes
St-Junien
Limoges
Clermont-Ferrand
Royan
Cognac
Angoulême
LIMOUSIN
Ussel
Gironde
Périgueux
Tulle
Plomb du Cantal
BAY OF BISCAY
NORTH SEA
xiv
vi
1:4 654 000
0
100
200 km
0
50
100 miles
10°
8°
6°
4°
2°
0°
2°
56°
54°
50°
48°
46°

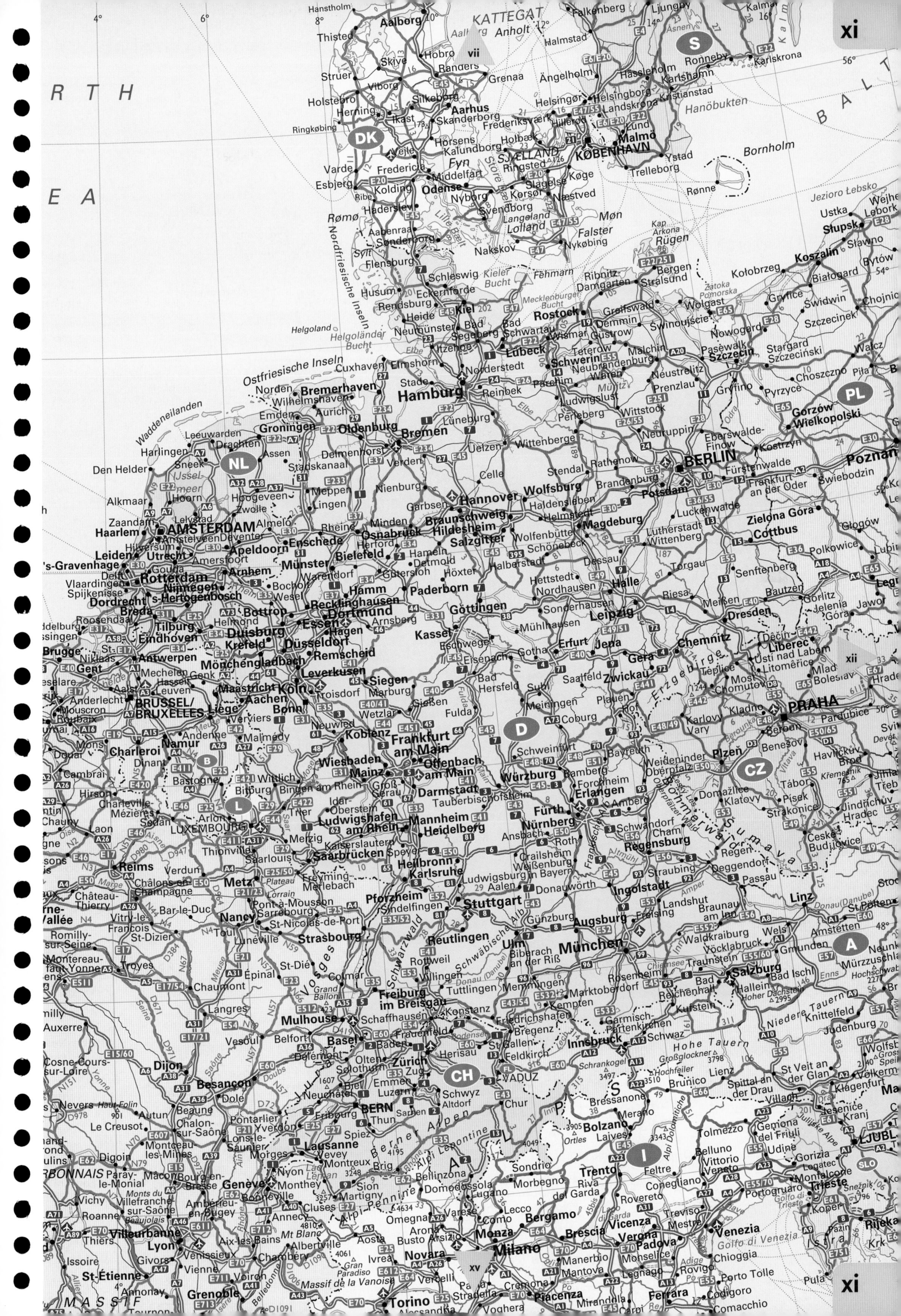
KATTEGAT
R T H
E A
B A L T
DK
S
NL
B
L
D
PL
CZ
CH
A
I
SLO
vii
xii
xv
KØBENHAVN
Malmö
Aarhus
Aalborg
Odense
Bornholm
Rügen
Kiel
Lübeck
Rostock
Hamburg
Bremen
Bremerhaven
Groningen
Hannover
BERLIN
Szczecin
Poznań
Wolfsburg
Braunschweig
Magdeburg
Potsdam
Cottbus
Zielona Góra
AMSTERDAM
Haarlem
Leiden
Utrecht
Rotterdam
Arnhem
Nijmegen
Eindhoven
Antwerpen
Gent
Brugge
BRUSSEL/BRUXELLES
Liège
Namur
Charleroi
Maastricht
Aachen
Köln
Bonn
Düsseldorf
Duisburg
Essen
Dortmund
Münster
Bielefeld
Osnabrück
Paderborn
Göttingen
Kassel
Halle
Leipzig
Dresden
Chemnitz
Erfurt
Jena
Gera
Zwickau
PRAHA
Plzeň
Liberec
Koblenz
Frankfurt am Main
Wiesbaden
Mainz
Darmstadt
Mannheim
Heidelberg
Würzburg
Nürnberg
Fürth
Erlangen
Regensburg
Ingolstadt
Augsburg
München
Salzburg
Linz
LUXEMBOURG
Metz
Nancy
Reims
Strasbourg
Saarbrücken
Karlsruhe
Stuttgart
Pforzheim
Ulm
Freiburg im Breisgau
Mulhouse
Basel
Zürich
BERN
Lausanne
Genève
Innsbruck
VADUZ
Bolzano
Trento
Milano
Bergamo
Brescia
Verona
Vicenza
Padova
Venezia
Trieste
Torino
Novara
Lyon
Villeurbanne
Grenoble
Dijon
Besançon
Saint-Étienne
LJUBLJANA

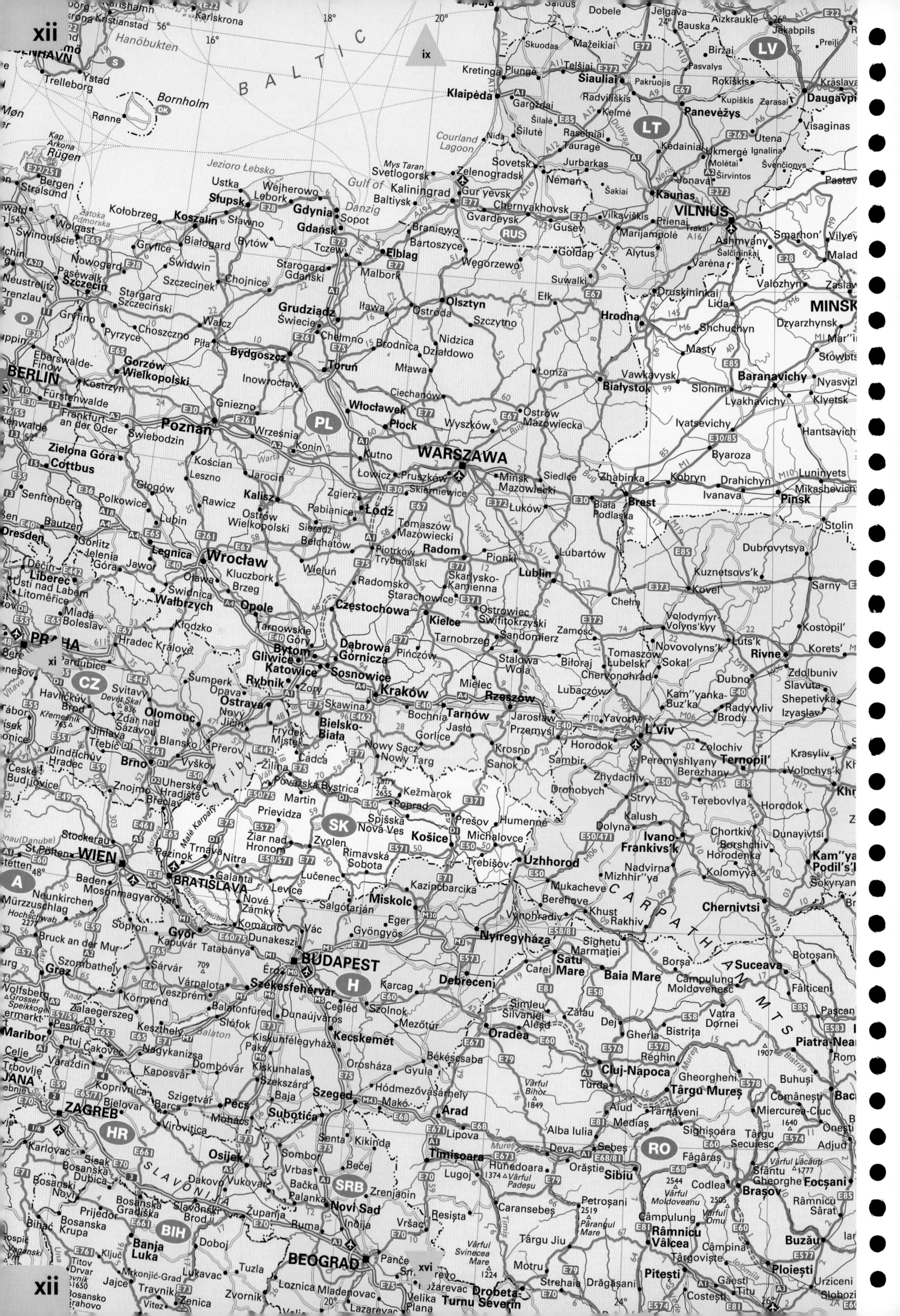

BALTIC
ix
Hanöbukten
Karlskrona
Kristianstad
Ystad
Trelleborg
Bornholm
Rønne
DK
Møn
Kap Arkona
Rügen
Stralsund
Bergen
Wolgast
Swinoujście
Neustrelitz
Prenzlau
Pasewalk
Szczecin
Nowogard
Gryfice
Kołobrzeg
Koszalin
Sławno
Słupsk
Ustka
Jezioro Łebsko
Lebork
Wejherowo
Gdynia
Sopot
Gdańsk
Gulf of Danzig
Tczew
Elbląg
Malbork
Starogard Gdański
Chojnice
Szczecinek
Świdwin
Białogard
Bytów
Stargard Szczeciński
Gryfino
Pyrzyce
Choszczno
Wałcz
Piła
Bydgoszcz
Grudziądz
Świecie
Chełmno
Toruń
Brodnica
Iława
Ostróda
Olsztyn
Nidzica
Działdowo
Mława
Szczytno
Ełk
Suwałki
Gołdap
Węgorzewo
Bartoszyce
Braniewo
Baltiysk
Kaliningrad
Svetlogorsk
Zelenogradsk
Gur'yevsk
Chernyakhovsk
Gvardeysk
Gusev
Sovetsk
Neman
RUS
Courland Lagoon
Nida
Klaipėda
Kretinga
Plungė
Telšiai
Šiauliai
Gargždai
Šilalė
Šilutė
Tauragė
Raseiniai
Jurbarkas
Kelmė
Radviliškis
Pakruojis
Panevėžys
Kėdainiai
Ukmergė
Kaunas
Jonava
Šakiai
Vilkaviškis
Marijampolė
Prienai
Alytus
Trakai
VILNIUS
Ashmyany
Šalčininkai
Varėna
Druskininkai
Lida
Hrodna
LT
LV
Jelgava
Bauska
Dobele
Aizkraukle
Jēkabpils
Biržai
Pasvalys
Rokiškis
Kupiškis
Zarasai
Daugavpils
Utena
Ignalina
Visaginas
Molėtai
Švenčionys
Širvintos
Pastavy
Smarhon'
Vilyeyka
Maladzyechna
Valozhyn
Zaslawye
MINSK
Dzyarzhynsk
Stowbtsy
Nyasvizh
Baranavichy
Shchuchyn
Masty
Slonim
Vawkavysk
Lyakhavichy
Klyetsk
Ivatsevichy
Hantsavichy
Byaroza
Kobryn
Drahichyn
Luninyets
Mikashevichy
Pinsk
Ivanava
Zhabinka
Brest
Biała Podlaska
Białystok
Łomża
Ostrów Mazowiecka
Wyszków
Ciechanów
Płock
Włocławek
Inowrocław
Gniezno
Poznań
Września
Konin
Kutno
WARSZAWA
Łowicz
Pruszków
Skierniewice
Mińsk Mazowiecki
Siedlce
Łuków
Łódź
Zgierz
Pabianice
Tomaszów Mazowiecki
Piotrków Trybunalski
Bełchatów
Sieradz
Kalisz
Ostrów Wielkopolski
Jarocin
Kościan
Leszno
Rawicz
Głogów
Polkowice
Lubin
Legnica
Wrocław
Oława
Kluczbork
Brzeg
Opole
Wieluń
Radomsko
Częstochowa
Radom
Pionki
Skarżysko-Kamienna
Starachowice
Ostrowiec Świętokrzyski
Kielce
Lublin
Lubartów
Chełm
Zamość
Tomaszów Lubelski
Biłgoraj
Stalowa Wola
Sandomierz
Tarnobrzeg
Mielec
Rzeszów
Tarnów
Jasło
Krosno
Sanok
Przemyśl
Jarosław
Lubaczów
Dębica
Kraków
Bochnia
Nowy Sącz
Nowy Targ
Gorlice
Skawina
Bielsko-Biała
Żory
Rybnik
Katowice
Gliwice
Bytom
Sosnowiec
Dąbrowa Górnicza
Tarnowskie Góry
Pińczów
PL
Berlin
Eberswalde-Finow
Kostrzyn
Fürstenwalde
Frankfurt an der Oder
Gorzów Wielkopolski
Świebodzin
Zielona Góra
Cottbus
Senftenberg
Bautzen
Görlitz
Dresden
Jelenia Góra
Jawor
Świdnica
Wałbrzych
Kłodzko
Děčín
Liberec
Ústí nad Labem
Litoměřice
Mladá Boleslav
PRAHA
Hradec Králové
Pardubice
Havlíčkův Brod
Svitavy
Šumperk
Opava
Ostrava
Nový Jičín
Frýdek-Místek
Olomouc
Přerov
Prostějov
Blansko
Vyškov
Brno
Jihlava
Třebíč
Žďár nad Sázavou
Jindřichův Hradec
Tábor
České Budějovice
Znojmo
Břeclav
Uherské Hradiště
Chřiby
CZ
Čadca
Žilina
Považská Bystrica
Martin
Prievidza
Žiar nad Hronom
Zvolen
Banská Bystrica
Tatry
Poprad
Kežmarok
Spišská Nová Ves
Prešov
Košice
Humenné
Michalovce
Trebišov
Rimavská Sobota
Lučenec
Nitra
Trnava
Levice
Nové Zámky
Komárno
Galanta
BRATISLAVA
Pezinok
Malé Karpaty
SK
WIEN
Stockerau
St Pölten
Baden
Neunkirchen
Mürzzuschlag
Hochschwab
Bruck an der Mur
Graz
Wolfsberg
Maribor
Ptuj
Celje
A
Sopron
Mosonmagyaróvár
Győr
Tatabánya
Kapuvár
Dunakeszi
Vác
Szombathely
Sárvár
Várpalota
Veszprém
Székesfehérvár
Érd
BUDAPEST
Cegléd
Szolnok
Karcag
Debrecen
Nyíregyháza
Miskolc
Eger
Gyöngyös
Salgótarján
Kazincbarcika
Balatonfüred
Siófok
Balaton
Keszthely
Zalaegerszeg
Körmend
Nagykanizsa
Kaposvár
Dombóvár
Dunaújváros
Kecskemét
Kiskunfélegyháza
Kiskunhalas
Szekszárd
Baja
Paks
Mezőtúr
Orosháza
Békéscsaba
Gyula
Hódmezővásárhely
Makó
Szeged
Pécs
Mohács
Szigetvár
Barcs
H
Varaždin
Čakovec
Koprivnica
Bjelovar
Virovitica
ZAGREB
Karlovac
Sisak
Slavonija
Osijek
Vukovar
Đakovo
Slavonski Brod
Županja
HR
Bosanska Dubica
Bosanska Gradiška
Bosanski Novi
Prijedor
Bosanska Krupa
Bihać
Banja Luka
Doboj
Tuzla
Lukavac
Zvornik
Travnik
Zenica
Jajce
BIH
Subotica
Sombor
Senta
Kikinda
Vrbas
Bačka Palanka
Bečej
Novi Sad
Zrenjanin
Inđija
Ruma
Pančevo
Vršac
BEOGRAD
Smederevo
Požarevac
Velika Plana
Loznica
Mladenovac
Lazarevac
SRB
Uzhhorod
Mukacheve
Berehove
Vynohradiv
Khust
Rakhiv
CARPATHIAN MTS
L'viv
Horodok
Yavoriv
Sambir
Drohobych
Stryy
Zhydachiv
Dolyna
Kalush
Ivano-Frankivs'k
Nadvirna
Kolomyya
Chernivtsi
Sokyryany
Kam"yanets'-Podil's'kyy
Horodok
Chortkiv
Borshchiv
Horodenka
Terebovlya
Ternopil'
Zolochiv
Peremyshlyany
Berezhany
Brody
Radyvyliv
Dubno
Zdolbuniv
Slavuta
Shepetivka
Izyaslav
Rivne
Kostopil'
Korets'
Luts'k
Kovel'
Volodymyr-Volyns'kyy
Novovolyns'k
Sokal'
Chervonohrad
Kam"yanka-Buz'ka
Kuznetsovs'k
Dubrovytsya
Sarny
Stolin
Krasyliv
Volochys'k
Dunayivtsi
Satu Mare
Carei
Baia Mare
Sighetu Marmaţiei
Borşa
Suceava
Botoşani
Câmpulung Moldovenesc
Fălticeni
Paşcani
Vatra Dornei
Piatra-Neamţ
Roman
Bacău
Buhuşi
Comăneşti
Miercurea-Ciuc
Oneşti
Adjud
Focşani
Râmnicu Sărat
Buzău
Ploieşti
Urziceni
Slobozia
Braşov
Sfântu Gheorghe
Târgu Secuiesc
Codlea
Făgăraş
Sibiu
Sighişoara
Mediaş
Târnăveni
Târgu Mureş
Reghin
Gheorgheni
Bistriţa
Dej
Gherla
Cluj-Napoca
Turda
Aiud
Alba Iulia
Sebeş
Orăştie
Deva
Hunedoara
Petroşani
Târgu Jiu
Râmnicu Vâlcea
Câmpulung
Piteşti
Câmpina
Târgovişte
Găeşti
Titu
Costeşti
Drăgăşani
Strehaia
Motru
Drobeta-Turnu Severin
Caransebeş
Reşiţa
Lugoj
Timişoara
Arad
Lipova
Oradea
Simleu Silvaniei
Zalău
Aleşd
RO
xi
xvi

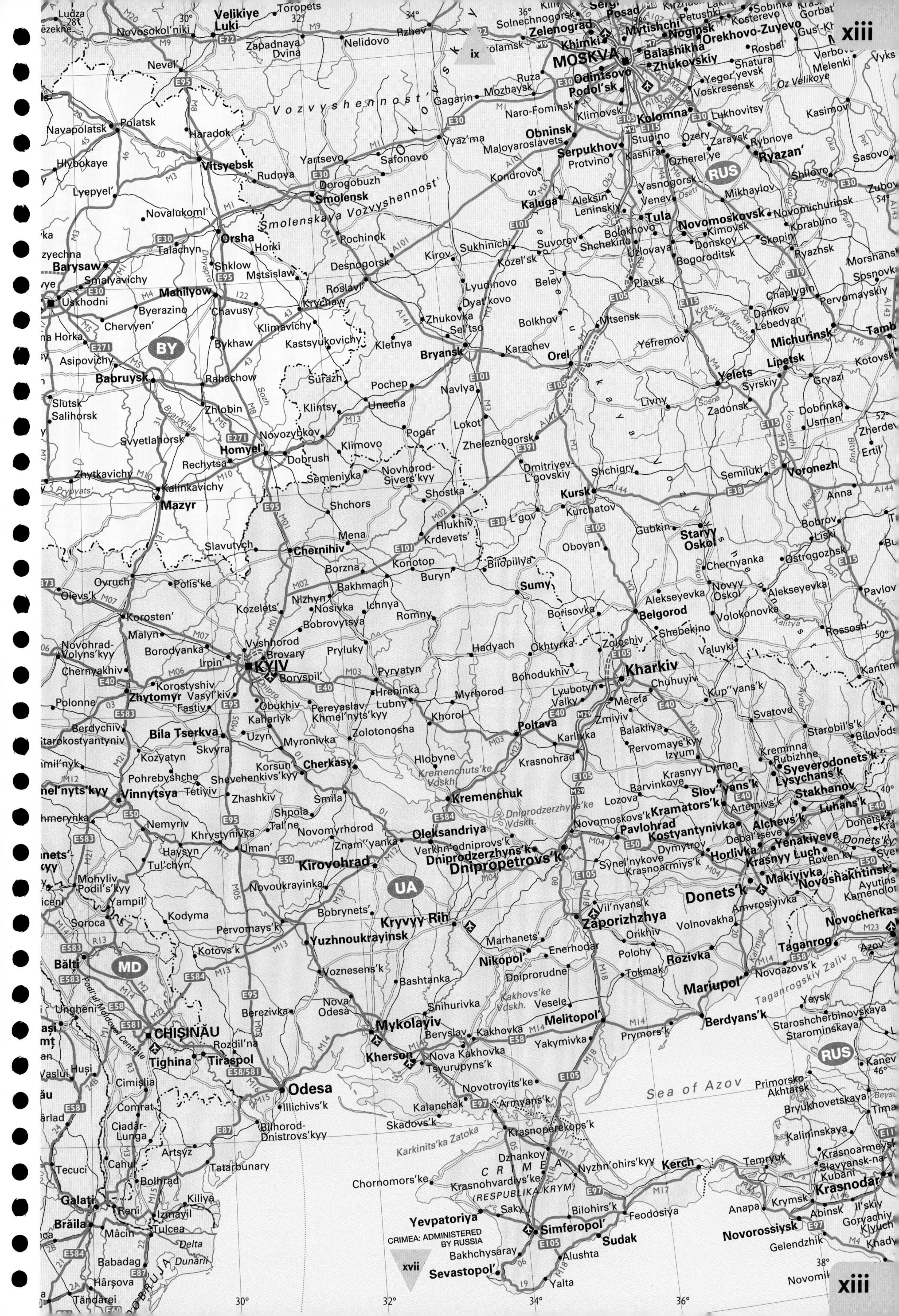

MOSKVA
Zelenograd
Khimki
Mytishchi
Sergiev Posad
Noginsk
Orekhovo-Zuyevo
Balashikha
Zhukovskiy
Odintsovo
Podol'sk
Kolomna
Serpukhov
Obninsk
Kaluga
Tula
Novomoskovsk
Ryazan'
RUS
Velikiye Luki
Toropets
Nelidovo
Rzhev
Zapadnaya Dvina
Nevel'
Polatsk
Navapolatsk
Vitsyebsk
Smolensk
Vozvyshennost'
Smolenskaya Vozvyshennost'
Orsha
Barysaw
Mahilyow
Uskhodni
BY
Babruysk
Slutsk
Salihorsk
Homyel'
Mazyr
Kalinkavichy
Rechytsa
Bryansk
Orel
Kursk
Lipetsk
Yelets
Michurinsk
Voronezh
Belgorod
Staryy Oskol
Sumy
Chernihiv
Konotop
KYIV
Brovary
Boryspil'
Zhytomyr
Korosten'
Bila Tserkva
Cherkasy
Kremenchuk
Poltava
Kharkiv
Izyum
Lysychans'k
Syeverodonets'k
Luhans'k
Stakhanov
Alchevs'k
Kramators'k
Slov"yans'k
Horlivka
Makiyivka
Donets'k
Mariupol'
Taganrog
Novocherkassk
Zaporizhzhya
Dnipropetrovs'k
Dniprodzerzhyns'k
Kryvyy Rih
Kirovohrad
Oleksandriya
Uman'
Vinnytsya
UA
Mykolayiv
Kherson
Odesa
Illichivs'k
Bilhorod-Dnistrovs'kyy
MD
CHIŞINĂU
Tiraspol
Tighina
Bălţi
Galaţi
Brăila
Tulcea
Izmayil
Melitopol'
Berdyans'k
Nikopol'
Sea of Azov
Taganrogskiy Zaliv
Karkinits'ka Zatoka
CRIMEA (RESPUBLIKA KRYM)
CRIMEA: ADMINISTERED BY RUSSIA
Yevpatoriya
Simferopol'
Sevastopol'
Kerch
Feodosiya
Sudak
Yalta
Alushta
Dzhankoy
Krasnodar
Novorossiysk
Anapa
Yeysk
30°
32°
34°
36°
38°
ix
xvii

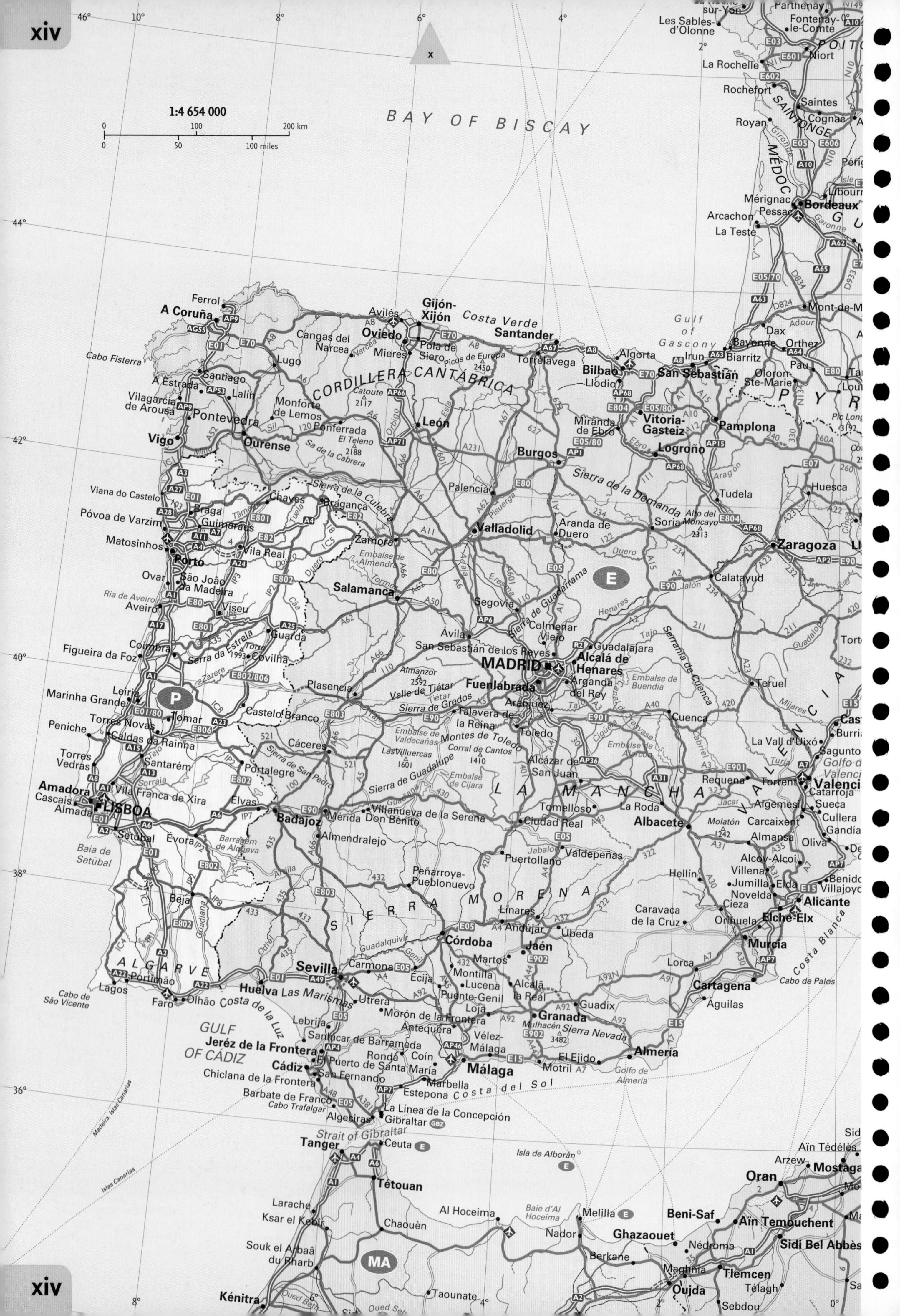

xiv
1:4 654 000
0 100 200 km
0 50 100 miles
BAY OF BISCAY
Costa Verde
Gulf of Gascony
CORDILLERA CANTÁBRICA
Picos de Europa 2450
Catoute 2117
El Teleno 2188
Sierra de la Cabrera
Sierra de la Culebra
Sierra de la Demanda
Alto del Moncayo 2313
Sierra de Guadarrama
Serranía de Cuenca
Serra da Estrela
Torre 1993
Almanzor 2592
Sierra de Gredos
Montes de Toledo
Corral de Cantos 1410
Las Villuercas 1601
Sierra de Guadalupe
Sierra de San Pedro
LA MANCHA
SIERRA MORENA
VALENCIA
ALGARVE
Sierra Nevada
Mulhacén 3482
Molatón 1242
Costa Blanca
Costa de la Luz
Costa del Sol
GULF OF CÁDIZ
Golfo de Almería
Golfo de Valencia
Strait of Gibraltar
Las Marismas
Cabo Fisterra
Cabo de São Vicente
Cabo Trafalgar
Cabo de Palos
Baía de Setúbal
Ria de Aveiro
Isla de Alborán
Baie d'Al Hoceima
Madeira, Islas Canarias
Islas Canarias
Embalse de Almendra
Embalse de Valdecañas
Embalse de Cíjara
Embalse de Buendía
Embalse de Alarcón
Barragem de Alqueva
P
E
MA
GBZ
A Coruña
Ferrol
Santiago
A Estrada
Lalín
Vilagarcía de Arousa
Pontevedra
Vigo
Ourense
Lugo
Monforte de Lemos
Ponferrada
Gijón-Xijón
Avilés
Oviedo
Cangas del Narcea
Mieres
Pola de Siero
León
Santander
Torrelavega
Bilbao
Algorta
Llodio
Miranda de Ebro
Vitoria-Gasteiz
San Sebastián
Irun
Pamplona
Logroño
Tudela
Burgos
Palencia
Valladolid
Aranda de Duero
Soria
Zaragoza
Calatayud
Huesca
Teruel
Zamora
Salamanca
Segovia
Ávila
San Sebastián de los Reyes
Colmenar Viejo
Guadalajara
MADRID
Alcalá de Henares
Fuenlabrada
Arganda del Rey
Aranjuez
Toledo
Talavera de la Reina
Plasencia
Valle de Tiétar
Cáceres
Badajoz
Mérida
Don Benito
Villanueva de la Serena
Almendralejo
Cuenca
Requena
Alcázar de San Juan
Tomelloso
Ciudad Real
Puertollano
Valdepeñas
La Roda
Albacete
Hellín
Peñarroya-Pueblonuevo
Linares
Andújar
Úbeda
Jaén
Córdoba
Martos
Montilla
Lucena
Puente-Genil
Alcalá la Real
Granada
Guadix
Loja
Antequera
Écija
Carmona
Sevilla
Utrera
Morón de la Frontera
Lebrija
Huelva
Sanlúcar de Barrameda
Jeréz de la Frontera
El Puerto de Santa María
Cádiz
San Fernando
Chiclana de la Frontera
Barbate de Franco
Algeciras
La Línea de la Concepción
Gibraltar
Ronda
Coín
Marbella
Estepona
Málaga
Vélez-Málaga
Motril
El Ejido
Almería
Lorca
Águilas
Cartagena
Murcia
Orihuela
Elche-Elx
Alicante
Caravaca de la Cruz
Cieza
Jumilla
Yecla
Villena
Novelda
Elda
Alcoy-Alcoi
Almansa
Villajoyosa
Benidorm
Gandía
Oliva
Cullera
Sueca
Alzira
Carcaixent
Algemesí
Catarroja
Torrent
Valencia
Sagunto
Burriana
La Vall d'Uixó
Castellón
Tortosa
Lleida
Viana do Castelo
Póvoa de Varzim
Braga
Guimarães
Chaves
Bragança
Matosinhos
Porto
Vila Real
Ovar
São João da Madeira
Aveiro
Viseu
Guarda
Coimbra
Figueira da Foz
Covilhã
Leiria
Marinha Grande
Torres Novas
Tomar
Castelo Branco
Peniche
Caldas da Rainha
Santarém
Torres Vedras
Portalegre
Elvas
Vila Franca de Xira
Amadora
Cascais
LISBOA
Almada
Setúbal
Évora
Beja
Portimão
Lagos
Faro
Olhão
Tanger
Ceuta
Tétouan
Larache
Ksar el Kebir
Chaouèn
Al Hoceima
Souk el Arbaâ du Rharb
Kénitra
Taounate
Melilla
Nador
Berkane
Oujda
Ghazaouet
Nédroma
Maghnia
Tlemcen
Sebdou
Beni-Saf
Aïn Temouchent
Sidi Bel Abbès
Oran
Arzew
Mostaganem
Aïn Tédélès
La Roche-sur-Yon
Les Sables-d'Olonne
Fontenay-le-Comte
Parthenay
Niort
POITOU
La Rochelle
Rochefort
Saintes
Cognac
SAINTONGE
Royan
MÉDOC
Gironde
Libourne
Mérignac
Bordeaux
Pessac
Arcachon
La Teste
Garonne
Mont-de-Marsan
Dax
Adour
Bayonne
Biarritz
Orthez
Pau
Oloron-Ste-Marie
Lourdes
Pic Long 3192
PYRENEES
Duero
Tajo
Ebro
Guadiana
Guadalquivir
Henares
Jalón
Cinca
Júcar
Cabriel
Segura

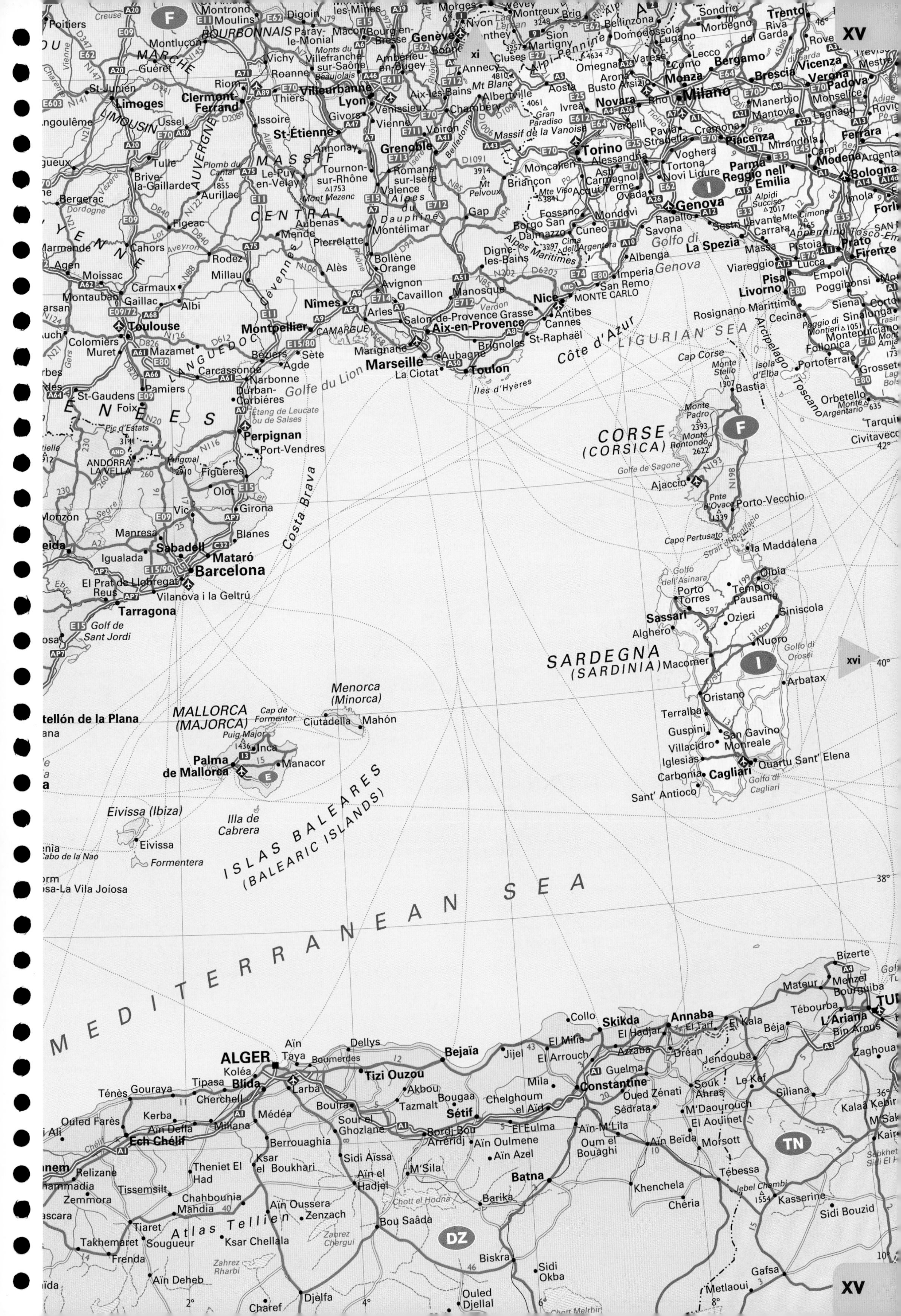
MEDITERRANEAN SEA
LIGURIAN SEA
Golfe du Lion
Golfo di Genova
Côte d'Azur
Costa Brava
CORSE
(CORSICA)
SARDEGNA
(SARDINIA)
ISLAS BALEARES
(BALEARIC ISLANDS)
MALLORCA
(MAJORCA)
Menorca
(Minorca)
Eivissa (Ibiza)
Formentera
Illa de
Cabrera
Arcipelago Toscano
Isola d'Elba
MASSIF CENTRAL
AUVERGNE
LIMOUSIN
MARCHE
BOURBONNAIS
LANGUEDOC
CAMARGUE
Alpes du Dauphiné
Alpes Maritimes
Alpi Pennine
Appennino Tosco-Emiliano
Cévennes
Atlas Tellien
Chott el Hodna
Zahrez Chergui
Zahrez Rharbi
Jebel Chambi
Golfe de Sagone
Strait of Bonifacio
Golfo dell'Asinara
Golfo di Orosei
Golfo di Cagliari
Golf de Sant Jordi
Étang de Leucate ou de Salses
Îles d'Hyères
Cap Corse
Capo Pertusato
Cap de Formentor
Cabo de la Nao
F
I
E
DZ
TN
AND
Poitiers
Limoges
Clermont-Ferrand
Vichy
Montluçon
Moulins
Roanne
Villeurbanne
Lyon
Vénissieux
St-Étienne
Grenoble
Valence
Annecy
Chambéry
Genève
Montreux
Lausanne
Sion
Brig
Aosta
Torino
Milano
Monza
Bergamo
Brescia
Verona
Vicenza
Padova
Trento
Piacenza
Parma
Reggio nell' Emilia
Modena
Bologna
Genova
La Spezia
Pisa
Livorno
Firenze
Prato
Siena
Cuneo
Nice
Monte Carlo
Cannes
Antibes
Toulon
Marseille
Aix-en-Provence
Avignon
Nîmes
Montpellier
Béziers
Narbonne
Carcassonne
Toulouse
Perpignan
Andorra la Vella
Figueres
Girona
Barcelona
Sabadell
Mataró
Tarragona
Reus
Castellón de la Plana
Palma de Mallorca
Mahón
Ciutadella
Manacor
Inca
Eivissa
Bastia
Ajaccio
Porto-Vecchio
Sassari
Olbia
Nuoro
Oristano
Cagliari
Alger
Blida
Tizi Ouzou
Bejaïa
Sétif
Constantine
Skikda
Annaba
Batna
Biskra
Djelfa
Tiaret
Ech Chélif
M'Sila
Bizerte
Jendouba
Le Kef
Kasserine
Tébessa
Gafsa
xi
xvi
2°
4°
6°
8°
10°
36°
38°
40°
42°
46°

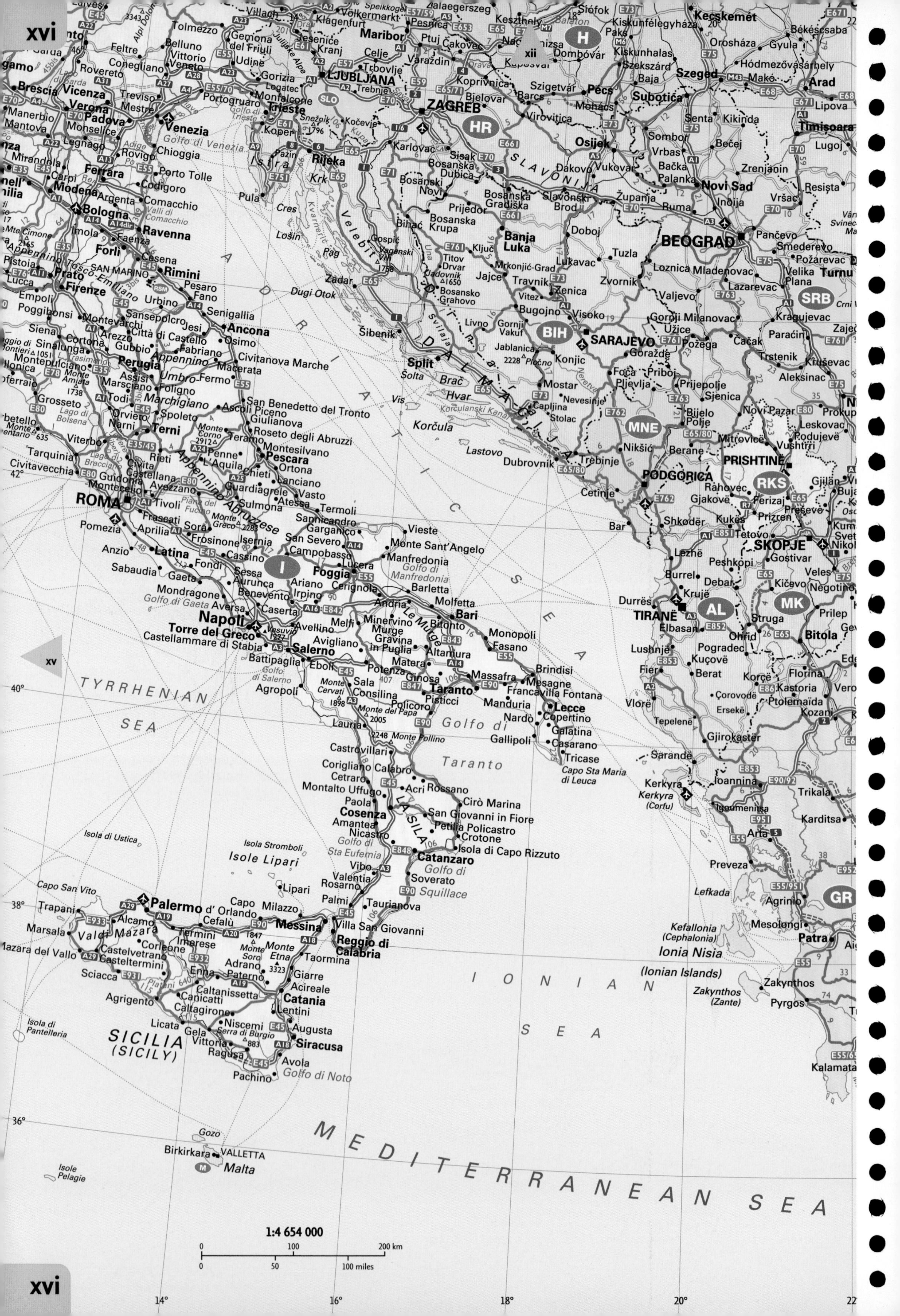
Tolmezzo
Villach
Klagenfurt
Völkermarkt
Zalaegerszeg
Keszthely
Siófok
Kecskemét
Békéscsaba
Belluno
Vittorio Veneto
Gemona del Friuli
Udine
Jesenice
Kranj
Maribor
Ptuj
Čakovec
Kiskunfélegyháza
Orosháza
Gyula
Feltre
Conegliano
Rovereto
Gorizia
LJUBLJANA
Celje
Varaždin
Dombóvár
Kiskunhalas
Hódmezővásárhely
Brescia
Vicenza
Treviso
Mestre
Portogruaro
Monfalcone
Trieste
Trbovlje
Koprivnica
Szigetvár
Pécs
Szekszárd
Baja
Szeged
Makó
Arad
Verona
Padova
Monselice
Manerbio
Mantova
Venezia
Golfo di Venezia
Koper
Kočevje
Trebnje
ZAGREB
Bjelovar
Barcs
Mohács
Subotica
Lipova
Legnago
Rovigo
Chioggia
Rijeka
Karlovac
Virovitica
Osijek
Senta
Kikinda
Timişoara
Lugoj
Mirandola
Carpi
Modena
Ferrara
Porto Tolle
Codigoro
Argenta
Comacchio
Istra
Pula
Krk
Cres
Lošinj
Sisak
Bosanska Dubica
Bosanski Novi
SLAVONIJA
Đakovo
Vukovar
Sombor
Vrbas
Bečej
Bačka Palanka
Novi Sad
Zrenjanin
Resita
Vršac
Inđija
Ruma
Županja
Slavonski Brod
Bosanska Gradiška
Prijedor
Bosanska Krupa
Bihać
Bologna
Imola
Faenza
Ravenna
Forlì
Cesena
Rimini
SAN MARINO
Pesaro
Fano
Urbino
Prato
Pistoia
Lucca
Firenze
Empoli
Poggibonsi
Siena
Montevarchi
Arezzo
Sansepolcro
Città di Castello
Gubbio
Jesi
Senigallia
Ancona
Osimo
Fabriano
Cortona
Sinalunga
Montepulciano
Perugia
Assisi
Foligno
Marsciano
Todi
Orvieto
Spoleto
Terni
Narni
Viterbo
Tarquinia
Civitavecchia
Grosseto
Lago di Bolsena
Banja Luka
Doboj
Tuzla
Lukavac
Zvornik
BEOGRAD
Pančevo
Smederevo
Požarevac
Loznica
Mladenovac
Velika Plana
Lazarevac
Valjevo
Kragujevac
Paraćin
Gospić
Velebit
Pag
Zadar
Dugi Otok
Šibenik
Ključ
Titov Drvar
Jajce
Mrkonjić-Grad
Travnik
Zenica
Vitez
Bugojno
Visoko
Livno
SARAJEVO
Jablanica
Konjic
Goražde
Foča
Priboj
Užice
Požega
Čačak
Kruševac
Aleksinac
Trstenik
Split
Šolta
Brač
Hvar
Vis
Korčula
Lastovo
Mostar
Nevesinje
Čapljina
Stolac
Pljevlja
Prijepolje
Sjenica
Novi Pazar
Bijelo Polje
Leskovac
Podujevë
Mitrovicë
Vushtrri
Prishtinë
Berane
Nikšić
Trebinje
Dubrovnik
PODGORICA
Cetinje
Bar
Rahovec
Gjakovë
Ferizaj
Prizren
Gjilan
Preševo
Shkodër
Kukës
Tetovo
SKOPJE
Gostivar
Veles
Kičevo
Negotino
Peshkopi
Debar
Burrel
Lezhë
Krujë
Durrës
TIRANË
Elbasan
Struga
Ohrid
Prilep
Bitola
Lushnjë
Pogradec
Fier
Kuçovë
Berat
Korçë
Florina
Kastoria
Ptolemaïda
Kozani
Vlorë
Tepelenë
Gjirokastër
Sarandë
Ioannina
Trikala
Kerkyra
(Corfu)
Igoumenitsa
Karditsa
Arta
Preveza
Lefkada
Agrinio
Mesolongi
Patra
Kefallonia
(Cephalonia)
Ionia Nisia
(Ionian Islands)
Zakynthos
(Zante)
Pyrgos
Kalamata
Civitanova Marche
Macerata
Fermo
San Benedetto del Tronto
Ascoli Piceno
Giulianova
Roseto degli Abruzzi
Teramo
Montesilvano
Pescara
Ortona
Chieti
Lanciano
Vasto
Termoli
L'Aquila
Rieti
Penne
Avezzano
Sulmona
Guardiagrele
Atessa
ROMA
Tivoli
Frascati
Pomezia
Aprilia
Anzio
Latina
Sabaudia
Frosinone
Sora
Isernia
Cassino
Fondi
Gaeta
Sessa Aurunca
Mondragone
Golfo di Gaeta
Benevento
Caserta
Aversa
Napoli
Torre del Greco
Castellammare di Stabia
Vesuvio
Avellino
Salerno
Battipaglia
Eboli
Golfo di Salerno
Agropoli
San Severo
Sannicandro Garganico
Vieste
Monte Sant'Angelo
Manfredonia
Golfo di Manfredonia
Campobasso
Lucera
Foggia
Ariano Irpino
Cerignola
Barletta
Andria
Molfetta
Bari
Bitonto
Monopoli
Fasano
Melfi
Minervino Murge
Gravina in Puglia
Altamura
Matera
Avigliano
Potenza
Ginosa
Massafra
Taranto
Brindisi
Mesagne
Francavilla Fontana
Manduria
Lecce
Copertino
Nardò
Galatina
Gallipoli
Casarano
Tricase
Capo Sta Maria di Leuca
Sala Consilina
Lauria
Policoro
Pisticci
Golfo di Taranto
Castrovillari
Corigliano Calabro
Cetraro
Montalto Uffugo
Acri
Rossano
Cosenza
Paola
Amantea
Cirò Marina
San Giovanni in Fiore
Petilia Policastro
Crotone
Nicastro
Isola di Capo Rizzuto
Catanzaro
Golfo di Sta Eufemia
Golfo di Squillace
Soverato
Vibo Valentia
Rosarno
Palmi
Taurianova
Villa San Giovanni
Reggio di Calabria
Isola di Ustica
Isola Stromboli
Isole Lipari
Lipari
Capo San Vito
Trapani
Palermo
Capo d' Orlando
Milazzo
Messina
Alcamo
Cefalù
Termini Imerese
Marsala
Val di Mazara
Mazara del Vallo
Castelvetrano
Corleone
Castelterminini
Sciacca
Agrigento
Enna
Adrano
Paternò
Monte Etna
Taormina
Giarre
Acireale
Catania
Caltanissetta
Canicattì
Caltagirone
Lentini
Licata
Gela
Niscemi
Vittoria
Ragusa
Augusta
Siracusa
Avola
Golfo di Noto
Pachino
Isola di Pantelleria
SICILIA
(SICILY)
Gozo
Birkirkara
VALLETTA
Malta
Isole Pelagie
TYRRHENIAN SEA
ADRIATIC SEA
DALMACIJA
IONIAN SEA
MEDITERRANEAN SEA
SLO
HR
H
BIH
SRB
MNE
RKS
AL
MK
GR
I
M
1:4 654 000
0
100
200 km
50
100 miles
14°
16°
18°
20°
22°
42°
40°
38°
36°

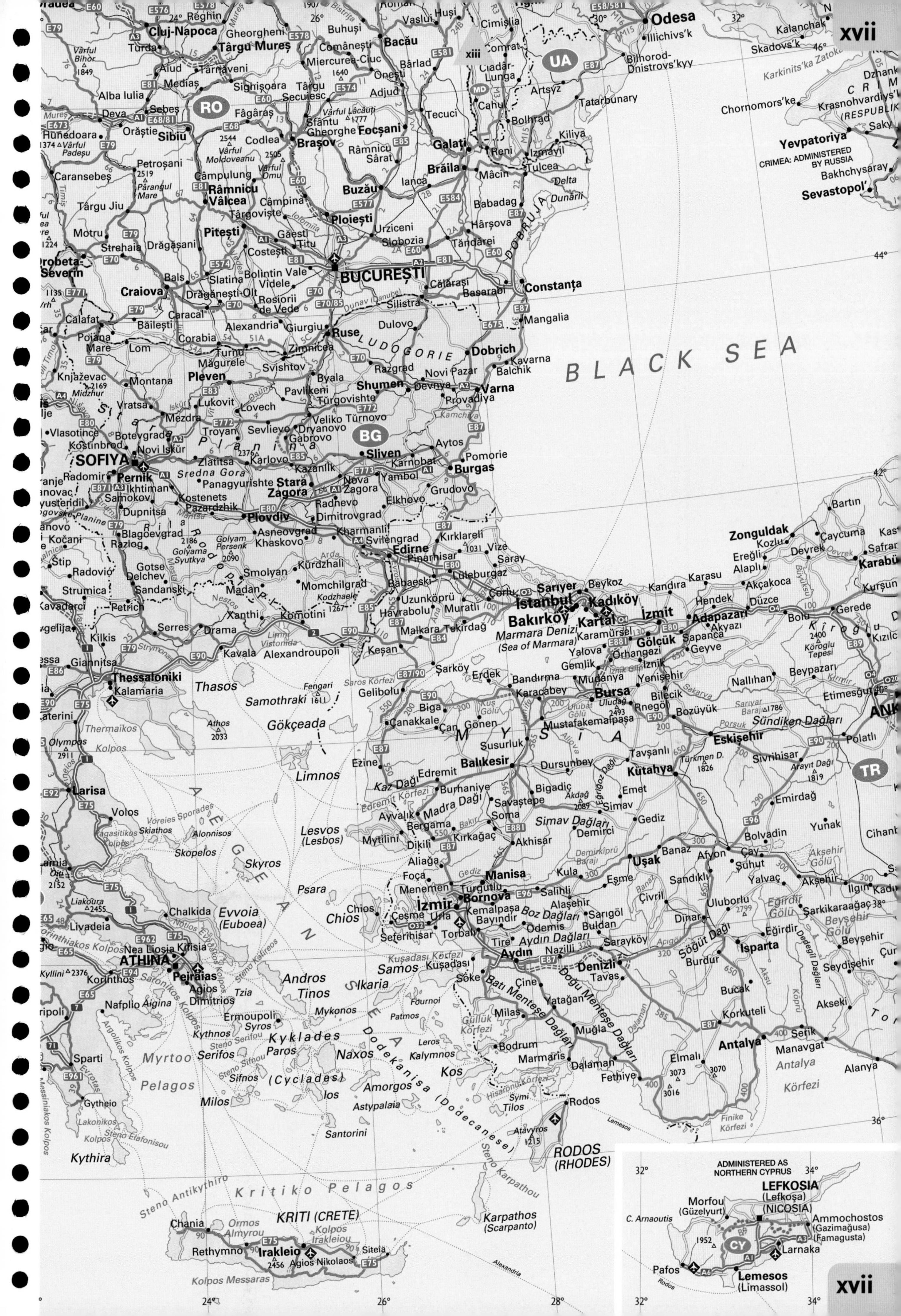
Cluj-Napoca
Târgu Mureş
Gheorgheni
Bacău
Vaslui
Huşi
Cimişlia
Odesa
Illichivs'k
Kalanchak
Skadovs'k
Bilhorod-Dnistrovs'kyy
Karkinits'ka Zatoka
Dzhankoy
CRIMEA
Krasnohvardiys'ke
(RESPUBLIKA)
Chornomors'ke
Saky
Yevpatoriya
CRIMEA: ADMINISTERED BY RUSSIA
Bakhchysaray
Sevastopol'
Turda
Aiud
Târnăveni
Mediaş
Sighişoara
Alba Iulia
Deva
Sebeş
Orăştie
Sibiu
Hunedoara
Făgăraş
Sfântu Gheorghe
Braşov
Codlea
Focşani
Miercurea-Ciuc
Comăneşti
Oneşti
Adjud
Bârlad
Târgu Secuiesc
Tecuci
Comrat
Ciadâr-Lunga
Cahul
Artsyz
Tatarbunary
Bolhrad
Galaţi
Reni
Izmayil
Kiliya
Tulcea
Brăila
Măcin
Râmnicu Sărat
Buzău
Ianca
Delta Dunării
Babadag
Hârşova
DOBRUJA
Caransebeş
Petroşani
Câmpulung
Râmnicu Vâlcea
Câmpina
Târgu Jiu
Târgovişte
Ploieşti
Urziceni
Slobozia
Ţăndărei
Motru
Piteşti
Găeşti
Titu
Strehaia
Drăgăşani
Costeşti
Drobeta-Turnu Severin
BUCUREŞTI
Craiova
Bals
Slatina
Bolintin Vale
Videle
Călăraşi
Basarabi
Constanţa
Drăgăneşti-Olt
Roşiorii de Vede
Dunav (Danube)
Silistra
Mangalia
Calafat
Caracal
Băileşti
Alexandria
Giurgiu
Ruse
Dulovo
Corabia
Turnu Măgurele
Zimnicea
Lom
Dobrich
Kavarna
Balchik
LUDOGORIE
BLACK SEA
Pleven
Svishtov
Razgrad
Novi Pazar
Montana
Byala
Shumen
Devnya
Varna
Knjaževac
Pavlikeni
Provadiya
Vratsa
Lukovit
Lovech
Targovishte
Mezdra
Troyan
Sevlievo
Veliko Tŭrnovo
Dryanovo
Gabrovo
Vlasotince
Kostinbrod
Botevgrad
Novi Iskŭr
SOFIYA
Stara Planina
Sliven
Aytos
Pomorie
Burgas
Karlovo
Kazanlŭk
Zlatitsa
Karnobat
Radomir
Pernik
Sredna Gora
Panagyurishte
Stara Zagora
Nova Zagora
Yambol
Ikhtiman
Samokov
Kostenets
Pazardzhik
Plovdiv
Radnevo
Dimitrovgrad
Elkhovo
Grudovo
Dupnitsa
Blagoevgrad
Asenovgrad
Khaskovo
Kharmanli
Svilengrad
Kırklareli
Vize
Edirne
Saray
Kočani
Razlog
Rila
Rodopi
Smolyan
Kŭrdzhali
Momchilgrad
Pinarhisar
Lüleburgaz
Štip
Radoviš
Gotse Delchev
Sandanski
Madan
Babaeski
Strumica
Petrich
Xanthi
Komotini
Uzunköprü
Çorlu
Sarıyer
Beykoz
Kavadarci
Kilkis
Serres
Drama
Kavala
Alexandroupoli
Havrabolu
Muratlı
Tekirdağ
Malkara
İstanbul
Kadıköy
Bakırköy
Kartal
Marmara Denizi (Sea of Marmara)
İzmit
Adapazarı
Akyazı
Sapanca
Geyve
Gölcük
Karamürsel
Yalova
Orhangazi
Gemlik
İznik
Thessaloniki
Kalamaria
Giannitsa
Thasos
Samothraki
Keşan
Şarköy
Erdek
Bandırma
Mudanya
Bursa
Yenişehir
Bilecik
Gelibolu
Saros Körfezi
Fengari
Karacabey
Uludağ
İnegöl
Bozüyük
Katerini
Thermaikos Kolpos
Gökçeada
Athos
Biga
Çanakkale
Çan
Gönen
Mustafakemalpaşa
Eskişehir
Sündiken Dağları
Polatlı
Olympos
MYSIA
Susurluk
Tavşanlı
Sivrihisar
Limnos
Ezine
Edremit
Balıkesir
Dursunbey
Kütahya
Emet
Larisa
Kaz Dağı
Burhaniye
Edremit Körfezi
Madra Dağı
Bigadiç
Savaştepe
Simav
Emirdağ
Volos
Voreies Sporades
Skiathos
Alonnisos
Skopelos
Ayvalık
Bergama
Soma
Simav Dağları
Demirci
Gediz
Lesvos (Lesbos)
Mytilini
Dikili
Kırkağaç
Akhisar
Bolvadin
Yunak
Cihanbeyli
Skyros
Aliağa
Manisa
Kula
Uşak
Banaz
Afyon
Çay
Şuhut
Akşehir
Akşehir Gölü
Foça
Menemen
Turgutlu
Salihli
Eşme
Sandıklı
Yalvaç
Ilgın
Kadınhanı
Lamia
Liakoura
Psara
Chios
İzmir
Bornova
Alaşehir
Çivril
Uluborlu
Eğirdir Gölü
Şarkikaraağaç
Beyşehir Gölü
AEGEAN SEA
Chalkida
Evvoia (Euboea)
Çeşme
Urla
Kemalpaşa
Boz Dağları
Sarıgöl
Bayındır
Ödemiş
Buldan
Dinar
Eğirdir
Livadeia
Seferihisar
Torbalı
Tire
Aydın Dağları
Sarayköy
Isparta
Beyşehir
Korinthiakos Kolpos
Nea Liosia
Kifisia
ATHINA
Peiraias
Agios Dimitrios
Kuşadası Körfezi
Kuşadası
Samos
Aydın
Nazilli
Denizli
Söğüt Dağı
Burdur
Dedegöl Dağları
Seydişehir
Korinthos
Saronikos Kolpos
Andros
Tinos
Ikaria
Söke
Batı Menteşe Dağları
Çine
Doğu Menteşe Dağları
Tavas
Bucak
Akseki
Tripoli
Nafplio
Aigina
Tzia
Kythnos
Ermoupoli
Syros
Mykonos
Fournoi
Patmos
Milas
Yatağan
Güllük Körfezi
Muğla
Korkuteli
Argolikos Kolpos
Kyklades (Cyclades)
Paros
Naxos
Leros
Kalymnos
Dodekanisa (Dodecanese)
Bodrum
Kos
Marmaris
Dalaman
Fethiye
Elmalı
Antalya
Serik
Manavgat
Antalya Körfezi
Alanya
Sparti
Myrtoo Pelagos
Serifos
Sifnos
Amorgos
Astypalaia
Milos
Ios
Santorini
Symi
Tilos
Rodos
Hisarönü Körfezi
Finike Körfezi
Gytheio
Lakonikos Kolpos
Steno Elafonisou
Kythira
Atavyros
RODOS (RHODES)
Steno Antikythiro
Kritiko Pelagos
Steno Karpathou
Karpathos (Scarpanto)
Chania
Ormos Almyrou
KRITI (CRETE)
Kolpos Irakleiou
Rethymno
Irakleio
Agios Nikolaos
Siteia
Kolpos Messaras
Alexandria
ADMINISTERED AS NORTHERN CYPRUS
LEFKOSIA (Lefkoşa) (NICOSIA)
Morfou (Güzelyurt)
C. Arnaoutis
Ammochostos (Gazimağusa) (Famagusta)
Larnaka
Pafos
Lemesos (Limassol)
RO
UA
MD
BG
TR
CY
Zonguldak
Kozlu
Ereğli
Alaplı
Çaycuma
Devrek
Bartın
Karabük
Safranbolu
Kandıra
Karasu
Akçakoca
Hendek
Düzce
Bolu
Gerede
Köroğlu Tepesi
Köroğlu
Kızılcahamam
Beypazarı
Nallıhan
Etimesgut
Sakarya
Sarıyar Barajı
Porsuk
Türkmen D.
Arayıt Dağı

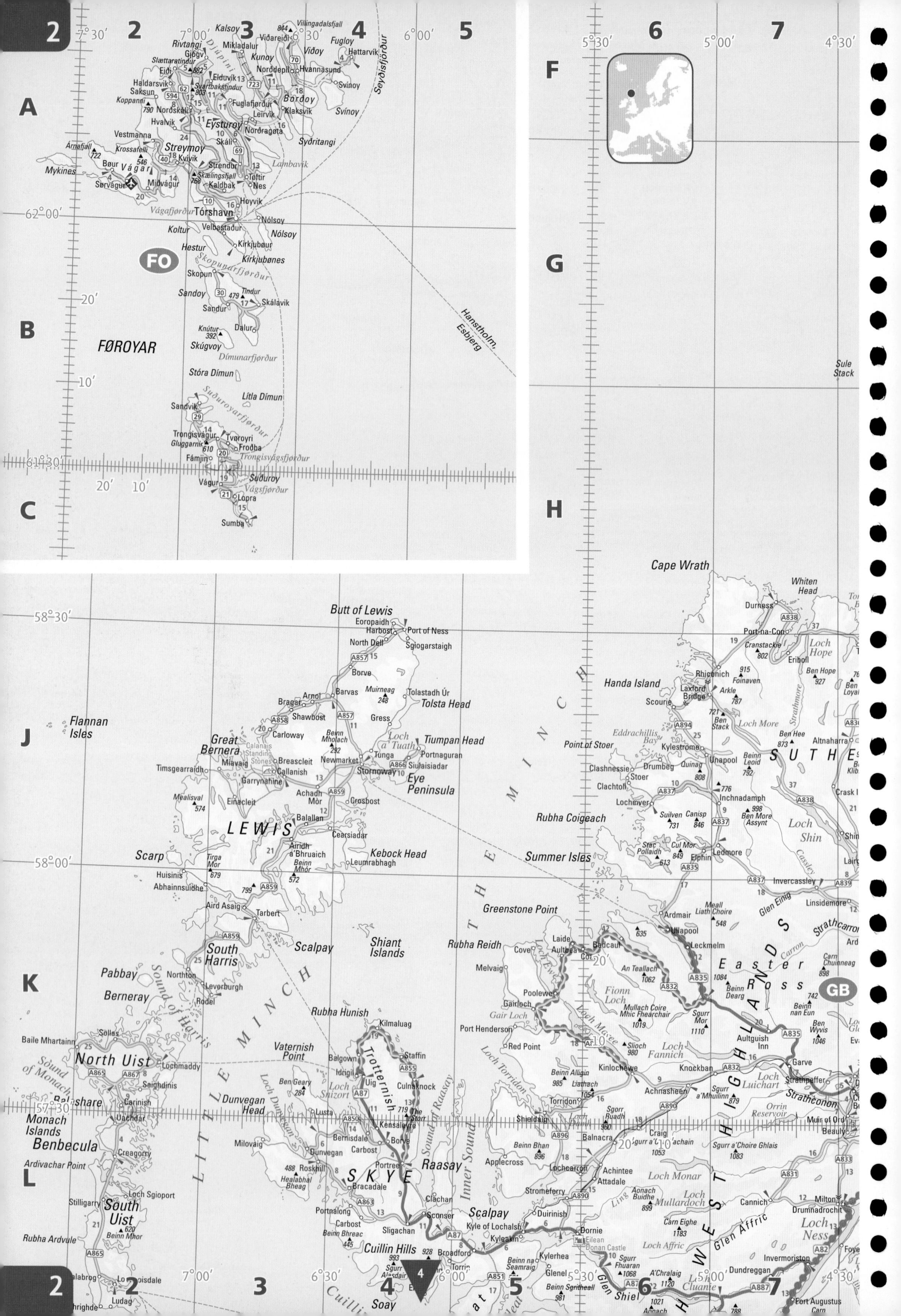
7°30′
7°00′
6°30′
6°00′
5°30′
5°00′
4°30′
A
B
C
F
G
H
J
K
L
Kalsoy
Villingadalsfjall
Fugloy
Hattarvík
Rivtangi
Mikladalur
Viðareiði
Viðoy
Slættaratindur
Gjógv
Kunoy
Norðdepil
Hvannasund
Seyðisfjørður
Eiði
Elduvík
Svínoy
Haldarsvík
Svartbakstindur
Borðoy
Saksun
Koppenni
Fuglafjørður
Klaksvík
Svínoy
Norðskáli
Leirvík
Hvalvík
Eysturoy
Norðragøta
Syðritangi
Vestmanna
Skáli
Árnafjall
Krossafelli
Streymoy
Kvívík
Mykines
Bøur
Vágar
Strendur
Lambavík
Sørvágur
Miðvágur
Skælingsfjall
Toftir
Kaldbak
Nes
Hoyvík
Vágafjørður
Tórshavn
62°00′
Nólsoy
Koltur
Velbastaður
Nólsoy
Hestur
Kirkjubøur
Kirkjubønes
FO
Skopunarfjørður
Skopun
Sandoy
Tindur
Skálavík
Sandur
Hanstholm, Esbjerg
Knútur
Dalur
FØROYAR
Skúgvoy
Dímunarfjørður
Stóra Dímun
Lítla Dímun
Suðuroyarfjørður
Sandvík
Trongisvágur
Tvøroyri
Gluggarnir
Froðba
Fámjin
Trongisvágsfjørður
61°30′
Suðuroy
Vágur
Vágsfjørður
Lopra
Sumba
Sule Stack
Cape Wrath
Whiten Head
Durness
Butt of Lewis
Eoropaidh
Harbost
Port of Ness
58°30′
Port-na-Con
North Dell
Sgiogarstaigh
Cranstackie
Loch Hope
Eriboll
Borve
Rhiconich
Foinaven
Ben Hope
Arnol
Barvas
Muirneag
Tolastadh Úr
Handa Island
Laxford Bridge
Arkle
Bragar
Tolsta Head
Scourie
Shawbost
Gress
Ben Stack
Loch More
Flannan Isles
Carloway
Loch a' Tuath
Tiumpan Head
Eddrachillis Bay
Ben Hee
Altnaharra
Great Bernera
Beinn Mholach
Calanais Standing Stones
Point of Stoer
Kylestrome
Breascleit
Newmarket
Tunga
Portnaguran
Unapool
Timsgearraidh
Miavaig
Callanish
Stornoway
Siulaisiadar
Clashnessie
Drumbeg
Quinag
Beinn Leoid
Garrynahine
Eye Peninsula
Stoer
Clachtoll
Crask Inn
Achadh Mòr
Inchnadamph
Mealisval
Einacleit
Grosbost
Lochinver
Ben More Assynt
Loch Shin
Balallan
Suilven
Canisp
LEWIS
Rubha Coigeach
Cearsiadar
Stac Pollaidh
Cul Mor
Ledmore
Airidh a' Bhruaich
Kebock Head
Elphin
Scarp
Tirga Mor
Beinn Mhòr
Leumrabhagh
Summer Isles
58°00′
Huisinis
Abhainnsuidhe
Invercassley
Linsidemore
Aird Asaig
Tarbert
Greenstone Point
Ardmair
Meall Liath Choire
Glen Einig
Ullapool
Strathcarron
Laide
Aultbea
Dundonnell
South Harris
Scalpay
Shiant Islands
Rubha Reidh
Cove
Leckmelm
An Teallach
Easter Ross
Melvaig
Northton
Pabbay
Leverburgh
Poolewe
Fionn Loch
Beinn Dearg
GB
Berneray
Rodel
Sound of Harris
Gairloch
Mullach Coire Mhic Fhearchair
Rubha Hunish
Port Henderson
Gair Loch
Sgurr Mor
Ben Wyvis
Kilmaluag
Loch Maree
Baile Mhartainn
Sollas
Vaternish Point
Red Point
Slioch
Aultguish Inn
Loch Fannich
North Uist
Lochmaddy
Balgown
Trotternish
Staffin
Loch Torridon
Garve
Sound of Monach
Sgiogarstaigh
Idrigil
Kinlochewe
Knockban
Strathpeffer
Loch Luichart
Ben Geary
Uig
Loch Snizort
Culnaknock
Beinn Alligin
Liathach
Achnasheen
Sgurr a' Mhuilinn
Strathconon
Dunvegan Head
Carinish
Torridon
Baleshare
57°30′
Monach Islands
Lusta
Sgurr Ruadh
Orrin Reservoir
Uachdar
Sound of Raasay
The Storr
Shieldaig
Muir of Ord
Benbecula
Kensaleyre
Bernisdale
Borve
Inner Sound
Balnacra
Craig
Beauly
Milovaig
Carbost
Beinn Bhan
Sgurr a' Chaorachain
Sgurr a' Choire Ghlais
Creagorry
Dunvegan
Ardivachar Point
Roskhill
Portree
Raasay
Applecross
Lochcarron
Achintee
Healabhal Bheag
SKYE
Attadale
Loch Monar
Bracadale
Stromeferry
Aonach Buidhe
Loch Mullardoch
Loch Sgioport
Clachan
Cannich
Milton
Stilligarry
South Uist
Portnalong
Sconser
Scalpay
Duirinish
Drumnadrochit
Beinn Mhor
Carbost
Kyle of Lochalsh
Dornie
Carn Eighe
Loch Ness
Rubha Ardvule
Sligachan
Kyleakin
Eilean Donan Castle
Glen Affric
Beinn Bhreac
Loch Affric
Cuillin Hills
Broadford
Kylerhea
Sgurr Fhuaran
Invermoriston
Glenel
Beinn na Seamraig
A'Chralaig
Dundreggan
Torrin
Loch Cluanie
Sgurr Alasdair
Glen Shiel
Beinn Sgritheall
Aonach
Fort Augustus
Soay
Cuillin
Lochboisdale
Ludag
Carn
1
2
3
4
5
6
7

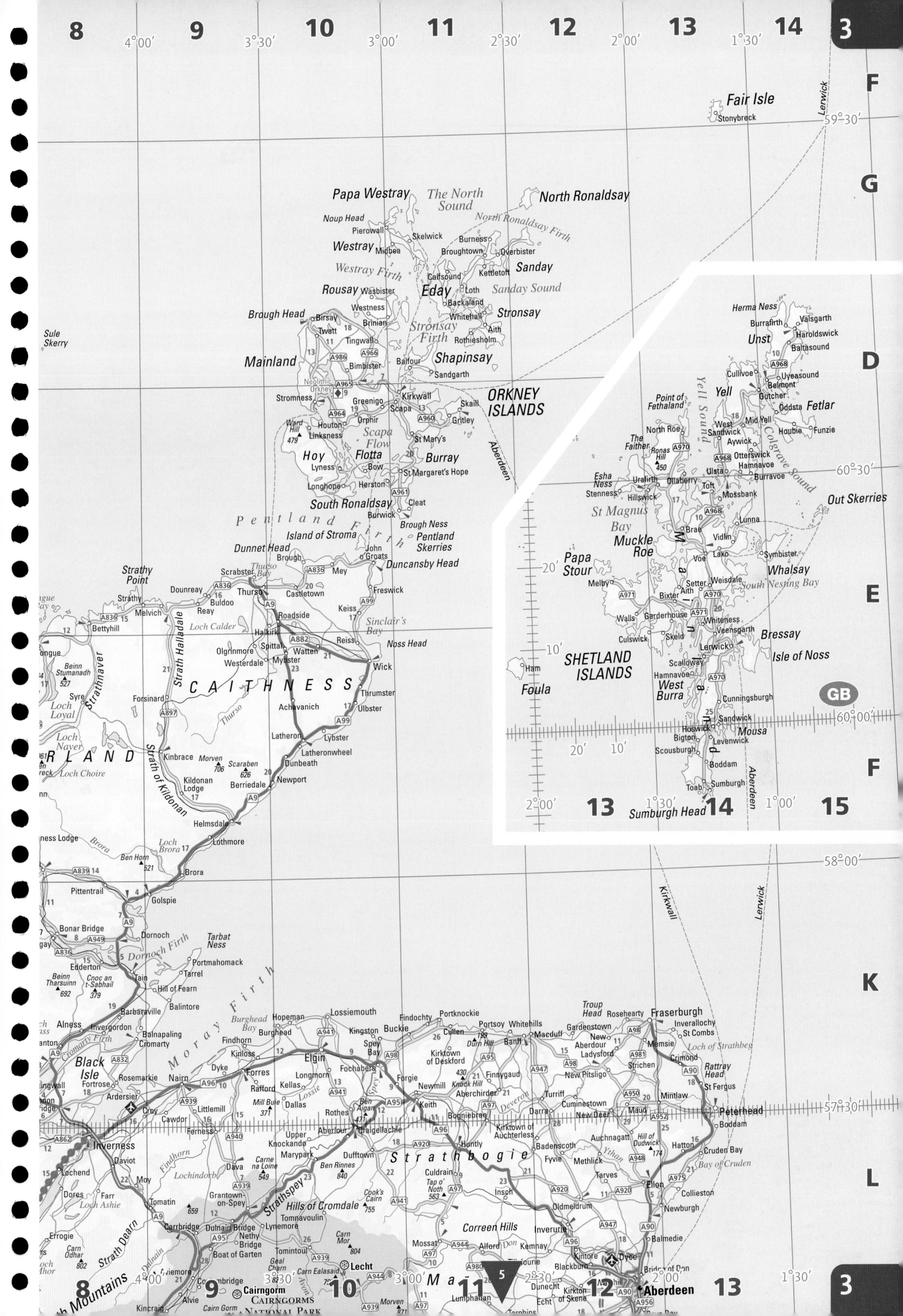

F
59°30'

G

Fair Isle
Stonybreck

Lerwick

Papa Westray
The North Sound
North Ronaldsay
Noup Head
North Ronaldsay Firth
Pierowall
Skelwick
Burness
Westray
Midbea
Broughtown
Overbister
Sanday
Calfsound
Kettletoft
Rousay
Wasbister
Loth
Sanday Sound
Brough Head
Westness
Brinian
Eday
Backaland
Stronsay
Birsay
Whitehall
Twatt
18
Aith
Stronsay Firth
Rothiesholm
Tingwall
11
Shapinsay
Mainland
13
A986
A966
Bimbister
Balfour
Sandgarth
A965
Neolithic
Orkney
9
Kirkwall
ORKNEY
Stromness
Greenigo
Scapa
13
ISLANDS
19
A964
Orphir
Skaill
A960
Ward
Houton
Gritley
Aberdeen
Hill
Linksness
St Mary's
479
Scapa
Hoy
Flow
Flotta
Burray
Lyness
Bow
20
Burray
St Margaret's Hope
Longhope
Herston
A961
South Ronaldsay
Cleat
Pentland　Firth
Burwick
Brough Ness
Island of Stroma
Pentland
Dunnet Head
John
Skerries
Thurso
o'Groats
Brough
Bay
Duncansby Head
Strathy
Scrabster
A836
Mey
Point
Dounreay
Thurso
A9
Freswick
Strathy
Buldoo
Castletown
A836
16
Melvich
Reay
Roadside
Keiss
A99
A836
15
Loch Calder
Halkirk
Sinclair's
Bettyhill
12
Spittal
Reiss
Bay
Olgrinmore
Watten
Noss Head
Westerdale
Mybster
21
Wick
Beinn
21
23
Stumanadh
CAITHNESS
Thrumster
527
Forsinard
Achavanich
Ulbster
Syre
A897
17
Loch
Latheron
Lybster
Loyal
Kinbrace
Morven
Latheronwheel
706
Scaraben
Loch
Dunbeath
626
Choire
Kildonan
Berriedale
20
Lodge
Newport
17
A9
Helmsdale
ness Lodge
Brora
Loch
Lothmore
Brora
17
Ben Horn
Brora
A839
14
521
Pittentrail
Golspie
7
A9
11
Bonar Bridge
Dornoch
8
A949
Tarbat
gay
A836
Dornoch Firth
Ness
15
Edderton
Portmahomack
5
7
Beinn
Cnoc an
Tarrel
Tharsuinn
t-Sabhail
Tain
692
379
Hill of Fearn
19
Barbaraville
Balintore
Alness
Invergordon
Balnapaling
nton
Cromarty
A9
Black
Cromarty Firth
gwall
A832
Isle
Rosemarkie
Fortrose
A96
Ardersier
dge
Croy
A939
Littlemill
Cawdor
A862
Inverness
Daviot
Moy
Dores
Loch Ashie
Farr
Errogie
Carn
Odhar
802
hor

Herma Ness
Burrafirth
Valsgarth
Haroldswick
Unst
Baltasound
10
A968
Cullivoe
Uyeasound
Yell
Belmont
Gutcher
Fetlar
Oddsta
Point of
Houbie
Fethaland
North Roe
Mid Yell
Funzie
The
Ronas
18
West
Aywick
Faither
Hill
Sandwick
450
A970
Otterswick
Esha
A968
Hamnavoe
Ness
Urafirth
Ulsta
Burravoe
Stenness
Ollaberry
Toft
St Magnus
Brae
Mossbank
Bay
A968
Lunna
Papa
Muckle
Vidlin
Stour
Roe
Voe
Laxo
Symbister
Whalsay
Melby
Setter
Weisdale
Bixter
Aith
A970
South Nesting Bay
Walls
Garderhouse
A971
Whiteness
Veensgarth
Bressay
Culswick
Skeld
A971
Lerwick
Isle of Noss
Ham
SHETLAND
Scalloway
Hamnavoe
GB
Foula
ISLANDS
West
A970
Cunningsburgh
Burra
25
Sandwick
60°00'
20'
10'
Hoswick
Mousa
Bigton
Levenwick
Boddam
Scousburgh
Toab
Sumburgh
Aberdeen
2°00'
13
Sumburgh Head
14
1°00'
15

58°00'

K

Out Skerries
Colgrave Sound
Yell Sound
60°30'

Kirkwall
Lerwick

Troup
Rosehearty
Fraserburgh
Burghead
Lossiemouth
Portknockie
Head
Inverallochy
Bay
Hopeman
Findochty
Whitehills
Gardenstown
St Combs
Burghead
Spey
Buckie
Portsoy
Macduff
New
11
A98
Findhorn
Bay
Kingston
Cullen
199
Banff
Aberdour
Memsie
Kinloss
A941
26
Dun Hill
Ladysford
A981
Elgin
A95
Strichen
Crimond
Dyke
Longmorn
Fochabers
Kirktown
A98
Rattray
Forres
of Deskford
Finnygaud
New Pitsligo
Head
Nairn
A96
Rafford
A941
Forgie
A98
18
St Fergus
Kellas
Newmill
430
A947
A90
10
Mill Buie
Dallas
Ben
Keith
Knock Hill
Turriff
Cuminestown
Peterhead
371
Aigan
A95
Aberchirder
Darra
New Deer
Maud
A952
Boddam
Rothes
A95
Bogniebrae
A96
Kirktown of
Craigellachie
11
Huntly
Auchterless
A950
Mintlaw
57°30'
Upper
Aberlour
Kirkton
Darnaway
Ferness
A940
Knockando
A96
28
Cruden Bay
Badenscoth
Auchnagatt
Hill of
Dufftown
Fyvie
Methlick
Dudwick
Hatton
Maryvark
Ben Rinnes
Strathbogie
174
Bay of Cruden
Dava
840
Ythan
Carne
na Loine
Culdrain
Tarves
A975
549
Tap o'
A920
Ellon
Collieston
Tomnavoulin
Cook's
Noth
Insch
A920
Cairn
563
Newburgh
Lynemore
755
A941
A97
Carrbridge
Dulnain Bridge
Oldmeldrum
A947
Nethy
Correen Hills
Inverurie
Balmedie
Bridge
Mossat
A944
Alford
Don
Kemnay
A96
Boat of Garten
Tomintoul
A939
Kintore
A90
Carn
Lecht
Mor
Kincraig
804
Lumphanan
Dunecht
Echt
Aberdeen
Alvie
Cairngorm
Morven
CAIRNGORMS
871
Kirkton of Skene
A956
Cairn Gorm
NATIONAL PARK

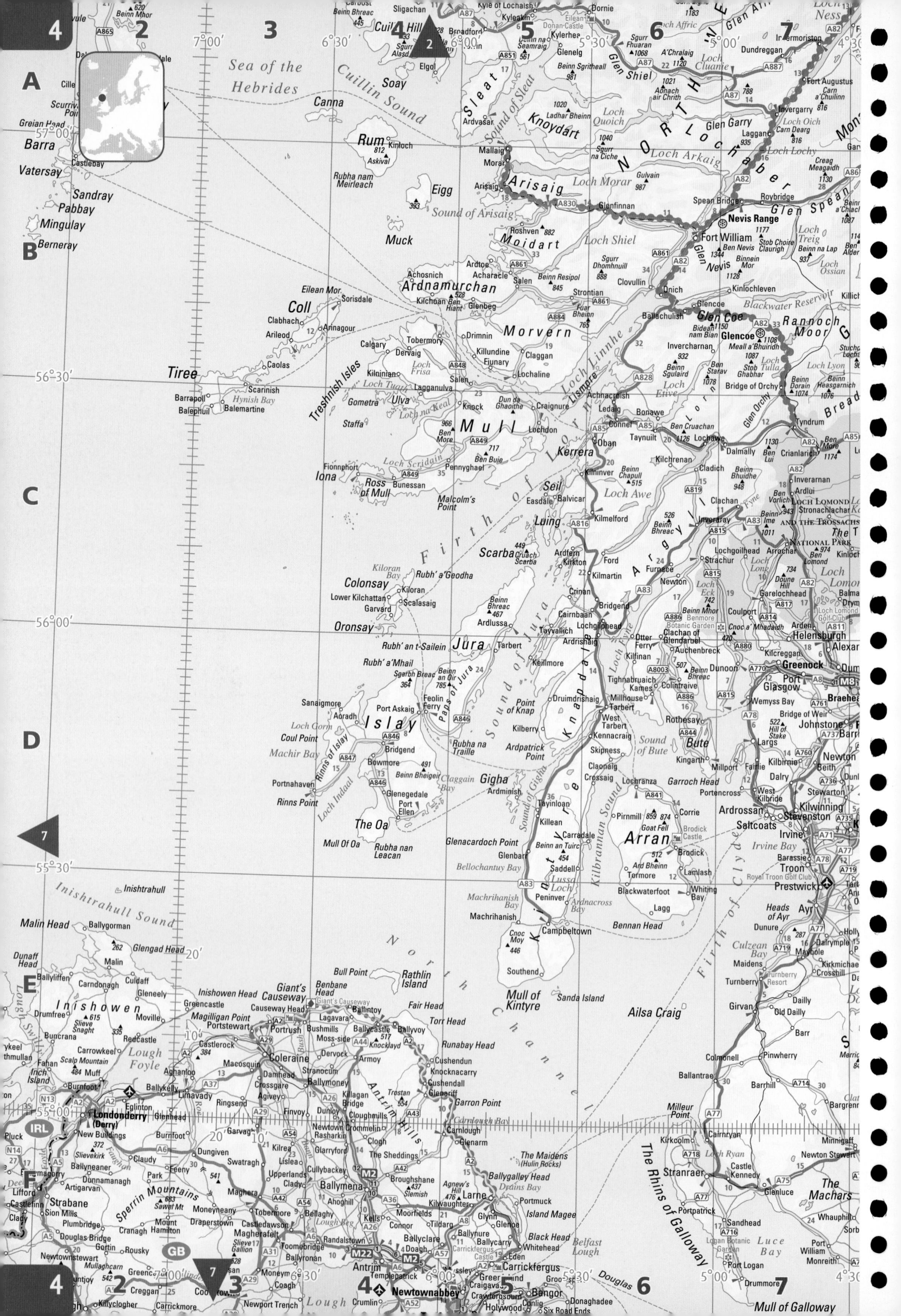

4
Sea of the Hebrides
Cuillin Sound
Soay
Canna
Elgol
Rum
Kinloch
Askival
Rubha nam Meirleach
Eigg
Muck
Sound of Arisaig
Barra
Castlebay
Vatersay
Sandray
Pabbay
Mingulay
Berneray
Sleat
Sound of Sleat
Knoydart
Loch Quoich
Glen Shiel
Loch Cluanie
Glenelg
Dornie
Broadford
Invermoriston
Dundreggan
Fort Augustus
Invergarry
Glen Garry
Laggan
Loch Oich
Loch Lochy
Loch Arkaig
Loch Morar
Mallaig
Morar
Arisaig
Glenfinnan
Spean Bridge
Roybridge
Glen Spean
Nevis Range
Fort William
Ben Nevis
Glen Nevis
Moidart
Loch Shiel
Ardnamurchan
Kilchoan
Acharacle
Salen
Strontian
Clovullin
Onich
Kinlochleven
Blackwater Reservoir
Glencoe
Glen Coe
Ballachulish
Rannoch Moor
Coll
Arinagour
Tiree
Scarinish
Hynish Bay
Balemartine
Tobermory
Dervaig
Morvern
Lochaline
Treshnish Isles
Ulva
Gometra
Staffa
Mull
Craignure
Lochdon
Loch Linnhe
Lismore
Oban
Kerrera
Connel
Taynuilt
Bonawe
Loch Etive
Dalmally
Tyndrum
Crianlarich
Bridge of Orchy
Iona
Fionnphort
Bunessan
Ross of Mull
Malcolm's Point
Pennyghael
Loch Scridain
Seil
Easdale
Luing
Loch Awe
Kilmelford
Scarba
Firth of Lorn
Colonsay
Scalasaig
Oronsay
Kilmartin
Crinan
Lochgilphead
Ardrishaig
Tarbert
Jura
Sound of Jura
Islay
Port Askaig
Bridgend
Bowmore
Port Ellen
The Oa
Mull Of Oa
Rinns of Islay
Loch Indaal
Gigha
Knapdale
Kintyre
Campbeltown
Southend
Mull of Kintyre
Sanda Island
Inveraray
Strachur
Loch Fyne
Dunoon
Rothesay
Bute
Sound of Bute
Arran
Brodick
Lamlash
Lochranza
Kilbrannan Sound
Ailsa Craig
Firth of Clyde
Loch Lomond
Arrochar
Helensburgh
Greenock
Port Glasgow
Largs
Ardrossan
Saltcoats
Irvine
Troon
Prestwick
Ayr
Girvan
Ballantrae
Cairnryan
Stranraer
Loch Ryan
Portpatrick
The Rhins of Galloway
Luce Bay
Newton Stewart
Glenluce
The Machars
Mull of Galloway
Inishtrahull Sound
Malin Head
Inishowen
Lough Foyle
Londonderry (Derry)
Limavady
Coleraine
Portrush
Portstewart
Bushmills
Giant's Causeway
Ballycastle
Rathlin Island
Fair Head
Torr Head
Antrim Hills
Ballymena
Larne
Island Magee
Carrickfergus
Belfast Lough
Bangor
Newtownabbey
Antrim
Strabane
Sperrin Mountains
Magherafelt
North Channel
The Maidens
IRL
GB
1 2 3 4 5 6 7
A B C D E F

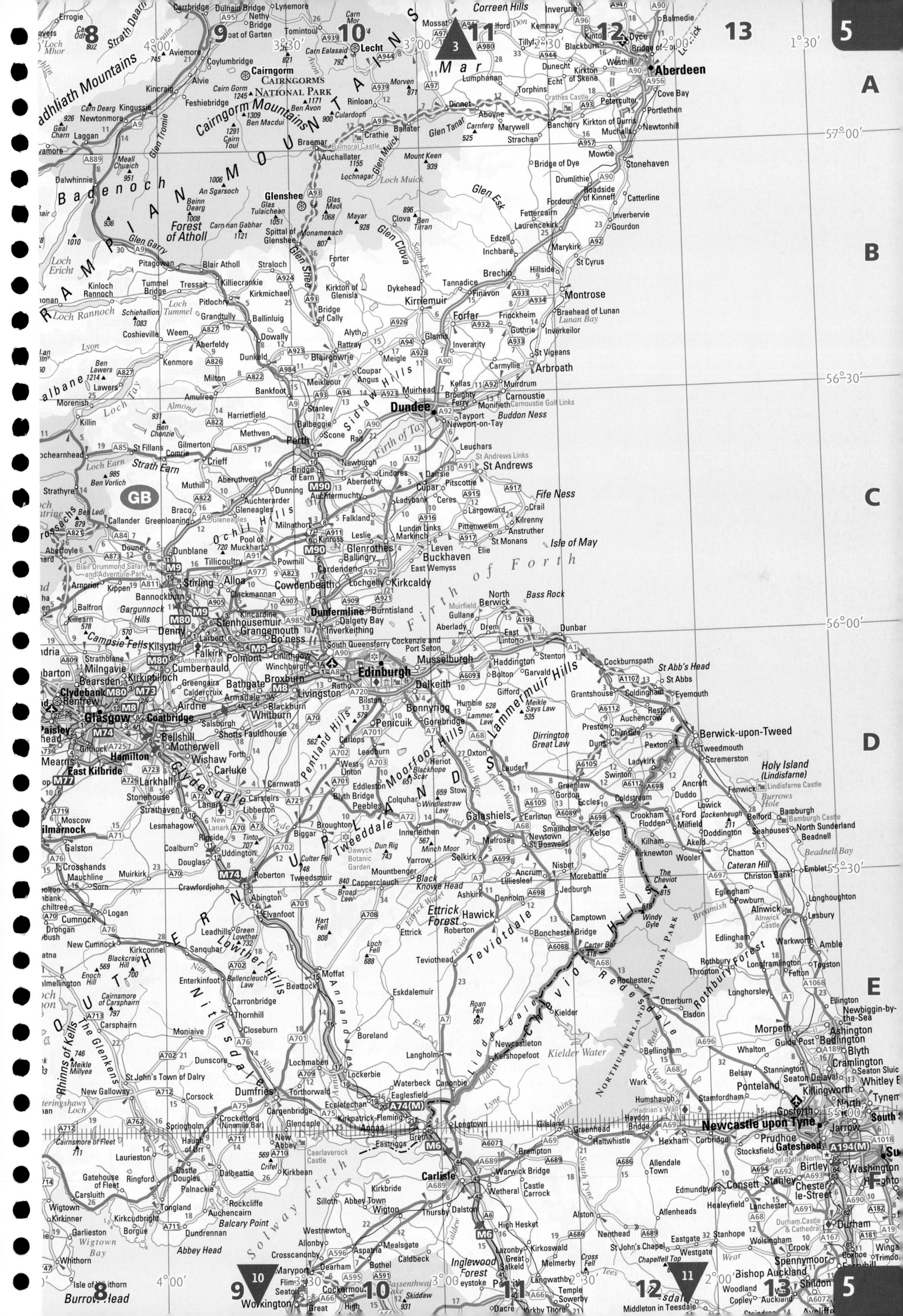
5
8
9
10
11
12
13
A
B
C
D
E
F
4°00′
3°30′
3°00′
2°30′
2°00′
1°30′
57°00′
56°30′
56°00′
55°30′
55°00′
Aberdeen
Dyce
Westhill
Cove Bay
Portlethen
Newtonhill
Peterculter
Banchory
Aboyne
Ballater
Braemar
Inverurie
Kemnay
Stonehaven
Inverbervie
Montrose
Brechin
Arbroath
Carnoustie
Forfar
Kirriemuir
Dundee
Perth
St Andrews
Cupar
Glenrothes
Kirkcaldy
Dunfermline
Stirling
Alloa
Falkirk
Grangemouth
Edinburgh
Musselburgh
Dalkeith
Livingston
Bathgate
Glasgow
Paisley
Coatbridge
Motherwell
Hamilton
East Kilbride
Kilmarnock
Lanark
Peebles
Galashiels
Melrose
Selkirk
Hawick
Kelso
Jedburgh
Dunbar
North Berwick
Berwick-upon-Tweed
Holy Island
(Lindisfarne)
Bamburgh
Alnwick
Amble
Morpeth
Ashington
Blyth
Cramlington
Newcastle upon Tyne
Gateshead
Hexham
Durham
Carlisle
Dumfries
Moffat
Lockerbie
Annan
Gretna
Penrith
Workington
Aviemore
Kingussie
Pitlochry
Aberfeldy
Crieff
Callander
Cairngorm Mountains
CAIRNGORMS
NATIONAL PARK
GRAMPIAN MOUNTAINS
Badenoch
Forest of Atholl
Firth of Tay
Firth of Forth
Ochil Hills
Sidlaw Hills
Pentland Hills
Moorfoot Hills
Lammermuir Hills
SOUTHERN UPLANDS
Cheviot Hills
NORTHUMBERLAND NATIONAL PARK
Kielder Water
Solway Firth
Isle of May
Fife Ness
Bass Rock
St Abb's Head
GB
M90
M9
M8
M80
M74
M6
A1
A74(M)
A194(M)

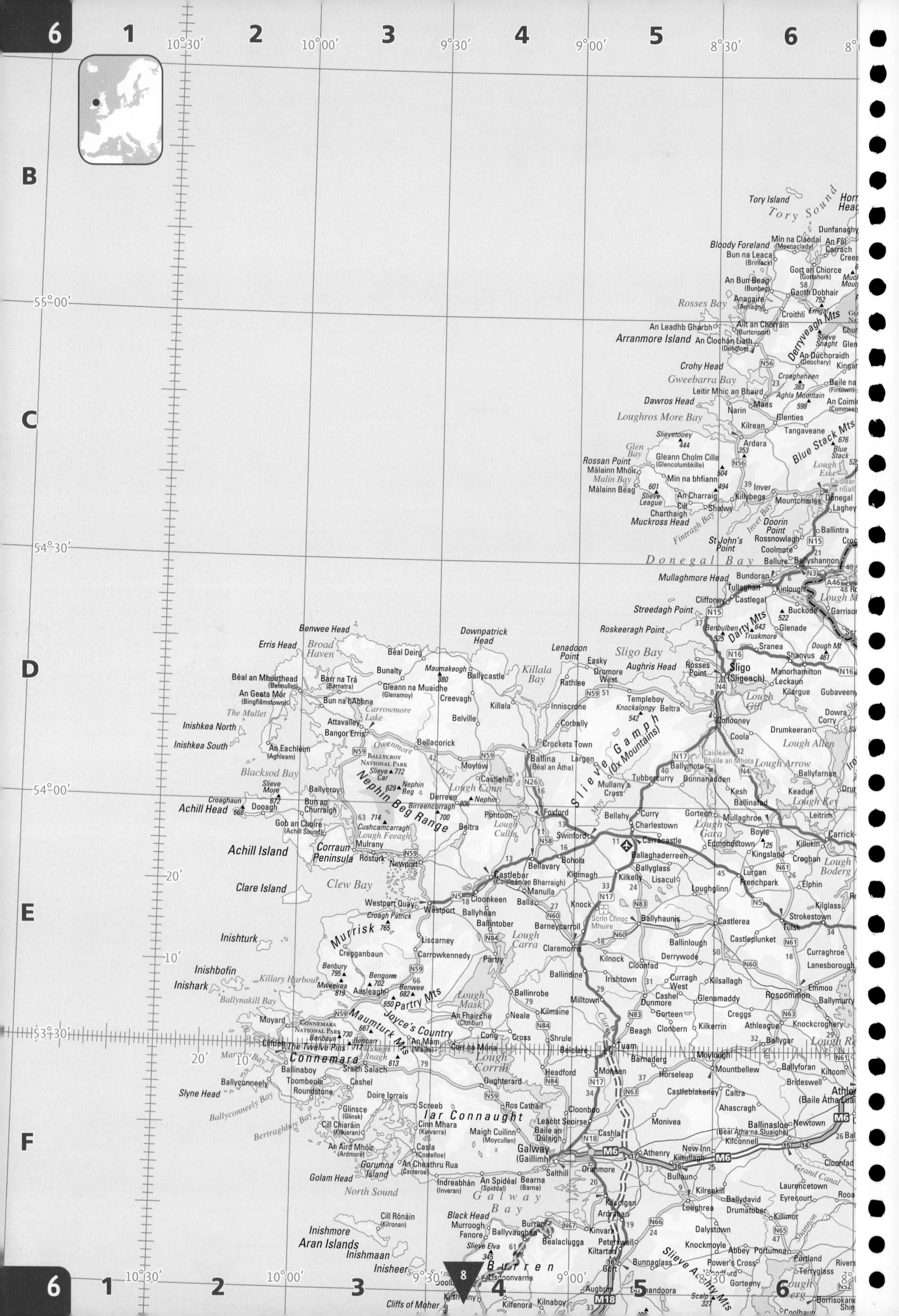

6
1 2 3 4 5 6
10°30′ 10°00′ 9°30′ 9°00′ 8°30′
B
C
D
E
F
55°00′
54°30′
54°00′
53°30′
Tory Island
Tory Sound
Bloody Foreland
Dunfanaghy
Mín na Cláodaí (Meenaclady)
An Fál Carrach
Bun na Leaca (Brinlack)
Gort an Chiorce (Gortahork)
An Bun Beag (Bunbeg)
Gaoth Dobhair
Errigal 752
Rosses Bay
Anagaire (Annagry)
Croithlí
An Leadhb Gharbh
Allt an Chorráin (Burtonport)
Arranmore Island
An Clochán Liath (Dungloe)
Derryveagh Mts
Slieve Snaght
An Dúchoraidh (Doochary)
Crohy Head
Gweebarra Bay
Croaghcheen 383
Aghla Mountain 598
Leitir Mhic an Bhaird
Dawros Head
Narin
Maas
Loughros More Bay
Glenties
Kilrean
Tangaveane
Slievetooey 444
Ardara 353
Blue Stack Mts
Glen Bay
Gleann Cholm Cille (Glencolumbkille)
Rossan Point
Málainn Mhóir
Malin Bay
Málainn Beag
Mín na bhfiann
601 Slieve League
An Charraig
Cill
Shalwy
Charthaigh
Muckross Head
Killybegs
Inver
Mountcharles
Donegal
Laghey
Lough Eske
Fintragh Bay
Inver Bay
Doorin Point
St John's Point
Rossnowlagh
Ballintra
Coolmore
Donegal Bay
Ballure
Ballyshannon
Mullaghmore Head
Bundoran
Tullaghan
Kinlough
Cliffoney
Castlegal
Streedagh Point
Buckode
Garrison
Benbulben 525
Dartry Mts
Truskmore 643
Glenade
Roskeeragh Point
Sranea
Dough Mt 461
Sligo Bay
Aughris Head
Rosses Point
Sligo (Sligeach)
Shanvus
Manorhamilton
Leckaun
Kilargue
Gubaveeny
Lough Gill
Collooney
Dowra
Corry
Drumkeeran
Coola
Lough Allen
Ballymote
Lough Arrow
Ballyfarnan
Bunnanadden
Keadue
Kesh
Ballinafad
Lough Key
Gorteen
Mullaghroe
Leitrim
Lough Gara
Boyle
Carrick-
Edmondstown
Kingsland
Kilrukin
Croghan
Lough Boderg
Lurgan
Frenchpark
Elphin
Loughglinn
Kilglass
Castlerea
Strokestown
Tulsk
Castleplunket
Curraghroe
Lanesborough
Kilsallagh
Emmoo
Roscommon
Ballymurry
Creggs
Athleague
Knockcroghery
Ballygar
Moylough
Mountbellew
Ballyforan
Kiltoom
Brideswell
Athlone (Baile Átha Luain)
Ahascragh
Caltra
Castleblakeney
Horseleap
Barnaderg
Monivea
Ballinasloe (Béal Átha na Sluaighe)
Newtown
Kilconnell
Athenry
New Inn
Kiltullagh
Grand Canal
Cloonfad
Bullaun
Laurencetown
Eyrecourt
Kilreekill
Ballydavid
Loughrea
Drumatober
Killimor
Dalystown
Knockmoyle
Abbey
Portumna
Power's Cross
Portland
Terryglass
Gorteeny
Slieve Aughty Mts
Benwee Head
Erris Head
Broad Haven
Béal Deirg
Downpatrick Head
Lenadoon Point
Easky
Killala Bay
Dromore West
Bunalty
Maumakeogh 380
Ballycastle
Rathlee
Béal an Mhuirthead (Belmullet)
Barr na Trá (Barnatra)
Gleann na Muaidhe (Glenamoy)
An Geata Mór (Binghamstown)
Creevagh
Killala
Inniscrone
Templeboy
Knockalongy 542
Beltra
Bun na hAbhna
The Mullet
Carrowmore Lake
Attavalley
Belville
Corbally
Inishkea North
Bangor Erris
Slieve Gamph (Ox Mountains)
Inishkea South
An Eachléim (Aghleam)
Owenmore
Bellacorick
Crockets Town
Ballycroy National Park
Slieve Car 772
Ballina (Béal an Átha)
Largan
Moylaw
Blacksod Bay
Castlehill
Slieve More 672
Nephin Beg Range
Nephin Beg 629
Lough Conn
Ballycroy
Croaghaun 668
Dooagh
Achill Head
Bun an Churraigh
Derreen
Birreencorragh 700
Nephin 806
Mullany's Cross
Tubbercurry
Gob an Choire (Achill Sound)
Cushcamcarragh 714
Pontoon
Lough Cullin
Foxford
Bellahy
Curry
Charlestown
Lough Feeagh
Beltra
Swinford
Carracastle
Achill Island
Corraun Peninsula
Mulrany
Rosturk
Newport
Bohola
Ballaghaderreen
Bellavary
Castlebar (Caisleán an Bharraigh)
Kiltimagh
Kilkelly
Ballyglass
Lisacul
Clare Island
Clew Bay
Manulla
Westport Quay
Westport
Cloonkeen
Balla
Knock
Croagh Patrick 765
Ballyheán
Scrín Cnoc Mhuire
Ballyhaunis
Ballintober
Barnecarroll
Inishturk
Murrisk
Lough Carra
Claremorris
Liscarney
Ballinlough
Cregganbaun
Carrowkennedy
Partry
Kilnock
Cloonfad
Derrywode
Inishbofin
Benbury 795
Bengorm 702
Ballindine
Irishtown
Curragh West
Glenamaddy
Inishark
Killary Harbour
Mweelrea 819
Aasleagh
Benwee 682
Lough Mask
Ballinrobe
Cashel
Dunmore
Ballynakill Bay
Partry Mts
Kilmaine
Milltown
Gorteen
Moyard
Connemara National Park
Benbaun 730
Maumturk Mts
Joyce's Country
An Fhairche (Clonbur)
Neale
Clonbern
Kilkerrin
Benbaun
Bencorr
Beagh
Clifden
The Twelve Pins
An Mám (Maam)
Cong
Cross
Shrule
Corr na Móna
Belclare
Tuam
Connemara
Inagh
Lough Corrib
Ballinaboy
Sraith Salach
Headford
Mohean
Ballyconneely
Toombeola
Roundstone
Cashel
Oughterard
Slyne Head
Doire Iorrais
Ballyconneely Bay
Glinsce (Glinsk)
Screeb
Ros Cathail
Cloonboo
Iar Connaught
Bertraghboy Bay
Cill Chiaráin (Kilkieran)
Cinn Mhara (Kinvarra)
Leacht Seoirse
Maigh Cuilinn (Moycullen)
Baile an Dúlaigh
Cashla
An Aird Mhóir (Ardmore)
Casla (Costelloe)
Galway (Gaillimh)
Gorumna Island
An Cheathrú Rua (Carraroe)
Salthill
Oranmore
Golam Head
Indreabhán (Inverean)
An Spidéal (Spiddal)
Bearna (Barna)
North Sound
Galway Bay
Kilcolgan
Ardrahan
Cill Rónáin (Kilronan)
Black Head
Burren
Inishmore
Murroogh
Fanore
Ballyvaughan
Kinvara
Aran Islands
Slieve Elva 345
Bealaclugga
Peterswell
Kiltartan
Inishmaan
Inisheer
Burren
Lisdoonvarna
Gort
Bunnaglass
Kilfenora
Kilnaboy
Aughrim
Cliffs of Moher
Kilshanny
Doolin
Shannon
Lough Derg
Scalp 327
Borrisokane
Clonfert
Slieve Aughty Mts
M6
M17
M18
N4
N5
N15
N16
N17
N26
N56
N58
N59
N60
N61
N63
N65
N66
N67
N83
N84
A46
8

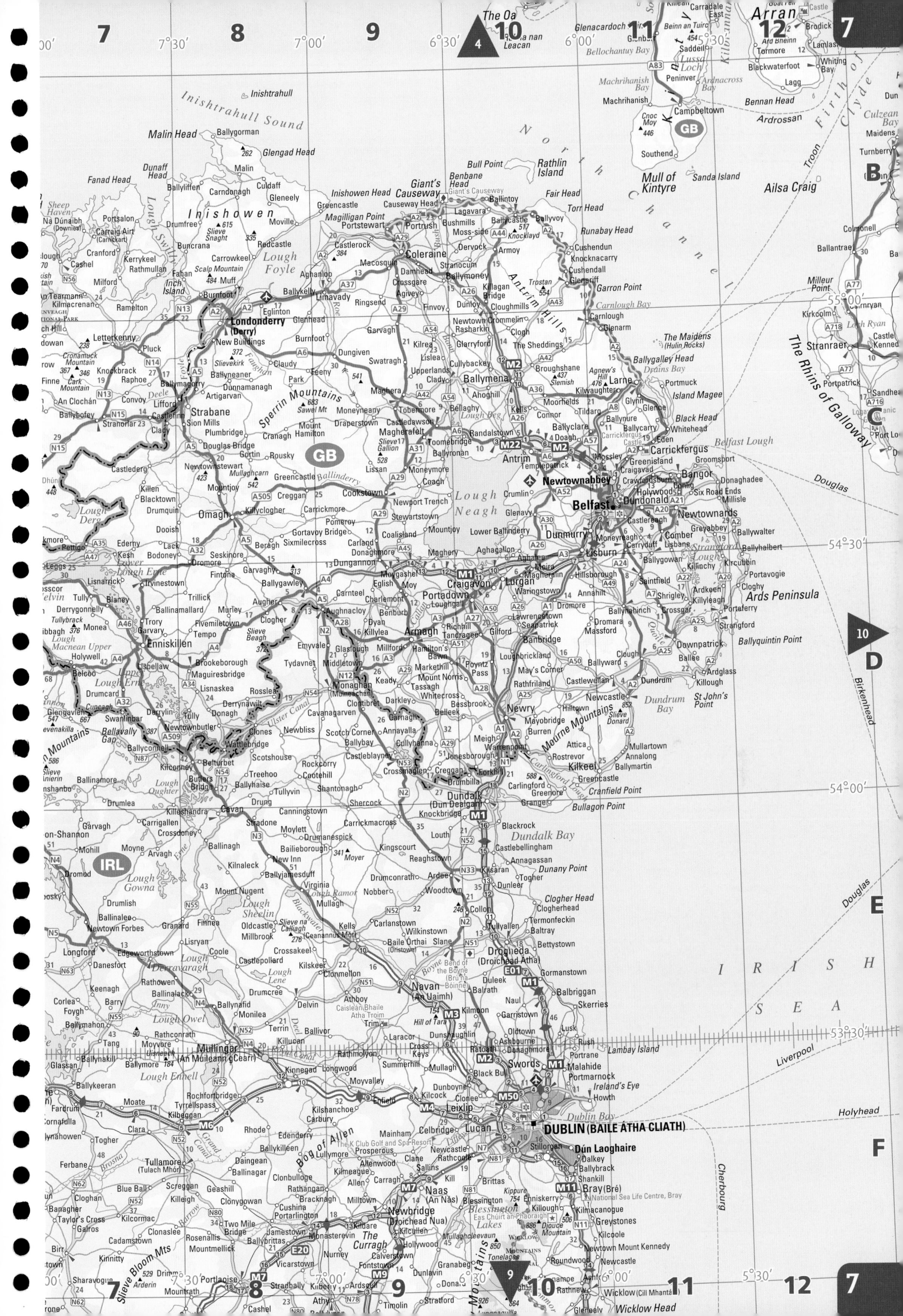
7
8
9
10
11
12
7°30′
7°00′
6°30′
6°00′
5°30′
4
The Oa
Rubha nan Leacan
Glenacardoch
Bellochantuy Bay
Beinn an Tuirc
454
Saddell
Carradale East
Arran
Brodick
Lamlash
Tormore
Whiting Bay
Blackwaterfoot
Lagg
Machrihanish Bay
Machrihanish
Peninver
Ardnacross Bay
Campbeltown
Cnoc Moy
446
GB
Southend
Sanda Island
Mull of Kintyre
Ailsa Craig
Bennan Head
Ardrossan
Firth of Clyde
Troon
Culzean Bay
Maidens
Turnberry
B
Colmonell
Ballantrae
Milleur Point
A77
55°00′
Kirkcolm
Loch Ryan
Stranraer
Cairnryan
Castle Kennedy
A718
A716
A77
Portpatrick
The Rhins of Galloway
Sandhead
C
Port Logan
Inishtrahull
Inishtrahull Sound
Malin Head
Ballygorman
262
Glengad Head
Malin
Dunaff Head
Fanad Head
Ballyliffen
Culdaff
Carndonagh
Gleneely
Inishowen
Inishowen Head
Greencastle
Moville
Slieve Snaght
615
Lough Swilly
Portsalon
Na Dúnaibh (Downies)
Carraig Airt (Carrickart)
Buncrana
Redcastle
Drumfree
Cranford
Kerrykeel
Rathmullan
Fahan
Carrowkeel
Lough Foyle
Scalp Mountain
484
Muff
Inch Island
Cashel
Milford
N56
Burnfoot
Ramelton
Kilmacrenan
Letterkenny
Londonderry (Derry)
New Buildings
Eglinton
Glenhead
Cronamuck Mountain
Cark Mountain
Knockbrack
Raphoe
Pluck
N14
N13
N15
Convoy
Lifford
Strabane
Sion Mills
Ballybofey
Stranorlar
An Clochán
Finne
Slievekirk
Ballyneaner
Claudy
Ballymagorry
Artigarvan
Dunnamanagh
Sperrin Mountains
Sawel Mt
683
Plumbridge
Clady
Douglas Bridge
Castlederg
Newtownstewart
Gortin
Rousky
GB
Mullaghcarn
Greencastle
Ballinderry
Mountjoy
Killen
Blacktown
Drumquin
Omagh
Killyclogher
Creggan
Carrickmore
Cookstown
Pomeroy
Dooish
Gortavoy Bridge
Sixmilecross
Beragh
Lough Derg
Pettigo
Ederny
Lack
Kesh
Bodoney
Seskinore
Dromore
Fintona
Lower Lough Erne
Irvinestown
Lisnarick
Trillick
Garvaghy
Ballygawley
Dungannon
Tully
Blaney
Derrygonnelly
Ballinamallard
Murley
Augher
Clogher
Aughnacloy
Monea
Trory
Garvary
Fivemiletown
Tempo
Enniskillen
Lough Macnean Upper
Holywell
Belcoo
Lisbellaw
Brookeborough
Maguiresbridge
Lisnaskea
Upper Lough Erne
Slieve Beagh
Drumcard
Derrylin
Tully
Donagh
Newtownbutler
Derrynawilt
Rosslea
Swanlinbar
Bellavally Gap
Cuilcagh
667
Glengavlen
Wattlebridge
Clones
Newbliss
Ballyconnell
Belturbet
Kilconny
Butlers Bridge
Scotshouse
Treehoo
Ballyhaise
Cavan
Killeshandra
Ballinamore
Lough Oughter
Drumlea
Carrigallen
Crossdoney
Garvagh
Arvagh
Moyne
Mohill
IRL
Dromod
Lough Gowna
Drumlish
Ballinalee
Newtown Forbes
Granard
Finnea
Longford
Danesfort
Edgeworthstown
Lough Derravaragh
Rathowen
Ballinalack
Keenagh
Corlea
Foygh
Ballymahon
Barry
Lough Owel
Ballynafid
Rathconrath
Mullingar (An Muileann gCearr)
Lough Ennell
Moyvore
Tang
Ballynakill
Ballymore
Glassan
Ballykeeran
Moate
Tyrrellspass
Kilbeggan
Rochfortbridge
M6
Clara
Tullamore (Tulach Mhór)
Ferbane
Blue Ball
Cloghan
Banagher
Taylor's Cross
Kilcormac
Clonaslee
Cadamstown
Kinnitty
Slieve Bloom Mts
Arderin
Mountrath
Portlaoise
Rosenallis
Mountmellick
Geashill
Killeigh
Clonygowan
Daingean
Ballinagar
Rhode
Edenderry
Bog of Allen
Monasterevin
The Curragh
Kildare
Newbridge (Droichead Nua)
Naas (An Nás)
Kilcullen
Portarlington
Jamestown
Vicarstown
Stradbally
Athy
Ballitore
Timolin
Fontstown
Calverstown
Nurney
Dunlavin
Donard
Stratford
Blessington
Blessington Lakes
Hollywood
Wicklow Mountains
Tonelagee
Clane
Sallins
Kill
Prosperous
Allenwood
Carragh
Mainham
Celbridge
Newcastle
Rathcoole
Lucan
Leixlip
Maynooth
Kilcock
Enfield
Kinnegad
Moyvalley
Longwood
Summerhill
Kilshanchoe
Carbury
Mullagh
Dunboyne
Clonee
Ratoath
Swords
Ashbourne
Donabate
Malahide
Portmarnock
Ireland's Eye
Howth
Lambay Island
Portrane
Rush
Lusk
Skerries
Balbriggan
Gormanstown
Naul
Garristown
Oldtown
Balrath
Duleek
Drogheda (Droichead Átha)
Bettystown
Termonfeckin
Baltray
Clogherhead
Clogher Head
Dunany Point
Dunleer
Togher
Annagassan
Castlebellingham
Dundalk Bay
Blackrock
Dundalk (Dún Dealgan)
Knockbridge
Louth
Ardee
Collon
Slane
Navan (An Uaimh)
Kells (Ceanannus Mór)
Athboy
Trim
Hill of Tara
Kilmoon
Dunshaughlin
Dunboyne
DUBLIN (BAILE ÁTHA CLIATH)
Dublin Bay
Dún Laoghaire
Dalkey
Ballybrack
Shankill
Bray (Bré)
National Sea Life Centre, Bray
Enniskerry
Kilmacanogue
Greystones
Kilcoole
Newtown Mount Kennedy
Newcastle
Roundwood
Djouce Mountain
Kippure
Wicklow (Cill Mhantáin)
Wicklow Head
Rathnew
Ashford
Glenealy
Stillorgan
Irish Sea
Holyhead
Liverpool
Douglas
Cherbourg
Birkenhead
F
E
D
53°30′
54°00′
54°30′
Coleraine
Portrush
Portstewart
Castlerock
Magilligan Point
Limavady
Aghanloo
Ballykelly
Dungiven
Feeny
Park
Garvagh
Ringsend
Macosquin
Bushmills
Giant's Causeway
Benbane Head
Bull Point
Rathlin Island
Ballintoy
Ballycastle
Ballyvoy
Fair Head
Torr Head
Runabay Head
Cushendun
Knocknacarry
Cushendall
Glenariff
Garron Point
Carnlough Bay
Carnlough
Glenarm
Antrim Hills
Trostan
554
Knocklayd
517
Armoy
Dervock
Stranocum
Ballymoney
Dunloy
Cloughmills
Killagan Bridge
Newtown Crommelin
Rasharkin
Clogh
Glarryford
The Sheddings
Broughshane
Slemish
437
Ballymena
Ahoghill
Cullybackey
Kilrea
Swatragh
Upperlands
Clady
Maghera
Tobermore
Draperstown
Moneyneany
Magherafelt
Castledawson
Bellaghy
Toomebridge
Slieve Gallion
528
Lissan
Moneymore
Coagh
Ballyronan
Randalstown
Antrim
Templepatrick
Newtownabbey
Belfast
Dundonald
Holywood
Crawfordsburn
Bangor
Donaghadee
Groomsport
Conlig
Six Road Ends
Millisle
Newtownards
Comber
Greyabbey
Ballywalter
Ballyhalbert
Kircubbin
Portavogie
Cloghy
Ards Peninsula
Portaferry
Strangford
Strangford Lough
Killinchy
Lisbane
Ballygowan
Carryduff
Moneyreagh
Castlereagh
Lisburn
Dunmurry
Hillsborough
Saintfield
Annahilt
Shrigley
Crossgar
Killyleagh
Ardkeen
Ballynahinch
Dromara
Massford
Dromore
Waringstown
Lurgan
Craigavon
Portadown
Moira
Magheralin
Aghalee
Aghagallon
Lower Ballinderry
Glenavy
Crumlin
Lough Neagh
Coalisland
Stewartstown
Newport Trench
Mountjoy
Maghery
Moygashel
Eglish
Moy
Charlemont
Carnteel
Benburb
Loughgall
Richhill
Tandragee
Armagh
Gilford
Lawrencetown
Seapatrick
Banbridge
Loughbrickland
Ballyward
Castlewellan
Newcastle
Dundrum
Dundrum Bay
Clough
Downpatrick
Ballee
Ardglass
Killough
St John's Point
Quoile
Ballyquintin Point
Slieve Donard
852
Mourne Mountains
Hilltown
Mayobridge
Burren
Attica
Rostrevor
Kilkeel
Annalong
Mullartown
Ballymartin
Greencastle
Cranfield Point
Greenore
Carlingford
Carlingford Lough
Bullagon Point
Grange
Warrenpoint
Newry
Jonesborough
Forkhill
Creggan
Crossmaglen
Drumbilla
Meigh
Bessbrook
Belleek
Whitecross
Tassagh
Mount Norris
Markethill
Hamilton's Bawn
Poyntz Pass
Rathfriland
May's Corner
Keady
Middletown
Glaslough
Emyvale
Tydavnet
Monaghan (Muineachán)
Clontibret
Darkley
Castleblayney
Cullyhanna
Annayalla
Ballybay
Scotch Corner
Cavanagarven
Carrickmacross
Shercock
Rockcorry
Cootehill
Shantonagh
Tullyvin
Drung
Canningstown
Stradone
Moylett
Drumanespick
Bailieborough
Kingscourt
Reaghstown
New Inn
Ballyjamesduff
Virginia
Lough Ramor
Nobber
Drumconrath
Mount Nugent
Lough Sheelin
Oldcastle
Millbrook
Carlanstown
Wilkinstown
Crossakeel
Kilskeer
Clonmellon
Castlepollard
Lough Lene
Drumcree
Delvin
Coole
Lisryan
Killucan
Rathmolyon
Ballivor
Laracor
Terrin
Monilea
Lough Larne
Larne
Ballygalley Head
Drains Bay
Island Magee
Portmuck
Black Head
Whitehead
Glynn
Glenoe
Kilwaughter
Agnew's Hill
Ballycarry
Ballynure
Ballyclare
Carrickfergus
Greenisland
Belfast Lough
Mossley
Craigavad
Doagh
Tildarg
Connor
Kells
Moorfields
Eden
North Channel
The Maidens (Hulin Rocks)
Boyne
Bend of the Boyne (Brú na Bóinne)
Ulster Canal
Royal Canal
Grand Canal
Blackwater
Brosna
Barrow
Liffey
10
9
7

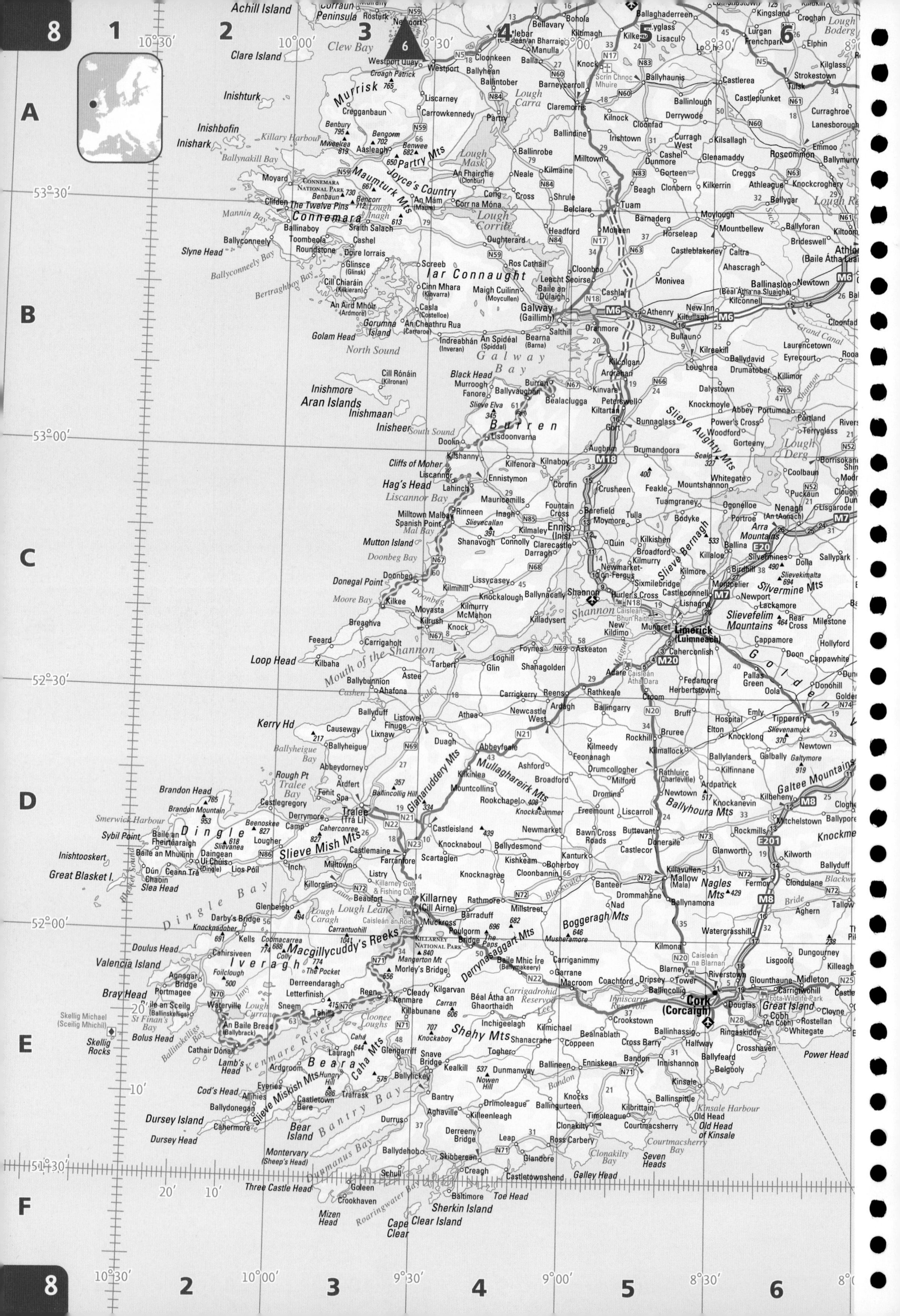

1
2
3
4
5
6
A
B
C
D
E
F
10°30′
10°00′
9°30′
9°00′
8°30′
8°0
53°30′
53°00′
52°30′
52°00′
51°30′
20′
10′
Achill Island
Clare Island
Inishturk
Inishbofin
Inishark
Clew Bay
Westport
Croagh Patrick
Murrisk
Killary Harbour
Partry Mts
Joyce's Country
Maumturk Mts
The Twelve Pins
Connemara
Clifden
Slyne Head
Ballyconneely Bay
Bertraghboy Bay
Iar Connaught
Castlebar
Ballinrobe
Lough Mask
Lough Corrib
Lough Carra
Claremorris
Knock
Ballyhaunis
Castlerea
Roscommon
Tuam
Galway
(Gaillimh)
Galway Bay
Salthill
Oranmore
Athenry
Ballinasloe
Loughrea
Gort
Golam Head
North Sound
Inishmore
Aran Islands
Inishmaan
Inisheer
Black Head
Burren
Lisdoonvarna
Doolin
Cliffs of Moher
Hag's Head
Liscannor Bay
Lahinch
Ennistymon
Milltown Malbay
Spanish Point
Mal Bay
Mutton Island
Doonbeg Bay
Ennis
(Inis)
Slieve Aughty Mts
Lough Derg
Slieve Bernagh
Donegal Point
Kilkee
Kilrush
Shannon
Limerick
(Luimneach)
Nenagh
Silvermine Mts
Slievefelim Mountains
Loop Head
Mouth of the Shannon
Tarbert
Foynes
Askeaton
Adare
Rathkeale
Newcastle West
Ballybunnion
Listowel
Kerry Hd
Ballyheigue Bay
Tralee Bay
Tralee
(Trá Lí)
Brandon Head
Dingle
Slieve Mish Mts
Sybil Point
Inishtooskert
Great Blasket I.
Slea Head
Dingle Bay
Castlemaine
Killorglin
Killarney
(Cill Airne)
Lough Leane
Macgillycuddy's Reeks
Iveragh
Valencia Island
Doulus Head
Bray Head
Portmagee
Waterville
Skellig Michael
(Sceilig Mhichíl)
Skellig Rocks
Bolus Head
Kenmare
Kenmare River
Sneem
Beara
Caha Mts
Slieve Miskish Mts
Glengarriff
Cod's Head
Dursey Island
Dursey Head
Bantry Bay
Bear Island
Bantry
Dunmanus Bay
Mizen Head
Three Castle Head
Crookhaven
Schull
Skibbereen
Baltimore
Sherkin Island
Cape Clear
Clear Island
Toe Head
Galley Head
Clonakilty
Ross Carbery
Courtmacsherry
Seven Heads
Old Head of Kinsale
Kinsale
Kinsale Harbour
Bandon
Cork
(Corcaigh)
Cobh
Great Island
Midleton
Power Head
Macroom
Shehy Mts
Derrynasaggart Mts
Boggeragh Mts
Mallow
(Mala)
Nagles Mts
Fermoy
Mitchelstown
Galtee Mountains
Ballyhoura Mts
Charleville
Tipperary
Mullaghareirk Mts
Glanaruddery Mts
Abbeyfeale
Killarney National Park
Golden Vale

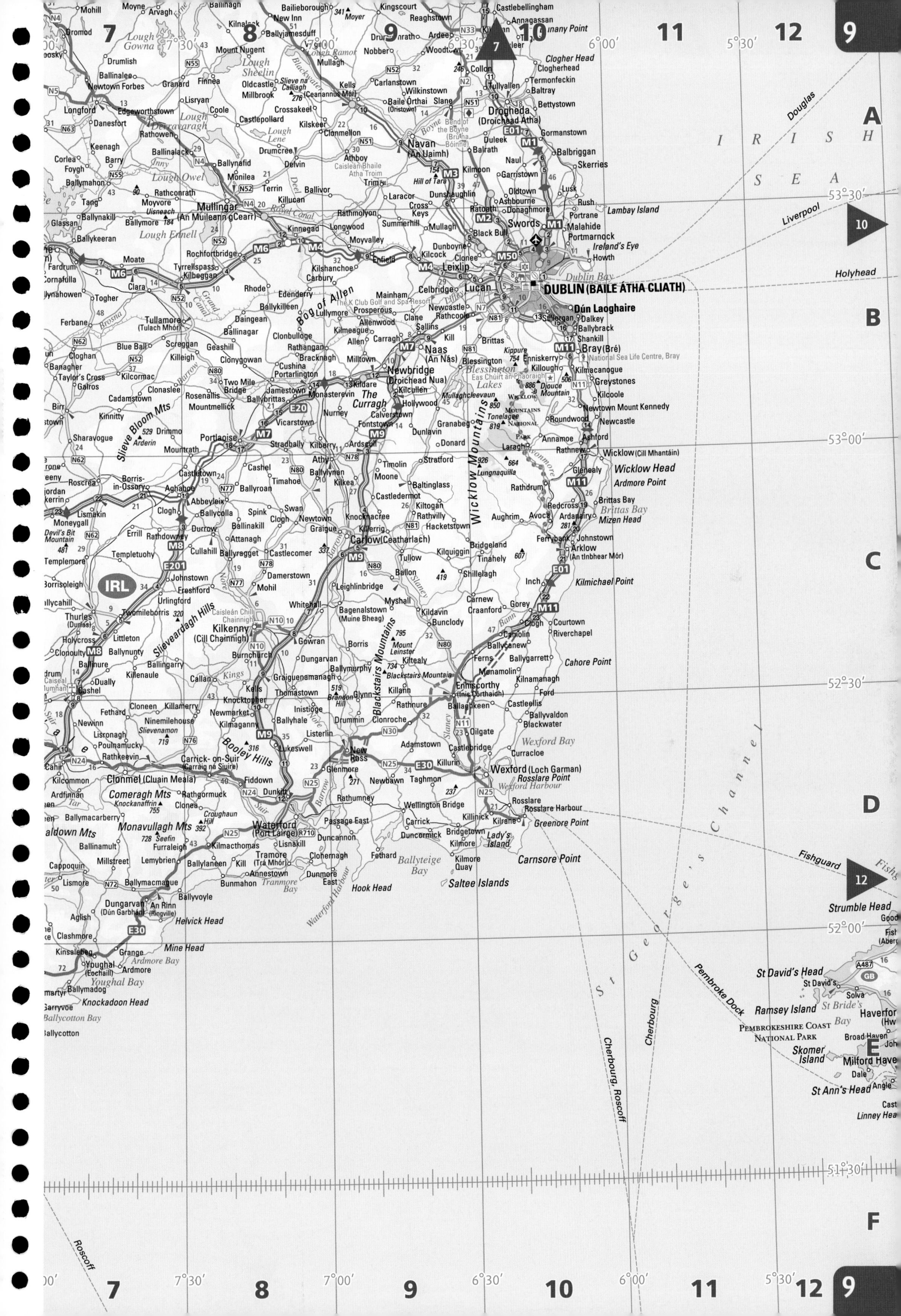

7
8
9
10
11
12
A
B
C
D
E
F
I R I S H
S E A
Douglas
Liverpool
Holyhead
Fishguard
Cherbourg
Cherbourg, Roscoff
Roscoff
Pembroke Dock
St George's Channel
53°30′
53°00′
52°30′
52°00′
51°30′
6°00′
5°30′
7°00′
6°30′
7°30′
IRL
GB
DUBLIN (BAILE ÁTHA CLIATH)
Dún Laoghaire
Drogheda (Droichead Átha)
Navan (An Uaimh)
Mullingar (An Muileann gCearr)
Tullamore (Tulach Mhór)
Naas (An Nás)
Newbridge (Droichead Nua)
Portlaoise
Kilkenny (Cill Chainnigh)
Carlow (Ceatharlach)
Wexford (Loch Garman)
Waterford (Port Láirge)
Clonmel (Cluain Meala)
Dungarvan (Dún Garbhán)
Youghal (Eochaill)
Enniscorthy (Inis Córthaidh)
Arklow (An tInbhear Mór)
Wicklow (Cill Mhantáin)
Bray (Bré)
Swords
Lucan
Leixlip
Celbridge
Malahide
Howth
Balbriggan
Skerries
Kells
Trim
Longford
Thurles (Durlas)
Cashel
Lambay Island
Ireland's Eye
Dublin Bay
Wicklow Head
Ardmore Point
Brittas Bay
Mizen Head
Kilmichael Point
Cahore Point
Wexford Bay
Rosslare Harbour
Greenore Point
Carnsore Point
Saltee Islands
Hook Head
Ballyteige Bay
Tramore Bay
Helvick Head
Mine Head
Ardmore Bay
Youghal Bay
Knockadoon Head
Ballycotton Bay
Clogher Head
Wicklow Mountains
Blackstairs Mountains
Slieve Bloom Mts
Slieveardagh Hills
Comeragh Mts
Monavullagh Mts
Knockmealdown Mts
Booley Hills
Bog of Allen
The Curragh
Blessington Lakes
Wicklow Mountains National Park
Lough Owel
Lough Ennell
Lough Sheelin
Lough Derravaragh
Lough Lene
Royal Canal
Grand Canal
Strumble Head
St David's Head
St David's
Ramsey Island
St Bride's Bay
Pembrokeshire Coast National Park
Skomer Island
Milford Haven
Dale
St Ann's Head
Angle
Haverfordwest
Broad Haven
Solva
M1
M2
M3
M4
M6
M7
M8
M9
M11
M50
E01
E20
E30
E201
N11
N25
N24
N52
N80

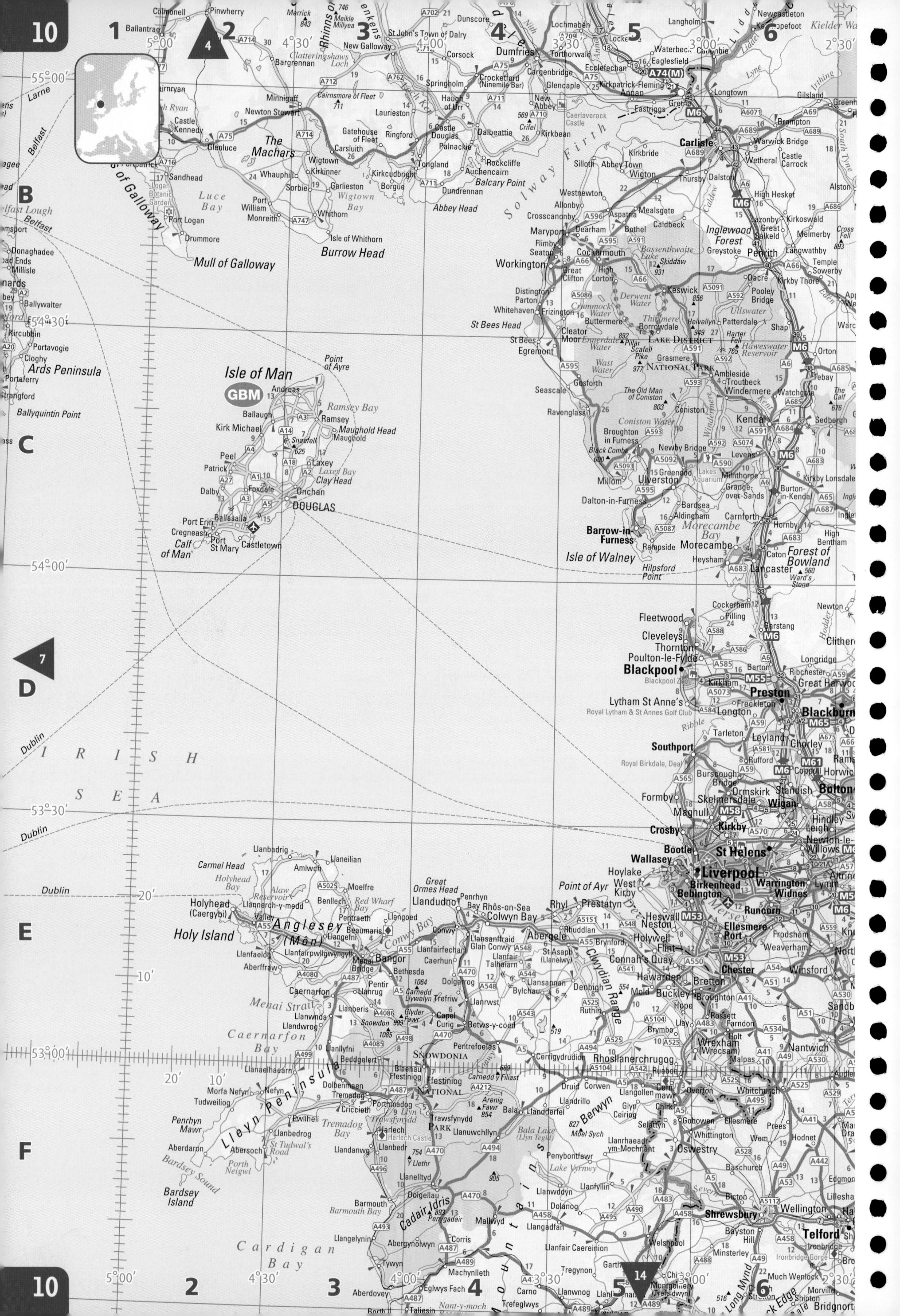

Isle of Man
GBM
Andreas
Point of Ayre
Ramsey Bay
Ballaugh
Kirk Michael
Ramsey
Maughold Head
Peel
Patrick
Laxey
Clay Head
Dalby
Foxdale
Onchan
DOUGLAS
Port Erin
Ballasalla
Cregneash
Port St Mary
Castletown
Calf of Man
Mull of Galloway
Burrow Head
Isle of Whithorn
Whithorn
The Machars
Luce Bay
Wigtown Bay
Newton Stewart
Glenluce
Castle Kennedy
Stranraer
Drummore
Port Logan
Sandhead
Kirkcudbright
Castle Douglas
Dalbeattie
Dumfries
Annan
Gretna
Carlisle
Solway Firth
Silloth
Wigton
Maryport
Workington
Cockermouth
Keswick
Whitehaven
St Bees Head
Egremont
Seascale
Ravenglass
Penrith
Ullswater
LAKE DISTRICT NATIONAL PARK
Ambleside
Windermere
Coniston
Kendal
Ulverston
Dalton-in-Furness
Millom
Barrow-in-Furness
Isle of Walney
Morecambe Bay
Morecambe
Lancaster
Heysham
Forest of Bowland
Fleetwood
Cleveleys
Thornton
Poulton-le-Fylde
Blackpool
Lytham St Anne's
Preston
Blackburn
Southport
Formby
Ormskirk
Skelmersdale
Wigan
Bolton
Crosby
Bootle
St Helens
Wallasey
Liverpool
Birkenhead
Bebington
Warrington
Widnes
Runcorn
Hoylake
West Kirby
Point of Ayr
Rhyl
Prestatyn
Holywell
Flint
Connah's Quay
Chester
Ellesmere Port
Neston
Heswall
Wrexham (Wrecsam)
Mold
Buckley
Denbigh
Ruthin
Clwydian Range
Abergele
Colwyn Bay
Llandudno
Great Ormes Head
Conwy
Bangor
Menai Bridge
Anglesey (Môn)
Holyhead (Caergybi)
Holy Island
Amlwch
Carmel Head
Caernarfon
Menai Strait
Caernarfon Bay
Llanberis
Snowdon
SNOWDONIA NATIONAL PARK
Betws-y-coed
Blaenau Ffestiniog
Porthmadog
Criccieth
Pwllheli
Lleyn Peninsula
Tremadog Bay
Harlech
Bardsey Island
Bardsey Sound
Abersoch
Bala
Bala Lake (Llyn Tegid)
Berwyn
Llangollen
Oswestry
Dolgellau
Cadair Idris
Barmouth
Barmouth Bay
Cardigan Bay
Tywyn
Aberdovey
Machynlleth
Welshpool
Shrewsbury
Telford
Wellington
Whitchurch
Nantwich
Winsford
Northwich
IRISH SEA
Dublin
Belfast
Larne
Belfast Lough
Ards Peninsula
Donaghadee
Portavogie
Ballyquintin Point
Strangford
Newcastleton
Kielder Water
Langholm
Lochmaben
Lockerbie
Brampton
Alston
M6
M55
M58
M53
M65
M61
A74(M)
55°00′
54°30′
54°00′
53°30′
53°00′
5°00′
4°30′
4°00′
3°30′
3°00′
2°30′
1
2
3
4
5
6
B
C
D
E
F
4
7
14

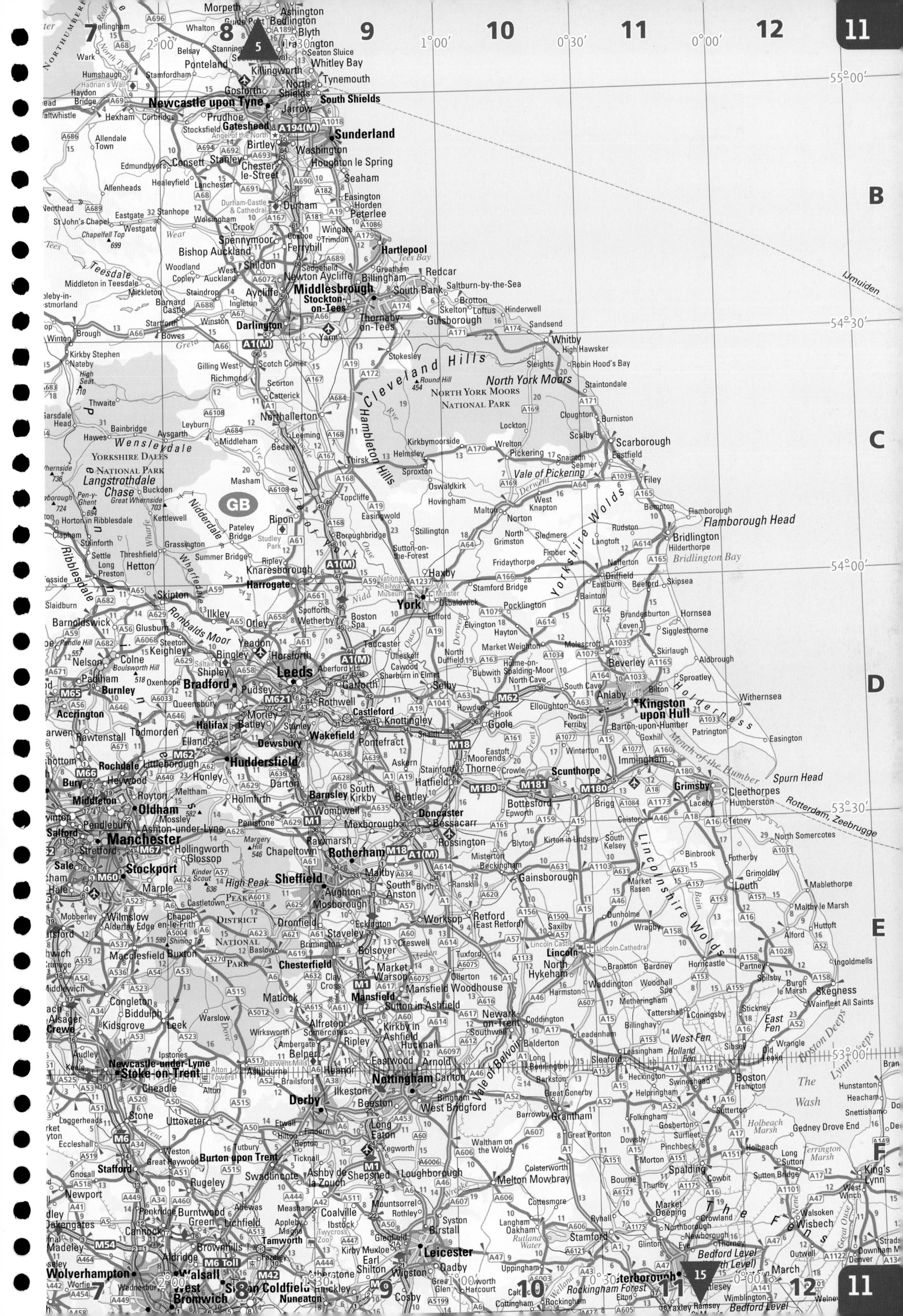

11
7
8
9
10
11
12
5
15
B
C
D
E
F
55°00′
54°30′
54°00′
53°30′
53°00′
1°00′
0°30′
0°00′
2°00′
IJmuiden
Rotterdam, Zeebrugge
Morpeth
Ashington
Bedlington
Blyth
Whitley Bay
Tynemouth
North Shields
South Shields
Ponteland
Killingworth
Gosforth
Newcastle upon Tyne
Jarrow
Gateshead
Sunderland
Hexham
Corbridge
Prudhoe
Washington
Houghton le Spring
Seaham
Consett
Stanley
Chester-le-Street
Durham
Peterlee
Easington
Horden
Spennymoor
Crook
Bishop Auckland
Ferryhill
Hartlepool
Tees Bay
Shildon
Newton Aycliffe
Billingham
Redcar
Saltburn-by-the-Sea
Middlesbrough
Stockton-on-Tees
South Bank
Thornaby-on-Tees
Guisborough
Darlington
Yarm
Whitby
Robin Hood's Bay
Cleveland Hills
North York Moors
North York Moors National Park
Scarborough
Filey
Flamborough Head
Bridlington
Bridlington Bay
Northallerton
Richmond
Catterick
Thirsk
Hambleton Hills
Vale of Pickering
Pickering
Malton
Yorkshire Dales National Park
Wensleydale
Ripon
Harrogate
Knaresborough
Vale of York
Yorkshire Wolds
Driffield
York
Selby
Goole
Beverley
Kingston upon Hull
Hornsea
Withernsea
Holderness
Spurn Head
Mouth of the Humber
Grimsby
Cleethorpes
Immingham
Scunthorpe
Skipton
Ilkley
Otley
Keighley
Bradford
Leeds
Wetherby
Tadcaster
Halifax
Huddersfield
Dewsbury
Wakefield
Castleford
Pontefract
Barnsley
Doncaster
Rotherham
Sheffield
Burnley
Accrington
Rochdale
Bury
Oldham
Manchester
Stockport
High Peak
Peak District National Park
Chesterfield
Worksop
Retford
Gainsborough
Lincoln
Lincolnshire Wolds
Louth
Skegness
Mansfield
Matlock
Macclesfield
Buxton
Congleton
Crewe
Stoke-on-Trent
Newcastle-under-Lyme
Derby
Nottingham
Newark-on-Trent
Vale of Belvoir
Grantham
Sleaford
Boston
The Wash
Stafford
Burton upon Trent
Loughborough
Melton Mowbray
Spalding
King's Lynn
Leicester
Stamford
Tamworth
Lichfield
Wolverhampton
Walsall
West Bromwich
Sutton Coldfield
Nuneaton
Peterborough
The Fens
Bedford Level
GB

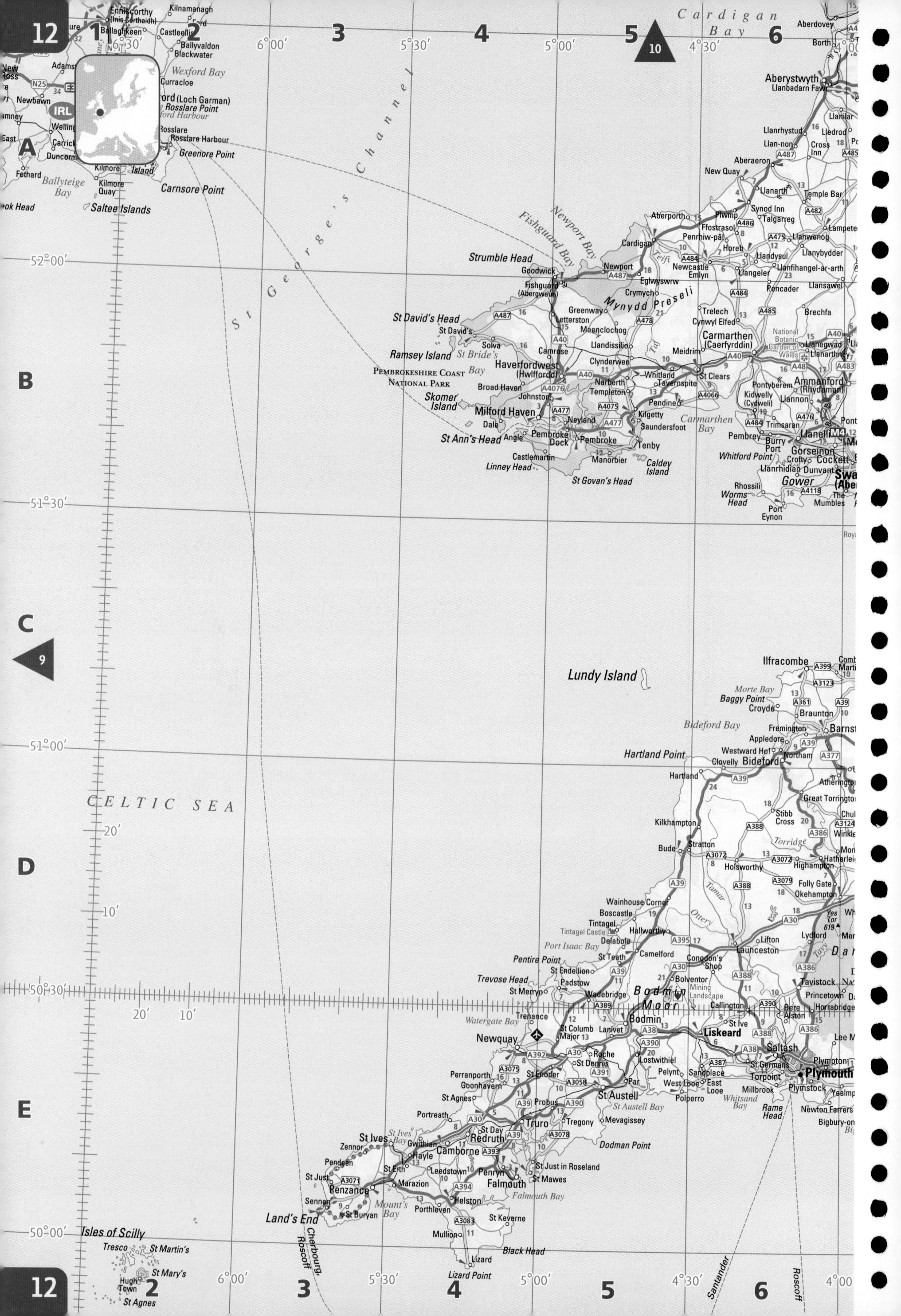
1
2
3
4
5
6
10
9
A
B
C
D
E
6°30′
6°00′
5°30′
5°00′
4°30′
4°00′
52°00′
51°30′
51°00′
50°30′
50°00′
20′
10′
Cardigan Bay
St George's Channel
CELTIC SEA
IRL
Enniscorthy (Inis Córthaidh)
Kilnamanagh
Ballaghkeen
Castleellis
Ballyvaldon
Blackwater
Wexford Bay
Curracloe
Wexford (Loch Garman)
Rosslare Point
Wexford Harbour
Rosslare
Rosslare Harbour
Greenore Point
Carnsore Point
New Ross
Adamstown
Newbawn
Wellington
Carrick
Duncormick
Fethard
Ballyteige Bay
Kilmore
Kilmore Quay
Saltee Islands
Hook Head
Aberdovey
Borth
Aberystwyth
Llanbadarn Fawr
Llanrhystud
Llan-non
Lledrod
Cross Inn
Aberaeron
New Quay
Llanarth
Temple Bar
Synod Inn
Talgarreg
Aberporth
Plwmp
Ffostrasol
Penrhiw-pâl
Horeb
Llanwenog
Lampeter
Llanybydder
Cardigan
Newcastle Emlyn
Llandysul
Llangeler
Llanfihangel-ar-arth
Pencader
Llansawel
Newport Bay
Fishguard Bay
Strumble Head
Goodwick
Fishguard (Abergwaun)
Newport
Eglwyswrw
Crymych
Mynydd Preseli
Greenway
Letterston
Maenclochog
Trelech
Cynwyl Elfed
Brechfa
St David's Head
St David's
Solva
Ramsey Island
St Bride's Bay
Camrose
Llandissilio
Carmarthen (Caerfyrddin)
National Botanic Garden of Wales
Llanegwad
Llanarthney
Meidrim
Clynderwen
Haverfordwest (Hwlffordd)
Whitland
St Clears
Tavernspite
Narberth
Templeton
PEMBROKESHIRE COAST NATIONAL PARK
Broad Haven
Johnston
Skomer Island
Milford Haven
Dale
St Ann's Head
Angle
Pembroke Dock
Neyland
Pembroke
Kilgetty
Saundersfoot
Pendine
Tenby
Carmarthen Bay
Castlemartin
Linney Head
Manorbier
Caldey Island
St Govan's Head
Ammanford (Rhydaman)
Pontyberem
Kidwelly (Cydweli)
Llannon
Trimsaran
Pembrey
Burry Port
Llanelli
Gorseinon
Whitford Point
Crofty
Cockett
Llanrhidian
Dunvant
Gower
Rhossili
Worms Head
Port Eynon
The Mumbles
Lundy Island
Ilfracombe
Morte Bay
Baggy Point
Croyde
Braunton
Bideford Bay
Fremington
Barnstaple
Appledore
Westward Ho!
Northam
Hartland Point
Clovelly
Bideford
Hartland
Atherington
Great Torrington
Stibb Cross
Kilkhampton
Torridge
Bude
Stratton
Holsworthy
Highampton
Hatherleigh
Folly Gate
Okehampton
Tamar
Wainhouse Corner
Boscastle
Tintagel
Tintagel Castle
Ottery
Hallworthy
Delabole
Lifton
Lydford
Yes Tor 619
Port Isaac Bay
Camelford
Congdon's Shop
Launceston
Pentire Point
St Teath
St Endellion
Padstow
Bolventor
Mining Landscape
Trevose Head
St Merryn
Wadebridge
Bodmin Moor
Callington
Tavistock
Princetown
Horrabridge
Bere Alston
Watergate Bay
Trenance
St Columb Major
Lanivet
Bodmin
St Ive
Liskeard
Saltash
Newquay
Roche
St Dennis
Lostwithiel
Pelynt
Sandplace
St Germans
Torpoint
Plympton
Plymouth
Plymstock
Perranporth
Goonhavern
St Enoder
Par
West Looe
East Looe
Polperro
Millbrook
Yealmpton
St Agnes
Probus
St Austell
St Austell Bay
Whitsand Bay
Rame Head
Newton Ferrers
Bigbury-on-Sea
Portreath
Truro
Tregony
Mevagissey
St Ives
St Ives Bay
Gwithian
St Day
Redruth
Zennor
Hayle
Camborne
Dodman Point
Pendeen
St Erth
Leedstown
Penryn
St Just in Roseland
St Just
Penzance
Marazion
Falmouth
St Mawes
Falmouth Bay
Sennen
St Buryan
Mount's Bay
Helston
Porthleven
Land's End
St Keverne
Mullion
Black Head
Lizard
Lizard Point
Cherbourg, Roscoff
Santander
Roscoff
Isles of Scilly
Tresco
St Martin's
St Mary's
Hugh Town
St Agnes
A487
A40
A4076
A477
A4075
A478
A484
A485
A486
A475
A482
A4066
A483
A476
A4118
M4
A399
A3123
A361
A39
A377
A3124
A386
A388
A3072
A3079
A30
A395
A389
A390
A38
A387
A392
A3075
A3058
A391
A3078
A393
A394
A3071
A3083
N25
N11

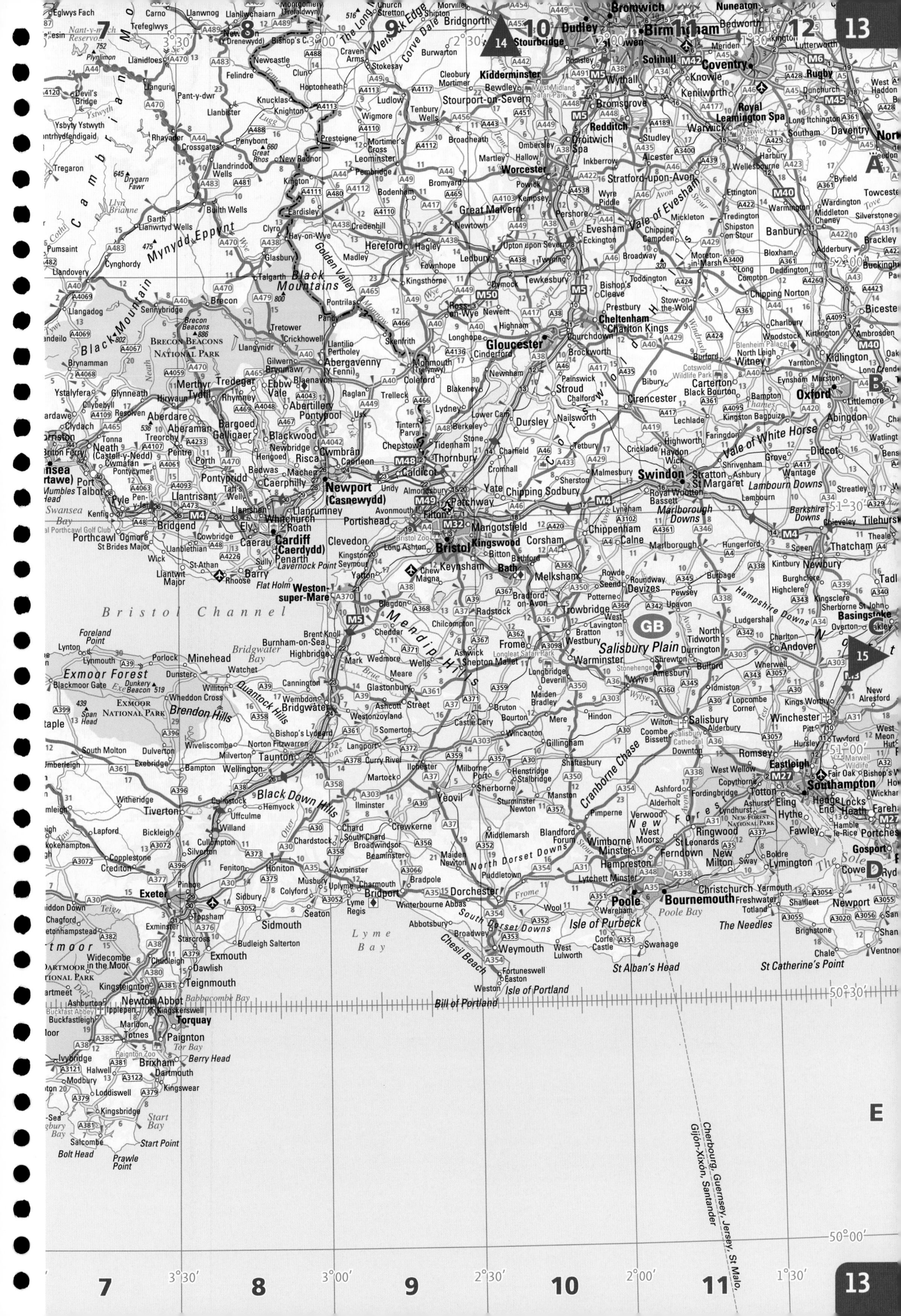
7
8
9
10
11
12
A
B
C
D
E
14
15
3°30′
3°00′
2°30′
2°00′
1°30′
52°00′
51°30′
51°00′
50°30′
50°00′
Birmingham
Coventry
Dudley
Stourbridge
Kidderminster
Worcester
Hereford
Gloucester
Cheltenham
Stroud
Cirencester
Swindon
Oxford
Abingdon
Newbury
Basingstoke
Andover
Winchester
Southampton
Salisbury
Salisbury Plain
Devizes
Melksham
Chippenham
Bath
Bristol
Weston-super-Mare
Newport (Casnewydd)
Cardiff (Caerdydd)
Barry
Bridgend
Port Talbot
Neath
Merthyr Tydfil
Abergavenny
Brecon
Black Mountain
Brecon Beacons National Park
Black Mountains
Cambrian Mountains
Bristol Channel
Exmoor Forest
Exmoor National Park
Minehead
Bridgwater
Taunton
Yeovil
Dorchester
Weymouth
Poole
Bournemouth
Christchurch
Exeter
Exmouth
Teignmouth
Newton Abbot
Torquay
Paignton
Brixham
Dartmouth
Kingsbridge
Start Point
Prawle Point
Bolt Head
Lyme Bay
Isle of Portland
Bill of Portland
Isle of Purbeck
St Alban's Head
The Needles
St Catherine's Point
New Forest
Cotswold Hills
Mendip Hills
Quantock Hills
Brendon Hills
Black Down Hills
Vale of White Horse
Vale of Evesham
Cranborne Chase
North Dorset Downs
Marlborough Downs
Lambourn Downs
Hampshire Downs
Chesil Beach
Golden Valley
Wenlock Edge
Corve Dale
GB
Cherbourg, Guernsey, Jersey, St Malo,
Gijón-Xixón, Santander

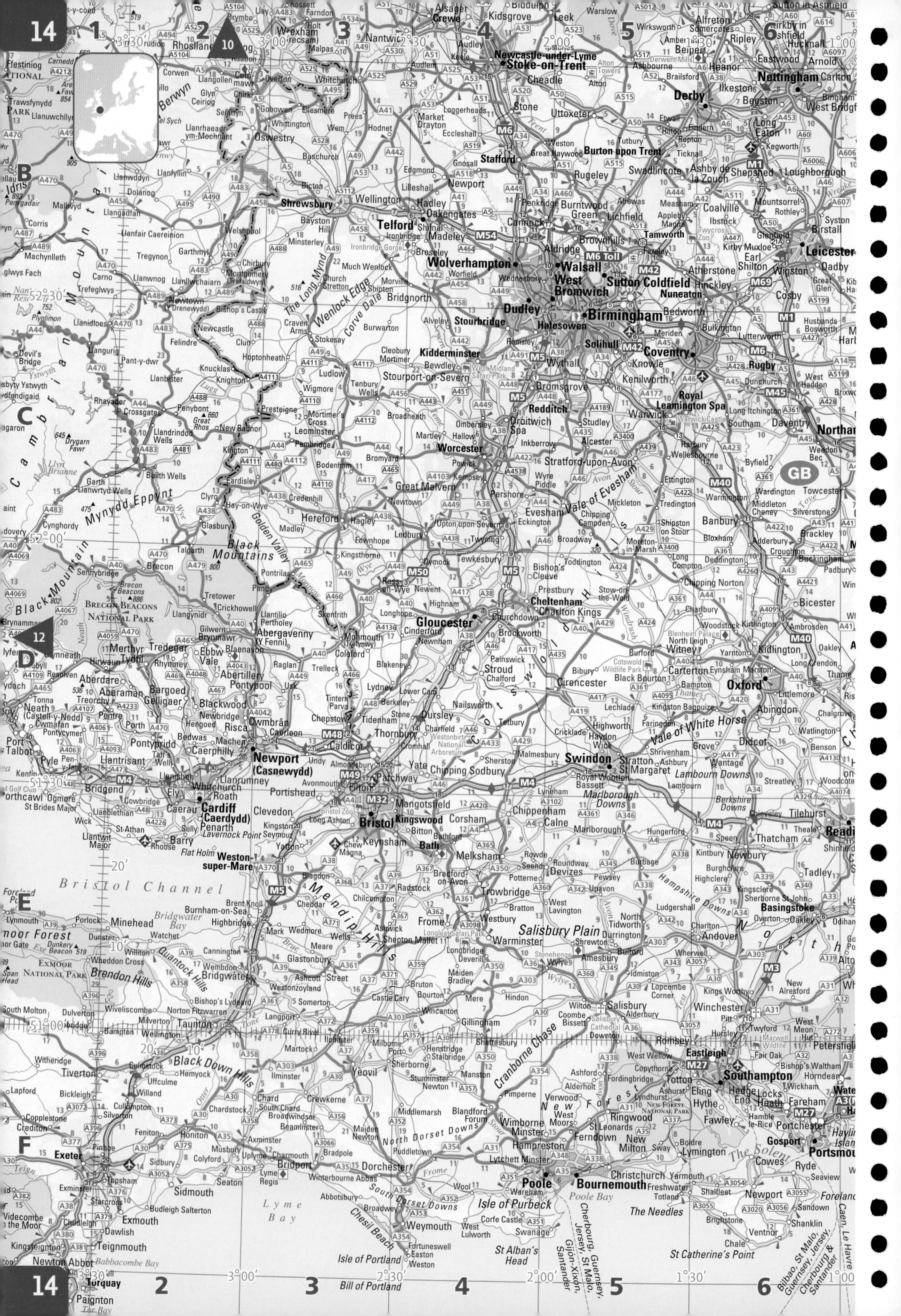
14
1
2
3
4
5
6
B
C
D
E
F
GB
10
12
Wrexham
Crewe
Kidsgrove
Leek
Alsager
Nantwich
Whitchurch
Newcastle-under-Lyme
Stoke-on-Trent
Cheadle
Stone
Uttoxeter
Derby
Nottingham
Ilkeston
Beeston
Long Eaton
Ripley
Heanor
Eastwood
Arnold
Hucknall
Ashbourne
Belper
Alfreton
Llangollen
Oswestry
Ellesmere
Wem
Market Drayton
Stafford
Burton upon Trent
Tutbury
Swadlincote
Ashby de la Zouch
Shepshed
Loughborough
Coalville
Mountsorrel
Leicester
Oadby
Wigston
Birstall
Shrewsbury
Wellington
Telford
Newport
Lichfield
Rugeley
Cannock
Tamworth
Atherstone
Hinckley
Nuneaton
Bedworth
Coventry
Rugby
Lutterworth
Welshpool
Newtown
Machynlleth
Llanidloes
Rhayader
Llandrindod Wells
Builth Wells
Knighton
Presteigne
New Radnor
Kington
Leominster
Ludlow
Bridgnorth
Church Stretton
Much Wenlock
Wolverhampton
Walsall
West Bromwich
Sutton Coldfield
Dudley
Birmingham
Halesowen
Solihull
Stourbridge
Kidderminster
Bewdley
Stourport-on-Severn
Bromsgrove
Redditch
Droitwich Spa
Worcester
Great Malvern
Pershore
Evesham
Stratford-upon-Avon
Warwick
Royal Leamington Spa
Kenilworth
Daventry
Banbury
Brackley
Towcester
Bicester
Buckingham
Hereford
Ledbury
Tewkesbury
Cheltenham
Gloucester
Ross-on-Wye
Monmouth
Abergavenny (Y Fenni)
Brecon
Hay-on-Wye
Crickhowell
Merthyr Tydfil
Tredegar
Ebbw Vale
Aberdare
Pontypool
Cwmbrân
Newport (Casnewydd)
Caerphilly
Pontypridd
Neath (Castell-y-Nedd)
Port Talbot
Bridgend
Cardiff (Caerdydd)
Penarth
Barry
Chepstow
Lydney
Stroud
Cirencester
Witney
Oxford
Abingdon
Didcot
Kidlington
Swindon
Chippenham
Malmesbury
Marlborough
Devizes
Hungerford
Newbury
Thatcham
Basingstoke
Andover
Bristol
Kingswood
Bath
Keynsham
Clevedon
Weston-super-Mare
Portishead
Yate
Chipping Sodbury
Trowbridge
Melksham
Frome
Warminster
Salisbury
Amesbury
Winchester
Romsey
Eastleigh
Southampton
Fareham
Gosport
Portsmouth
Lymington
Ringwood
Wimborne Minster
Poole
Bournemouth
Christchurch
Dorchester
Weymouth
Bridport
Lyme Regis
Yeovil
Sherborne
Shaftesbury
Gillingham
Wincanton
Glastonbury
Wells
Street
Bridgwater
Burnham-on-Sea
Minehead
Taunton
Wellington
Tiverton
Honiton
Chard
Crewkerne
Ilminster
Axminster
Exeter
Exmouth
Sidmouth
Teignmouth
Dawlish
Newton Abbot
Torquay
Paignton
Cowes
Newport
Ryde
Shanklin
Ventnor
Cambrian Mountains
Black Mountain
Black Mountains
Brecon Beacons National Park
Bristol Channel
Mendip Hills
Cotswold Hills
Salisbury Plain
Exmoor National Park
Quantock Hills
Brendon Hills
Black Down Hills
North Dorset Downs
Cranborne Chase
New Forest
Vale of White Horse
Lambourn Downs
North Downs
Hampshire Downs
Vale of Evesham
Wenlock Edge
The Long Mynd
Golden Valley
Lyme Bay
Isle of Portland
Bill of Portland
Chesil Beach
Isle of Purbeck
Poole Bay
The Solent
The Needles
St Catherine's Point
St Alban's Head
Cherbourg, Guernsey, Jersey, St Malo, Gijón-Xixón, Santander
Bilbao, St Malo, Guernsey, Jersey, Cherbourg & Santander
Caen, Le Havre
M1
M4
M5
M6
M6 Toll
M40
M42
M45
M48
M49
M50
M54
M69
M3
M27
M32
52°30′
52°00′
51°30′
51°00′
3°00′
2°30′
2°00′
1°30′
1°00′

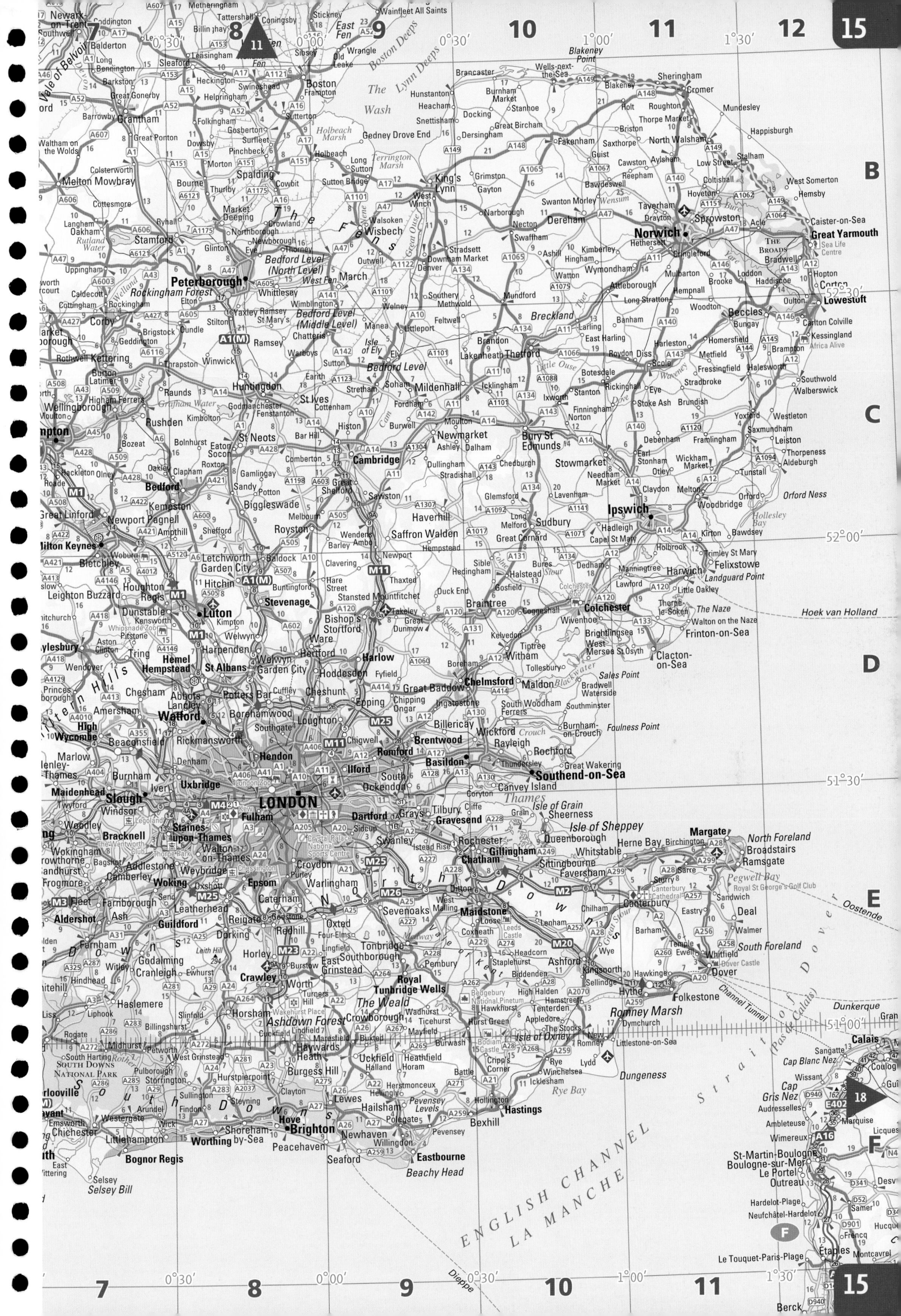
7
8
9
10
11
12
B
C
D
E
F
11
18
The Wash
Boston Deeps
Lynn Deeps
The Fens
Bedford Level (North Level)
Bedford Level (Middle Level)
Breckland
Norwich
Great Yarmouth
Lowestoft
King's Lynn
Peterborough
Cambridge
Ipswich
Colchester
Chelmsford
LONDON
Southend-on-Sea
Isle of Sheppey
Margate
Canterbury
Dover
Folkestone
Maidstone
Brighton
Hastings
Eastbourne
Romney Marsh
Dungeness
Beachy Head
Rye Bay
North Downs
South Downs
The Weald
Ashdown Forest
Chiltern Hills
Harwich
Felixstowe
Clacton-on-Sea
Hoek van Holland
Oostende
Dunkerque
Calais
Boulogne-sur-Mer
Étaples
Berck
Strait of Dover (Pas de Calais)
Channel Tunnel
ENGLISH CHANNEL
LA MANCHE
Dieppe
Luton
Bedford
Milton Keynes
Watford
Slough
Guildford
Crawley
Worthing
Chichester
Bognor Regis
Selsey Bill
Grantham
Boston
Spalding
Wisbech
Huntingdon
Thetford
Bury St Edmunds
Stowmarket
Sudbury
Newmarket
Saffron Walden
Stevenage
St Albans
Harlow
Basildon
Gravesend
Gillingham
Chatham
Ashford
Royal Tunbridge Wells
Sevenoaks
52°30′
52°00′
51°30′
51°00′
0°30′
0°00′
1°00′
1°30′

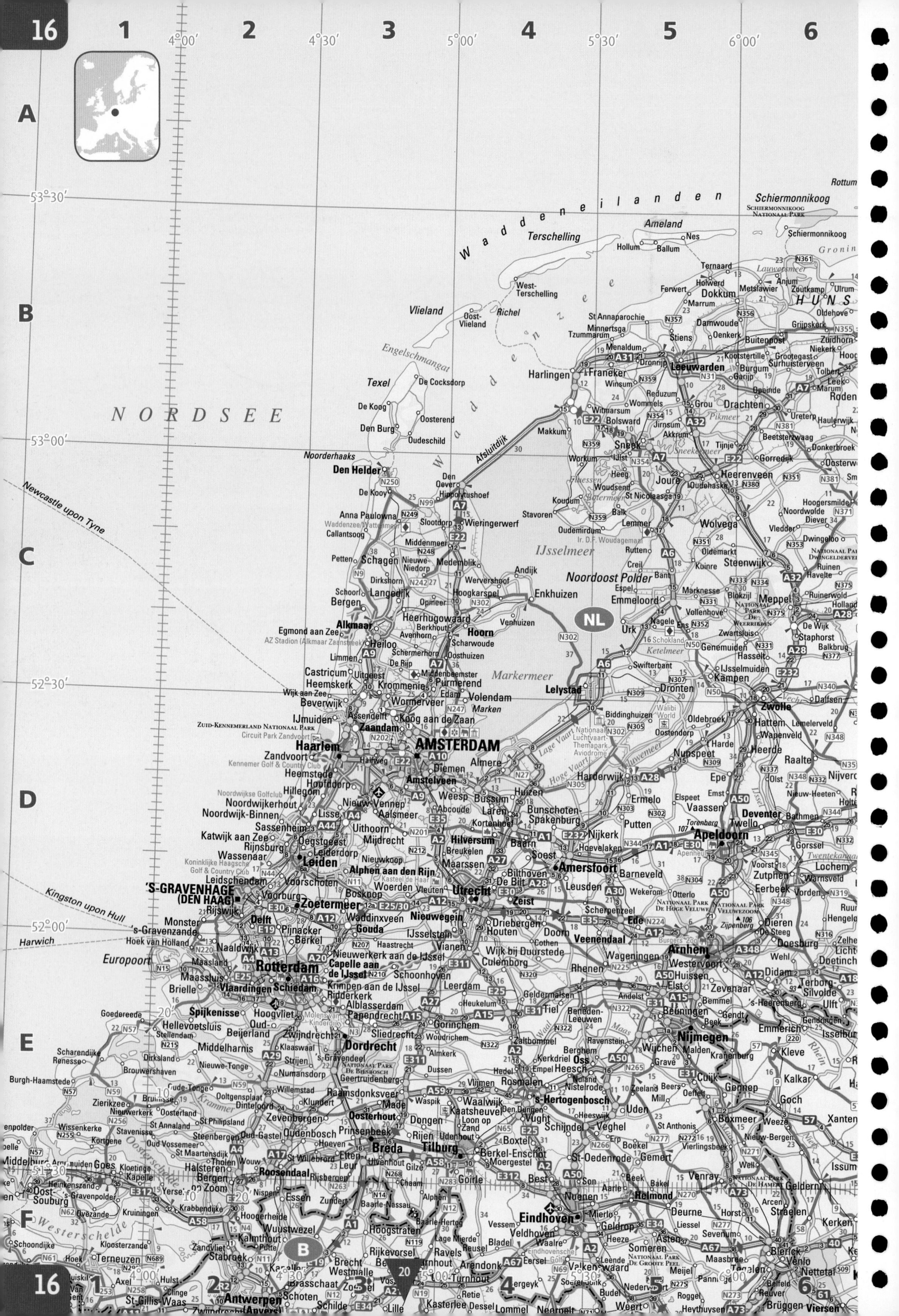
1
2
3
4
5
6
4°00'
4°30'
5°00'
5°30'
6°00'
A
B
C
D
E
F
53°30'
53°00'
52°30'
52°00'
51°30'
NORDSEE
Waddeneilanden
Waddenzee
Schiermonnikoog
Ameland
Terschelling
Vlieland
Texel
Engelschmangat
Noorderhaaks
Afsluitdijk
IJsselmeer
Markermeer
Noordoost Polder
NL
B
Newcastle upon Tyne
Kingston upon Hull
Harwich
Europoort
Den Helder
Alkmaar
Haarlem
AMSTERDAM
Zaandam
Hoorn
Enkhuizen
Lelystad
Leeuwarden
Harlingen
Franeker
Dokkum
Drachten
Sneek
Heerenveen
Joure
Wolvega
Steenwijk
Meppel
Emmeloord
Urk
Kampen
Zwolle
Dronten
Harderwijk
Apeldoorn
Deventer
Zutphen
Amersfoort
Hilversum
Utrecht
Zeist
Ede
Arnhem
Nijmegen
Leiden
'S-GRAVENHAGE (DEN HAAG)
Delft
Zoetermeer
Gouda
Rotterdam
Schiedam
Vlaardingen
Dordrecht
Gorinchem
Breda
Tilburg
Oosterhout
Roosendaal
's-Hertogenbosch
Oss
Eindhoven
Helmond
Venlo
Goes
Middelburg
Vlissingen
Terneuzen
Antwerpen (Anvers)
Bergen op Zoom
Westerschelde
Oosterschelde
Rhein
Maas
Waal
IJssel
20

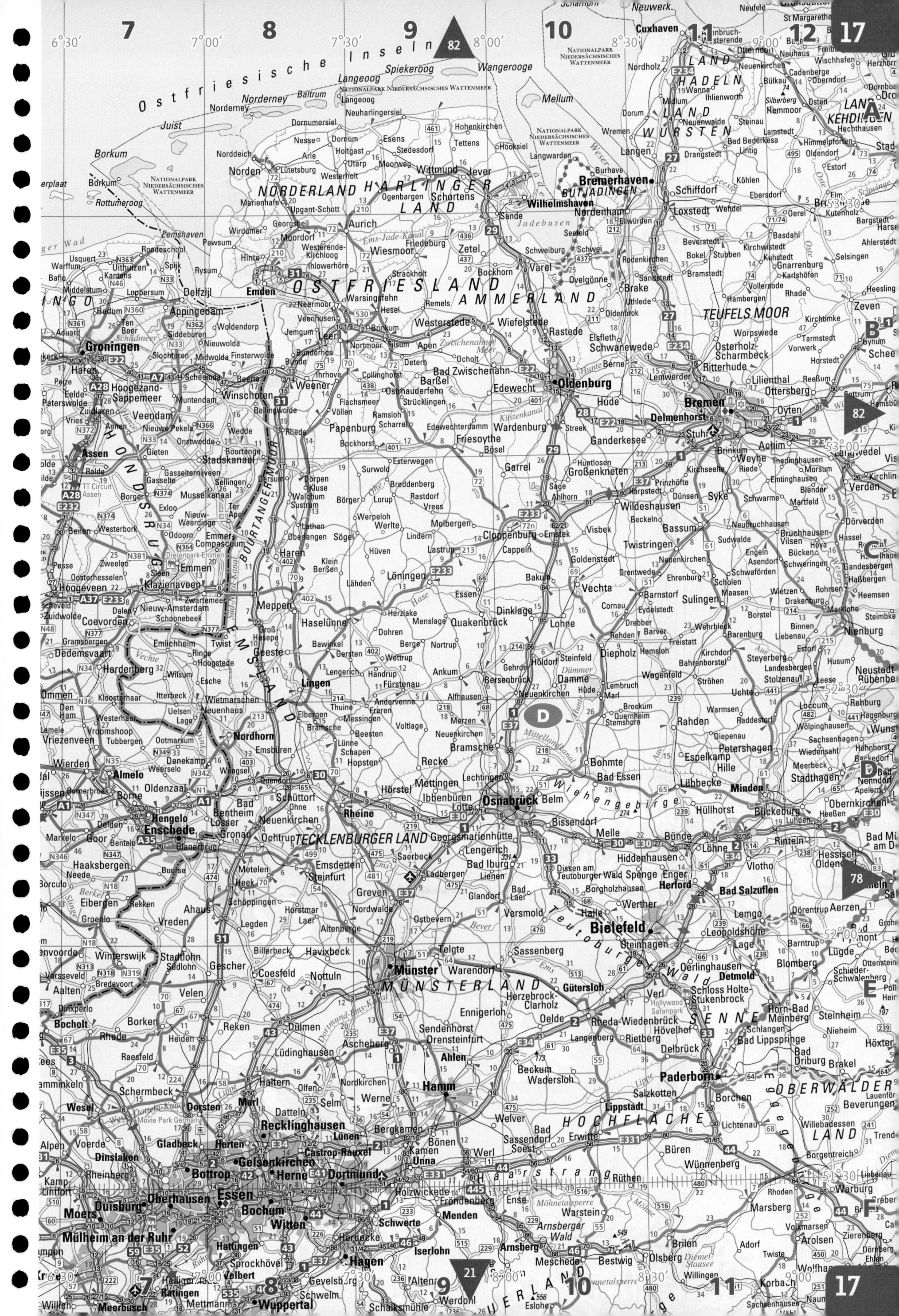17
7
8
9
10
11
12
82
Ostfriesische Inseln
Borkum
Juist
Norderney
Baltrum
Langeoog
Spiekeroog
Wangerooge
Mellum
Nationalpark Niedersächsisches Wattenmeer
Cuxhaven
Land Hadeln
Land Wursten
Land Kehdingen
Bremerhaven
Butjadingen
Wilhelmshaven
Jadebusen
Nordenham
Norden
Emden
Aurich
Wittmund
Jever
Norderland
Harlinger Land
Ostfriesland
Ammerland
Leer
Oldenburg
Delmenhorst
Bremen
Teufels Moor
Osterholz-Scharmbeck
Zeven
Groningen
Delfzijl
Assen
Emmen
Hondsrug
Bourtanger Moor
Emsland
Papenburg
Meppen
Lingen
Cloppenburg
Vechta
Wildeshausen
Verden
Nienburg
Diepholz
Nordhorn
Almelo
Hengelo
Enschede
Rheine
Tecklenburger Land
Osnabrück
Wiehengebirge
Bielefeld
Teutoburger Wald
Minden
Herford
Bad Salzuflen
Detmold
Münster
Münsterland
Gütersloh
Paderborn
Senne
Hamm
Recklinghausen
Gelsenkirchen
Dortmund
Bochum
Essen
Oberhausen
Duisburg
Mülheim an der Ruhr
Wuppertal
Hagen
Iserlohn
Unna
Soest
Lippstadt
Arnsberg
Arnsberger Wald
Haarstrang
Hochfläche
Oberwälder Land
Warburg
Höxter
Meerbusch
Sauerland
D
78
21

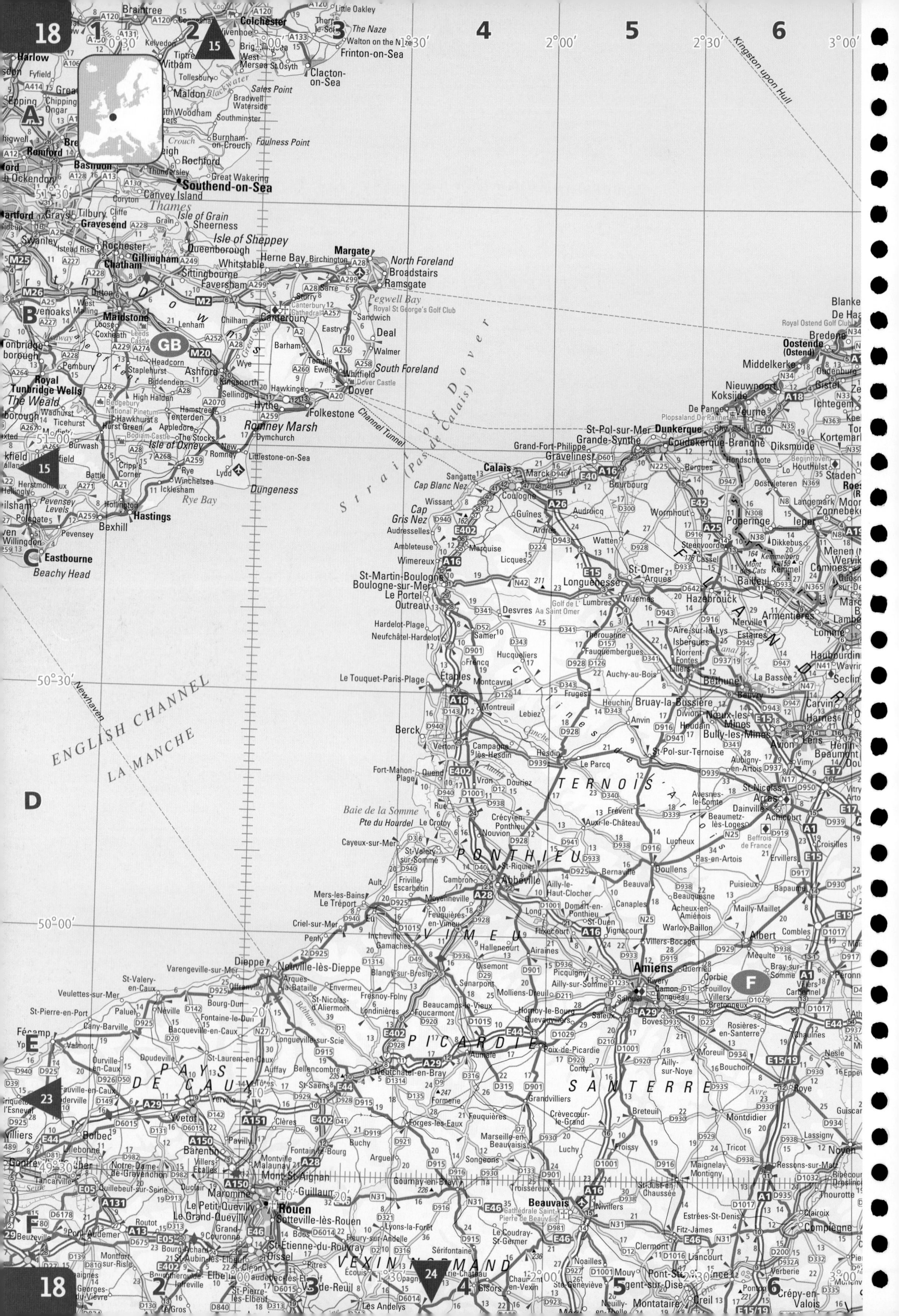
1
2
3
4
5
6
A
B
C
D
E
F
15
GB
F
23
24
Braintree
Colchester
Little Oakley
The Naze
Walton on the Naze
Frinton-on-Sea
Clacton-on-Sea
Harlow
Witham
Tiptree
West Mersea
St Osyth
Tollesbury
Maldon
Sales Point
Bradwell Waterside
Southminster
Burnham-on-Crouch
Foulness Point
Romford
Basildon
Rochford
Great Wakering
Southend-on-Sea
Canvey Island
Thames
Dartford
Grays
Tilbury
Gravesend
Isle of Grain
Sheerness
Isle of Sheppey
Queenborough
Swanley
Rochester
Chatham
Gillingham
Whitstable
Herne Bay
Birchington
Margate
North Foreland
Broadstairs
Ramsgate
Sittingbourne
Faversham
Pegwell Bay
Sandwich
Canterbury
Sturry
Deal
Walmer
Eastry
Barham
Maidstone
Sevenoaks
West Malling
Lenham
Chilham
Tonbridge
Headcorn
Ashford
Wye
Royal Tunbridge Wells
The Weald
Staplehurst
Biddenden
High Halden
Hawkhurst
Tenterden
Hamstreet
Appledore
Ticehurst
Hurst Green
Burwash
The Stocks
Isle of Oxney
Rye
Winchelsea
Battle
Crowhurst
Icklesham
Rye Bay
Cripp's Corner
New Romney
Littlestone-on-Sea
Lydd
Dungeness
Romney Marsh
Dymchurch
Hythe
Folkestone
Dover
Whitfield
South Foreland
Temple Ewell
Hawkinge
Channel Tunnel
Strait of Dover
(Pas de Calais)
Pevensey Levels
Pevensey
Polegate
Willingdon
Eastbourne
Beachy Head
Bexhill
Hastings
Hollington
ENGLISH CHANNEL
LA MANCHE
Newhaven
Kingston upon Hull
Blankenberge
De Haan
Bredene
Oostende (Ostend)
Middelkerke
Nieuwpoort
Koksijde
De Panne
Veurne
Gistel
Ichtegem
Diksmuide
Kortemark
Houthulst
Staden
Poperinge
Ieper
Zonnebeke
Langemark
Menen
Wervik
Comines
Dunkerque
St-Pol-sur-Mer
Grande-Synthe
Coudekerque-Branche
Grand-Fort-Philippe
Gravelines
Bourbourg
Bergues
Hondschoote
Calais
Marck
Sangatte
Cap Blanc Nez
Coquelles
Guînes
Ardres
Audruicq
Wissant
Cap Gris Nez
Audresselles
Ambleteuse
Marquise
Wimereux
Licques
Watten
Wormhout
Steenvoorde
Cassel
St-Omer
Arques
Longuenesse
Hazebrouck
Bailleul
Armentières
St-Martin-Boulogne
Boulogne-sur-Mer
Le Portel
Outreau
Desvres
Lumbres
Wizernes
Hardelot-Plage
Neufchâtel-Hardelot
Samer
Thérouanne
Fauquembergues
Aire-sur-la-Lys
Isbergues
Merville
Estaires
Lomme
Norrent-Fontes
Lillers
Béthune
La Bassée
Haubourdin
Seclin
Le Touquet-Paris-Plage
Étaples
Montcavrel
Hucqueliers
Fruges
Auchy-au-Bois
Bruay-la-Buissière
Beuvry
Carvin
Montreuil
Heuchin
Divion
Noeux-les-Mines
Houdain
Bully-les-Mines
Lens
Harnes
Avion
Hénin-Beaumont
Berck
Verton
Campagne-lès-Hesdin
Hesdin
Anvin
St-Pol-sur-Ternoise
Aubigny-en-Artois
Vimy
Fort-Mahon-Plage
Quend
Vron
Dourlez
Le Parcq
TERNOIS
Avesnes-le-Comte
St-Nicolas
Arras
Dainville
Achicourt
Baie de la Somme
Pte du Hourdel
Le Crotoy
Rue
Crécy-en-Ponthieu
Nouvion
Frévent
Auxi-le-Château
Beaumetz-lès-Loges
Cayeux-sur-Mer
St-Valery-sur-Somme
PONTHIEU
St-Riquier
Abbeville
Lucheux
Pas-en-Artois
Doullens
Bernaville
Croisilles
Ervillers
Ault
Friville-Escarbotin
Cambron
Aillly-le-Haut-Clocher
Beauval
Puisieux
Bapaume
Mers-les-Bains
Le Tréport
Moyenneville
Feuquières-en-Vimeu
Domart-en-Ponthieu
Canaples
Beauquesne
Acheux-en-Amiénois
Mailly-Maillet
Eu
Criel-sur-Mer
Incheville
Gamaches
VIMEU
Long
St-Ouen
Flixecourt
Vignacourt
Warloy-Baillon
Albert
Combles
Penly
Hallencourt
Airaines
Villers-Bocage
Méaulte
Bray-sur-Somme
Dieppe
Neuville-lès-Dieppe
Varengeville-sur-Mer
Arques-la-Bataille
Blangy-sur-Bresle
Oisemont
Picquigny
Ailly-sur-Somme
Amiens
Querrieu
Corbie
Rivery
Camon
Longueau
Fouilloy
Villers-Bretonneux
St-Valery-en-Caux
Veulettes-sur-Mer
Offranville
Envermeu
Bourg-Dun
St-Nicolas-d'Aliermont
Fresnoy-Folny
Senarpont
Molliens-Dreuil
Salouël
Saleux
Boves
Péronne
St-Pierre-en-Port
Paluel
Néville
Fontaine-le-Dun
Londinières
Beaucamps-le-Vieux
Foucarmont
Hornoy-le-Bourg
Quevauvillers
Rosières-en-Santerre
Chaulnes
Fécamp
Cany-Barville
Bacqueville-en-Caux
Longueville-sur-Scie
PICARDIE
Aumale
Poix-de-Picardie
Moreuil
Nesle
Valmont
Ourville-en-Caux
Doudeville
St-Laurent-en-Caux
Auffay
Bellencombre
Neufchâtel-en-Bray
Conty
Ailly-sur-Noye
Bouchoir
Roye
PAYS DE CAUX
St-Saëns
Formerie
Grandvilliers
SANTERRE
Fauville-en-Caux
Yerville
Yvetot
Clères
Forges-les-Eaux
Feuquières
Crèvecoeur-le-Grand
Breteuil
Montdidier
Bolbec
Lillebonne
Pavilly
Barentin
Buchy
Argueil
Marseille-en-Beauvaisis
Luchy
Froissy
Lassigny
Noyon
Notre-Dame-de-Gravenchon
Tancarville
Yvetot
Fontaine-le-Bourg
Montville
Malaunay
Songeons
Maignelay-Montigny
Tricot
Ressons-sur-Matz
Quillebeuf-sur-Seine
Duclair
Mont-St-Aignan
St-Guillaume
Gournay-en-Bray
Troissereux
St-Just-en-Chaussée
Thourotte
Le Petit-Quevilly
Le Grand-Quevilly
Maromme
Rouen
Sotteville-lès-Rouen
Beauvais
Nivillers
Estrées-St-Denis
Clairoix
Compiègne
Pont-Audemer
Routot
Grand-Couronne
St-Étienne-du-Rouvray
Oissel
Lyons-la-Forêt
Fleury-sur-Andelle
Le Coudray-St-Germer
Fitz-James
Clermont
Liancourt
Beuzeville
Montfort-sur-Risle
St-Aubin-lès-Elbeuf
Elbeuf
Caudebec-lès-Elbeuf
Sérifontaine
VEXIN NORMAND
Noailles
Mouy
Pont-Ste-Maxence
Ste-Geneviève
Écouis
Étrépagny
Gisors
Chaumont-en-Vexin
Neuilly-en-Thelle
Montataire
Creil
Crépy-en-Valois
St-Pierre-lès-Elbeuf
Pont-de-l'Arche
Le Vaudreuil
Les Andelys
Georges-du-Vièvre
Le Gros
A12
A13
A16
A26
A28
A29
A131
A150
A151
A20
A249
A299
A256
A258
A259
A21
M2
M20
M25
M26
E15
E40
E402
E44
E46
N42
N25
N31
1° 00′
1° 30′
2° 00′
2° 30′
3° 00′
0° 30′
51° 30′
51° 00′
50° 30′
50° 00′
49° 30′

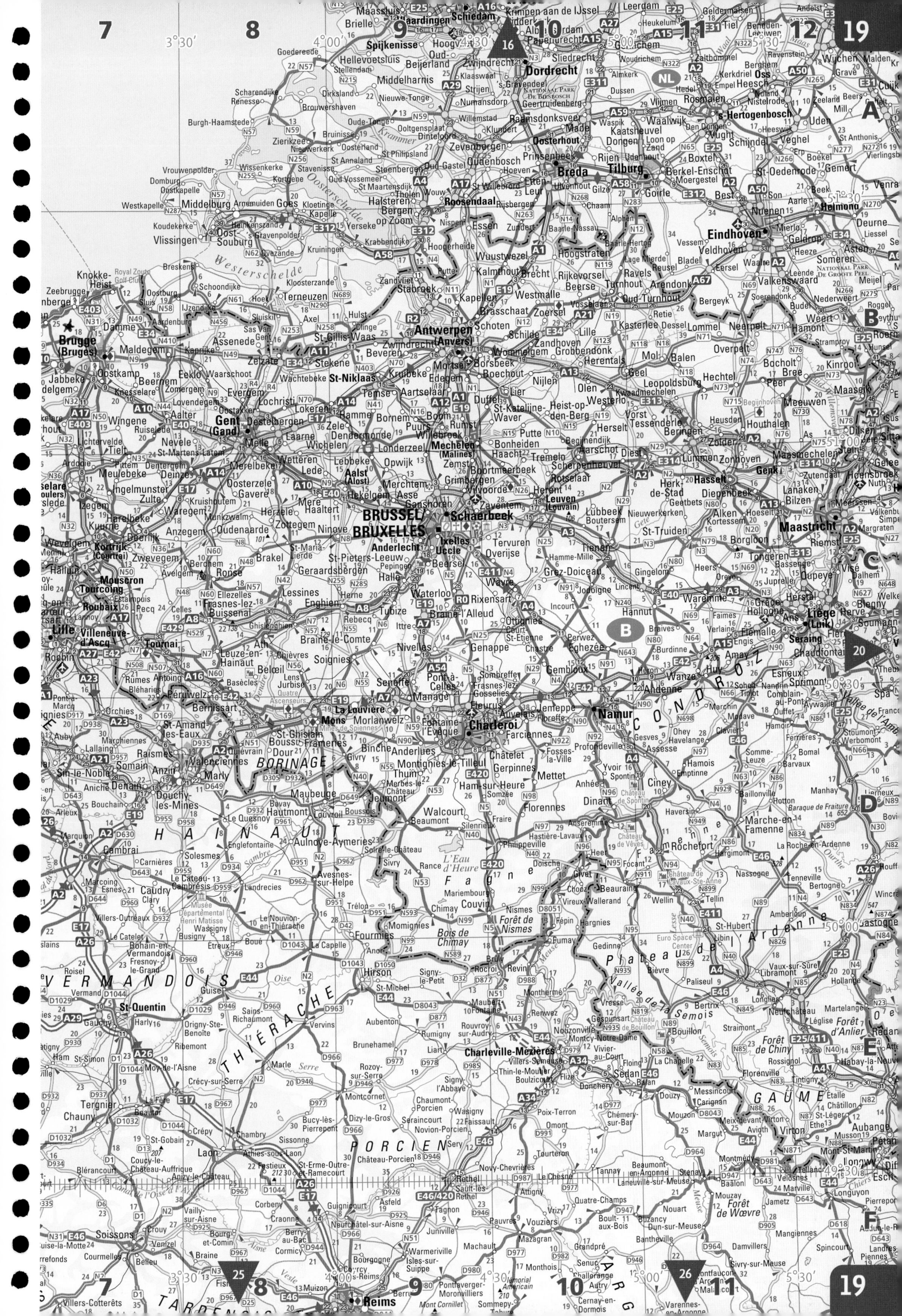
7
8
9
10
11
12
Schiedam
Spijkenisse
Dordrecht
Gorinchem
Middelharnis
NL
'sHertogenbosch
Oss
Breda
Tilburg
Roosendaal
Bergen op Zoom
Middelburg
Goes
Vlissingen
Eindhoven
Helmond
Terneuzen
Knokke-Heist
Brugge (Bruges)
Antwerpen (Anvers)
St-Niklaas
Gent (Gand)
Aalst (Alost)
Mechelen (Malines)
Lier
Turnhout
Geel
Hasselt
Genk
Maastricht
Tongeren
Leuven (Louvain)
BRUSSEL/ BRUXELLES
Schaerbeek
Anderlecht
Kortrijk (Courtrai)
Mouscron
Tourcoing
Roubaix
Lille
Villeneuve-d'Ascq
Tournai
Mons
La Louvière
Charleroi
Namur
Liège (Luik)
Seraing
Huy
Wavre
Waterloo
Nivelles
B
CONDROZ
BORINAGE
HAINAUT
Valenciennes
Cambrai
Maubeuge
Dinant
Rochefort
Marche-en-Famenne
Bastogne
Fagne
Plateau de l'Ardenne
Vallée de la Semois
THIÉRACHE
VERMANDOIS
St-Quentin
Charleville-Mézières
Sedan
Bouillon
GAUME
Arlon
Virton
Laon
Soissons
Reims
PORCIEN
Rethel
20
16
25
26

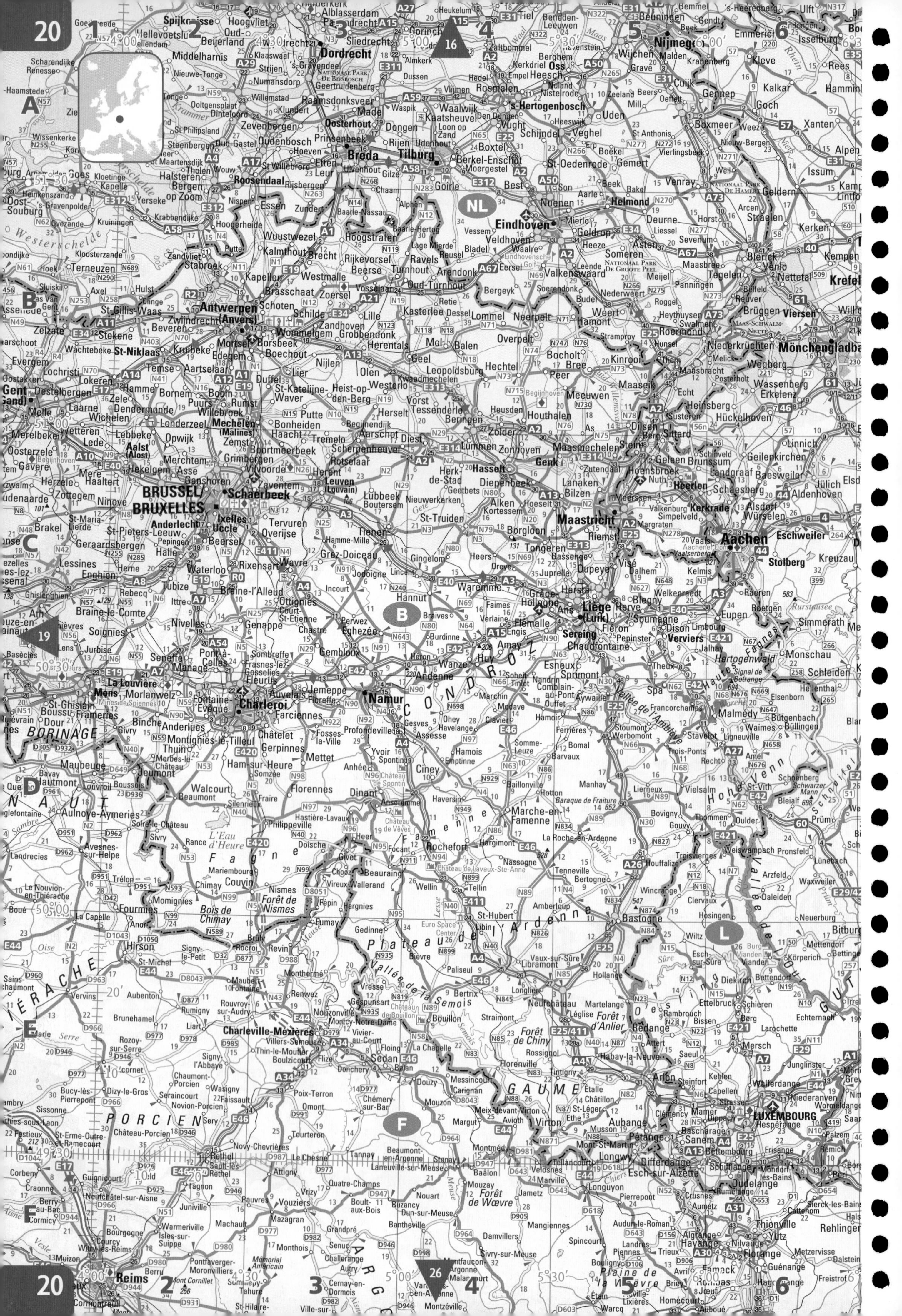

1
2
3
4
5
6
A
B
C
D
E
F
16
19
26
NL
B
L
F
Dordrecht
Breda
Tilburg
Roosendaal
Oosterhout
'sHertogenbosch
Eindhoven
Helmond
Nijmegen
Uden
Venlo
Krefeld
Mönchengladbach
Viersen
Roermond
Weert
Antwerpen (Anvers)
St-Niklaas
Gent
Aalst (Alost)
Mechelen (Malines)
BRUSSEL/ BRUXELLES
Schaerbeek
Anderlecht
Ixelles
Uccle
Leuven (Louvain)
Hasselt
Genk
Maastricht
Aachen
Eschweiler
Heerlen
Kerkrade
Liège (Luik)
Seraing
Verviers
Namur
Charleroi
La Louvière
Mons
Wavre
Huy
Dinant
Rochefort
Marche-en-Famenne
Bastogne
Arlon
LUXEMBOURG
Esch-sur-Alzette
Thionville
Charleville-Mézières
Sedan
Reims
C O N D R O Z
F a g n e
F a m e n n e
P l a t e a u d e l ' A r d e n n e
G A U M E
P O R C I E N
B O R I N A G E
T H I É R A C H E
A R G O N N E
Hohe Venn
Schneifel
Oesling
GUTLAND

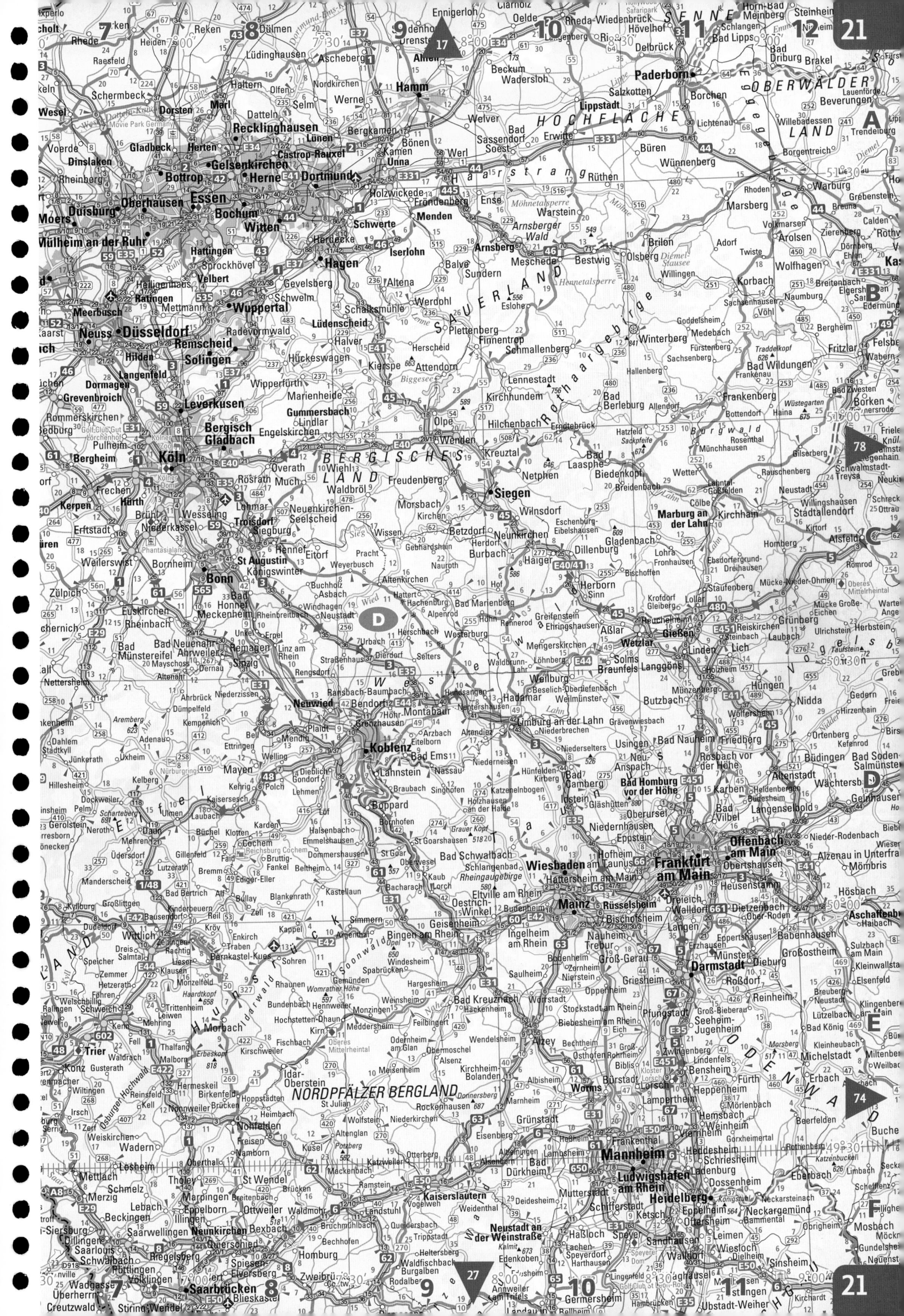

21
Dülmen
Hamm
Paderborn
Lippstadt
Recklinghausen
Gelsenkirchen
Bottrop
Herne
Dortmund
Unna
Oberhausen
Essen
Bochum
Duisburg
Moers
Mülheim an der Ruhr
Witten
Hagen
Iserlohn
Wuppertal
Düsseldorf
Neuss
Remscheid
Solingen
Leverkusen
Bergisch Gladbach
Köln
Bonn
Siegburg
St Augustin
Siegen
Olpe
Marburg an der Lahn
Gießen
Wetzlar
Koblenz
Neuwied
Limburg an der Lahn
Wiesbaden
Mainz
Frankfurt am Main
Offenbach am Main
Darmstadt
Aschaffenburg
Trier
Kaiserslautern
Mannheim
Ludwigshafen am Rhein
Heidelberg
Worms
Saarbrücken
Neunkirchen
Neustadt an der Weinstraße
HOCHFLÄCHE
OBERWÄLDER LAND
SAUERLAND
Rothaargebirge
BERGISCHES LAND
Westerwald
Taunus
Eifel
Hunsrück
NORDPFÄLZER BERGLAND
ODENWALD
Vogelsberg
D
17
27
74
78
21

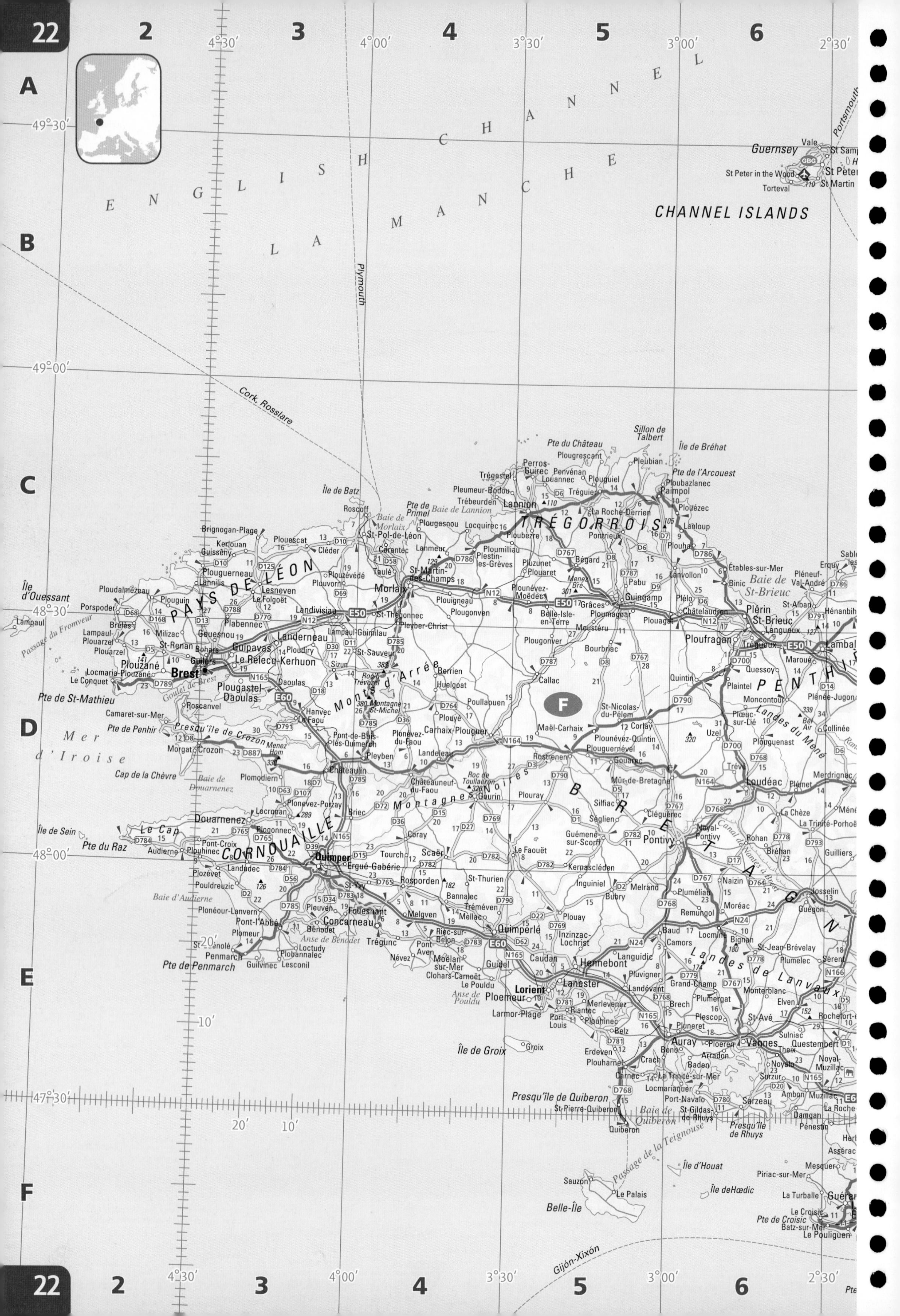
2
3
4
5
6
A
B
C
D
E
F
4°30′
4°00′
3°30′
3°00′
2°30′
49°30′
49°00′
48°30′
48°00′
47°30′
ENGLISH CHANNEL
LA MANCHE
CHANNEL ISLANDS
Guernsey
Vale
St Peter in the Wood
Torteval
St Martin
Portsmouth
Plymouth
Cork, Rosslare
Gijón-Xixón
F
PAYS DE LÉON
TRÉGORROIS
CORNOUAILLE
BRETAGNE
PENTHIÈVRE
Monts d'Arrée
Montagnes Noires
Landes de Lanvaux
Landes du Mené
Mer d'Iroise
Île d'Ouessant
Île de Batz
Île de Bréhat
Île de Sein
Île de Groix
Belle-Île
Île d'Houat
Île de Hœdic
Presqu'île de Crozon
Presqu'île de Quiberon
Presqu'île de Rhuys
Baie de Morlaix
Baie de Lannion
Baie de St-Brieuc
Baie de Douarnenez
Baie d'Audierne
Baie de Quiberon
Anse de Bénodet
Goulet de Brest
Passage du Fromveur
Passage de la Teignouse
Pte du Raz
Pte de Penmarch
Pte de St-Mathieu
Pte de Penhir
Cap de la Chèvre
Pte du Château
Pte de l'Arcouest
Pte de Primel
Pte de Croisic
Sillon de Talbert
Le Cap
Brest
Quimper
Lorient
Vannes
St-Brieuc
Morlaix
Lannion
Guingamp
Pontivy
Loudéac
Carhaix-Plouguer
Concarneau
Quimperlé
Douarnenez
Châteaulin
Auray
Hennebont
Lanester
Landerneau
Roscoff
St-Pol-de-Léon
Paimpol
Perros-Guirec
Tréguier
Lamballe
Plérin
Ploufragan
Crozon
Morgat
Camaret-sur-Mer
Le Conquet
Plouzané
Guipavas
Le Relecq-Kerhuon
Plougastel-Daoulas
Audierne
Pont-l'Abbé
Fouesnant
Bénodet
Rosporden
Gourin
Rostrenen
Callac
Quiberon
Carnac
Le Palais
Sauzon
Guérande
La Turballe
Le Croisic
Batz-sur-Mer
Le Pouliguen
Sarzeau
Muzillac
Questembert
Josselin
Ploërmel
Ploemeur
Guidel
Port-Louis
Belz
Erdeven
Locminé
Baud
Guémené-sur-Scorff
Le Faouët
Scaër
Bannalec
Pleyben
Le Faou
Daoulas
Landivisiau
Lesneven
Plabennec
St-Renan
Ploudalmézeau
Plouguerneau
Huelgoat
Pleyber-Christ
St-Thégonnec
Bégard
Pontrieux
Lanvollon
Plouha
Binic
Étables-sur-Mer
Quintin
Uzel
Corlay
Mûr-de-Bretagne
Gouarec
Cléguérec
Rohan
E50
E60
N12
N164
N165
N24
D786
D767
D768

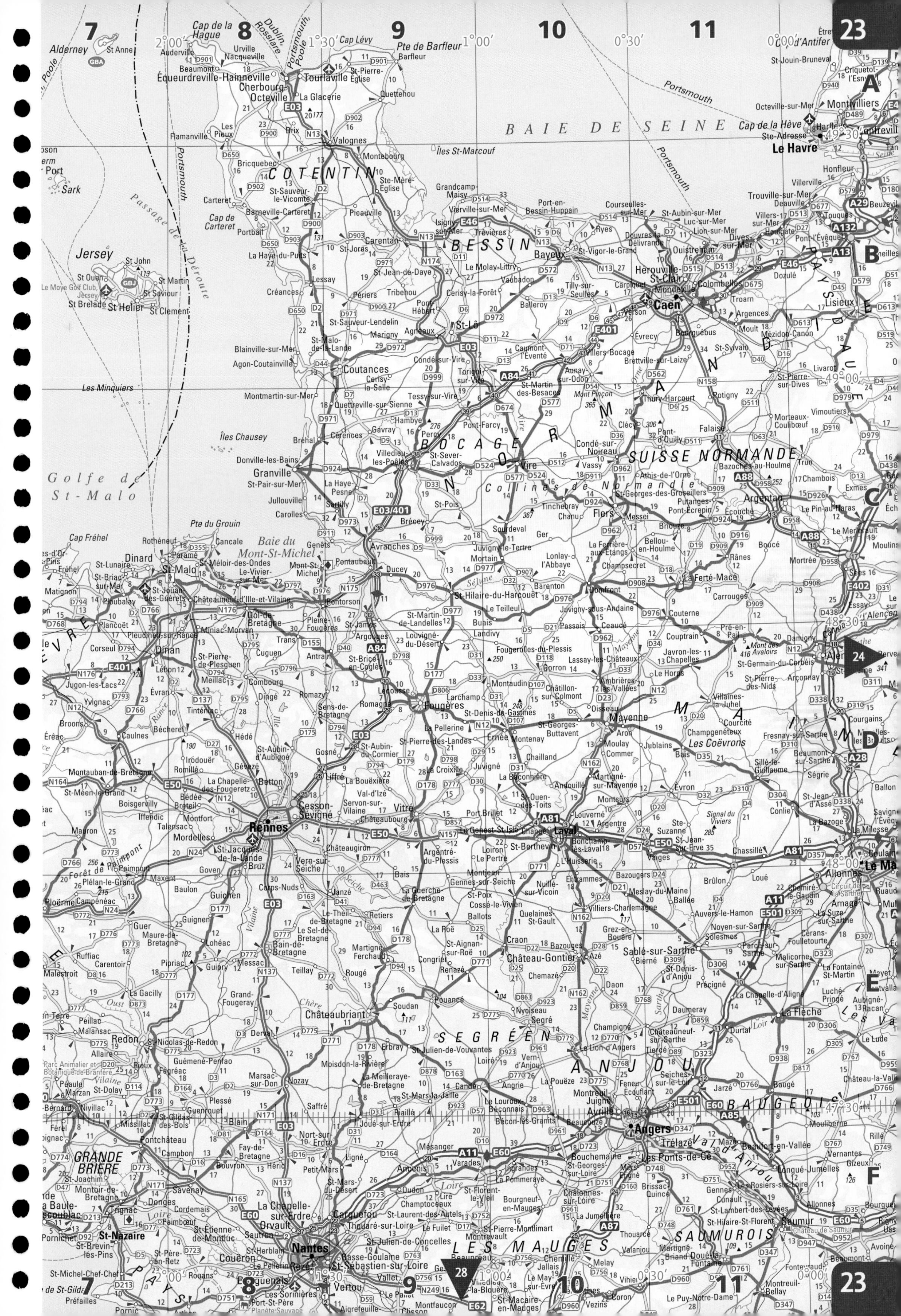
7
8
9
10
11
Alderney
Cap de la Hague
Dublin, Rosslare
Portsmouth, Poole
Cap Lévy
Pte de Barfleur
Barfleur
Auderville
Urville Nacqueville
Beaumont
Équeurdreville-Hainneville
Cherbourg-Octeville
Tourlaville
St-Pierre-Église
La Glacerie
Quettehou
Flamanville
Les Pieux
Brix
Valognes
Montebourg
Îles St-Marcouf
BAIE DE SEINE
Portsmouth
Cap d'Antifer
St-Jouin-Bruneval
Criquetot-l'Esneval
Octeville-sur-Mer
Montivilliers
Cap de la Hève
Ste-Adresse
Harfleur
Le Havre
Gonfreville
Honfleur
Sark
Passage de la Déroute
Bricquebec
COTENTIN
St-Sauveur-le-Vicomte
Ste-Mère-Église
Carteret
Cap de Carteret
Barneville-Carteret
Portbail
Picauville
Grandcamp-Maisy
Vierville-sur-Mer
Port-en-Bessin-Huppain
Courseulles-sur-Mer
St-Aubin-sur-Mer
Luc-sur-Mer
Lion-sur-Mer
Villerville
Trouville-sur-Mer
Deauville
Villers-sur-Mer
Houlgate
Touques
Pont-l'Évêque
Beuzeville
Jersey
St John
St Ouen
St Martin
St Saviour
St Brelade
St Helier
St Clement
Le Moye Golf Club, Jersey
La Haye-du-Puits
St-Jores
Carentan
Isigny-sur-Mer
Trévières
BESSIN
Bayeux
St-Vigor-le-Grand
Ryes
Douvres-la-Délivrande
Ouistreham
Dives-sur-Mer
PAYS D'AUGE
Lessay
St-Jean-de-Daye
Le Molay-Littry
Vaubadon
Hérouville-St-Clair
Colombelles
Dozulé
Créances
Périers
Tribehou
Cerisy-la-Forêt
Tilly-sur-Seulles
Carpiquet
Mondeville
Caen
Troarn
Lisieux
Pont-Hébert
Balleroy
Verson
Ifs
Argences
St-Sauveur-Lendelin
Agneaux
St-Lô
Bourguébus
Moult
Mézidon-Canon
Marigny
Évrecy
Blainville-sur-Mer
St-Malo-de-la-Lande
Caumont-l'Éventé
Villers-Bocage
St-Sylvain
Agon-Coutainville
Coutances
Condé-sur-Vire
Torigni-sur-Vire
Aunay-sur-Odon
Bretteville-sur-Laize
Cerisy-la-Salle
St-Martin-des-Besaces
Livarot
St-Pierre-sur-Dives
Les Minquiers
Montmartin-sur-Mer
Tessy-sur-Vire
Mont Pinçon
Thury-Harcourt
NORMANDIE
Potigny
Quettreville-sur-Sienne
Hambye
Percy
Pont-Farcy
Clécy
Pont-d'Ouilly
Falaise
Morteaux-Coulibœuf
Vimoutiers
Îles Chausey
Bréhal
Cérences
Gavray
BOCAGE
Condé-sur-Noireau
SUISSE NORMANDE
Villedieu-les-Poêles
St-Sever-Calvados
Vire
Vassy
Athis-de-l'Orne
Bazoches-au-Houlme
Trun
Chambois
Exmes
Donville-les-Bains
Granville
St-Pair-sur-Mer
Golfe de St-Malo
La Haye-Pesnel
Collines de Normandie
St-Georges-des-Groseillers
Putanges-Pont-Écrepin
Argentan
Écouché
Le Pin-au-Haras
Jullouville
Sartilly
St-Pois
Tinchebray
Chanu
Flers
Messei
Carolles
Brécey
Sourdeval
Briouze
Pte du Grouin
Cap Fréhel
Rothéneuf
Cancale
Baie du Mont-St-Michel
Genêts
Avranches
Ger
Bellou-en-Houlme
Juvigny-le-Tertre
Lonlay-l'Abbaye
La Ferrière-aux-Étangs
Rânes
Boucé
Mortrée
Le Merlerault
Moulins
Dinard
Paramé
St-Malo
St-Lunaire
St-Briac-sur-Mer
St-Méloir-des-Ondes
Le Vivier-sur-Mer
Mont-St-Michel
Pontaubault
Ducey
Mortain
Champsecret
Matignon
Ploubalay
St-Jouan-des-Guérets
Châteauneuf-d'Ille-et-Vilaine
Pontorson
Sélune
St-Hilaire-du-Harcouët
Barenton
Domfront
La Ferté-Macé
Carrouges
Sées
Plancoët
Dol-de-Bretagne
Pleine-Fougères
St-Martin-de-Landelles
Le Teilleul
Juvigny-sous-Andaine
Couterne
Miniac-Morvan
Pleudihen-sur-Rance
St-James
Buais
Passais
Ceaucé
Pré-en-Pail
Mont des Avaloirs
Alençon
Corseul
Dinan
Trans
Argouges
Louvigné-du-Désert
Landivy
Couptrain
Damigny
St-Pierre-de-Plesguen
Cuguen
Antrain
St-Brice-en-Coglès
Fougerolles-du-Plessis
Lassay-les-Châteaux
Javron-les-Chapelles
St-Germain-du-Corbéis
Jugon-les-Lacs
Léhon
Évran
Meillac
Combourg
Gorron
Le Horps
St-Pierre-des-Nids
Arçonnay
Yvignac
Dingé
Romazy
Larchamp
Montaudin
Châtillon-sur-Colmont
Ambrières-les-Vallées
Villaines-la-Juhel
Broons
Tinténiac
Sens-de-Bretagne
Romagné
Fougères
St-Denis-de-Gastines
Oisseau
Mayenne
Courcité
Courgains
Éréac
Caulnes
Bécherel
Hédé
La Pellerine
Ernée
Montenay
St-Georges-Buttavent
Aron
Champgenéteux
Les Coëvrons
Fresnay-sur-Sarthe
St-Aubin-d'Aubigné
St-Aubin-du-Cormier
St-Pierre-des-Landes
Jublains
Moulay
Commer
Bais
Beaumont-sur-Sarthe
Irodouër
Romillé
Gévezé
Gosné
Chailland
Sillé-le-Guillaume
Montauban-de-Bretagne
La Chapelle-des-Fougeretz
Betton
Liffré
La Bouëxière
La Croixille
Juvigné
La Baconnière
Martigné-sur-Mayenne
Ségrie
St-Méen-le-Grand
Bédée
Breteil
Andouillé
Évron
Ballon
Boisgervilly
Cesson-Sévigné
Val-d'Izé
Servon-sur-Vilaine
Vitré
St-Ouen-des-Toits
Montsûrs
St-Jean-d'Assé
Iffendic
Montfort
Talensac
Rennes
Châteaubourg
Port Brillet
Louverné
Argentré
Signal du Viviers
Conlie
Savigné-l'Évêque
Mauron
Mordelles
Le Genest-St-Isle
Changé
Laval
Ste-Suzanne
La Bazoge
La Milesse
Forêt de Paimpont
Paimpont
St-Jacques-de-la-Lande
Bruz
Vern-sur-Seiche
Châteaugiron
Argentré-du-Plessis
Loiron
St-Berthevin
Bonchamp-lès-Laval
Vaiges
St-Jean-sur-Erve
Chassillé
Coulaines
Le Mans
Plélan-le-Grand
Goven
Maxent
Baulon
Corps-Nuds
Bais
Le Pertre
L'Huisserie
Entrammes
Bazougers
Brûlon
Loué
Allonnes
Ploërmel
Campénéac
Guichen
Janzé
Montjean
Gennes-sur-Seiche
La Guerche-de-Bretagne
Nuillé-sur-Vicoin
Meslay-du-Maine
Ballée
Chemiré-le-Gaudin
Arnage
Circuit de la Sarthe
Guignen
Le Theil-de-Bretagne
Retiers
St-Poix
Cossé-le-Vivien
Ballots
Quelaines-St-Gault
Villiers-Charlemagne
Auvers-le-Hamon
La Suze-sur-Sarthe
Guer
Maure-de-Bretagne
Lohéac
Le Sel-de-Bretagne
Bain-de-Bretagne
La Roë
Grez-en-Bouère
Noyen-sur-Sarthe
Solesmes
Cérans-Foulletourte
Ruffiac
Carentoir
Pipriac
Messac
Martigné-Ferchaud
St-Aignan-sur-Roë
Craon
Bazouges
Château-Gontier
Azé
Sablé-sur-Sarthe
Bierné
Parcé-sur-Sarthe
Malicorne-sur-Sarthe
La Fontaine-St-Martin
Malestroit
Guipry
Teillay
Rougé
Congrier
Renazé
Chemazé
St-Denis-d'Anjou
Précigné
La Gacilly
Grand-Fougeray
Chère
Châteaubriant
Pouancé
Daon
La Chapelle-d'Aligné
Luché-Pringé
Aubigné-Racan
Oust
Soudan
Noyellant
Segré
Daumeray
La Flèche
Peillac
Malansac
Redon
St-Nicolas-de-Redon
Derval
Erbray
SEGRÉEN
Champigné
Châteauneuf-sur-Sarthe
Durtal
Le Lude
Allaire
Guémené-Penfao
Moisdon-la-Rivière
St-Julien-de-Vouvantes
Loiré
Vern-d'Anjou
Le Lion-d'Angers
Tiercé
Parc Animalier et Botanique de Branféré
Rieux
Fégréac
Marsac-sur-Don
Nozay
La Meilleraye-de-Bretagne
Candé
Angrie
La Pouëze
ANJOU
Feneu
Seiches-sur-le-Loir
Jarzé
Baugé
Château-la-Vallière
Péaule
Marzan
St-Dolay
Plessé
Guenrouet
St-Mars-la-Jaille
Saffré
Le Louroux-Béconnais
Montreuil-Juigné
Écuillé
Avrillé
BAUGEOIS
Nivillac
Missillac
St-Gildas-des-Bois
Blain
Riaillé
Joué-sur-Erdre
Bécon-les-Granits
Beaucouzé
Angers
Trélazé
Val d'Anjou
Mazé
Beaufort-en-Vallée
Moulihernе
Rillé
Férel
Pontchâteau
Nort-sur-Erdre
Fay-de-Bretagne
Héric
Ligné
Mésanger
Ancenis
Varades
Ingrandes
Bouchemaine
St-Georges-sur-Loire
Les Ponts-de-Cé
Mûrs-Érigné
Vernantes
Longué-Jumelles
GRANDE BRIÈRE
Campbon
Bouvron
Petit-Mars
St-Mars-du-Désert
La Pommeraye
Brissac-Quincé
Gennes
Les Rosiers-sur-Loire
St-Joachim
Montoir-de-Bretagne
Savenay
La Chapelle-sur-Erdre
Oudon
Loire
Liré
Champtoceaux
St-Florent-le-Vieil
Bourgneuf-en-Mauges
Chalonnes-sur-Loire
La Jumellière
Coutures
St-Lambert-des-Levées
Allonnes
La Baule-Escoublac
Trignac
Donges
Cordemais
Carquefou
St-Laurent-des-Autels
Le Fuilet
Montrevault
St-Pierre-Montlimart
Thouarcé
SAUMUROIS
St-Hilaire-St-Florent
Saumur
Château de Saumur
Pornichet
St-Nazaire
Paimbœuf
St-Étienne-de-Montluc
Sautron
Orvault
Nantes
Thouaré-sur-Loire
St-Julien-de-Concelles
LES MAUGES
Valanjou
Martigné-Briand
Doué-la-Fontaine
St-Brevin-les-Pins
St-Père-en-Retz
St-Herblain
Couëron
Le Pellerin
Rezé
Basse-Goulaine
St-Sébastien-sur-Loire
Vallet
Beaupréau
Chemillé
Jallais
Melay
Vihiers
Fontevraud-l'Abbaye
Beaumont
Avoine
St-Michel-Chef-Chef
Rouans
Bouguenais
Vertou
Le Pallet
Villedieu-la-Blouère
Le May-sur-Èvre
St-Macaire-en-Mauges
Coron
Le Puy-Notre-Dame
Montreuil-Bellay
Préfailles
Pornic
Les Sorinières
Port-St-Père
Planète Sauvage
Aigrefeuille
Clisson
Montfaucon
Vezins
Torfou
PAYS
24
28

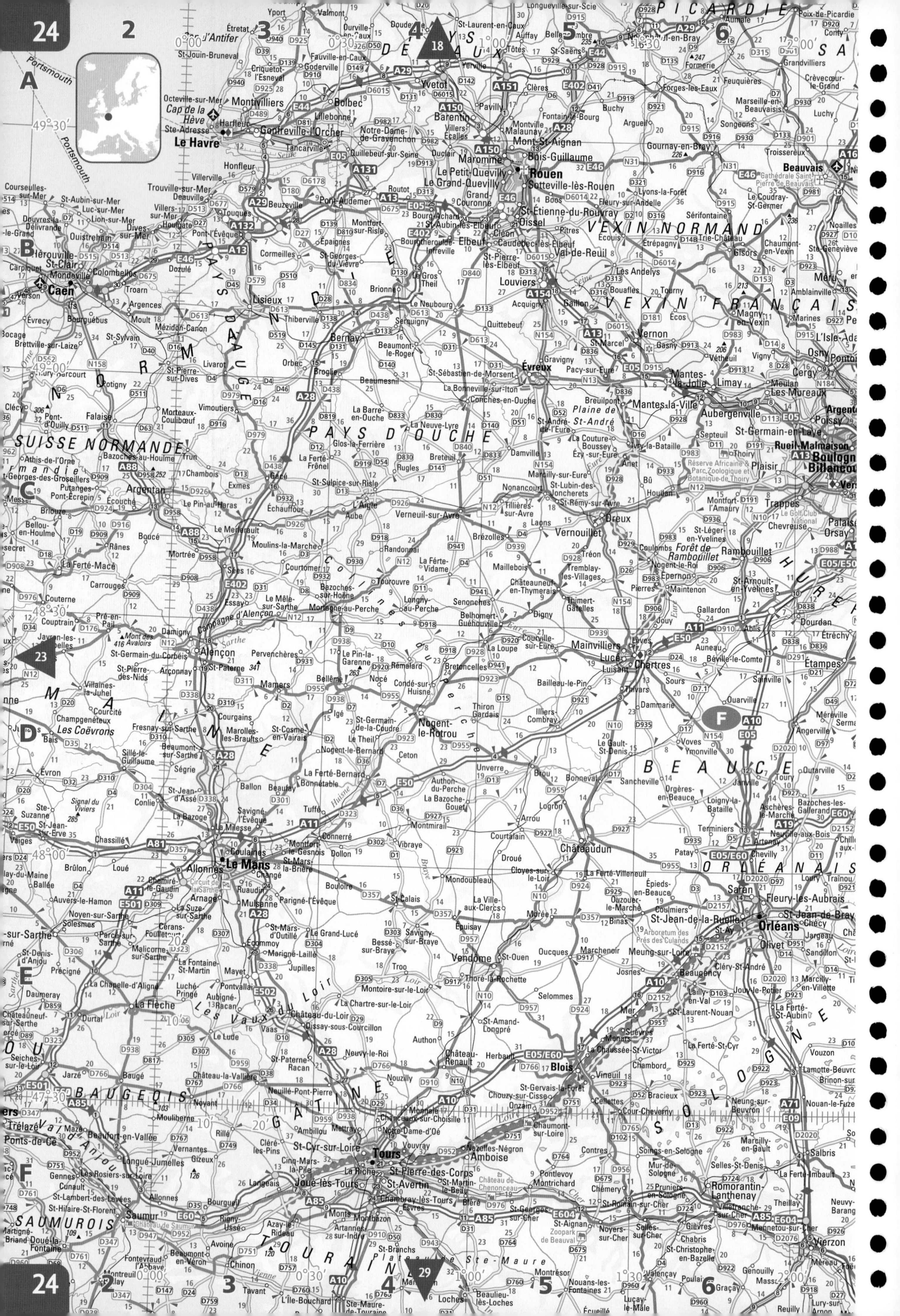
2
3
4
5
6
A
B
C
D
E
F
18
23
29
Portsmouth
PICARDIE
PAYS DE CAUX
Le Havre
Rouen
Caen
Beauvais
Lisieux
VEXIN NORMAND
VEXIN FRANÇAIS
PAYS D'AUGE
NORMANDIE
PAYS D'OUCHE
SUISSE NORMANDE
Évreux
Vernon
Mantes-la-Jolie
Dreux
Chartres
Alençon
Le Mans
Nogent-le-Rotrou
Collines du Perche
Châteaudun
BEAUCE
Orléans
ORLÉANAIS
Vendôme
Blois
SOLOGNE
Tours
Amboise
Saumur
SAUMUROIS
La Flèche
BAUGEOIS
GÂTINE
TOURAINE
Les Vaux du Loir
Romorantin-Lanthenay
Vierzon
Rambouillet
Étampes
Évreux
Argentan
Falaise
Bernay
Mamers
Honfleur
Fécamp
Yvetot
Dieppe
Gisors
Cergy
Poissy
Versailles
Trappes
Chinon
Loches
Joué-lès-Tours
Plateau de Ste-Maure

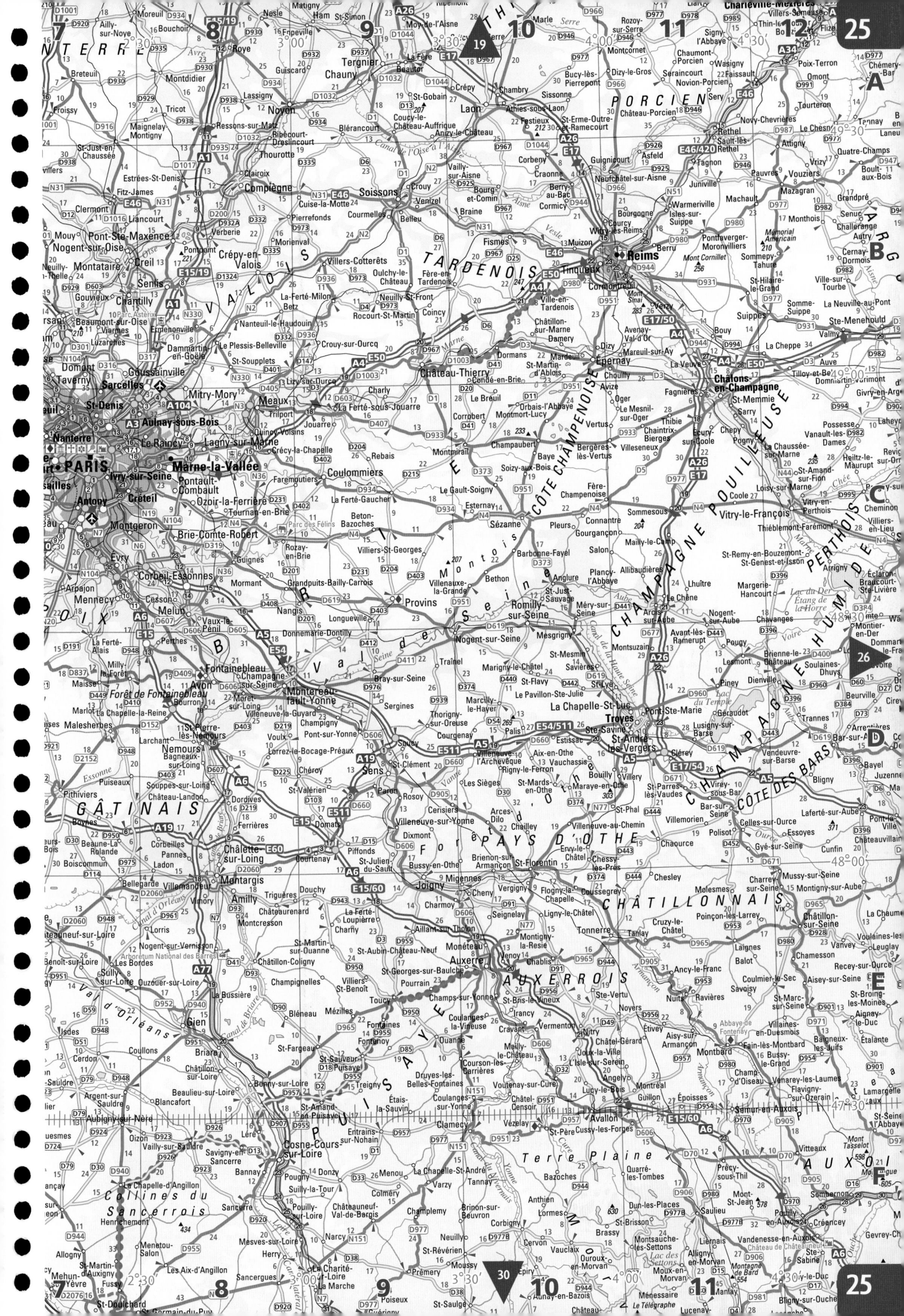
PARIS
Reims
Troyes
Auxerre
Châlons-en-Champagne
Épernay
Meaux
Provins
Sens
Fontainebleau
Melun
Montargis
Gien
Nevers
Soissons
Laon
Compiègne
Noyon
Château-Thierry
Coulommiers
Nogent-sur-Seine
Montereau-fault-Yonne
Joigny
Tonnerre
Avallon
Clamecy
Cosne-Cours-sur-Loire
Vitry-le-François
Charleville-Mézières
Rethel
Sézanne
Romilly-sur-Seine
Bar-sur-Aube
Châtillon-sur-Seine
Montbard
Semur-en-Auxois
Marne-la-Vallée
Évry
Corbeil-Essonnes
Pithiviers
Nemours
TARDENOIS
PORCIEN
VALOIS
BRIE
CÔTE CHAMPENOISE
CHAMPAGNE POUILLEUSE
CHAMPAGNE HUMIDE
PERTHOIS
CÔTE DES BARS
PAYS D'OTHE
CHÂTILLONNAIS
AUXERROIS
PUISAYE
GÂTINAIS
Forêt de Fontainebleau
Val d'Orléans
Collines du Sancerrois
Terre Plaine
AUXOIS
Val de Seine
Montois
19
26
30

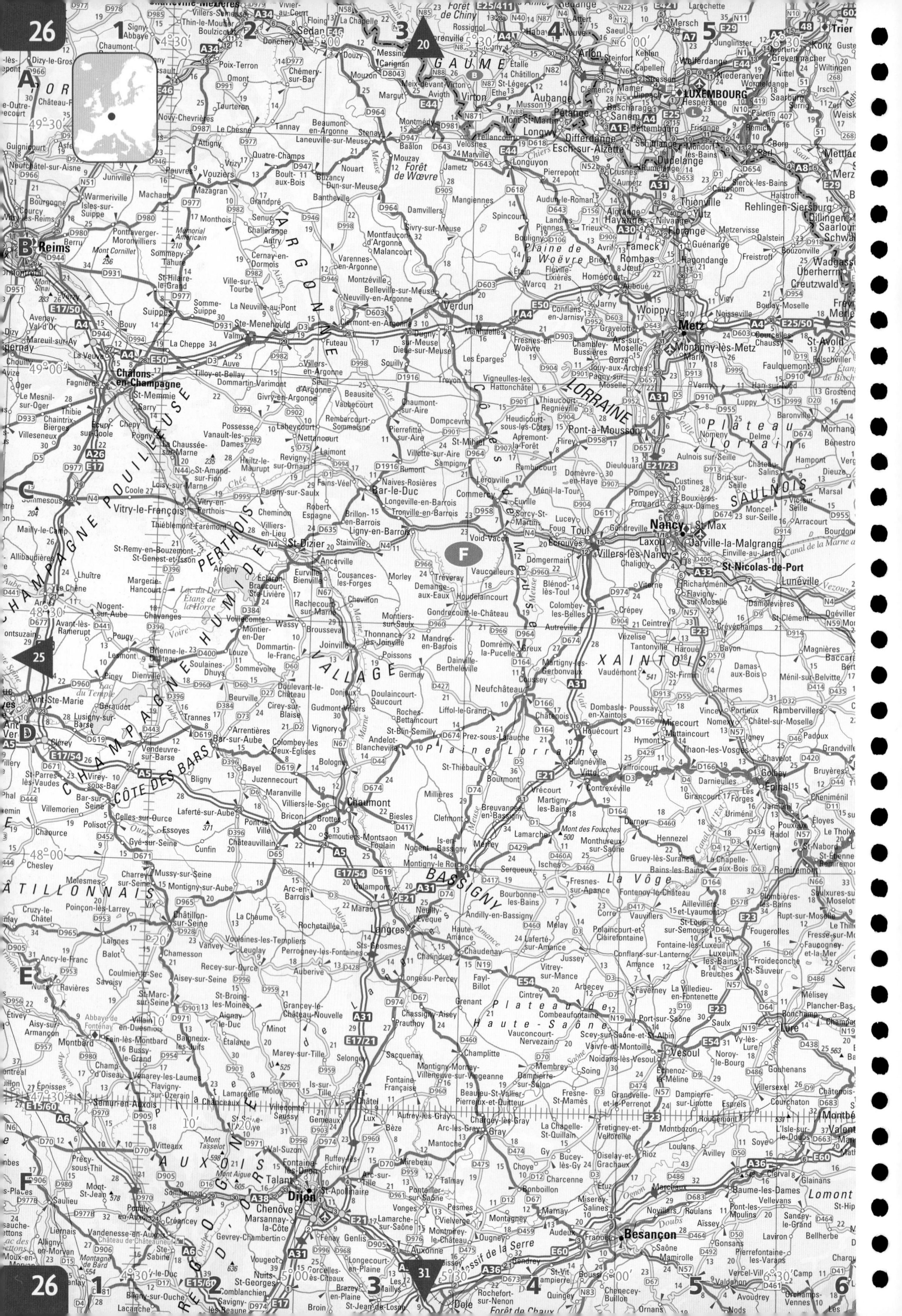

1
2
3
4
5
A
B
C
D
E
F
20
25
31
Reims
Sedan
Charleville-Mézières
Arlon
LUXEMBOURG
Trier
Thionville
Metz
Verdun
Châlons-en-Champagne
Vitry-le-François
St-Dizier
Bar-le-Duc
Commercy
Toul
Nancy
Lunéville
St-Nicolas-de-Port
Pont-à-Mousson
Neufchâteau
Chaumont
Langres
Épinal
Vittel
Contrexéville
Mirecourt
Vesoul
Lure
Dijon
Besançon
Montbard
Bar-sur-Aube
Sarreguemines
St-Avold
Forbach
Longwy
Ste-Menehould
Joinville
Châtillon-sur-Seine
Gray
Auxonne
Dole
ARGONNE
LORRAINE
GAUME
CHAMPAGNE POUILLEUSE
CHAMPAGNE HUMIDE
PERTHOIS
VALLAGE
BASSIGNY
XAINTOIS
SAULNOIS
CÔTE DES BARS
AUXOIS
Plaine Lorraine
Plateau Lorrain
Plaine de la Woëvre
Côtes de Meuse
Plateau de Haute-Saône
La Vôge
CHÂTILLONNAIS
Forêt de Wœvre
Forêt de Chiny

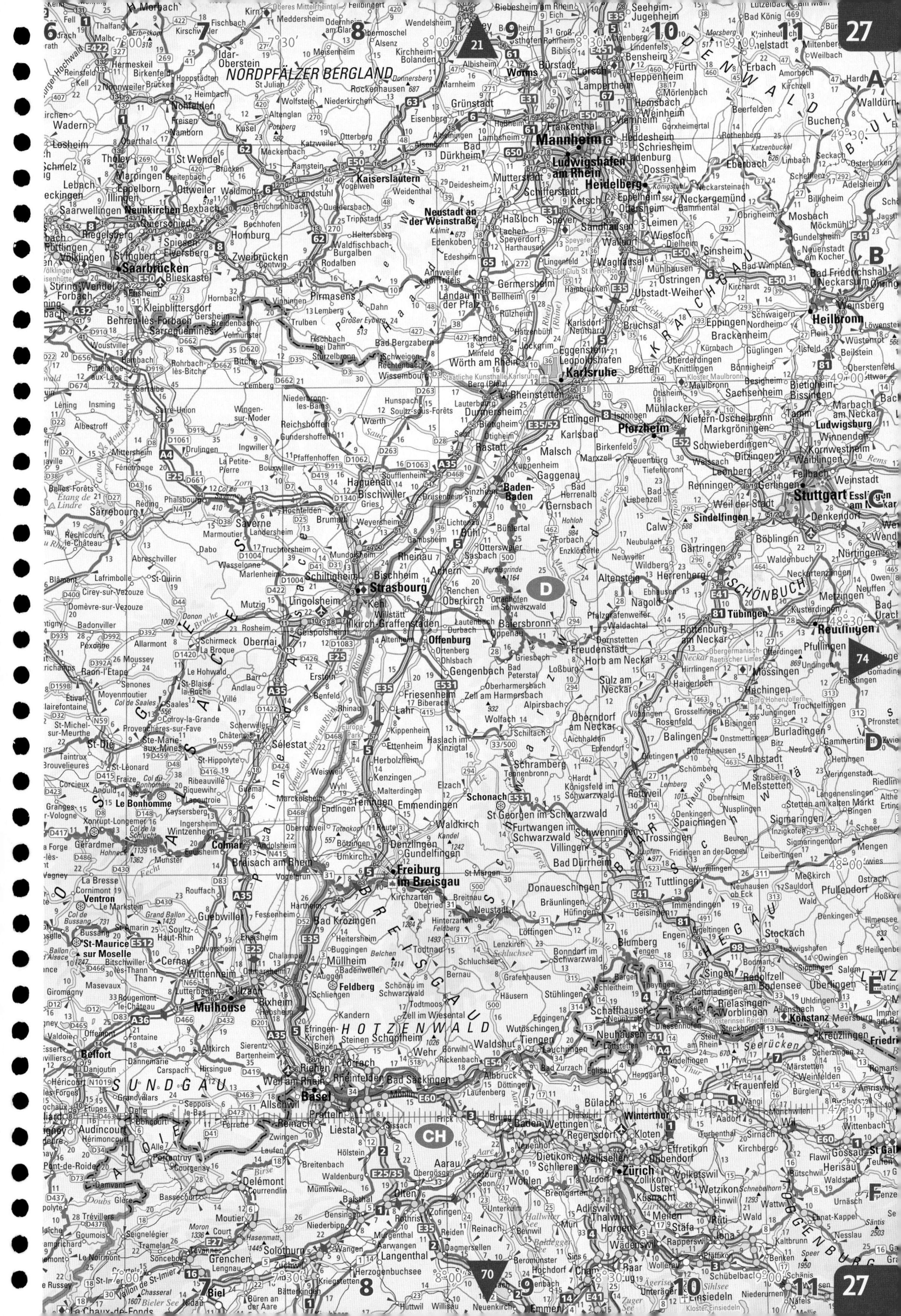

NORDPFÄLZER BERGLAND
Kaiserslautern
Mannheim
Ludwigshafen am Rhein
Heidelberg
Worms
Saarbrücken
Neunkirchen
Homburg
Zweibrücken
Pirmasens
Landau in der Pfalz
Neustadt an der Weinstraße
Speyer
Karlsruhe
Pforzheim
Heilbronn
Ludwigsburg
Stuttgart
Sindelfingen
Böblingen
Tübingen
Reutlingen
Rastatt
Baden-Baden
Offenburg
Strasbourg
Haguenau
Saverne
Sarrebourg
Sarreguemines
Colmar
Sélestat
Mulhouse
Freiburg im Breisgau
Basel
Belfort
Lörrach
Villingen
Schwenningen
Tuttlingen
Singen
Konstanz
Schaffhausen
Winterthur
Zürich
Baden
Aarau
Olten
Solothurn
Grenchen
Biel
Delémont
Liestal
D
CH
ODENWALD
KRAICHGAU
SCHÖNBUCH
HEGAU
BREISGAU
HOTZENWALD
SUNDGAU
ALSACE
Feldberg
Le Bonhomme
Ventron
St-Maurice sur Moselle
Schonach
St Georgen im Schwarzwald
21
74
70
6
7
8
9
10
11
A
B
C
D
E
F

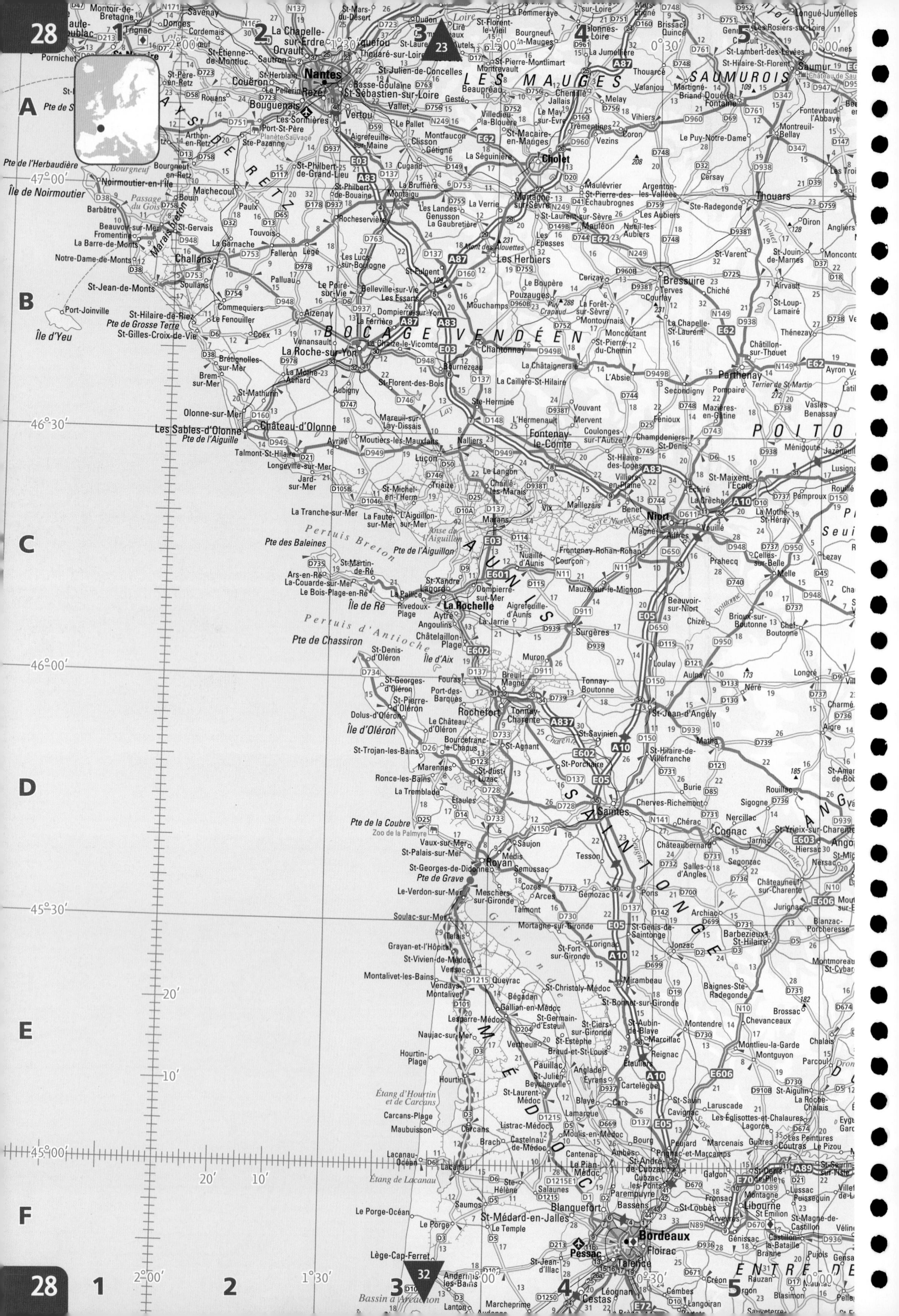

Nantes
Cholet
LES MAUGES
SAUMUROIS
Saumur
PAYS DE RETZ
Île de Noirmoutier
Noirmoutier-en-l'Île
Île d'Yeu
Port-Joinville
Challans
St-Jean-de-Monts
St-Gilles-Croix-de-Vie
BOCAGE VENDÉEN
La Roche-sur-Yon
Les Herbiers
Bressuire
Thouars
Parthenay
Les Sables-d'Olonne
Château-d'Olonne
Luçon
Fontenay-le-Comte
Niort
POITOU
Pertuis Breton
Île de Ré
La Rochelle
AUNIS
Pertuis d'Antioche
Île d'Oléron
Rochefort
Surgères
St-Jean-d'Angély
Saintes
SAINTONGE
Cognac
Royan
Pte de Grave
Le Verdon-sur-Mer
Soulac-sur-Mer
MÉDOC
Pauillac
Lacanau
Étang de Lacanau
Étang d'Hourtin et de Carcans
Blanquefort
St-Médard-en-Jalles
Bordeaux
Pessac
Libourne
St-Émilion
ENTRE-DEUX-MERS
Lège-Cap-Ferret
Bassin d'Arcachon
A83
A87
A10
E03
E05
47°00′
46°30′
46°00′
45°30′
45°00′
2°00′
1°30′
1°00′
0°30′
0°00′
A
B
C
D
E
F
1
2
3
4
5
23
32

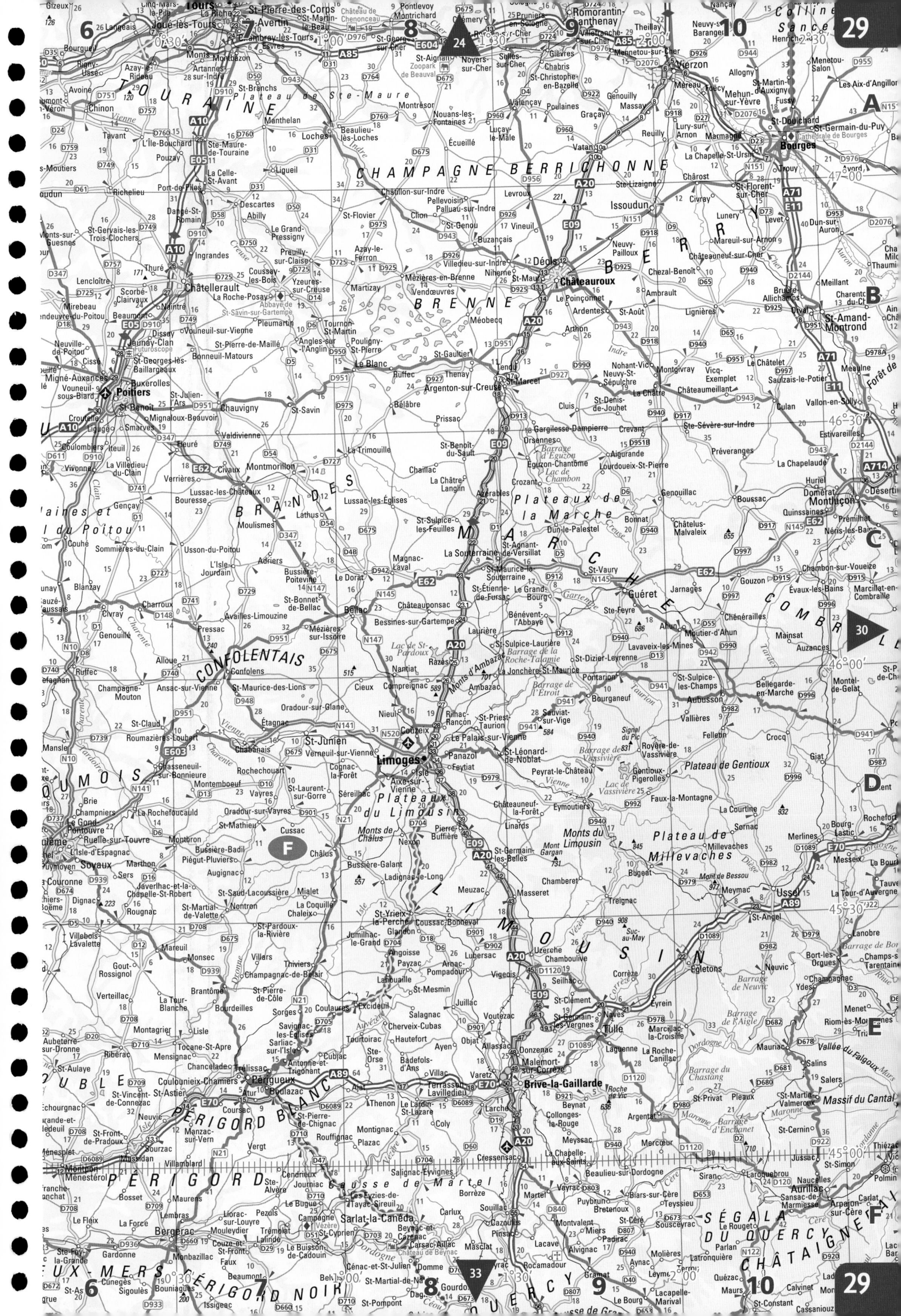
6
7
8
9
10
24
Tours
Joué-lès-Tours
St-Pierre-des-Corps
St-Avertin
Chambray-lès-Tours
Montbazon
Romorantin-Lanthenay
Vierzon
Bourges
TOURAINE
Chinon
Loches
Manthelan
Ste-Maure-de-Touraine
L'Île-Bouchard
Richelieu
Montrichard
St-Aignan
Zoopark de Beauval
Selles-sur-Cher
Valençay
Vatan
Issoudun
Mehun-sur-Yèvre
CHAMPAGNE BERRICHONNE
BERRY
Châtillon-sur-Indre
Buzançais
Déols
Châteauroux
Levroux
Châtellerault
Dangé-St-Romain
La Roche-Posay
Abbaye de St-Savin-sur-Gartempe
Mézières-en-Brenne
BRENNE
Méobecq
Futuroscope
Jaunay-Clan
Poitiers
Chauvigny
St-Savin
Le Blanc
Argenton-sur-Creuse
St-Marcel
La Châtre
St-Amand-Montrond
Châteaumeillant
Culan
Montmorillon
BRANDES
Lussac-les-Châteaux
Lussac-les-Églises
La Souterraine
MARCHE
Plateau de la Marche
Dun-le-Palestel
Guéret
Boussac
Montluçon
COMBRAILLE
30
Bellac
Le Dorat
Civray
Confolens
CONFOLENTAIS
Monts d'Ambazac
Ambazac
Bourganeuf
Aubusson
Felletin
St-Junien
Rochechouart
Limoges
Oradour-sur-Glane
Plateau du Limousin
Plateau de Gentioux
Plateau de Millevaches
Monts du Limousin
Eymoutiers
Lac de Vassivière
Ussel
St-Yrieix-la-Perche
Châlus
Nontron
LIMOUSIN
Uzerche
Égletons
Tulle
Brive-la-Gaillarde
Périgueux
PÉRIGORD BLANC
DOUBLE
Ribérac
Brantôme
Excideuil
Sarlat-la-Canéda
Bergerac
PÉRIGORD
PÉRIGORD NOIR
Causse de Martel
Souillac
Gourdon
QUERCY
Aurillac
SÉGALA
CHÂTAIGNERAIE
Massif du Cantal
Salers
Mauriac
Argentat
Beaulieu-sur-Dordogne
Figeac
33
Angoulême
ANGOUMOIS
La Rochefoucauld
Soyaux
Ruffec
F

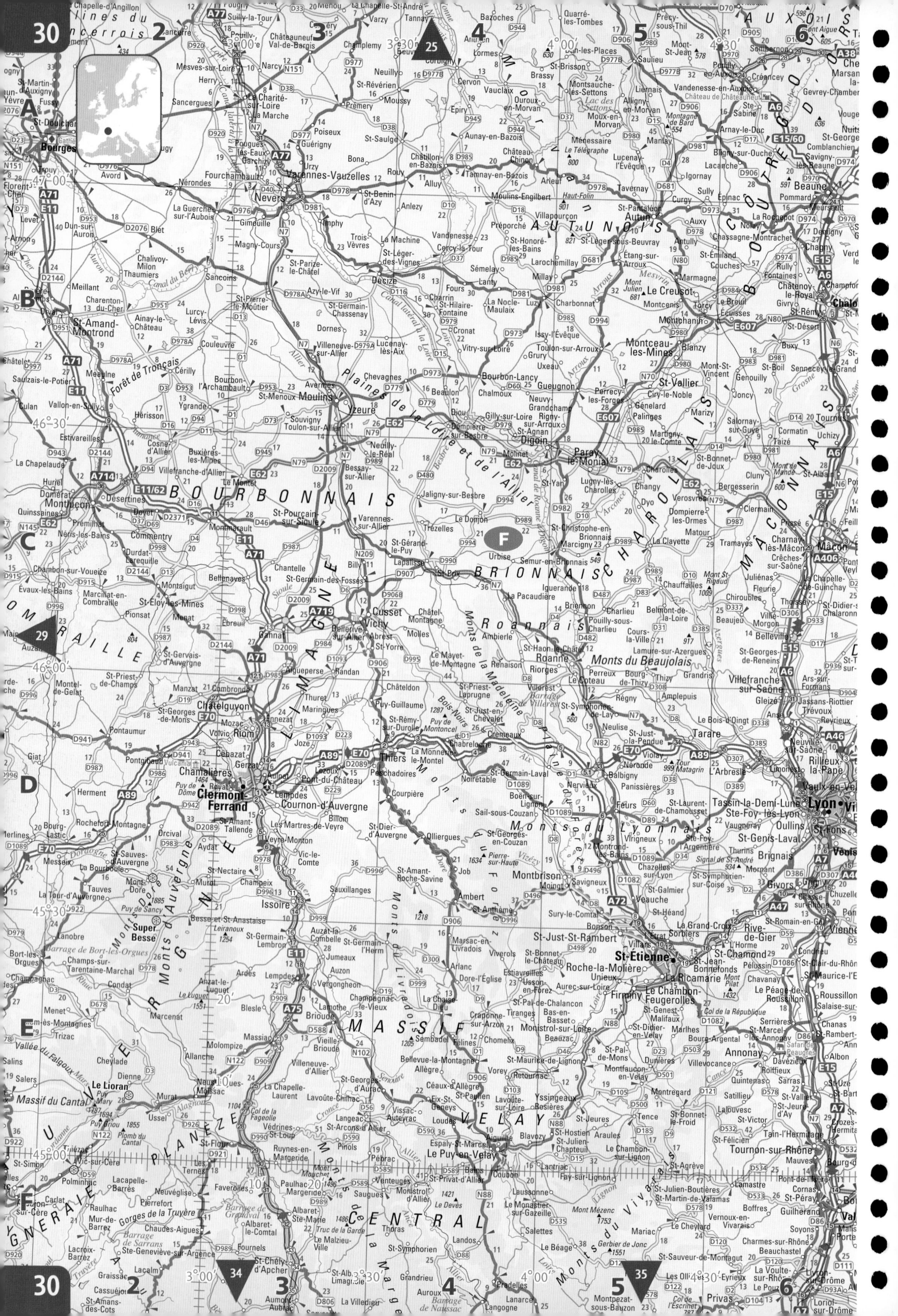

Bourges
Nevers
Moulins
Montluçon
Vichy
Clermont-Ferrand
Thiers
Roanne
Autun
Beaune
Le Creusot
Montceau-les-Mines
Mâcon
Lyon
St-Étienne
Le Puy-en-Velay
Issoire
Riom
Châtelguyon
Cusset
Digoin
Paray-le-Monial
Villefranche-sur-Saône
Tarare
Feurs
Montbrison
Ambert
Brioude
St-Flour
Annonay
Tournon-sur-Rhône
Vienne
Givors
Firminy
Yssingeaux
Privas
BOURBONNAIS
AUTUNOIS
CHAROLLAIS
BRIONNAIS
LIMAGNE
MASSIF CENTRAL
VELAY
MÂCONNAIS
COMBRAILLE
Monts du Beaujolais
Monts du Lyonnais
Monts du Forez
Monts de la Madeleine
Monts du Vivarais
Monts Dore
Monts du Livradois
Massif du Cantal
Planèze
Forêt de Tronçais
Roannais
Plaines de la Loire et de l'Allier
A71
A72
A89
A75
E62
E11
E70
N7
A6
A7

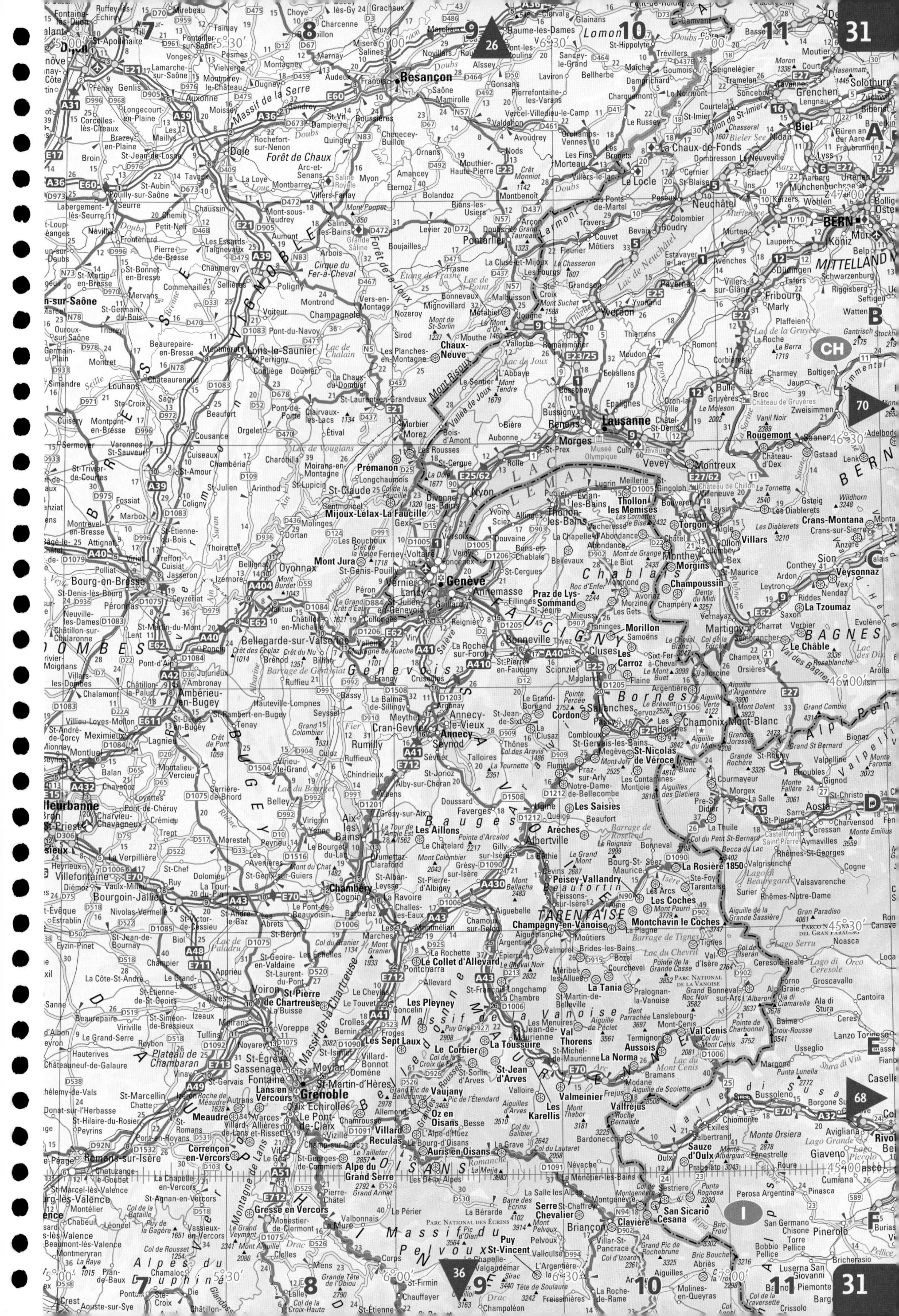
31
Dijon
Besançon
Dole
Forêt de Chaux
Massif de la Serre
Pontarlier
La Chaux-de-Fonds
Le Locle
Neuchâtel
Biel
Solothurn
Grenchen
BERN
Köniz
MITTELLAND
Fribourg
Lac de Neuchâtel
Yverdon
Lausanne
Morges
Vevey
Montreux
LAC LEMAN
Genève
Annemasse
Thonon-les-Bains
Evian-les-Bains
Nyon
Lons-le-Saunier
Bourg-en-Bresse
Oyonnax
St-Claude
Bellegarde-sur-Valserine
Annecy
Chamonix-Mont-Blanc
Martigny
Sion
Aosta
Chambéry
Aix-les-Bains
Albertville
Grenoble
Voiron
Briançon
Pinerolo
Susa
Chaux-Neuve
Champagnole
Poligny
Arbois
Salins-les-Bains
Morez
Les Rousses
Mont Jura
Chablais
Faucigny
Genevois
Bornes
Bauges
Bugey
Dombes
Beaufortin
Tarentaise
Massif de la Vanoise
Massif de Belledonne
Massif de la Chartreuse
Oisans
Massif du Pelvoux
Alpes du Dauphiné
Plateau de Chambaran
Vignoble
Bresse
Revermont
Valle di Susa
Mont Blanc 4810
Gran Paradiso 4061
CH
I
26
70
68
36
7
8
9
10
11
A
B
C
D
E
F
31

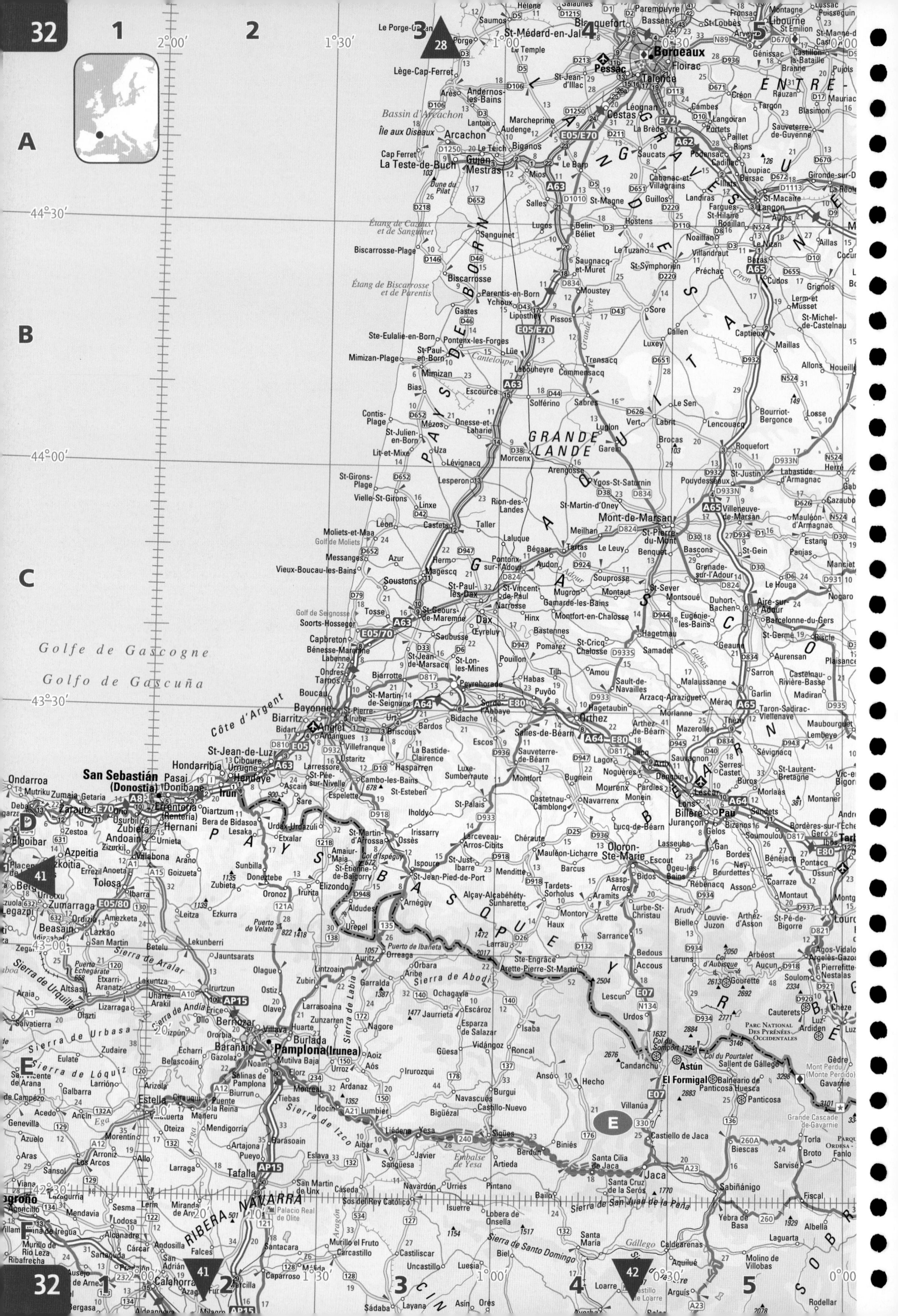
Golfe de Gascogne
Golfo de Gascuña
Côte d'Argent
Bordeaux
Pessac
Talence
Floirac
Libourne
St-Médard-en-Jalles
Blanquefort
Lège-Cap-Ferret
Arcachon
La Teste-de-Buch
Bassin d'Arcachon
Île aux Oiseaux
Dune du Pilat
Biganos
Andernos-les-Bains
Langon
St-Macaire
Bazas
Biscarrosse
Parentis-en-Born
Mimizan
Mimizan-Plage
Labouheyre
Sabres
Morcenx
Roquefort
Mont-de-Marsan
Aire-sur-l'Adour
St-Sever
Hagetmau
Dax
Soustons
Capbreton
Bayonne
Biarritz
Anglet
St-Jean-de-Luz
Hendaye
Irun
Hondarribia
San Sebastián (Donostia)
Tolosa
Orthez
Pau
Lescar
Lons
Billère
Jurançon
Oloron-Ste-Marie
Mauléon-Licharre
St-Jean-Pied-de-Port
Pamplona (Iruñea)
Burlada
Estella
Tafalla
Jaca
Sabiñánigo
Lourdes
Gavarnie
Cauterets
El Formigal
Astún
Candanchú
Sangüesa
Olite
Calahorra
Logroño
Zarautz
Zumarraga
Beasain
Azpeitia
Hernani
Errenteria
Pasai Donibane
Pays Basque
Pays de Born
Grande Lande
Landes de Gascogne
Graves
Entre-Deux-Mers
Béarn
Bigorre
Sierra de Aralar
Sierra de Urbasa
Sierra de Andía
Sierra de Abodi
Sierra de Leyre
Sierra de Santo Domingo
Sierra de San Juan de la Peña
Ribera Navarra
Parc National des Pyrénées Occidentales
Embalse de Yesa
E05/E70
E80
E72
E07
A63
A64
A65
A62
AP15
E
41
42
28
1
2
3
4
5
A
B
C
D
E
F
2°00'
1°30'
1°00'
0°30'
0°00'
44°30'
44°00'
43°30'
43°00'
42°30'

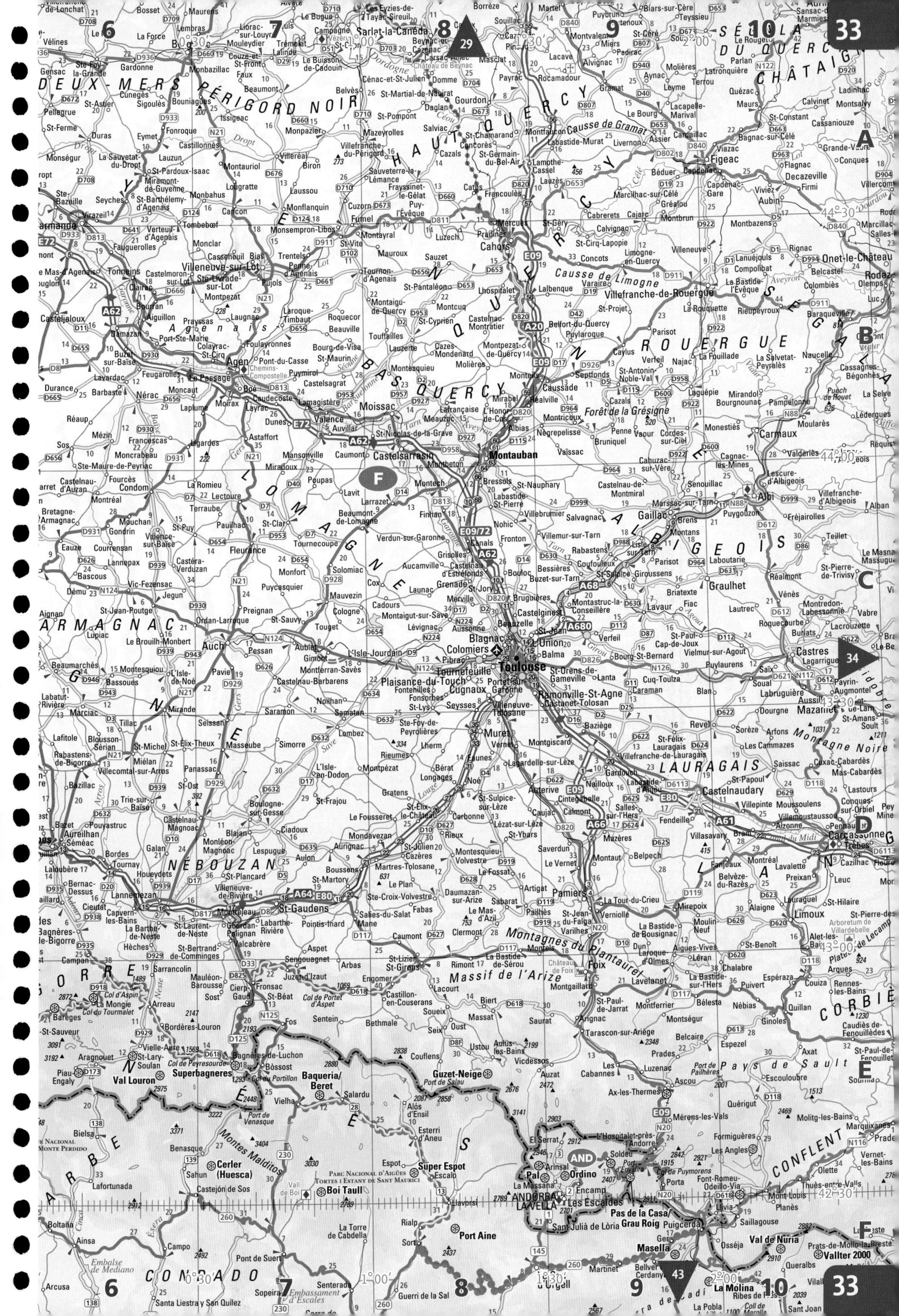
PÉRIGORD NOIR
DEUX-MERS
HAUT QUERCY
QUERCY
DU QUERCY
CHÂTAIGN
Causse de Gramat
Causse de Limogne
Agenais
BAS QUERCY
ROUERGUE
SÉGALA
LOMAGNE
ALBIGEOIS
ARMAGNAC
GASCOGNE
LAURAGAIS
Montagne Noire
NÉBOUZAN
Massif de l'Arize
Montagnes du Plantaurel
Pays de Sault
CORBIÈRES
CONFLENT
BIGORRE
Montes Malditos
Forêt de la Grésigne
Sarlat-la-Canéda
Bergerac
Villeneuve-sur-Lot
Marmande
Agen
Moissac
Castelsarrasin
Montauban
Cahors
Figeac
Villefranche-de-Rouergue
Decazeville
Rodez
Albi
Carmaux
Gaillac
Graulhet
Castres
Mazamet
Toulouse
Blagnac
Colomiers
Muret
Auch
Condom
Nérac
Lectoure
Castelnaudary
Carcassonne
Limoux
Pamiers
Foix
St-Gaudens
Lannemezan
Bagnères-de-Luchon
Saint-Girons
Ax-les-Thermes
Andorra la Vella
Les Escaldes
Puigcerdà
La Seu d'Urgell
Parc Nacional d'Aigües Tortes i Estany de Sant Maurici
Baqueira/Beret
Super Espot
Port Aine
Boi Taull
Superbagneres
Val Louron
Guzet-Neige
Cerler (Huesca)
Pas de la Casa/Grau Roig
Masella
Val de Núria
Vallter 2000
AND
F
29
34
43
6
7
8
9
10
A
B
C
D
E
F
44°30'
44°00'
43°30'
43°00'
42°30'
0°30'
1°00'
1°30'
2°00'

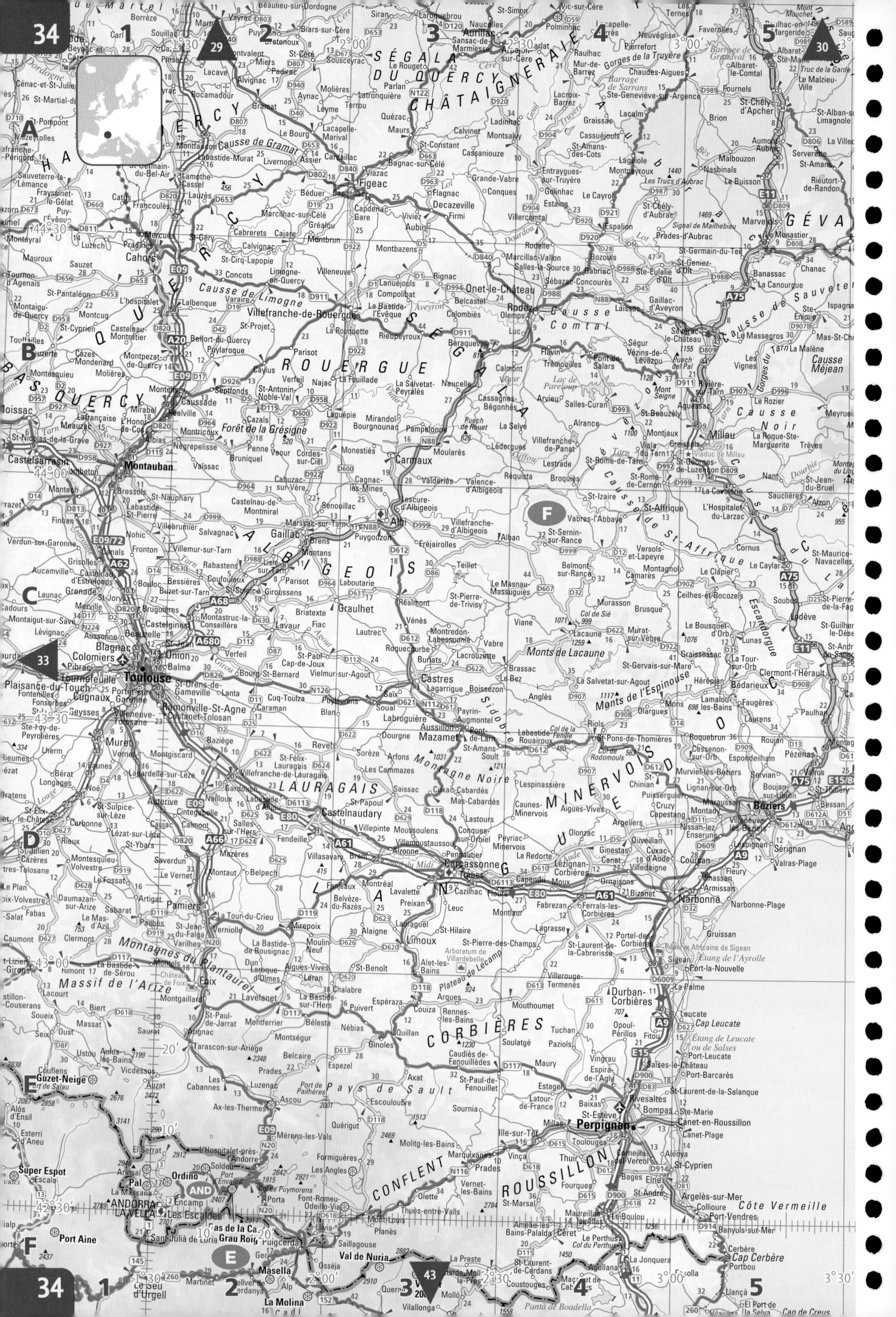

1
2
3
4
5
A
B
C
D
E
F
29
30
33
43
QUERCY
BAS QUERCY
SÉGALA DU QUERCY
CHÂTAIGNERAIE
AUBRAC
GÉVAUDAN
ROUERGUE
SÉGALA
ALBIGEOIS
LAURAGAIS
LÉVÉZOU
Causse de Gramat
Causse de Limogne
Causse Comtal
Causse de Sauveterre
Causse Méjean
Causse Noir
Causse du Larzac
Causse de St-Affrique
Monts de Lacaune
Monts de l'Espinouse
Montagne Noire
Sidobre
MINERVOIS
LANGUEDOC
CORBIÈRES
Pays de Sault
CONFLENT
ROUSSILLON
Côte Vermeille
Massif de l'Arize
Montagnes du Plantaurel
Forêt de la Grésigne
Gorges de la Truyère
Gorges du Tarn
Étang de Leucate ou de Salses
Étang de l'Ayrolle
Cap Leucate
Cap Cerbère
Aurillac
Figeac
Cahors
Montauban
Rodez
Millau
Albi
Toulouse
Castres
Mazamet
Carcassonne
Narbonne
Béziers
Perpignan
Foix
Pamiers
Limoux
Castelnaudary
Villefranche-de-Rouergue
Decazeville
Carmaux
Gaillac
Lodève
Bédarieux
Pézenas
Agde
St-Affrique
Espalion
Mende
St-Flour
Castelsarrasin
Moissac
Muret
Colomiers
Blagnac
Tournefeuille
Ax-les-Thermes
Quillan
Prades
Céret
Argelès-sur-Mer
Collioure
Port-Vendres
Banyuls-sur-Mer
Cerbère
Portbou
Le Perthus
La Jonquera
Andorra la Vella
Puigcerdà
La Seu d'Urgell
Font-Romeu-Odeillo-Via
Viaduc de Millau
AND

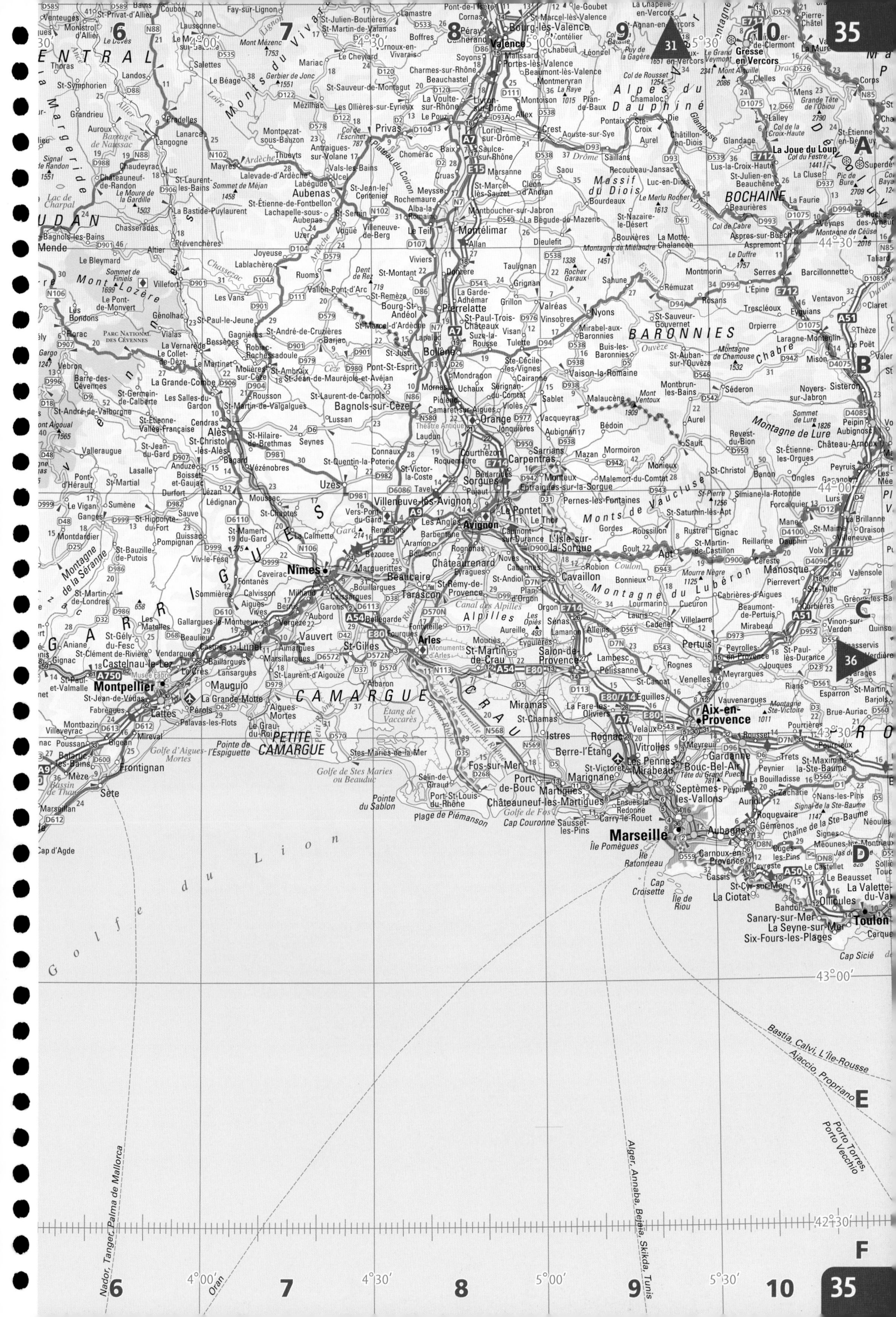

6
7
8
9
10
31
36
A
B
C
D
E
F
4°00′
4°30′
5°00′
5°30′
44°30′
44°00′
43°30′
43°00′
42°30′
Valence
Bourg-lès-Valence
Portes-lès-Valence
Privas
Aubenas
Montélimar
Pierrelatte
Bollène
Orange
Carpentras
Avignon
Nîmes
Beaucaire
Tarascon
Arles
Alès
Uzès
Bagnols-sur-Cèze
Montpellier
Sète
Lunel
Vauvert
St-Gilles
Cavaillon
Apt
Manosque
Sisteron
Die
Crest
Nyons
Valréas
Vaison-la-Romaine
Mende
Le Vigan
Salon-de-Provence
Istres
Martigues
Marignane
Vitrolles
Aix-en-Provence
Marseille
Aubagne
La Ciotat
Toulon
Sanary-sur-Mer
La Seyne-sur-Mer
Six-Fours-les-Plages
Gresse en Vercors
La Joue du Loup
Villeneuve-lès-Avignon
L'Isle-sur-la-Sorgue
Châteaurenard
Sorgues
Pertuis
Gardanne
Miramas
Berre-l'Étang
Lattes
Mauguio
La Grande-Motte
Aigues-Mortes
Le Grau-du-Roi
Frontignan
Stes-Maries-de-la-Mer
Port-St-Louis-du-Rhône
Fos-sur-Mer
Port-de-Bouc
Châteauneuf-les-Martigues
Cassis
Forcalquier
Digne
Serres
Laragne-Montéglin
Mont Lozère
Monts du Vivarais
Mont Mézenc
Gerbier de Jonc
Alpes du Dauphiné
Massif du Diois
BOCHAINE
BARONNIES
Montagne de Lure
Mont Ventoux
Monts de Vaucluse
Montagne du Lubéron
Alpilles
GARRIGUES
CAMARGUE
PETITE CAMARGUE
CRAU
Golfe du Lion
Golfe d'Aigues-Mortes
Golfe de Stes Maries ou Beauduc
Golfe de Fos
Étang de Vaccarès
Étang de Berre
Cap Couronne
Cap Croisette
Cap Sicié
Île de Riou
Pointe de l'Espiguette
Pointe du Sablon
Plage de Piémanson
Bastia, Calvi, L'Île-Rousse
Ajaccio, Propriano
Porto Torres, Porto Vecchio
Alger, Annaba, Bejaïa, Skikda, Tunis
Oran
Nador, Tanger, Palma de Mallorca
A7
A9
A54
A51
A50
A750
E15
E80
E712
E714

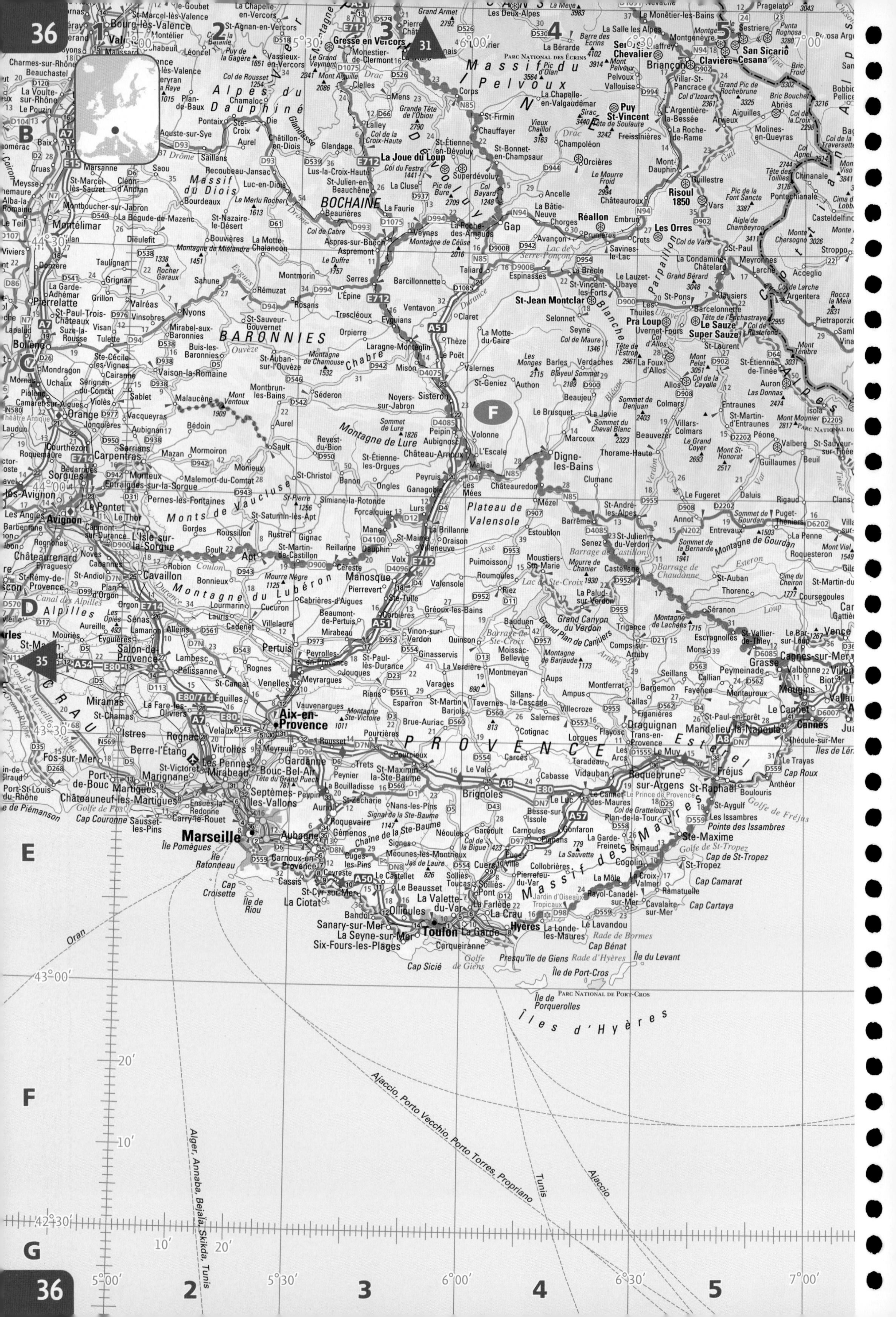

Bourg-lès-Valence
Valence
Montélimar
Pierrelatte
Bollène
Orange
Carpentras
Avignon
Cavaillon
Apt
Arles
Salon-de-Provence
Aix-en-Provence
Marseille
Aubagne
La Ciotat
Toulon
Hyères
Draguignan
Fréjus
St-Raphaël
Cannes
Grasse
Vence
Digne-les-Bains
Sisteron
Manosque
Gap
Briançon
Barcelonnette
Nyons
Vaison-la-Romaine
Die
Castellane
Brignoles
Martigues
Istres
Vitrolles
Massif du Pelvoux
Alpes du Dauphiné
Massif du Diois
BOCHAINE
BARONNIES
Montagne de Lure
Plateau de Valensole
Montagne du Lubéron
Monts de Vaucluse
Alpilles
CRAU
PROVENCE
Massif des Maures
Esterel
Grand Canyon du Verdon
Lac de Ste-Croix
Lac de Serre-Ponçon
Mont Ventoux
Golfe de Fos
Golfe de Fréjus
Cap Camarat
Presqu'île de Giens
Île de Porquerolles
Île de Port-Cros
Île du Levant
Îles d'Hyères
Parc National des Écrins
Parc National de Port-Cros
Ajaccio, Porto Vecchio, Porto Torres, Propriano
Alger, Annaba, Bejaïa, Skikda, Tunis
Tunis
Ajaccio
Oran
43°00′
42°30′
5°00′
5°30′
6°00′
6°30′
7°00′
35
31
F

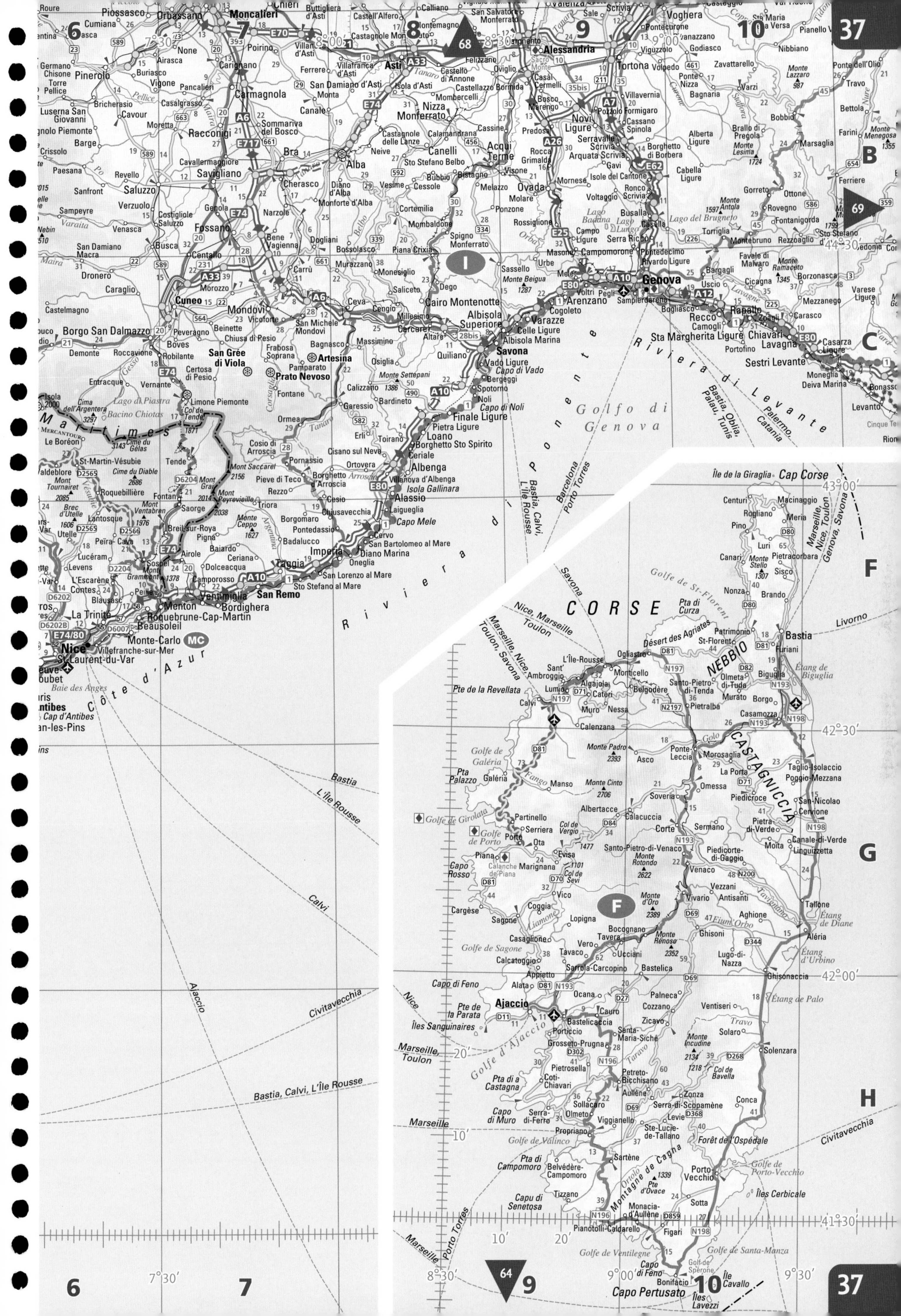
6
7
8
9
10
68
69
64
B
C
F
G
H
I
F
Moncalieri
Orbassano
Piossasco
Cumiana
Pinerolo
Carignano
Carmagnola
Poirino
Asti
Alessandria
Voghera
Tortona
Novi Ligure
Serravalle Scrivia
Arquata Scrivia
Acqui Terme
Ovada
Nizza Monferrato
Canelli
Alba
Bra
Racconigi
Savigliano
Saluzzo
Fossano
Cuneo
Mondovì
Borgo San Dalmazzo
Ceva
Cairo Montenotte
Savona
Albisola Superiore
Varazze
Arenzano
Genova
Recco
Camogli
Rapallo
Chiavari
Lavagna
Sestri Levante
Sta Margherita Ligure
Portofino
Finale Ligure
Loano
Albenga
Alassio
Imperia
Taggia
San Remo
Bordighera
Ventimiglia
Menton
Roquebrune-Cap-Martin
Beausoleil
Monte-Carlo
MC
Nice
Villefranche-sur-Mer
St-Laurent-du-Var
Antibes
Cap d'Antibes
Baie des Anges
Côte d'Azur
Riviera di Ponente
Riviera di Levante
Golfo di Genova
Limone Piemonte
Col de Tende
Tende
Saorge
Breil-sur-Roya
Sospel
Lago di Piastra
Bacino Chiotas
Le Boréon
St-Martin-Vésubie
Roquebillière
Lantosque
Utelle
Levens
L'Escarène
Contes
La Trinité
Prato Nevoso
Artesina
San Grée di Viola
Garessio
Ormea
Bastia
L'Île Rousse
Calvi
Ajaccio
Civitavecchia
Bastia, Calvi, L'Île Rousse
Barcelona Porto Torres
Bastia, Olbia, Palau, Tunis
Palermo, Catania
CORSE
Cap Corse
Île de la Giraglia
Désert des Agriates
St-Florent
Golfe de St-Florent
NEBBIO
CASTAGNICCIA
Calvi
L'Île-Rousse
Calenzana
Monte Padro 2393
Monte Cinto 2706
Corte
Golfe de Galéria
Golfe de Girolata
Golfe de Porto
Porto
Piana
Cargèse
Sagone
Golfe de Sagone
Vico
Monte Rotondo 2622
Monte d'Oro 2389
Venaco
Vivario
Aléria
Étang de Diane
Étang d'Urbino
Ghisonaccia
Étang de Palo
Ajaccio
Golfe d'Ajaccio
Îles Sanguinaires
Capo di Feno
Propriano
Golfe de Valinco
Sartène
Montagne de Cagna
Porto-Vecchio
Golfe de Porto-Vecchio
Îles Cerbicale
Bonifacio
Capo Pertusato
Îles Lavezzi
Île Cavallo
Golfe de Ventilegne
Golfe de Santa-Manza
Solenzara
Forêt de l'Ospédale
Marseille, Nice, Toulon
Marseille, Nice, Toulon, Savona
Nice, Marseille, Toulon
Marseille, Porto Torres
Livorno
Savona
43°00'
42°30'
42°00'
41°30'
44°30'
7°30'
8°30'
9°00'
9°30'

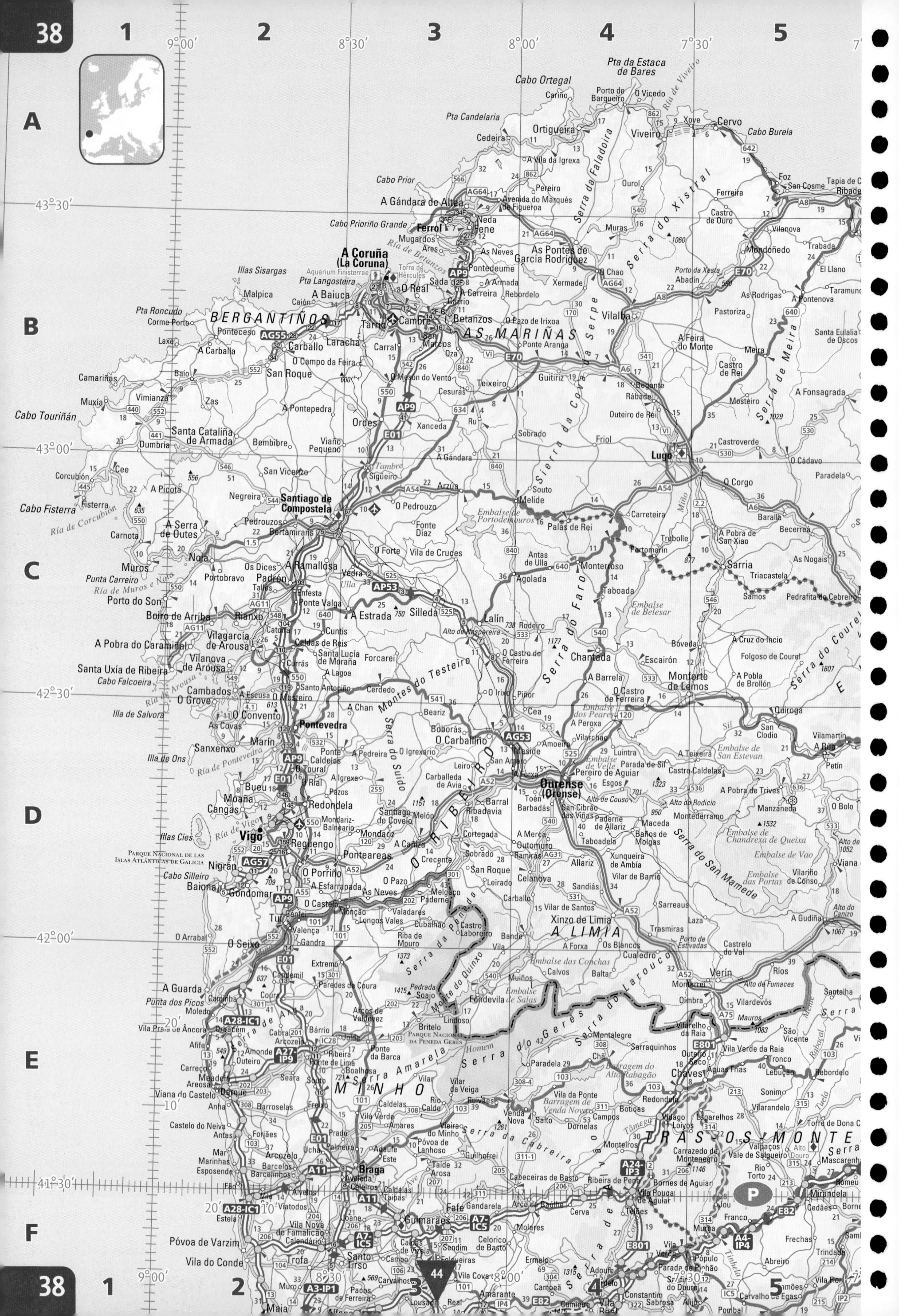
1
2
3
4
5
9°00′
8°30′
8°00′
7°30′
A
B
C
D
E
F
43°30′
43°00′
42°30′
42°00′
41°30′
Pta da Estaca de Bares
Cabo Ortegal
Pta Candelaria
Cabo Prior
Cabo Prioriño Grande
Illas Sisargas
Pta Langosteira
Pta Roncudo
Cabo Touriñán
Cabo Fisterra
Ría de Corcubión
Punta Carreiro
Ría de Muros e Noia
Cabo Falcoeira
Ría de Arousa
Illa de Salvora
Illa de Ons
Ría de Pontevedra
Illas Cíes
Ría de Vigo
Parque Nacional de las Islas Atlánticas de Galicia
Cabo Silleiro
Punta dos Picos
Cabo Burela
Ría de Viveiro
Ría de Betanzos
A Coruña
(La Coruna)
Aquarium Finisterrae
Torre de Hércules
Ferrol
Neda
Fene
Mugardos
Ares
Pontedeume
A Gándara de Altea
Cedeira
Cariño
Ortigueira
Porto do Barqueiro
O Vicedo
Viveiro
Xove
Cervo
Foz
San Cosme
Ribadeo
Ferreira
Castro de Ouro
Vilanova
Mondoñedo
Trabada
El Llano
Abadín
As Rodrigas
A Pontenova
Pastoriza
A Feira do Monte
Meira
Castro de Rei
Santa Eulalia de Oscos
A Fonsagrada
Mosteiro
Outeiro de Rei
Rábade
Begonte
Vilalba
As Pontes de García Rodríguez
O Chao
Xermade
Muras
Ourol
Serra da Faladoira
Serra do Xistral
Serra de Meira
Serra da Cova da Serpe
A Vila da Igrexa
Pereiro
Avenida do Marqués de Figueroa
As Neves
A Armada
A Carreira
Rebordelo
Sada
O Real
Carrio
Betanzos
Cambre
Tarrío
A Baiuca
Malpica
Caión
BERGANTIÑOS
AS MARIÑAS
Corme-Porto
Ponteceso
Laxe
A Carballa
Carballo
Laracha
O Campo da Feira
Carral
San Marcos
Oza
O Pazo de Irixoa
Ponte Aranga
Guitiriz
Teixeiro
Cesuras
O Mesón do Vento
Camariñas
Baio
San Roque
Vimianzo
Zas
Muxía
A Pontepedra
Ordes
Xanceda
Ru
Santa Cataliña de Armada
Dumbría
Bembibre
Viaño Pequeno
Sobrado
Friol
Lugo
Castroverde
O Cádavo
Paradela
O Corgo
Baralla
Becerreá
As Nogais
Triacastela
Samos
Pedrafita do Cebreiro
Sarria
A Pobra de San Xiao
Portomarín
Trebolle
Carreteira
Palas de Rei
Melide
Souto
Arzúa
A Gándara
Sigüeiro
Tambre
Santiago de Compostela
O Pedrouzo
Fonte Díaz
O Forte
Vila de Cruces
Embalse de Portodemouros
Sierra da Cova
Serra do Faro
Antas de Ulla
Monterroso
Agolada
Taboada
Embalse de Belesar
Corcubión
Cee
A Picota
Fisterra
Negreira
San Vicenzo
Pedrouzos
Bertamirans
A Serra de Outes
Carnota
Nois
Muros
Portobravo
Os Dices
A Ramallosa
Padrón
Vedra
Ulla
Taifas
Enfesta
Ponte Valga
A Estrada
Silleda
Lalín
Alto de Nespereira
Rodeiro
Chantada
Bóveda
A Cruz do Incio
Folgoso de Courel
A Pobla de Brollón
Serra do Courel
Escairón
Monforte de Lemos
A Barrela
O Castro de Ferreira
Porto do Son
Boiro de Arriba
Rianxo
Catoira
Cuntis
Caldas de Reis
Santa Lucía de Moraña
Forcarei
A Lagoa
A Pobra do Caramiñal
Vilagarcía de Arousa
Vilanova de Arousa
Santa Uxía de Ribeira
Cambados
A Escusa
O Mosteiro
Santo Antoniño
Cerdedo
Montes do Testeiro
O Irixo
Piñor
O Grove
O Convento
As Covas
Sanxenxo
Marín
Pontevedra
A Chan
Serra do Suído
Beariz
Boborás
O Carballiño
Cea
Amoeiro
Vilarchao
Embalse dos Peares
A Peroxa
Quiroga
San Clodio
Vilamartín
A Rúa
Petín
Embalse de San Estevan
Sil
Luintra
Parada de Sil
A Teixeira
Castro Caldelas
Embalse de Velle
Pereiro de Aguiar
Esgos
A Pobra de Trives
Manzaneda
O Bolo
Ponte Caldelas
A Pedreira
O Igrexario
O Toural
O Rial
A Igrexa
Pazos
Carballeda de Avia
Leiro
San Amaro
Maside
Ourense
(Orense)
A Forxa
Toén
Barbadás
San Cibrao das Viñas
Paderne de Allariz
Maceda
Baños de Molgas
Alto do Rodicio
Montederramo
Embalse de Chandrexa de Queixa
Embalse de Vao
Embalse das Portas
Vilariño de Conso
Alto de Couso
Bueu
Moaña
Cangas
Redondela
Vigo
Mondariz-Balneario
Mondariz
Santiago de Covelo
Melón
Barral
Ribadavia
O RIBEIRO
Cortegada
A Merca
Outomuro
Ramirás
Allariz
Xunqueira de Ambía
Vilar de Barrio
Serra do San Mamede
A Gudiña
Alto do Canizo
Nigrán
Baiona
Gondomar
Reguengo
Ponteareas
A Caniza
Crecente
Sobrado
San Roque
Leirado
Celanova
Sandiás
Sarreaus
O Porriño
A Esfarrapada
O Pazo
As Neves
Melgaço
Paderne
Carballo
Vilar de Santos
Xinzo de Limia
A LIMIA
Laza
Trasmiras
Porto de Estivadas
Castrelo do Val
O Castelo
Monção
Valadares
Longos Vales
Cubalhão
Castro Laboreiro
Serra da Peneda
Bande
Vila
A Forxa
Os Blancos
Cualedro
Verín
Ríos
Tui
Ganfei
Valença
Gandra
Riba de Mouro
O Arrabal
O Seixo
Extremo
Serra do Quinxo
Embalse das Conchas
Calvos
Baltar
Serra do Larouco
Monterrei
Oímbra
Alto de Fumaces
Vilardevós
Santalha
A Guarda
Caminha
Moledo
Cerdal
Coura
Paredes de Coura
Pedrada
Soajo
Embalse de Salas
Fondevila
Muiños
Arcos de Valdevez
Lindoso
Britelo
Parque Nacional da Peneda Gerês
Serra do Gerês
Montalegre
Sarraquinhos
Vilarelho da Raia
Vila Verde da Raia
São Vicente
Tronco
Lebução
Rebordelo
Vila Praia de Âncora
Orbacém
Afife
Amonde
Outeiro
Cabra
Arcozelo
Bárrio
Jolda
Ponte da Barca
Ponte de Lima
Ribeira
Boalhosa
Serra Amarela
Homem
Paradela
Chã
Barragem do Alto Rabagão
Chaves
Outeiro Seco
Águas Frias
Carreço
Meadela
Areosa
Darque
Viana do Castelo
Seara
Souto
Vilar
Vila Verde
MINHO
Vila da Ponte
Barragem de Venda Nova
Rio Caldo
Ruivães
Venda Nova
Salto
Dornelas
Campos
Boticas
Redondela
Vidago
Loivos
Lagarelhos
Sonim
Vilarandelo
Anha
Barroselas
Freixo
Caldelas
Amares
Serra da Cabreira
Castelo do Neiva
Antas
Forjães
Mar
Marinhas
Esposende
Arcozelo
Prado
Ucha
Palmeira
Vieira do Minho
Póvoa de Lanhoso
Adaúfe
Este
Guilhofrei
Monteiros
TRÁS-OS-MONTES
Carrazedo de Montenegro
Valpaços
Vale de Salgueiro
Alto Douro
Torre de Dona Chama
Mascarenhas
Rio Torto
Barcelos
Barcelinhos
Braga
Taíde
Arosa
Aveleda
Celeiros
Cabeceiras de Basto
Ribeira de Pena
Bornes de Aguiar
Mirandela
Romeu
Fão
Alvelos
Viatodos
Taipas
Caldelas
Fafe
Gandarela
Vila Pouca de Aguiar
Cerva
Telões
Jou
Franco
Cedães
Borne
Estela
Joane
Vila Nova de Famalicão
Calendário
Guimarães
Moreira de Cónegos
Molares
Celorico de Basto
Murça
Frechas
Póvoa de Varzim
Caldas de Vizela
Sendim
Vila Verde
Pópulo
Parada de Pinhão
Abreiro
Trindade
Vila do Conde
Trofa
Santo Tirso
Campo
Felgueiras
Ermelo
Serra do Alvão
Adoufe
Sabrosa
Carvalho de Egas
Vila Flor
Muro
Carvalhosa
Pacos de Ferreira
Vila Cova
Amarante
Campeã
Constantim
Pombal
Maia
Lousada
Vila Real
Alijó
Sabrosa
Cumieira
Sanfins do Douro
Aguiã
Moncorvo
P
44

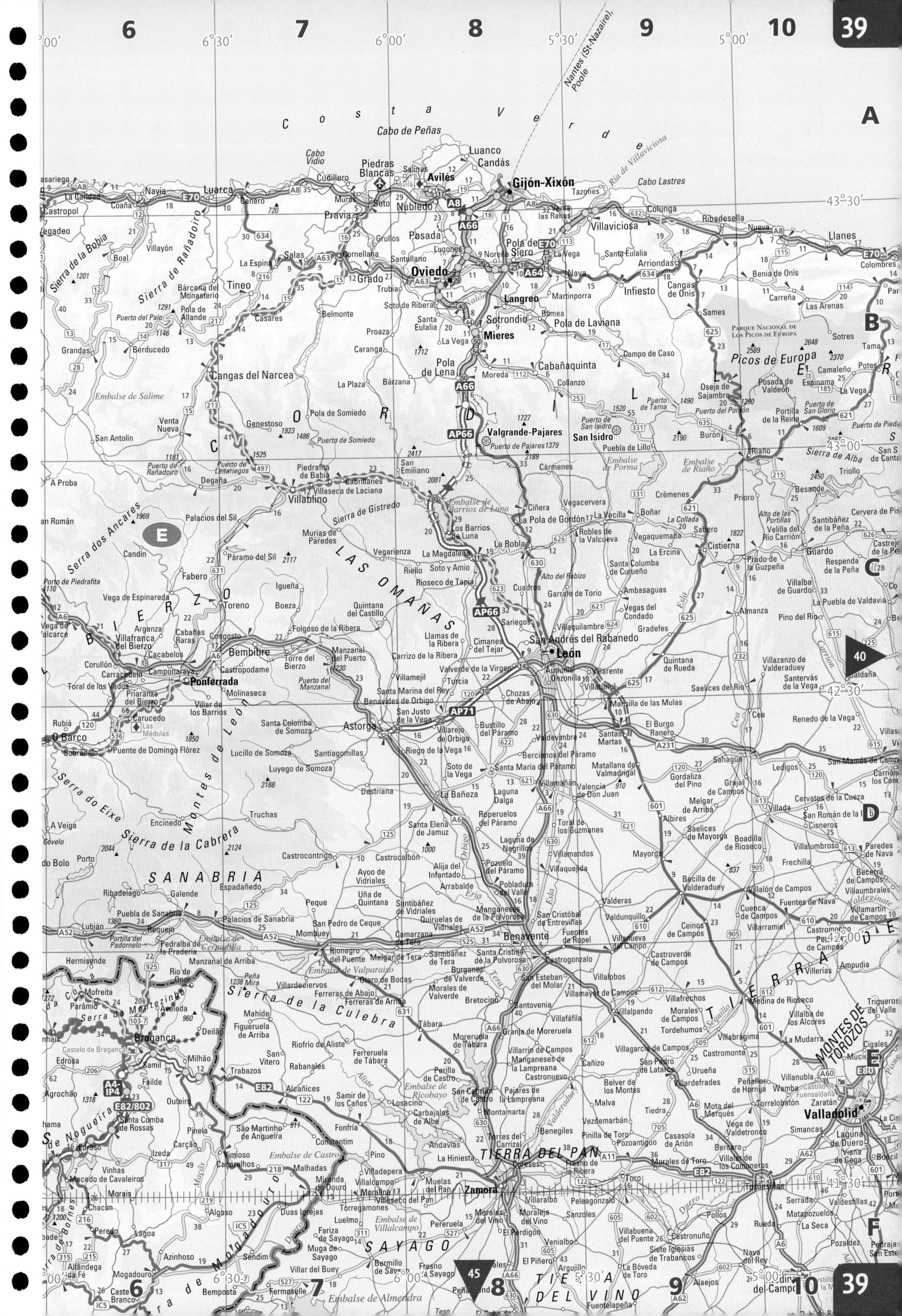
6
7
8
9
10
A
B
C
D
E
F
6°30′
6°00′
5°30′
5°00′
43°30′
43°00′
42°30′
42°00′
41°30′
Nantes (St-Nazaire), Poole
Costa Verde
Cabo de Peñas
Cabo Vidio
Piedras Blancas
Luanco
Candás
Avilés
Gijón-Xixón
Ría de Villaviciosa
Cabo Lastres
Navia
Luarca
Castropol
Vegadeo
Cudillero
Salinas
Muros
Soto
Nubledo
Pravia
Posada
Tazones
Colunga
Villaviciosa
Ribadesella
Llanes
Sierra de la Bobia
Sierra de Rañadoiro
Villayón
Boal
La Espina
Salas
Cornellana
Grullos
Grado
Oviedo
Lugones
Noreña
Pola de Siero
La Vega
Nava
Santa Eulalia
Arriondas
Benia de Onís
Cangas de Onís
Infiesto
Carreña
Las Arenas
Tineo
Bárcena del Monasterio
Pola de Allande
Puerto del Palo
Berducedo
Grandas
Trubia
Soto de Ribera
Langreo
Martinporra
Belmonte
Santa Eulalia
Sotrondio
Blimea
Pola de Laviana
Mieres
Proaza
Caranga
La Vega
Pola de Lena
Moreda
Cabañaquinta
Campo de Caso
Sames
Parque Nacional de los Picos de Europa
Picos de Europa
Sotres
Tama
Potes
Camaleño
Posada de Valdeón
Espinama
Oseja de Sajambre
Puerto del Pontón
Portilla de la Reina
Puerto de San Glorio
Embalse de Salime
Cangas del Narcea
La Plaza
Bárzana
Collanzo
Puerto de Tarna
Venta Nueva
Genestoso
Pola de Somiedo
Puerto de Somiedo
Valgrande-Pajares
Puerto de Pajares
Puerto de San Isidro
San Isidro
Burón
Riaño
San Antolín
Puerto de Rañadoiro
Puerto de Leitariegos
Piedrafita de Babia
San Emiliano
Embalse de Porma
Puebla de Lillo
Embalse de Riaño
Sierra de Alba
Triollo
A Proba
Degaña
Cabrillanes
Villaseca de Laciana
Villablino
Cármenes
Crémenes
Besande
Sierra dos Ancares
Palacios del Sil
Sierra de Gistredo
Embalse de Barrios de Luna
Ciñera
La Pola de Gordón
Vegacervera
La Vecilla
Boñar
La Collada
Sabero
Santibáñez de la Peña
Cervera de Pisuerga
San Román
Candín
Murias de Paredes
Los Barrios de Luna
La Robla
Robles de la Valcueva
Vegaquemada
Cistierna
Guardo
Páramo del Sil
Las Omañas
Vegarienza
La Magdalena
Riello
Soto y Amío
Rioseco de Tapia
Santa Colomba de Curueño
La Ercina
Prado de la Guzpeña
Respenda de la Peña
Porto de Piedrafita
Fabero
Alto del Rabizo
Cuadros
Garrafe de Torio
Ambasaguas
Vega de Espinareda
Bierzo
Toreno
Igueña
Boeza
Quintana del Castillo
Vegas del Condado
Almanza
Pino del Río
La Puebla de Valdavia
Vega de Valcarce
Arganza
Villafranca del Bierzo
Cabañas Raras
Congosto
Folgoso de la Ribera
Llamas de la Ribera
Sariegos
Villaquilambre
Gradefes
Cacabelos
Camponaraya
Bembibre
Torre del Bierzo
Manzanal del Puerto
Carrizo de la Ribera
Cimanes del Tejar
San Andrés del Rabanedo
León
Quintana de Rueda
Villazanzo de Valderaduey
Saldaña
Corullón
Carracedelo
Castropodame
Puerto del Manzanal
Villamejil
Valverde de la Virgen
Armunia
Onzonilla
Villarente
Villaturiel
Santervás de la Vega
Saelices del Río
Toral de los Vados
Ponferrada
Priaranza del Bierzo
Molinaseca
Turcia
Santa Marina del Rey
Chozas de Abajo
Mansilla de las Mulas
Villar de los Barrios
Benavides de Órbigo
Carucedo
Las Médulas
Santa Colomba de Somoza
Astorga
San Justo de la Vega
Villarejo de Órbigo
Bustillo del Páramo
Valdevimbre
Santas Martas
El Burgo Ranero
Cea
Renedo de la Vega
Rubiá
O Barco
Sobradelo
Puente de Domingo Flórez
Montes de León
Lucillo de Somoza
Santiagomillas
Riego de la Vega
Bercianos del Páramo
Sahagún
Luyego de Somoza
Soto de la Vega
Santa María del Páramo
Matallana de Valmadrigal
Gordaliza del Pino
Ledigos
San Mamés de Campos
Serra do Eixe
Destriana
La Bañeza
Laguna Dalga
Villamañán
Valencia de Don Juan
Grajal de Campos
Cervatos de la Cueza
Melgar de Arriba
Villada
San Román de la Cuba
Sierra de la Cabrera
Encinedo
Truchas
Roperuelos del Páramo
Toral de los Guzmanes
Albires
A Veiga
Santa Elena de Jamuz
Laguna de Negrillos
Saelices de Mayorga
Boadilla de Rioseco
Cisneros
Villamandos
Mayorga
Villaumbroso
Paredes de Nava
Castrocontrigo
Castrocalbón
Pozuelo del Páramo
Villaquejida
Frechilla
Sanabria
Ayoo de Vidriales
Alija del Infantado
Arrabalde
Pobladura del Valle
Becerril de Campos
Bolo
Ribadelago
Galende
Espadañedo
Uña de Quintana
Santibáñez de Vidriales
Villalón de Campos
Villaumbrales
Peque
Bercillo de Valderaduey
Valderas
Fuentes de Nava
Villamartín de Campos
Puebla de Sanabria
Lubián
Requejo
Palacios de Sanabria
San Pedro de Ceque
Quiruelas de Vidriales
Manganeses de la Polvorosa
San Cristóbal de Entreviñas
Valdunquillo
Cuenca de Campos
Villarramiel
Portilla del Padornelo
Pedralba de la Pradería
Embalse de Cernadilla
Mombuey
Camarzana de Tera
Benavente
Fuentes de Ropel
Villanueva del Campo
Ceinos de Campos
Castromocho
Hermisende
Manzanal de Arriba
Rionegro del Puente
Melgar de Tera
Santibáñez de Tera
Santa Cristina de la Polvorosa
Castrogonzalo
Castroverde de Campos
Tierra de Campos
Ampudia
Río de Onor
Embalse de Valparaíso
Otero de Bodas
Burganes de Valverde
San Esteban del Molar
Villalobos
Villerías
Mofreita
Parâmio
Serra de Montezinho
Aveleda
Villardeciervos
Ferreras de Abajo
Ferreras de Arriba
Morales de Valverde
Villamayor de Campos
Villafrechós
Medina de Rioseco
Trigueros del Valle
Sierra de la Culebra
Bretocino
Santovenia
Villalpando
Morales de Campos
Villalba de los Alcores
Montes de Torozos
Bragança
Deilão
Castelo de Bragança
Mahíde
Figueruela de Arriba
Tábara
Granja de Moreruela
Villafáfila
Tordehumos
Villabrágima
La Mudarra
Cigales
Mucientes
Edrosa
Samil
Milhão
Riofrío de Aliste
San Vitero
Ferreruela de Tábara
Moreruela de Tábara
Villarrín de Campos
Manganeses de la Lampreana
Villagarcía de Campos
San Pedro de Latarce
Castromonte
Urueña
Villanubla
Agrochão
Failde
Trabazos
Rabanales
Perilla de Castro
Castronuevo
Cañizo
Villardefrades
Peñaflor de Hornija
Wamba
Castillo de Fuensaldaña
Valladolid
Outeiro
Alcañices
Samir de los Caños
Embalse de Ricobayo
San Cebrián de Castro
Pajares de la Lampreana
Belver de los Montes
Zaratán
Serra de Nogueira
Santa Comba de Rossas
São Martinho de Angueira
Losacino
Carbajales de Alba
Montamarta
Malva
Tiedra
Mota del Marqués
Torrelobatón
Simancas
Pinela
Fonfría
Vezdemarbán
Vega de Valdetronco
Laguna de Duero
Izeda
Carção
Vimioso
Constantim
Andavías
Benegiles
Pinilla de Toro
Pozoantiguo
Casasola de Arión
Bercero
Villalar de los Comuneros
Viana de Cega
Embalse de Castro
Pino
La Hiniesta
Tierra del Pan
Coreses
Fresno de la Ribera
Morales de Toro
Vinhas
Macedo de Cavaleiros
Caçarelhos
Malhadas
Villadepera
Villalcampo
Miranda do Douro
Moralina
Muelas del Pan
Zamora
Toro
Tordesillas
Morais
Villaseco del Pan
Villaralbo
Peleagonzalo
Serrada
Valdestillas
Chacim
Algoso
Duas Igrejas
Torregamones
Moraleja del Vino
Sanzoles
Pollos
Matapozuelos
Peredo
Lagoa
Luelmo
Embalse de Villalcampo
Pereruela
Morales del Vino
El Perdigón
Villabuena del Puente
Castronuño
Rueda
La Seca
Fariza de Sayago
Sayago
Venialbo
Siete Iglesias de Trabancos
Pozaldez
Azinhoso
Sendim
Muga de Sayago
Villar del Buey
Bermillo de Sayago
Fresno de Sayago
El Piñero
Arguijo
La Bóveda de Toro
Nava del Rey
Alfândega da Fé
Mogadouro
Serra de Mogadouro
Bemposta
Fermoselle
Embalse de Almendra
Tierra del Vino
Alaejos
Fuentelapeña
Pedrajas de San Esteban
Castelo Branco
40
45
E70
A8
A63
A64
A66
AP66
AP71
A6
A52
A11
A60
A62
A231
E82
E80
IC5
IP4
E82/802

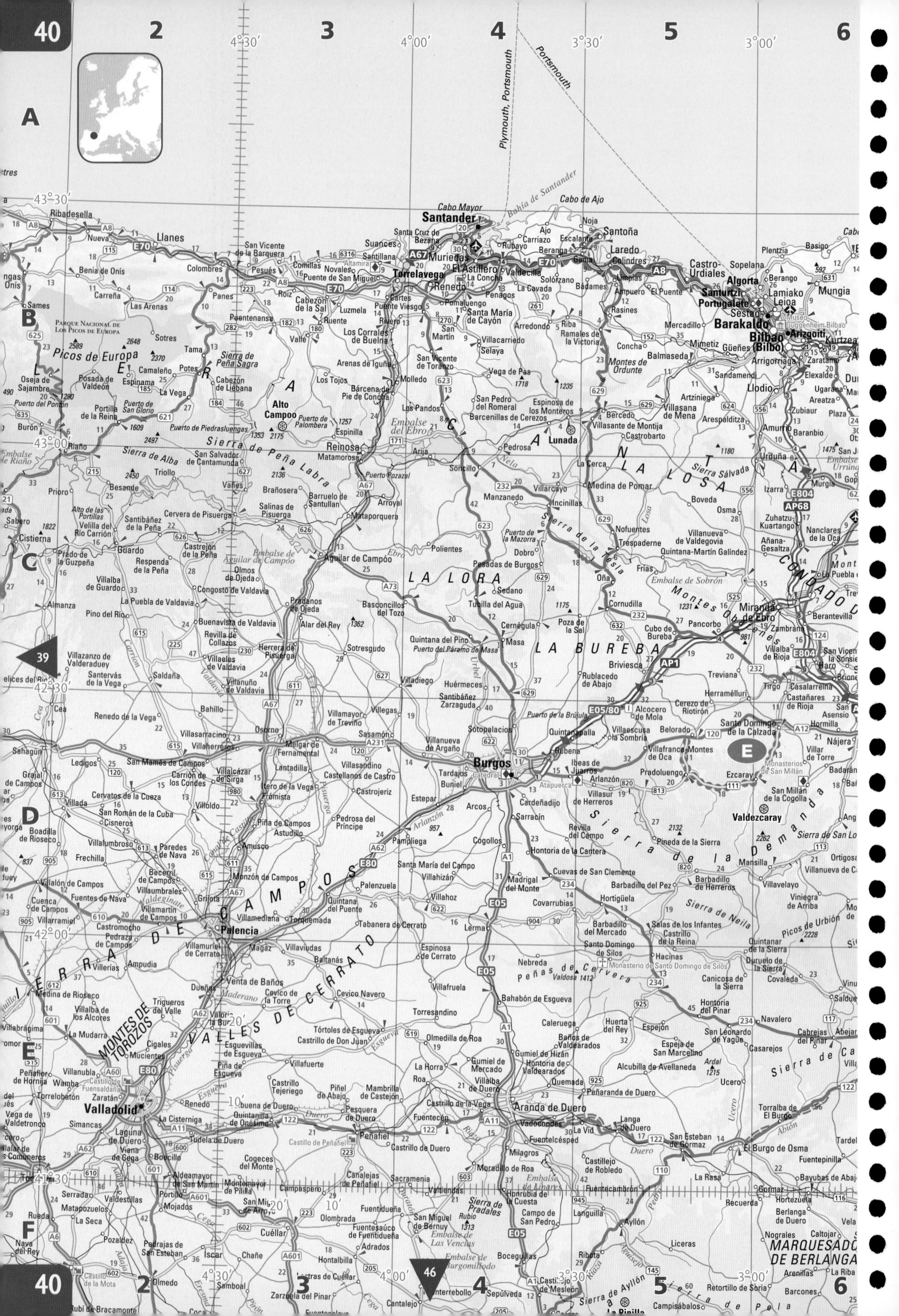
2
3
4
5
6
A
B
C
D
E
F
4°30′
4°00′
3°30′
3°00′
43°30′
43°00′
42°30′
42°00′
41°30′
Plymouth, Portsmouth
Portsmouth
Cabo Mayor
Santander
Bahía de Santander
Cabo de Ajo
Santoña
Laredo
Noja
Ajo
Castro-Urdiales
Algorta
Santurtzi
Portugalete
Sestao
Barakaldo
Bilbao (Bilbo)
Lamiako
Leioa
Mungia
Guggenheim Bilbao
Arrigorriaga
Ribadesella
Llanes
San Vicente de la Barquera
Colombres
Comillas
Santillana
Altamira
Torrelavega
Muriedas
El Astillero
Renedo
Suances
Santa Cruz de Bezana
Puente Viesgo
Santa María de Cayón
Parque Nacional de los Picos de Europa
Picos de Europa
Sierra de Peña Sagra
Potes
Camaleño
Posada de Valdeón
Oseja de Sajambre
Puerto del Pontón
Riaño
Embalse de Riaño
Puerto de San Glorio
Puerto de Piedrasluengas
Alto Campoo
Puerto de Palombera
Reinosa
Embalse del Ebro
Espinilla
Arija
Lunada
Espinosa de los Monteros
Villasante de Montija
Sierra de Peña Labra
Sierra de Alba
Cervera de Pisuerga
Guardo
Cistierna
Aguilar de Campóo
Embalse de Aguilar de Campóo
Medina de Pomar
Villarcayo
Sierra Sálvada
Orduña
Amurrio
Llodio
Villasana de Mena
Balmaseda
Montes de Ordunte
Sierra de la Tesla
Embalse de Sobrón
Montes Obarenes
Miranda de Ebro
Condado de Treviño
La Lora
La Bureba
Briviesca
Pancorbo
Oña
Frías
Trespaderne
Poza de la Sal
Sedano
Villadiego
Herrera de Pisuerga
Alar del Rey
Saldaña
Osorno
Melgar de Fernamental
Sasamón
Burgos
Atapuerca
Belorado
Santo Domingo de la Calzada
Ezcaray
Nájera
Haro
Valdezcaray
San Millán de la Cogolla
Monasterios de San Millán
Sierra de la Demanda
Pineda de la Sierra
Salas de los Infantes
Sierra de Neila
Picos de Urbión
Castrillo de la Reina
Covarrubias
Santo Domingo de Silos
Monasterio de Santo Domingo de Silos
Peñas de Cervera
Lerma
Castrojeriz
Frómista
Carrión de los Condes
Sahagún
Villalón de Campos
Tierra de Campos
Palencia
Dueñas
Venta de Baños
Baltanás
Valles de Cerrato
Montes de Torozos
Medina de Rioseco
Valladolid
Simancas
Tudela de Duero
Peñafiel
Castillo de Peñafiel
Aranda de Duero
Roa
Gumiel de Mercado
San Esteban de Gormaz
El Burgo de Osma
Sierra de Cabrejas
Navaleno
San Leonardo de Yagüe
Cuéllar
Íscar
Olmedo
Sierra de Pradales
Embalse de Las Vencías
Embalse de Burgomillodo
Riaza
Ayllón
Sierra de Ayllón
La Pinilla
Marquesado de Berlanga
Sepúlveda
Cantalejo
39
46
E
E70
A8
A67
A73
A62
A231
E80
E05
E05/80
E804
AP68
AP1
A1
A11
A12
A60
A601

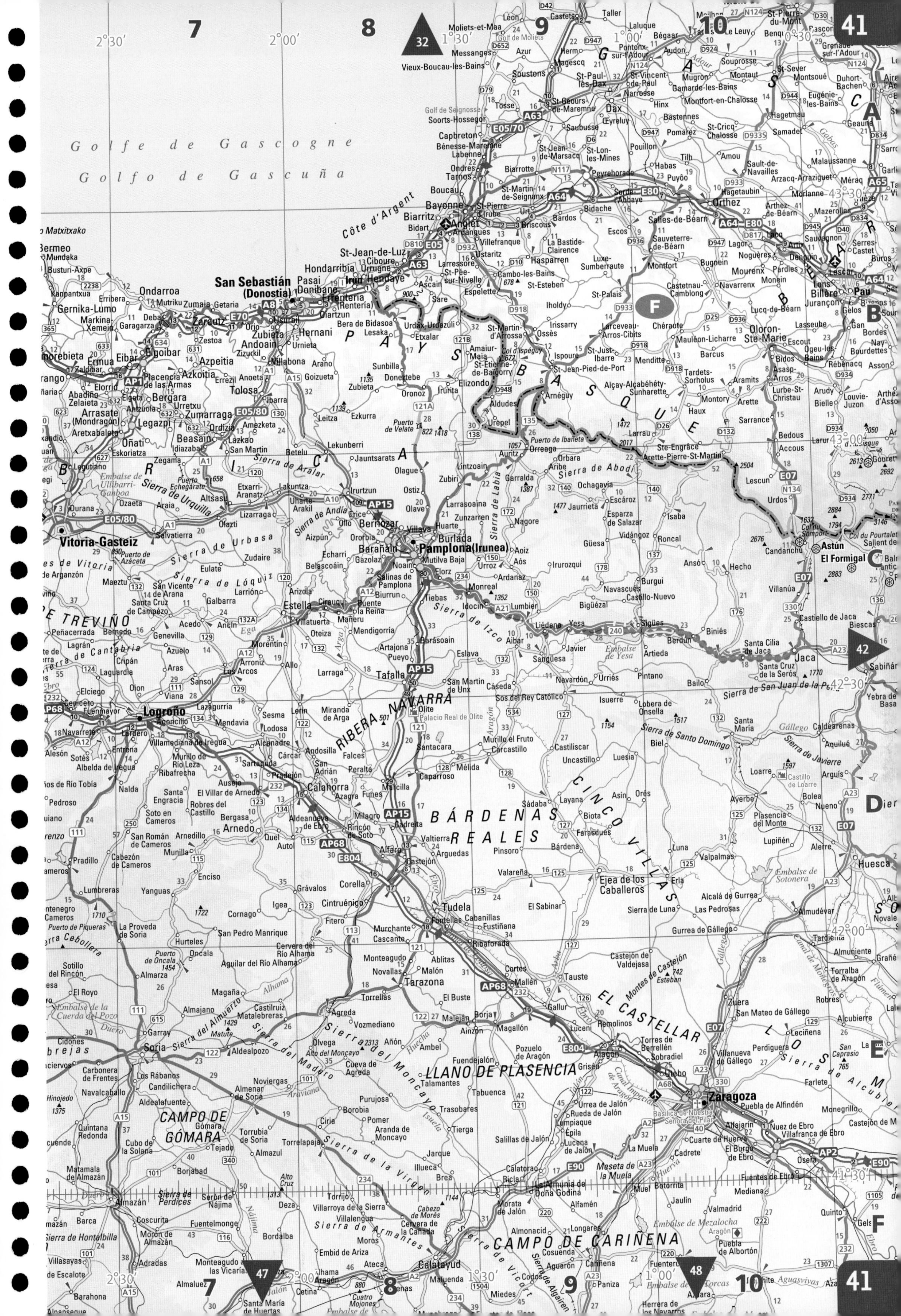
7
8
9
10
32
42
47
48
A
B
C
D
E
F
Golfe de Gascogne
Golfo de Gascuña
Côte d'Argent
PAYS BASQUE
Bayonne
Biarritz
Anglet
St-Jean-de-Luz
Hendaye
Irun
San Sebastián (Donostia)
Dax
Orthez
Pau
Oloron-Ste-Marie
Pamplona(Iruñea)
Vitoria-Gasteiz
Logroño
Estella
Tafalla
Olite
RIBERA NAVARRA
BÁRDENAS REALES
CINCO VILLAS
Tudela
Calahorra
Tarazona
Jaca
Huesca
Zaragoza
EL CASTELLAR
LLANO DE PLASENCIA
CAMPO DE GÓMARA
CAMPO DE CARIÑENA
Soria
Calatayud
Almazán
Sierra de Urbasa
Sierra del Moncayo
Sierra de la Virgen
Sierra de Armantes
Sierra de San Juan de la Peña
Sierra de Santo Domingo
Montes de Castejón
Meseta de la Muela
Sierra de Abodi
Sierra de Izco
Sierra de Andía
Sierra de Aralar
Sierra de Urquilla
Sierra de Lóquiz
Embalse de Yesa
Palacio Real de Olite

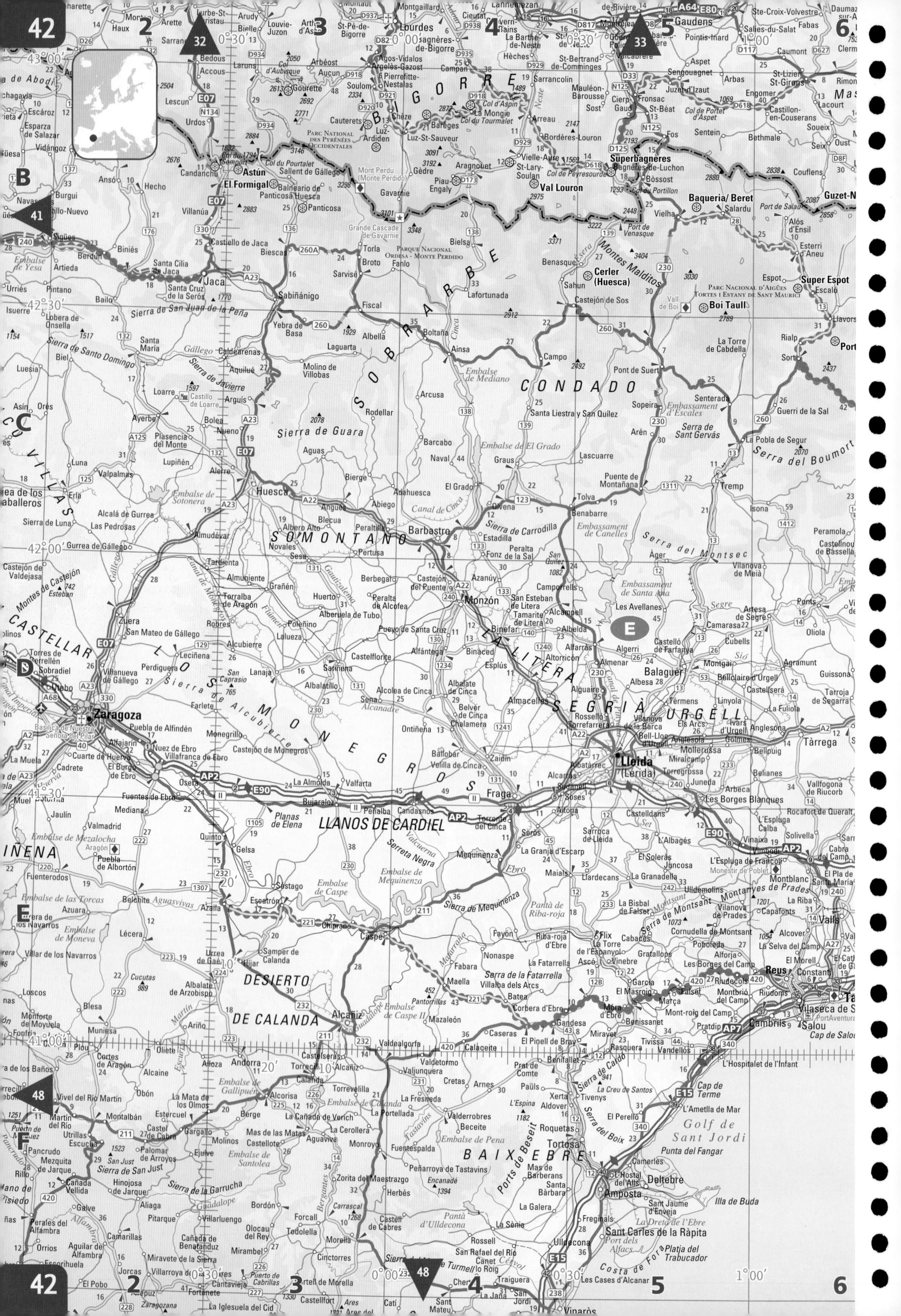
42
2
3
4
5
6
32
33
41
48
B
C
D
E
F
Lourdes
Argelès-Gazost
Gourette
Cauterets
Luz-St-Sauveur
Barèges
La Mongie
Col du Tourmalet
Col d'Aspin
BIGORRE
Bagnères-de-Bigorre
Lannemezan
St-Gaudens
St-Bertrand-de-Comminges
Sarrancolin
Arreau
Bordères-Louron
Vielle-Aure
St-Lary-Soulan
Val Louron
Superbagnères
Bagnères-de-Luchon
Bossòst
Baqueria/ Beret
Salardu
Vielha
Guzet-Neige
St-Girons
Castillon-en-Couserans
Aspet
Fronsac
Fos
Bedous
Accous
Laruns
Arudy
Oloron-Ste-Marie
Aretteia
Lescun
Urdos
Candanchú
Astún
El Formigal
Sallent de Gállego
Panticosa
Balneario de Panticosa
Biescas
Torla
Broto
Fanlo
Gavarnie
Gèdre
Piau-Engaly
Aragnouet
Mont Perdu (Monte Perdido)
PARC NATIONAL DES PYRÉNÉES OCCIDENTALES
PARQUE NACIONAL ORDESA - MONTE PERDIDO
Grande Cascade de Gavarnie
Bielsa
Benasque
Cerler (Huesca)
Montes Malditos
Castejón de Sos
Vall de Boí
Boi Taull
PARC NACIONAL D'AIGÜES TORTES I ESTANY DE SANT MAURICI
Espot
Super Espot
Esterri d'Àneu
Llavorsí
Rialp
Sort
Port del Comte
La Torre de Cabdella
Pont de Suert
Sopeira
Embassament d'Escales
Senterada
Serra de Sant Gervás
La Pobla de Segur
Serra del Boumort
Tremp
Isona
Guerri de la Sal
Canfranc
Jaca
Santa Cilia de Jaca
Castiello de Jaca
Villanúa
Sabiñánigo
Fiscal
Boltaña
Aínsa
Lafortunada
SOBRARBE
Sierra de San Juan de la Peña
Yebra de Basa
Embalse de Yesa
Sigüés
Berdún
Artieda
Biniés
Hecho
Ansó
Burgui
Navascués
Urriés
Pintano
Bailo
Isuerre
Lobera de Onsella
Sierra de Santo Domingo
Biel
Luesia
Santa María
Caldearenas
Sierra de Javierre
Loarre
Castillo de Loarre
Arguís
Ayerbe
Bolea
Nueno
Plasencia del Monte
Lupiñén
Alerre
Huesca
Sierra de Guara
Aguas
Barcabo
Rodellar
Arcusa
Campo
CONDADO
Embalse de Mediano
Santa Liestra y San Quílez
Embalse de El Grado
Graus
El Grado
Naval
Lascuarre
Arén
Puente de Montañana
Tolva
Benabarre
Embassament de Canelles
Serra del Montsec
Àger
Vilanova de Meià
Embassament de Santa Ana
Les Avellanes
Artesa de Segre
Ponts
Camarasa
Cubells
Oliola
Guissona
Agramunt
Balaguer
Bellcaire d'Urgell
Castellserà
Tarroja de Segarra
La Fuliola
Anglesola
Tàrrega
Bellpuig
Belianes
Vallfogona de Riucorb
Cinco Villas
Ejea de los Caballeros
Erla
Luna
Valpalmas
Sierra de Luna
Alcalá de Gurrea
Las Pedrosas
Almudévar
Gurrea de Gállego
Castejón de Valdejasa
Montes de Castejón
Esteban
Tardienta
Almuniente
Grañén
Torralba de Aragón
Robres
Alcubierre
Perdiguera
Leciñena
Sierra de Alcubierre
LOS MONEGROS
Monegrillo
Farlete
Castejón de Monegros
Sariñena
Lanaja
Lalueza
Poleñino
Alberuela de Tubo
Huerto
Berbegal
Peralta de Alcofea
Castejón del Puente
Monzón
Pueyo de Santa Cruz
Alfántega
Binaced
Binéfar
LA LITERA
Tamarite de Litera
San Esteban de Litera
Alcampell
Albelda
Alfarràs
Algerri
Almenar
Alguaire
Almacelles
SEGRIÀ
URGELL
Rosselló
Torrefarrera
Vilanova de la Barca
Bell-Lloc d'Urgell
Mollerussa
Golmés
Miralcamp
Torregrossa
Juneda
Lleida (Lérida)
Alcarràs
Albatàrrec
Sudanell
Soses
Aitona
Fraga
Zaidín
Velilla de Cinca
Ballobar
Chalamera
Belver de Cinca
Alcolea de Cinca
Albalate de Cinca
Esplús
Barbastro
SOMONTANO
Sierra de Carrodilla
Estadilla
Fonz
Peralta de la Sal
Azanúy
Olvena
Berbegal
Abiego
Adahuesca
Bierge
Canal de Cinca
Angüés
Peraltilla
Blecua
Novales
Sesa
Pertusa
Ontiñena
Valfarta
Candasnos
Peñalba
Bujaraloz
LLANOS DE CARDIEL
Torrente de Cinca
Serós
Mequinenza
Embalse de Mequinenza
Serreta Negra
La Granja d'Escarp
Maials
Llardecans
Castelldans
Les Borges Blanques
Arbeca
L'Espluga Calba
Vinaixa
Vimbodí
Monestir de Poblet
L'Espluga de Francolí
Montblanc
Valls
Zaragoza
Basílica de Nuestra Señora del Pilar
Utebo
Sobradiel
Torres de Berrellén
Villanueva de Gállego
Zuera
San Mateo de Gállego
CASTELLAR
Puebla de Alfindén
Alfajarín
Nuez de Ebro
Villafranca de Ebro
Cuarte de Huerva
Cadrete
El Burgo de Ebro
La Muela
María de Huerva
Muel
Jaulín
Osera
Fuentes de Ebro
Mediana
Valmadrid
Quinto
Gelsa
Planas de Elena
Embalse de Mezalocha
Aragón
Puebla de Albortón
CARIÑENA
Fuenterodos
Belchite
Aguasvivas
Embalse de las Torcas
Azuara
Herrera de los Navarros
Embalse de Moneva
Lécera
Villar de los Navarros
Cucutas
Albalate de Arzobispo
Loscos
Blesa
Monforte de Moyuela
Muniesa
Azaila
Escatrón
Sástago
Embalse de Caspe
Chiprana
Caspe
Sierra de Mequinenza
Samper de Calanda
Híjar
Urrea de Gaén
DESIERTO DE CALANDA
Alcañiz
Embalse de Caspe II
Mazaleón
Fabara
Nonaspe
Maella
Fayón
Riba-roja d'Ebre
Pantà de Riba-roja
Flix
La Torre de l'Espanyol
Ascó
Vinebre
La Fatarrella
Serra de la Fatarrella
Villalba dels Arcs
Batea
Corbera d'Ebre
Gandesa
Móra d'Ebre
El Masroig
Falset
Marçà
La Bisbal de Falset
Serra de Montsant
Cabacés
Cornudella de Montsant
Poboleda
Vilanova de Prades
Montanyes de Prades
Ulldemolins
Alforja
Les Borges del Camp
Reus
Montbrió del Camp
Riudoms
Mont-roig del Camp
Cambrils
Salou
Vila-seca
PortAventura
Cap de Salou
Tarragona
Benissanet
Miravet
Tivissa
Vandellòs
Pratdip
L'Hospitalet de l'Infant
L'Ametlla de Mar
Cap de Terme
Golf de Sant Jordi
Punta del Fangar
El Perelló
Camarles
Deltebre
Amposta
Sant Jaume d'Enveja
Illa de Buda
La Dreta de l'Ebre
Sant Carles de la Ràpita
Port dels Alfacs
Platja del Trabucador
Costa de Fora
Les Cases d'Alcanar
Ulldecona
Freginals
La Galera
Santa Bàrbara
Mas de Barberans
Tortosa
BAIX EBRE
Ports de Beseit
Roquetas
Aldover
Xerta
Tivenys
Serra de Cardó
La Creu de Santos
Serra del Boix
Paüls
Prat de Comte
Benifallet
Rasquera
El Pinell de Bray
Caseras
Calaceite
Valdealgorfa
Valdetormo
Valjunquera
Cretas
Arnes
Beceite
Valderrobres
Embalse de Pena
Fuentespalda
Peñarroya de Tastavins
Tastavins
La Fresneda
La Portellada
Torrevelilla
La Cañada de Verich
Calanda
Embalse de Calanda
Alcorisa
Castelserás
Torrecilla de Alcañiz
Alcañiz
Andorra
Alloza
Oliete
Ariño
Alcaine
Obón
Embalse de Gallipuén
La Mata de los Olmos
Berge
Mas de las Matas
Aguaviva
Castellote
Embalse de Santolea
Molinos
Ejulve
Gargallo
Castel de Cabra
Estercuel
Montalbán
Martín del Río
Utrillas
Escucha
Pancrudo
Mezquita de Jarque
Sierra de San Just
Palomar de Arroyos
Hinojosa de Jarque
Cañada Vellida
Sierra de la Garrucha
Aliaga
Pitarque
Villarluengo
Cañada de Benatanduz
Miravete de la Sierra
Mirambel
Olocau del Rey
Bordón
Forcall
Todolella
Morella
Zorita del Maestrazgo
Herbés
Monroyo
Encanadé
Pantà d'Ulldecona
Castell de Cabres
La Sènia
Rossell
San Rafael del Río
Canet lo Roig
Traiguera
La Jana
Chert
Sant Mateu
San Jordi
Vinaròs
Catí
Castellfort
Ares del Maestrat
Cantavieja
Villarroya de los Pinares
Fortanete
Jorcas
Allepuz
El Pobo
Camarillas
Aguilar de Alfambra
Orrios
Perales del Alfambra
Galve
LLANOS DE CARDIEL
Sierra de Tornell lo Roig
Cinctorres
Puerto de Cabrillas
La Iglesuela del Cid
Tronchón
Villarluengo
Valdealgorfa
Plou
Cortes de Aragón
Vivel del Río Martín
Llanos de Visiedo
Rillo
Alfambra
Escorihuela

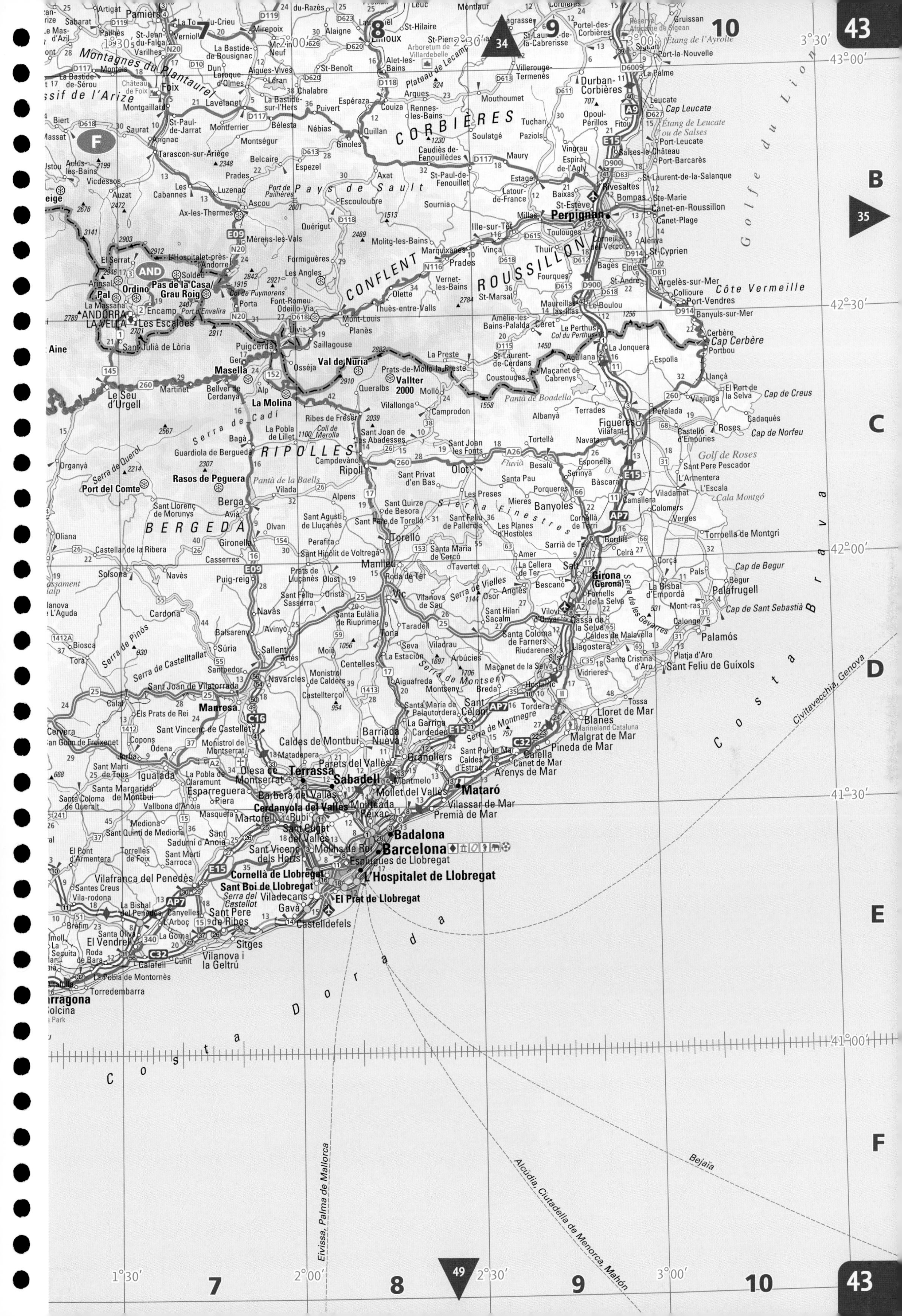
43
7
8
9
10
34
35
49
B
C
D
E
F
1°30′
2°00′
2°30′
3°00′
3°30′
43°00′
42°30′
42°00′
41°30′
41°00′
Pamiers
Mirepoix
Limoux
St-Hilaire
Gruissan
Montagnes du Plantaurel
Massif de l'Arize
Foix
Lavelanet
Quillan
CORBIÈRES
Durban-Corbières
Leucate
Cap Leucate
Étang de Leucate ou de Salses
Port-Leucate
Port-Barcarès
Tarascon-sur-Ariège
Pays de Sault
Ax-les-Thermes
Rivesaltes
Perpignan
Canet-en-Roussillon
Golfe du Lion
ROUSSILLON
CONFLENT
Prades
Argelès-sur-Mer
Côte Vermeille
Port-Vendres
Banyuls-sur-Mer
Cerbère
Cap Cerbère
Portbou
L'Hospitalet-près-l'Andorre
AND
Pas de la Casa/Grau Roig
Ordino
ANDORRA LA VELLA
Les Escaldes
Encamp
Sant Julià de Lòria
Puigcerdà
Masella
Val de Núria
Vallter 2000
La Molina
Le Seu d'Urgell
Serra del Cadí
RIPOLLES
Ripoll
Olot
Figueres
Roses
Cap de Creus
Cadaqués
Cap de Norfeu
Golf de Roses
Banyoles
Serra de Queralt
Port del Comte
Rasos de Peguera
Berga
BERGEDÀ
Torelló
Manlleu
Vic
Girona (Gerona)
Palafrugell
Cap de Begur
Cap de Sant Sebastià
Palamós
Sant Feliu de Guíxols
Costa Brava
Solsona
Cardona
Manresa
Serra de Castelltallat
Serra de Montseny
Lloret de Mar
Blanes
Malgrat de Mar
Pineda de Mar
Calella
Arenys de Mar
Mataró
Granollers
Terrassa
Sabadell
Igualada
Badalona
Barcelona
L'Hospitalet de Llobregat
Cornellà de Llobregat
Sant Boi de Llobregat
El Prat de Llobregat
Castelldefels
Sitges
Vilanova i la Geltrú
Vilafranca del Penedès
El Vendrell
Tarragona
Costa Dorada
Civitavecchia, Genova
Bejaïa
Alcúdia, Ciutadella de Menorca, Mahón
Elvissa, Palma de Mallorca

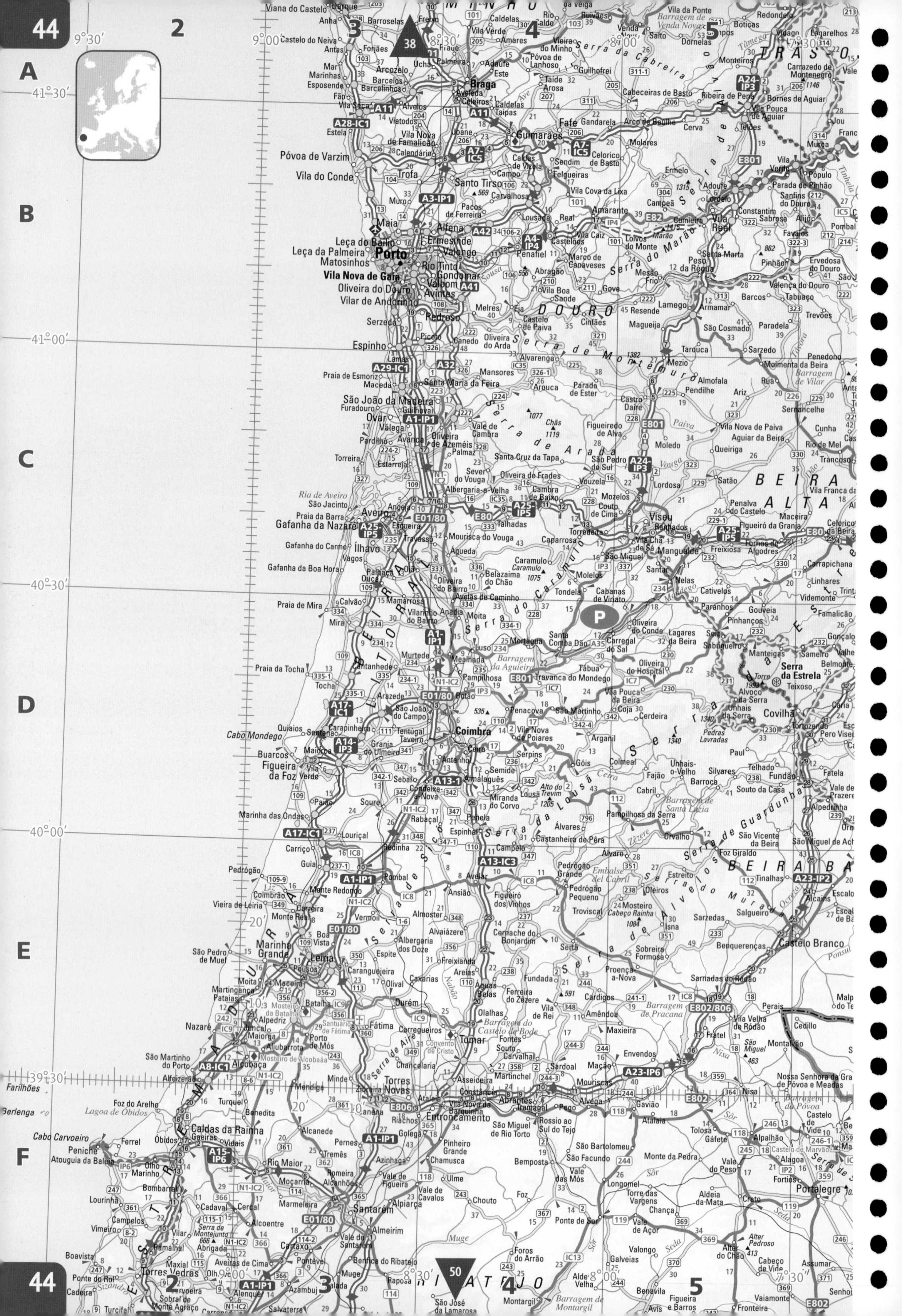

A
B
C
D
E
F
2
3
4
5
9°30′
9°00′
8°30′
8°00′
7°30′
41°30′
41°00′
40°30′
40°00′
39°30′
38
50
M I N H O
T R Á S - O S
D O U R O
B E I R A
A L T A
B E I R A B A
L I T O R A L
R I B A T E J O
Viana do Castelo
Anha
Barroselas
Castelo do Neiva
Antas
Forjães
Mar
Marinhas
Esposende
Fão
Vila Seca
Arcozelo
Barcelos
Barcelinhos
Ucha
Alvelos
Viatodos
Estela
Póvoa de Varzim
Vila do Conde
Vila Nova de Famalicão
Calendário
Trofa
Santo Tirso
Muro
Maia
Leça do Balio
Leça da Palmeira
Matosinhos
Porto
Vila Nova de Gaia
Oliveira do Douro
Vilar de Andorinho
Ermesinde
Valongo
Rio Tinto
Gondomar
Valbom
Avintes
Alfena
Pedroso
Serzedo
Espinho
Lamas
Praia de Esmoriz
Maceda
São João da Madeira
Furadouro
Ovar
Válega
Pardilhó
Avanca
Oliveira de Azeméis
Torreira
Estarreja
Ria de Aveiro
São Jacinto
Praia da Barra
Gafanha da Nazaré
Aveiro
Esgueira
Gafanha do Carmo
Ílhavo
Vagos
Gafanha da Boa Hora
Oliveira do Bairro
Praia de Mira
Mira
Calvão
Mamarrosa
Anadia
Praia da Tocha
Tocha
Cantanhede
Mealhada
Luso
Murtede
Quiaios
Cabo Mondego
Buarcos
Figueira da Foz
Coimbra
Condeixa-a-Nova
Soure
Marinha das Ondas
Louriçal
Carriço
Guia
Pedrógão
Pombal
Monte Redondo
Vieira de Leiria
Monte Real
São Pedro de Muel
Marinha Grande
Leiria
Maceira
Batalha
Nazaré
Alcobaça
Porto de Mós
Fátima
São Martinho do Porto
Foz do Arelho
Caldas da Rainha
Óbidos
Berlenga
Farilhões
Cabo Carvoeiro
Peniche
Atouguia da Baleia
Lourinhã
Bombarral
Cadaval
Rio Maior
Santarém
Almeirim
Cartaxo
Torres Vedras
Alenquer
Azambuja
Benavente
Torres Novas
Entroncamento
Tomar
Abrantes
Constância
Golegã
Chamusca
Alpiarça
Ponte de Sor
Gavião
Nisa
Castelo Branco
Portalegre
Alter do Chão
Crato
Braga
Guimarães
Fafe
Felgueiras
Amarante
Penafiel
Paredes
Lousada
Marco de Canaveses
Castelo de Paiva
Cinfães
Resende
Lamego
Peso da Régua
Vila Real
Mesão Frio
Arouca
Santa Maria da Feira
Vale de Cambra
Sever do Vouga
Albergaria-a-Velha
Águeda
Oliveira de Frades
Vouzela
São Pedro do Sul
Castro Daire
Viseu
Mangualde
Nelas
Tondela
Santa Comba Dão
Mortágua
Penacova
Arganil
Góis
Lousã
Miranda do Corvo
Penela
Ansião
Figueiró dos Vinhos
Pedrógão Grande
Sertã
Oleiros
Fundão
Covilhã
Serra da Estrela
Manteigas
Seia
Gouveia
Celorico da Beira
Trancoso
Moimenta da Beira
Tarouca
Sernancelhe
Penedono
Vila Nova de Paiva
Sátão
Penalva do Castelo
Fornos de Algodres
Oliveira do Hospital
Tábua
Carregal do Sal
Oliveira de Conde
Chaves
Ribeira de Pena
Cabeceiras de Basto
Celorico de Basto
Mondim de Basto
Vila Pouca de Aguiar
Sabrosa
Alijó
Murça
Serra do Marão
Serra de Montemuro
Serra do Caramulo
Serra da Lousã
Serra de Alvelos
Serra de Aire
Serra da Gardunha
Serra de Arada
Serra de Estrela
Barragem da Aguieira
Barragem de Santa Luzia
Barragem do Castelo de Bode
Barragem de Pracana
Barragem de Montargil
Vila Velha de Ródão
Proença-a-Nova
Mação
Sardoal
Vila de Rei
Ferreira do Zêzere
Ourém
Vila Nova da Barquinha
Montargil
Coruche
São José da Lamarosa
Fronteira
Avis
Sousel
Figueira e Barros
Galveias
Benavila
Ponte de Sor
Montalvão
Castelo de Vide
Marvão
Alpalhão
Tolosa
Gáfete
Fratel
Cedillo
P

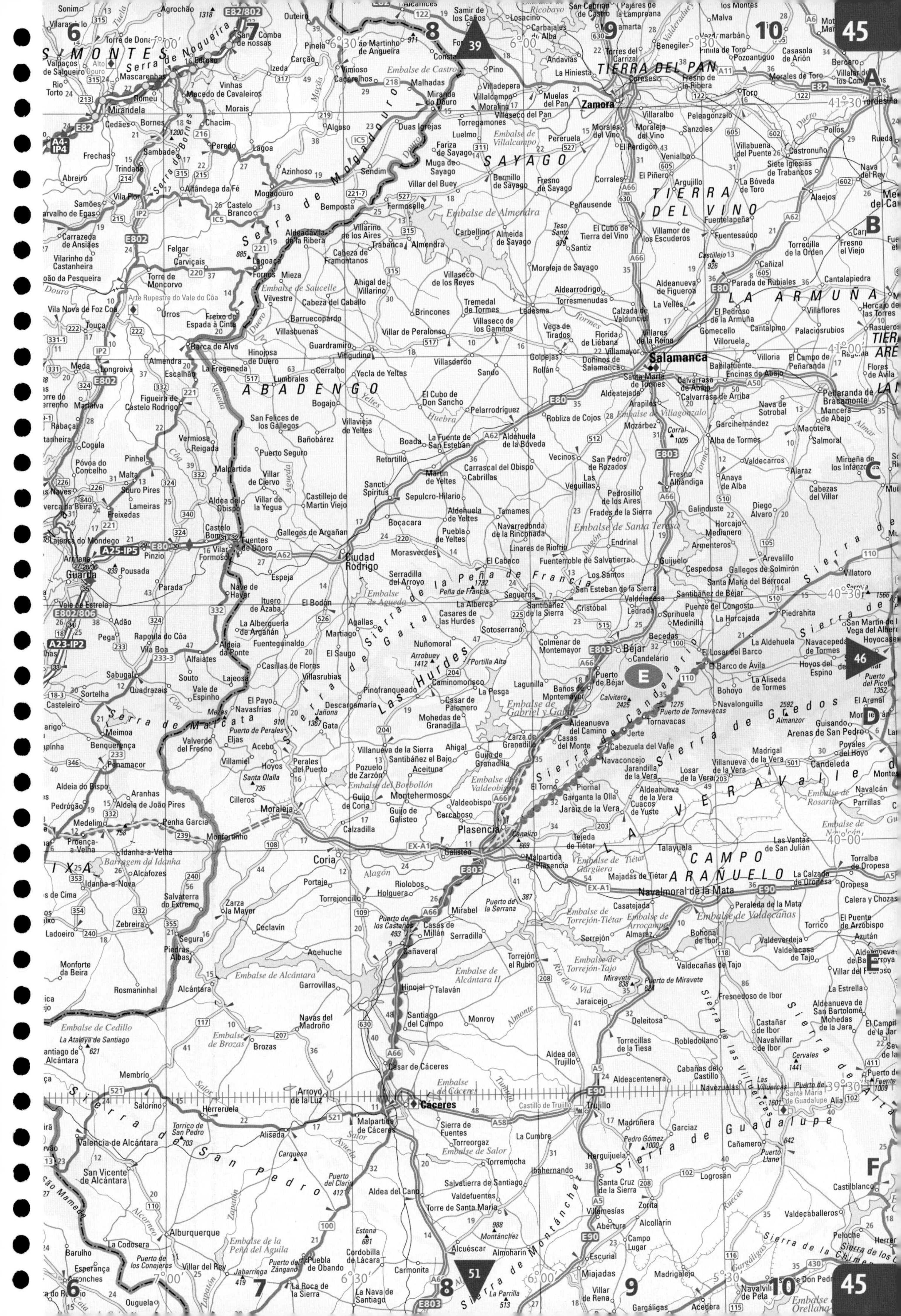

6
7
8
9
10
39
A
B
C
D
E
F
46
51
Zamora
Salamanca
Ciudad Rodrigo
Béjar
Plasencia
Coria
Cáceres
Trujillo
Miajadas
Navalmoral de la Mata
Mirandela
Guarda
Alcántara
Valencia de Alcántara
Alburquerque
TIERRA DEL PAN
SAYAGO
TIERRA DEL VINO
LA ARMUÑA
ABADENGO
Las Hurdes
LA VERA
CAMPO ARAÑUELO
Serra de Nogueira
Serra de Bornes
Sierra de Mogadouro
Sierra de Gata
Sierra de la Peña de Francia
Serra de Malcata
Sierra de Candelario
Sierra de Gredos
Sierra de San Pedro
Sierra de Guadalupe
Sierra de Montánchez
Sierra de las Villuercas
Sierra de Altamira
Embalse de Almendra
Embalse de Ricobayo
Embalse de Castro
Embalse de Villalcampo
Embalse de Saucelle
Embalse de Santa Teresa
Embalse de Villagonzalo
Embalse de Águeda
Embalse de Gabriel y Galán
Embalse de Valdeobispo
Embalse del Borbollón
Embalse de Alcántara
Embalse de Alcántara II
Embalse de Torrejón-Tajo
Embalse de Torrejón-Tiétar
Embalse de Valdecañas
Embalse de Arrocampo
Embalse de Cedillo
Embalse de Brozas
Embalse de Cáceres
Embalse de Salor
Embalse de la Peña del Águila
Embalse de Rosarito
Barragem da Idanha
Torre de Moncorvo
Vila Nova de Foz Côa
Barca de Alva
Figueira de Castelo Rodrigo
Almeida
Vilar Formoso
Fuentes de Oñoro
Sabugal
Penamacor
Idanha-a-Nova
Castelo Branco
Vitigudino
Lumbrales
Ledesma
Alba de Tormes
Peñaranda de Bracamonte
Guijuelo
La Alberca
Hervás
El Barco de Ávila
Jarandilla de la Vera
Moraleja
Montehermoso
Galisteo
Malpartida de Plasencia
Casar de Cáceres
Arroyo de la Luz
Malpartida de Cáceres
Brozas
Logrosán
Zorita
Madrigalejo
Navalvillar de Pela
Oropesa
Toro
Fermoselle
Miranda do Douro
Mogadouro
E80
E82
E90
E802
E803
A62
A66
A5
A50
EX-A1
A58
A23-IP2
A25-IP5

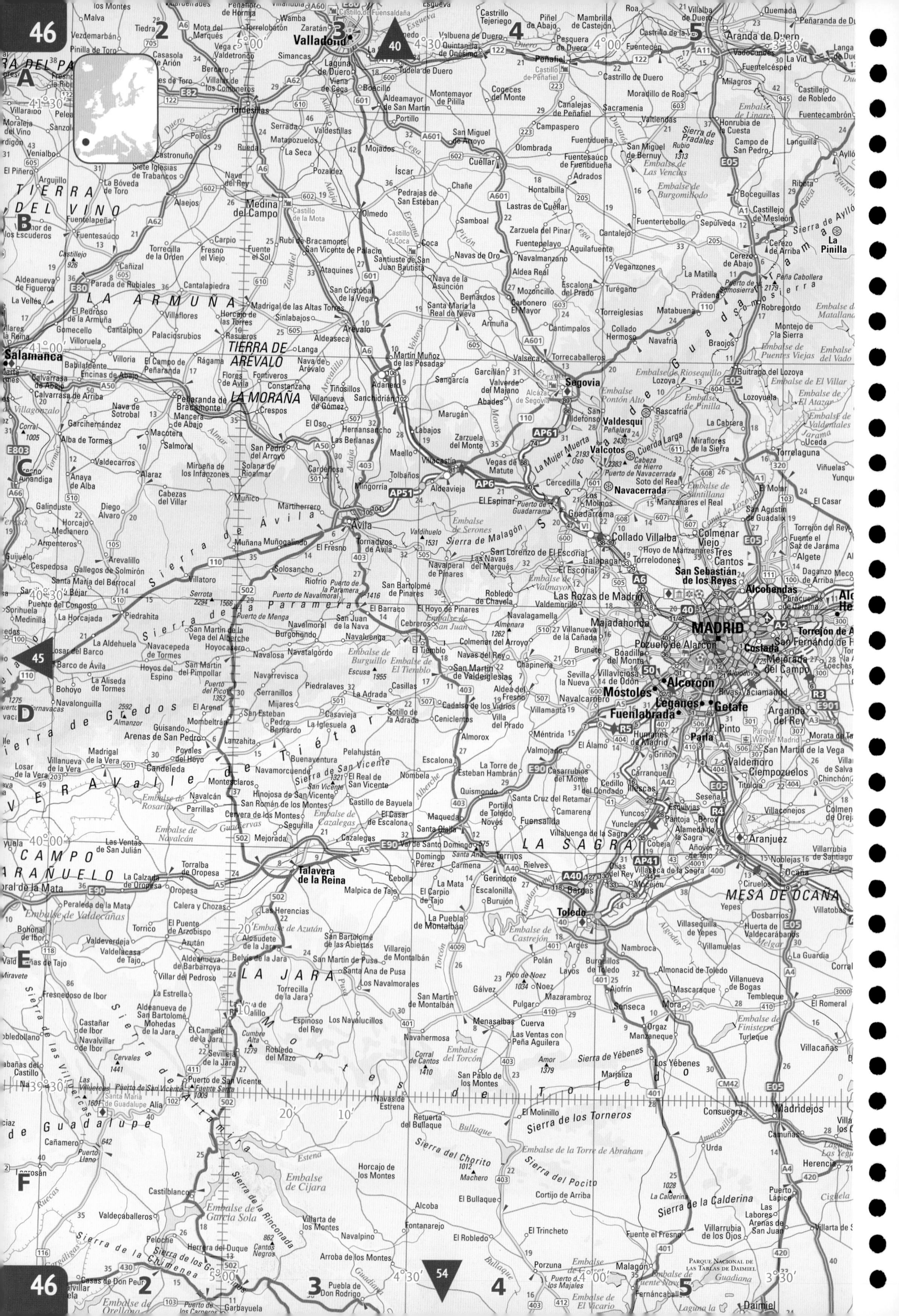

Valladolid
Tordesillas
Medina del Campo
Salamanca
Peñaranda de Bracamonte
Arévalo
Ávila
Segovia
Cuéllar
Peñafiel
Aranda de Duero
MADRID
Alcobendas
San Sebastián de los Reyes
Collado Villalba
Colmenar Viejo
Las Rozas de Madrid
Majadahonda
Pozuelo de Alarcón
Móstoles
Alcorcón
Leganés
Getafe
Fuenlabrada
Parla
Torrejón de Ardoz
Costada
Pinto
Valdemoro
Ciempozuelos
Aranjuez
Ocaña
Toledo
Talavera de la Reina
Torrijos
Illescas
Consuegra
Madridejos
Béjar
Piedrahita
Barco de Ávila
Arenas de San Pedro
Oropesa
TIERRA DEL VINO
LA ARMUÑA
TIERRA DE ARÉVALO
LA MORAÑA
LA SAGRA
MESA DE OCAÑA
LA JARA
CAMPO ARAÑUELO
Sierra de Ávila
Sierra de Gredos
Sierra de Guadarrama
Sierra de Ayllón
Sierra de Malagón
Sierra de la Paramera
Sierra de San Vicente
Montes de Toledo
Sierra de Guadalupe
Sierra de Altamira
Sierra de los Torneros
Sierra del Chorito
Sierra del Pocito
Sierra de la Calderina
Sierra de Yébenes
Valle del Tiétar
Embalse de Cíjara
Embalse de García Sola
Embalse de Valdecañas
Embalse de Azután
Embalse de Burguillo
Embalse de Rosarito
Parque Nacional de las Tablas de Daimiel
Valdesquí
Valcotos
Navacerrada
La Pinilla

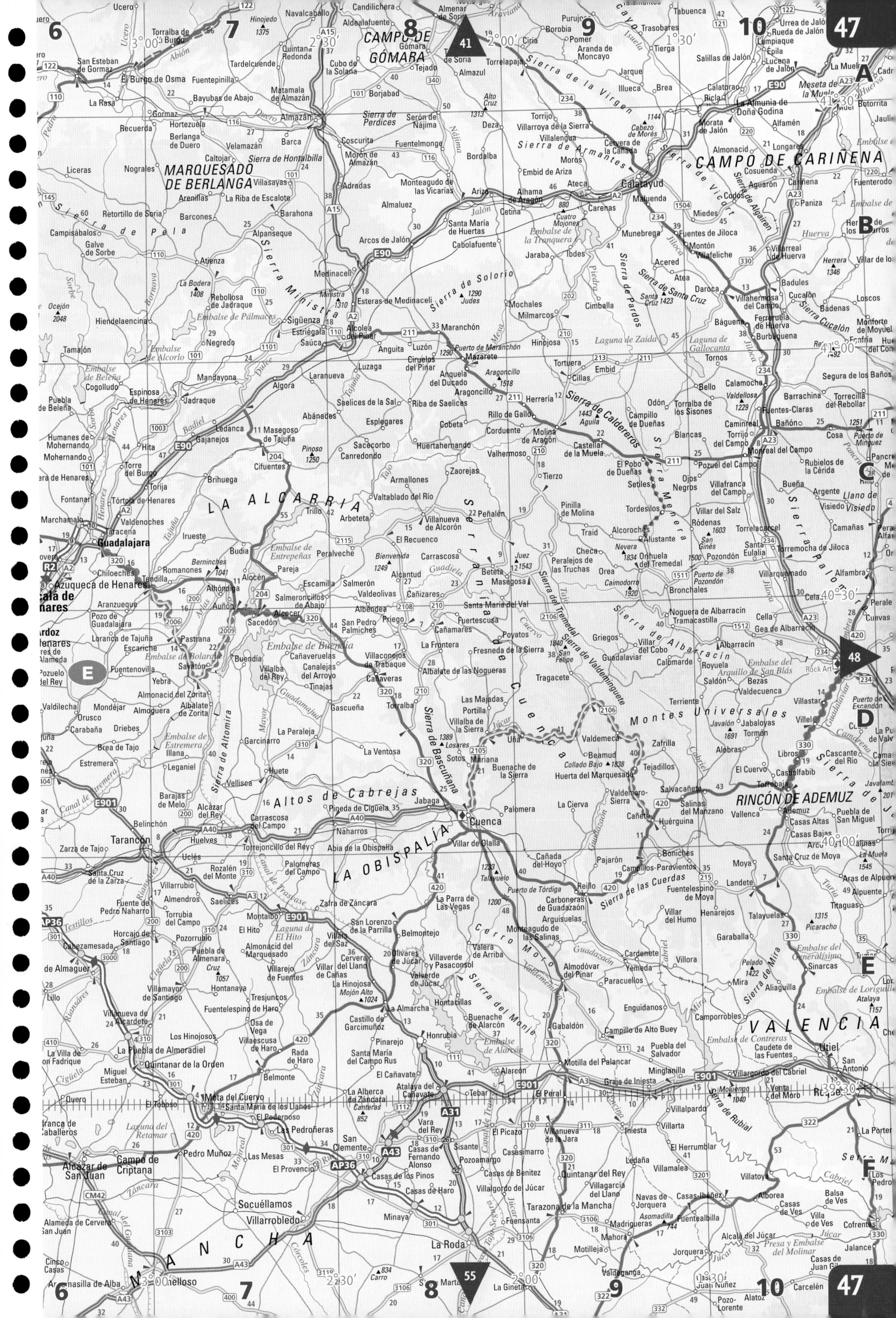

47
6
7
8
9
10
41
48
55
A
B
C
D
E
F
CAMPO DE GÓMARA
MARQUESADO DE BERLANGA
CAMPO DE CARIÑENA
LA ALCARRIA
Serranía de Cuenca
LA OBISPALÍA
Altos de Cabrejas
Montes Universales
RINCÓN DE ADEMUZ
VALENCIA
MANCHA
Sierra de la Virgen
Sierra de Armantes
Sierra de Vicort
Sierra de Algairén
Sierra de Pela
Sierra Ministra
Sierra de Solorio
Sierra de Pardos
Sierra de Santa Cruz
Sierra Cucalón
Sierra de Caldereros
Sierra Menera
Sierra Palomera
Sierra de Albarracín
Sierra del Tremedal
Sierra de Valdeminguete
Sierra de Bascuñana
Sierra de Altomira
Sierra de las Cuerdas
Sierra de Mira
Sierra del Monje
Cerro Moro
Sierra de Rubial
Soria
El Burgo de Osma
San Esteban de Gormaz
Almazán
Medinaceli
Sigüenza
Atienza
Calatayud
Daroca
Calamocha
Monreal del Campo
Molina de Aragón
Guadalajara
Azuqueca de Henares
Alcalá de Henares
Pastrana
Sacedón
Cuenca
Tarancón
Huete
Albarracín
Teruel
Ademuz
Utiel
Requena
Motilla del Palancar
San Clemente
La Roda
Villarrobledo
Socuéllamos
Alcázar de San Juan
Campo de Criptana
Quintanar de la Orden
Mota del Cuervo
Belmonte
Tarazona de la Mancha
Casas-Ibáñez
La Gineta
Embalse de Entrepeñas
Embalse de Buendía
Embalse de Bolarque
Embalse de Alarcón
Embalse de Contreras
Embalse de Beleña
Embalse de Pálmaces
Embalse de la Tranquera
Laguna de Gallocanta
Laguna de Zaida
Laguna de El Hito
E901
E90
A2
A3
A23
A31
A40
A43
AP36

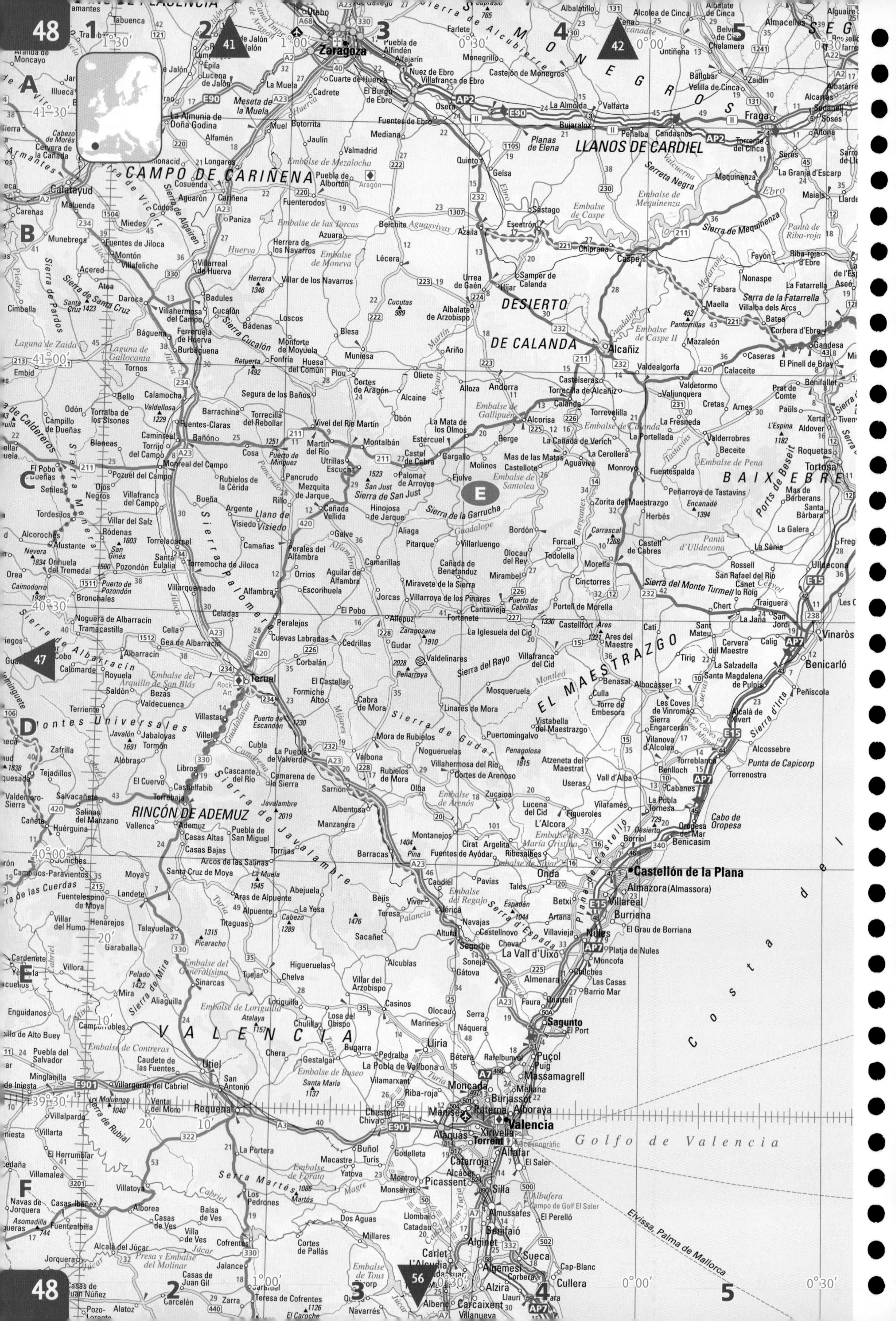

Zaragoza
Calatayud
CAMPO DE CARIÑENA
Cariñena
Puebla de Alfindén
Alfajarín
Nuez de Ebro
Villafranca de Ebro
Cuarte de Huerva
El Burgo de Ebro
Fuentes de Ebro
La Muela
Cadrete
Meseta de la Muela
La Almunia de Doña Godina
Alfamén
Muel
Botorrita
Jaulín
Mediana
Valmadrid
Embalse de Mezalocha
Puebla de Albortón
Aragón
Fuenterodos
Belchite
Azuara
Lécera
Herrera de los Navarros
Embalse de las Torcas
Embalse de Moneva
Villar de los Navarros
Villarreal de Huerva
Paniza
Aguarón
Cosuenda
Longares
Sierra de Vicort
Sierra de Algairén
Daroca
Atea
Acered
Sierra de Santa Cruz
Badules
Villahermosa del Campo
Cucalón
Bádenas
Loscos
Sierra Cucalón
Ferreruela de Huerva
Báguena
Burbáguena
Laguna de Gallocanta
Laguna de Zaida
Monforte de Moyuela
Huesa del Común
Blesa
Muniesa
Plou
Fonfría
Tornos
Bello
Calamocha
Odón
Torralba de los Sisones
Campillo de Dueñas
Fuentes-Claras
Barrachina
Torrecilla del Rebollar
Segura de los Baños
Vivel del Río Martín
Martín del Río
Montalbán
Utrillas
Escucha
Bañón
Caminreal
Torrijo del Campo
Blancas
Cosa
Monreal del Campo
Pozuel del Campo
Rubielos de la Cérida
Pancrudo
Mezquita de Jarque
Palomar de Arroyos
Castel de Cabra
Ejulve
Gargallo
Molinos
Aliaga
Hinojosa de Jarque
Sierra de San Just
Sierra de la Garrucha
Cañada Vellida
Villafranca del Campo
Bueña
Argente
Visiedo
Llano de Visiedo
Villar del Salz
Ródenas
Torrelacárcel
Alustante
Orihuela del Tremedal
Pozondón
Santa Eulalia
Torremocha de Jiloca
Villarquemado
Alfambra
Camañas
Perales del Alfambra
Galve
Camarillas
Aguilar de Alfambra
Orrios
Escorihuela
Jorcas
El Pobo
Celadas
Cella
Noguera de Albarracín
Tramacastilla
Gea de Albarracín
Albarracín
Sierra de Albarracín
Royuela
Calomarde
Saldón
Bezas
Valdecuenca
Teruel
Peralejos
Cuevas Labradas
Cedrillas
Corbalán
El Castellar
Formiche Alto
Cabra de Mora
Gúdar
Alcalá de la Selva
Valdelinares
Peñarroya
Sierra de Gúdar
Mora de Rubielos
Rubielos de Mora
Nogueruelas
Linares de Mora
Mosqueruela
Puertomingalvo
Villahermosa del Río
Cortes de Arenoso
Zucaina
Montes Universales
Javalón
Jabaloyas
Tormón
Terriente
Villastar
Villel
Cubla
La Puebla de Valverde
Camarena de la Sierra
Sarrión
Albentosa
Manzanera
Olba
Libros
Cascante del Río
Castielfabib
Torrebaja
Ademuz
RINCÓN DE ADEMUZ
Sierra de Javalambre
Javalambre
Casas Altas
Casas Bajas
Puebla de San Miguel
Torrijas
Arcos de las Salinas
Santa Cruz de Moya
Moya
Landete
Salvacañete
Salinas del Manzano
Vallanca
Huérguina
Cañete
Boniches
Campillos-Paravientos
Fuentelespino de Moya
Henarejos
Talayuelas
Garaballa
Aras de Alpuente
Alpuente
Abejuela
La Yesa
Titaguas
Tuéjar
Chelva
Higueruelas
Villar del Arzobispo
Alcublas
Casinos
Losa del Obispo
Chulilla
Sinarcas
Aliaguilla
Mira
Sierra de Mira
Embalse de Loriguilla
Camporrobles
VALENCIA
Embalse de Contreras
Caudete de las Fuentes
Utiel
Villargordo del Cabriel
Venta del Moro
Requena
San Antonio
Siete Aguas
Chiva
Cheste
Buñol
Turís
Godelleta
Macastre
Yátova
Embalse de Forata
Sierra Martés
Montroy
Monserrat
Picassent
Llombai
Catadau
Carlet
L'Alcúdia
Alginet
Benifaió
Almussafes
Sueca
Cullera
Algemesí
Alzira
Carcaixent
Alberic
Villanueva
Cortes de Pallás
Millares
Dos Aguas
Embalse de Tous
Navarrés
Cofrentes
Jalance
Jarafuel
Teresa de Cofrentes
Zarra
Casas de Juan Gil
Carcelén
Alatoz
Alcalá del Júcar
Jorquera
Presa y Embalse del Molinar
Villa de Ves
Balsa de Ves
Casas de Ves
Alborea
Villatoya
Casas-Ibáñez
Fuentealbilla
Navas de Jorquera
Villamalea
El Herrumblar
Villarta
Villalpardo
Minglanilla
Puebla del Salvador
Sierra de Rubial
Valencia
Torrent
Xirivella
Alaquàs
Manises
Paterna
Burjassot
Moncada
Alboraya
Meliana
Massamagrell
Puçol
Puig
Rafelbunyol
Bétera
Náquera
Serra
Olocau
Marines
Llíria
Pedralba
Bugarra
Gestalgar
Chera
La Pobla de Vallbona
Riba-roja
Vilamarxant
Embalse de Buseo
Catarroja
Alfafar
Silla
Alcàsser
El Saler
L'Albufera
Campo de Golf El Saler
El Perelló
Golfo de Valencia
Eivissa, Palma de Mallorca
Sagunto
El Port
Gilet
Faura
Quartell
Almenara
Chilches
Moncofa
Las Casas
Barrio Mar
La Vall d'Uixó
Nules
Platja de Nules
Vilavella
Sierra de Espadán
Chóvar
Castellnovo
Segorbe
Navajas
Altura
Jérica
Viver
Teresa
Bejís
Embalse del Regajo
Caudiel
Pavías
Soneja
Gátova
Sacañet
Barracas
Pina
Montanejos
Cirat
Argelita
Fuentes de Ayódar
Ribesalbes
Embalse de María Cristina
Embalse de Sichar
Onda
Tales
Betxí
Artana
Vila-real
Burriana
El Grau de Borriana
Almazora (Almassora)
Castellón de la Plana
Benicasim
Oropesa del Mar
Cabo de Oropesa
Borriol
Costa del Azahar
Plana de Castelló
Lucena del Cid
L'Alcora
Figueroles
Vilafamés
La Pobla Tornesa
Cabanes
Useras
Vall d'Alba
Atzeneta del Maestrat
Penagolosa
Vistabella del Maestrazgo
Benlloch
Torreblanca
Torrenostra
Alcossebre
Punta de Capicorp
Sierra d'Irta
Alcalà de Xivert
Peñíscola
Benicarló
Vinaròs
Santa Magdalena de Pulpis
Les Coves de Vinromà
Sierra Engarcerán
Vilanova d'Alcolea
Torre d'en Besora
Albocàsser
Benasal
Culla
EL MAESTRAZGO
Villafranca del Cid
Ares del Maestre
Catí
Tírig
La Salzadella
Sant Mateu
Cervera del Maestre
Calig
San Jordi
La Jana
Traiguera
Chert
Canet lo Roig
Rossell
San Rafael del Río
Ulldecona
La Sénia
La Galera
Sierra del Monte Turmell
Castellfort
Portell de Morella
Cinctorres
Morella
Forcall
Todolella
Olocau del Rey
Castell de Cabres
Herbés
Zorita del Maestrazgo
Cantavieja
La Iglesuela del Cid
Fortanete
Villarroya de los Pinares
Miravete de la Sierra
Cañada de Benatanduz
Villarluengo
Pitarque
Bordón
Mirambel
Tronchón
Sierra del Rayo
Montalbán
Estercuel
La Mata de los Olmos
Obón
Alcaine
Oliete
Ariño
Alloza
Andorra
Berge
Alcorisa
Calanda
Embalse de Calanda
Mas de las Matas
Aguaviva
Castellote
Embalse de Santolea
La Cerollera
La Ginebrosa
La Cañada de Verich
Torrevelilla
Monroyo
Fuentespalda
Peñarroya de Tastavins
Valderrobres
Beceite
Embalse de Pena
Puertos de Beseit
La Portellada
La Fresneda
Valjunquera
Valdetormo
Castelserás
Torrecilla de Alcañiz
Alcañiz
Valdealgorfa
Mazaleón
Calaceite
Cretas
Arnes
Lledó
Caseras
Gandesa
El Pinell de Bray
Benifallet
Prat de Comte
Paüls
Xerta
Tivenys
Aldover
Roquetas
Tortosa
Mas de Barberans
Santa Bàrbara
BAIX EBRE
Sierra de Cardó
DESIERTO DE CALANDA
Híjar
Urrea de Gaén
Samper de Calanda
Albalate del Arzobispo
Azaila
Escatrón
Sástago
Chiprana
Caspe
Embalse de Caspe
Embalse de Caspe II
Fabara
Nonaspe
Maella
Batea
Villalba dels Arcs
Corbera d'Ebre
Serra de la Fatarrella
La Fatarrella
Fayón
Riba-roja d'Ebre
Pantà de Riba-roja
Sierra de Mequinenza
Mequinenza
Embalse de Mequinenza
Serreta Negra
LLANOS DE CARDIEL
Planas de Elena
Bujaraloz
Peñalba
Candasnos
Fraga
Torrente del Cinca
Zaidín
Ballobar
Velilla de Cinca
Albalate de Cinca
Belver de Cinca
Chalamera
Ontiñena
Alcolea de Cinca
Alcubierre
Sierra de Alcubierre
MONEGROS
Monegrillo
Farlete
Perdiguera
Castejón de Monegros
La Almolda
Valfarta
Osera
Pina de Ebro
Quinto
Gelsa
Alfajarín
Utebo
Villanueva de Gállego
Canal Imperial de Aragón
Épila
Lumpiaque
Lucena de Jalón
Rueda de Jalón
Calatorao
Jarque
Illueca
Morata de Jalón
Maluenda
Munébrega
Miedes
Codos
Fuentes de Jiloca
Montón
Villafeliche
Cimballa
Sierra de Pardos
Embid
Odón
Sierra de Caldereros
Sierra Menera
El Pobo de Dueñas
Setiles
Tordesilos
Alcoroches
Bronchales
Puerto de Pozondón
Sierra de Albarracín
Golfo de Valencia

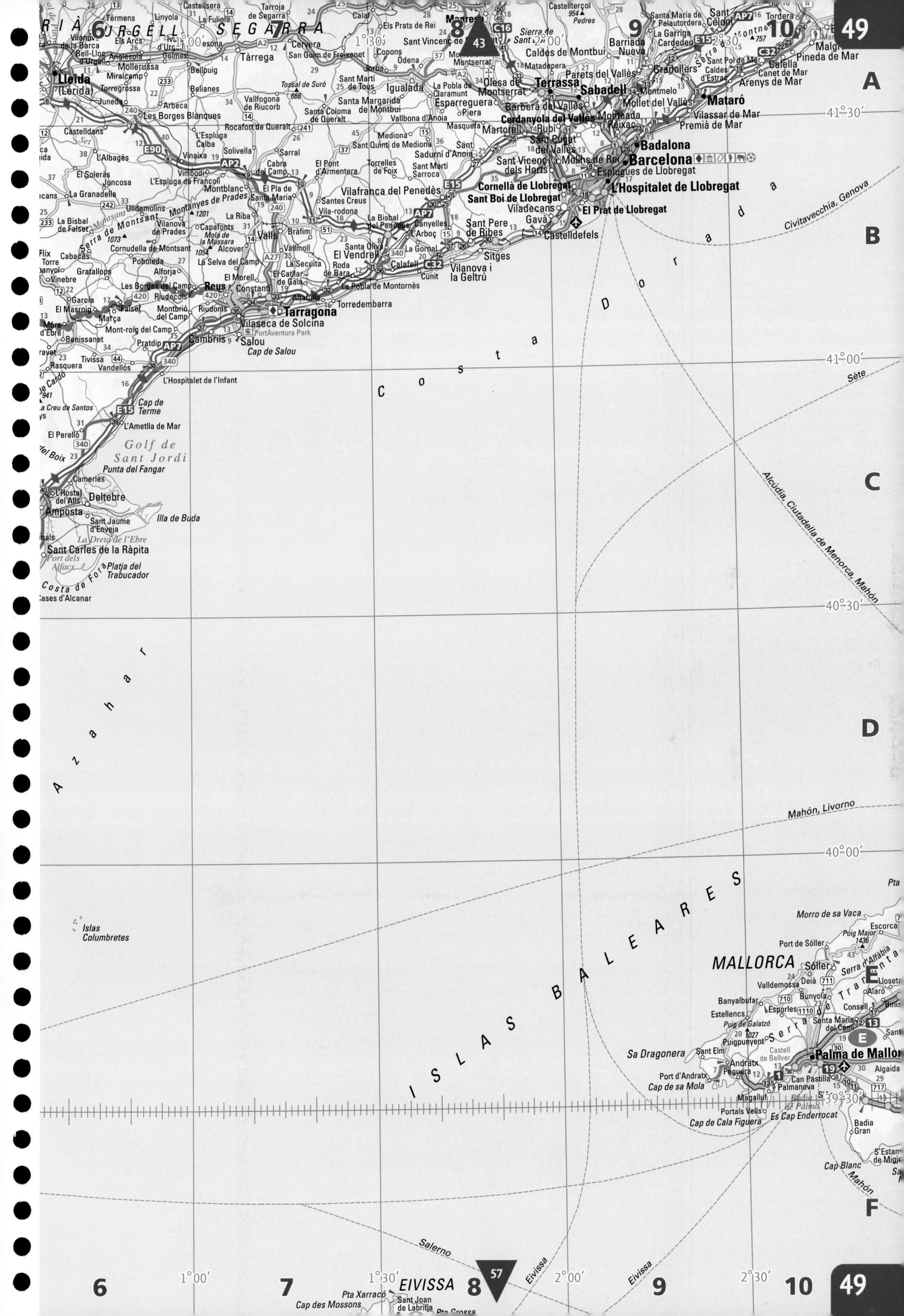

URGELL
SEGARRA
Lleida
(Lérida)
Tàrrega
Cervera
Igualada
Manresa
43
Terrassa
Sabadell
Mataró
Granollers
Arenys de Mar
Calella
Pineda de Mar
Badalona
Barcelona
L'Hospitalet de Llobregat
Cornellà de Llobregat
Sant Boi de Llobregat
El Prat de Llobregat
Castelldefels
Gavà
Viladecans
Sitges
Vilanova i la Geltrú
Vilafranca del Penedès
El Vendrell
Calafell
Tarragona
Reus
Valls
Vilaseca de Solcina
Salou
Cambrils
Cap de Salou
PortAventura Park
Montblanc
Les Borges Blanques
L'Hospitalet de l'Infant
L'Ametlla de Mar
Golf de Sant Jordi
Punta del Fangar
Amposta
Deltebre
Sant Carles de la Ràpita
Illa de Buda
Platja del Trabucador
Costa Dorada
Azahar
Islas Columbretes
ISLAS BALEARES
MALLORCA
Sa Dragonera
Palma de Mallorca
Sóller
Port de Sóller
Andratx
Magalluf
Cap de Cala Figuera
Es Cap Enderrocat
Cap Blanc
Civitavecchia, Genova
Sète
Alcúdia, Ciutadella de Menorca, Mahón
Mahón, Livorno
Salerno
Eivissa
EIVISSA
57
41°30′
41°00′
40°30′
40°00′
39°30′
1°00′
1°30′
2°00′
2°30′
A
B
C
D
E
F
6
7
8
9
10

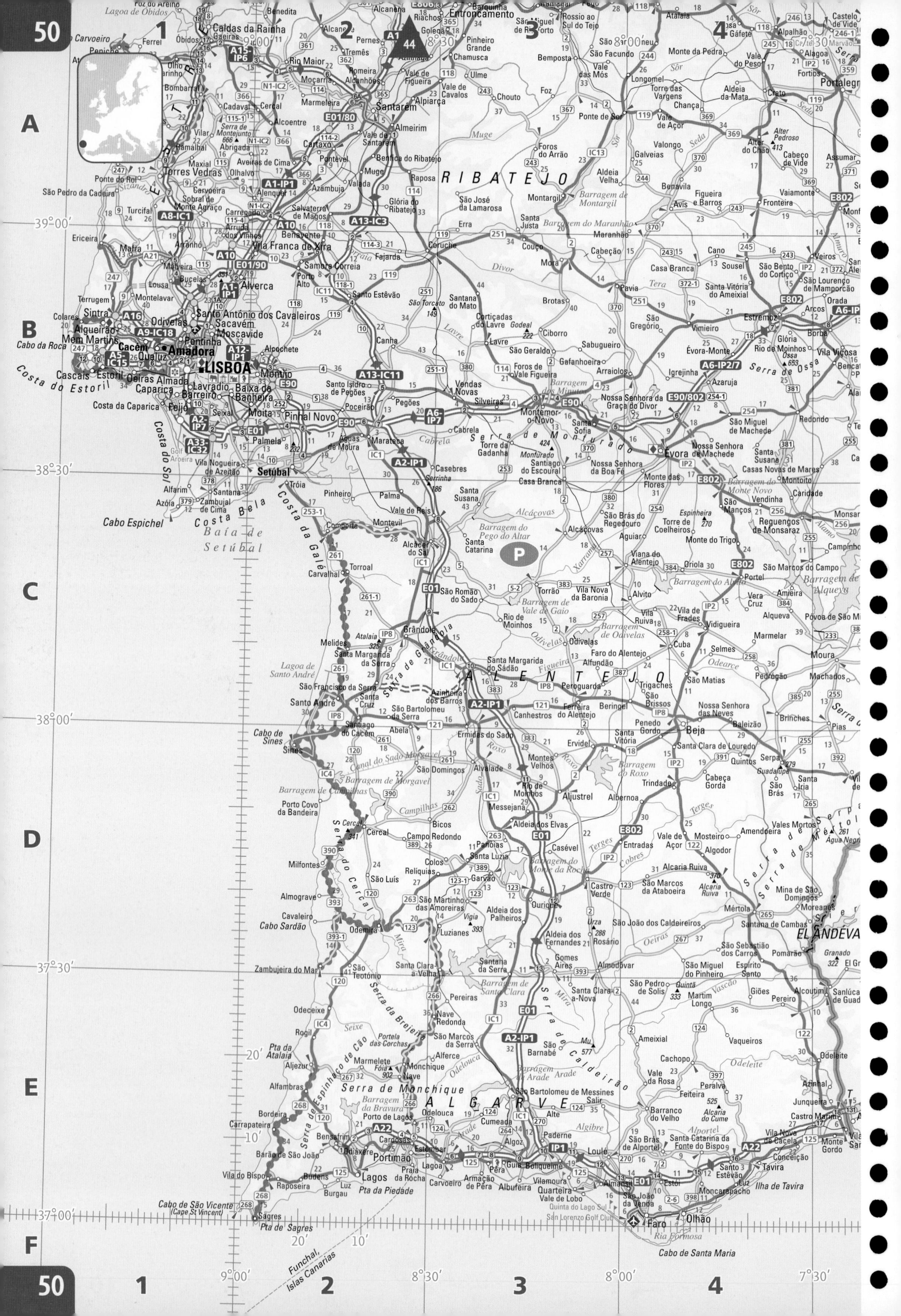

Caldas da Rainha
Óbidos
Benedita
Alcanena
Riachos
Entroncamento
Barquinha
Golegã
Rossio ao Sul do Tejo
Atalaia
Castelo de Vide
Peniche
Ferrel
Rio Maior
Pernes
Tremês
Azinhaga
Pinheiro Grande
Chamusca
São Facundo
Bemposta
Gáfete
Alpalhão
Alagoa
Portalegre
Fortios
Bombarral
Romeira
Alcanhões
Vale de Figueira
Ulme
Vale das Mós
Longomel
Torre das Vargens
Chança
Aldeia da Mata
Crato
Vale de Cavalos
Santarém
Alpiarça
Chouto
Foz
Ponte de Sor
Vale de Açor
Cadaval
Cercal
Alcoentre
Marmeleira
Almeirim
Vale de Santarém
Cartaxo
Pontével
Benfica do Ribatejo
Muge
Foros do Arrão
Galveias
Valongo
Alter do Chão
Alter Pedroso
Cabeço de Vide
Assumar
Ramalhal
Abrigada
Aveiras de Cima
Maxial
Torres Vedras
Olhalvo
Azambuja
Valada
Raposa
RIBATEJO
Aldeia Velha
Benavila
Figueira e Barros
Avis
Vaiamonte
Fronteira
Ponte do Rol
São Pedro da Cadeira
Carvoeira
Sobral de Monte Agraço
Alenquer
Salvaterra de Magos
Glória do Ribatejo
São José da Lamarosa
Montargil
Barragem de Montargil
Santa Justa
Barragem do Maranhão
Maranhão
Turcifal
Carregado
Arruda dos Vinhos
Benavente
Erra
Ericeira
Mafra
Arranhó
Vila Franca de Xira
Coruche
Couço
Cabeção
Cano
Sousel
São Bento do Cortiço
Veiros
Fajarda
Samora Correia
Mora
Casa Branca
São Lourenço de Mamporcão
Malveira
Bucelas
Alverca
Porto Alto
Santo Estêvão
Pavia
Santa Vitória do Ameixial
Terrugem
Lousa
Montelavar
Sintra
Colares
Algueirão
Mem Martins
Cabo da Roca
Odivelas
Santo António dos Cavaleiros
Sacavém
Moscavide
São Torcato
Santana do Mato
Brotas
São Gregório
Vimieiro
Estremoz
Orada
Arcos
Borba
Cacém
Amadora
Queluz
Pontinha
LISBOA
Alcochete
Canha
Cortiçadas do Lavre
Lavre
Godeal
Ciborro
Sabugueiro
Glória
Rio de Moinhos
Vila Viçosa
Cascais
Estoril
Oeiras
Almada
Montijo
Costa do Estoril
Caparica
Lavradio
Barreiro
Baixa da Banheira
Santo Isidro de Pegões
São Geraldo
Foros de Vale Figueira
Gafanhoeira
Arraiolos
Igrejinha
Évora-Monte
Azaruja
Serra de Ossa
Costa da Caparica
Feijó
Seixal
Moita
Pinhal Novo
Poceirão
Pegões
Vendas Novas
Silveiras
Montemor-o-Novo
Barragem dos Minutos
Nossa Senhora da Graça do Divor
Redondo
Costa do Sol
Palmela
Águas de Moura
Marateca
Cabrela
Serra de Monfurado
Torre da Gadanha
Santa Sofia
São Miguel de Machede
Évora
Nossa Senhora de Machede
Vila Nogueira de Azeitão
Setúbal
Casebres
Santiago do Escoural
Nossa Senhora da Boa Fé
Casa Branca
Santa Susana
Casas Novas de Mares
Montoito
Alfarim
Santana
Tróia
Pinheiro
Palma
Monte das Flores
Barragem do Monte Novo
São Manços
Vendinha
Caridade
Azóia
Zambujal de Cima
Cabo Espichel
Costa Bela
Baía de Setúbal
Costa da Galé
Comporta
Montevil
Vale de Reis
Alcáçovas
São Brás do Regedouro
Torre de Coelheiros
Espinheira
Aguiar
Reguengos de Monsaraz
Alcácer do Sal
Barragem do Pego do Altar
Santa Catarina
Monte do Trigo
Torroal
Carvalhal
Viana do Alentejo
Oriola
Portel
São Marcos do Campo
Barragem de Alqueva
São Romão do Sado
Torrão
Vila Nova da Baronia
Alvito
Barragem do Alvito
Amieira
Vera Cruz
Alqueva
Póvoa de São Miguel
Barragem de Vale de Gaio
Rio de Moinhos
Vila Ruiva
Vila de Frades
Vidigueira
Marmelar
Melides
Atalaia
Grândola
Serra de Grândola
Barragem de Odivelas
Odivelas
Faro do Alentejo
Cuba
Selmes
Moura
Santa Margarida da Serra
Lagoa de Santo André
Santa Margarida do Sádão
Alfundão
ALENTEJO
Pedrógão
Machados
São Francisco da Serra
Santa Cruz
Azinheira dos Barros
Peroguarda
Trigaches
São Brissos
São Matias
Santo André
São Bartolomeu da Serra
Canhestros
Ferreira do Alentejo
Beringel
Nossa Senhora das Neves
Brinches
Pias
Cabo de Sines
Sines
Santiago do Cacém
Abela
Ermidas do Sado
Ervidel
Santa Vitória
Penedo Gordo
Beja
Baleizão
São Domingos
Barragem de Morgavel
Alvalade
Montes Velhos
Barragem do Roxo
Santa Clara de Louredo
Quintos
Serpa
Guadalupe
Barragem de Campilhas
Porto Covo da Bandeira
Rio de Moinhos
Aljustrel
Albernoa
Trindade
Cabeça Gorda
São Brás
Santa Iria
Campilhas
Messejana
Bicos
Aldeia dos Elvas
Vales Mortos
Serra de Serpa
Cercal
Serra do Cercal
Campo Redondo
Panóias
Casével
Entradas
Vale de Açor
Mosteiro
Amendoeira
Algodor
Milfontes
Colos
Santa Luzia
Barragem do Monte da Rocha
Serra de Mértola
Relíquias
Garvão
Castro Verde
Alcaria Ruiva
São Luís
São Marcos da Ataboeira
Almograve
São Martinho das Amoreiras
Ourique
Aldeia dos Palheiros
Vigia
Mértola
Mina de São Domingos
Moreanes
Cavaleiro
Cabo Sardão
Odemira
Luzianes
Aldeia dos Fernandes
Urze
Rosário
São João dos Caldeireiros
Santana de Cambas
EL ANDÉVALO
Oeiras
São Sebastião dos Carros
Pomarão
Zambujeira do Mar
São Teotónio
Santa Clara-a-Velha
Santana da Serra
Gomes Aires
Almodôvar
São Miguel do Pinheiro
Espírito Santo
Barragem de Santa Clara
Santa Clara-a-Nova
São Pedro de Solis
Martim Longo
Gióes
Pereiro
Alcoutim
Sanlúcar de Guadiana
Odeceixe
Pereiras
Serra de Caldeirão
Serra da Brejeira
Nave Redonda
Rogil
Portela das Corchas
São Marcos da Serra
Ameixial
Vaqueiros
Pta da Atalaia
Marmelete
Fóia
Monchique
Alferce
São Barnabé
Cachopo
Odeleite
Aljezur
Nave
Serra de Espinhaço de Cão
Barragem do Arade
Vale da Rosa
Peralva
Alfambras
Serra de Monchique
São Bartolomeu de Messines
Feiteira
Azinhal
Barragem da Bravura
ALGARVE
Salir
Junqueira
Bordeira
Odelouca
Cumeada
Alte
Barranco do Velho
Alcaria do Cume
Castro Marim
Carrapateira
Porto de Lagos
Bensafrim
Cardosas
Algoz
Paderne
São Brás de Alportel
Santa Catarina da Fonte do Bispo
Vila Nova de Cacela
Monte Gordo
Odiáxere
Portimão
Estômbar
Loulé
Conceição
Barão de São João
Santo Estêvão
Tavira
Vila do Bispo
Raposeira
Budens
Lagos
Praia da Rocha
Lagoa
Pêra
Guia
Boliqueime
Almancil
Estói
Moncarapacho
Ilha de Tavira
Luz
Burgau
Pta da Piedade
Carvoeiro
Armação de Pêra
Albufeira
Vilamoura
Quarteira
Vale de Lobo
Quinta do Lago Sul
São Lorenzo Golf Club
São João da Venda
Faro
Olhão
Cabo de São Vicente (Cape St Vincent)
Sagres
Pta de Sagres
Ria Formosa
Cabo de Santa Maria
Funchal, Islas Canarias
A
B
C
D
E
F
1
2
3
4
39°00′
38°30′
38°00′
37°30′
37°00′
9°00′
8°30′
8°00′
7°30′

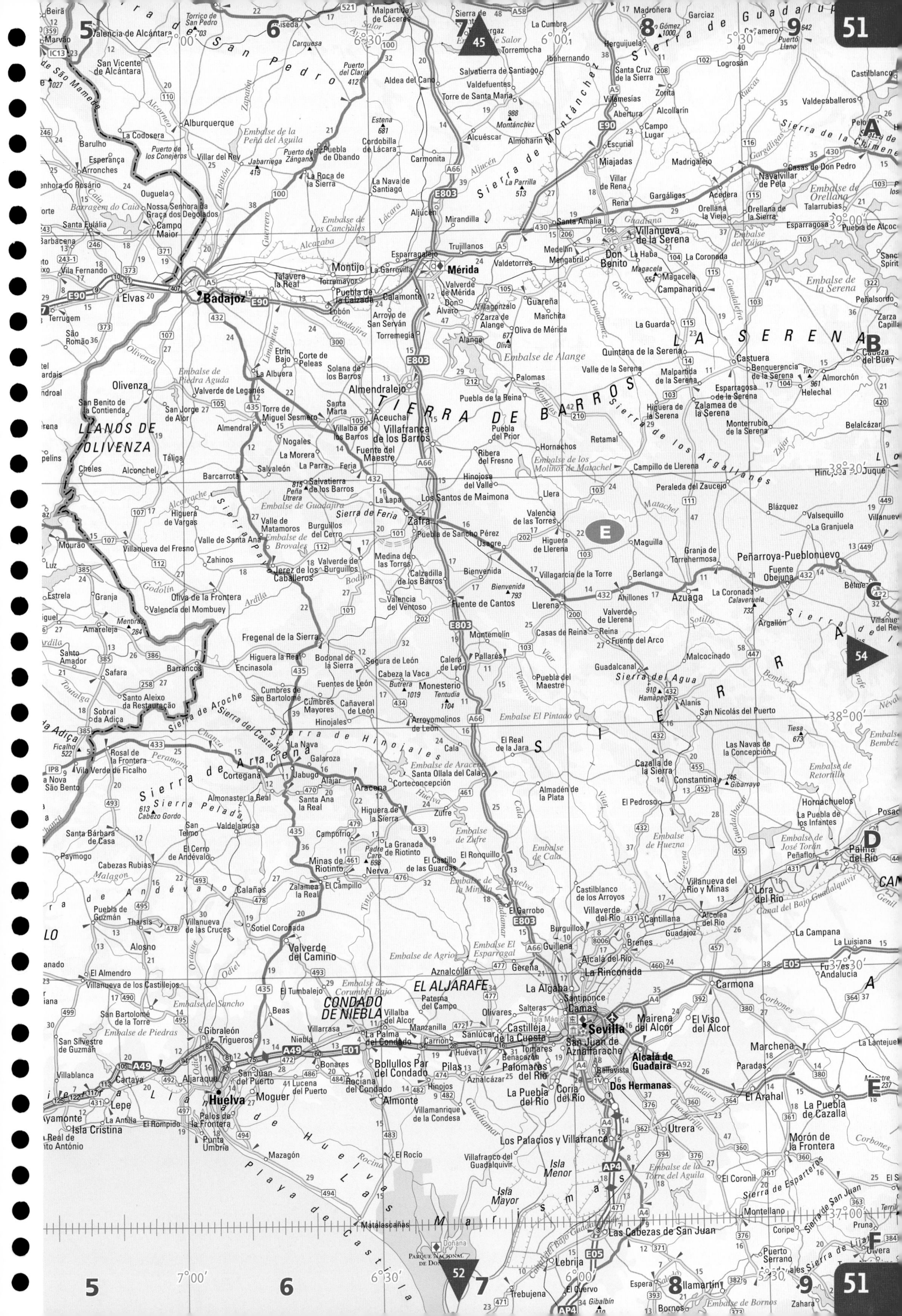

5
6
7
8
9
45
Valencia de Alcántara
Sierra de San Pedro
Sierra de Montánchez
Sierra de Guadalupe
San Vicente de Alcántara
Alburquerque
Cáceres
Miajadas
Logrosán
Mérida
Badajoz
Elvas
Montijo
Villanueva de la Serena
Don Benito
Medellín
Campanario
Castuera
LA SERENA
Embalse de la Serena
Embalse de Orellana
Olivenza
LLANOS DE OLIVENZA
Almendralejo
TIERRA DE BARROS
Villafranca de los Barros
Zafra
Jerez de los Caballeros
Fregenal de la Sierra
Llerena
Azuaga
Peñarroya-Pueblonuevo
Fuente Obejuna
Sierra de Aroche
Sierra de Aracena
Sierra de Hinojales
Aracena
Cortegana
Jabugo
Sierra Morena
Sierra del Agua
Cazalla de la Sierra
Constantina
Lora del Río
Carmona
Sevilla
EL ALJARAFE
CONDADO DE NIEBLA
Huelva
Lepe
Ayamonte
Isla Cristina
Moguer
Almonte
El Rocío
Matalascañas
Playa de Castilla
Parque Nacional de Doñana
Alcalá de Guadaira
Dos Hermanas
Utrera
Marchena
Morón de la Frontera
Las Cabezas de San Juan
Lebrija
Marismas
Isla Mayor
Isla Menor
A
B
C
D
E
F
54
52
7°00′
6°30′
6°00′
5°30′
39°00′
38°30′
38°00′
37°30′
37°00′

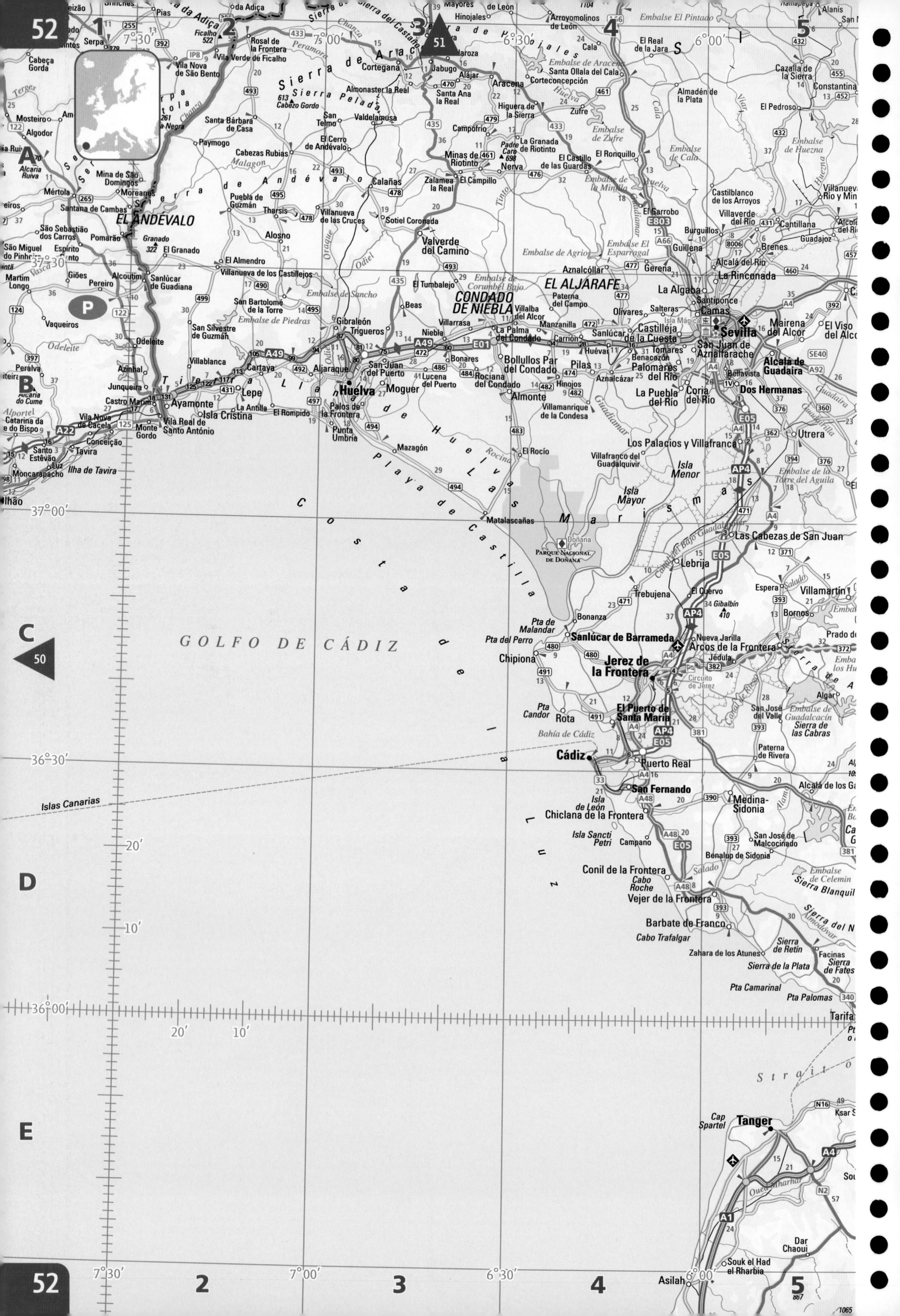

1
2
3
4
5
A
B
C
D
E
51
50
7°30′
7°00′
6°30′
6°00′
37°30′
37°00′
36°30′
36°00′
20′
10′
Serpa
Pias
Ficalho 522
Rosal de la Frontera
Vila Verde de Ficalho
Vila Nova de São Bento
Cabeça Gorda
Mosteiro
Algodor
Alcaria Ruiva
Mértola
Santana de Cambas
Moreanes
Mina de São Domingos
EL ANDÉVALO
São Sebastião dos Carros
Pomarão
Granado 322
El Granado
São Miguel do Pinheiro
Espírito Santo
Martim Longo
Giões
Pereiro
Alcoutim
Sanlúcar de Guadiana
Vaqueiros
Odeleite
Peralva
Azinhal
Junqueira
Castro Marim
Ayamonte
Vila Real de Santo António
Monte Gordo
Vila Nova de Cacela
Conceição
Tavira
Santo Estêvão
Luz
Moncarapacho
Ilha de Tavira
Catarina da Fonte do Bispo
Alcaria do Cume
Alportel
Olhão
Sierra de Aracena
Sierra Pelada
613 Cabezo Gordo
Cortegana
Almonaster la Real
Jabugo
Alájar
Aracena
Santa Ana la Real
San Telmo
Valdelamusa
Santa Bárbara de Casa
Paymogo
Cabezas Rubias
El Cerro de Andévalo
Sierra de Andévalo
Puebla de Guzmán
Tharsis
Alosno
Calañas
Villanueva de las Cruces
Sotiel Coronada
Zalamea la Real
El Campillo
Minas de Riotinto
Nerva
Padre Caro 698
La Granada de Riotinto
Campofrío
Higuera de la Sierra
Zufre
Santa Olalla del Cala
Corteconcepción
Embalse de Aracena
Embalse de Zufre
El Castillo de las Guardas
El Ronquillo
Embalse de la Minilla
El Garrobo
Embalse de Cala
Embalse El Pintado
El Real de la Jara
Cala
Cazalla de la Sierra
Constantina
Almadén de la Plata
El Pedroso
Embalse de Huezna
Castilblanco de los Arroyos
Villaverde del Río
Cantillana
Burguillos
Guillena
Brenes
Alcalá del Río
La Rinconada
Gerena
Valverde del Camino
El Almendro
Villanueva de los Castillejos
San Bartolomé de la Torre
Embalse de Sancho
Embalse de Piedras
San Silvestre de Guzmán
El Tumbalejo
Beas
Gibraleón
Trigueros
CONDADO DE NIEBLA
EL ALJARAFE
Embalse de Corumbel Bajo
Embalse de Agrio
Embalse El Esparragal
Aznalcóllar
Paterna del Campo
Villalba del Alcor
Villarrasa
Niebla
La Palma del Condado
Manzanilla
Olivares
Salteras
La Algaba
Santiponce
Camas
Isla Mágica
Sevilla
Mairena del Alcor
El Viso del Alcor
Villablanca
Cartaya
Lepe
La Antilla
Isla Cristina
El Rompido
Aljaraque
Huelva
San Juan del Puerto
Moguer
Palos de la Frontera
Punta Umbría
Lucena del Puerto
Bonares
Rociana del Condado
Bollullos Par del Condado
Almonte
Villamanrique de la Condesa
Hinojos
Pilas
Carrión
Huévar
Sanlúcar la Mayor
Castilleja de la Cuesta
San Juan de Aznalfarache
Tomares
Benacazón
Aznalcázar
Palomares del Río
La Puebla del Río
Coria del Río
Bellavista
Dos Hermanas
Alcalá de Guadaira
Utrera
Los Palacios y Villafranca
Villafranco del Guadalquivir
Isla Menor
Isla Mayor
Marismas
Mazagón
El Rocío
Playa de Castilla
Costa de Huelva
Matalascañas
Doñana
PARQUE NACIONAL DE DOÑANA
Las Cabezas de San Juan
Lebrija
Canal del Bajo Guadalquivir
Trebujena
El Cuervo
34 Gibalbín 410
Espera
Villamartín
Bornos
Bonanza
Pta de Malandar
Pta del Perro
Sanlúcar de Barrameda
Nueva Jarilla
Arcos de la Frontera
Prado del Rey
Chipiona
Jerez de la Frontera
Jédula
Circuito de Jerez
Algar
San José del Valle
Embalse de Guadalcacín
Sierra de las Cabras
Pta Candor
Rota
El Puerto de Santa María
Bahía de Cádiz
Cádiz
Puerto Real
Paterna de Rivera
San Fernando
Isla de León
Chiclana de la Frontera
Medina-Sidonia
Alcalá de los Gazules
Isla Sancti Petri
Campano
San José de Malcocinado
Benalup de Sidonia
Embalse de Celemín
Sierra Blanquilla
Conil de la Frontera
Cabo Roche
Vejer de la Frontera
Barbate de Franco
Cabo Trafalgar
Zahara de los Atunes
Sierra de Retín
Sierra de la Plata
Facinas
Sierra de Fates
Sierra del Niño
Pta Camarinal
Pta Palomas
Tarifa
GOLFO DE CÁDIZ
Costa de la Luz
Islas Canarias
Strait of
Cap Spartel
Tanger
Oued Mharhar
Dar Chaoui
Souk el Had el Rharbia
Asilah
A49
E01
A4
E05
AP4
A48
A22
E803
A66
N16
N2
A1

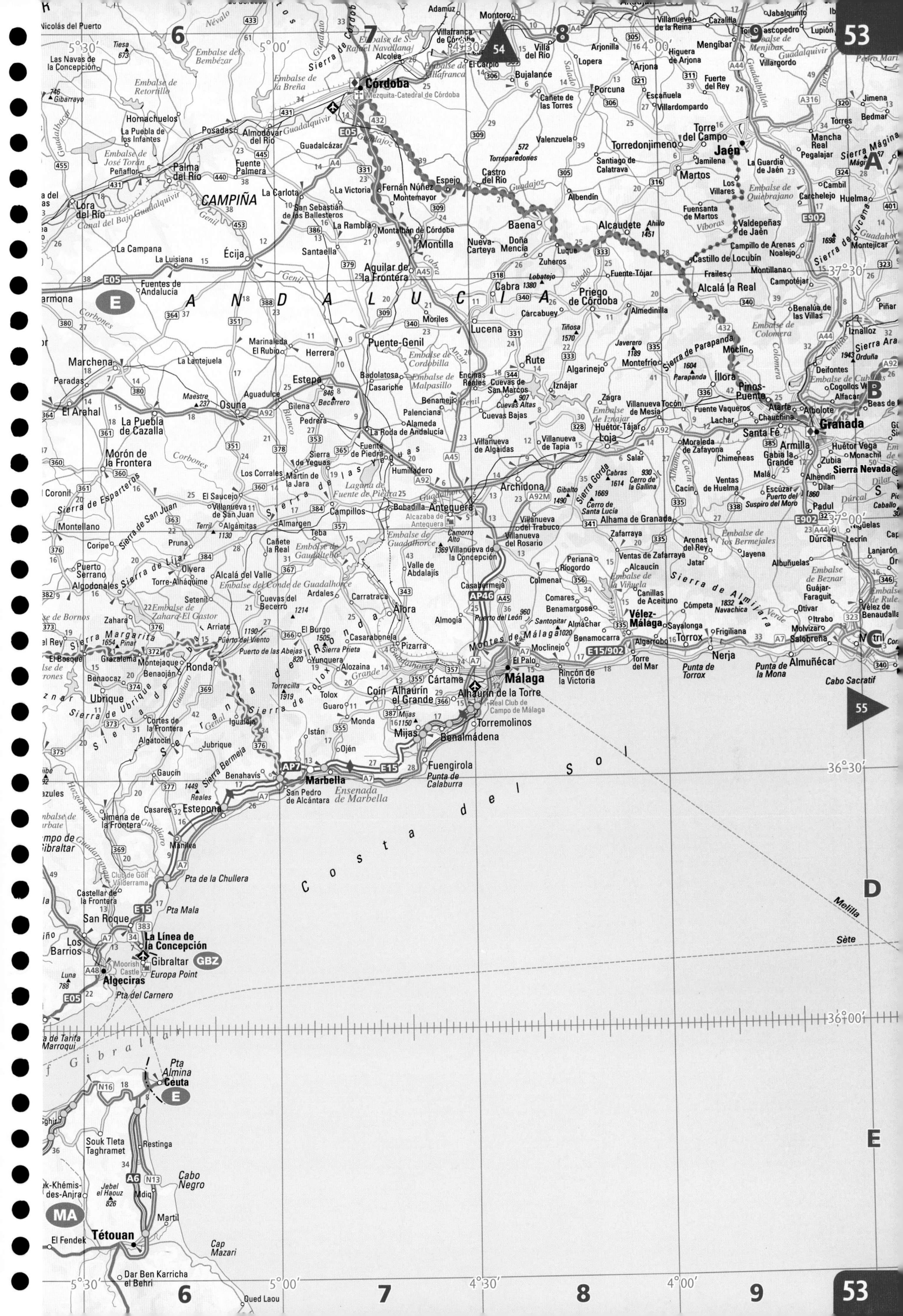
54
55
A
B
C
D
E
6
7
8
9
5°30′
5°00′
4°30′
4°00′
37°30′
37°00′
36°30′
36°00′
A N D A L U C I A
CAMPIÑA
Costa del Sol
Montoro
Adamuz
Villafranca de Córdoba
Alcolea
Córdoba
Mezquita-Catedral de Córdoba
Embalse de S. Rafael Navallana
Sierra de Córdoba
Embalse de la Breña
Embalse de Retortillo
Embalse del Bembézar
Nicolás del Puerto
Las Navas de la Concepción
Tiesa 673
Gibiarrayo 746
Hornachuelos
La Puebla de los Infantes
Embalse de José Torán
Peñaflor
Posadas
Almodóvar del Río
Palma del Río
Fuente Palmera
Lora del Río
Canal del Bajo Guadalquivir
Guadalquivir
Guadalcázar
La Carlota
La Victoria
San Sebastián de los Ballesteros
Fernán Núñez
Montemayor
Espejo
Castro del Río
Valenzuela
Torreparedones 572
El Carpio
Bujalance
Villa del Río
Cañete de las Torres
Porcuna
Lopera
Arjonilla
Arjona
Villanueva de la Reina
Cazalilla
Jabalquinto
Lupión
Mengíbar
Higuera de Arjona
Villargordo
Escañuela
Villardompardo
Fuerte del Rey
Torredonjimeno
Torre del Campo
Jaén
Jamilena
Martos
Santiago de Calatrava
La Guardia de Jaén
Mancha Real
Pegalajar
Sierra Mágina
Jimena
Torres
Bedmar
Cambil
Carchelejo
Huelma
Los Villares
Embalse de Quiebrajano
Fuensanta de Martos
Valdepeñas de Jaén
Víboras
Campillo de Arenas
Noalejo
Montejícar
Sierra de Lucena
Castillo de Locubín
Alcaudete
Ahillo 1451
Albendín
Baena
Doña Mencía
Nueva Carteya
Montilla
Montalbán de Córdoba
La Rambla
Santaella
Aguilar de la Frontera
Luque
Zuheros
Cabra
Lobatejo 1380
Priego de Córdoba
Carcabuey
Fuente-Tójar
Frailes
Alcalá la Real
Montillana
Campotéjar
Benalúa de las Villas
Iznalloz
Piñar
Almedinilla
Embalse de Colomera
Colomera
Sierra de Parapanda
Parapanda 1604
Moclín
Íllora
Pinos-Puente
Atarfe
Albolote
Granada
Deifontes
Cogollos Vega
Alfacar
Orduña 1943
Sierra Arana
Embalse de Cubillas
Chauchina
Santa Fe
Armilla
Huétor Vega
Monachil
Gabia la Grande
Zubia
Sierra Nevada
Alhendín
Dílar
Malá
Escúzar
Puerto del Moro 1860
Suspiro del Moro
Padul
Dúrcal
Lecrín
Nigüelas
Lanjarón
Albuñuelas
Embalse de Béznar
Guájar-Faraguit
Vélez de Benaudalla
Ítrabo
Otívar
Molvízar
Salobreña
Motril
Almuñécar
Punta de la Mona
Cabo Sacratif
La Campana
Écija
La Luisiana
Fuentes de Andalucía
Carmona
Marchena
Paradas
El Arahal
La Lantejuela
Marinaleda
El Rubio
Herrera
Puente-Genil
Estepa
Badolatosa
Casariche
Embalse de Cordobilla
Embalse de Malpasillo
Moriles
Lucena
Encinas Reales
Cuevas de San Marcos
Cuevas Altas 907
Cuevas Bajas
Rute
Iznájar
Algarinejo
Montefrío
Javerero 1189
Tiñosa 1570
Zagra
Embalse de Iznájar
Villanueva de Mesía
Huétor-Tájar
Loja
Tocón
Fuente Vaqueros
Lachar
Moraleda de Zafayona
Chimeneas
Ventas de Huelma
Cacín
Salar
Osuna
Maestre 237
Aguadulce
Gilena
Pedrera
Becerrero 846
La Puebla de Cazalla
Morón de la Frontera
Corbones
Los Corrales
Martín de la Jara
Sierra de Yeguas
Fuente de Piedra
Laguna de Fuente de Piedra
Humilladero
La Roda de Andalucía
Alameda
Palenciana
Benamejí
Villanueva de Algaidas
Villanueva de Tapia
Archidona
Antequera
Alcazaba de Antequera
Bobadilla
Campillos
Almargen
Teba
El Saucejo
Villanueva de San Juan
Algámitas
Terril 1130
Sierra de Esparteros
Sierra de San Juan
Coronil
Montellano
Coripe
Pruna
Puerto Serrano
Algodonales
Olvera
Torre-Alháquime
Sierra de Líjar
Alcalá del Valle
Embalse del Conde de Guadalhorce
Embalse de Guadalhorce
Embalse de Gaudalteba
Cañete la Real
Valle de Abdalajís
Camorro Alto
Villanueva de la Concepción
Villanueva del Trabuco
Villanueva del Rosario
Gibalto 1490
Sierra Gorda
Cerro de Santa Lucía 1669
Cabras 1614
Cerro de la Gallina 930
Alhama de Granada
Zafarraya
Ventas de Zafarraya
Arenas del Rey
Jatar
Jayena
Embalse de los Bermejales
Sierra de Almijara
Navachica 1832
Cómpeta
Periana
Riogordo
Colmenar
Alcaucín
Embalse de la Viñuela
Canillas de Aceituno
Vélez-Málaga
Sayalonga
Frigiliana
Torrox
Nerja
Punta de Torrox
Torre del Mar
Algarrobo
Benamargosa
Almáchar
Comares
Benamocarra
Moclinejo
Santopitar 1020
Montes de Málaga
Puerto del León 960
Casabermeja
Almogía
Álora
Carratraca
Ardales
Cuevas del Becerro
Setenil
Zahara
Embalse de Zahara-El Gastor
Sierra Margarita
Pinar 1654
Arriate
Puerto del Viento 1190
Puerto de las Abejas
El Burgo
Sierra Prieta 1505
Casarabonela
Pizarra
Yunquera
Alozaina
Tolox
Serranía de Ronda
Sierra de Tolox
Torrecilla 1919
Ronda
Montejaque
Benaoján
Grazalema
El Bosque
Benaocaz
Ubrique
Sierra de Ubrique
Cortes de la Frontera
Algatocín
Jubrique
Gaucín
Igualeja
Sierra Bermeja
Reales 1449
Benahavís
Casares
Estepona
Jimena de la Frontera
Manilva
Pta de la Chullera
Club de Golf Valderrama
Castellar de la Frontera
San Roque
Pta Mala
La Línea de la Concepción
Los Barrios
Gibraltar
GBZ
Moorish Castle
Europa Point
Algeciras
Luna 788
Pta del Carnero
Guaro
Monda
Istán
Ojén
Coín
Alhaurín el Grande
Cártama
Alhaurín de la Torre
Real Club de Campo de Málaga
Málaga
El Palo
Rincón de la Victoria
Mijas 1150
Mijas
Torremolinos
Benalmádena
Fuengirola
Punta de Calaburra
Marbella
San Pedro de Alcántara
Ensenada de Marbella
Melilla
Sète
E
MA
Gibraltar
Pta Almina
Ceuta
Souk Tleta Taghramet
Restinga
Cabo Negro
Jebel el Haouz 826
Mdiq
Martil
Tétouan
El Fendek
Cap Mazari
Dar Ben Karricha el Behri
Oued Laou
E05
E15
E15/902
E902
AP7
AP46
A4
A7
A44
A45
A48
A92
A92M
A316
N13
N16
A6

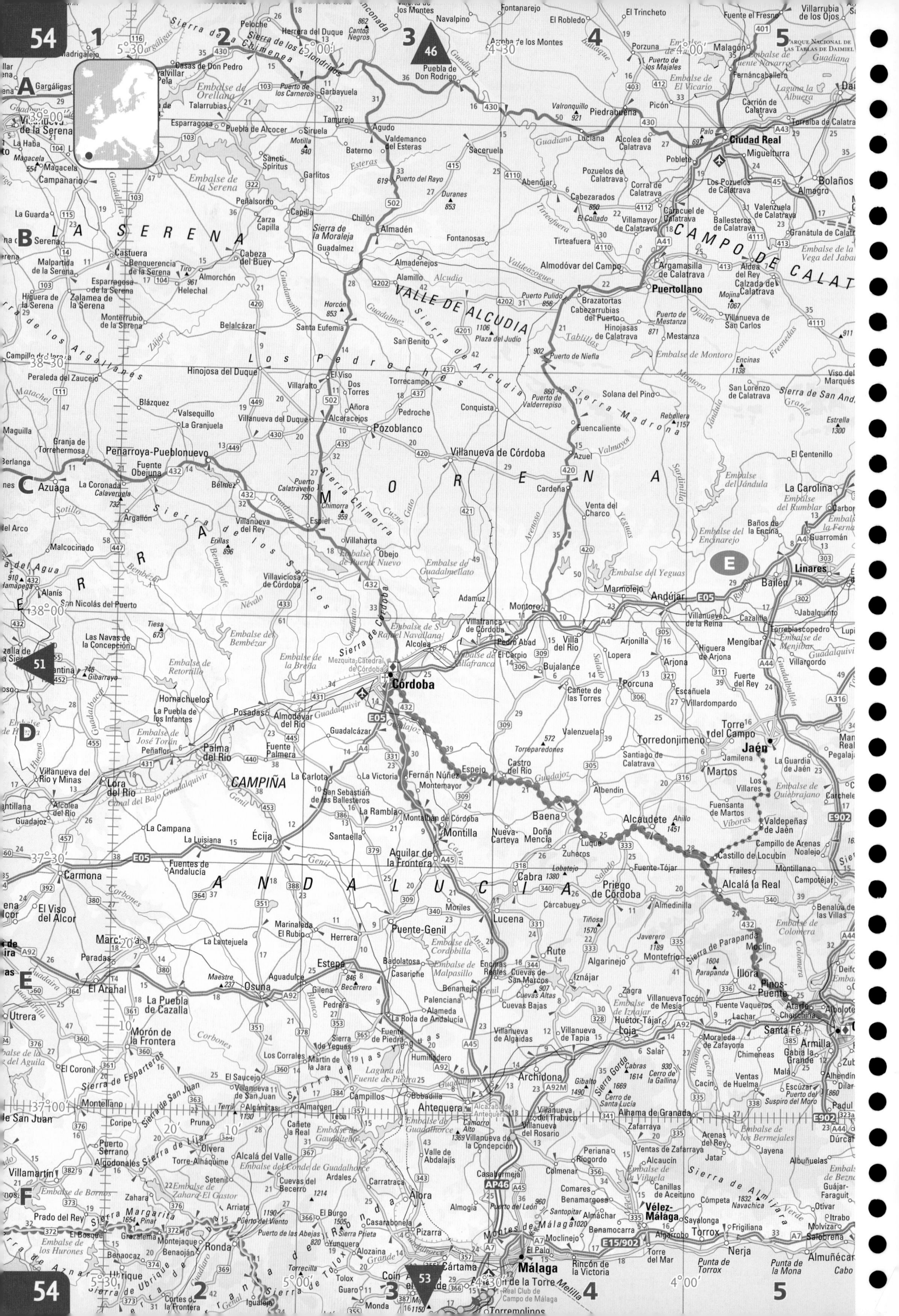

54
1
2
3
4
5
A
B
C
D
E
F
46
51
53
LA SERENA
CAMPO DE CALATRAVA
VALLE DE ALCUDIA
Sierra de Alcudia
Los Pedroches
Sierra Madrona
MORENA
SIERRA
Sierra de los Santos
Sierra de Córdoba
CAMPIÑA
ANDALUCIA
Sierra de Parapanda
Sierra de Almijara
Sierra de Tolox
Sierra de Ubrique
Sierra de Lijar
Sierra de Esparteros
Sierra de Yeguas
Sierra de San Andrés
Sierra de la Chimenea
Sierra de los Golondrinos
Sierra de los Argallanes
Sierra Chimorra
Sierra Gorda
Sierra de la Moraleja
Parque Nacional de las Tablas de Daimiel
Embalse de Orellana
Embalse de la Serena
Embalse de Montoro
Embalse del Jándula
Embalse del Rumblar
Embalse del Encinarejo
Embalse del Yeguas
Embalse de Guadalmellato
Embalse de Puente Nuevo
Embalse del Bembézar
Embalse de Retortillo
Embalse de la Breña
Embalse de S. Rafael Navallana
Embalse de Villafranca
Embalse de José Torán
Embalse de Cordobilla
Embalse de Malpasillo
Embalse de Iznájar
Embalse de Guadalhorce
Embalse del Conde de Guadalhorce
Embalse de Zahara-El Gastor
Embalse de Bornos
Embalse de los Hurones
Embalse de la Viñuela
Embalse de los Bermejales
Embalse de Colomera
Embalse de Quiebrajano
Embalse de Gasset
Embalse de El Vicario
Laguna de Fuente de Piedra
Ciudad Real
Puertollano
Almadén
Córdoba
Mezquita-Catedral de Córdoba
Jaén
Linares
Bailén
Andújar
Montoro
Pozoblanco
Villanueva de Córdoba
Peñarroya-Pueblonuevo
Hinojosa del Duque
Palma del Río
Écija
Carmona
Osuna
Estepa
Antequera
Lucena
Cabra
Priego de Córdoba
Alcalá la Real
Loja
Málaga
Vélez-Málaga
Ronda
Nerja
Torrox
Martos
Baena
Montilla
Puente-Genil
Aguilar de la Frontera
Morón de la Frontera
Utrera
Archidona
Almodóvar del Campo
Villanueva de la Serena
Campanario
Castuera
Cabeza del Buey
Fuente Obejuna
Azuaga
Lora del Río
Santa Fé
Armilla
Alhama de Granada
Torremolinos
Alcaucín
Alcaudete
E05
E15/902
E902
A4
A44
A45
A92
A92M
A7
AP46

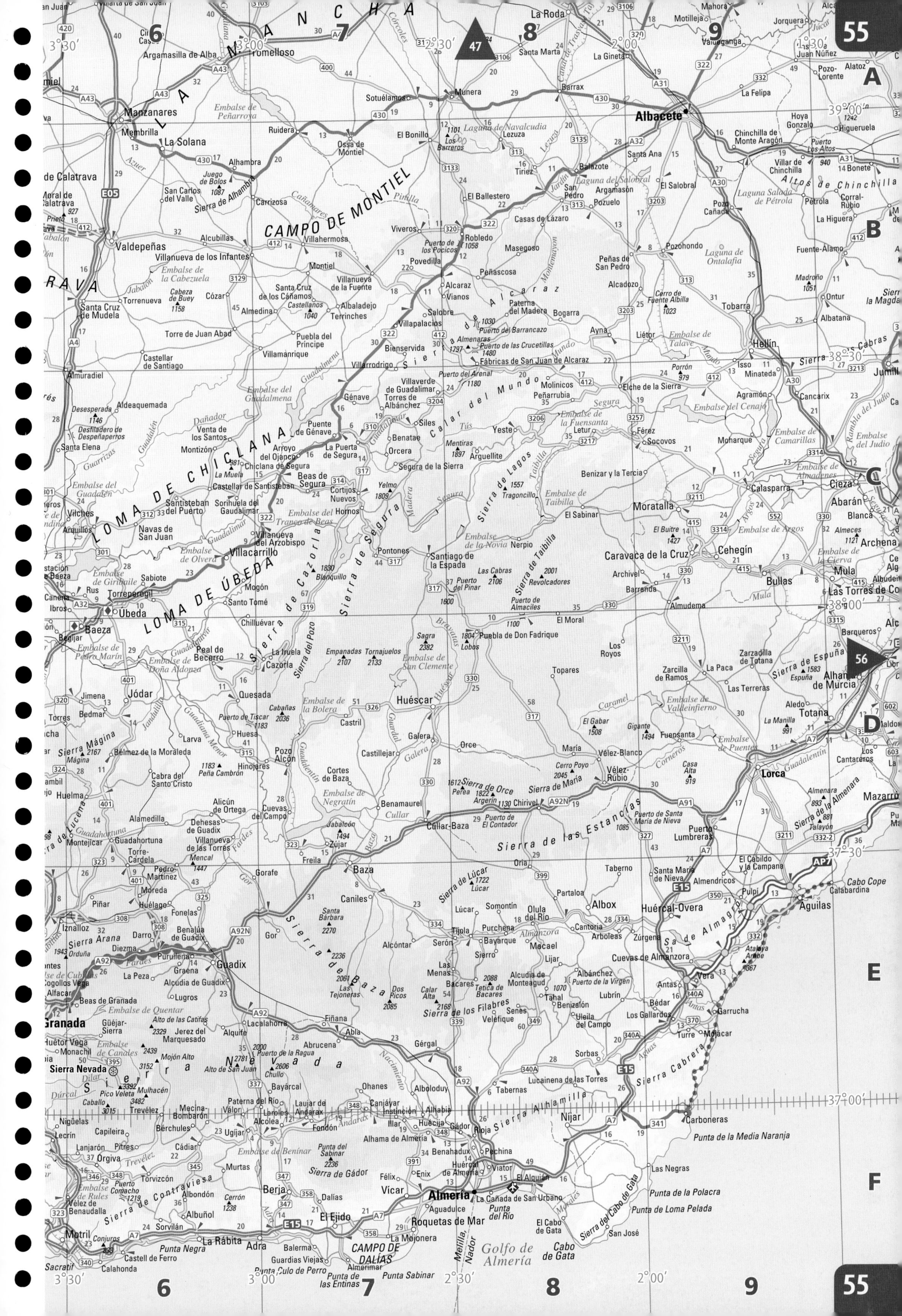

55
LA MANCHA
Argamasilla de Alba
Tomelloso
Manzanares
Membrilla
La Solana
Embalse de Peñarroya
Ruidera
Ossa de Montiel
Sotuélamos
Munera
El Bonillo
Laguna de Navalcudia
Lezuza
La Roda
Santa Marta
La Gineta
Barrax
Albacete
Motilleja
Mahora
Valdeganga
Jorquera
Juan Núñez
Pozo-Lorente
Alatoz
La Felipa
Hoya Gonzalo
Higueruela
Chinchilla de Monte Aragón
Villar de Chinchilla
Bonete
Altos de Chinchilla
Laguna Salada de Pétrola
Pétrola
Corral-Rubio
La Higuera
Fuente-Álamo
Ontur
Albatana
Sierra de la Magdalena
Santa Ana
El Salobral
Balazote
Laguna del Salobral
Argamasón
Pozuelo
San Pedro
Pozo Cañada
Pozohondo
Laguna de Ontalafia
Peñas de San Pedro
Alcadozo
Tobarra
Hellín
Isso
Minateda
Sierra de Cabras
Agramón
Cancarix
Jumilla
Embalse del Cenajo
Embalse de Camarillas
Embalse del Judío
Rambla del Judío
Embalse de Talave
Liétor
Ayna
Bogarra
Paterna del Madera
Masegoso
Casas de Lázaro
El Ballestero
Robledo
Viveros
Tiriez
CAMPO DE MONTIEL
Carrizosa
Alhambra
San Carlos del Valle
Sierra de Alhambra
de Calatrava
Moral de Calatrava
Valdepeñas
Alcubillas
Villanueva de los Infantes
Villahermosa
Montiel
Santa Cruz de los Cañamos
Almedina
Cózar
Torrenueva
Santa Cruz de Mudela
Embalse de la Cabezuela
Villanueva de la Fuente
Albaladejo
Terrinches
Puebla del Príncipe
Villamanrique
Torre de Juan Abad
Castellar de Santiago
Almuradiel
Povedilla
Alcaraz
Vianos
Salobre
Villapalacios
Bienservida
Villarrodrigo
Sierra de Alcaraz
Peñascosa
Fábricas de San Juan de Alcaraz
Puerto de las Crucetillas
Puerto del Barrancazo
Molinicos
Peñarrubia
Elche de la Sierra
Villaverde de Guadalimar
Torres de Albánchez
Génave
Puente de Génave
Siles
Benatae
Orcera
Segura de la Sierra
Calar del Mundo
Yeste
Letur
Embalse de la Fuensanta
Férez
Socovos
Moratalla
Calasparra
Cieza
Abarán
Blanca
Archena
Embalse de Argos
Cehegín
Caravaca de la Cruz
Archivel
Bullas
Mula
Barranda
Almudema
Las Torres de Cotillas
Alguazas
Benizar y la Tercia
Sierra de Lagos
Tragoncillo
Embalse de Taibilla
El Sabinar
Nerpio
Sierra de Taibilla
Embalse de la Novia
Santiago de la Espada
Pontones
Hornos
Sierra de Segura
Cortijos Nuevos
Beas de Segura
Arroyo del Ojanco
La Puerta de Segura
Chiclana de Segura
LOMA DE CHICLANA
Castellar de Santisteban
Santisteban del Puerto
Sorihuela del Guadalimar
Montizón
Venta de los Santos
Aldeaquemada
Desfiladero de Despeñaperros
Santa Elena
Vilches
Arquillos
Navas de San Juan
Villacarrillo
Villanueva del Arzobispo
Embalse del Tranco de Beas
LOMA DE ÚBEDA
Sabiote
Torreperogil
Úbeda
Baeza
Rus
Ibros
Begíjar
Santo Tomé
Mogón
Chilluévar
Sierra de Cazorla
Cazorla
La Iruela
Peal de Becerro
Quesada
Embalse de Pedro Marín
Embalse de Doña Aldonza
Jódar
Jimena
Bedmar
Torres
Larva
Huesa
Hinojares
Pozo Alcón
Sierra Mágina
Bélmez de la Moraleda
Cabra del Santo Cristo
Huelma
Alicún de Ortega
Dehesas de Guadix
Villanueva de las Torres
Cuevas del Campo
Sierra del Pozo
Puebla de Don Fadrique
Huéscar
Castril
Embalse de la Bolera
Embalse de San Clemente
Galera
Orce
Castillejar
Cortes de Baza
Embalse de Negratín
Benamaurel
Cúllar
Cúllar-Baza
Sierra de Orce
Chirivel
Sierra de María
María
Vélez-Blanco
Vélez-Rubio
Topares
El Moral
Los Royos
Zarcilla de Ramos
La Paca
Zarzadilla de Totana
Sierra de Espuña
Alhama de Murcia
Las Terreras
Embalse de Valdeinfierno
Fuensanta
Embalse de Puentes
Totana
Aledo
Lorca
Cantareros
Mazarrón
Sierra de la Almenara
Puerto Lumbreras
Sierra de las Estancias
Puerto de Santa María de Nieva
Oria
Taberno
Santa María de Nieva
El Cabildo y la Campana
Almendricos
Pulpí
Águilas
Cabo Cope
Calabardina
Huércal-Overa
Partaloa
Albox
Olula del Río
Cantoria
Arboleas
Zúrgena
Sierra de Almagro
Cuevas del Almanzora
Vera
Antas
Garrucha
Bédar
Los Gallardos
Turre
Mojácar
Sorbas
Lucainena de las Torres
Sierra Cabrera
Carboneras
Punta de la Media Naranja
Níjar
Sierra Alhamilla
Las Negras
Punta de la Polacra
Punta de Loma Pelada
Sierra del Cabo de Gata
San José
Cabo de Gata
El Cabo de Gata
Golfo de Almería
Almería
La Cañada de San Urbano
Punta del Río
Huércal de Almería
Viator
El Alquián
Pechina
Benahadux
Rioja
Gádor
Alhama de Almería
Tabernas
Alboloduy
Gérgal
Nacimiento
Abla
Fiñana
Abrucena
Sierra de los Filabres
Tahal
Senés
Velefique
Uleila del Campo
Lubrín
Benizalón
Alcudia de Monteagud
Macael
Lijar
Albánchez
Purchena
Serón
Tíjola
Bayarque
Sierro
Lúcar
Somontín
Sierra de Lúcar
Bacares
Las Menas
Alcóntar
Sierra de Baza
Caniles
Baza
Zújar
Freila
Gor
Gorafe
Guadix
Purullena
Graena
Alcudia de Guadix
Lugros
Benalúa de Guadix
Fonelas
Huélago
Moreda
Pedro Martínez
Torre-Cardela
Guadahortuna
Alamedilla
Montejícar
Piñar
Iznalloz
Sierra Arana
Darro
Diezma
La Peza
Beas de Granada
Embalse de Quéntar
Granada
Güéjar-Sierra
Jerez del Marquesado
Lacalahorra
Alquife
Huétor Vega
Monachil
Sierra Nevada
Mulhacén
Pico Veleta
Caballo
Trevélez
Dúrcal
Nigüelas
Lecrín
Capileira
Lanjarón
Pitres
Órgiva
Bérchules
Mecina-Bombarón
Válor
Ugíjar
Cádiar
Paterna del Río
Laroles
Laujar de Andarax
Alcolea
Fondón
Ohanes
Canjáyar
Instinción
Alhabia
Huécija
Íllar
Bayárcal
Puerto de la Ragua
Embalse de Beninar
Sierra de Gádor
Murtas
Torvizcón
Sierra de Contraviesa
Albondón
Albuñol
Embalse de Rules
Vélez de Benaudalla
Motril
Sorvilán
La Rábita
Adra
Berja
Dalías
El Ejido
Félix
Vícar
Enix
Aguadulce
Roquetas de Mar
La Mojonera
Balerma
Guardias Viejas
Almerimar
CAMPO DE DALÍAS
Punta Culo de Perro
Punta de las Entinas
Punta Sabinar
Punta Negra
Castell de Ferro
Calahonda
Melilla, Nador
56
47
55

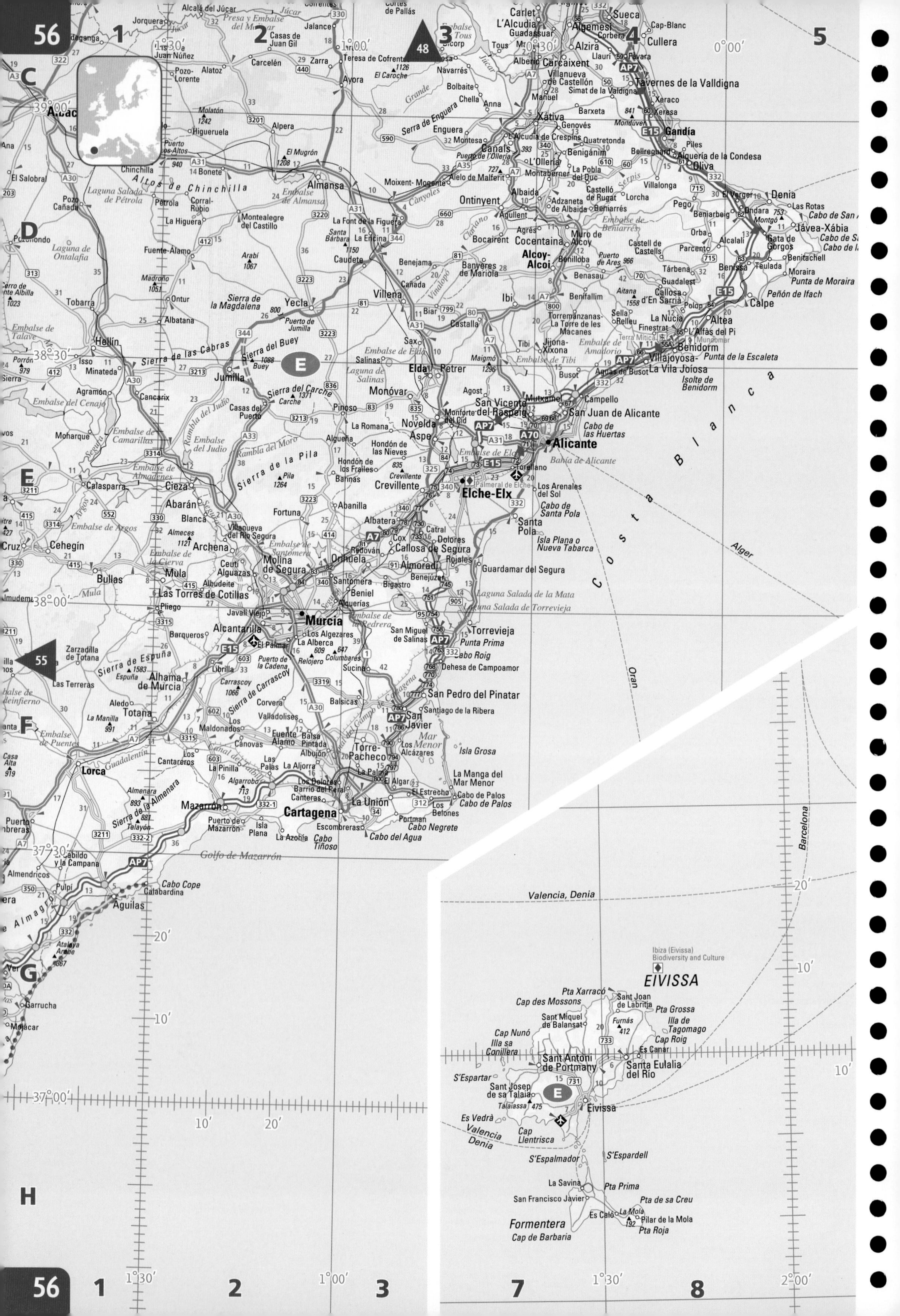

56
1
2
3
4
5
C
D
E
F
G
H
48
55
7
8
Alcalá del Júcar
Jorquera
Casas de Juan Gil
Jalance
Cortes de Pallás
Carlet
L'Alcudia
Guadassuar
Algemesí
Sueca
Cap-Blanc
Cullera
Alzira
Carcaixent
Corbera
Llauri
Favara
Villanueva de Castellón
Tavernes de la Valldigna
Simat de la Valldigna
Xeraco
Xeresa
Gandia
Piles
Alquería de la Condesa
Oliva
Xàtiva
Genovés
L'Alcudia de Crespins
Quatretonda
Benigánim
L'Olleria
Montaberner
La Pobla del Duc
Bellreguard
Villalonga
Pego
Castelló de Rugat
Lorcha
Albaida
Adzaneta de Albaida
Beniarrés
Ontinyent
Agullent
Bocairent
Agrés
Cocentaina
Muro de Alcoy
Alcoy-Alcoi
Benilloba
Banyeres de Mariola
Benasau
Ibi
Benifallim
Torremanzanas-La Torre de les Macanes
Jijona-Xixona
Tibi
Busot
Aguas de Busot
Villajoyosa-La Vila Joíosa
Benidorm
Finestrat
La Nucía
L'Alfàs del Pi
Altea
Calpe
Polop
Callosa d'En Sarrià
Sella
Relleu
Guadalest
Tárbena
Benissa
Teulada
Moraira
Punta de Moraira
Peñón de Ifach
Benitachell
Jávea-Xàbia
Cabo de San Antonio
Gata de Gorgos
Alcalalí
Parcent
Orba
Beniarbeig
Ondara
Denia
Las Rotas
El Verger
Montgó
Castell de Castells
Punta de la Escaleta
Isolte de Benidorm
Costa Blanca
Campello
Mutxamel
San Vicente del Raspeig
San Juan de Alicante
Cabo de las Huertas
Alicante
Bahía de Alicante
Agost
Monforte del Cid
Novelda
Aspe
Elda
Petrer
Sax
Biar
Castalla
Villena
Cañada
Benejama
Caudete
La Encina
La Font de la Figuera
Almansa
Moixent-Mogente
Alelo de Malferit
Montesa
Canals
Enguera
Serra de Enguera
Navarrés
Bolbaite
Chella
Anna
Bicorp
Ayora
Zarra
Teresa de Cofrentes
El Caroche
Carcelén
Alpera
Higueruela
Pozo-Lorente
Alatoz
Chinchilla
Bonete
Altos de Chinchilla
Laguna Salada de Pétrola
Pétrola
Corral-Rubio
La Higuera
Montealegre del Castillo
El Mugrón
Fuente-Álamo
Ontur
Albatana
Tobarra
Hellín
Isso
Minateda
Agramón
Cancarix
Jumilla
Sierra de las Cabras
Sierra del Buey
Yecla
Sierra de la Magdalena
Pinoso
Monóvar
Salinas
Laguna de Salinas
Embalse de Elda
La Romana
Algueña
Hondón de las Nieves
Hondón de los Frailes
Barinas
Crevillente
Elche-Elx
Torrellano
Los Arenales del Sol
Santa Pola
Cabo de Santa Pola
Isla Plana o Nueva Tabarca
Guardamar del Segura
Rojales
Dolores
Catral
Callosa de Segura
Almoradí
Benejúzar
Cox
Redován
Orihuela
Albatera
Abanilla
Fortuna
Santomera
Beniel
Alquerías
Bigastro
Laguna Salada de la Mata
Laguna Salada de Torrevieja
Torrevieja
Punta Prima
Cabo Roig
Dehesa de Campoamor
San Miguel de Salinas
San Pedro del Pinatar
Santiago de la Ribera
San Javier
Los Alcázares
Mar Menor
Isla Grosa
La Manga del Mar Menor
Cabo de Palos
Los Belones
Portman
Cabo Negrete
El Algar
La Palma
La Unión
Cartagena
Escombreras
Cabo Tiñoso
Cabo del Agua
Torre-Pacheco
Balsicas
Sucina
Murcia
Los Algezares
La Alberca
El Palmar
Alcantarilla
Javalí Viejo
Molina de Segura
Archena
Ceutí
Alguazas
Albudeite
Mula
Bullas
Cehegín
Calasparra
Cieza
Abarán
Blanca
Villanueva del Río Segura
Las Torres de Cotillas
Pliego
Barqueros
Librilla
Alhama de Murcia
Sierra de España
Totana
Aledo
Las Terreras
Zarzadilla de Totana
Lorca
Puerto Lumbreras
Mazarrón
Puerto de Mazarrón
Isla Plana
La Azohía
Golfo de Mazarrón
Cabildo y la Campana
Almendricos
Pulpí
Águilas
Calabardina
Cabo Cope
Garrucha
Mojácar
Fuente Álamo
Balsa Pintada
Albujón
Las Palas
La Aljorra
Los Dolores
Barrio del Peral
Canteras
Cánovas
Maldonados
Los Cantareros
La Pinilla
Corvera
Valladolises
Sierra de Carrascoy
Sierra de la Almenara
Valencia, Denia
Oran
Alger
Barcelona
EIVISSA
Ibiza (Eivissa) Biodiversity and Culture
Pta Xarracó
Sant Joan de Labritja
Pta Grossa
Illa de Tagomago
Cap Roig
Es Canar
Cap des Mossons
Sant Miquel de Balansat
Furnás
Cap Nunó
Illa sa Conillera
Sant Antoni de Portmany
Santa Eulalia del Río
S'Espartar
Sant Josep de sa Talaia
Talaiassa
Eivissa
Es Vedrà
Cap Llentrisca
S'Espalmador
S'Espardell
La Savina
Pta Prima
San Francisco Javier
Pta de sa Creu
Es Caló
La Mola
Pilar de la Mola
Pta Roja
Formentera
Cap de Barbaria
AP7
A7
A31
A30
A33
A35
E15
A70

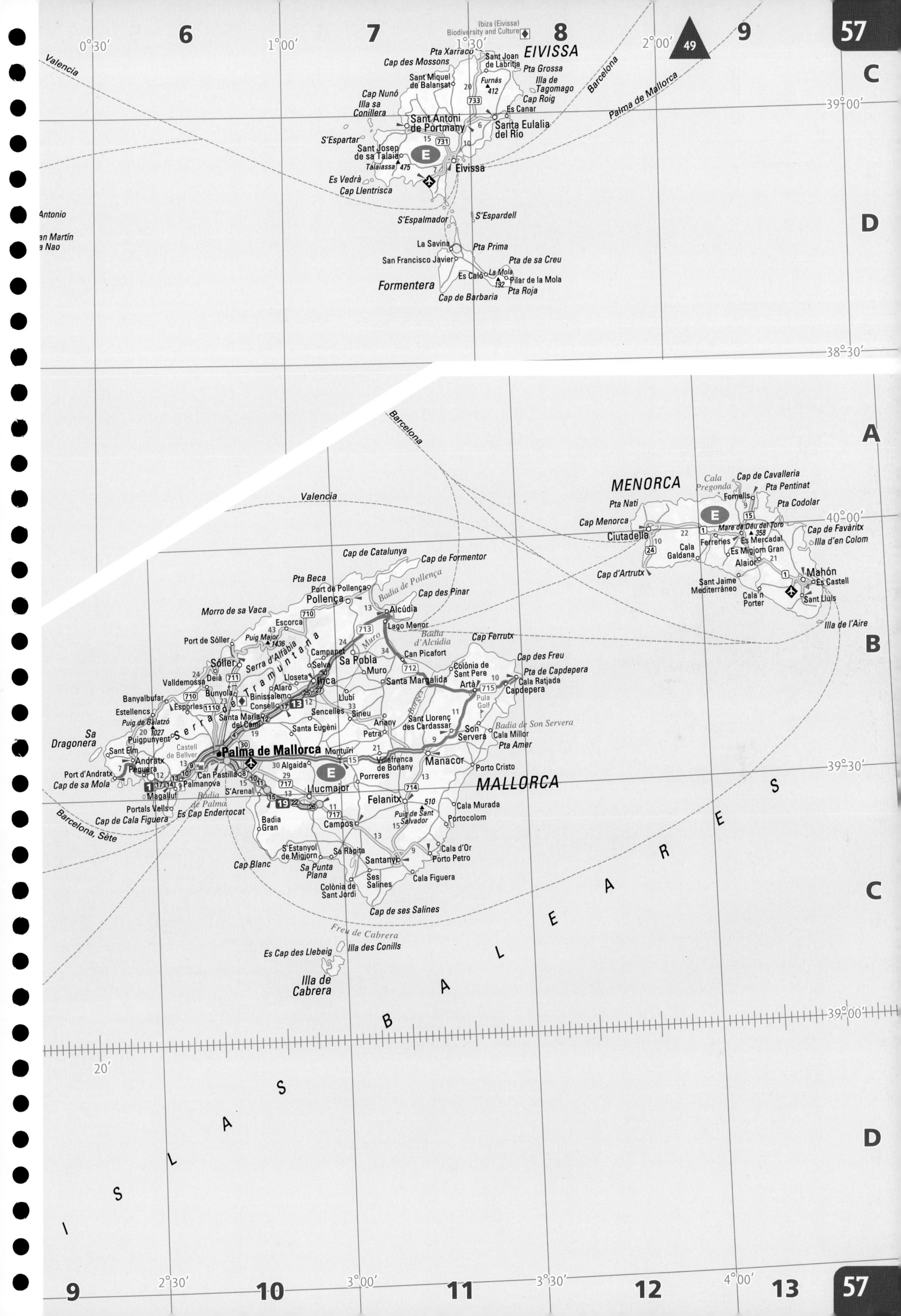

Valencia

0°30'　　　1°00'

Ibiza (Eivissa)
Biodiversity and Culture ◆

Pta Xarraco
Cap des Mossons
Sant Joan
de Labritja

Pta Grossa
Illa de
Tagomago
Cap Roig
Es Canar

Sant Miquel
de Balansat
Furnàs
▲412
733

Cap Nunó
Illa sa
Conillera

Barcelona
Palma de Mallorca

39°00'

Sant Antoni
de Portmany
15
6
731
Santa Eulalia
del Río

S'Espartar
Sant Josep
de sa Talaia
10

E

Talaiassa ▲475

Es Vedrà
7
Cap Llentrisca

Eivissa

D

an Antonio
an Martín
e Nao

S'Espardell
S'Espalmador

La Savina
Pta Prima
Pta de sa Creu

San Francisco Javier
Es Caló
La Mola
Pilar de la Mola
▲192
Pta Roja

Formentera
Cap de Barbaria

38°30'

Barcelona

Valencia

A

MENORCA
Cala
Pregonda
Cap de Cavalleria
Pta Pentinat
Fornells
9
Pta Codolar

Pta Nati
Cap Menorca
Mare de Déu del Toro
▲358
15
Cap de Favàritx

Ciutadella
10
24
22
Ferreries
Es Mercadal
Es Migjorn Gran
Alaior
21
1
Illa d'en Colom

Cala
Galdana
Mahón
Es Castell

Cap d'Artrutx
Sant Jaime
Mediterráneo
Cala'n
Porter
Sant Lluís

40°00'

Illa de l'Aire

B

Cap de Catalunya
Cap de Formentor

Pta Beca
Port de Pollença
Badia de Pollença
Cap des Pinar

Pollença
13
Alcúdia

Morro de sa Vaca
710
713
Lago Menor

Escorca
43
Puig Major
▲1436
24
Campanet
Sa Pobla
Muro
34
Can Picafort
Badia
d'Alcúdia
Cap Ferrutx

Port de Sóller
Selva
Santa Margalida
712
Colònia de
Sant Pere
Cap des Freu
Pta de Capdepera

Sóller
Serra d'Alfàbia
Lloseta
30
Inca
Llubí
10
Artà
715
Cala Ratjada
Capdepera

Valldemossa
Deià
711
Bunyola
Alaró
25
Binissalem
Consell
17
Sineu
33
Sant Llorenç
des Cardassar
Pula
Golf

Banyalbufar
Espporles
710
23
12
1110
Santa Maria
del Camí
13
Sencelles
11
Son
Servera
Badia de Son Servera

Estellencs
Puig de Galatzó
▲1027
20
Puigpunyent
19
Santa Eugèni
Ariany
Petra
9
Cala Millor

Sa
Dragonera
Castell
de Bellver
Montuïri
21
Villafranca
de Bonany
Manacor
Pta Amer

Sant Elm
Andratx
Can Pastilla
30
Algaida
15
Porreres
Porto Cristo

Palma de Mallorca

E

MALLORCA

39°30'

Port d'Andratx
Peguera
7
Magaluf
13
Palmanova
8
29
717
S'Arenal
Llucmajor
Felanitx
714
510
Cala Murada

Cap de sa Mola
1
17
14

Portocolom

Barcelona, Sète
Portals Vells
19
22
Campos
Puig de Sant
Salvador
15

Cap de Cala Figuera
Es Cap Enderrocat
Badia
de Palma
717
11
13

Badia
Gran
Santanyí
9
Cala d'Or
Porto Petro

S'Estanyol
de Migjorn
Sa Ràpita
Ses
Salines
Cala Figuera

Cap Blanc
Sa Punta
Plana

Colònia de
Sant Jordi
Cap de ses Salines

Freu de Cabrera

Es Cap des Llebeig
Illa des Conills

Illa de
Cabrera

C

B
A
L
E
A
R
E
S

39°00'

20'

I
S
L
A
S

B
A
L
E
A
R
S

I
S
L
A
S

D

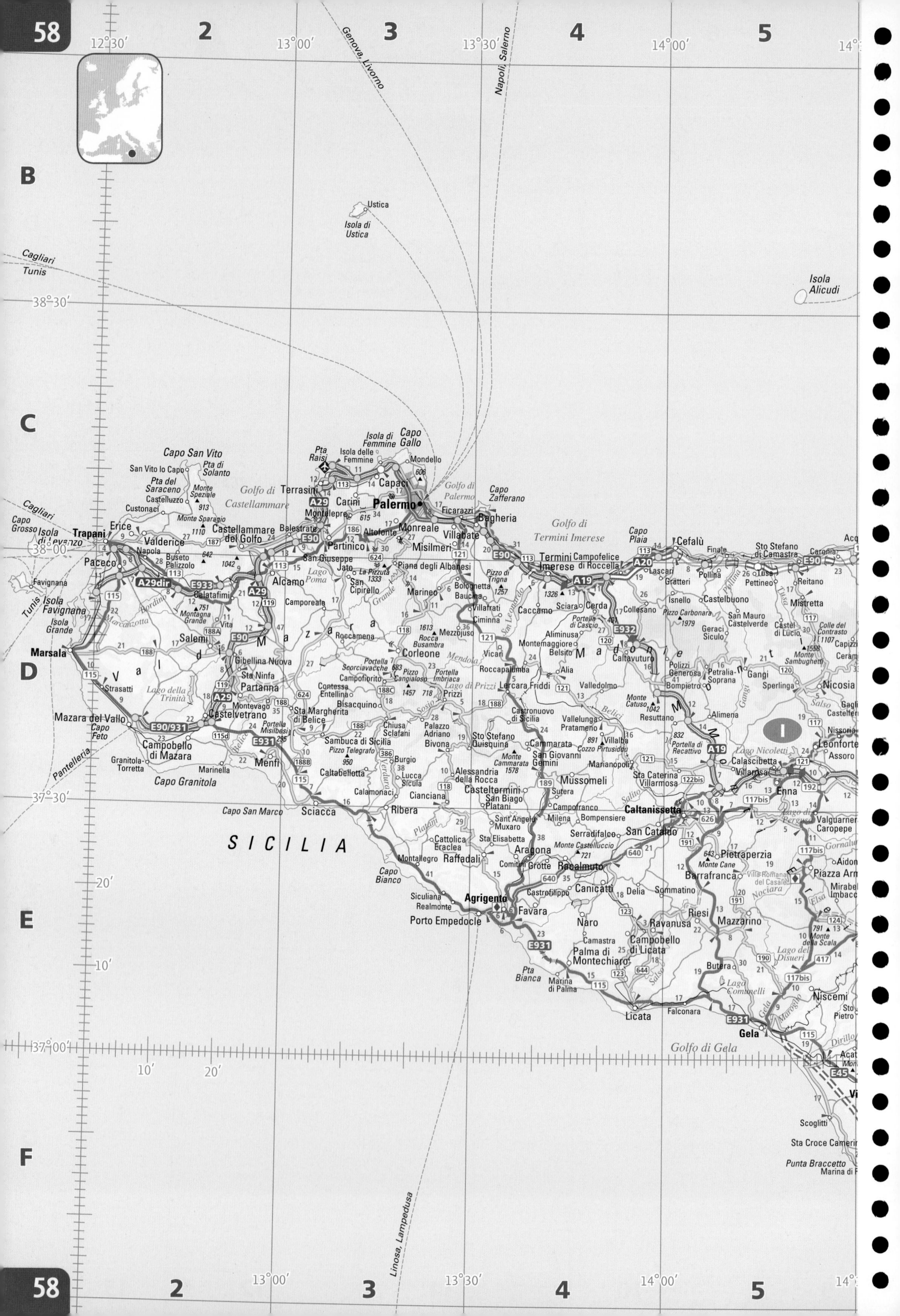
58
2
3
4
5
12°30′
13°00′
13°30′
14°00′
Genova, Livorno
Napoli, Salerno
B
C
D
E
F
Ustica
Isola di Ustica
Cagliari
Tunis
38°30′
Isola Alicudi
Capo San Vito
San Vito lo Capo
Pta di Solanto
Pta del Saraceno
Monte Speziale 913
Castelluzzo
Custonaci
Monte Sparagio 1110
Golfo di Castellammare
Capo Grosso
Isola di Levanzo
Trapani
Erice
Valderice
Castellammare del Golfo
Balestrate
Terrasini
Carini
Capaci
Pta Raisi
Isola delle Femmine
Isola di Femmine
Capo Gallo
Mondello
Golfo di Palermo
Palermo
Monreale
Montelepre
Altofonte
Partinico
Capo Zafferano
Ficarazzi
Bagheria
Villabate
Misilmeri
Golfo di Termini Imerese
Termini Imerese
Campofelice di Roccella
Capo Plaia
Cefalù
Finale
Sto Stefano di Camastra
Caronia
Napola
Paceco
Buseto Palizzolo
Favignana
Isola Favignana
Isola Grande
Marsala
Salemi
Calatafimi
Alcamo
San Giuseppe Jato
San Cipirello
Lago Poma
La Pizzuta 1333
Piana degli Albanesi
Camporeale
Marineo
Bolognetta
Baucina
Pizzo di Trigna 1257
Villafrati
Ciminna
Caccamo
Sciara
Cerda
Collesano
Lascari
Gratteri
Pollina
Isnello
Castelbuono
Pizzo Carbonara 1979
San Mauro Castelverde
Geraci Siculo
Tusa
Pettineo
Reitano
Mistretta
Castel di Lucio
Monte Sambughetti
Capizzi
Montagna Grande 751
Vita
Gibellina Nuova
Sta Ninfa
Partanna
Lago della Trinità
Montevago
Castelvetrano
Roccamena
Corleone
Rocca Busambra 1613
Mezzojuso
Portella Scorciavacche
Campofiorito
Pizzo Cangialoso 1457
Contessa Entellina
Bisacquino
Prizzi
Lago di Prizzi
Roccapalumba
Vicari
Lercara Friddi
Aliminusa
Montemaggiore Belsito
Caltavuturo
Alia
Valledolmo
Polizzi Generosa
Petralia Soprana
Bompietro
Gangi
Sperlinga
Nicosia
Monte Catuso 1042
Resuttano
Alimena
Strasatti
Mazara del Vallo
Capo Feto
Campobello di Mazara
Granitola-Torretta
Capo Granitola
Marinella
Menfi
Sta Margherita di Belice
Sambuca di Sicilia
Pizzo Telegrafo 950
Chiusa Sclafani
Palazzo Adriano
Bivona
Burgio
Caltabellotta
Lucca Sicula
Calamonaci
Cianciana
Sto Stefano Quisquina
Castronuovo di Sicilia
Cammarata
Monte Cammarata 1578
San Giovanni Gemini
Vallelunga Pratameno
Villalba
Marianopoli
Portella di Recattivo
Calascibetta
Villarosa
Sta Caterina Villarmosa
Enna
Leonforte
Assoro
Lago Nicoletti
Alessandria della Rocca
Casteltermini
San Biagio Platani
Mussomeli
Sutera
Campofranco
Milena
Bompensiere
Caltanissetta
San Cataldo
Serradifalco
Monte Castelluccio 721
Capo San Marco
Sciacca
Ribera
SICILIA
Sant'Angelo Muxaro
Cattolica Eraclea
Sta Elisabetta
Aragona
Montallegro
Raffadali
Comitini
Grotte
Racalmuto
Capo Bianco
Siciliana
Realmonte
Agrigento
Porto Empedocle
Favara
Castrofilippo
Canicattì
Delia
Sommatino
Naro
Camastra
Palma di Montechiaro
Campobello di Licata
Ravanusa
Riesi
Mazzarino
Pietraperzia
Monte Cane
Barrafranca
Villa Romana del Casale
Piazza Armerina
Valguarnera Caropepe
Lago di Pergusa
Butera
Lago Comunelli
Niscemi
Pta Bianca
Marina di Palma
Licata
Falconara
Gela
Golfo di Gela
Pantelleria
Linosa, Lampedusa
37°30′
37°00′
20′
10′
Scoglitti
Sta Croce Camerina
Punta Braccetto
A29
A29dir
A19
A20
E90
E931
E932
E933
E90/931
E45
I

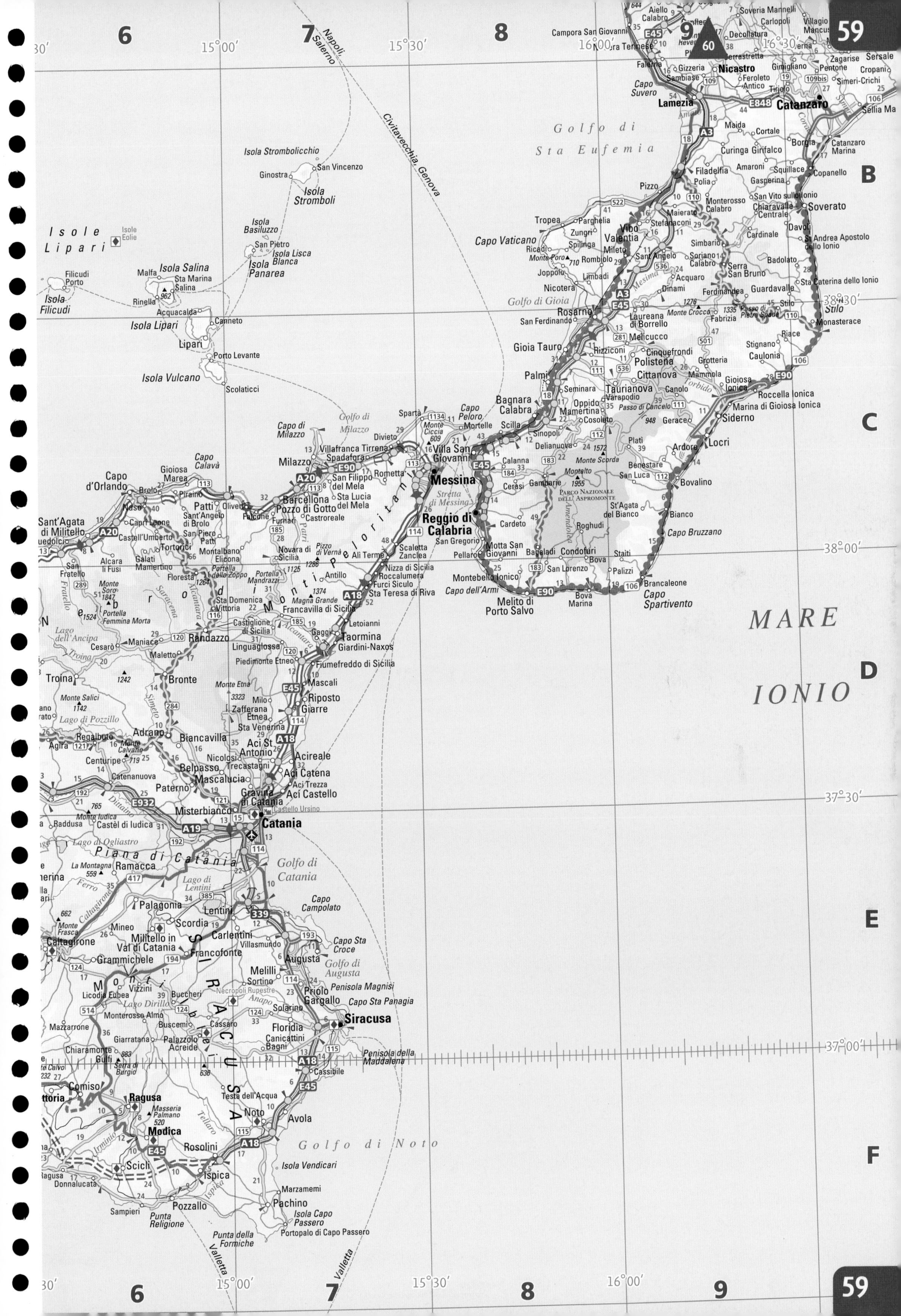
6
7
8
9
60
15°00′
15°30′
16°00′
16°30′
B
C
D
E
F
38°30′
38°00′
37°30′
37°00′
Napoli Salerno
Civitavecchia, Genova
Isole Lipari
Isole Eolie
Isola Strombolicchio
Ginostra
San Vincenzo
Isola Stromboli
Isola Basiluzzo
San Pietro
Isola Lisca Bianca
Isola Panarea
Filicudi Porto
Isola Filicudi
Malfa
Isola Salina
Sta Marina Salina
Rinella
Acquacalda
Isola Lipari
Canneto
Lipari
Porto Levante
Isola Vulcano
Scolaticci
Golfo di Milazzo
Capo di Milazzo
Milazzo
Capo Calavà
Capo d'Orlando
Gioiosa Marea
Brolo
Piraino
Patti
Oliveri
Falcone
Naso
Capri Leone
Sant'Agata di Militello
Castell'Umberto
Tortorici
Sant'Angelo di Brolo
San Piero Patti
Montalbano Elicona
Galati Mamertino
Alcara li Fusi
San Fratello
Floresta
Portella dello Zoppo
Portella Mandrazzi
Monte Soro 1847
Portella Femmina Morta
Lago dell'Ancipa
Cesarò
Maniace
Randazzo
Maletto
Troina
Bronte
Monte Salici 1142
Lago di Pozzillo
Adrano
Biancavilla
Regalbuto
Agira
Monte Calvario 719
Centuripe
Catenanuova
Paterno
Belpasso
Nicolosi
Trecastagni
Mascalucia
Gravina di Catania
Misterbianco
Catania
Castello Ursino
Monte Iudica 765
Raddusa
Castèl di Iudica
Lago di Ogliastro
Piana di Catania
La Montagna 559
Ramacca
Lago di Lentini
Palagonia
Lentini
Scordia
Carlentini
Mineo
Militello in Val di Catania
Caltagirone
Francofonte
Grammichele
Villasmundo
Augusta
Melilli
Sortino
Licodia Eubea
Vizzini
Buccheri
Necropoli Rupestre
Lago Dirillo
Monterosso Almo
Buscemi
Cassaro
Palazzolo Acreide
Giarratana
Chiaramonte Gulfi
Mazzarrone
Comiso
Vittoria
Ragusa
Masseria Palmano
Modica
Scicli
Rosolini
Ispica
Donnalucata
Sampieri
Pozzallo
Punta Religione
Pachino
Marzamemi
Isola Capo Passero
Portopalo di Capo Passero
Punta della Formiche
Valletta
Isola Vendicari
Golfo di Noto
Noto
Avola
Testa dell'Acqua
Cassibile
Penisola della Maddalena
Siracusa
Floridia
Canicattini Bagni
Solarino
Priolo Gargallo
Penisola Magnisi
Capo Sta Panagia
Golfo di Augusta
Capo Sta Croce
Capo Campolato
Golfo di Catania
Acireale
Aci Catena
Aci Trezza
Aci Castello
Aci St Antonio
Sta Venerina
Zafferana Etnea
Milo
Monte Etna 3323
Giarre
Riposto
Mascali
Fiumefreddo di Sicilia
Piedimonte Etneo
Linguaglossa
Castiglione di Sicilia
Francavilla di Sicilia
Gaggi
Taormina
Giardini-Naxos
Letojanni
Sta Teresa di Riva
Furci Siculo
Roccalumera
Nizza di Sicilia
Antillo
Monti Peloritani
Monti Nebrodi
Novara di Sicilia
Pizzo di Vernà
Ali Terme
Scaletta Zanclea
Barcellona Pozzo di Gotto
Sta Lucia del Mela
San Filippo del Mela
Castroreale
Furnari
Rometta
Spadafora
Villafranca Tirrena
Divieto
Spartà
Monte Ciccia 609
Capo Peloro
Mortelle
Villa San Giovanni
Messina
Stretta di Messina
Reggio di Calabria
San Gregorio
Pellaro
Motta San Giovanni
Montebello Ionico
Capo dell'Armi
Melito di Porto Salvo
Bagaladi
San Lorenzo
Condofuri
Bova
Bova Marina
Palizzi
Staiti
Brancaleone
Capo Spartivento
Cardeto
Roghudi
Parco Nazionale dell'Aspromonte
Montalto 1955
Gambarie
Cerasi
Calanna
Delianuova
Monte Scorda
Sinopoli
Scilla
Bagnara Calabra
Palmi
Seminara
Oppido Mamertina
Cosoleto
Varapodio
Taurianova
Cittanova
Polistena
Cinquefrondi
Rizziconi
Gioia Tauro
San Ferdinando
Rosarno
Golfo di Gioia
Laureana di Borrello
Melicucco
Canolo
Passo di Cancello
Gerace
Platì
Ardore
Benestare
San Luca
Bovalino
Sant'Agata del Bianco
Bianco
Capo Bruzzano
Locri
Siderno
Marina di Gioiosa Ionica
Gioiosa Ionica
Roccella Ionica
Mammola
Grotteria
Caulonia
Stignano
Riace
Monasterace
Stilo
Fabrizia
Monte Crocco
Passo di Pietra Spada
Guardavalle
Sta Caterina dello Ionio
Badolato
Serra San Bruno
Ferdinandea
Nicotera
Joppolo
Limbadi
Rombiolo
Capo Vaticano
Ricadi
Monte Poro 710
Spilinga
Zungri
Tropea
Parghelia
Vibo Valentia
Mileto
Sant'Angelo
Soriano Calabro
Simbario
Dinami
Acquaro
Maierato
Stefanaconi
Pizzo
Monterosso Calabro
Cardinale
Chiaravalle Centrale
San Vito sullo Ionio
Soverato
Davoli
Sant'Andrea Apostolo dello Ionio
Filadelfia
Polia
Gasperina
Squillace
Copanello
Amaroni
Curinga
Girifalco
Borgia
Catanzaro Marina
Maida
Cortale
Golfo di Sta Eufemia
Lamezia
Catanzaro
Capo Suvero
Sambiase
Gizzeria
Falerna
Nicastro
Feroleto Antico
Tiriolo
Gimigliano
Pentone
Simeri-Crichi
Sellia Marina
Cropani
Zagarise
Sersale
Decollatura
Carlopoli
Soveria Mannelli
Villagio Mancuso
Aiello Calabro
Campora San Giovanni
Nocera Terinese
Serrastretta
MARE IONIO
A3
A18
A19
A20
E45
E90
E848
E932

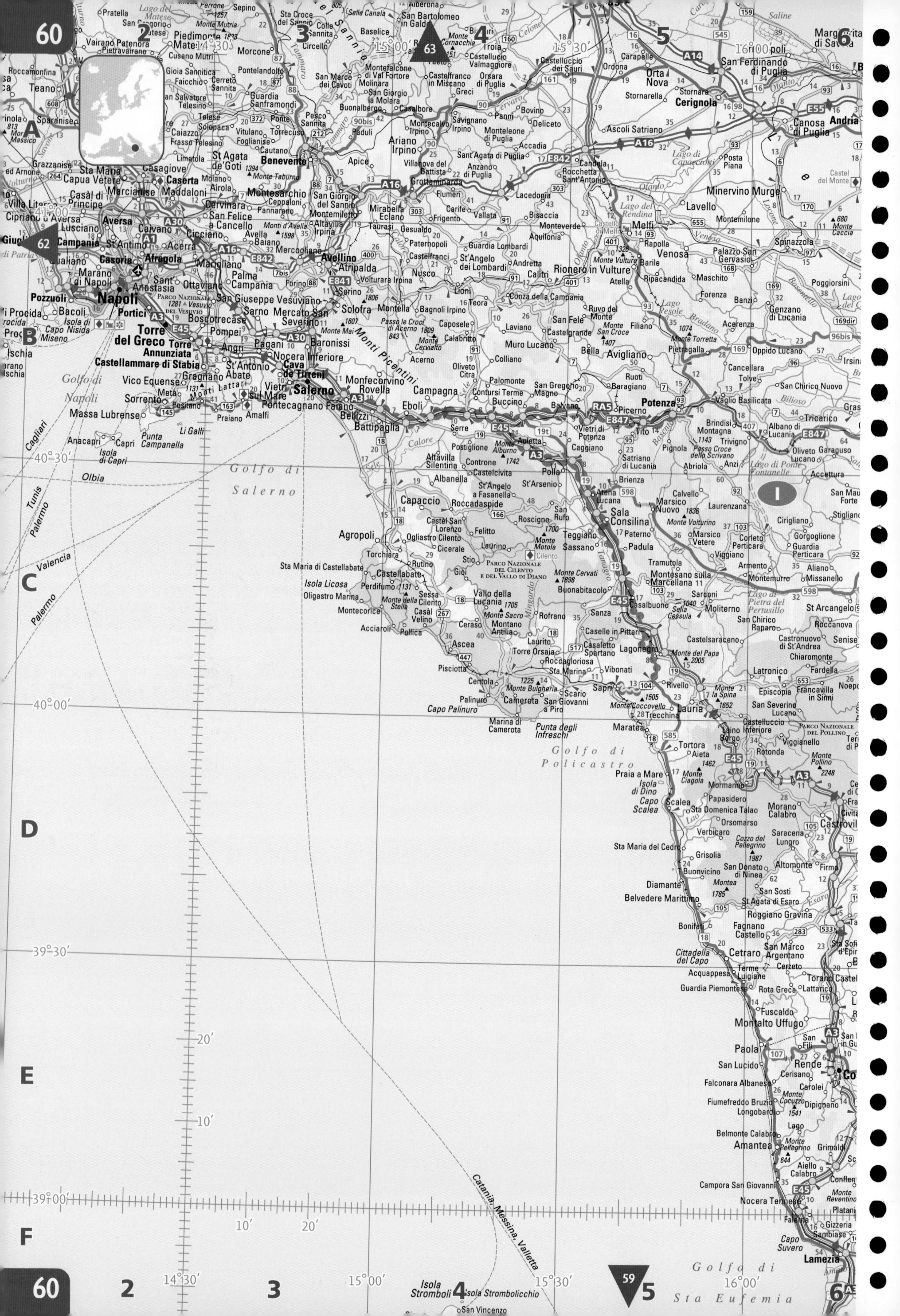

2
3
4
5
6
63
62
59
A
B
C
D
E
F
I
14°30′
15°00′
15°30′
16°00′
41°00′
40°30′
40°00′
39°30′
39°00′
20′
10′
Pratella
Sepino
Sta Croce del Sannio
Colle Sannita
Alberona
San Bartolomeo in Galdo
Piedimonte Matese
Vairano Patenora
Pietravairano
Teano
Roccamonfina
Cusano Mutri
Morcone
Baselice
Circello
Troia
Castelluccio Valmaggiore
Castelluccio dei Sauri
Ordona
Carapelle
Orta Nova
Stornarella
Stornara
Cerignola
San Ferdinando di Puglia
Margherita di Savoia
Canosa di Puglia
Andria
Gioia Sannitica
Faicchio
Cerreto Sannita
Pontelandolfo
Guardia Sanframondi
San Salvatore Telesino
San Marco dei Cavoti
Montefalcone di Val Fortore
Molinara
San Giorgio la Molara
Buonalbergo
Casalbore
Castelfranco in Miscano
Greci
Orsara di Puglia
Bovino
Deliceto
Panni
Ascoli Satriano
Sparanise
Telese
Solopaca
Ponte
Torrecuso
Pesco Sannita
Paduli
Montecalvo Irpino
Savignano Irpino
Monteleone di Puglia
Accadia
Caiazzo
Vitulano
Foglianise
Frasso Telesino
Cautano
Limatola
St Agata de' Goti
Benevento
Apice
Ariano Irpino
Sant'Agata di Puglia
Anzano di Puglia
Candela
Rocchetta Sant'Antonio
Posta Piana
Lago di Capaciotti
Grazzanise
Sta Maria Capua Vetere
Casagiove
Caserta
Moiano
Monte Taburno
Marcianise
Maddaloni
Airola
Montesarchio
San Giorgio del Sannio
Villanova del Battista
Grottaminarda
Flumeri
Lacedonia
Minervino Murge
Castel del Monte
Casal di Principe
Villa Literno
Cervinara
Ceppaloni
Pannarano
San Felice a Cancello
Montemiletto
Mirabella Eclano
Taurasi
Frigento
Carife
Vallata
Bisaccia
Lago del Rendina
Lavello
Montemilone
Spinazzola
Cipriano d'Aversa
Aversa
Lusciano
Calvano
Cicciano
Avella
Monti d'Avella
Altavilla Irpina
Gesualdo
Paternopoli
Guardia Lombardi
Monteverde
Aquilonia
Melfi
Rapolla
Venosa
Palazzo San Gervasio
Campania
St'Antimo
Acerra
Baiano
Mercogliano
Avellino
Atripalda
Castelfranci
St'Angelo dei Lombardi
Andretta
Calitri
Rionero in Vulture
Monte Vulture
Barile
Atella
Ripacandida
Maschito
Giugliano
Casoria
Afragola
Marigliano
Palma Campania
Forino
Volturara Irpina
Nusco
Lioni
Teora
Conza della Campania
Ruvo del Monte
Forenza
Banzi
Genzano di Lucania
Poggiorsini
Qualiano
Marano di Napoli
Sant'Anastasia
Ottaviano
Pozzuoli
Napoli
Parco Nazionale del Vesuvio
Vesuvio
San Giuseppe Vesuviano
Sarno
Mercato San Severino
Serino
Solofra
Montella
Bagnoli Irpino
Laviano
San Fele
Castelgrande
Filiano
Lago Pesole
Acerenza
Oppido Lucano
Procida
Bacoli
Portici
Boscotrecase
Isola di Capo Nisida
Capo Miseno
Ischia
Torre del Greco
Torre Annunziata
Pompei
Angri
Pagani
Baronissi
Nocera Inferiore
Monte Mai
Monti Picentini
Passo le Croci di Acerno
Caposele
Calabritto
Monte Cervialto
Acerno
Muro Lucano
Bella
Avigliano
Monte Torretta
Pietragalla
Cancellara
Tolve
Irsina
Castellammare di Stabia
St'Antonio Abate
Gragnano
Cava de' Tirreni
Salerno
Monfecorvino Rovella
Oliveto Citra
Colliano
Palomonte
Contursi Terme
Buccino
San Gregorio Magno
Balvano
Ruoti
Baragiano
Potenza
Vaglio Basilicata
San Chirico Nuovo
Golfo di Napoli
Vico Equense
Meta
Monti Lattari
Sorrento
Positano
Vietri sul Mare
Pontecagnano Faiano
Campagna
Eboli
Bellizzi
Battipaglia
Picerno
Tito
Massa Lubrense
Praiano
Amalfi
Serre
Postiglione
Monte Alburno
Auletta
Vietri di Potenza
Caggiano
Satriano di Lucania
Pignola
Brindisi Montagna
Trivigno
Albano di Lucania
Tricarico
Anacapri
Capri
Punta Campanella
Isola di Capri
Li Galli
Calore
Altavilla Silentina
Controne
Castelcivita
Polla
Passo Croce dello Scrivano
Abriola
Anzi
Lago di Ponte Fontanelle
Oliveto Lucano
Garaguso
Accettura
Cagliari
Olbia
Golfo di Salerno
Albanella
St'Angelo a Fasanella
St'Arsenio
Atena Lucana
Brienza
Calvello
Marsico Nuovo
Monte Volturino
Laurenzana
San Mauro Forte
Tunis
Palermo
Valencia
Capaccio
Roccadaspide
Roscigno
San Rufo
Sala Consilina
Castel San Lorenzo
Felitto
Monte Motola
Teggiano
Sassano
Paterno
Padula
Marsico Vetere
Viggiano
Corleto Perticara
Guardia Perticara
Cirigliano
Gorgoglione
Stigliano
Agropoli
Ogliastro Cilento
Cicerale
Laurino
Cilento
Torchiara
Rutino
Stio
Gioi
Parco Nazionale del Cilento e del Vallo di Diano
Monte Cervati
Tramutola
Montesano sulla Marcellana
Armento
Montemurro
Aliano
Missanello
Sta Maria di Castellabate
Castellabate
Isola Licosa
Perdifumo
Sessa Cilento
Oligastro Marina
Monte della Stella
Montecorice
Casal Velino
Vallo della Lucania
Monte Sacro
Montano Antilia
Rofrano
Buonabitacolo
Sanza
Casalbuono
Sarconi
Sella Cessula
Moliterno
Lago di Pietra del Pertusillo
San Chirico Raparo
Sant'Arcangelo
Roccanova
Acciaroli
Pollica
Cerasò
Laurito
Caselle in Pittari
Castelsaraceno
Castronuovo di St'Andrea
Senise
Chiaromonte
Ascea
Torre Orsaia
Casaletto Spartano
Roccagloriosa
Lagonegro
Monte del Papa
Pisciotta
Centola
Sta Marina
Vibonati
Latronico
Fardella
Monte Bulgheria
Scario
Sapri
Rivello
Monte la Spina
Episcopia
Francavilla in Sinni
Noepoli
Palinuro
Capo Palinuro
Camerota
San Giovanni a Piro
Monte Coccovello
Trecchina
Lauria
San Severino Lucano
Marina di Camerota
Punta degli Infreschi
Maratea
Tortora
Aieta
Laino Borgo
Castelluccio Inferiore
Parco Nazionale del Pollino
Viggianello
Rotonda
Monte Pollino
Golfo di Policastro
Praia a Mare
Isola di Dino
Monte Ciagola
Mormanno
Capo Scalea
Scalea
Papasidero
Sta Domenica Talao
Orsomarso
Morano Calabro
Castrovillari
Verbicaro
Saracena
Lungro
Sta Maria del Cedro
Grisolia
Cozzo del Pellegrino
Altomonte
Firmo
Buonvicino
San Donato di Ninea
Diamante
Monte Montea
San Sosti
Belvedere Marittimo
St Agata di Esaro
Roggiano Gravina
Bonifati
Fagnano Castello
Tarsia
Cetraro
San Marco Argentano
Cittadella del Capo
Cerzeto
Acquappesa
Terme Luigiane
Torano Castello
Guardia Piemontese
Rota Greca
Lattarico
Fuscaldo
Montalto Uffugo
Paola
San Fili
San Lucido
Rende
Cosenza
Falconara Albanese
Cerisano
Carolei
Fiumefreddo Bruzio
Monte Cocuzzo
Dipignano
Longobardi
Lago
Belmonte Calabro
Amantea
Monte Pellegrino
Grimaldi
Aiello Calabro
Campora San Giovanni
Conflenti
Nocera Terinese
Monte Reventino
Falerna
Gizzeria
Sambiase
Capo Suvero
Lamezia
Golfo di Sta Eufemia
Catania, Messina, Valletta
Isola Stromboli
Isola Strombolicchio
San Vincenzo
A1
A3
A14
A16
A30
E45
E55
E841
E842
E847
RA5

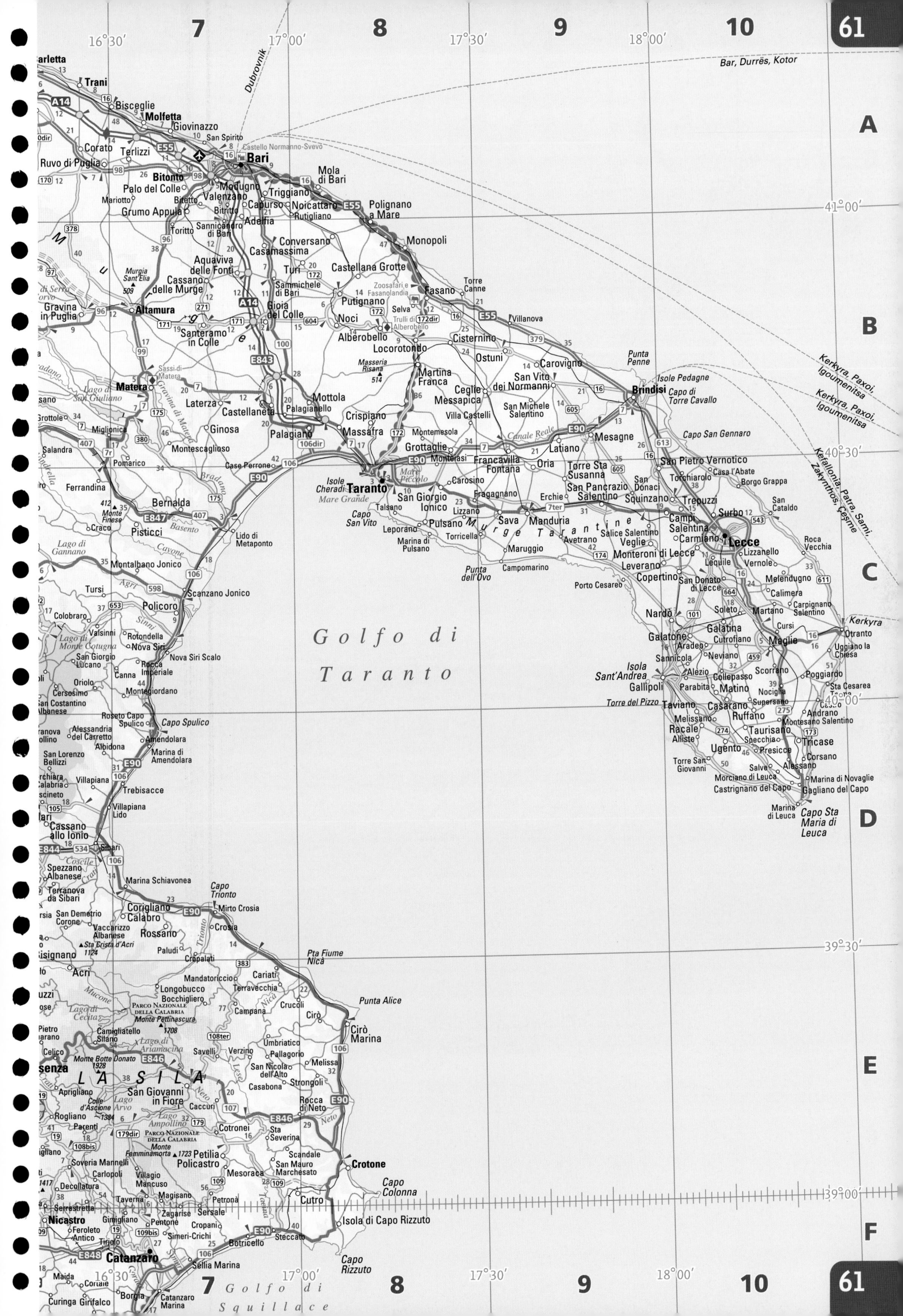
7
8
9
10
A
B
C
D
E
F
16°30′
17°00′
17°30′
18°00′
41°00′
40°30′
40°00′
39°30′
39°00′
Dubrovnik
Bar, Durrës, Kotor
Kerkyra, Paxoi, Igoumenitsa
Kerkyra, Paxoi, Igoumenitsa
Kefallonia, Patra, Sami, Zakynthos, Çesme
Kerkyra
Barletta
Trani
Bisceglie
Molfetta
Giovinazzo
San Spirito
Castello Normanno-Svevo
Bari
Corato
Terlizzi
Ruvo di Puglia
Bitonto
Palo del Colle
Modugno
Valenzano
Triggiano
Mola di Bari
Mariotto
Bitetto
Capurso
Noicattaro
Polignano a Mare
Grumo Appula
Bitritto
Adelfia
Rutigliano
Toritto
Sannicandro di Bari
Monopoli
Conversano
Casamassima
Acquaviva delle Fonti
Turi
Castellana Grotte
Murgia Sant'Elia
Cassano delle Murge
Sammichele di Bari
Zoosafari e Fasanolandia
Fasano
Torre Canne
Gravina in Puglia
Altamura
Gioia del Colle
Putignano
Selva
Noci
Trulli di Alberobello
Villanova
Santeramo in Colle
Alberobello
Locorotondo
Cisternino
Ostuni
Carovigno
Punta Penne
Masseria Risana
Martina Franca
San Vito dei Normanni
Isole Pedagne
Brindisi
Capo di Torre Cavallo
Sassi di Matera
Matera
Lago di San Giuliano
Laterza
Castellaneta
Mottola
Palagianello
Ceglie Messapica
San Michele Salentino
Crispiano
Villa Castelli
Miglionica
Ginosa
Palagiano
Massafra
Montemesola
Canale Reale
Mesagne
Capo San Gennaro
Salandra
Montescaglioso
Grottaglie
Latiano
San Pietro Vernotico
Pomarico
Case Perrone
Monteiasi
Francavilla Fontana
Oria
Torre Sta Susanna
Casa l'Abate
Ferrandina
Isole Cheradi
Taranto
Mare Piccolo
Carosino
San Pancrazio Salentino
San Donaci
Torchiarolo
Borgo Grappa
Mare Grande
San Giorgio Ionico
Fragagnano
Erchie
Squinzano
Trepuzzi
San Cataldo
Monte Finese
Bernalda
Talsano
Lizzano
Sava
Manduria
Surbo
Craco
Pisticci
Basento
Capo San Vito
Leporano
Pulsano
Torricella
Murge Tarantine
Campi Salentina
Lago di Gannano
Lido di Metaponto
Marina di Pulsano
Maruggio
Avetrano
Salice Salentino
Carmiano
Lecce
Roca Vecchia
Veglie
Cavone
Montalbano Jonico
Monteroni di Lecce
Lizzanello
Leverano
Lequile
Vernole
Punta dell'Ovo
Campomarino
Porto Cesareo
Copertino
San Donato di Lecce
Melendugno
Tursi
Scanzano Jonico
Calimera
Policoro
Nardò
Soleto
Martano
Carpignano Salentino
Colobraro
Galatina
Cursi
Otranto
Valsinni
Rotondella
Galatone
Cutrofiano
Maglie
Lago di Monte Cotugna
Nova Siri
Aradeo
Uggiano la Chiesa
San Giorgio Lucano
Nova Siri Scalo
Sannicola
Neviano
Rocca Imperiale
Golfo di Taranto
Isola Sant'Andrea
Alezio
Scorrano
Poggiardo
Oriolo
Canna
Gallipoli
Collepasso
Parabita
Matino
Nociglia
Sta Cesarea Terme
Cersosimo
Montegiordano
Torre del Pizzo
Taviano
Casarano
Supersano
San Costantino Albanese
Andrano
Roseto Capo Spulico
Capo Spulico
Melissano
Ruffano
Montesano Salentino
Alessandria del Carretto
Racale
Alliste
Taurisano
Specchia
Tricase
Amendolara
Albidona
Ugento
Presicce
San Lorenzo Bellizzi
Marina di Amendolara
Corsano
Torre San Giovanni
Salve
Alessano
Villapiana
Trebisacce
Morciano di Leuca
Marina di Novaglie
Castrignano del Capo
Gagliano del Capo
Villapiana Lido
Marina di Leuca
Capo Sta Maria di Leuca
Cassano allo Ionio
Sibari
Coscile
Spezzano Albanese
Terranova da Sibari
Marina Schiavonea
Capo Trionto
San Demetrio Corone
Corigliano Calabro
Mirto Crosia
Vaccarizzo Albanese
Rossano
Crosia
Sta Cristia d'Acri
Paludi
Trionto
Bisignano
Cropalati
Pta Fiume Nicà
Acri
Mandatoriccio
Cariati
Mucone
Longobucco
Terravecchia
Bocchigliero
Campana
Crucoli
Punta Alice
Lago di Cecita
Parco Nazionale della Calabria
Monte Pettinascura
Cirò
Camigliatello Silano
Cirò Marina
Lago di Ariamacina
Umbriatico
Celico
Monte Botte Donato
Savelli
Verzino
Pallagorio
Cosenza
La Sila
San Nicola dell'Alto
Melissa
Neto
Strongoli
Aprigliano
San Giovanni in Fiore
Casabona
Colle d'Ascione
Lago Arvo
Caccuri
Rocca di Neto
Rogliano
Parenti
Lago Ampollino
Cotronei
Sta Severina
Monte Femminamorta
Petilia Policastro
Scandale
San Mauro Marchesato
Soveria Mannelli
Carlopoli
Villagio Mancuso
Mesoraca
Crotone
Decollatura
Tacina
Capo Colonna
Taverna
Magisano
Petronà
Cutro
Serrastretta
Nicastro
Gimigliano
Zagarise
Sersale
Isola di Capo Rizzuto
Pentone
Feroleto Antico
Cropani
Tiriolo
Simeri-Crichi
Steccato
Botricello
Catanzaro
Sellia Marina
Capo Rizzuto
Maida
Cortale
Golfo di Squillace
Borgia
Curinga
Girifalco
Catanzaro Marina

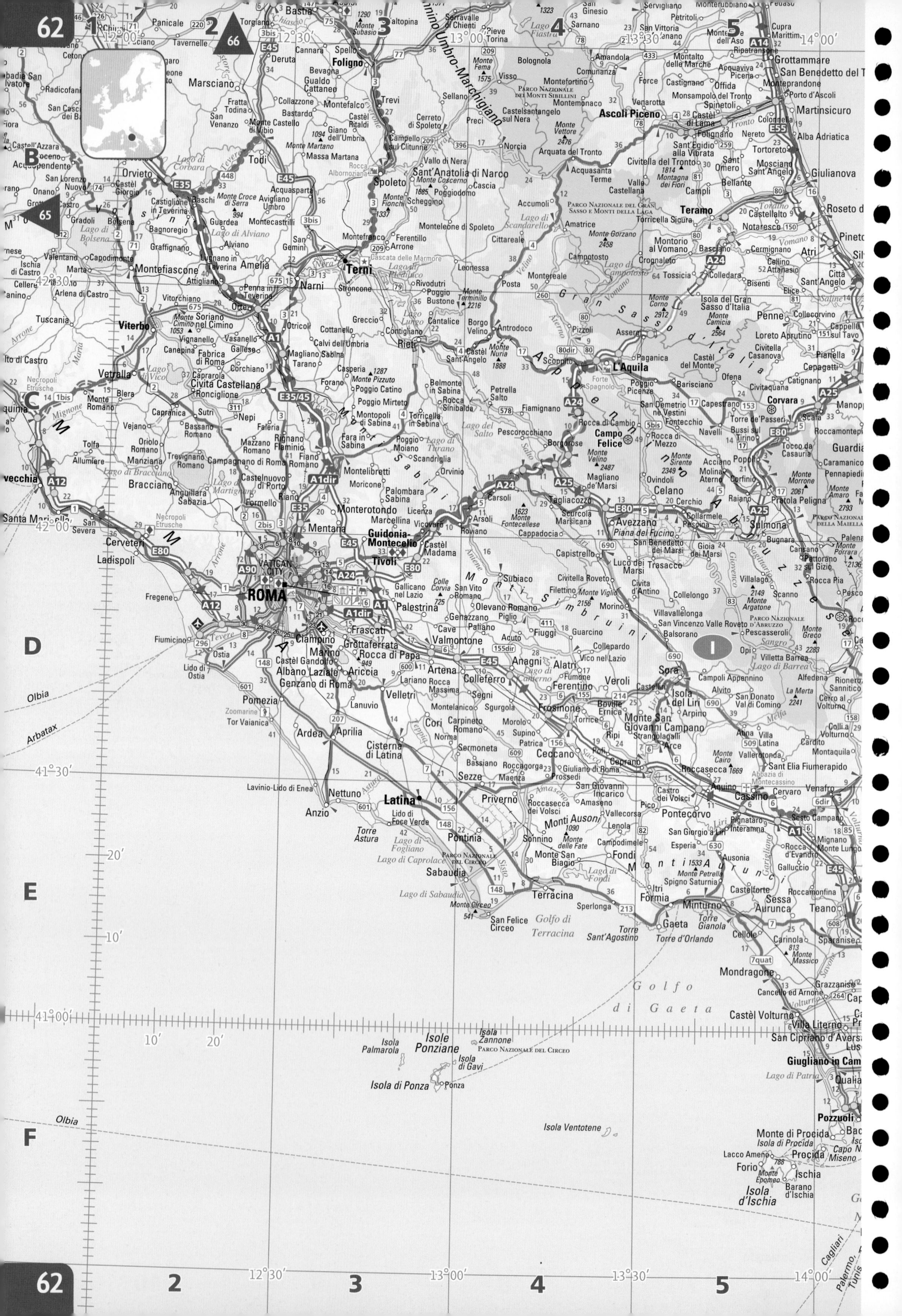

66
65
Roma
Vatican City
Latina
Frosinone
Rieti
Terni
L'Aquila
Teramo
Ascoli Piceno
Viterbo
Foligno
Spoleto
Orvieto
Todi
Tivoli
Guidonia-Montecelio
Avezzano
Sulmona
Cassino
Gaeta
Formia
Terracina
Sabaudia
Anzio
Nettuno
Pomezia
Velletri
Frascati
Ciampino
Fiumicino
Ostia
Ladispoli
Cerveteri
Bracciano
Civita Castellana
Montefiascone
Narni
Amelia
Sora
Alatri
Anagni
Colleferro
Palestrina
Valmontone
Aprilia
Pontinia
Priverno
Ceccano
Fondi
Minturno
Sessa Aurunca
Teano
Mondragone
Castèl Volturno
Pozzuoli
Giugliano in Campania
Procida
Ischia
Forio
Isola d'Ischia
Isole Ponziane
Isola di Ponza
Isola Palmarola
Isola Zannone
Isola di Gavi
Isola Ventotene
Golfo di Gaeta
Golfo di Terracina
Lago di Bolsena
Lago di Bracciano
Lago di Vico
Lago del Salto
Lago di Sabaudia
Lago di Fogliano
Lago di Caprolace
Lago di Patria
Parco Nazionale dei Monti Sibillini
Parco Nazionale del Gran Sasso e Monti della Laga
Parco Nazionale d'Abruzzo
Parco Nazionale della Maiella
Parco Nazionale del Circeo
Gran Sasso d'Italia
Appennino Umbro-Marchigiano
Appennino Abruzzese
Monti Sabini
Monti Simbruini
Monti Ausoni
Monti Aurunci
Giulianova
Roseto degli Abruzzi
San Benedetto del Tronto
Grottammare
Martinsicuro
Alba Adriatica
Tortoreto
Atri
Penne
Corvara
Celano
Campo Felice
Olbia
Arbatax
Cagliari
Palermo, Tunis
41°00′
41°30′
42°00′
42°30′
12°00′
12°30′
13°00′
13°30′
14°00′
A1
A12
A24
A25
A14
A90
A1dir
E35
E45
E80
E55

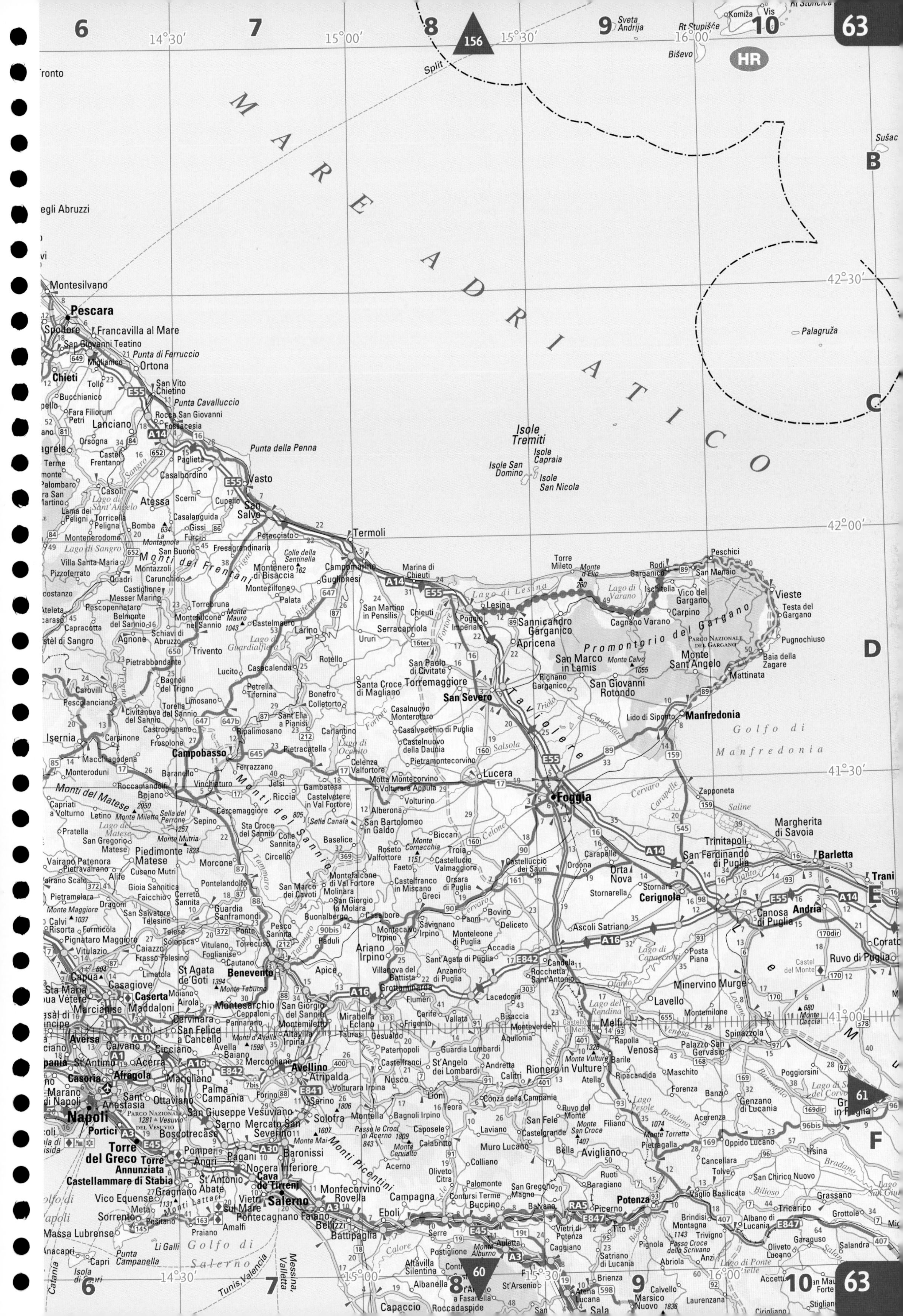
6
7
8
9
10
156
14°30'
15°00'
15°30'
16°00'
Sveta Andrija
Rt Stupišće
Komiža
Vis
Biševo
HR
Split
Sušac
Palagruža
42°30'
42°00'
41°30'
41°00'
B
C
D
E
F
MARE ADRIATICO
Isole Tremiti
Isole Capraia
Isole San Domino
Isole San Nicola
Tronto
Montesilvano
Pescara
Spoltore
Francavilla al Mare
San Giovanni Teatino
Punta di Ferruccio
Ortona
Chieti
Tollo
San Vito Chietino
Bucchianico
Fara Filiorum Petri
Punta Cavalluccio
Rocca San Giovanni
Fossacesia
Lanciano
Orsogna
Castel Frentano
Paglieta
Punta della Penna
Casalbordino
Vasto
Casoli
Lago di Sant'Angelo
Atessa
Scerni
Cupello
San Salvo
Torricella Peligna
Bomba
Casalanguida
Gissi
Furci
Montenerodomo
Lago di Sangro
Villa Santa Maria
Petacciato
Termoli
Fresagrandinaria
San Buono
Colle della Sentinella
Montenero di Bisaccia
Campomarino
Marina di Chieuti
Monti dei Frentani
Pizzoferrato
Quadri
Carunchio
Montazzoli
Guglionesi
Montecilfone
Palata
Castiglione Messer Marino
Torrebruna
Pescopennataro
Belmonte del Sannio
Capracotta
Agnone
Montefalcone nel Sannio
Monte Mauro
Castelmauro
Larino
San Martino in Pensilis
Chieuti
Serracapriola
Ururi
Trivento
Schiavi di Abruzzo
Pietrabbondante
Lucito
Casacalenda
Rotello
Bagnoli del Trigno
Petrella Tifernina
Bonefro
Colletorto
Carovilli
Pescolanciano
Civitanova del Sannio
Torella del Sannio
Limosano
Sant'Elia a Pianisi
Castropignano
Frosolone
Ripalimosano
Carlantino
Isernia
Carpinone
Macchiagodena
Campobasso
Pietracatella
Monteroduni
Baranello
Ferrazzano
Celenza Valfortore
Lago di Occhito
Roccamandolfi
Vinchiaturo
Jelsi
Gambatesa
Monti del Matese
Bojano
Monti del Sannio
Riccia
Castelvetere in Val Fortore
Capriati a Volturno
Letino
Monte Miletto
Sella del Perrone
Sepino
Cercemaggiore
Alberona
Pratella
Lago del Matese
Monte Mutria
Sta Croce del Sannio
San Bartolomeo in Galdo
San Gregorio Matese
Colle Sannita
Baselice
Piedimonte Matese
Circello
Roseto Valfortore
Monte Cornacchia
Vairano Patenora
Pietravairano
Morcone
Alife
Cusano Mutri
Faeto
Montefalcone di Val Fortore
Castelfranco in Miscano
Gioia Sannitica
Pontelandolfo
San Marco dei Cavoti
Molinara
Greci
Pietramelara
Faicchio
Cerreto Sannita
San Giorgio la Molara
Monte Maggiore
Dragoni
San Salvatore Telesino
Guardia Sanframondi
Buonalbergo
Casalbore
Calvi Risorta
Formicola
Telese
Ponte
Pesco Sannita
Montecalvo Irpino
Savignano Irpino
Pignataro Maggiore
Solopaca
Vitulano
Torrecuso
Paduli
Ariano Irpino
Vitulazio
Caiazzo
Frasso Telesino
Foglianise
Cautano
Apice
Capua
Limatola
St Agata de' Goti
Benevento
Villanova del Battista
Casagiove
Caserta
Monte Taburno
Grottaminarda
Sta Maria Capua Vetere
Maddaloni
Moiano
Airola
Montesarchio
San Giorgio del Sannio
Flumeri
Marcianise
Cervinara
Ceppaloni
Mirabella Eclano
Frigento
Aversa
Calvano
San Felice a Cancello
Pannarano
Montemiletto
Taurasi
Gesualdo
Cicciano
Monti d'Avella
Altavilla Irpina
Sant'Antimo
Afragola
Acerra
Avella
Baiano
Mercogliano
Avellino
Atripalda
Casoria
Marigliano
Palma Campania
Forino
Volturara Irpina
Nusco
Napoli
Portici
Sant'Anastasia
Ottaviano
Parco Nazionale del Vesuvio
Vesuvio
San Giuseppe Vesuviano
Sarno
Mercato San Severino
Solofra
Serino
Montella
Bagnoli Irpino
Boscotrecase
Baronissi
Monti Picentini
Torre del Greco
Torre Annunziata
Pompei
Angri
Pagani
Nocera Inferiore
Castellammare di Stabia
Gragnano
Sant'Antonio Abate
Cava de' Tirreni
Monti Lattari
Vico Equense
Vietri sul Mare
Salerno
Meta
Positano
Sorrento
Amalfi
Pontecagnano Faiano
Massa Lubrense
Praiano
Bellizzi
Battipaglia
Eboli
Li Galli
Golfo di Salerno
Anacapri
Capri
Punta Campanella
Isola di Capri
Catania
Tunis, Valencia
Messina, Valletta
Monfecorvino Rovella
Campagna
Acerno
Calabritto
Caposele
Lioni
Teora
Conza della Campania
Laviano
Muro Lucano
Colliano
Oliveto Citra
Palomonte
Contursi Terme
Buccino
Serre
Postiglione
Monte Alburno
Altavilla Silentina
Albanella
Capaccio
Roccadaspide
St'Arsenio
Auletta
Caggiano
Sala
Atena Lucana
Brienza
Marsico Nuovo
Calvello
Laurenzana
Sant'Angelo dei Lombardi
Guardia Lombardi
Paternopoli
Castelfranci
Andretta
Calitri
Lacedonia
Bisaccia
Aquilonia
Monteverde
Vallata
Carife
Candela
Rocchetta Sant'Antonio
Sant'Agata di Puglia
Accadia
Monteleone di Puglia
Anzano di Puglia
Panni
Bovino
Deliceto
Orsara di Puglia
Troia
Castelluccio Valmaggiore
Biccari
Castelluccio dei Sauri
Volturino
Volturara Appula
Motta Montecorvino
Pietramontecorvino
Castelnuovo della Daunia
Casalvecchio di Puglia
Casalnuovo Monterotaro
Santa Croce di Magliano
Torremaggiore
San Paolo di Civitate
San Severo
Lucera
Foggia
Tavoliere
Poggio Imperiale
Lesina
Lago di Lesina
Torre Mileto
Monte d'Elio
Lago di Varano
Rodi Garganico
Ischitella
Cagnano Varano
Sannicandro Garganico
Apricena
San Marco in Lamis
Monte Calvo
Rignano Garganico
San Giovanni Rotondo
Promontorio del Gargano
Parco Nazionale del Gargano
Monte Sant'Angelo
Carpino
Vico del Gargano
Peschici
San Menaio
Vieste
Testa del Gargano
Pugnochiuso
Baia delle Zagare
Mattinata
Manfredonia
Lido di Siponto
Golfo di Manfredonia
Zapponeta
Saline
Margherita di Savoia
Trinitapoli
San Ferdinando di Puglia
Barletta
Trani
Carapelle
Ordona
Orta Nova
Stornara
Stornarella
Cerignola
Canosa di Puglia
Andria
Corato
Ascoli Satriano
Lago di Capaccioli
Posta Piana
Castel del Monte
Ruvo di Puglia
Minervino Murge
Lavello
Montemilone
Monte Caccia
Lago del Rendina
Melfi
Rapolla
Barile
Venosa
Palazzo San Gervasio
Spinazzola
Monte Vulture
Rionero in Vulture
Atella
Ripacandida
Maschito
Forenza
Banzi
Poggiorsini
Lago di Serra del Corvo
Genzano di Lucania
Gravina in Puglia
Ruvo del Monte
San Fele
Castelgrande
Monte Santa Croce
Filiano
Lago Pesole
Bradano
Acerenza
Monte Torretta
Bella
Avigliano
Pietragalla
Oppido Lucano
Irsina
Cancellara
Tolve
San Chirico Nuovo
Baragiano
Ruoti
Vaglio Basilicata
Grassano
San Gregorio Magno
Balvano
Picerno
Potenza
Tito
Brindisi Montagna
Albano di Lucania
Tricarico
Grottole
Vietri di Potenza
Satriano di Lucania
Pignola
Passo Croce dello Scrivano
Trivigno
Anzi
Abriola
Garaguso
Oliveto Lucano
Salandra
Lago di Ponte
Accettura
Ciriligno
Stigliano
A14
A16
A3
A30
A1
RA5
E55
E45
E842
E841
E847
60
61

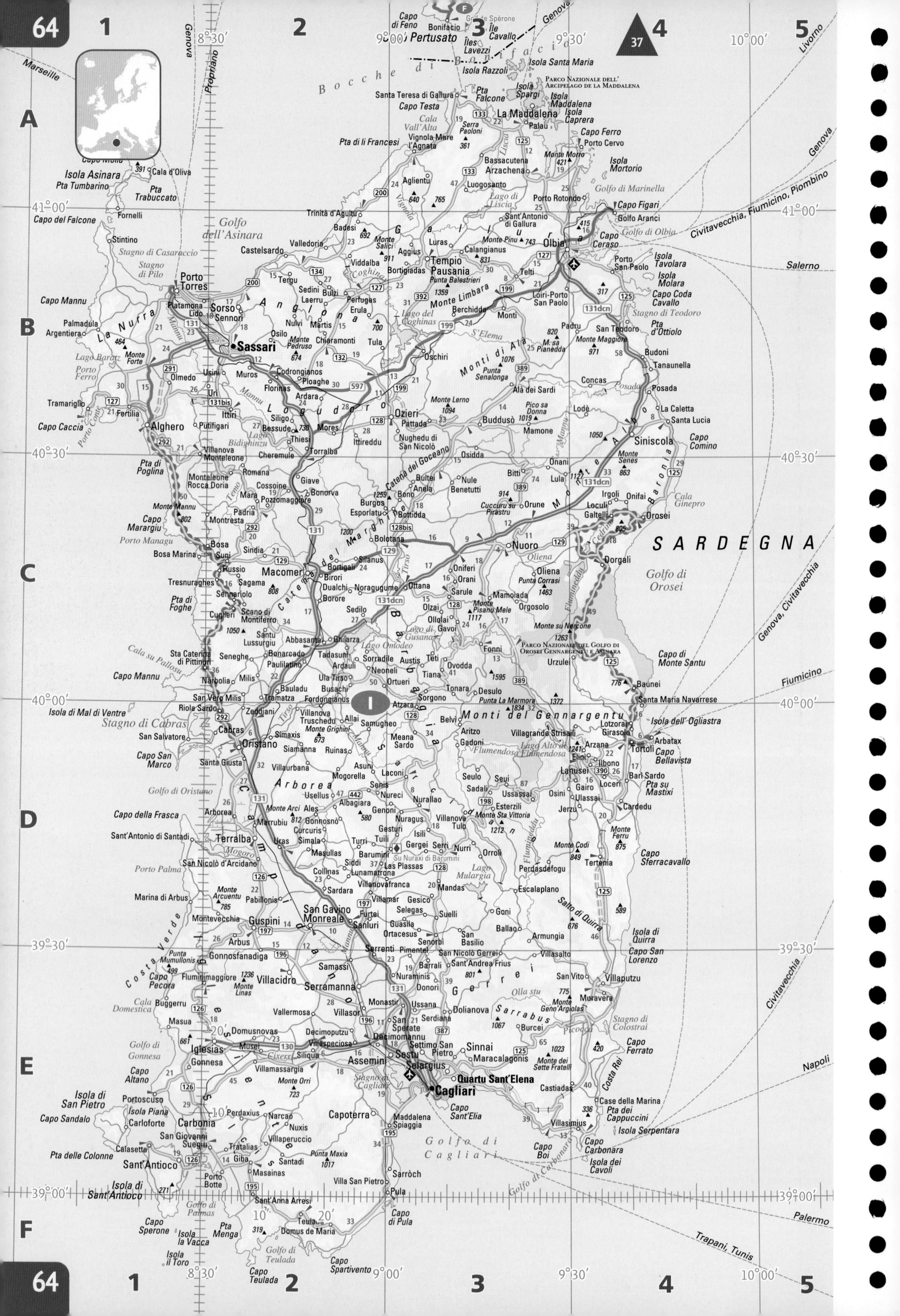

SARDEGNA
Bocche di Bonifacio
Capo di Feno
Bonifacio
Capo Pertusato
Îles Lavezzi
Isola Santa Maria
Isola Razzoli
Parco Nazionale dell' Arcipelago de la Maddalena
Santa Teresa di Gallura
Capo Testa
Pta Falcone
Isola Spargi
Isola Maddalena
La Maddalena
Isola Caprera
Palau
Capo Ferro
Porto Cervo
Pta di li Francesi
Vignola Mare
Isola Asinara
Pta Tumbarino
Cala d'Oliva
Pta Trabuccato
Capo del Falcone
Fornelli
Stintino
Golfo dell'Asinara
Stagno di Casaraccio
Stagno di Pilo
Porto Torres
Castelsardo
Valledoria
Trinità d'Agultu
Badesi
Luogosanto
Arzachena
Bassacutena
Isola Mortorio
Golfo di Marinella
Porto Rotondo
Capo Figari
Golfo Aranci
Sant'Antonio di Gallura
Olbia
Golfo di Olbia
Capo Ceraso
Tempio Pausania
Luras
Calangianus
Aggius
Bortigiadas
Viddalba
Telti
Isola Tavolara
Porto San Paolo
Isola Molara
Capo Coda Cavallo
Loiri-Porto San Paolo
Monte Limbara
Berchidda
Monti
San Teodoro
Stagno di Teodoro
Pta d'Ottiolo
Budoni
Tanaunella
Posada
La Caletta
Santa Lucia
Siniscola
Capo Comino
Capo Mannu
Palmadula
Argentiera
La Nurra
Sorso
Sennori
Platamona Lido
Sassari
Anglona
Sedini
Bulzi
Perfugas
Erula
Laerru
Nulvi
Martis
Osilo
Chiaramonti
Tula
Oschiri
Lago del Coghinas
Monti di Alà
Alà dei Sardi
Padru
Monte Maggiore
Lago Baratz
Porto Ferro
Olmedo
Usini
Muros
Codrongianos
Florinas
Ploaghe
Ardara
Logudoro
Ozieri
Pattada
Buddusò
Concas
Lodè
Tramariglio
Fertilia
Capo Caccia
Alghero
Putifigari
Ittiri
Uri
Siligo
Bessude
Thiesi
Mores
Ittireddu
Nughedu di San Nicolò
Mamone
Torralba
Cheremule
Villanova Monteleone
Pta di Poglina
Monteleone Rocca Doria
Romana
Cossoine
Giave
Bonorva
Mara
Pozzomaggiore
Padria
Montresta
Capo Marargiu
Porto Managu
Bosa
Bosa Marina
Suni
Sindia
Osidda
Catena del Goceano
Bultei
Anela
Nule
Benetutti
Bono
Burgos
Esporlatu
Bottidda
Bitti
Onani
Lula
Irgoli
Onifai
Loculi
Galtelli
Orosei
Cala Ginepro
Baronia
Bolotana
Silanus
Bortigali
Macomer
Birori
Dualchi
Noragugume
Ottana
Oniferi
Orani
Nuoro
Oliena
Dorgali
Golfo di Orosei
Orune
Flussio
Tresnuraghes
Sagama
Sennariolo
Cuglieri
Pta di Foghe
Scano di Montiferro
Sarule
Mamoiada
Orgosolo
Olzai
Ollolai
Gavoi
Lago di Gusana
Monte su Nercone
Santu Lussurgiu
Abbasanta
Ghilarza
Lago Omodeo
Sedilo
Sta Caterina di Pittinuri
Seneghe
Bonarcado
Paulilatino
Tadasuni
Sorradile
Ardauli
Neoneli
Austis
Teti
Tiana
Ovodda
Fonni
Parco Nazionale del Golfo di Orosei Gennargentu e Asinara
Urzulei
Capo di Monte Santu
Baunei
Cala su Pallosu
Capo Mannu
Narbolia
Milis
Ula Tirso
Busachi
Ortueri
Tonara
Desulo
Punta La Marmora
San Vero Milis
Bauladu
Tramatza
Fordongianus
Sorgono
Atzara
Isola di Mal di Ventre
Riola Sardo
Zeddiani
Villanova Truschedu
Allai
Samugheo
Belvi
Monti del Gennargentu
Santa Maria Navarrese
Isola dell' Ogliastra
Lotzorai
Girasole
Arbatax
Tortolì
Capo Bellavista
Stagno di Cabras
Cabras
San Salvatore
Oristano
Simaxis
Siamanna
Ruinas
Meana Sardo
Aritzo
Gadoni
Villagrande Strisaili
Lago Alto di Flumendosa
Arzana
Elini
Ilbono
Lanusei
Capo San Marco
Santa Giusta
Villaurbana
Mogorella
Asuni
Laconi
Seulo
Seui
Sadali
Ussassai
Gairo
Loceri
Bari Sardo
Pta su Mastixi
Golfo di Oristano
Arborea
Usellus
Senis
Nureci
Nurallao
Esterzili
Osini
Ulassai
Jerzu
Cardedu
Capo della Frasca
Monte Arci
Ales
Albagiara
Gonnosnò
Genoni
Nuragus
Villanova Tulo
Marrubiu
Curcuris
Sant'Antonio di Santadi
Terralba
Uras
Simala
Gesturi
Tuili
Isili
Gergei
Serri
Nurri
Orroli
Monte Ferru
Capo Sferracavallo
Tertenia
Porto Palma
Masullas
Barumini
Su Nuraxi di Barumini
San Nicolò d'Arcidano
Siddi
Las Plassas
Lunamatrona
Collinas
Villanovafranca
Mandas
Lago Mulargia
Perdasdefogu
Escalaplano
Sardara
Marina di Arbus
Pabillonis
Villamar
Gesico
Salto di Quirra
Montevecchia
Guspini
San Gavino Monreale
Furtei
Sanluri
Selegas
Suelli
Goni
Guasila
Ortacesus
Ballao
Armungia
Isola di Quirra
Capo San Lorenzo
Costa Verde
Arbus
Senorbì
San Basilio
Serrenti
Pimentel
San Nicolò Gerrei
Sant'Andrea Frius
Villasalto
Gonnosfanadiga
Samassi
Barrali
Gerrei
San Vito
Villaputzu
Capo Pecora
Fluminimaggiore
Villacidro
Serramanna
Nuraminis
Donori
Olla stu
Muravera
Cala Domestica
Buggerru
Monastir
Ussana
Dolianova
Sarrabus
Stagno di Colostrai
Masua
Vallermosa
Villasor
San Sperate
Serdiana
Burcei
Golfo di Gonnesa
Domusnovas
Decimoputzu
Decimomannu
Settimo San Pietro
Sinnai
Maracalagonis
Capo Ferrato
Iglesias
Musei
Villaspeciosa
Siliqua
Gonnesa
Assemini
Sestu
Selargius
Monte dei Sette Fratelli
Costa Rei
Capo Altano
Villamassargia
Monte Orri
Stagno di Cagliari
Quartu Sant'Elena
Cagliari
Castiadas
Isola di San Pietro
Portoscuso
Isola Piana
Carloforte
Capo Sandalo
Carbonia
Perdaxius
Narcao
Nuxis
Capoterra
Maddalena Spiaggia
Capo Sant'Elia
Villasimius
Cala Sinzias
Case della Marina
Pta dei Cappuccini
Isola Serpentara
San Giovanni Suergiu
Villaperuccio
Golfo di Cagliari
Capo Boi
Capo Carbonara
Calasetta
Tratalias
Giba
Santadi
Punta Maxia
Pta delle Colonne
Sant'Antioco
Masainas
Sarroch
Isola dei Cavoli
Porto Botte
Villa San Pietro
Isola di Sant'Antioco
Pula
Golfo di Carbonara
Sant'Anna Arresi
Golfo di Palmas
Teulada
Capo di Pula
Capo Sperone
Isola la Vacca
Pta Menga
Domus de Maria
Isola il Toro
Golfo di Teulada
Capo Spartivento
Capo Teulada
Marseille
Genova
Livorno
Civitavecchia, Fiumicino, Piombino
Salerno
Genova, Civitavecchia
Fiumicino
Civitavecchia
Napoli
Palermo
Trapani, Tunis
Propriano
41°00′
40°30′
40°00′
39°30′
39°00′
8°30′
9°00′
9°30′
10°00′
1 2 3 4 5
A B C D E F
37

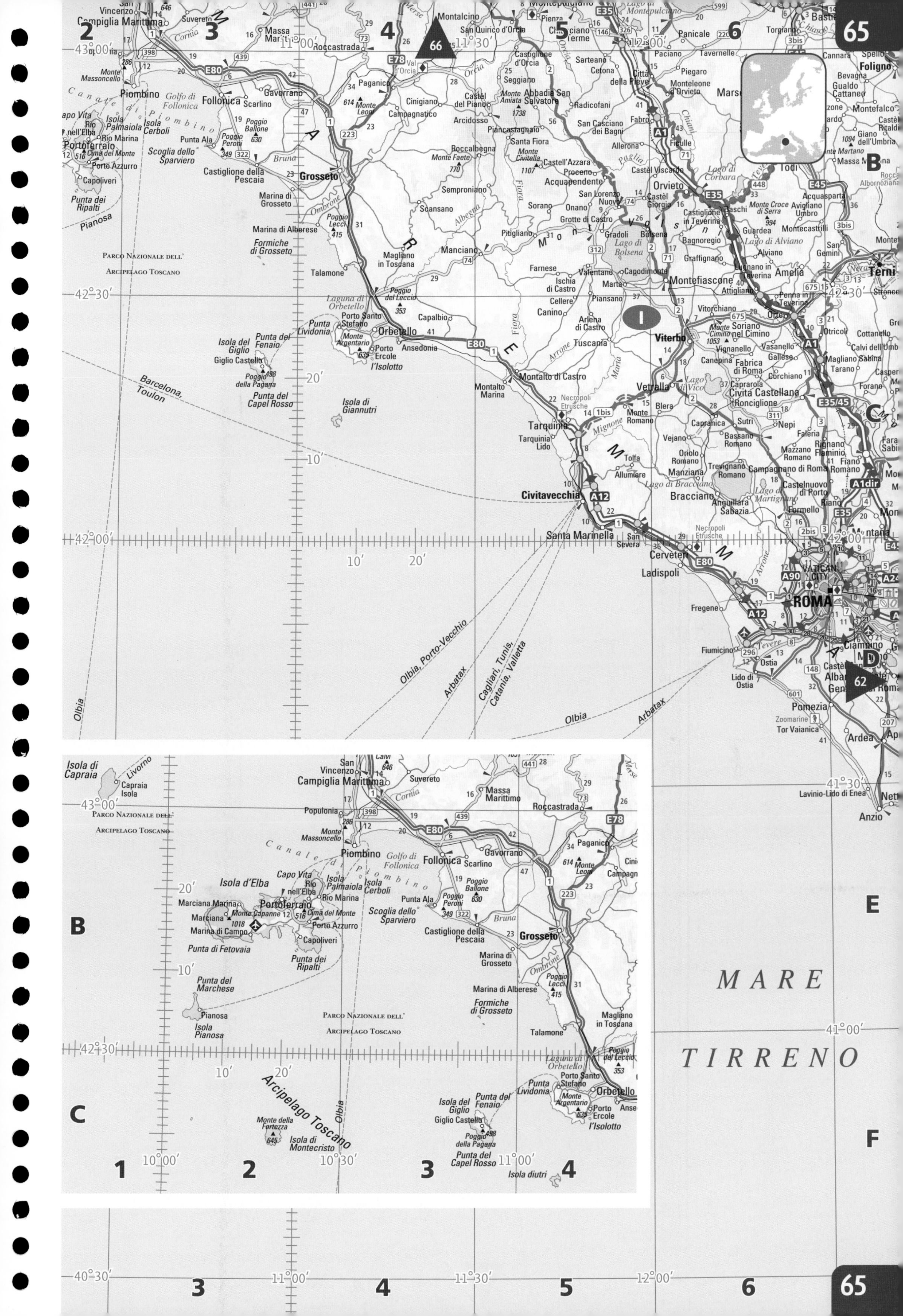
65
Campiglia Marittima
Suvereto
Massa Marittima
Roccastrada
Montalcino
San Quirico d'Orcia
Pienza
Chianciano Terme
Montepulciano
Panicale
Torgiano
Bastia
Piombino
Golfo di Follonica
Follonica
Scarlino
Gavorrano
Paganico
Castel del Piano
Abbadia San Salvatore
Radicofani
Sarteano
Cetona
Città della Pieve
Piegaro
Monteleone d'Orvieto
Foligno
Bevagna
Gualdo Cattaneo
Montefalco
Portoferraio
Rio Marina
Porto Azzurro
Capoliveri
Punta dei Ripalti
Pianosa
Punta Ala
Scoglia dello Sparviero
Castiglione della Pescaia
Grosseto
Marina di Grosseto
Cinigiano
Campagnatico
Arcidosso
Piancastagnaio
Santa Fiora
Seggiano
Roccalbegna
Semproniano
Scansano
San Casciano dei Bagni
Allerona
Fabro
Ficulle
Castel Viscardo
Orvieto
Proceno
Acquapendente
Castel Giorgio
Sorano
Onano
San Lorenzo Nuovo
Grotte di Castro
Gradoli
Bolsena
Lago di Bolsena
Pitigliano
Bagnoregio
Lago di Alviano
Alviano
Guardea
Montecastrilli
Acquasparta
Avigliano Umbro
Todi
Lago di Corbara
Marina di Alberese
Formiche di Grosseto
Parco Nazionale dell' Arcipelago Toscano
Magliano in Toscana
Manciano
Farnese
Ischia di Castro
Valentano
Capodimonte
Marta
Montefiascone
Graffignano
Lugnano in Teverina
Amelia
Attigliano
Terni
Talamone
Laguna di Orbetello
Porto Santo Stefano
Capalbio
Orbetello
Ansedonia
Porto Ercole
l'Isolotto
Monte Argentario
Cellere
Canino
Arlena di Castro
Tuscania
Piansano
Viterbo
Vitorchiano
Soriano nel Cimino
Orte
Otricoli
Isola del Giglio
Giglio Castello
Punta del Fenaio
Punta del Capel Rosso
Poggio della Pagana
Isola di Giannutri
Barcelona, Toulon
Montalto di Castro
Montalto Marina
Vignanello
Vasanello
Gallese
Canepina
Fabrica di Roma
Corchiano
Magliano Sabina
Tarano
Caprarola
Civita Castellana
Ronciglione
Lago di Vico
Vetralla
Necropoli Etrusche
Tarquinia
Tarquinia Lido
Monte Romano
Blera
Capranica
Sutri
Nepi
Vejano
Bassano Romano
Faleria
Rignano Flaminio
Oriolo Romano
Mazzano Romano
Fiano Romano
Tolfa
Allumiere
Manziana
Trevignano Romano
Campagnano di Roma
Lago di Bracciano
Bracciano
Anguillara Sabazia
Lago di Martignano
Castelnuovo di Porto
Riano
Formello
Civitavecchia
Santa Marinella
San Severa
Cerveteri
Ladispoli
Vatican City
ROMA
Fregene
Fiumicino
Ostia
Lido di Ostia
Ciampino
Pomezia
Zoomarine
Tor Vaianica
Ardea
Anzio
Lavinio-Lido di Enea
Olbia, Porto-Vecchio
Arbatax
Cagliari, Tunis, Catania, Valletta
Olbia
MARE TIRRENO
Isola di Capraia
Capraia Isola
Populonia
Isola d'Elba
Marciana Marina
Marciana
Marina di Campo
Monte Capanne
Punta di Fetovaia
Punta del Marchese
Isola Pianosa
Arcipelago Toscano
Monte della Fortezza
Isola di Montecristo
Isola diutri
42°30′
42°00′
41°30′
41°00′
40°30′
43°00′
10°00′
10°30′
11°00′
11°30′
12°00′
A
B
C
D
E
F
1
2
3
4
5
6
66
62
65

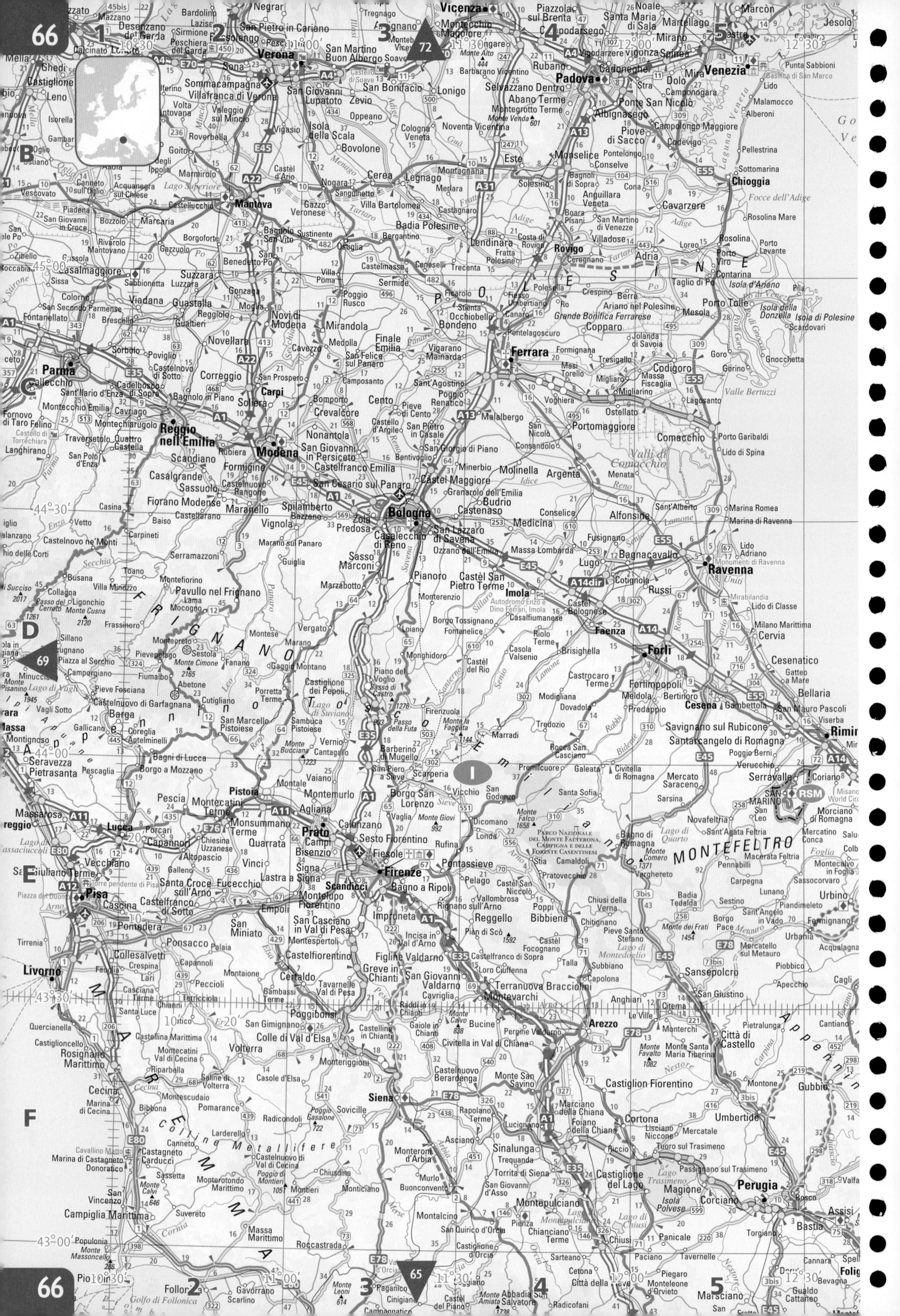
1
2
3
4
5
B
C
D
E
F
72
69
65
Desenzano del Garda
Bardolino
Lazise
Sirmione
Peschiera del Garda
Negrar
San Pietro in Cariano
Verona
Vicenza
Montecchio Maggiore
Piazzola sul Brenta
Santa Maria di Sala
Martellago
Mestre
Marcòn
Jesolo
Noale
Mirano
Padova
Venezia
Punta Sabbioni
Lido
Malamocco
Alberoni
Pellestrina
Sottomarina
Chioggia
Calcinato
Lonato
Ghedi
Castiglione
Leno
Isorella
Gambara
Sona
Sommacampagna
Villafranca di Verona
Valeggio sul Mincio
Volta Mantovana
Roverbella
Goito
San Martino Buon Albergo
Soave
San Bonifacio
San Giovanni Lupatoto
Zevio
Lonigo
Oppeano
Isola della Scala
Vigasio
Bovolone
Cologna Veneta
Noventa Vicentina
Selvazzano Dentro
Abano Terme
Montegrotto Terme
Monte Venda 601
Cadoneghe
Stra
Dolo
Mira
Campagna Lupia
Ponte San Nicolò
Albignasego
Campolongo Maggiore
Piove di Sacco
Codevigo
Monselice
Este
Pontelongo
Conselve
Castèl d'Ario
Mantova
Cerea
Legnago
Nogara
Sanguinetto
Gazzo Veronese
Villa Bartolomea
Castagnaro
Badia Polesine
Montagnana
Merlara
Solesino
Bagnoli di Sopra
Cona
Anguillara Veneta
Cavarzere
Boara Pisani
San Martino di Venezze
Rosolina Mare
Rosolina
Porto Levante
Rovigo
Lendinara
Costa di Rovigo
Fratta Polesine
Villadose
Adria
Loreo
Porto Viro
Contarina
Taglio di Po
Isola d'Ariano
Porto Tolle
Isola della Donzella
Isola di Polesine
Scardovari
Canneto sull'Oglio
Acquanegra sul Chiese
Marmirolo
Castellucchio
Marcaria
Piadena
San Giovanni in Croce
Bozzolo
Rivarolo Mantovano
Borgoforte
Bagnolo San Vito
Sustinente
Ostiglia
Bergantino
Castelmassa
Ceneselli
Trecenta
Sermide
Ficarolo
Stienta
Occhiobello
Fiesso Umbertiano
Canaro
Polesella
Crespino
Berra
Ariano nel Polesine
Mesola
Gazzuolo
Casalmaggiore
Sabbioneta
Sissa
Suzzara
Luzzara
Colorno
San Secondo Parmense
Viadana
Guastalla
Gonzaga
Moglia
Reggiolo
Gualtieri
Brescello
Fontanellato
Poggio Rusco
Novi di Modena
Mirandola
Finale Emilia
Bondeno
Vigarano Mainarda
Ferrara
Pontelagoscuro
Grande Bonifica Ferrarese
Copparo
Jolanda di Savoia
Formignana
Tresigallo
Codigoro
Goro
Gorino
Gnocchetta
Massa Fiscaglia
Migliaro
Migliarino
Lagosanto
Valle Bertuzzi
Parma
Collecchio
Sorbolo
Poviglio
Novellara
Castelnovo di Sotto
Correggio
Cadelbosco di Sopra
Sant'Ilario d'Enza
Bagnolo in Piano
Carpi
Soliera
San Prospero
Medolla
San Felice sul Panaro
Camposanto
Cavezzo
Sant'Agostino
Poggio Renatico
Cento
Pieve di Cento
Bomporto
Crevalcore
Fornovo di Taro
Felino
Montecchio Emilia
Cavriago
Montechiarugolo
Reggio nell'Emilia
Modena
Nonantola
San Giovanni in Persiceto
Castello d'Argile
San Pietro in Casale
Malalbergo
Voghiera
Portomaggiore
Ostellato
Comacchio
Porto Garibaldi
Lido di Spina
Valli di Comacchio
Langhirano
Traversetolo
Quattro Castella
San Polo d'Enza
Scandiano
Rubiera
Formigine
Casalgrande
Sassuolo
Castelnuovo Rangone
Castelfranco Emilia
Bentivoglio
San Giorgio di Piano
Minerbio
Molinella
Argenta
Consandolo
Menata
San Cesario sul Panaro
Castel Maggiore
Granarolo dell'Emilia
Budrio
Castenaso
Fiorano Modense
Maranello
Spilamberto
Bologna
Medicina
Conselice
Alfonsine
Sant'Alberto
Marina Romea
Marina di Ravenna
Casina
Vetto
Baiso
Castellarano
Vignola
Bazzano
Zola Predosa
Casalecchio di Reno
San Lazzaro di Savena
Ozzano dell'Emilia
Fusignano
Bagnacavallo
Ravenna
Lido Adriano
Castelnovo ne' Monti
Carpineti
Marano sul Panaro
Serramazzoni
Guiglia
Sasso Marconi
Massa Lombarda
Lugo
Cotignola
Russi
Toano
Busana
Villa Minozzo
Montefiorino
Pavullo nel Frignano
Lama Mocogno
Marzabotto
Pianoro
Castèl San Pietro Terme
Imola
Autodromo Enzo e Dino Ferrari, Imola
Castel Bolognese
Faenza
Mirabilandia
Lido di Classe
Milano Marittima
Cervia
Passo del Cerreto
Ligonchio
Monte Cusna 2120
Collagna
Frassinoro
Sillano
Vergato
Monterenzio
Borgo Tossignano
Fontanelice
Casalfiumanese
Riolo Terme
Brisighella
Forlì
Forlimpopoli
Cesenatico
Gatteo a Mare
Bellaria
Montese
Marano
Montecreto
Sestola
Pievepelago
Monte Cimone 2165
Fanano
Fiumalbo
Abetone
Piazza al Serchio
Minucciano
Camporgiano
Gaggio Montano
Loiano
Monghidoro
Casola Valsenio
Castèl del Rio
Castrocaro Terme
Meldola
Bertinoro
Cesena
Gambettola
San Mauro Pascoli
Viserba
Rimini
Pieve Fosciana
Castelnuovo di Garfagnana
Cutigliano
Porretta Terme
Castiglione dei Pepoli
Lago di Suviana
Piano del Voglio
Sasso di Castro
Firenzuola
Monte la Faggeta
Marradi
Modigliana
Dovadola
Predappio
Tredozio
Savignano sul Rubicone
Santarcangelo di Romagna
Poggio Berni
Verucchio
Vagli Sotto
Barga
Coreglia Antelminelli
Gallicano
San Marcello Pistoiese
Sambuca Pistoiese
Passo della Futa
Monte Bucciana 1223
Cantagallo
Vernio
Barberino di Mugello
Rocca San Casciano
Premilcuore
Galeata
Civitella di Romagna
Mercato Saraceno
Sarsina
Serravalle
Coriano
San Marino
RSM
Misano
Massa
Montignoso
Seravezza
Pietrasanta
Pescaglia
Bagni di Lucca
Borgo a Mozzano
San Piero a Sieve
Scarperia
Vicchio
San Godenzo
Santa Sofia
Novafeltria
Sant'Agata Feltria
Mercatino Conca
Morciano di Romagna
Massarosa
Viareggio
Lucca
Porcari
Capannori
Pescia
Montecatini Terme
Monsummano Terme
Pistoia
Montale
Montemurlo
Agliana
Vaiano
Calenzano
Prato
Sesto Fiorentino
Borgo San Lorenzo
Dicomano
Londa
Rufina
Monte Giovi 992
Monte Falco 1658
Parco Nazionale del Monte Falterona, Campigna e delle Foreste Casentinesi
Bagno di Romagna
Lago di Quarto
Monte Comero 1371
Verghereto
Montefeltro
Macerata Feltria
Pennabilli
Carpegna
Sassocorvaro
Lago di Massaciuccoli
Vecchiano
San Giuliano Terme
Pisa
Torre pendente di Pisa
Piazza del Duomo
Chiesina Uzzanese
Altopascio
Quarrata
Campi Bisenzio
Fiesole
Firenze
Pontassieve
Pelago
Stia
Camaldoli
Pratovecchio
Santa Croce sull'Arno
Fucecchio
Vinci
Lastra a Signa
Signa
Scandicci
Bagno a Ripoli
Castel San Niccolò
Vallombrosa
Poppi
Badia Tedalda
Sestino
Urbino
Cascina
Castelfranco di Sotto
Empoli
Montelupo Fiorentino
Impruneta
Rignano sull'Arno
Reggello
Bibbiena
Chiusi della Verna
Borgo Pace
Sant'Angelo in Vado
Fermignano
Pontedera
San Miniato
San Casciano in Val di Pesa
Incisa in Val d'Arno
Pian di Scò
Chitignano
Pieve Santo Stefano
Monte dei Frati 1454
Urbania
Tirrenia
Ponsacco
Montespertoli
Figline Valdarno
Castelfranco di Sopra
Castel Focognano
Lago di Montedoglio
Mercatello sul Metauro
Acqualagna
Collesalvetti
Crespina
Lari
Capannoli
Palaia
Castelfiorentino
Greve in Chianti
San Giovanni Valdarno
Talla
Subbiano
Sansepolcro
Piobbico
Livorno
Montaione
Peccioli
Certaldo
Tavarnelle Val di Pesa
Loro Ciuffenna
Terranuova Bracciolini
Capolona
Apecchio
Cagli
Casciana Terme
Terricciola
Gambassi Terme
Montevarchi
Cavriglia
Anghiari
San Giustino
Santa Luce
Chianni
Poggibonsi
Radda in Chianti
Citerna
Quercianella
Castellina Marittima
San Gimignano
Colle di Val d'Elsa
Castellina in Chianti
Gaiole in Chianti
Monte Calvo 838
Bucine
Pergine Valdarno
Arezzo
Le Ville
Monterchi
Pietralunga
Cantiano
Castiglioncello
Rosignano Marittimo
Montescudaio
Riparbella
Montecatini Val di Cecina
Volterra
Saline di Volterra
Monteriggioni
Casole d'Elsa
Civitella in Val di Chiana
Città di Castello
Monte Favalto 1082
Monte Santa Maria Tiberina
Cecina
Marina di Cecina
Bibbona
Pomarance
Castelnuovo Berardenga
Monte San Savino
Castiglion Fiorentino
Montone
Gubbio
Siena
Sovicille
Radicondoli
Poggio Gasalone 722
Rapolano Terme
Lucignano
Marciano della Chiana
Foiano della Chiana
Cortona
Umbertide
Lisciano Niccone
Mercatale
Colline Metallifere
Larderello
Canneto
Castelnuovo di Val di Cecina
Poggio di Montieri 1051
Asciano
Sinalunga
Trequanda
Tuoro sul Trasimeno
Passignano sul Trasimeno
Cavallino Matto
Marina di Castagneto Donoratico
Castagneto Carducci
Sassetta
Monterotondo Marittimo
Montieri
Chiusdino
Monteroni d'Arbia
Murlo
Buonconvento
Monticiano
Torrita di Siena
San Giovanni d'Asso
Castiglione del Lago
Lago Trasimeno
Isola Polvese
Magione
Corciano
Perugia
Bosco
Monte Calvi 646
San Vincenzo
Campiglia Marittima
Suvereto
Massa Marittima
Roccastrada
Montalcino
San Quirico d'Orcia
Castiglione d'Orcia
Montepulciano
Pienza
Chianciano Terme
Lago di Montepulciano
Lago di Chiusi
Chiusi
Panicale
Paciano
Tavernelle
Torgiano
Bastia
Assisi
Bevagna
Gualdo Cattaneo
Foligno
Populonia
Monte Massoncello 286
Piombino
Follonica
Golfo di Follonica
Gavorrano
Scarlino
Monte Leoni 614
Paganico
Cinigiano
Castel del Piano
Monte Amiata 1738
Abbadia San Salvatore
Radicofani
Sarteano
Cetona
Città della Pieve
Piegaro
Monteleone d'Orvieto
Marsciano
Cannara
Frignano
Appennino Tosco-Emiliano
Alpi Apuane
Maremma
Appennino
Polesine
Laguna Veneta
Golfo di Venezia
10°30'
11°00'
11°30'
12°00'
12°30'
45°00'
44°30'
44°00'
43°30'
43°00'
I
E35
E45
E55
E70
E78
E80
A1
A4
A11
A12
A13
A14
A14dir
A22
A31

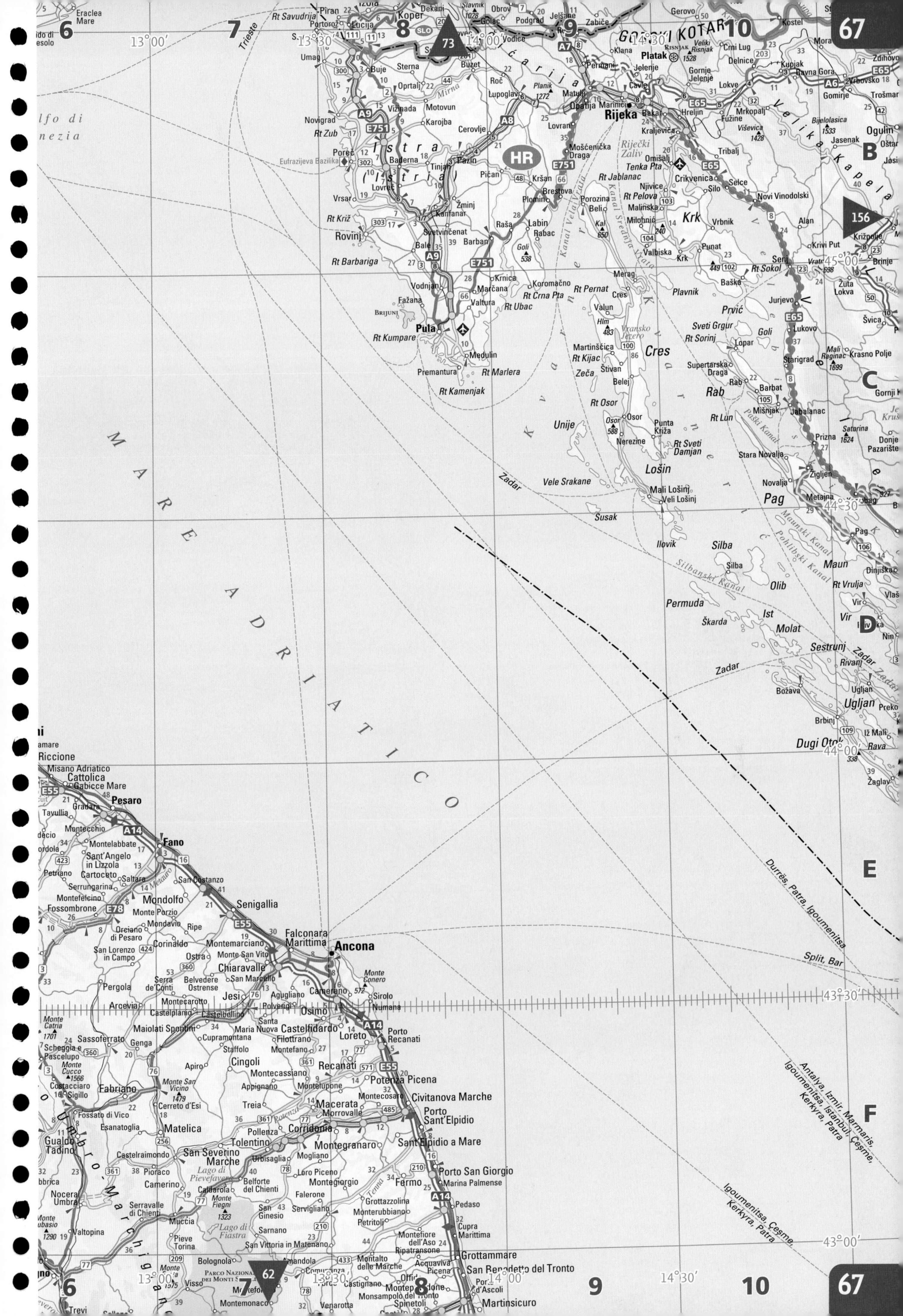
MARE ADRIATICO
Istra
(Istria)
HR
SLO
73
156
62
GORSKI KOTAR
Velika Kapela
Kvarner
Kvarnerić
Trieste
Zadar
Durrës, Patra, Igoumenitsa
Split, Bar
Antalya, Izmir, Marmaris, Igoumenitsa, Istanbul, Çesme, Kerkyra, Patra
Igoumenitsa, Çesme, Kerkyra, Patra
Eraclea Mare
Piran
Portorož
Lucija
Izola
Koper
Dekani
Rt Savudrija
Umag
Buje
Sterna
Oprtalj
Buzet
Roč
Lupoglav
Motovun
Vižinada
Karojba
Novigrad
Rt Zub
Cerovlje
Poreč
Eufrazijeva Bazilika
Baderna
Tinjan
Pazin
Pičan
Lovreč
Vrsar
Rt Križ
Žminj
Kanfanar
Rovinj
Svetvinčenat
Barban
Rt Barbariga
Bale
Vodnjan
Fažana
Brijuni
Pula
Rt Kumpare
Marčana
Valtura
Krnica
Medulin
Premantura
Rt Marlera
Rt Kamenjak
Raša
Labin
Rabac
Goli 538
Kršan
Plomin
Brestova
Koromačno
Rt Crna Pta
Rt Ubac
Učka
Planik 1272
Lovran
Opatija
Matulji
Mošćenička Draga
Rijeka
Bakar
Kraljevica
Klana
Platak
Risnjak
Jelenje
Čavle
Permani
Slavnik 1028
Obrov
Podgrad
Jelšane
Zabiče
Gerovo
Kostel
Crni Lug
Delnice
Gornje Jelenje
Lokve
Mrkopalj
Fužine
Hreljin
Bjelolasica 1533
Viševica 1428
Tribalj
Crikvenica
Selce
Novi Vinodolski
Rijecki Zaliv
Omišalj
Tenka Pta
Rt Jablanac
Njivice
Malinska
Rt Pelova
Porozina
Beli
Milohnić
Krk
Vrbnik
Punat
Baška
Valbiska
Kal 650
Merag
Cres
Rt Pernat
Valun
Hlm 483
Vransko Jezero
Martinšćica
Rt Kijac
Zeča
Štivan
Belej
Rt Osor
Osor
Osor 588
Unije
Nerezine
Punta Križa
Rt Sveti Damjan
Lošinj
Mali Lošinj
Veli Lošinj
Vele Srakane
Susak
Ilovik
Silba
Olib
Permuda
Škarda
Ist
Molat
Sestrunj
Rivanj
Božava
Ugljan
Brbinj
Dugi Otok
Iž Mali
Rava
Žaglav
Plavnik
Prvić
Sveti Grgur
Rt Sorinj
Goli
Lopar
Supertarska Draga
Rab
Barbat
Mišnjak
Rt Lun
Paški Kanal
Pag
Novalja
Stara Novalja
Metajna
Maun
Rt Vrulja
Vir
Dinjiško
Silbanski Kanal
Maunski Kanal
Pohlibski Kanal
Senj
Rt Sokol
Jurjevo
Lukovo
Starigrad
Jablanac
Prizna
Žigljen
Jbag
Mali Rajinac 1699
Krasno Polje
Satorina 1624
Donje Pazarište
Krivi Put
Krmpote
Brinje
Žuta Lokva
Švica
Alan
Ogulin
Jasenak
Josip
Mora
Kupjak
Ravna Gora
Vrbovsko
Zdihovo
Gomirje
Trošmar
Riccione
Misano Adriatico
Cattolica
Gabicce Mare
Gradara
Pesaro
Tavullia
Montecchio
Fano
Montelabbate
Sant'Angelo in Lizzola
Saltara
Cartoceto
Serrungarina
Petriano
Montefelcino
Fossombrone
Mondolfo
San Costanzo
Senigallia
Monte Porzio
Mondavio
Orciano di Pesaro
Ripe
San Lorenzo in Campo
Corinaldo
Montemarciano
Falconara Marittima
Ancona
Ostra
Monte San Vito
Chiaravalle
Serra de'Conti
Belvedere Ostrense
San Marcello
Pergola
Jesi
Agugliano
Camerano
Sirolo
Numana
Monte Conero 572
Polverigi
Arcevia
Castelplanio
Montecarotto
Castelbellino
Osimo
Santa Maria Nuova
Castelfidardo
Loreto
Porto Recanati
Maiolati Spontini
Cupramontana
Filottrano
Monte Catria 1701
Sassoferrato
Genga
Scheggia e Pascelupo
Staffolo
Montefano
Recanati
Cingoli
Apiro
Montecassiano
Potenza Picena
Monte Cucco 1566
Costacciaro
Sigillo
Fabriano
Monte San Vicino 1479
Appignano
Montelupone
Cerreto d'Esi
Treia
Macerata
Montecosaro
Civitanova Marche
Morrovalle
Porto Sant'Elpidio
Fossato di Vico
Esanatoglia
Matelica
Pollenza
Corridonia
Tolentino
Gualdo Tadino
Montegranaro
Sant'Elpidio a Mare
Castelraimondo
San Severino Marche
Urbisaglia
Mogliano
Loro Piceno
Porto San Giorgio
Marina Palmense
Fermo
Pioraco
Camerino
Lago di Pievefavera
Caldarola
Belforte del Chienti
Montegiorgio
Falerone
Nocera Umbra
Grottazzolina
Pedaso
Serravalle di Chienti
Monte Fiegni 1323
San Ginesio
Servigliano
Monterubbiano
Petritoli
Cupra Marittima
Muccia
Lago di Fiastra
Sarnano
Montefiore dell'Aso
Ripatransone
Valtopina
Pieve Torina
San Vittoria in Matenano
Grottammare
Montalto delle Marche
Acquaviva Picena
San Benedetto del Tronto
Amandola
Comunanza
Bolognola
Parco Nazionale dei Monti Sibillini
Visso
Montefortino
Montemonaco
Castignano
Offida
Monsampolo del Tronto
Spinetoli
Porto d'Ascoli
Martinsicuro
Venarotta
Trevi
Umbro-Marchigiano
E55
E65
E751
E78
A9
A8
A7
A6
A14
13°00′
13°30′
14°00′
14°30′
45°00′
44°30′
44°00′
43°30′
43°00′
6
7
8
9
10
B
C
D
E
F

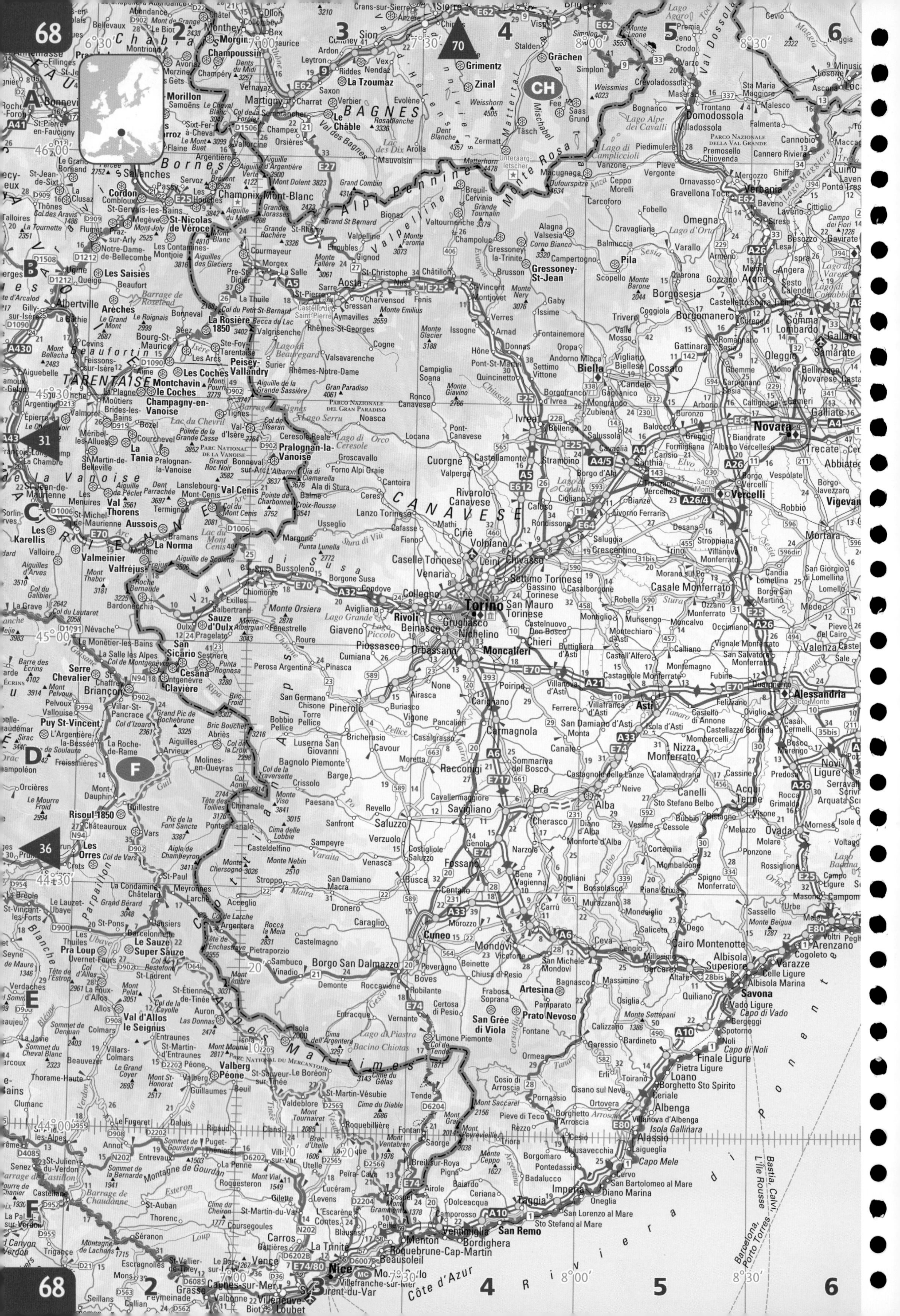
2
3
4
5
6
70
CH
A
B
C
D
E
F
31
36
F
6°30'
7°00'
7°30'
8°00'
8°30'
46°00'
45°30'
45°00'
44°30'
44°00'
Monthey
Morgins
Champoussin
Sion
Sierre
Crans-sur-Sierre
Visp
Brig
Grächen
Grimentz
Zinal
La Tzoumaz
Martigny
BAGNES
Le Châble
Verbier
Saas Fee
Saas Grund
Zermatt
Täsch
Simplon
Domodossola
Villadossola
Morillon
Samoëns
Chamonix-Mont-Blanc
Sallanches
Cordon
Combloux
Megève
St-Gervais-les-Bains
St-Nicolas de Véroce
Les Contamines-Montjoie
Les Houches
Albertville
Arêches
Les Saisies
Beaufort
Courmayeur
Morgex
La Thuile
La Rosière 1850
Aosta
Châtillon
Breuil-Cervinia
Champoluc
Gressoney-St-Jean
Gressoney-la-Trinite
Alagna Valsesia
Macugnaga
Monte Rosa
Alpi Pennine
Valpelline
Pila
Varallo
Omegna
Verbania
Stresa
Arona
Borgomanero
Borgosesia
Biella
Ivrea
Novara
Vercelli
Trecate
Vigevano
TARENTAISE
Les Coches
Montchavin
Peisey-Vallandry
Champagny-en-Vanoise
Tignes
Val-d'Isère
Courchevel
La Tania
Méribel-les-Allues
Pralognan-la-Vanoise
Val Thorens
Les Menuires
Val Cenis
Aussois
La Norma
Valfréjus
Valmeinier
Modane
Les Karellis
Gran Paradiso
Cogne
Ceresole Reale
CANAVESE
Cuorgnè
Rivarolo Canavese
Ciriè
Chivasso
Settimo Torinese
Torino
Collegno
Rivoli
Moncalieri
Chieri
Nichelino
Pinerolo
Carmagnola
Bra
Alba
Asti
Alessandria
Casale Monferrato
Valenza
Nizza Monferrato
Acqui Terme
Ovada
Novi Ligure
Sauze d'Oulx
Bardonecchia
San Sicario
Sestriere
Cesana
Clavière
Briançon
Serre Chevalier
Puy St-Vincent
Risoul 1850
Les Orres
Saluzzo
Savigliano
Fossano
Cuneo
Mondovì
Borgo San Dalmazzo
Limone Piemonte
Artesina
Prato Nevoso
San Grée di Viola
Savona
Albisola Superiore
Varazze
Arenzano
Cairo Montenotte
Finale Ligure
Loano
Albenga
Alassio
Imperia
Taggia
San Remo
Ventimiglia
Bordighera
Menton
Nice
Valberg
Péone
Val d'Allos le Seignus
Pra Loup
Le Sauze
Super Sauze
Barcelonnette
Isola 2000
Auron
Alpes Maritimes
Côte d'Azur
Riviera di Ponente
Bastia, Calvi, L'Ile Rousse
Barcelona, Porto Torres

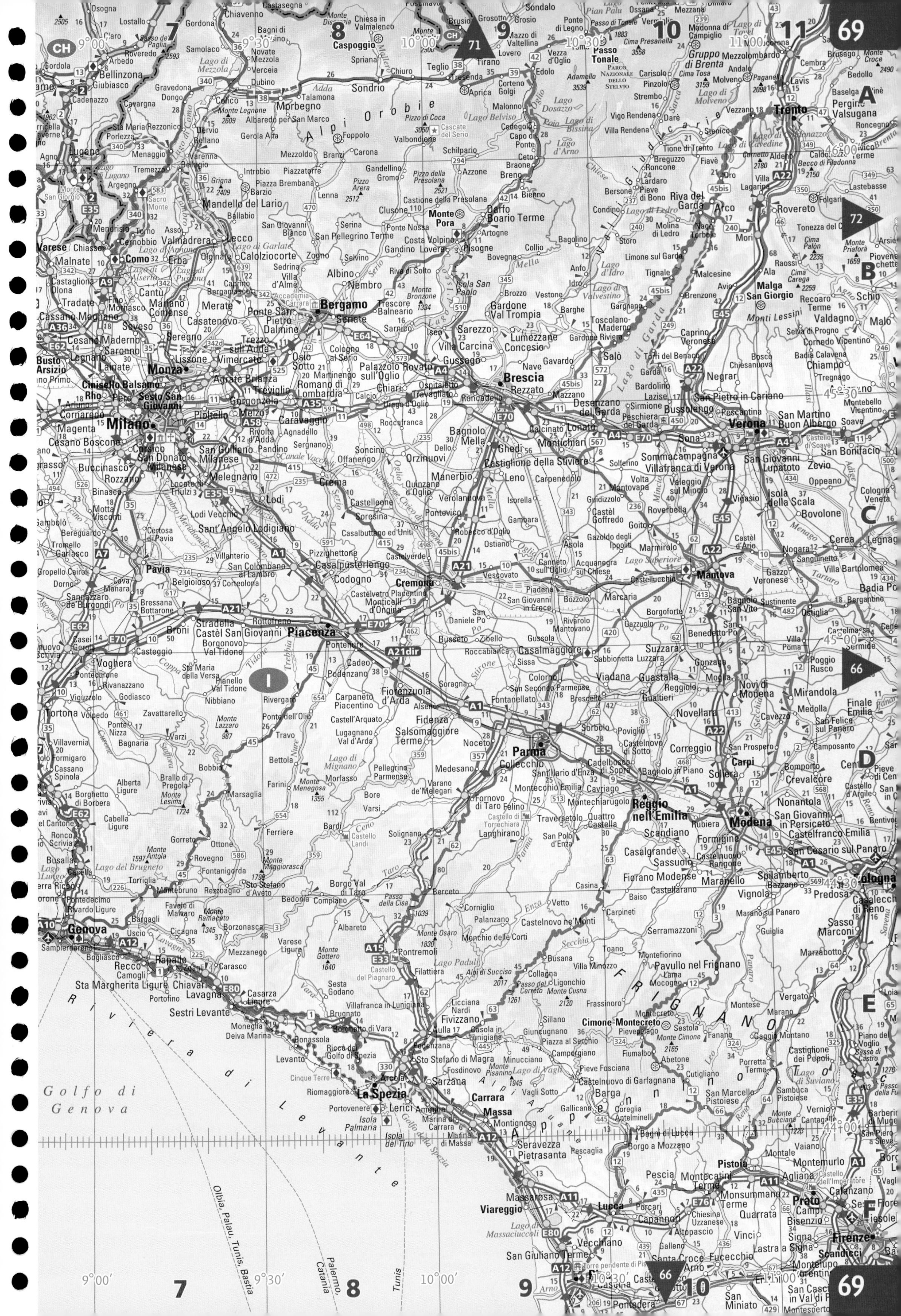
7
8
9
10
11
CH
I
71
72
66
A
B
C
D
E
F
9°00'
9°30'
10°00'
10°30'
11°00'
45°30'
45°00'
44°30'
44°00'
Alpi Orobie
Val Giudicarie
Lago di Garda
Lago di Como
Lago di Mezzola
Lago Maggiore
Frignano
Alpi Apuane
Appennino
Riviera di Levante
Golfo di Genova
Golfo della Spezia
Monti Lessini
Olbia, Palau, Tunis, Bastia
Palermo, Catania
Tunis
Chiavenna
Sondalo
Tirano
Sondrio
Morbegno
Bellinzona
Lugano
Mendrisio
Como
Lecco
Varese
Bergamo
Monza
Milano
Sesto San Giovanni
Legnano
Rho
Lodi
Pavia
Voghera
Tortona
Crema
Cremona
Brescia
Verona
Trento
Rovereto
Riva del Garda
Arco
Desenzano del Garda
Mantova
Piacenza
Fidenza
Parma
Reggio nell'Emilia
Modena
Carpi
Sassuolo
Bologna
Genova
Rapallo
Chiavari
Sestri Levante
La Spezia
Sarzana
Carrara
Massa
Viareggio
Lucca
Pistoia
Prato
Firenze
Scandicci
Pontremoli
Salsomaggiore Terme
Castelnovo ne' Monti
Pavullo nel Frignano
Cimone-Montecreto
Abetone
Camogli
Recco
Lavagna
Lerici
Portovenere
Pietrasanta
Montecatini Terme
Pescia
Vignola
Mirandola
Sirmione
Peschiera del Garda
Villafranca di Verona
Salò
Gardone Val Trompia
Darfo Boario Terme
Edolo
Pisogne
Iseo
Chiari
Treviglio
Caravaggio
Codogno
Casalpusterlengo
Stradella
Broni
Casteggio
Bobbio
Bardi
Borgo Val di Taro
Fornovo di Taro
Langhirano
Colorno
Guastalla
Suzzara
Viadana
Casalmaggiore
Sabbioneta
Ostiglia
Bussolengo
San Bonifacio
Soave
Schio
Valdagno
Recoaro Terme
Malga San Giorgio
Passo Tonale
Madonna di Campiglio
Pinzolo
Mezzolombardo
Pergine Valsugana
Levanto
Monterosso
Riomaggiore
Cinque Terre
Isola Palmaria
Isola del Tino
Lago di Massaciuccoli
Sesto Fiorentino
Calenzano
Fiesole
Empoli
San Miniato
Pontedera
Fucecchio
Vinci
Lastra a Signa
Campi Bisenzio
A1
A4
A7
A9
A10
A11
A12
A15
A21
A22
A35
A36
A58
E35
E45
E62
E70
E76
E80

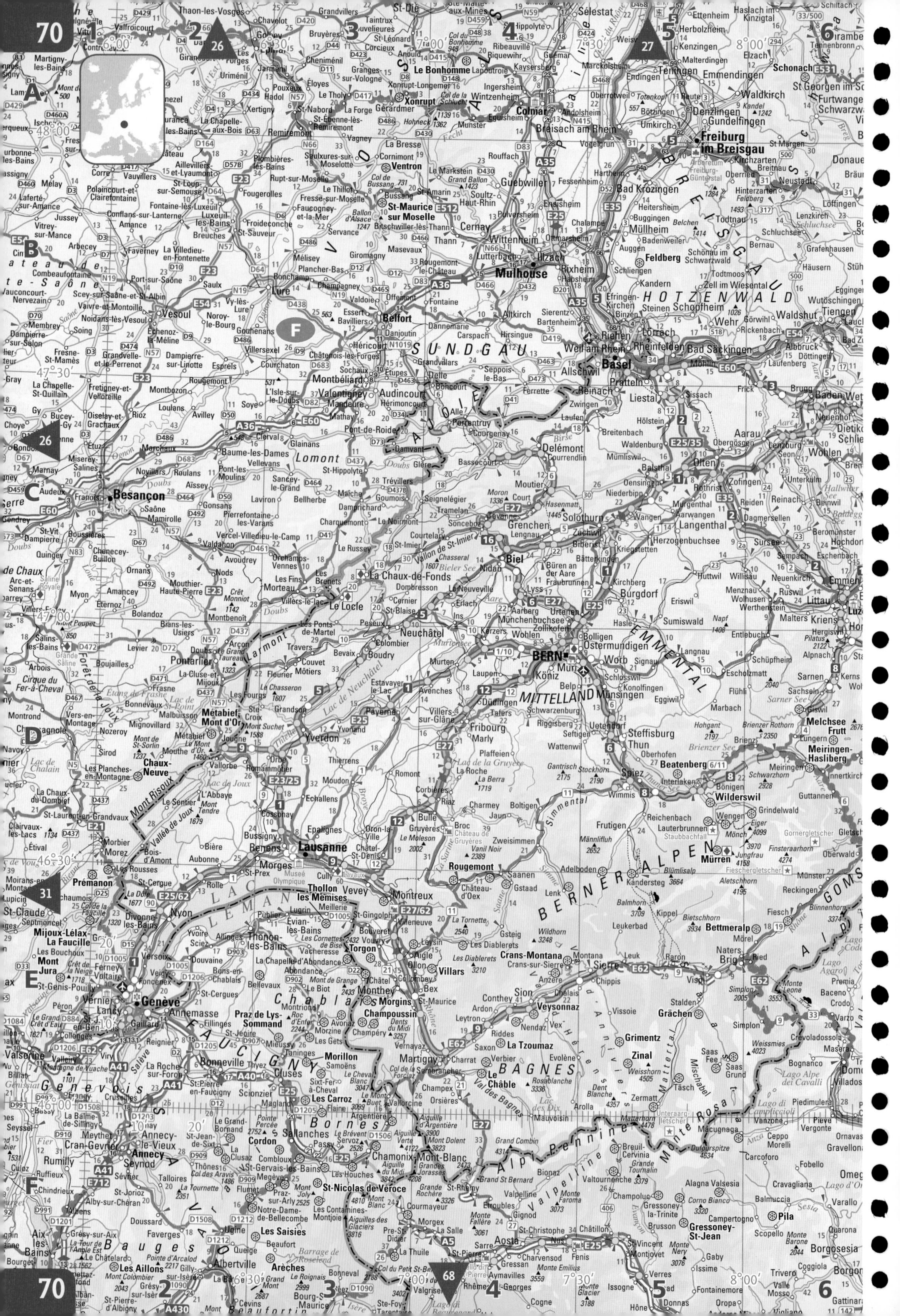

1
2
3
4
5
6
26
27
A
B
C
D
E
F
F
Sélestat
Colmar
Breisach am Rhein
Freiburg im Breisgau
Mulhouse
Belfort
Montbéliard
Vesoul
Lure
Besançon
Épinal
Gérardmer
Remiremont
Basel
Weil am Rhein
Lörrach
Rheinfelden
Bad Säckingen
Waldshut
Tiengen
Liestal
Delémont
Solothurn
Grenchen
Biel
La Chaux-de-Fonds
Le Locle
Neuchâtel
Pontarlier
Yverdon
Lausanne
Vevey
Montreux
Fribourg
BERN
Thun
Spiez
Interlaken
Burgdorf
Langenthal
Olten
Aarau
Zofingen
Genève
Annemasse
Annecy
Chamonix-Mont-Blanc
Sion
Sierre
Brig
Zermatt
Martigny
Aosta
Courmayeur
Albertville
Aix-les-Bains
St-Claude
Nyon
Morges
Thonon-les-Bains
Évian-les-Bains
Cluses
Sallanches
Megève
Bonneville
Verbier
Crans-Montana
Saanen
Gstaad
Grindelwald
Wengen
Mürren
Kandersteg
Leukerbad
Saas Fee
Grächen
Champoluc
Gressoney-St-Jean
Ivrea
Domodossola
SUNDGAU
HOTZENWALD
BREISGAU
EMMENTAL
MITTELLAND
BERNER ALPEN
LAC LÉMAN
FAUCIGNY
Chablais
BAGNES
Alpi Pennine
Monte Rosa
Genevois
Bauges
Beaufortin
Bornes
Jura
Lac de Neuchâtel
Bieler See
Thuner See
Brienzer See
Lac de Joux
Lomont
AJOIE
Mont Blanc 4810
Matterhorn 4478
Dufourspitze 4634
Eiger 3970
Mönch 4099
Jungfrau 4158
Finsteraarhorn 4274
Weisshorn 4505
Dent Blanche 4357
Grand Combin 4314
Feldberg 1493
Grand Ballon 1423
Chasseral 1607
Napf 1408
Pilatus 2122
47°30′
47°00′
46°30′
46°00′
6°00′
6°30′
7°00′
7°30′
8°00′
48°00′
E25
E27
E60
E62
A36
A35
A5
A41
A40
68
31

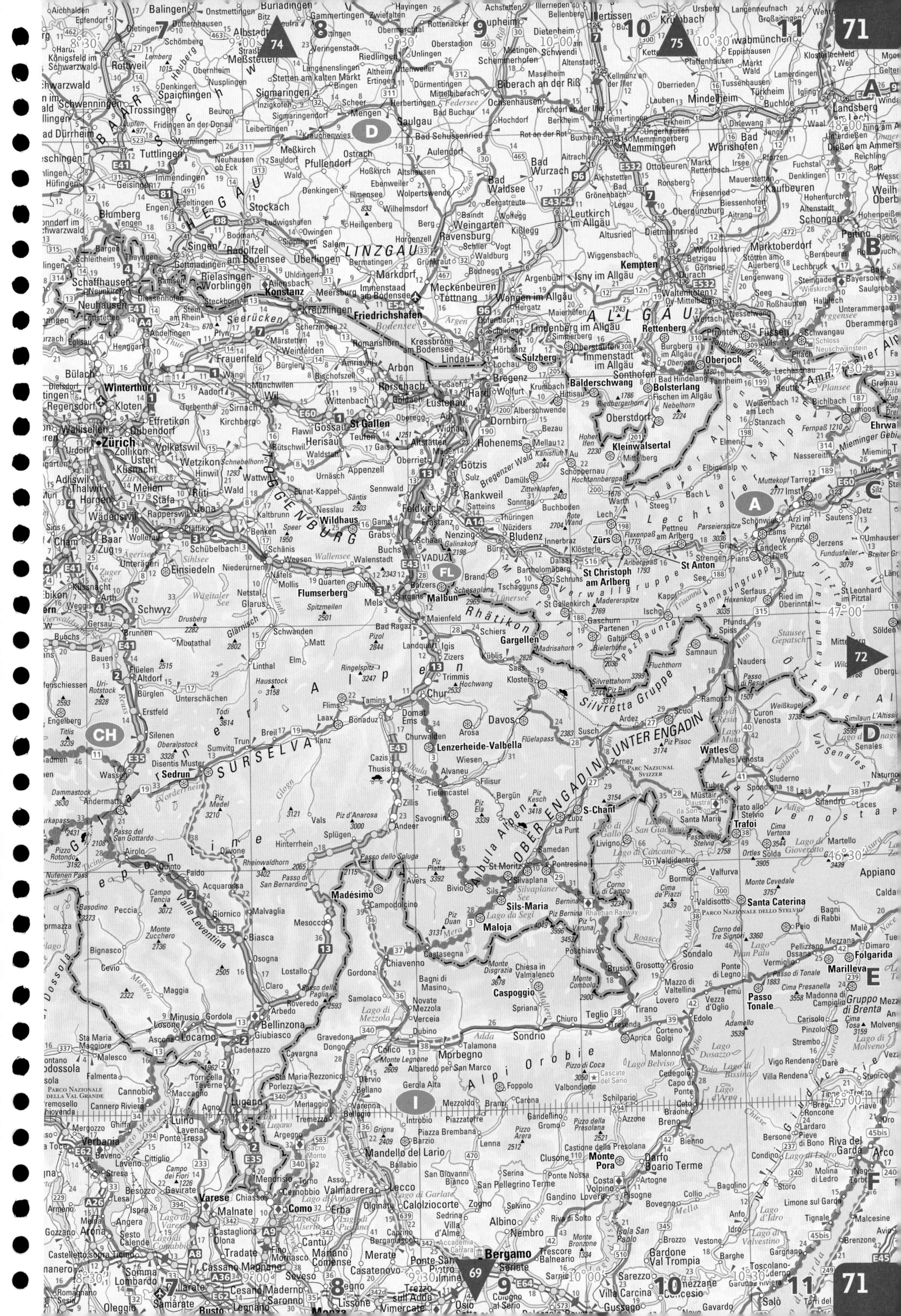
74
75
72
69
7
8
9
10
11
D
CH
FL
A
I
Balingen
Albstadt
Sigmaringen
Saulgau
Biberach an der Riß
Memmingen
Mindelheim
Landsberg
Bad Wörishofen
Kaufbeuren
Schongau
Marktoberdorf
Kempten
Füssen
Tuttlingen
Trossingen
Spaichingen
Rottweil
Villingen-Schwenningen
Bad Dürrheim
Donaueschingen
Stockach
Singen
Radolfzell am Bodensee
Überlingen
Meersburg
Konstanz
Friedrichshafen
Ravensburg
Weingarten
Bad Waldsee
Bad Wurzach
Leutkirch im Allgäu
Isny im Allgäu
Wangen im Allgäu
Lindau
Lindenberg im Allgäu
Immenstadt im Allgäu
Sonthofen
Oberstdorf
Bad Hindelang
Pfronten
Schaffhausen
Kreuzlingen
Frauenfeld
Winterthur
Zürich
Wil
St Gallen
Herisau
Rorschach
Arbon
Bregenz
Dornbirn
Hohenems
Feldkirch
Bludenz
VADUZ
Sargans
Chur
Davos
Klosters
Arosa
Lenzerheide-Valbella
St Moritz
Sils-Maria
Maloja
Samedan
Zernez
Scuol
Landeck
St Anton
Zürs
St Christoph am Arlberg
Lech
Reutte
Imst
Ehrwald
Nauders
Glarus
Schwyz
Zug
Einsiedeln
Altdorf
Andermatt
Airolo
Biasca
Bellinzona
Locarno
Lugano
Como
Varese
Lecco
Bergamo
Sondrio
Tirano
Chiavenno
Madésimo
Bormio
Livigno
Glurns
Malles Venosta
Mals
Silandro
Ponte di Legno
Edolo
Passo Tonale
Riva del Garda
Salò
Bodensee
Lago Maggiore
Lago di Como
Lago d'Iseo
Lago di Lugano
HEGAU
LINZGAU
ALLGÄU
Allgäuer Alpen
Lechtaler Alpen
Rhätikon
Silvretta Gruppe
Samnaungruppe
Verwallgruppe
UNTER ENGADIN
OBER ENGADIN
SURSELVA
Alpi Orobie
Lepontine Alpen
Ötztaler Alpen
Val Venosta
TOGGENBURG
Parco Nazionale dello Stelvio
Parc Naziunal Svizzer
Schloss Neuschwanstein
Rhaetian Railway
47°30'
47°00'
46°30'
46°00'
8°30'
9°00'
9°30'
10°00'
10°30'

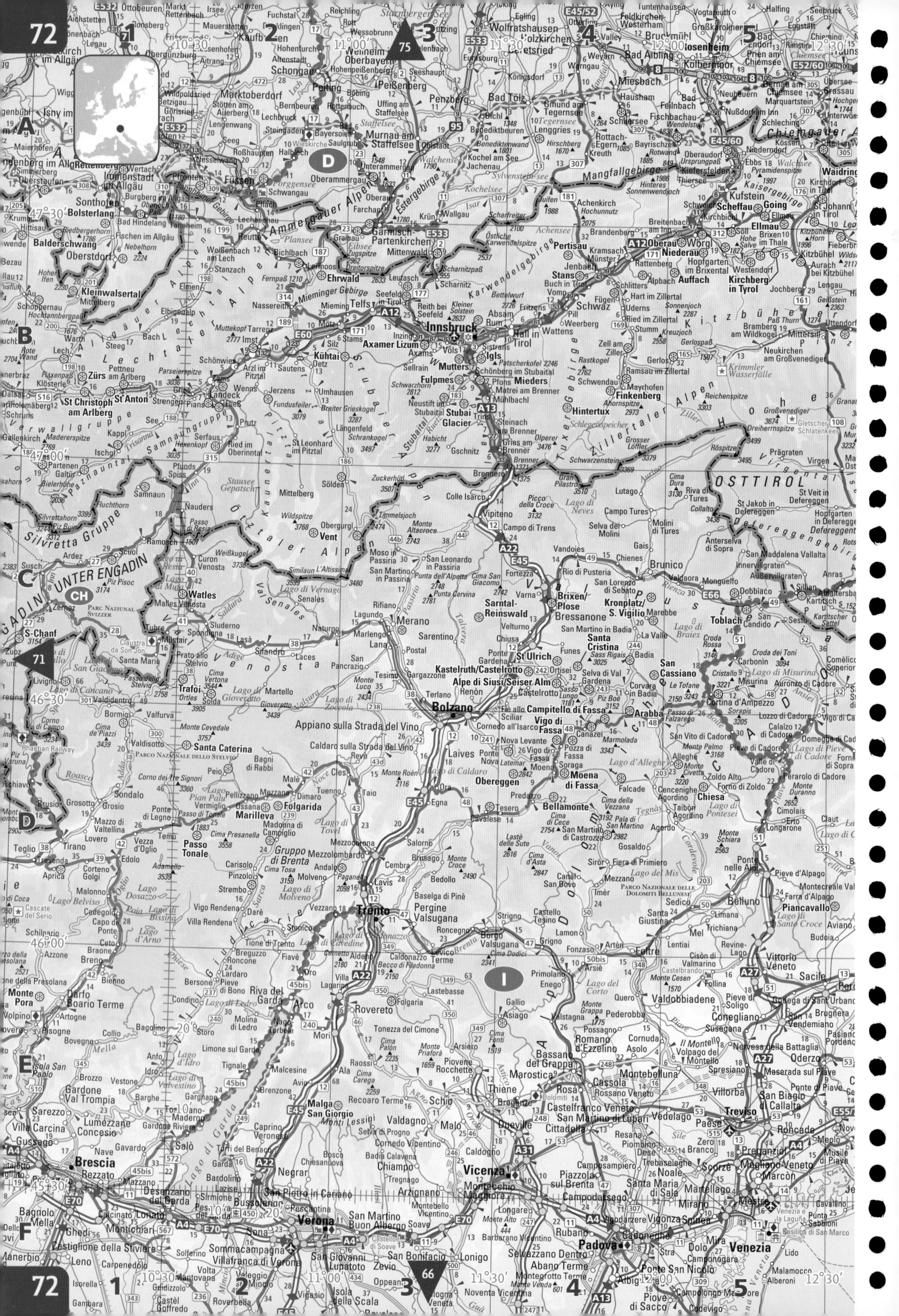
D
CH
I
OSTTIROL
UNTER ENGADIN
Innsbruck
Bolzano
Trento
Verona
Vicenza
Padova
Venezia
Treviso
Brescia
Merano
Brixen/Bressanone
Belluno
Rovereto
Kufstein
Rosenheim
Garmisch-Partenkirchen
Füssen
Kaufbeuren
Schongau
Weilheim in Oberbayern
Wolfratshausen
Bad Tölz
Miesbach
Bad Aibling
Kempten
Immenstadt im Allgäu
Sonthofen
Oberstdorf
Landeck
Imst
Telfs
Schwaz
Wörgl
Kitzbühel
Lienz
Brunico
Cortina d'Ampezzo
Bassano del Grappa
Castelfranco Veneto
Conegliano
Mestre
Allgäuer Alpen
Lechtaler Alpen
Ötztaler Alpen
Stubaier Alpen
Zillertaler Alpen
Kitzbüheler Alpen
Hohe Tauern
Karwendelgebirge
Mangfallgebirge
Ammergauer Alpen
Chiemgauer Alpen
Dolomiti
Alpi
Silvretta Gruppe
Samnaungruppe
Verwallgruppe
Val Venosta
Lago di Garda
Chiemsee
Tegernsee
A12
A13
A22
A4
A27
A31
E45
E60
E70
75
71
66
10°30′
11°00′
11°30′
12°00′
12°30′
47°30′
47°00′
46°30′
46°00′
45°30′
A
B
C
D
E
F
1
2
3
4
5

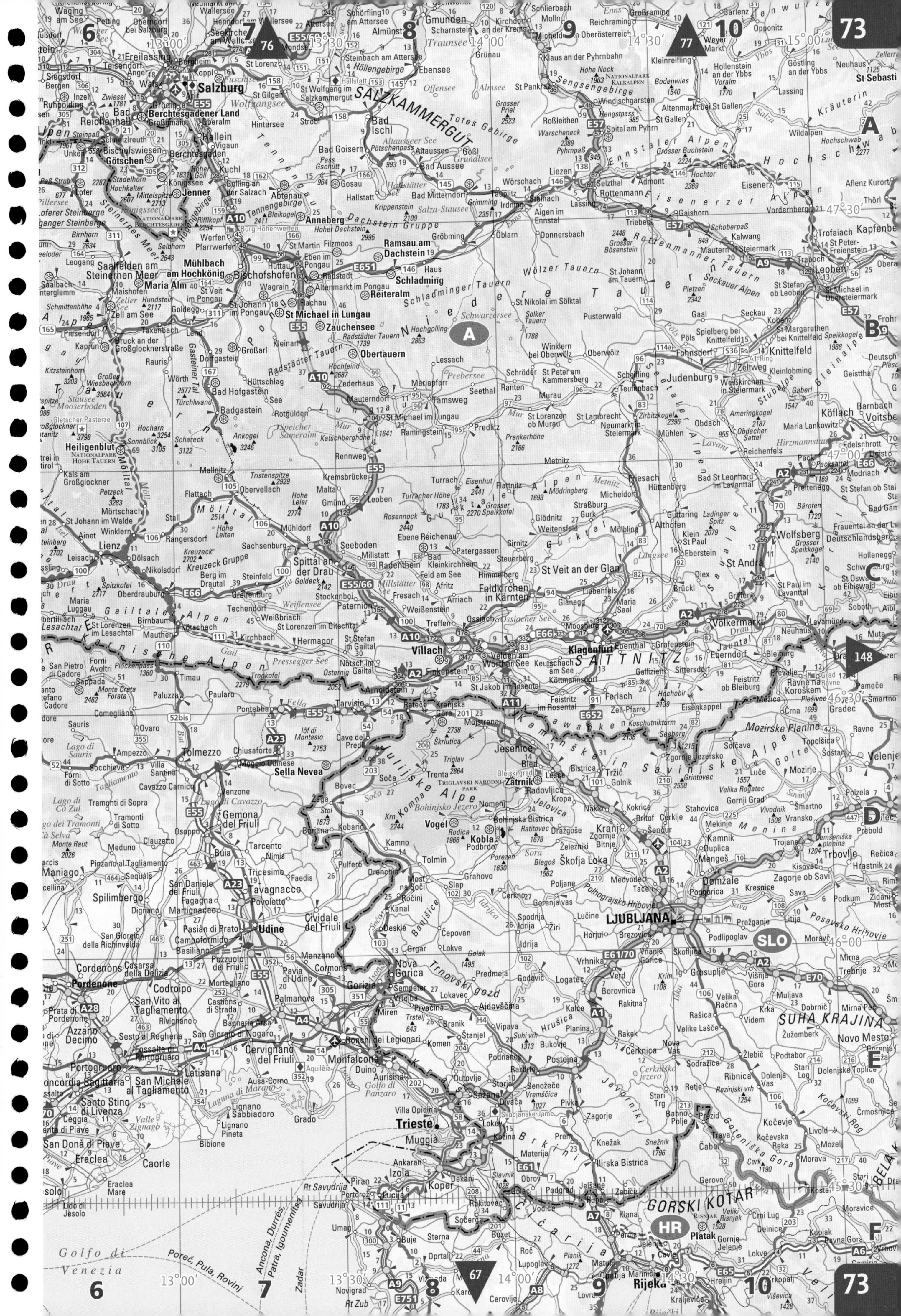
6
7
8
9
10
76
77
A
B
C
D
E
F
Salzburg
Berchtesgadener Land
Bad Reichenhall
Hallein
Berchtesgaden
Freilassing
Bad Ischl
Gmunden
SALZKAMMERGUT
Totes Gebirge
Bad Goisern
Bad Aussee
Altaussee
Gosau
Hallstatt
Bad Mitterndorf
Liezen
Admont
Rottenmann
Windischgarsten
Spital am Pyhrn
Sengsengebirge
Ennstaler Alpen
Eisenerz
Trofaiach
Leoben
Kapfenberg
Hochschwab
Schladming
Ramsau am Dachstein
Dachstein Gruppe
Tennengebirge
Annaberg
Reiteralm
Radstadt
Altenmarkt im Pongau
Bischofshofen
St Johann im Pongau
Mühlbach am Hochkönig
Saalfelden am Steinernen Meer
Maria Alm
Zell am See
Kaprun
St Michael in Lungau
Zauchensee
Obertauern
Niedere Tauern
Schladminger Tauern
Wölzer Tauern
Rottenmanner Tauern
Seckauer Alpen
Judenburg
Knittelfeld
Zeltweg
Fohnsdorf
Murau
Tamsweg
Mauterndorf
Lungau
Bad Hofgastein
Badgastein
Heiligenblut
Nationalpark Hohe Tauern
Mallnitz
Obervellach
Spittal an der Drau
Millstatt
Seeboden
Radenthein
Bad Kleinkirchheim
Turracher Höhe
Gurktaler Alpen
Feldkirchen in Kärnten
St Veit an der Glan
Wolfsberg
St Andrä
Völkermarkt
Klagenfurt
Moosburg
Velden am Wörther See
Villach
Ossiacher See
Hermagor
Kötschach
Lienz
Mauthen
Karnische Alpen
Gailtaler Alpen
Köflach
Voitsberg
Deutschlandsberg
Lavamünd
Bleiburg
148
Ravne na Koroškem
Dravograd
Slovenj Gradec
Kamniške in Savinjske Alpe
Mozirske Planine
Velenje
Jesenice
Bled
Kranjska Gora
Tarvisio
Pontebba
Sella Nevea
Tolmezzo
Julijske Alpe
Triglav
Bovec
Kobarid
Tolmin
Vogel
Kobla
Bohinjsko Jezero
Radovljica
Kranj
Škofja Loka
Tržič
Kamnik
Domžale
LJUBLJANA
SLO
Trbovlje
Vrhnika
Idrija
Nova Gorica
Gorizia
Cividale del Friuli
Udine
Gemona del Friuli
Tavagnacco
Spilimbergo
Maniago
Pordenone
Codroipo
Palmanova
Cervignano del Friuli
Latisana
Lignano Sabbiadoro
Grado
Monfalcone
Trieste
Muggia
Sežana
Postojna
Cerknica
Ajdovščina
Trnovski gozd
Koper
Izola
Piran
Portorož
Kočevje
Ribnica
Novo Mesto
SUHA KRAJINA
Ilirska Bistrica
GORSKI KOTAR
HR
Rijeka
Opatija
Umag
Buje
Caorle
San Donà di Piave
Eraclea
Jesolo
Golfo di Venezia
Poreč, Pula, Rovinj
Ancona, Durrës, Patra, Igoumenitsa
Zadar
67
13°00′
13°30′
14°00′
14°30′
15°00′
47°30′
47°00′
46°30′
46°00′
45°30′

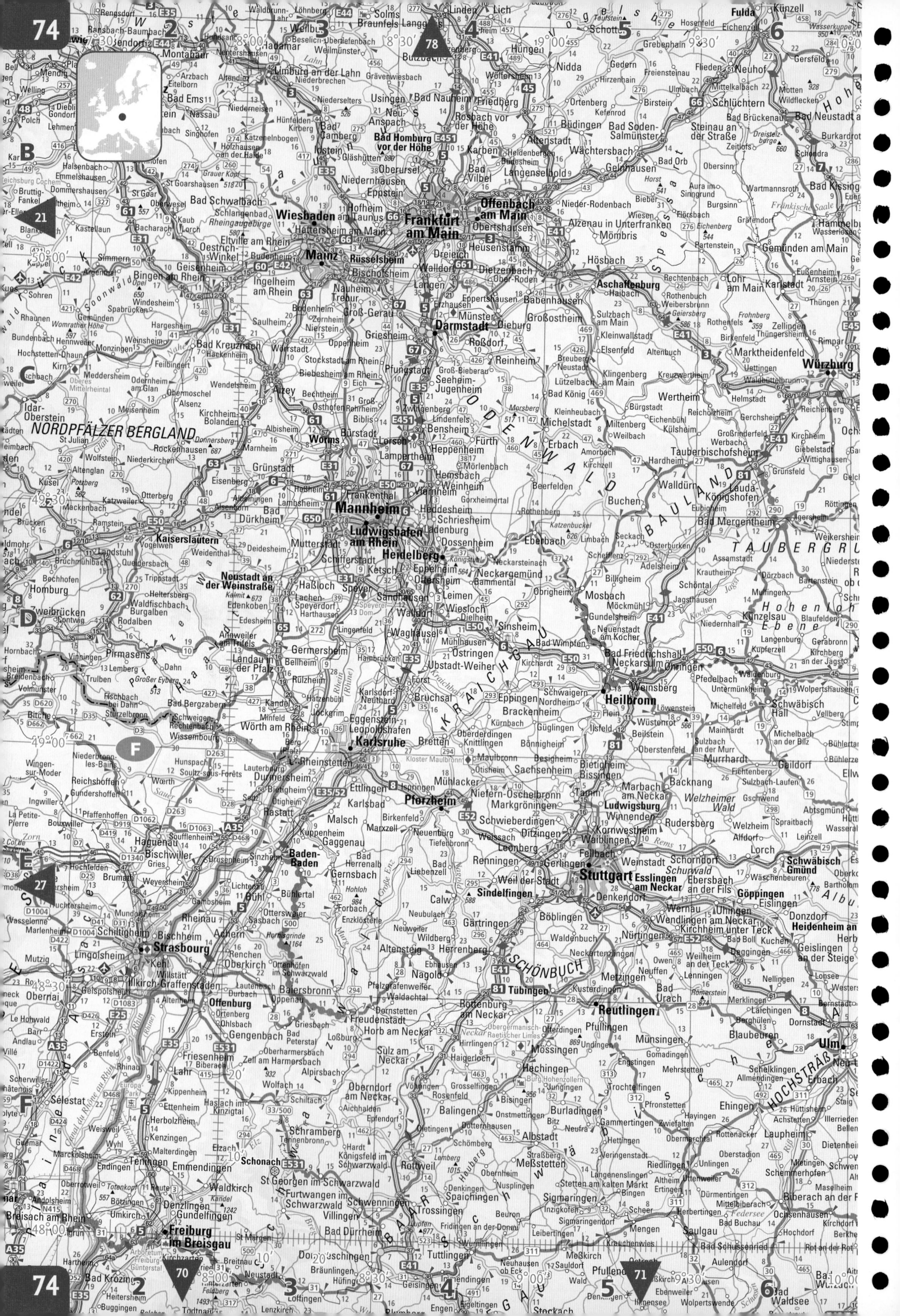
Frankfurt am Main
Offenbach am Main
Wiesbaden
Mainz
Darmstadt
Mannheim
Ludwigshafen am Rhein
Heidelberg
Karlsruhe
Stuttgart
Pforzheim
Heilbronn
Würzburg
Aschaffenburg
Kaiserslautern
Strasbourg
Freiburg im Breisgau
Offenburg
Baden-Baden
Tübingen
Reutlingen
Ulm
Worms
Speyer
Neustadt an der Weinstraße
Ludwigsburg
Esslingen am Neckar
Sindelfingen
Göppingen
Schwäbisch Hall
Schwäbisch Gmünd
Bad Homburg vor der Höhe
Fulda
Limburg an der Lahn
NORDPFÄLZER BERGLAND
ODENWALD
KRAICHGAU
BAULAND
SCHÖNBUCH
F

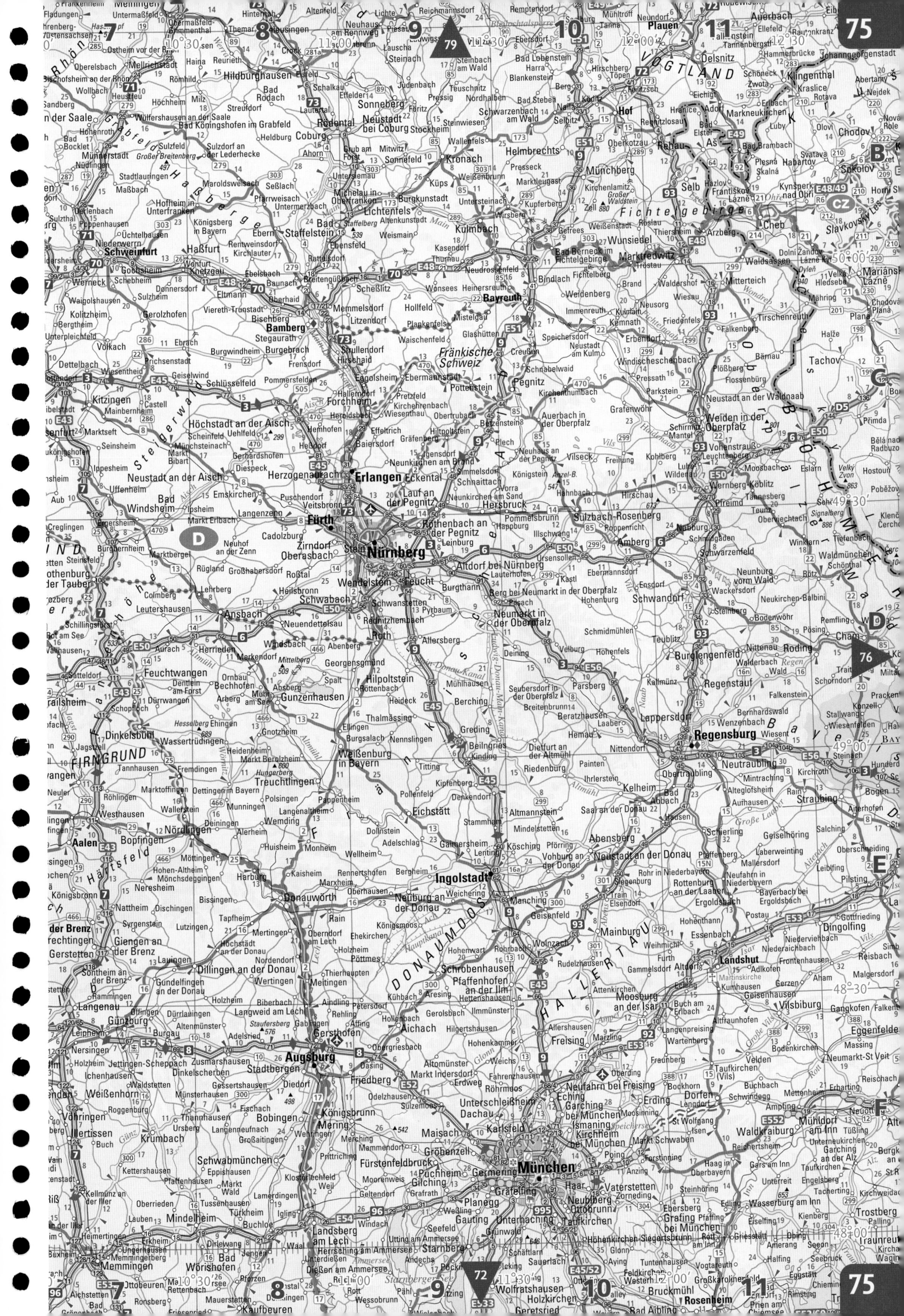
Rhön
Schweinfurt
Haßfurt
Hildburghausen
Coburg
Sonneberg
Kronach
Lichtenfels
Kulmbach
Bamberg
Bayreuth
Hof
Plauen
VOGTLAND
Oelsnitz
Klingenthal
Selb
Marktredwitz
Wunsiedel
Fichtelgebirge
Münchberg
Cheb
CZ
Mariánské Lázně
Tachov
Tirschenreuth
Weiden in der Oberpfalz
Neustadt an der Waldnaab
Fränkische Schweiz
Forchheim
Erlangen
Fürth
Nürnberg
Schwabach
Ansbach
Kitzingen
Steigerwald
Neustadt an der Aisch
Bad Windsheim
Rothenburg ob der Tauber
D
Amberg
Sulzbach-Rosenberg
Neumarkt in der Oberpfalz
Schwandorf
Cham
Regensburg
Kelheim
Straubing
Landshut
Dingolfing
Ingolstadt
Eichstätt
Weißenburg in Bayern
Gunzenhausen
Feuchtwangen
Dinkelsbühl
Nördlingen
Aalen
Donauwörth
Neuburg an der Donau
DONAUMOOS
HALLERTAU
Freising
Erding
Augsburg
Dachau
München
Landsberg am Lech
Memmingen
Mindelheim
Kaufbeuren
Starnberg
Wolfratshausen
Rosenheim
Mühldorf am Inn
Wasserburg am Inn
Günzburg
Ulm
Neu-Ulm
Frankenhöhe
Franken
Oberpfälzer Wald
BÖHMERWALD
Bayerischer Wald
79
72
76
10°30′
11°00′
11°30′
12°00′
12°30′
49°30′
49°00′
48°30′
48°00′

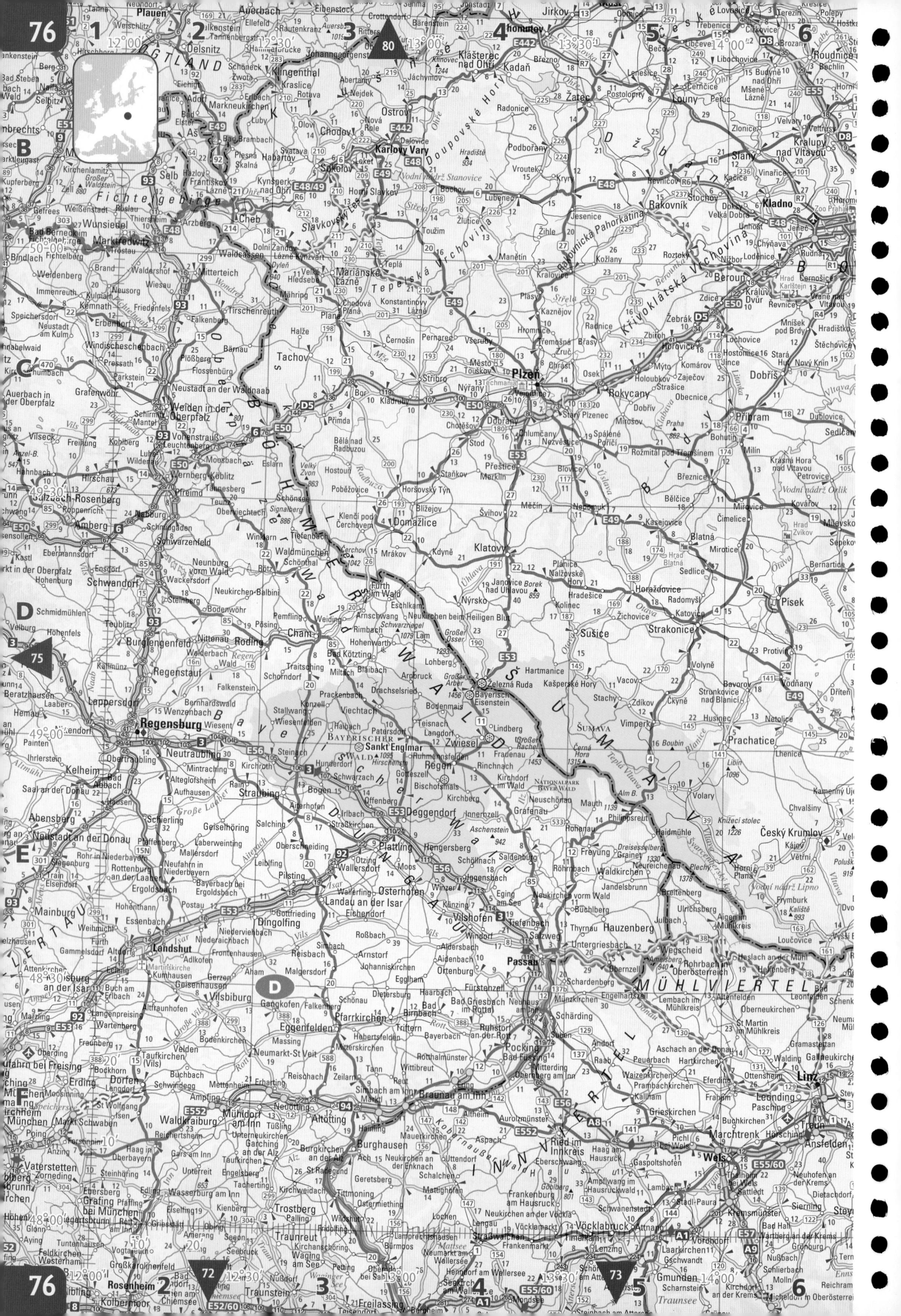

Plauen
Auerbach
Eibenstock
Jirkov
Chomutov
Klášterec nad Ohří
Kadaň
Žatec
Louny
Libochovice
Roudnice
Terezín
Oelsnitz
Klingenthal
Jáchymov
Ostrov
Karlovy Vary
Sokolov
Chodov
Cheb
Aš
Selb
Wunsiedel
Marktredwitz
Bad Berneck im Fichtelgebirge
Bindlach
Fichtelgebirge
VOGTLAND
Doupovské Hory
Slavkovský Les
Mariánské Lázně
Tepelská Vrchovina
Teplá
Toužim
Žlutice
Podbořany
Lubenec
Rakovník
Rakovnická Pahorkatina
Křivoklátská Vrchovina
Slaný
Kralupy nad Vltavou
Kladno
Beroun
Hořovice
Žebrák
Zbiroh
Rokycany
Plzeň
Stříbro
Tachov
Planá
Bor
Kladruby
Přimda
Weiden in der Oberpfalz
Neustadt an der Waldnaab
Grafenwöhr
Tirschenreuth
Waldsassen
Mitterteich
Kemnath
Pressath
Vohenstrauß
Amberg
Sulzbach-Rosenberg
Nabburg
Schwandorf
Neunburg vorm Wald
Oberviechtach
Waldmünchen
Domažlice
Horšovský Týn
Stod
Dobřany
Přeštice
Nepomuk
Klatovy
Sušice
Horažďovice
Strakonice
Blatná
Příbram
Dobříš
Písek
Vodňany
Prachatice
Vimperk
Volary
Český Krumlov
Kaplice
Cham
Roding
Furth im Wald
Bad Kötzting
Regen
Zwiesel
Železná Ruda
Bayerisch Eisenstein
Kašperské Hory
ŠUMAVA
BÖHMERWALD
BAYERISCHER WALD
Regensburg
Regenstauf
Burglengenfeld
Kelheim
Abensberg
Neustadt an der Donau
Straubing
Deggendorf
Plattling
Landau an der Isar
Dingolfing
Landshut
Vilshofen
Passau
Grafenau
Freyung
Waldkirchen
Hauzenberg
Rohrbach in Oberösterreich
MÜHLVIERTEL
Linz
Leonding
Traun
Wels
Marchtrenk
Eferding
Schärding
Pocking
Bad Füssing
Pfarrkirchen
Eggenfelden
Vilsbiburg
Simbach am Inn
Braunau am Inn
Altötting
Mühldorf am Inn
Waldkraiburg
Burghausen
Ried im Innkreis
Vöcklabruck
Gmunden
Traunreut
Traunstein
Trostberg
Wasserburg am Inn
Rosenheim
Erding
Dorfen
Freising
Mainburg
Grafing bei München
Vaterstetten
Deggendorf
DUNGAU
INNVIERTEL
HALLERTAU
Chiemsee
Traunsee
Mondsee
Attersee

80
75
72
73

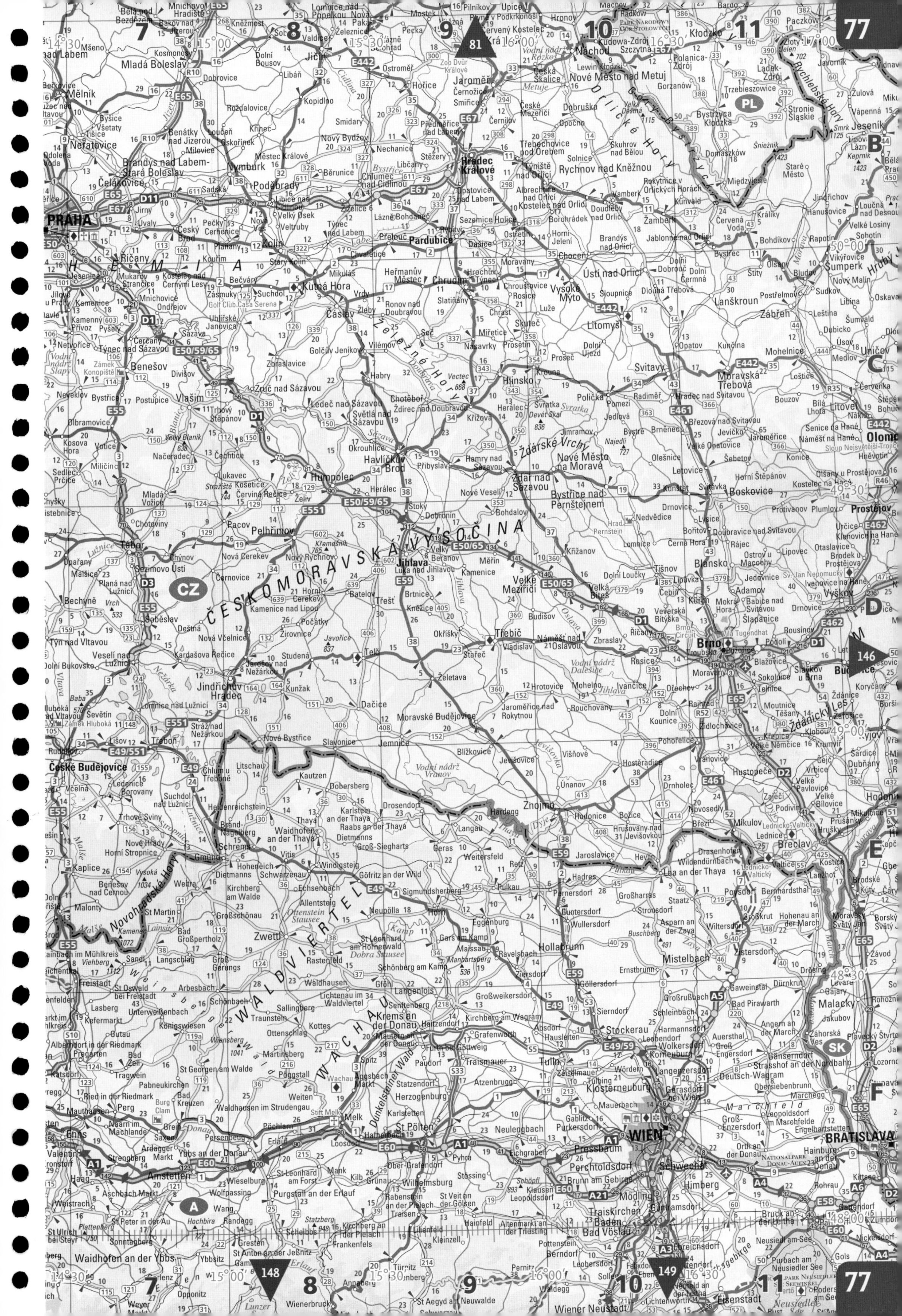
PRAHA
Mladá Boleslav
Mělník
Jičín
Jaroměř
Náchod
Kłodzko
Hradec Králové
Pardubice
Kolín
Kutná Hora
Chrudim
Čáslav
Nymburk
Poděbrady
Ústí nad Orlicí
Litomyšl
Svitavy
Šumperk
Jeseník
Zábřeh
Mohelnice
Benešov
Vlašim
Havlíčkův Brod
Humpolec
Pelhřimov
Tábor
Jihlava
Žďár nad Sázavou
Nové Město na Moravě
Boskovice
Blansko
Prostějov
Vyškov
Třebíč
Velké Meziříčí
Brno
Jindřichův Hradec
Telč
Dačice
Moravské Budějovice
Znojmo
České Budějovice
Třeboň
Český Krumlov
Kaplice
Mikulov
Břeclav
Hodonín
BOHEMIA
ČESKOMORAVSKÁ VYSOČINA
Žďárské Vrchy
Železné Hory
Orlické Hory
CZ
PL
SK
A
WALDVIERTEL
WACHAU
Gmünd
Zwettl
Horn
Hollabrunn
Mistelbach
Krems an der Donau
Stockerau
Tulln
Korneuburg
Klosterneuburg
WIEN
Schwechat
St. Pölten
Melk
Amstetten
Wieselburg
Mödling
Baden
Bad Vöslau
Traiskirchen
Wiener Neustadt
Eisenstadt
BRATISLAVA
Malacky
Freistadt
Enns
Waidhofen an der Ybbs
Laa an der Thaya
Marchfeld
81
146
148
149
7
8
9
10
11
B
C
D
E
F

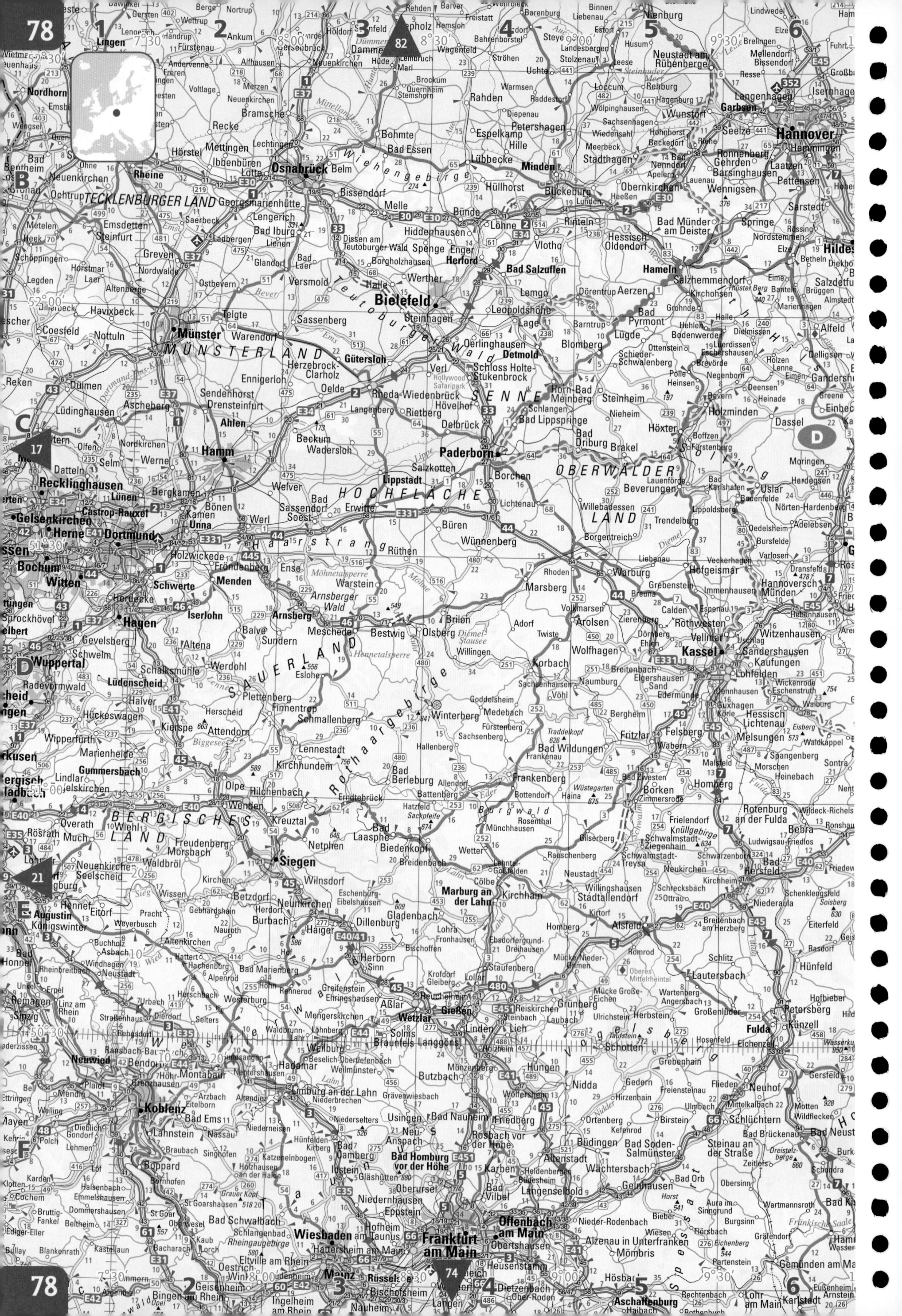

Lingen
Nordhorn
Bad Bentheim
Rheine
Ibbenbüren
Osnabrück
TECKLENBURGER LAND
Georgsmarienhütte
Lengerich
Bad Iburg
Greven
Emsdetten
Steinfurt
Münster
MÜNSTERLAND
Coesfeld
Dülmen
Lüdinghausen
Ahlen
Hamm
Recklinghausen
Gelsenkirchen
Herne
Dortmund
Bochum
Witten
Lünen
Castrop-Rauxel
Kamen
Unna
Werl
Soest
Hagen
Schwerte
Iserlohn
Menden
Wuppertal
Lüdenscheid
Gummersbach
Hückeswagen
Wipperfürth
Marienheide
Attendorn
Olpe
Siegen
Kreuztal
Hilchenbach
BERGISCHES LAND
Waldbröl
Neunkirchen-Seelscheid
Königswinter
Bad Honnef
Remagen
Neuwied
Koblenz
Bad Ems
Lahnstein
Boppard
St. Goarshausen
Montabaur
Limburg an der Lahn
Hadamar
Weilburg
Wetzlar
Gießen
Marburg an der Lahn
Biedenkopf
Bad Laasphe
Bad Berleburg
Winterberg
Rothaargebirge
SAUERLAND
Schmallenberg
Lennestadt
Meschede
Arnsberg
Sundern
Brilon
Olsberg
Warstein
Rüthen
Lippstadt
HOCHFLÄCHE
Haarstrang
Paderborn
Bad Lippspringe
Delbrück
Rietberg
Rheda-Wiedenbrück
Gütersloh
Bielefeld
Teutoburger Wald
SENNE
Schloss Holte-Stukenbrock
Oerlinghausen
Detmold
Lage
Lemgo
Bad Salzuflen
Herford
Bünde
Löhne
Vlotho
Minden
Bückeburg
Lübbecke
Espelkamp
Petershagen
Rahden
Bad Essen
Melle
Wiehengebirge
Bramsche
Damme
Diepholz
Nienburg
Neustadt am Rübenberge
Wunstorf
Garbsen
Hannover
Laatzen
Pattensen
Sarstedt
Hildesheim
Springe
Bad Münder am Deister
Hameln
Rinteln
Stadthagen
Hessisch Oldendorf
Bad Pyrmont
Lügde
Blomberg
Horn-Bad Meinberg
Steinheim
Bad Driburg
Brakel
Höxter
Holzminden
Solling
OBERWÄLDER LAND
Beverungen
Warburg
Marsberg
Bad Arolsen
Korbach
Wolfhagen
Kassel
Baunatal
Hann. Münden
Witzenhausen
Hessisch Lichtenau
Melsungen
Fritzlar
Felsberg
Homberg
Bad Wildungen
Frankenberg
Burgwald
Schwalmstadt
Alsfeld
Bad Hersfeld
Bebra
Rotenburg an der Fulda
Hünfeld
Fulda
Vogelsberg
Schotten
Lauterbach
Grünberg
Nidda
Friedberg
Bad Nauheim
Butzbach
Usingen
Bad Homburg vor der Höhe
Oberursel
Wiesbaden
Mainz
Frankfurt am Main
Offenbach am Main
Hanau
Gelnhausen
Wächtersbach
Büdingen
Schlüchtern
Bad Brückenau
Aschaffenburg
Spessart
Gemünden am Main
Lohr am Main
Karlstadt
Bingen am Rhein
Rüdesheim
Taunus
Westerwald
Weilmünster
Dillenburg
Herborn
Haiger
Betzdorf
Altenkirchen
Wissen
Eitorf
Much
Overath
Rösrath
Düren

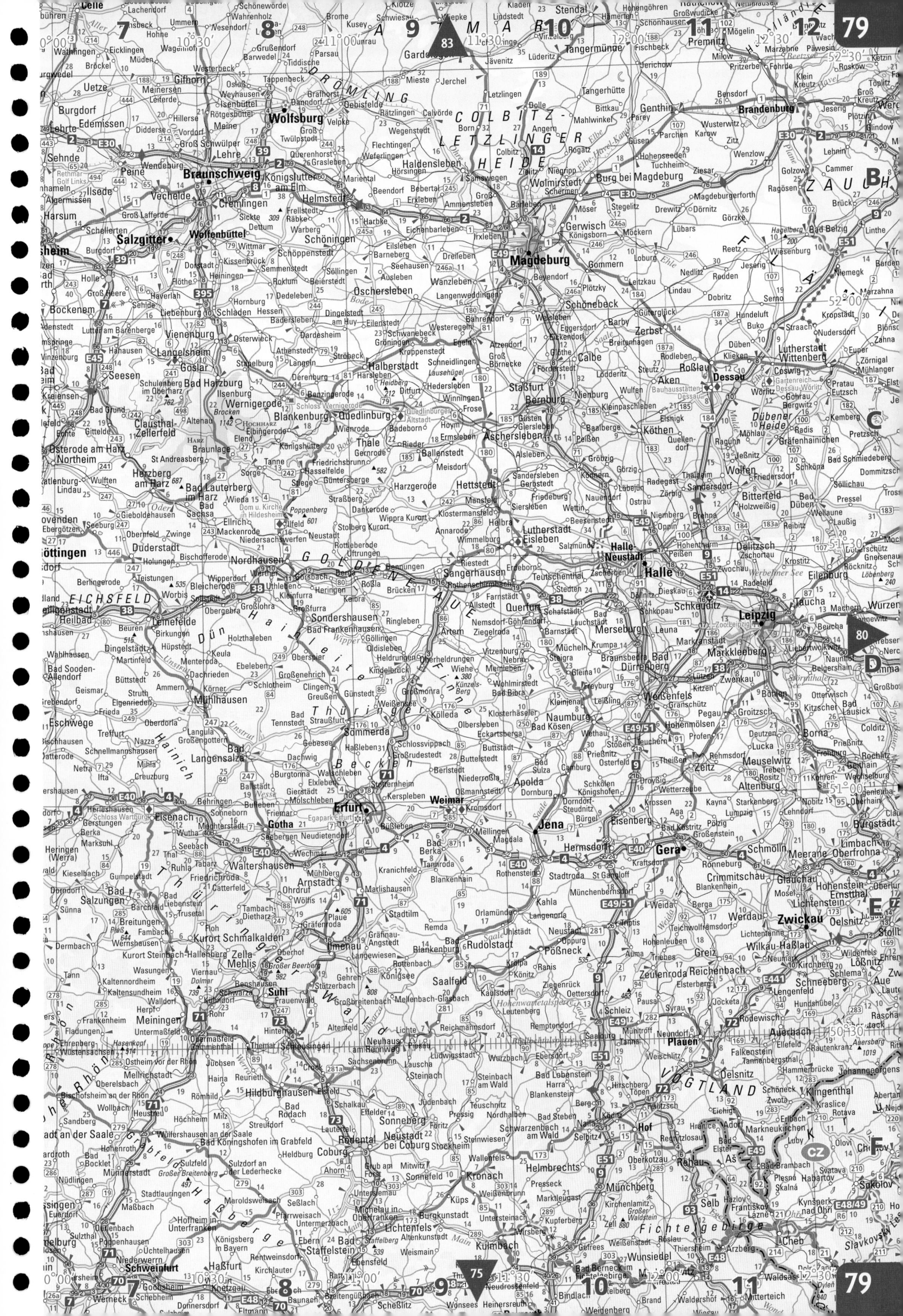
79
7
8
9
10
11
12
83
75
80
B
C
D
E
F
Celle
Stendal
Tangermünde
Premnitz
Rathenow
Gifhorn
Wolfsburg
DRÖMLING
COLBITZ-LETZLINGER HEIDE
Genthin
Brandenburg
Burgdorf
Lehrte
Sehnde
Peine
Braunschweig
Königslutter am Elm
Helmstedt
Haldensleben
Wolmirstedt
Burg bei Magdeburg
Salzgitter
Wolfenbüttel
Schöningen
Magdeburg
Schönebeck
Oschersleben
Zerbst
Goslar
Bad Harzburg
Wernigerode
Halberstadt
Quedlinburg
Blankenburg
Thale
Aschersleben
Staßfurt
Bernburg
Köthen
Dessau
Roßlau
Lutherstadt Wittenberg
Clausthal-Zellerfeld
Osterode am Harz
Northeim
Herzberg am Harz
Bad Lauterberg im Harz
Hettstedt
Lutherstadt Eisleben
Halle
Halle-Neustadt
Bitterfeld
Delitzsch
Eilenburg
Göttingen
Duderstadt
Nordhausen
Sangerhausen
GOLDENE AUE
Leipzig
Markkleeberg
EICHSFELD
Heilbad Heiligenstadt
Leinefelde
Worbis
Sondershausen
Querfurt
Merseburg
Schkeuditz
Taucha
Mühlhausen
Eschwege
Bad Langensalza
Sömmerda
Weißenfels
Naumburg
Borna
Zeitz
Hainich
Eisenach
Gotha
Erfurt
Weimar
Apolda
Jena
Eisenberg
Gera
Altenburg
Schmölln
Meerane
Crimmitschau
Glauchau
Zwickau
Arnstadt
Ilmenau
Bad Salzungen
Kurort Schmalkalden
Rudolstadt
Saalfeld
Pößneck
Greiz
Werdau
Reichenbach
Suhl
Zella-Mehlis
Meiningen
Hildburghausen
Sonneberg
Neuhaus am Rennweg
Plauen
Auerbach
Oelsnitz
VOGTLAND
Coburg
Neustadt bei Coburg
Kronach
Hof
Rehau
Selb
Münchberg
Kulmbach
Lichtenfels
Bad Staffelstein
Fichtelgebirge
Wunsiedel
Cheb
Aš
CZ
Sokolov
Schweinfurt
Haßfurt
Bad Neustadt an der Saale
Thüringer Wald
Thüringer Becken
Hainleite
Finne
Haßberge
Grabfeld
Rhön

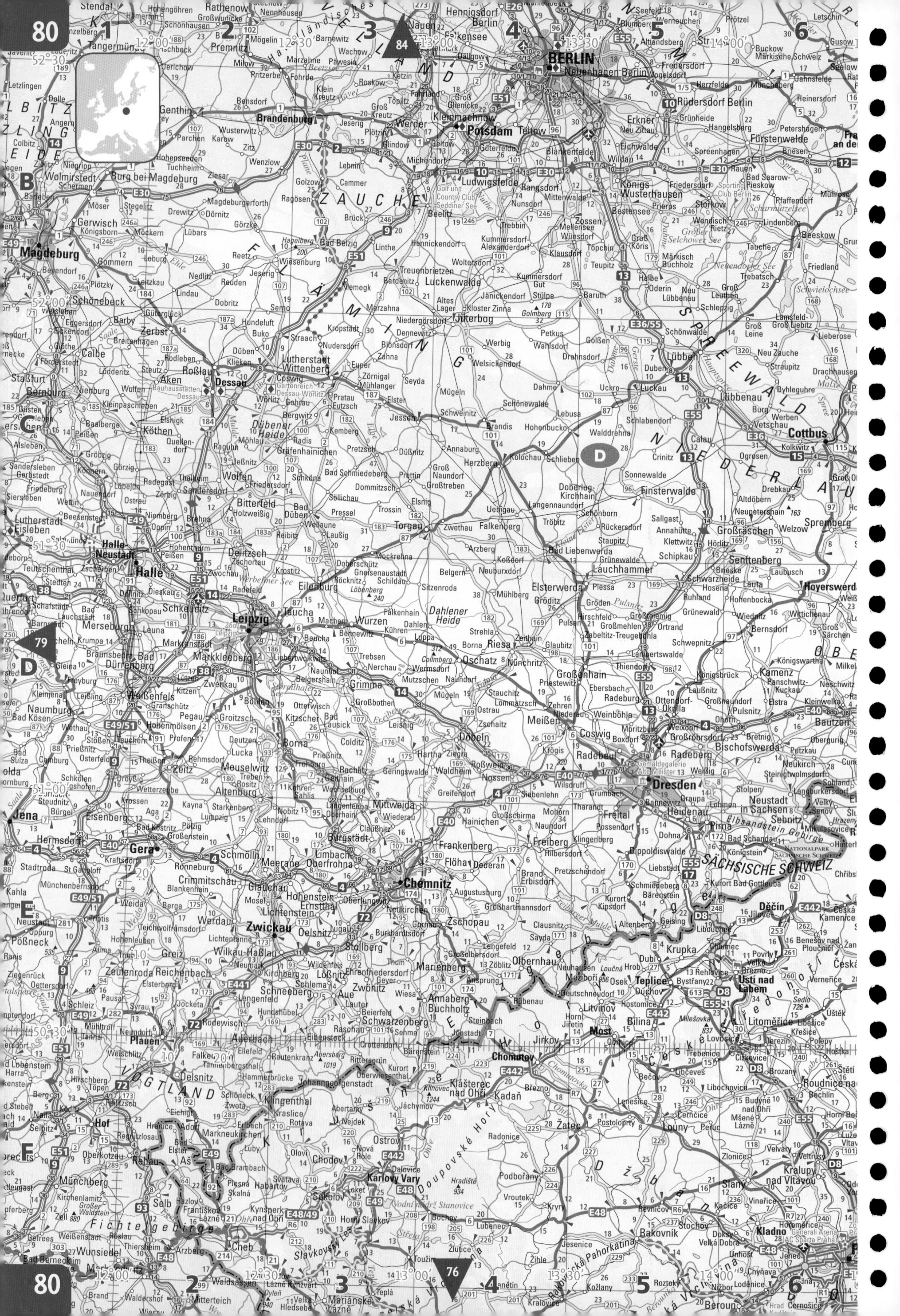

80
1
2
3
4
5
6
84
BERLIN
Potsdam
Brandenburg
Magdeburg
Dessau
Lutherstadt Wittenberg
Halle
Leipzig
Cottbus
Dresden
Chemnitz
Zwickau
Gera
Jena
Plauen
Hof
Cheb
Karlovy Vary
Chomutov
Most
Teplice
Ústí nad Labem
Kladno
Jüterbog
Luckenwalde
Torgau
Riesa
Meißen
Freiberg
Zeitz
Naumburg
Weißenfels
Merseburg
Bitterfeld
Köthen
Bernburg
Schönebeck
Eisleben
Lübben
Lübbenau
Finsterwalde
Elsterwerda
Hoyerswerda
Bautzen
Pirna
Děčín
Fürstenwalde
Beeskow
Spremberg
Senftenberg
Großenhain
Radebeul
Döbeln
Grimma
Wurzen
Eilenburg
Delitzsch
Altenburg
Greiz
Reichenbach
Aue
Annaberg-Buchholz
Marienberg
Žatec
Louny
Litoměřice
Rakovník
Sokolov
Selb
Wunsiedel
Münchberg
FLÄMING
ZAUCHE
SPREEWALD
NIEDERLAUSITZ
VOGTLAND
SÄCHSISCHE SCHWEIZ
Dübener Heide
Dahlener Heide
Fichtelgebirge
79
D
76
80
2
3
4
5
6

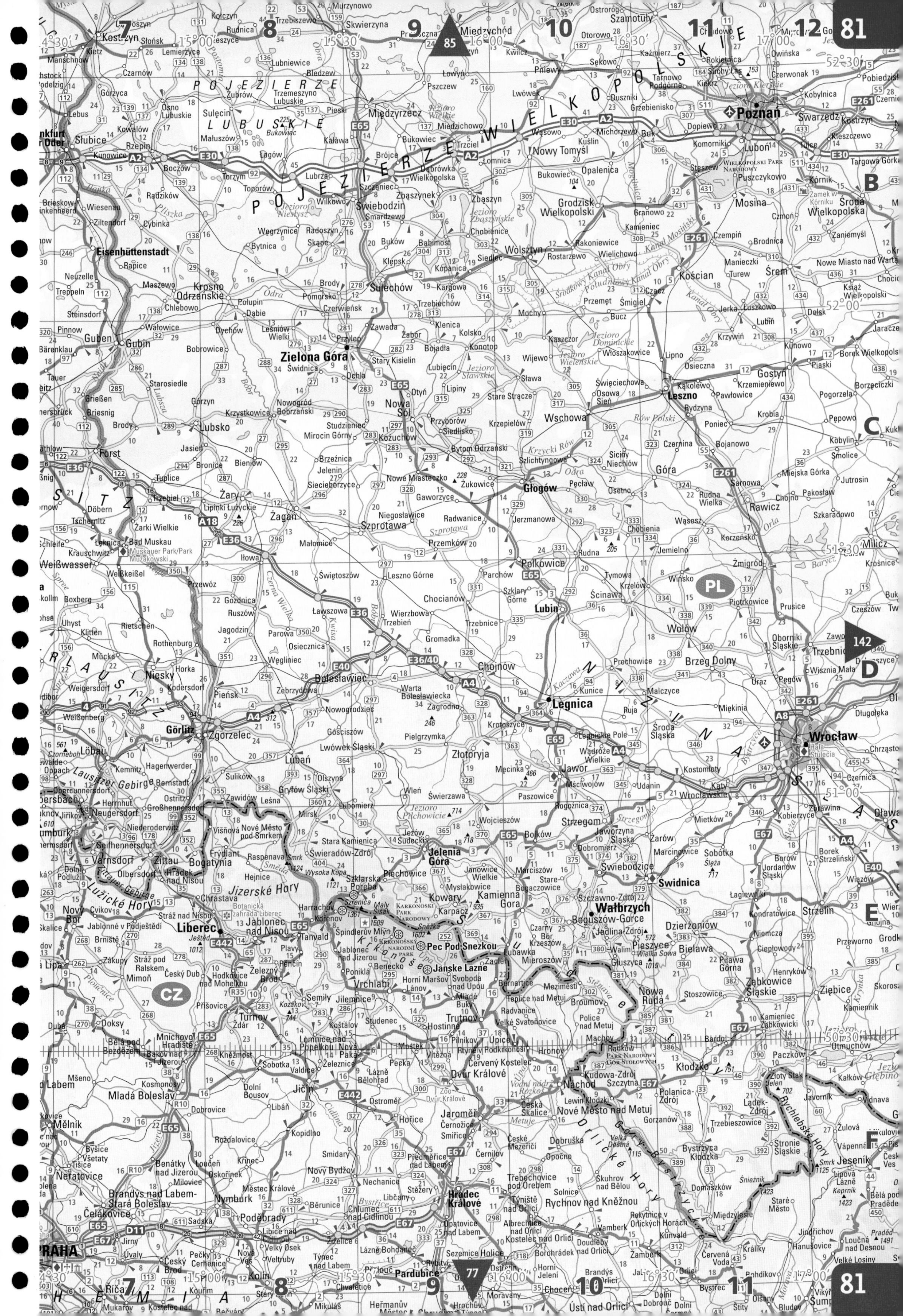

7
8
9
10
11
12
85
Międzychód
Szamotuły
Kostrzyn
Słońsk
Skwierzyna
Pniewy
Sękowo
Poznań
Swarzędz
Kostrzyn
POJEZIERZE LUBUSKIE
POJEZIERZE WIELKOPOLSKIE
WIELKOPOLSKIE
Frankfurt
Oder
Słubice
Rzepin
Sulęcin
Międzyrzecz
Trzciel
Nowy Tomyśl
Opalenica
Buk
Luboń
Stęszew
Mosina
Kórnik
Środa Wielkopolska
Świebodzin
Zbąszynek
Zbąszyń
Grodzisk Wielkopolski
Eisenhüttenstadt
Krosno Odrzańskie
Sulechów
Wolsztyn
Kościan
Śrem
Guben
Gubin
Zielona Góra
Nowa Sól
Leszno
Gostyń
Wschowa
Lubsko
Forst
Żary
Żagań
Szprotawa
Głogów
Góra
Rawicz
Milicz
Bad Muskau
Weißwasser
Iłowa
Polkowice
Lubin
Ścinawa
Wołów
Żmigród
PL
Oborniki Śląskie
Trzebnica
142
Niesky
Bolesławiec
Chojnów
Legnica
Brzeg Dolny
Wrocław
Görlitz
Zgorzelec
Lubań
Złotoryja
Jawor
Środa Śląska
Kąty Wrocławskie
Löbau
Zittau
Bogatynia
Jelenia Góra
Strzegom
Świebodzice
Świdnica
Sobótka
Wałbrzych
Dzierżoniów
Bielawa
Strzelin
Liberec
Jablonec nad Nisou
Tanvald
Karpacz
Kamienna Góra
Pec Pod Snezkou
Janske Lazne
Vrchlabí
Trutnov
Nowa Ruda
Ząbkowice Śląskie
Ziębice
CZ
Turnov
Česká Lípa
Mladá Boleslav
Jičín
Dvůr Králové
Náchod
Kłodzko
Polanica-Zdrój
Nové Město nad Metují
Jaroměř
Hořice
Mělník
Nový Bydžov
Hradec Králové
Rychnov nad Kněžnou
Bystrzyca Kłodzka
Stronie Śląskie
Jeseník
Nymburk
Poděbrady
Brandýs nad Labem-Stará Boleslav
PRAHA
Kolín
Pardubice
Ústí nad Orlicí
77
Karkonosze
Krkonoše
Góry Sowie
Orlické Hory
Góry Bystrzyckie
Rychlebské Hory
Jizerské Hory
Lužické Hory
Lausitzer Gebirge
LAUSITZ
NIZINA ŚLĄSKA
BOHEMIA
A2
E30
A4
E40
A18
E36
E65
E67
A8
E261
E442
B
C
D
E
F

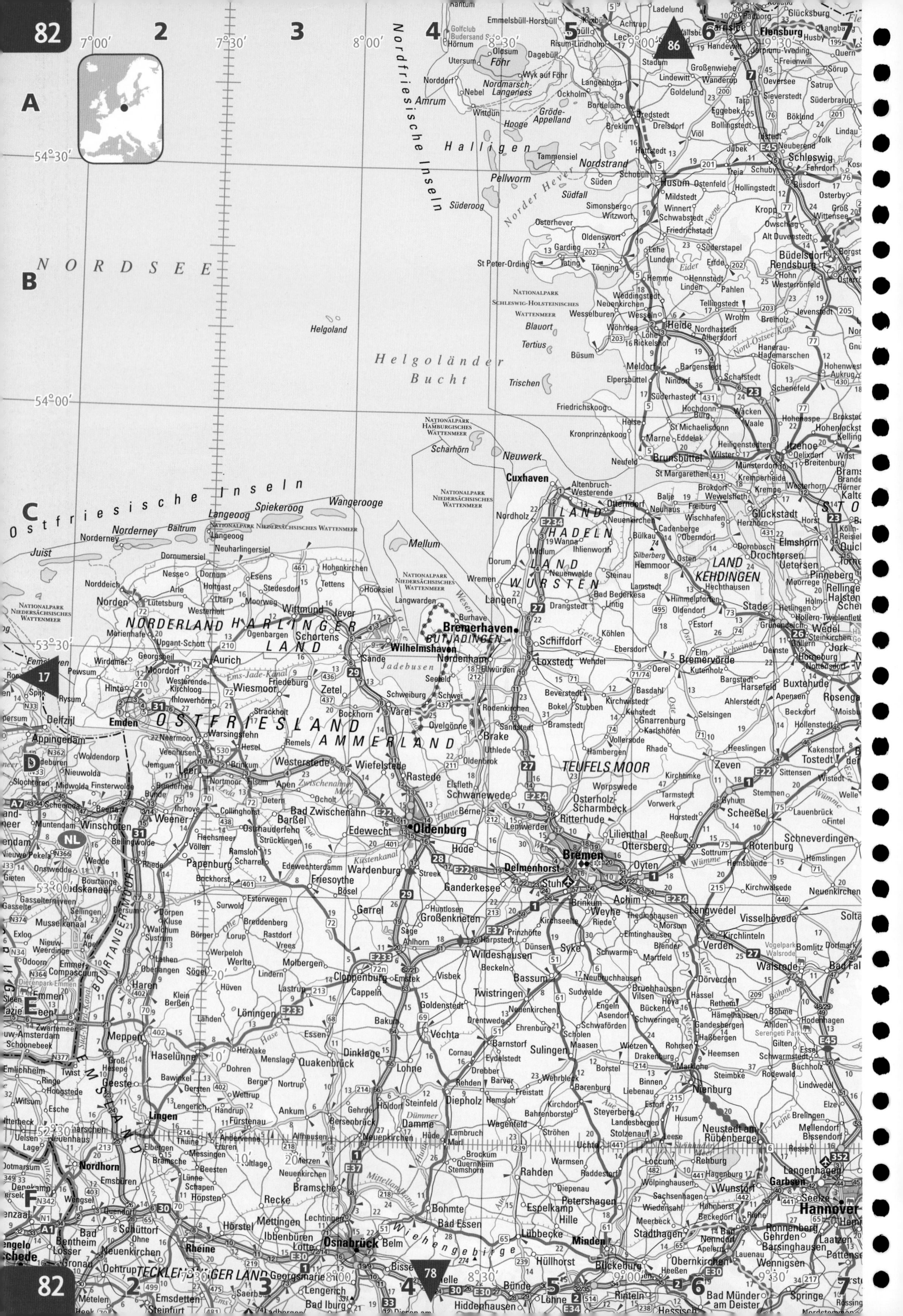

2
3
4
5
6
7
A
B
C
D
E
F
86
17
78
NL
N O R D S E E
Nordfriesische Inseln
Halligen
Föhr
Amrum
Pellworm
Nordstrand
Helgoland
Helgoländer Bucht
Ostfriesische Inseln
Juist
Norderney
Baltrum
Langeoog
Spiekeroog
Wangerooge
Mellum
Neuwerk
Scharhörn
Trischen
NATIONALPARK SCHLESWIG-HOLSTEINISCHES WATTENMEER
NATIONALPARK HAMBURGISCHES WATTENMEER
NATIONALPARK NIEDERSÄCHSISCHES WATTENMEER
NORDERLAND
HARLINGER LAND
OSTFRIESLAND
AMMERLAND
BUTJADINGEN
LAND HADELN
LAND WURSTEN
LAND KEHDINGEN
TEUFELS MOOR
EMSLAND
TECKLENBURGER LAND
Wiehengebirge
Jadebusen
Flensburg
Schleswig
Husum
Rendsburg
Heide
Itzehoe
Glückstadt
Elmshorn
Brunsbüttel
Cuxhaven
Bremerhaven
Wilhelmshaven
Emden
Aurich
Leer
Oldenburg
Delmenhorst
Bremen
Stade
Bremervörde
Zeven
Rotenburg
Verden
Walsrode
Nienburg
Cloppenburg
Vechta
Diepholz
Sulingen
Meppen
Lingen
Nordhorn
Rheine
Osnabrück
Minden
Wunstorf
Garbsen
Hannover
Springe
Bückeburg
Rinteln
Papenburg
Quakenbrück
Bramsche
Buxtehude
Achim
Syke
Wildeshausen
Tönning
Sankt Peter-Ording

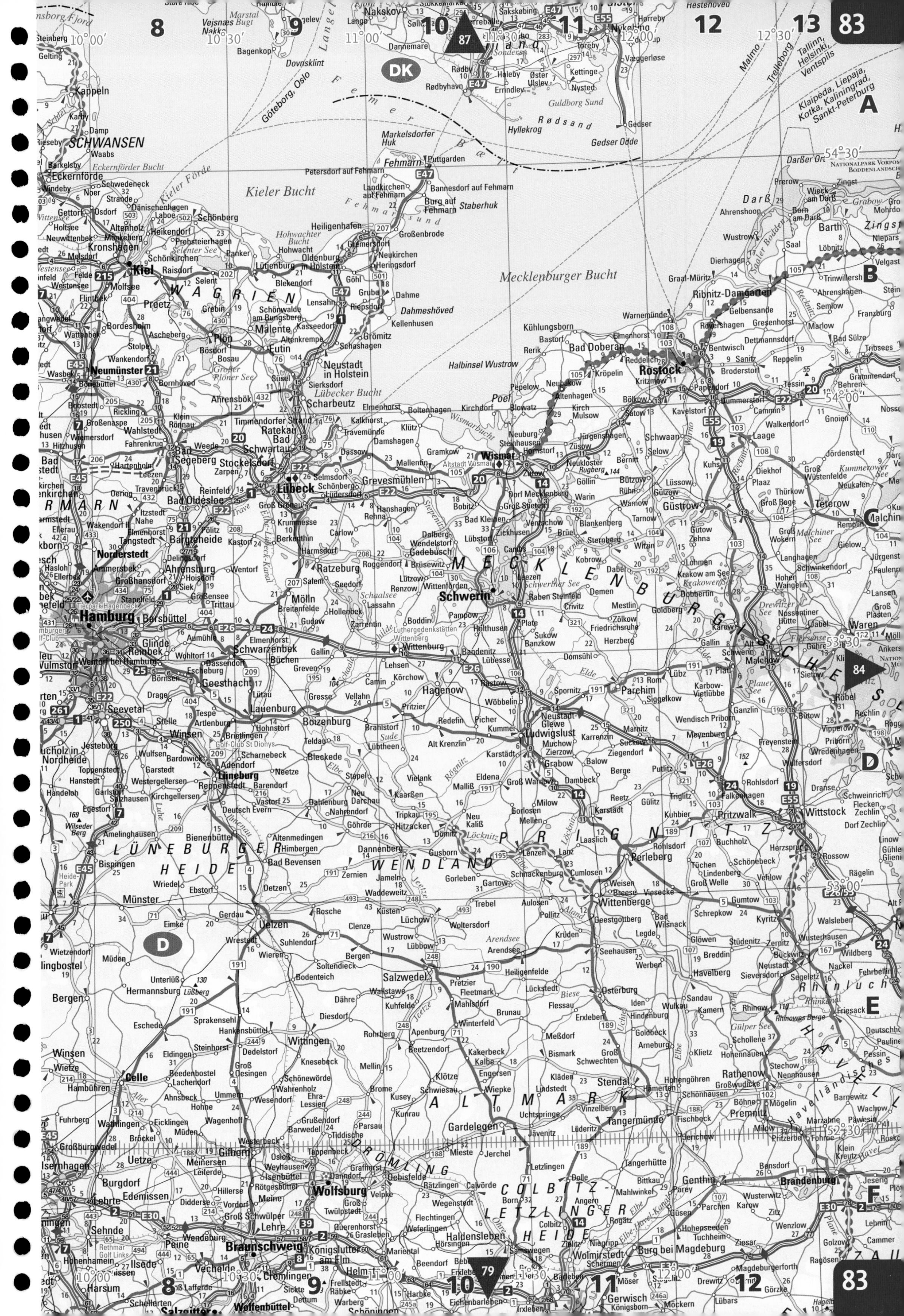
8
9
10
11
12
13
A
B
C
D
E
F
87
84
79
DK
D
10°00′
10°30′
11°00′
11°30′
12°00′
12°30′
54°30′
54°00′
53°30′
53°00′
52°30′
Fehmarn
Femer Bælt
Kieler Bucht
Mecklenburger Bucht
Lübecker Bucht
Halbinsel Wustrow
Nakskov
Sakskøbing
Nykøbing
Rødby
Rødbyhavn
Gedser
Gedser Odde
Guldborg Sund
Kappeln
SCHWANSEN
Eckernförde
Kiel
Kronshagen
Preetz
WAGRIEN
Plön
Eutin
Malente
Neumünster
Neustadt in Holstein
Heiligenhafen
Oldenburg in Holstein
Puttgarden
Burg auf Fehmarn
Scharbeutz
Bad Segeberg
Bad Oldesloe
Lübeck
Ratzeburg
Mölln
Norderstedt
Ahrensburg
Hamburg
Reinbek
Geesthacht
Lauenburg
Schwarzenbek
Winsen
Lüneburg
Buchholz in der Nordheide
Seevetal
LÜNEBURGER HEIDE
Munster
Uelzen
Celle
Wolfsburg
Gifhorn
Braunschweig
Peine
Wolfenbüttel
Salzgitter
Wismar
Schwerin
Rostock
Bad Doberan
Kühlungsborn
Warnemünde
Ribnitz-Damgarten
Graal-Müritz
Darß
Barth
Zingst
Güstrow
Teterow
Parchim
Ludwigslust
Hagenow
Boizenburg
Wittenberge
Perleberg
Pritzwalk
Wittstock
Waren
MECKLENBURGISCHE SEENPLATTE
PRIGNITZ
WENDLAND
Dannenberg
Salzwedel
Gardelegen
Stendal
Tangermünde
Rathenow
Brandenburg
Burg bei Magdeburg
ALTMARK
DRÖMLING
COLBITZ-LETZLINGER HEIDE
Haldensleben
Wolmirstedt
Helmstedt
Königslutter am Elm
Malmo
Trelleborg
Tallinn, Helsinki, Ventspils
Klaipėda, Liepaja, Kotka, Kaliningrad, Sankt-Peterburg
Göteborg, Oslo

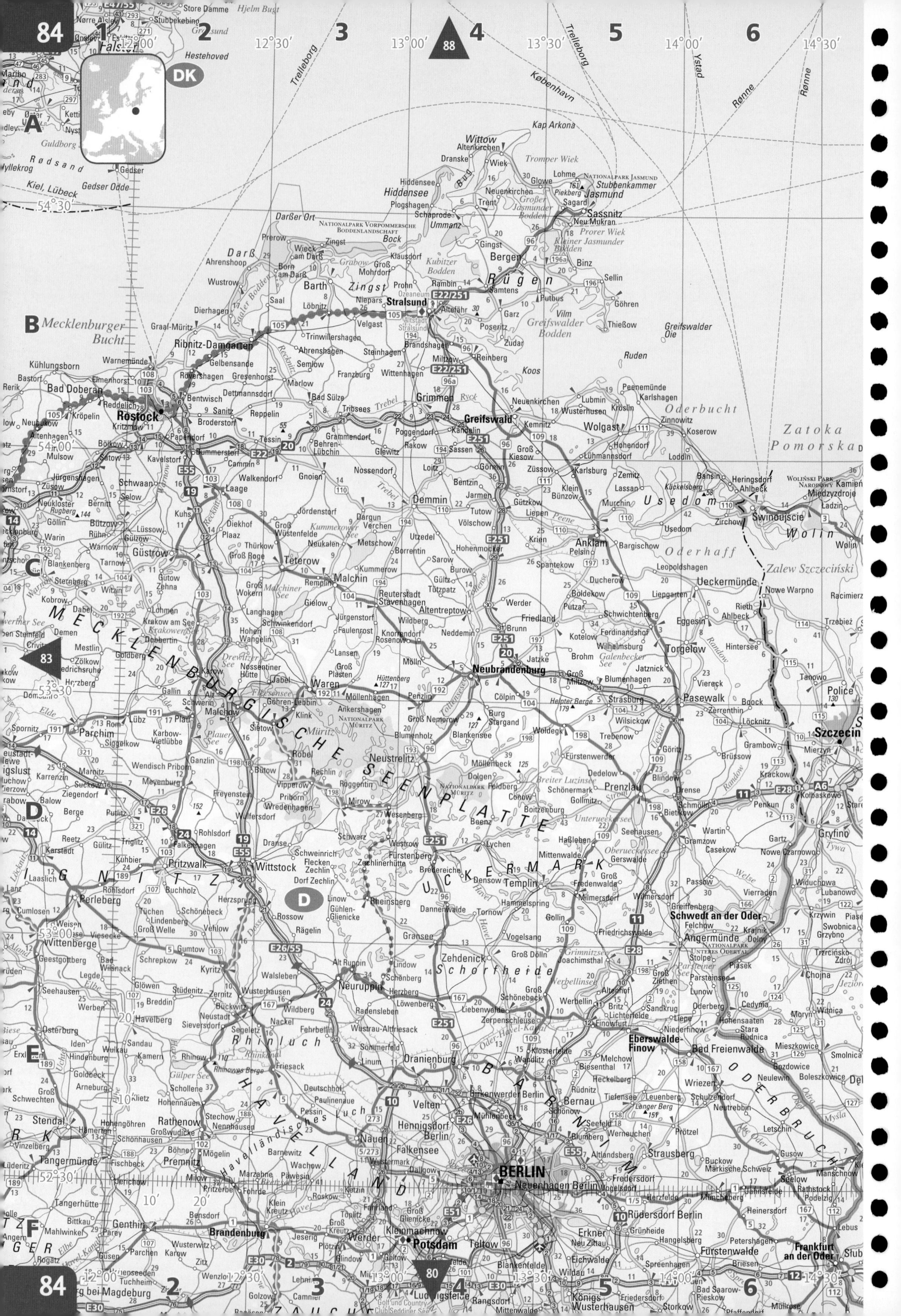
DK
88
1
2
3
4
5
6
12°00′
12°30′
13°00′
13°30′
14°00′
14°30′
Trelleborg
København
Ystad
Rønne
Kap Arkona
Wittow
Tromper Wiek
Hiddensee
Stubbenkammer
Jasmund
Sassnitz
Prorer Wiek
Rügen
Bergen
Binz
Sellin
Göhren
Putbus
Stralsund
Greifswalder Bodden
Greifswalder Oie
Ruden
Koos
Darßer Ort
Darß
Zingst
Barth
Prerow
Nationalpark Vorpommersche Boddenlandschaft
Mecklenburger Bucht
Gedser
Gedser Odde
Kiel, Lübeck
Rødsand
Guldborg
54°30′
A
B
C
D
E
F
Warnemünde
Rostock
Bad Doberan
Kühlungsborn
Ribnitz-Damgarten
Graal-Müritz
Grimmen
Greifswald
Wolgast
Peenemünde
Oderbucht
Zatoka Pomorska
Usedom
Heringsdorf
Ahlbeck
Świnoujście
Wolin
Międzyzdroje
Anklam
Oderhaff
Zalew Szczeciński
Ueckermünde
Nowe Warpno
Pasewalk
Police
Szczecin
Torgelow
Strasburg
Neubrandenburg
Demmin
Teterow
Malchin
Güstrow
Bützow
Schwaan
Laage
Tessin
Stavenhagen
Altentreptow
Friedland
Waren
Müritz
Nationalpark Müritz
Malchow
Plau
Parchim
Lübz
Goldberg
Sternberg
Mecklenburgische Seenplatte
Neustrelitz
Mirow
Wesenberg
Feldberg
Nationalpark Feldberg
Woldegk
Prenzlau
Templin
Lychen
Fürstenberg
Uckermark
Schwedt an der Oder
Angermünde
Nationalpark Unteres Odertal
Wittstock
Pritzwalk
Prignitz
Perleberg
Wittenberge
Kyritz
Neuruppin
Rheinsberg
Gransee
Zehdenick
Schorfheide
Eberswalde-Finow
Bad Freienwalde
Oderbruch
Oranienburg
Barnim
Bernau
Rhinluch
Havelland
Havelländisches Luch
Rathenow
Nauen
Falkensee
Hennigsdorf Berlin
BERLIN
Potsdam
Werder
Brandenburg
Genthin
Tangermünde
Stendal
Strausberg
Rüdersdorf Berlin
Erkner
Fürstenwalde
Frankfurt an der Oder
Königs Wusterhausen
Ludwigsfelde
Teltow
Kleinmachnow
Seelow
Kostrzyn
Chojna
Gryfino
Myślibórz
83
80
D
52°30′
53°00′
53°30′
54°00′
E22
E55
E251
E26
E28
E30
E51
A6
Kamień
Kolbaskowo
Lubanowo
Mieszkowice
Moryń
Cedynia

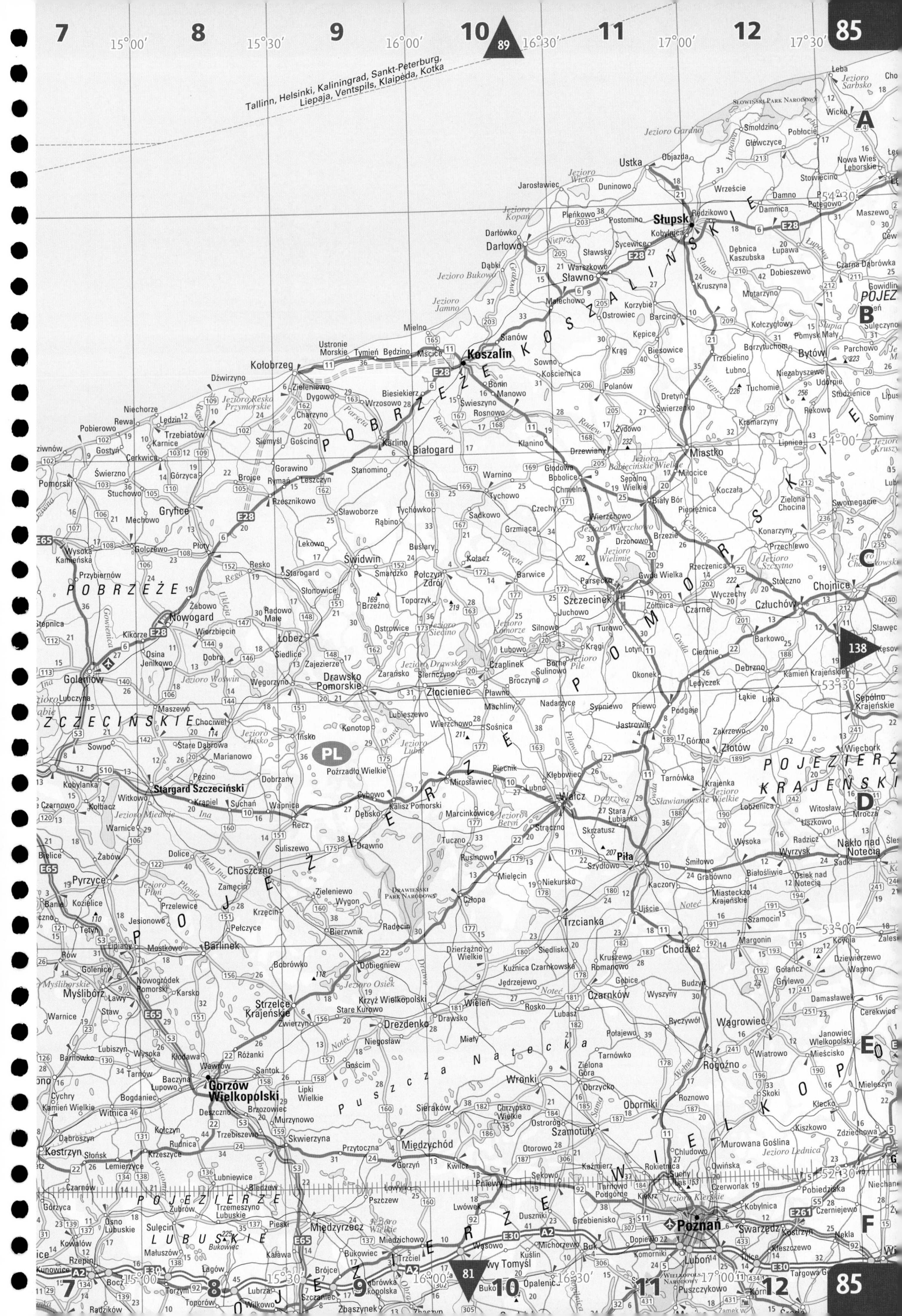
7
8
9
10
11
12
15°00′
15°30′
16°00′
16°30′
17°00′
17°30′
89
Tallinn, Helsinki, Kaliningrad, Sankt-Peterburg,
Liepaja, Ventspils, Klaipėda, Kotka
A
B
C
D
E
F
Łeba
Jezioro Sarbsko
Słowiński Park Narodowy
Jezioro Gardno
Smołdzino
Główczyce
Wicko
Ustka
Objazda
Nowa Wieś Lęborska
Jarosławiec
Jezioro Wicko
Duninowo
Wrzeście
Stowięcino
Damno
Potęgowo
Damnica
Maszewo
Jezioro Kopań
Pleńkowo
Postomino
Słupsk
Redzikowo
Kobylnica
Dargoleza
Darłówko
Darłowo
Sławsko
Sycewice
Dębnica Kaszubska
Łupawa
Dąbki
Jezioro Bukowo
Warszkowo
Sławno
Dobieszewo
Czarna Dąbrówka
Kruszyna
Motarzyno
Jezioro Jamno
Malechowo
Korzybie
Ostrowiec
Barcino
Kołczygłowy
Pomysk Mały
Sulęczyno
Mielno
Sianów
Kępice
Ustronie Morskie
Tymień
Będzino
Mścice
Koszalin
Krąg
Biesowice
Trzebielino
Borzytuchom
Bytów
Parchowo
Kołobrzeg
Sowno
Kościernica
Łubno
Niezabyszewo
Udorpie
Dźwirzyno
Zieleniewo
Dygowo
Biesiekierz
Bonin
Manowo
Polanów
Tuchomie
Studzienice
Jezioro Resko Przymorskie
Wrzosowo
Świeszyno
Rosnowo
Dretyń
Świerzenko
Rekowo
Niechorze
Rewal
Lędzin
Charzyno
Żydowo
Kramarzyny
Sominy
Pobierowo
Trzebiatów
Karnice
Siemyśl
Gościno
Karlino
Klanino
Lipnica
Gostyń
Cerkwica
Białogard
Drzewiany
Miastko
Górzyca
Brojce
Gorawino
Stanomino
Głodowa
Bobolice
Jezioro Bobięcińskie Wielkie
Miłocice
Pomorski
Świerzno
Stuchowo
Rymań
Leszczyn
Warnino
Chmielno
Sępolno Wielkie
Koczała
Tychowo
Biały Bór
Zielona Chocina
Swornegacie
Gryfice
Rzesznikowo
Sławoborze
Tychówko
Czechy
Pieniężnica
Mechowo
Rąbino
Sadkowo
Grzmiąca
Wierzchowo
Jezioro Wierzchowo
Konarzyny
Wysoka Kamieńska
Golczewo
Płoty
Lekowo
Buślary
Drzonowo
Brzezie
Przechlewo
Świdwin
Kołacz
Jezioro Wielimie
Rzeczenica
Jezioro Szczytno
Przybiernów
Resko
Starogard
Smardzko
Połczyn Zdrój
Barwice
Parsęcko
Gwda Wielka
POBRZEŻE
Słonowice
Szczecinek
Stołczno
Chojnice
Żabowo
Radowo Małe
Brzeżno
Toporzyk
Juchowo
Żółtnica
Wyczechy
Człuchów
Nowogard
Wierzbięcin
Łobez
Ostrowice
Jezioro Siecino
Jezioro Komorze
Silnowo
Czarne
Turowo
Barkowo
Kikorze
Osina
Dobra
Jenikowo
Siedlice
Zajezierze
Łubowo
Kragi
Lotyń
Cierznie
Goleniów
Jezioro Woświn
Węgorzyno
Drawsko Pomorskie
Zarańsko
Jezioro Drawsko
Sierniczyno
Czaplinek
Borne Sulinowo
Jezioro Pile
Okonek
Debrzno
Kamień Krajeński
Lubczyna
Broczyno
Ledyczek
Złocieniec
Sępólno Krajeńskie
Maszewo
Lubieszewo
Machliny
Nadarzyce
Sypniewo
Pniewo
Podgaje
Łąkie
Lipka
Chociwel
Konotop
Wierzchowo
Sośnica
Jastrowie
Zakrzewo
SZCZECIŃSKIE
Jezioro Ińsko
Ińsko
Stare Dąbrowa
Sowno
PL
Jezioro Lubie
Górzna
Złotów
Więcbork
Marianowo
Pożrzadło Wielkie
Piecnik
Kłębowiec
Tarnówka
Krajenka
POJEZIERZE KRAJEŃSKIE
Kobylanka
Pęzino
Dobrzany
Stargard Szczeciński
Cybowo
Mirosławiec
Lubno
Wałcz
Jezioro Sławianowskie Wielkie
Łobżenica
Witosław
Czarnowo
Kołbacz
Witkowo
Krąpiel
Suchań
Wapnica
Dębsko
Kalisz Pomorski
Marcinkowice
Jezioro Betyń
Stara Łubianka
Liszkowo
Jezioro Miedwie
Warnice
Recz
Tuczno
Strączno
Skrzatusz
Radzicz
Nakło nad Notecią
Bielice
Żabów
Suliszewo
Drawno
Piła
Wysoka
Wyrzysk
Śmiłowo
Sadki
Dolice
Choszczno
Rusinowo
Szydłowo
Białośliwie
Osiek nad Notecią
Pyrzyce
Jezioro Płoń
Zamęcin
Mielęcin
Niekursko
Kaczory
Grabówno
Miasteczko Krajeńskie
Banie
Kozielice
Przelewice
Zieleniewo
Wygoń
Drawieński Park Narodowy
Człopa
Ujście
Jesionowo
Krzęcin
Bierzwnik
Radęcin
Trzcianka
Szamocin
Tetyń
Pełczyce
Chodzież
Margonin
Lipiany
Mostkowo
Barlinek
Siedlisko
Kruszewo
Kcynia
Dzierżążno Wielkie
Kuźnica Czarnkowska
Romanowo
Gołańcz
Dziewierzewo
Golenice
Bobrówko
Dobiegniew
Grylewo
Wapno
Myśliborskie
Nowogródek Pomorski
Jezioro Osiek
Jędrzejewo
Gębice
Budzyń
Myślibórz
Karsko
Krzyż Wielkopolski
Czarnków
Wyszyny
Damasławek
Ławy
Staw
Strzelce Krajeńskie
Stare Kurowo
Wieleń
Rosko
Lubasz
Cerekwica
Warnice
Zwierzyn
Drezdenko
Drawsko
Byczywół
Wągrowiec
Połajewo
Janowiec Wielkopolski
Mieścisko
Lubiszyn
Wysoka
Kłodawa
Różanki
Niegosław
Mały
Puszcza Notecka
Tarnówko
Barnówko
Wawrów
Santok
Gościm
Zielona Góra
Rogoźno
Wiatrowo
Tarnów
Baczyna
Łupowo
Gorzów Wielkopolski
Lipki Wielkie
Wronki
Obrzycko
Skoki
Mieleszyn
Cychry
Kamień Wielki
Bogdaniec
Brzozowiec
Sieraków
Chrzypsko Wielkie
Oborniki
Roznowo
Kłecko
Witnica
Deszczno
Murzynowo
Ostroróg
Kiszkowo
Kołczyn
Trzebiszewo
Skwierzyna
Szamotuły
Zdziechowa
Dąbroszyn
Rudnica
Przytoczna
Międzychód
Otorowo
Murowana Goślina
Chludowo
Kostrzyn
Słońsk
Krzeszyce
Kwilcz
Kaźmierz
Rokietnica
Owińska
Jezioro Lednica
Lemierzyce
Lubniewice
Gorzyń
Sękowo
Suchy Las
Czerwonak
Czarnów
Bledzew
Pniewy
Tarnowo Podgórne
Kiekrz
Jezioro Kierskie
Pobiedziska
Niechanowo
POJEZIERZE LUBUSKIE
Pszczew
Lewice
Lwówek
Duszniki
Grzebienisko
Kobylnica
Czerniejewo
Górzyca
Ośno Lubuskie
Żubrów
Trzemeszno Lubuskie
Pieski
Międzyrzecz
Jezioro Wielkie
Poznań
Swarzędz
Kostrzyn
Nekla
Sulęcin
Miedzichowo
Wąsowo
Kuślin
Michorzewo
Buk
Dopiewo
Komorniki
Kleszczewo
Kowalów
Małuszów
Bukowiec
Kaława
Trzciel
Nowy Tomyśl
Opalenica
Luboń
Tolice
Kunowice
Rzepin
Łagów
Brójce
Dąbrówka Wielkopolska
Wielkopolski Park Narodowy
Puszczykowo
Targowa Górka
Boczów
Torzym
Lubrza
Szczaniec
Zbąszynek
Wilkowo
Toporów
Radzików
Zbąszyń
Wielkopolskie
POJEZIERZE WIELKOPOLSKIE
POJEZIERZE POMORSKIE
POBRZEŻE KOSZALIŃSKIE
138
81
E28
E65
E30
A2
S3
S5
S11
E261

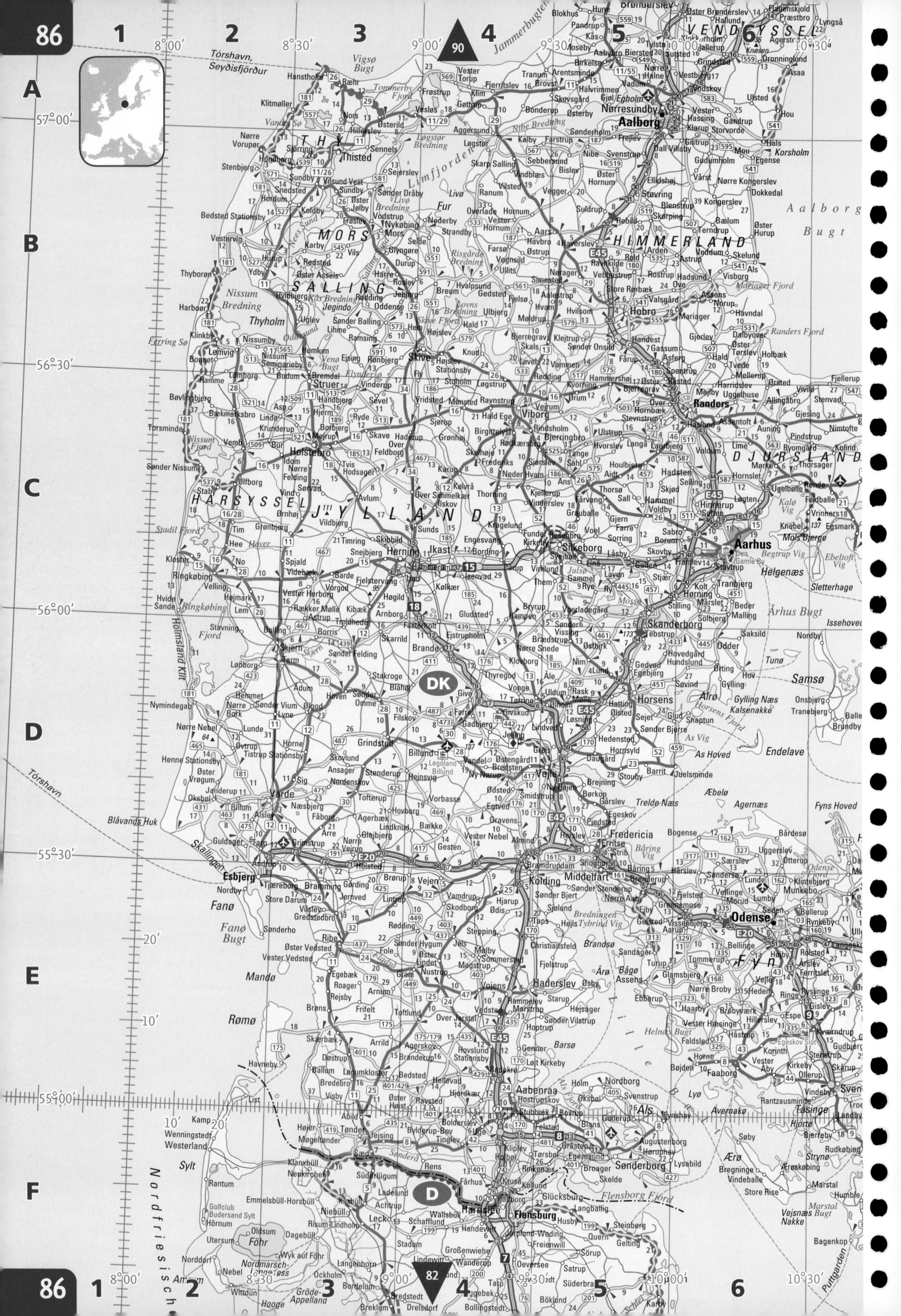

86
1
2
3
4
5
6
90
A
B
C
D
E
F
Tórshavn, Seyðisfjörður
Vigsø Bugt
Jammerbugten
VENDSYSSEL
Aalborg
Nørresundby
Thisted
THY
Limfjorden
MORS
Fur
SALLING
HIMMERLAND
Aalborg Bugt
Hobro
Mariager Fjord
Randers Fjord
Randers
Viborg
Skive
Struer
Holstebro
Lemvig
Nissum Bredning
Thyholm
Thyborøn
Ferring Sø
HARSYSSEL
JYLLAND
DJURSLAND
Silkeborg
Aarhus
Herning
Ikast
Ringkøbing
Stadil Fjord
Ringkøbing Fjord
Skjern
Brande
Skanderborg
Horsens
Horsens Fjord
Samsø
Helgenæs
Århus Bugt
DK
Billund
Legoland Billund
Grindsted
Vejle
Jelling
Varde
Blåvands Huk
Esbjerg
Fanø
Fanø Bugt
Ribe
Mandø
Rømø
Fredericia
Kolding
Middelfart
Odense
Fyn
Haderslev
Aabenraa
Sønderborg
Als
Tønder
Flensburg
Flensborg Fjord
D
Sylt
Westerland
Föhr
Niebüll
Husum
Nordfriesisch
Faaborg
Svendborg
Ærø
Marstal
Tåsinge
Helnæs Bugt
Lillebælt
Tórshavn
Skallingen
Holmsland Klit
82
86
1
2
3
4
5
6

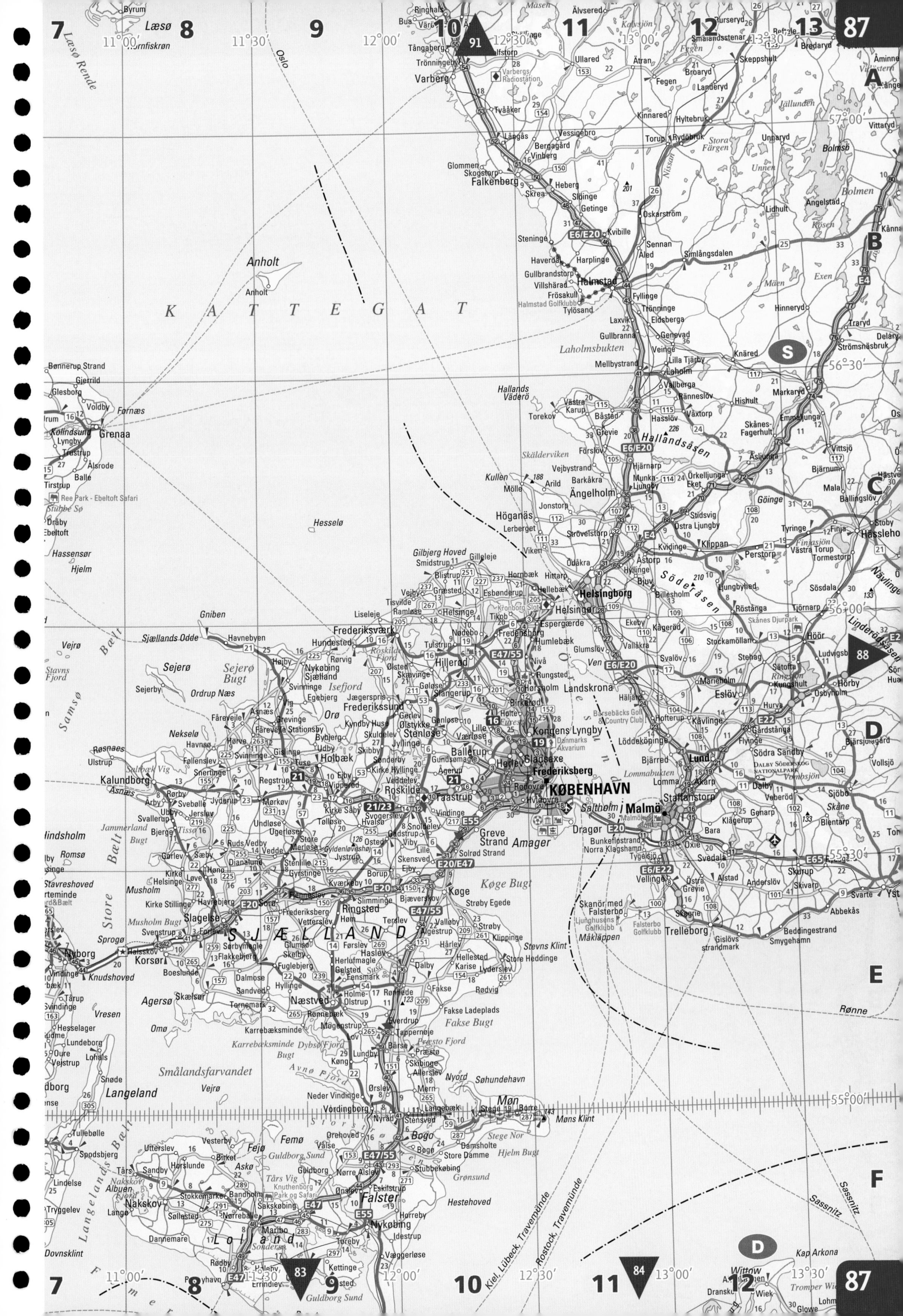
Læsø
Læsø Rende
Oslo
Varberg
Falkenberg
Halmstad
Anholt
K A T T E G A T
Laholmsbukten
Hallands Väderö
Grenaa
Hallandsåsen
Ängelholm
Höganäs
Kullen
Hesselø
Helsingborg
Helsingør
Söderåsen
Hässleholm
Hillerød
Frederiksværk
Frederikssund
Landskrona
Eslöv
Hörby
Lund
Malmö
KØBENHAVN
Frederiksberg
Kongens Lyngby
Gladsaxe
Herlev
Ballerup
Amager
Dragør
Saltholm
Roskilde
Holbæk
Kalundborg
Sejerø
Sejerø Bugt
Samsø
Slagelse
Korsør
Nyborg
S J Æ L L A N D
Køge
Køge Bugt
Ringsted
Næstved
Trelleborg
Falsterbo
Stevns Klint
Fakse Bugt
Vordingborg
Møn
Møns Klint
Smålandsfarvandet
Langeland
Falster
Nykøbing
Nakskov
L o l l a n d
Maribo
Kap Arkona
Sassnitz
Kiel, Lübeck, Travemünde
Rostock, Travemünde
Rønne
Ystad
Bolmen
Stora Färgen
Sjöbo
Skurup
Svedala
Vellinge
Staffanstorp
Kävlinge
Klippan
Höör

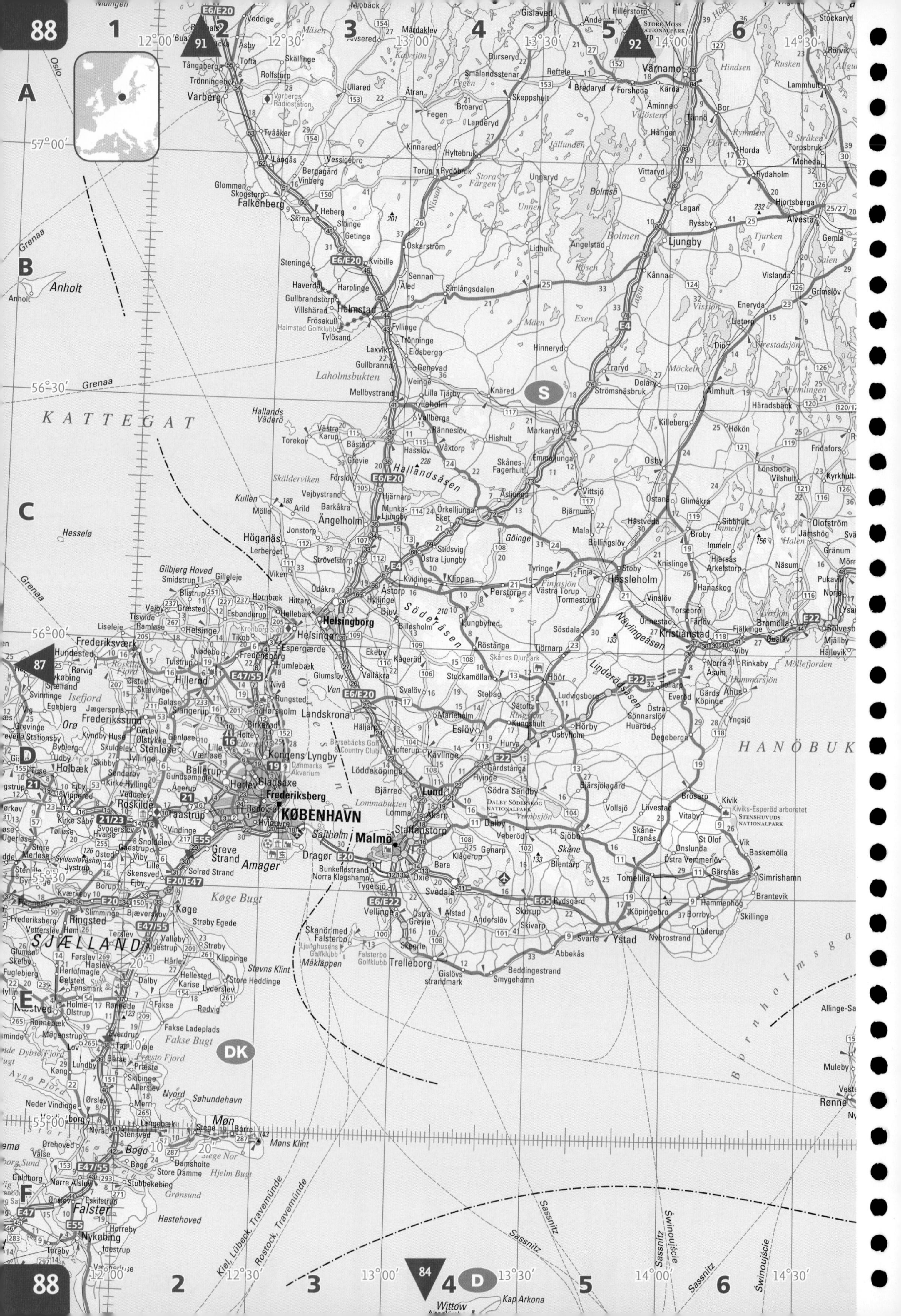

1
2
3
4
5
6
A
B
C
D
E
F
91
92
87
84
12°00′
12°30′
13°00′
13°30′
14°00′
14°30′
57°00′
56°30′
56°00′
55°30′
55°00′
KATTEGAT
HANÖBUK
S
DK
D
SJÆLLAND
Anholt
Hesselø
Varberg
Falkenberg
Halmstad
Laholmsbukten
Laholm
Hallandsåsen
Ängelholm
Höganäs
Helsingborg
Helsingør
Hillerød
Landskrona
Kongens Lyngby
Frederiksberg
KØBENHAVN
Malmö
Lund
Trelleborg
Ystad
Simrishamn
Kristianstad
Hässleholm
Ljungby
Värnamo
Alvesta
Markaryd
Eslöv
Höör
Hörby
Sjöbo
Tomelilla
Roskilde
Holbæk
Ringsted
Køge
Køge Bugt
Amager
Dragør
Næstved
Fakse Bugt
Møn
Falster
Nykøbing
Bolmen
Bolmsö
Söderåsen
Linderödsåsen
Nävlingeåsen
Osby
Olofström
Bromölla
Sölvesborg
Rønne
Kap Arkona
Wittow
Sassnitz
Świnoujście
Kiel, Lübeck, Travemünde
Rostock, Travemünde
Bornholmsgat
Grenaa
Oslo

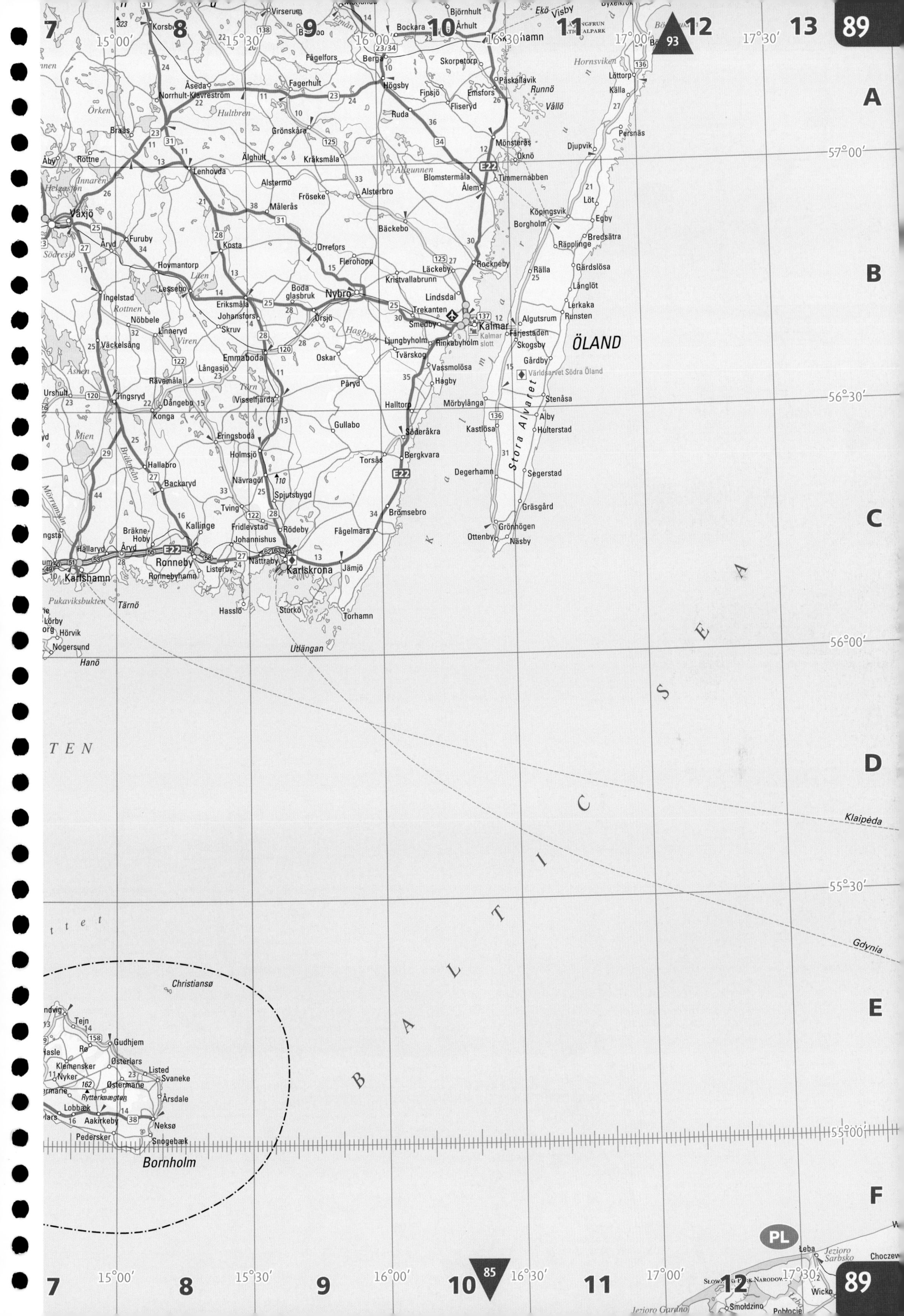
Växjö
Kalmar
Karlskrona
Karlshamn
Ronneby
Nybro
Emmaboda
Lessebo
Borgholm
Färjestaden
Mönsterås
Högsby
Ölland
Öland
Bornholm
Christiansø
Gudhjem
Svaneke
Neksø
Snogebæk
Årsdale
Hanö
Utlängan
Torhamn
Kalmar slott
Världsarvet Södra Öland
Stora Alvaret
BALTIC SEA
Klaipėda
Gdynia
Łeba
Wicko
Smołdzino
57°00′
56°30′
56°00′
55°30′
55°00′
15°00′
15°30′
16°00′
16°30′
17°00′
17°30′
A
B
C
D
E
F
7
8
9
10
11
12
13
93
85
PL

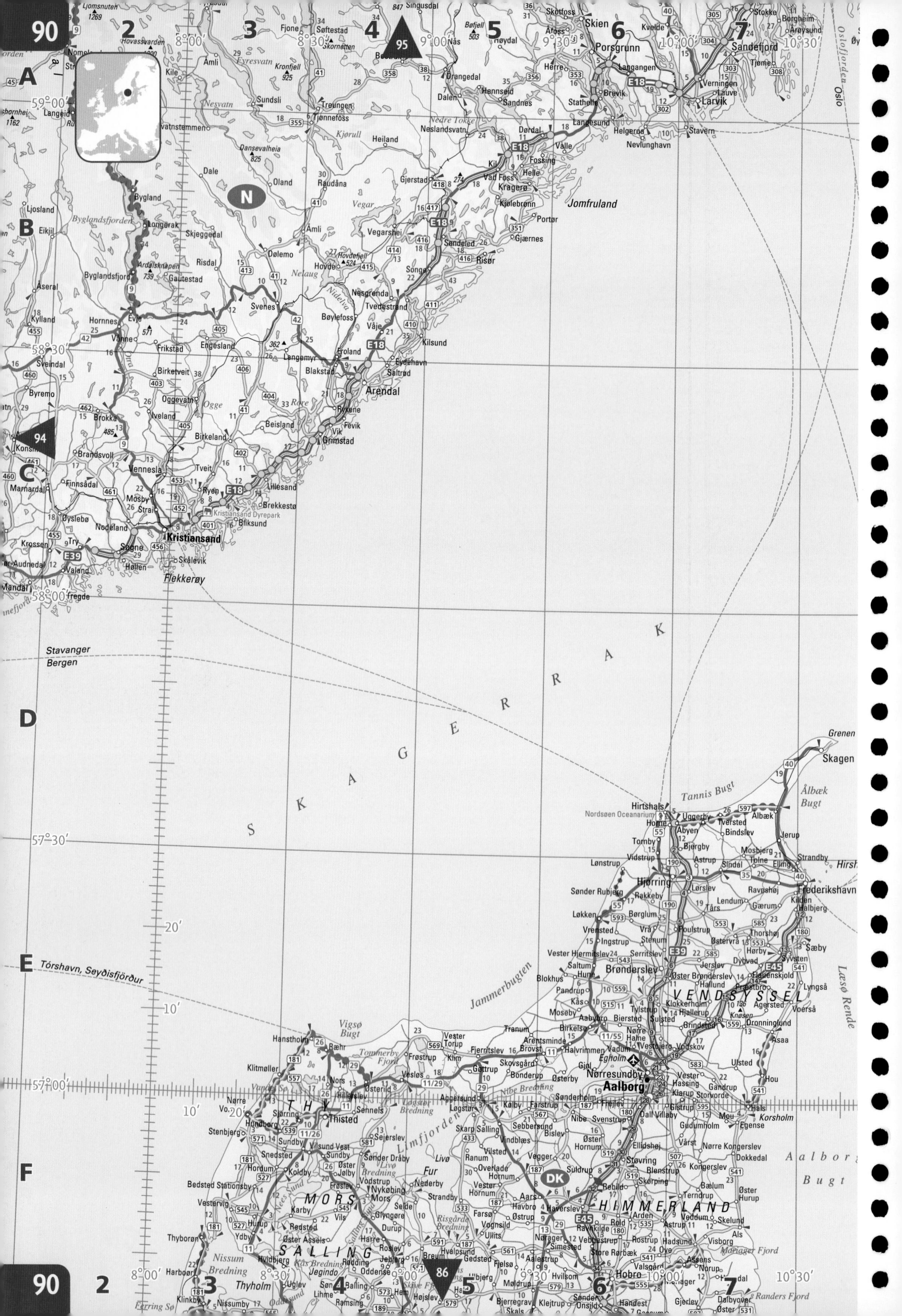
Skien
Porsgrunn
Sandefjord
Larvik
Langesund
Stavern
Kragerø
Jomfruland
Risør
Tvedestrand
Arendal
Grimstad
Lillesand
Kristiansand
Flekkerøy
Mandal
Vennesla
Evje
Bygland
Byglandsfjorden
Nesvatn
Nidelva
Stavanger
Bergen
S K A G E R R A K
Tórshavn, Seyðisfjörður
Jammerbugten
Skagen
Grenen
Hirtshals
Tannis Bugt
Ålbæk Bugt
Hjørring
Frederikshavn
Sæby
Brønderslev
Vendsyssel
Læsø Rende
Aalborg
Nørresundby
Limfjorden
Thisted
Thy
Mors
Salling
Himmerland
Hobro
Aalborg Bugt
Mariager Fjord
Randers Fjord
Hanstholm
Vigsø Bugt
Thyborøn
Nissum Bredning
Skive Fjord
DK
N
95
94
86
Oslofjorden
Oslo
59°00′
58°30′
58°00′
57°30′
57°00′
8°00′
8°30′
9°00′
9°30′
10°00′
10°30′
A
B
C
D
E
F
2
3
4
5
6
7

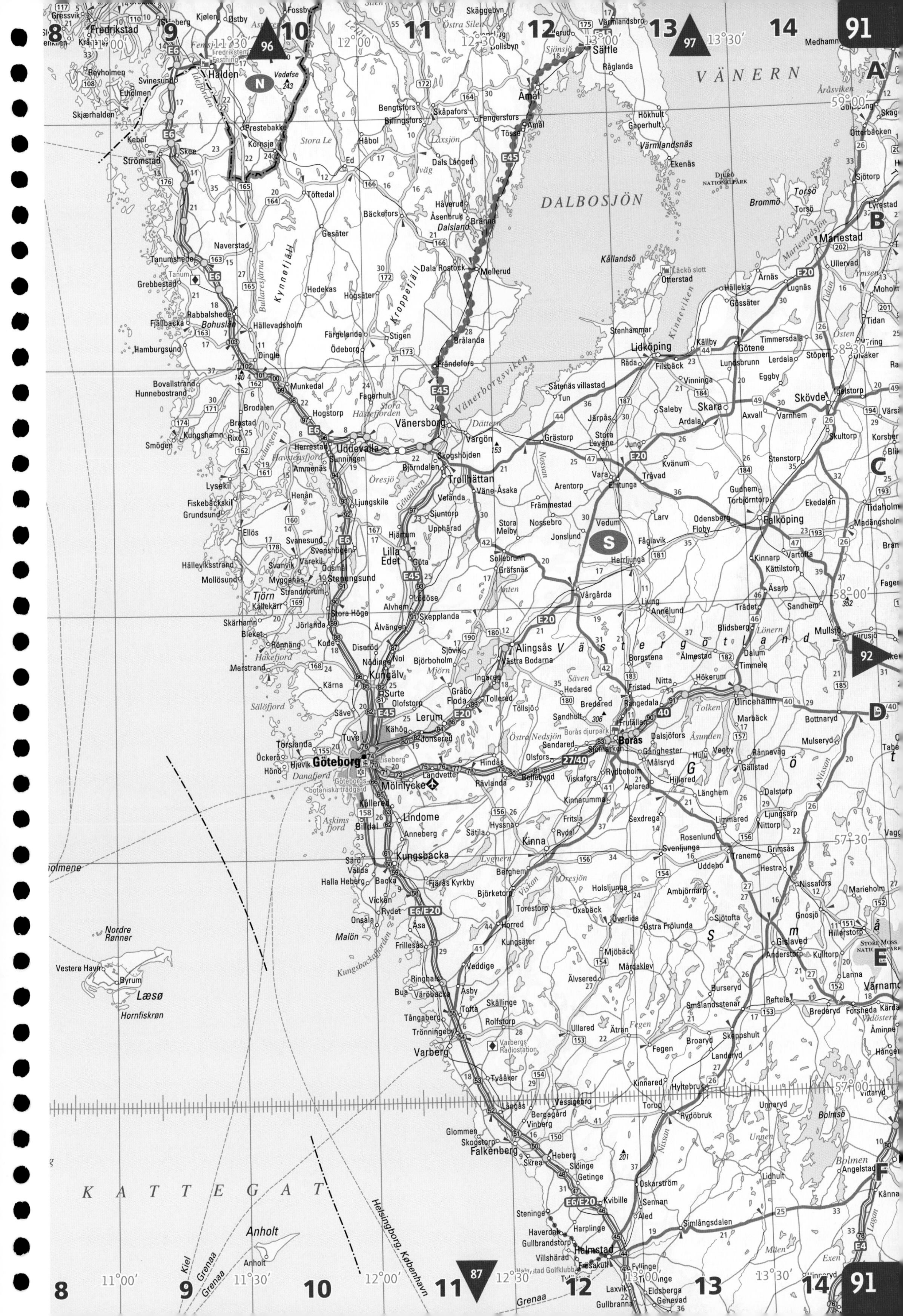

VÄNERN
DALBOSJÖN
KATTEGAT
Västergötland
Småland
Fredrikstad
Halden
Strömstad
Säffle
Åmål
Mariestad
Lidköping
Skövde
Skara
Götene
Falköping
Vänersborg
Trollhättan
Uddevalla
Lysekil
Stenungsund
Kungälv
Göteborg
Alingsås
Borås
Ulricehamn
Mölnlycke
Kungsbacka
Kinna
Varberg
Falkenberg
Halmstad
Gislaved
Värnamo
Tjörn
Läsø
Anholt
Vänerborgsviken
Kinneviken
Mellerud
Dals Långed
Bengtsfors
Munkedal
Tanumshede
Vårgårda
Herrljunga
Vara
Tranemo
Svenljunga
Lerum
Landvetter
Kattegat
Helsingborg, København
Grenaa
Kiel
N
S
E6
E20
E45
E6/E20
27/40
96
97
87
92
8
9
10
11
12
13
14
A
B
C
D
E
F

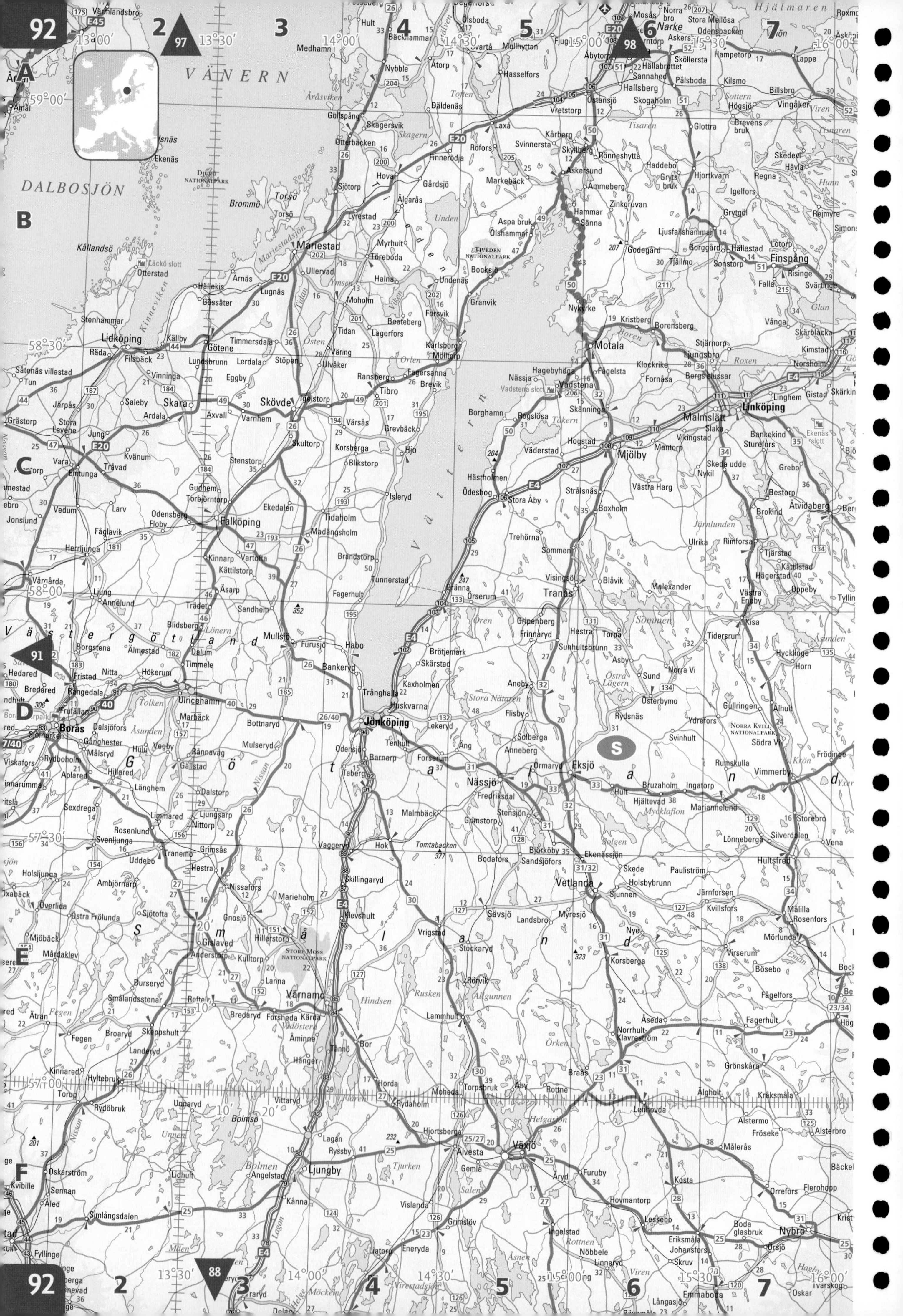
Vänern
Dalbosjön
Vättern
Hjälmaren
Djurö nationalpark
Tiveden nationalpark
Store Mosse nationalpark
Norra Kvill nationalpark
Västergötland
Götaland
Småland
Närke
Åmål
Mariestad
Lidköping
Skara
Skövde
Falköping
Borås
Ulricehamn
Jönköping
Huskvarna
Motala
Vadstena
Mjölby
Linköping
Finspång
Askersund
Hallsberg
Tranås
Nässjö
Eksjö
Vetlanda
Värnamo
Gislaved
Ljungby
Växjö
Alvesta
Vimmerby
Hultsfred
Nybro
Emmaboda
Gränna
Hjo
Tibro
Karlsborg
Laxå
Hova
Götene
Åtvidaberg
Kisa
Boxholm
Sävsjö
Lessebo
Kosta
Orrefors
92
2
3
4
5
6
7
A
B
C
D
E
F
97
98
91
88

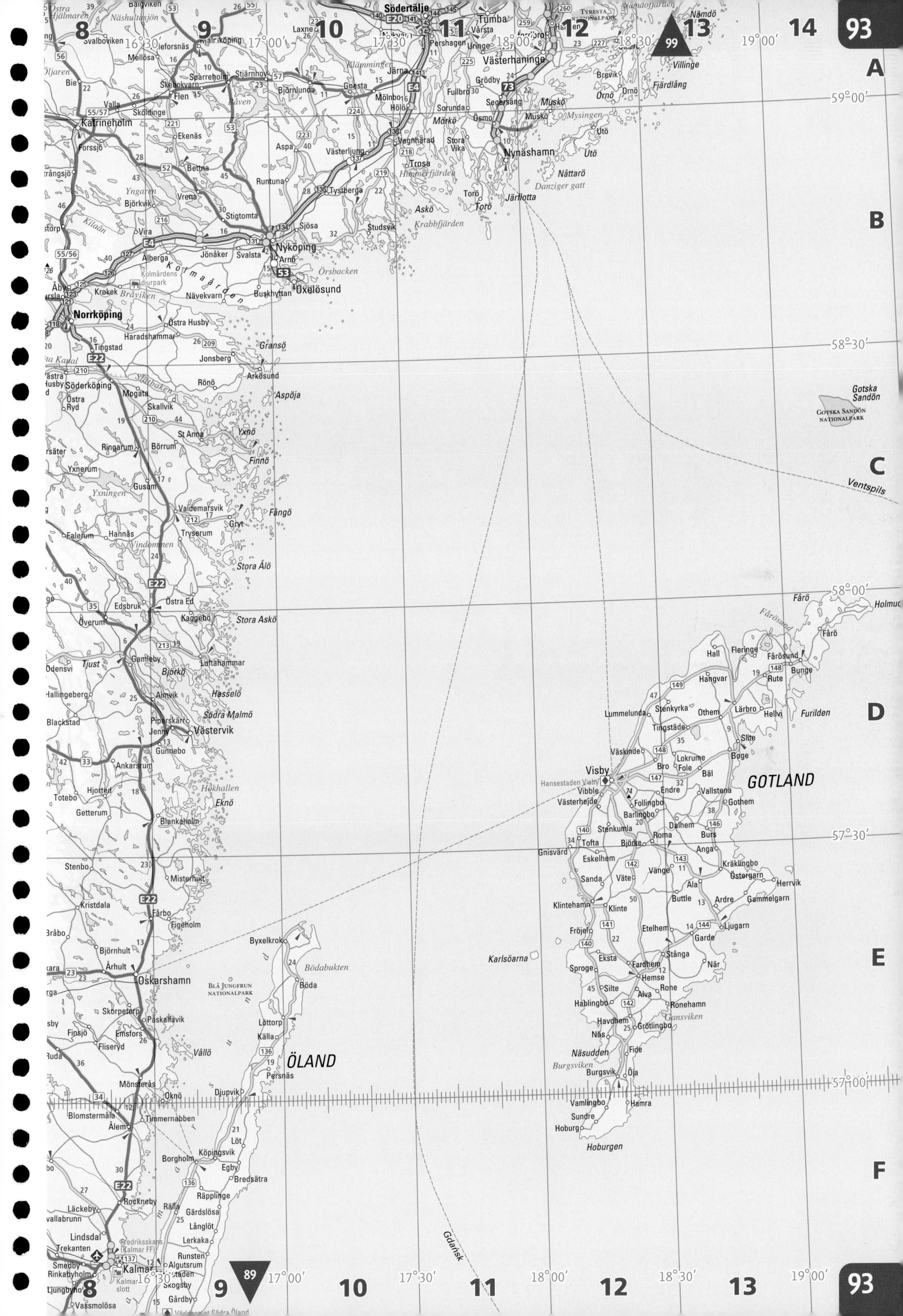

93
8
9
10
11
12
13
14
A
B
C
D
E
F
99
89
16°30′
17°00′
17°30′
18°00′
18°30′
19°00′
59°00′
58°30′
58°00′
57°30′
57°00′
Södertälje
Tumba
Vårsta
Västerhaninge
Nämdö
Villinge
Fjärdlång
Brevik
Ornö
Muskö
Mysingen
Utö
Nynäshamn
Nåttarö
Danziger gatt
Järflotta
Torö
Askö
Krabbfjärden
Trosa
Vagnhärad
Stora Vika
Sorunda
Mörkö
Ösmo
Segersäng
Gródby
Fullbro
Järna
Mölnbo
Hölö
Pershagen
Gnesta
Laxne
Björnlunda
Klämmingen
Västerljung
Tystberga
Aspa
Runtuna
Sjösa
Studsvik
Nyköping
Arnö
Örsbacken
Oxelösund
Buskhyttan
Nävekvarn
Svalsta
Jönåker
Stigtomta
Vrena
Bettna
Ekenäs
Flen
Sparreholm
Stjärnhov
Malmköping
Mellösa
Valla
Sköldinge
Katrineholm
Forssjö
Yngaren
Björkvik
Kilaån
Vira
Alberga
Kolmården
Kolmårdens djurpark
Krokek
Bråviken
Norrköping
Östra Husby
Haradshammar
Tingstad
Gransö
Jonsberg
Arkösund
Rönö
Aspöja
Söderköping
Mogata
Östra Ryd
Skallvik
St Anna
Yxnö
Finnö
Ringarum
Börrum
Yxnerum
Gusum
Yxningen
Valdemarsvik
Gryt
Fångö
Tryserum
Falerum
Hannäs
Vindommen
Stora Alö
Östra Ed
Edsbruk
Överum
Kaggebo
Stora Askö
Gamleby
Loftahammar
Tjust
Odensvi
Björkö
Hallingeberg
Almvik
Hasselö
Blackstad
Södra Malmö
Piperskärr
Jenny
Västervik
Gunnebo
Ankarsrum
Hjorted
Totebo
Hökhallen
Eknö
Getterum
Blankaholm
Stenbo
Misterhult
Kristdala
Fårbo
Figeholm
Björnhult
Århult
Oskarshamn
Blå Jungfrun Nationalpark
Byxelkrok
Bödabukten
Böda
Skorpetorp
Påskallavik
Emsfors
Fliseryd
Finsjö
Vållö
Löttorp
Källa
Persnäs
ÖLAND
Mönsterås
Djupvik
Timmernabben
Blomstermåla
Ålem
Löt
Köpingsvik
Borgholm
Egby
Bredsätra
Räpplinge
Rockneby
Rälla
Gärdslösa
Långlöt
Läckeby
Lindsdal
Trekanten
Lerkaka
Runsten
Algutsrum
Smedby
Rinkabyholm
Kalmar
Kalmar slott
Ljungbyholm
Vassmolösa
Skogsby
Gårdby
Gdansk
Ventspils
Gotska Sandön
Gotska Sandön Nationalpark
Fårö
Holmuddens
Fårösund
Hall
Fleringe
Bunge
Rute
Hangvar
Lummelunda
Stenkyrka
Othem
Lärbro
Hellvi
Furilden
Tingstäde
Slite
Väskinde
Lokrume
Bøge
Visby
Bro
Fole
Bäl
GOTLAND
Hansestaden Visby
Vibble
Västerhejde
Endre
Vallstena
Gothem
Follingbo
Barlingbo
Dalhem
Stenkumla
Roma
Tofta
Björke
Burs
Gnisvärd
Anga
Eskelhem
Kräklingbo
Östergarn
Herrvik
Sanda
Väte
Vänge
Ala
Buttle
Ardre
Gammelgarn
Klintehamn
Klinte
Ljugarn
Fröjel
Etelhem
Garde
Karlsöarna
Eksta
Stånga
Sproge
Fardhem
När
Hemse
Silte
Alva
Rone
Hablingbo
Ronehamn
Havdhem
Gansviken
Grötlingbo
Näs
Näsudden
Fide
Burgsviken
Burgsvik
Öja
Vamlingbo
Hamra
Sundre
Hoburg
Hoburgen
E4
E20
E22

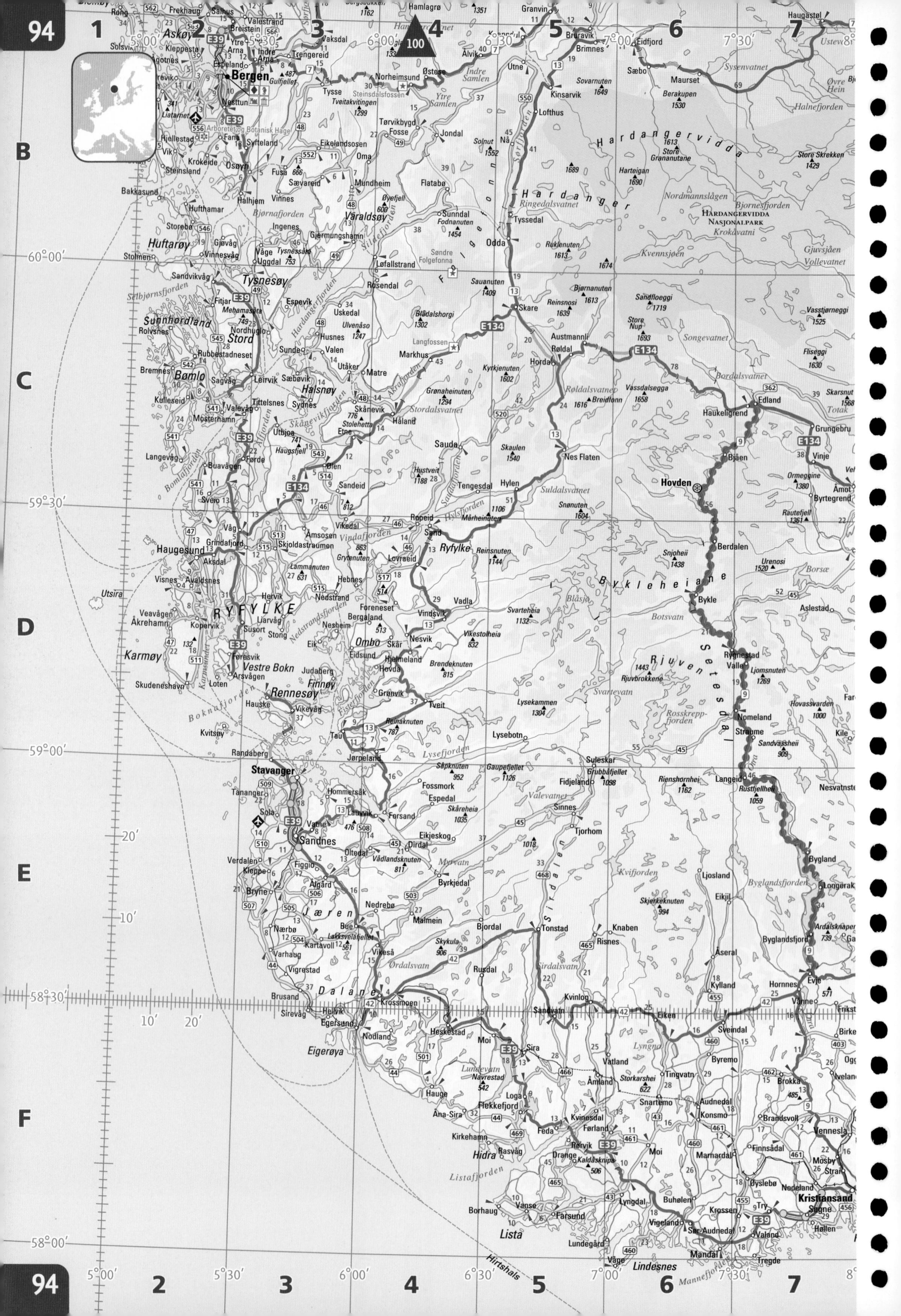

1
2
3
4
5
6
7
B
C
D
E
F
100
Askøy
Bergen
Kleppestø
Espeland
Arna
Ytre Arna
Indre Arna
Breistein
Valestrand
Salhus
Frekhaug
Rong
Trengereid
Vaksdal
Hamlagrø
Granvin
Bruravik
Brimnes
Eidfjord
Haugastøl
Ustevatn
Sæbø
Maurset
Sysenvatnet
Øvre Hein
Halnefjorden
Norheimsund
Øystese
Ålvik
Indre Samlen
Ytre Samlen
Utne
Kinsarvik
Lofthus
Sovarnuten 1649
Berakupen 1530
Tysse
Steinsdalsfossen
Tveitakvitingen 1299
Gulfjellet 487
Nesttun
Liataren 341
Arboretet og Botanisk Hage
Hjellestad
Fana
Sylteland
Vik
Krokeide
Steinsland
Os
Fusa
Eikelandsosen
Oma
Tørvikbygd
Fosse
Jondal
Solnut 1552
Nå
Hardangervidda
Store Grananutane 1613
Store Skrekken 1429
Harteigan 1690
1689
Sævareid
Mundheim
Flatabø
Bakkasund
Halhjem
Vinnes
Hufthamar
Storebø
Huftarøy
Gjøvåg
Vinnesvåg
Stolmen
Bjørnafjorden
Øyefjell 600
Våraldsøy
Ingenes
Gjermundshamn
Sunndal
Fodnanuten 1454
Hardanger
Ringedalsvatnet
Tyssedal
Nordmannslågen
Bjornesfjorden
Hardangervidda Nasjonalpark
Krokavatni
Odda
Ruklenuten 1613
Kvennsjøen
Gjuvsjåen
Vollevatnet
Søndre Folgefonna
Folgefonna
Våge
Tysnessåta 753
Uggdal
Tysnesøy
Løfallstrand
Rosendal
Sauanuten 1409
1674
Bjørnanuten 1613
Sandfloeggi 1719
Sandvikvåg
Selbjørnsfjorden
Fitjar
Mehamasåta 749
Sunnhordland
Rolvsnes
Nordhuglo
Stord
Espevik
Uskedal
Ulvenåso 1247
Hardangerfjorden
Skare
Reinsnosi 1639
Blådalshorgi 1302
Store Nup 1693
Vasstjørneggi 1525
Songevatnet
Rubbestadneset
Bremnes
Bømlo
Sagvåg
Leirvik
Husnes
Sunde
Valen
Langfossen
Markhus
Austmannli
Røldal
Horda
Fiseggi 1630
Utåker
Matre
Sæbøvik
Halsnøy
Kyrkjenuten 1602
Bordalsvatnet
Kulleseid
Tittelsnes
Sydnes
Skånevik
Stolehetta 776
Etne
Håland
Grønaheinuten 1294
Røldalsvatnet 1616
Breidfonn
Vassdalsegga 1658
Haukeligrend
Edland
Skarsnut 1568
Totak
Valevåg
Mosterhamn
Skånevikfjorden
Stordalsvatnet
Grungebu
Vinje
Langevåg
Utbjoa 741
Haugsfjell
Førde
Ølen
Sauda
Skaulen 1540
Nes Flaten
Bjåen
Bømlafjorden
Buavågen
Sandeid
Hustveit 1188
Tengesdal
Hylen
Hovden
Ormeggine 1380
Åmot
Byrtegrend
Sveio
812
Suldalsvatnet
Snønuten 1604
Rautefjell 1361
Vikedal
Vindafjorden
Ropeid
Sand
Hylsfjorden
Mårheinuten 1106
Våg
Grindafjord
Haugesund
Åmsosen
Skjoldastraumen
863
Grytenuten
Lovraeid
Ryfylke
Reinsnuten 1144
Berdalen
Snjoheii 1438
Urenosi 1520
Borsæ
Aksdal
Lammanuten 631
Hebnes
Nedstrand
Bykleheiane
Visnes
Avaldsnes
Utsira
Hervik
Vadla
Blåsjø
Bykle
Aslestad
Veavågen
Åkrehamn
Kopervik
RYFYLKE
Liarvåg
Foreneset
Bergaland
Vindsvik
Svartehela 1132
Botsvatn
Nesheim
513
Nedstrandsfjorden
Sørvik
Stong
Eik
Ombo
Skår
Nesvik
Vikestolheia 832
Karmøy
Eidsund
Hjelmeland
Brendeknuten 815
Rjuven
Setesdal
Rjuvbrokkene 1443
Rysstad
Valle
Ljomsnuten 1269
Skudeneshavn
Loten
Førrevik
Vestre Bokn
Arsvågen
Judaberg
Finnøy
Hovda
Grønvik
Svartevatn
Rennesøy
Hauske
Vikevåg
Boknafjorden
Tveit
Lysekammen 1304
Rosskrepp-fjorden
Nomeland
Hovassvarden 1000
Kvitsøy
Tau
Reinaknuten 787
Lysebotn
Straume
Sandvassheii 909
Kile
Randaberg
Jørpeland
Lysefjorden
Suleskar
Grubbåfjellet 1098
Fidjeland
Rjenshornhei 1162
Langeid
Rustfjellheii 1059
Nesvatnstemmen
Stavanger
Tananger
Hommersåk
Såpknuten 952
Gaupefjellet 1126
Fossmork
Valevatnet
Espedal
Skåreheia 1035
Sinnes
Sola
Lauvvik
Forsand
Tjorhom
Vatne
476
Sandnes
Eikjeskog
Dirdal
1018
Verdalen
Kleppe
Oltedal
Vådlandsknuten 811
Myrvatn
Byrkjedal
Sirdalen
Kvifjorden
Bygland
Figgjo
Ålgård
Bryne
Jøsland
Byglandsfjorden
Longerak
Eikjil
Skjerkeknuten 994
Jæren
Nedrebø
Malmein
Nærbø
Bue
Kartavoll
Lakksvelafjellet 561
Bjordal
Tonstad
Knaben
Risnes
Ardalsknapen 739
Byglandsfjord
Varhaug
Vikeså
Skykula 906
Ørdalsvatn
Sirdalsvatn
Åseral
Vigrestad
Rusdal
Kylland
Hornnes
Evje
Brusand
Dalane
Krossmoen
Kvinlog
Vanne
Sirevåg
Hellvik
Egersund
Heskestad
Sandvatn
Eiken
Sveindal
Frikstad
Nodland
Moi
Sira
Lyngna
Byremo
Birkeland
Eigerøya
Lundevatn
Navrestad 542
Vatland
Storkarshei 622
Tingvatn
Åmland
Ogge
Iveland
Hauge
Logan
Snartemo
Audnedal
Brokka 485
Åna-Sira
Flekkefjord
Kvinesdal
Konsmo
Brandsvoll
Feda
Førland
Vennesla
Kirkehamn
Hidra
Rasvåg
Rørvik
Moi
Marnardal
Finnsådal
Mosby
Strai
Drange
Kaldåsknipa 506
Listafjorden
Øyslebø
Nodeland
Borhaug
Vanse
Farsund
Lyngdal
Buhølen
Krossen
Try
Kristiansand
Søgne
Lista
Vigeland
Sør-Audnedal
Valand
Høllen
Lundegård
Mandal
Tregde
Våge
Lindesnes
Mannefjorden
Hirtshals
5°00′
5°30′
6°00′
6°30′
7°00′
7°30′
8°
60°00′
59°30′
59°00′
58°30′
58°00′
20′
10′
E39
E134

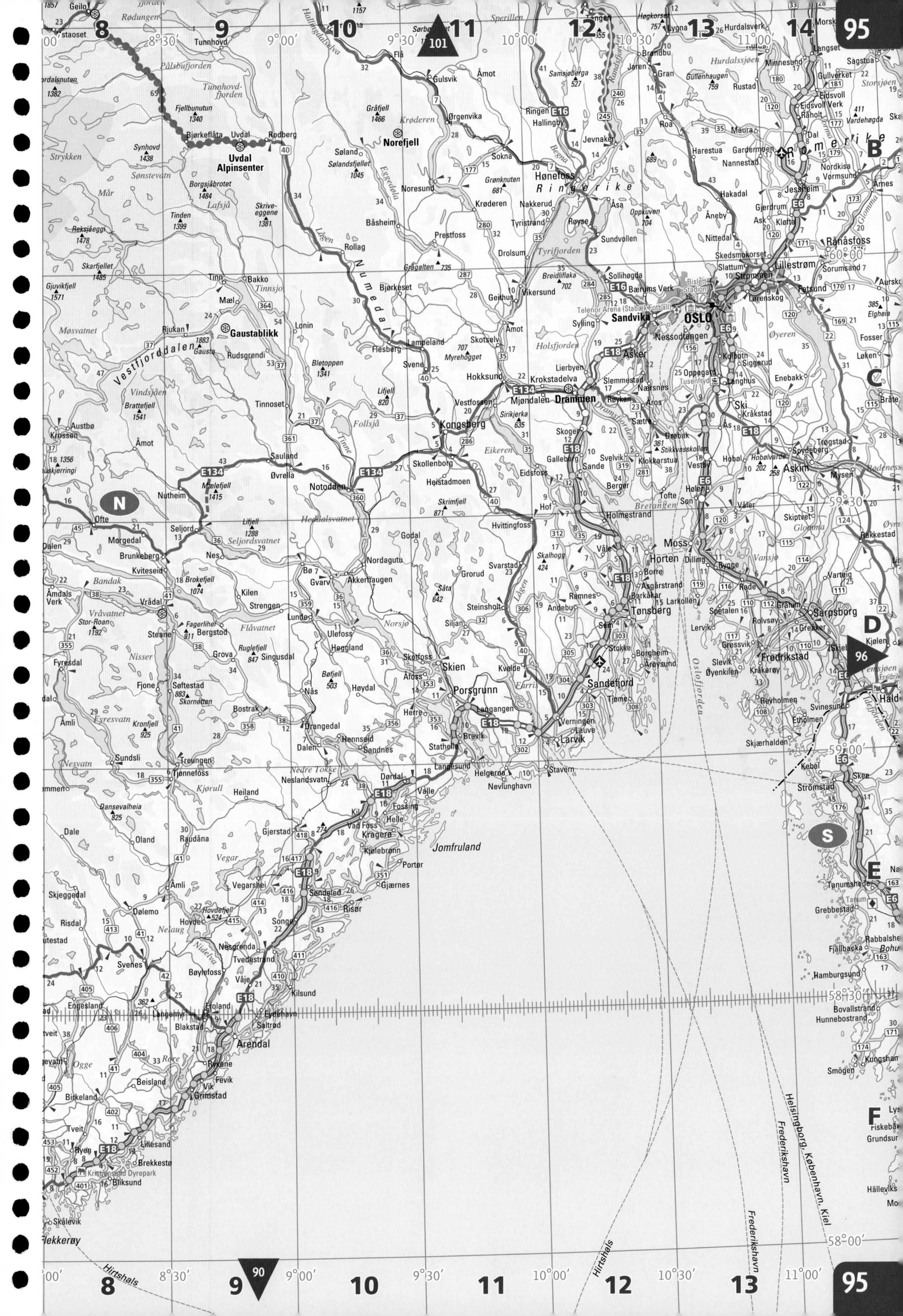
95
8
9
10
11
12
13
14
101
96
90
N
S
B
C
D
E
F
Geilo
Rødungen
Tunnhovd
Pålsbufjorden
Tunnhovdfjorden
Fjellbunutun
Bjørkefiåta
Uvdal
Rodberg
Uvdal Alpinsenter
Synhovd
Strykken
Sønstevatn
Borgsjåbrotet
Lafsjå
Mår
Tinden
Skriveeggene
Reksjåeggi
Skarfjellet
Gjuvikfjell
Tinn
Bakko
Tinnsjø
Mæl
Møsvatnet
Rjukan
Gaustablikk
Gausta
Vestfjorddalen
Rudsgrendi
Vindsjåen
Brattefjell
Tinnoset
Austbø
Krossen
Åmot
Sauland
Øvrella
Notodden
Nutheim
Mælefjell
Ofte
Seljord
Seljordsvatnet
Lifjell
Heddalsvatnet
Morgedal
Dalen
Brunkeberg
Kviteseid
Nes
Bandak
Åmdals Verk
Vrådal
Vråvatnet
Stor-Roan
Kilen
Strengen
Flåvatnet
Steane
Fagerlihei
Bergstod
Nisser
Grova
Ruglefjell
Singusdal
Fyresdal
Fjone
Søftestad
Skornetten
Bostrak
Fyresvatn
Kronfjell
Amli
Sundsli
Treungen
Tjønnefoss
Nesvatn
Kjørull
Heiland
Dansevalheia
Dale
Oland
Raudåna
Vegar
Åmli
Vegarshei
Skjeggedal
Dølemo
Hovdefjell
Risdal
Hovde
Nelaug
Nidelva
Nesgrenda
Tvedestrand
Svenes
Bøylefoss
Våje
Kilsund
Engesland
Langemyr
Froland
Eydehavn
Blakstad
Saltrød
Arendal
Rore
Ogge
Rykene
Fevik
Beisland
Vik
Grimstad
Birkeland
Tveit
Lillesand
Ryen
Brekkestø
Kristiansand Dyrepark
Bliksund
Skålevik
Flekkerøy
Hirtshals
Hallingdalselva
Flå
Sørbøhøgda
Gulsvik
Åmot
Gråfjell
Krøderen
Ørgenvika
Norefjell
Søland
Sølandsfjellet
Eggedøla
Sokna
Grønknuten
Noresund
Krøderen
Båsheim
Prestfoss
Lågen
Rollag
Numedal
Gråalten
Bjørkeset
Lonin
Flesberg
Lampeland
Myrehogget
Skotselv
Svene
Bletoppen
Lifjell
Follsjå
Kongsberg
Tinne
Skollenborg
Heistadmoen
Skrimfjell
Hvittingfoss
Godal
Nordagutu
Bø
Gvarv
Akkerhaugen
Grorud
Svarstad
Såta
Lunde
Ulefoss
Norsjø
Siljan
Steinsholt
Hegglang
Skotfoss
Skien
Bøfjell
Høydal
Afoss
Porsgrunn
Nås
Langangen
Drangedal
Herre
Brevik
Dalen
Hennseid
Sandnes
Stathelle
Langesund
Nedre Tokke
Neslandsvatn
Dørdal
Valle
Helgeroa
Nevlunghavn
Stavern
Larvik
Kil
Fossing
Helle
Vad Foss
Kragerø
Kjølebrønn
Jomfruland
Portør
Gjerstad
Gjærnes
Sandeled
Risør
Songe
Sperillen
Hønefoss
Ringerike
Ringen
Hallingby
Jevnaker
Randsfjorden
Begna
Nakkerud
Tyristrand
Røyse
Åsa
Sundvollen
Tyrifjorden
Drolsum
Breidliflaka
Geithus
Vikersund
Sollihøgda
Bærums Verk
Sandvika
Sylling
Holsfjorden
Asker
Lierbyen
Krokstadelva
Hokksund
Drammen
Mjøndalen
Vestfossen
Sirikjerka
Eikeren
Eidsfoss
Skoger
Galleberg
Sande
Svelvik
Dramsfjorden
Holmestrand
Hof
Skalhogg
Våle
Horten
Ramnes
Andebu
Tønsberg
Sem
Stokke
Borgheim
Årøysund
Sandefjord
Tjøme
Kvelde
Verningen
Lauve
Farris
Oslofjorden
Hurdalsverk
Lygna
Brandbu
Jaren
Gran
Samsjøberga
Gullenhaugen
Rustad
Roa
Hurdalssjøen
Harestua
Gardermoen
Nannestad
Romerike
Hakadal
Oppkuven
Åneby
Nittedal
Skedsmokorset
Slattum
Strømmen
Lillestrøm
Lørenskog
OSLO
Bislett Stadion
Telenor Arena (Stabæk Fotball)
Nessoddtangen
Kolbotn
Siggerud
Oppegård
Tusenfryd
Langhus
Slemmestad
Nærsnes
Røyken
Åros
Sætre
Drøbak
Stikkvasskollen
Klokkarstua
Ski
Kråkstad
Ås
Vestby
Hølen
Son
Tofte
Bretangen
Moss
Dilling
Rygge
Borre
Åsgårdstrand
Barkåker
Larkollen
Spetalen
Minnesund
Langset
Gullverket
Eidsvoll
Eidsvoll Verk
Råholt
Dal
Maura
Nordkisa
Vormsund
Jessheim
Gjerdrum
Ask
Kløfta
Rånåsfoss
Sorumsand
Fetsund
Øyeren
Elgheia
Fosser
Løken
Enebakk
Trøgstad
Spydeberg
Hobøl
Hobølvarde
Askim
Mysen
Våler
Skiptvet
Glomma
Rakkestad
Vansjø
Varteig
Råde
Grålum
Sarpsborg
Greåker
Rolvsøy
Lervik
Gressvik
Slevik
Øyenkilen
Fredrikstad
Kråkerøy
Skjeberg
Kjølen
Revholmen
Svinesund
Ethølmen
Skjærhalden
Halden
Iddefjorden
Kebal
Strømstad
Skee
Tanumshede
Grebbestad
Rabbalshede
Fjällbacka
Hamburgsund
Bovallstrand
Hunnebostrand
Kungshamn
Smögen
Hälleviks
Frederikshavn
Helsingborg, København, Kiel
Hirtshals
8°30′
9°00′
9°30′
10°00′
10°30′
11°00′
59°30′
59°00′
58°30′
58°00′
60°00′
E18
E134
E16
E6

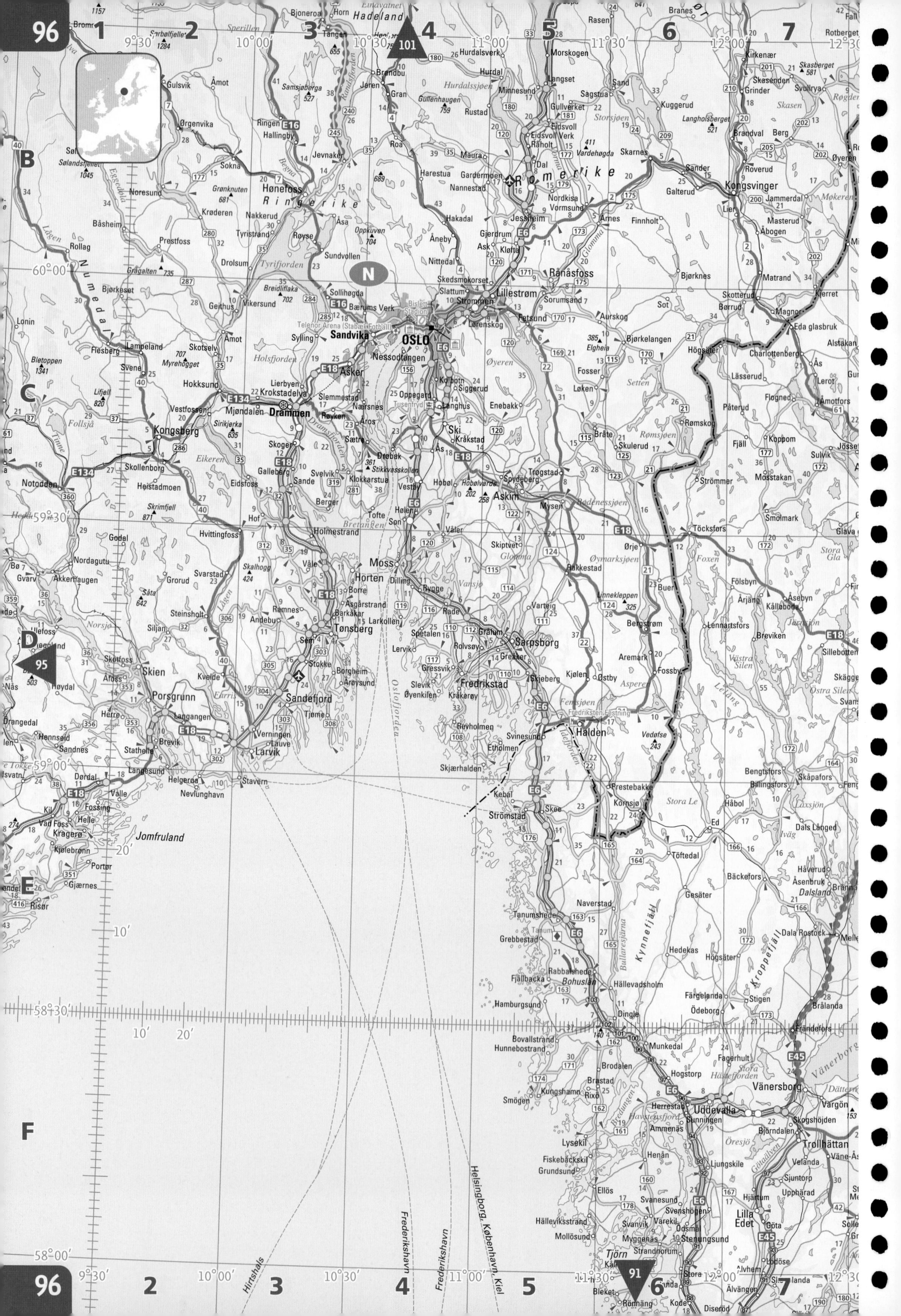
101
95
91
N
OSLO
Sandvika
Drammen
Hønefoss
Ringerike
Lillestrøm
Strømmen
Lørenskog
Jessheim
Gardermoen
Romerike
Kongsvinger
Kongsberg
Notodden
Numedal
Tyrifjorden
Holsfjorden
Asker
Nessodtangen
Ski
Askim
Mysen
Moss
Horten
Tønsberg
Sandefjord
Larvik
Porsgrunn
Skien
Brevik
Langesund
Stavern
Kragerø
Risør
Jomfruland
Sarpsborg
Fredrikstad
Halden
Strömstad
Skee
Tanumshede
Bohuslän
Kynnefjäll
Kroppefjäll
Dalsland
Uddevalla
Vänersborg
Trollhättan
Lilla Edet
Lysekil
Smögen
Kungshamn
Tjörn
Stenungsund
Hadeland
Hurdalssjøen
Øyeren
Glomma
Oslofjorden
Hirtshals
Frederikshavn
Helsingborg, København, Kiel
E6
E16
E18
E134
E45
59°30′
60°00′
58°30′
58°00′
9°30′
10°00′
10°30′
11°00′
11°30′
12°00′
B
C
D
E
F
1
2
3
4
5
6
7

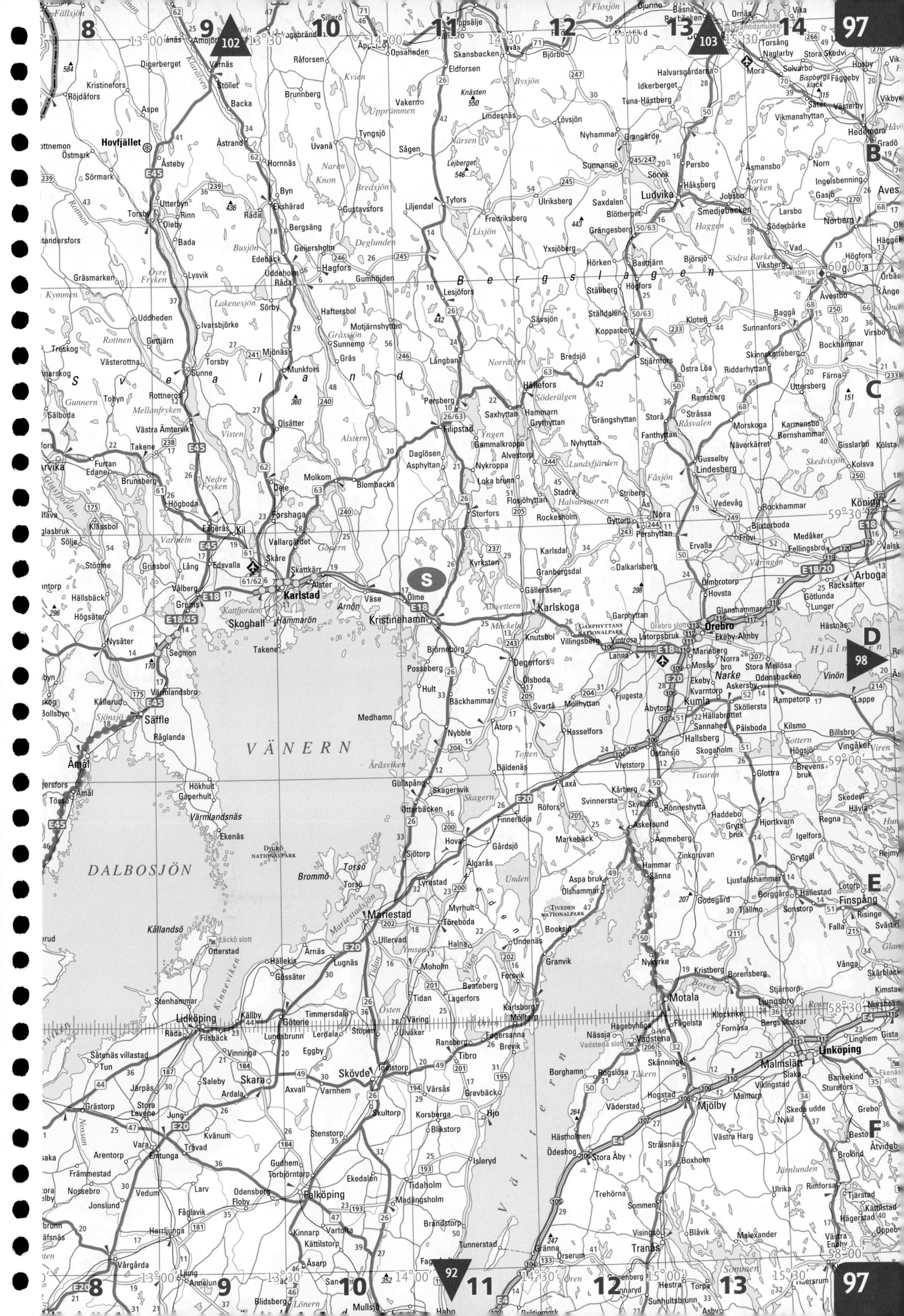
8
9
10
11
12
13
14
102
103
98
92
B
C
D
E
F
Bergslagen
Svealand
VÄNERN
DALBOSJÖN
Vättern
Narke
Karlstad
Kristinehamn
Karlskoga
Örebro
Ludvika
Smedjebacken
Hedemora
Avesta
Norberg
Köping
Arboga
Lindesberg
Nora
Hällefors
Filipstad
Hagfors
Munkfors
Sunne
Torsby
Arvika
Kil
Säffle
Åmål
Mora
Hovfjället
Kumla
Hallsberg
Askersund
Motala
Vadstena
Mjölby
Linköping
Tranås
Gränna
Hjo
Karlsborg
Mariestad
Töreboda
Skövde
Falköping
Skara
Lidköping
Vara
Vårgårda
Herrljunga
Tidaholm
Finspång
Djurö Nationalpark
Garphyttans Nationalpark
Tiveden Nationalpark
Läckö slott
Vadstena slott
Engelsbergs bruk

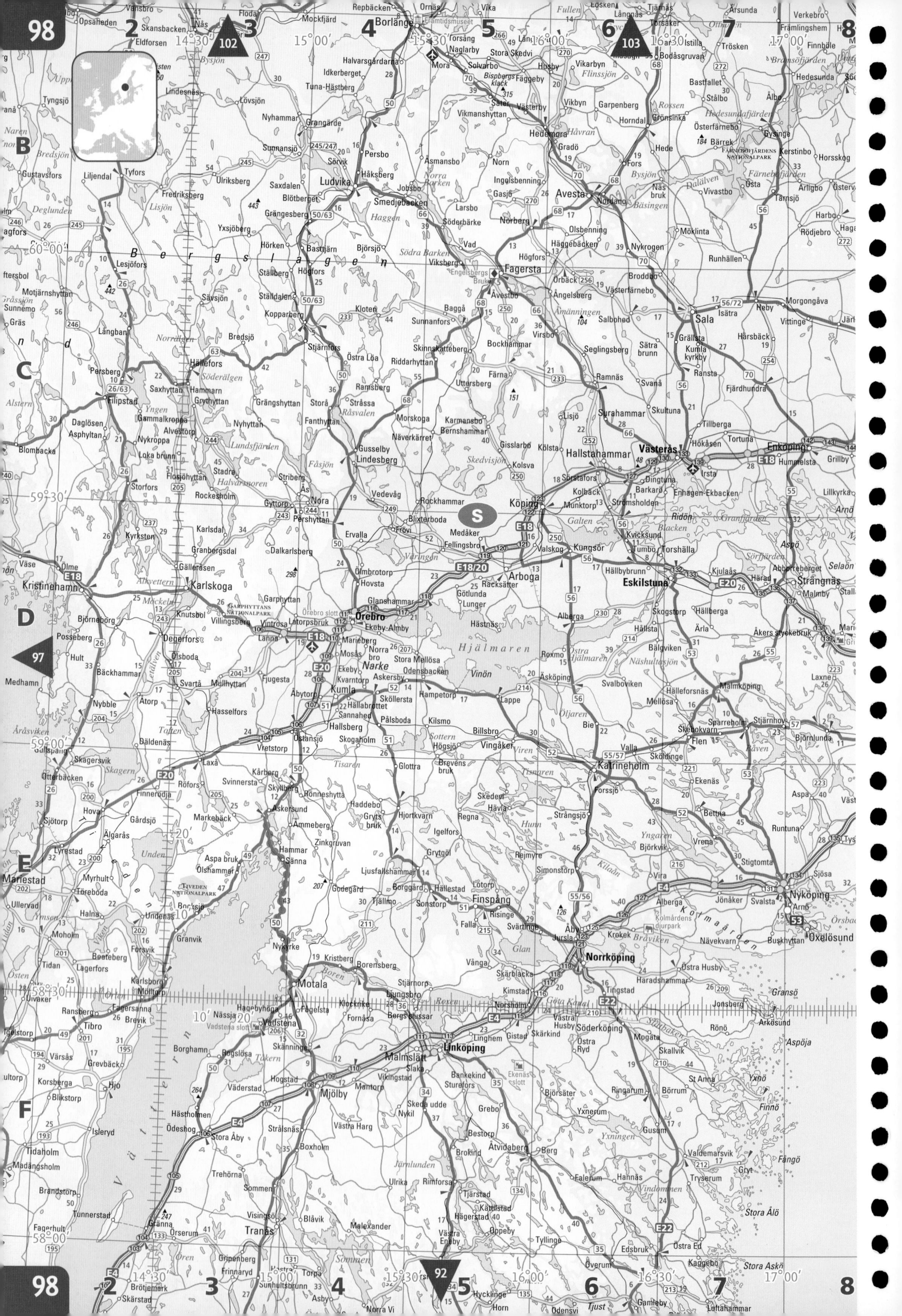
98
102
103
97
92
Bergslagen
Borlänge
Falun
Mora
Hedemora
Avesta
Sala
Ludvika
Smedjebacken
Fagersta
Norberg
Kopparberg
Hällefors
Filipstad
Karlskoga
Kristinehamn
Degerfors
Nora
Lindesberg
Örebro
Kumla
Hallsberg
Askersund
Laxå
Hova
Mariestad
Köping
Arboga
Kungsör
Västerås
Hallstahammar
Surahammar
Enköping
Strängnäs
Eskilstuna
Torshälla
Flen
Katrineholm
Vingåker
Nyköping
Oxelösund
Norrköping
Finspång
Söderköping
Linköping
Motala
Vadstena
Mjölby
Tranås
Gränna
Hjo
Tibro
Skövde
Åtvidaberg
Valdemarsvik
Hjälmaren
Vättern
Glan
Roxen
Boren
Sommen
Kolmården
Tiveden Nationalpark
Garphyttans Nationalpark
Färnebofjärdens Nationalpark
Engelsbergs Bruk
Göta Kanal
Gamleby
Västervik
Skärstad
E4
E18
E20
E22
E18/20
14°30′
15°00′
15°30′
16°00′
16°30′
17°00′
60°00′
59°30′
59°00′
58°30′
58°00′
S

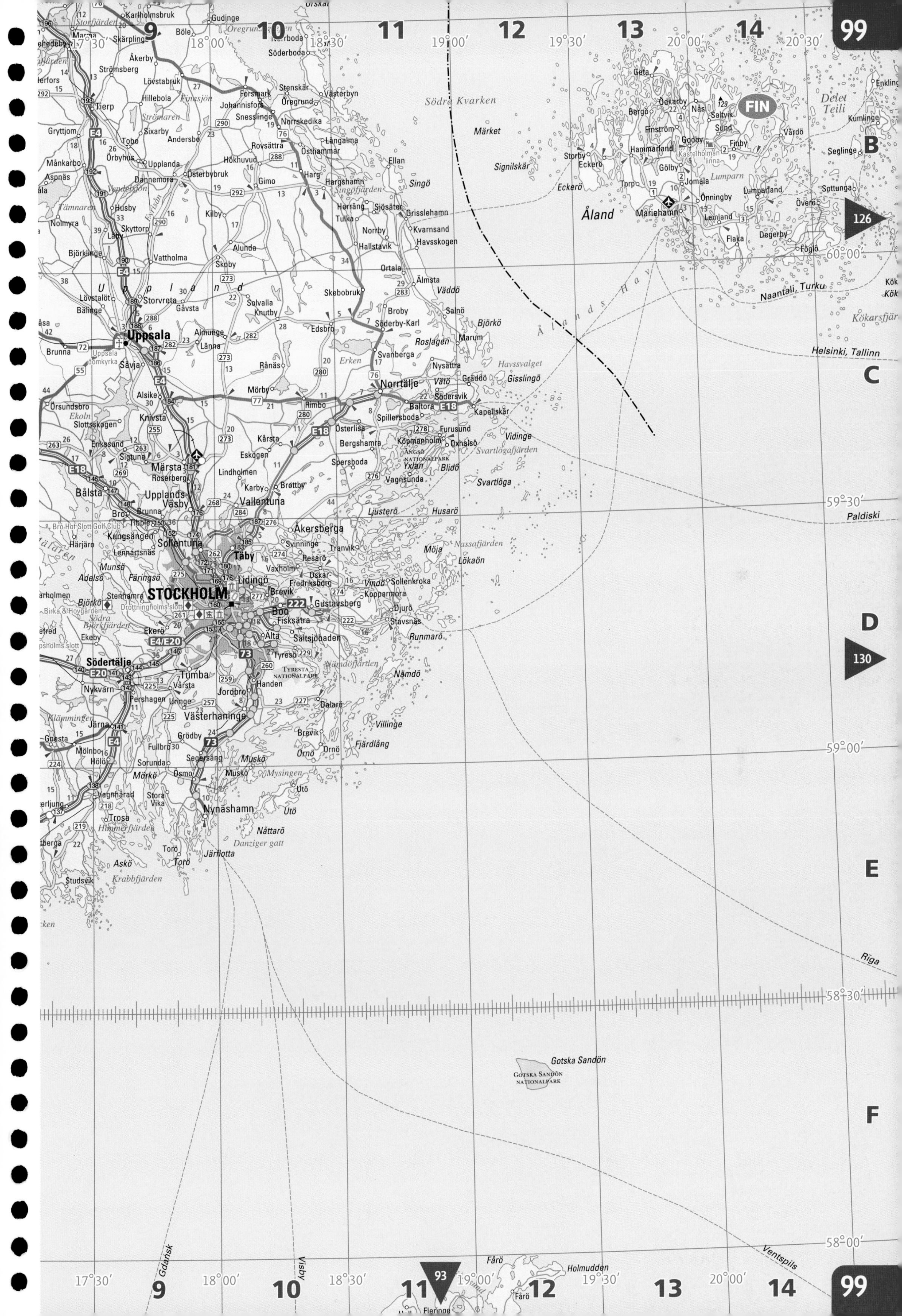
STOCKHOLM
Uppsala
Norrtälje
Södertälje
Nynäshamn
Åland
Mariehamn
FIN
Södra Kvarken
Ålands Hav
Gotska Sandön
Gotska Sandön Nationalpark
Helsinki, Tallinn
Paldiski
Riga
Ventspils
Visby
Gdańsk
Naantali, Turku
126
130
93

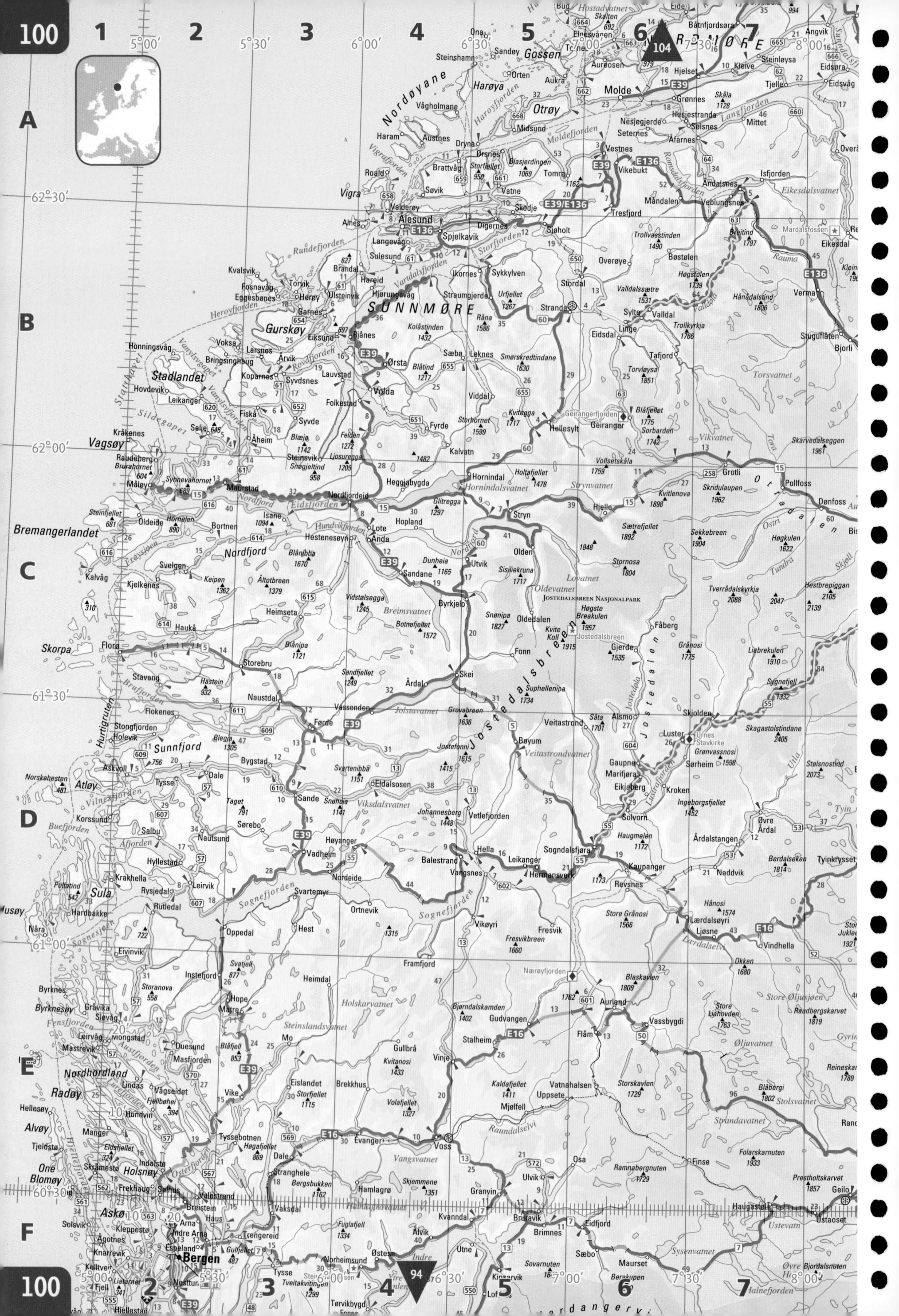

Nordøyane
Haramsøy
Harøya
Otrøy
Gossen
Molde
Romsdalsfjorden
Åndalsnes
Vigra
Ålesund
Spjelkavik
Storfjorden
Sykkylven
Stordal
Stranda
Valldal
Sunnmøre
Gurskøy
Ørsta
Volda
Stadlandet
Vagsøy
Måløy
Maurstad
Nordfjordeid
Eidsfjorden
Nordfjord
Bremangerlandet
Sandane
Byrkjelo
Stryn
Hjelle
Grotli
Otta
Hellesylt
Geiranger
Geirangerfjorden
Jostedalsbreen Nasjonalpark
Jostedalsbreen
Jostedalen
Olden
Lovatnet
Oldevatnet
Skei
Førde
Florø
Naustdal
Sunnfjord
Atløy
Dale
Sande
Vadheim
Høyanger
Balestrand
Leikanger
Hermansverk
Sogndalsfjøra
Kaupanger
Lærdalsøyri
Luster
Urnes Stavkirke
Skjolden
Sognefjorden
Sula
Rutledal
Oppedal
Vikøyri
Aurland
Flåm
Gudvangen
Nærøyfjorden
Nordhordland
Radøy
Holsnøy
Askøy
Bergen
Osterfjorden
Voss
Vangsvatnet
Evanger
Dale
Granvin
Ulvik
Eidfjord
Finse
Haugastøl
Geilo
Ustaoset
Hardangerfjorden
Norheimsund
Øystese
Kinsarvik
Utne
Hurtigruten
E39
E136
E16
104
94

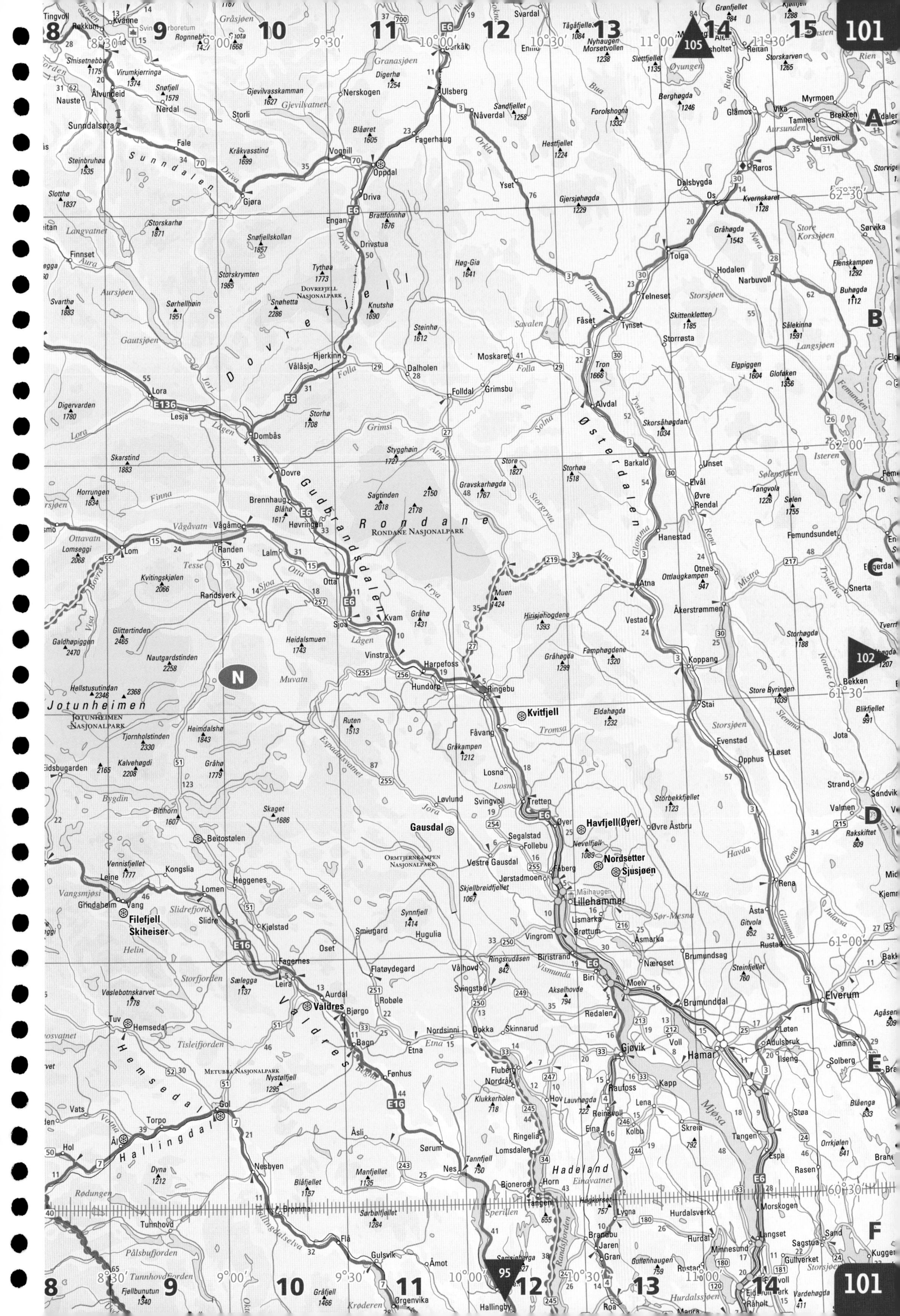
8
9
10
11
12
13
14
15
A
B
C
D
E
F
105
102
95
8°30'
9°00'
9°30'
10°00'
10°30'
11°00'
11°30'
62°30'
62°00'
61°30'
61°00'
60°30'
Tingvoll
Kvanne
Rognnebbe
Gråsjøen
Gjota
1668
Granasjøen
Svardal
Tågåfjellet
1084
Nyhaugen
Morsetvollen
1238
Grønfjellet
Kjølljen
1288
Smisetnebba
1175
Virumkjerringa
1374
Snøfjell
1579
Ålvundeid
Nauste
Nerdal
Sunndalsøra
Gjevilvasskamman
1627
Gjevilvatnet
Nerskogen
Digerhø
1254
Ulsberg
Berkåk
Nåverdal
Sandfjellet
1258
Slettfjellet
1135
Øyungen
Storskarven
1265
Rien
Myrmoen
Vika
Brekken
Tamnes
Aursunden
Glåmos
Berghøgda
1246
Forolshogna
1332
Storli
Bløøret
1605
Fagerhaug
Fale
Sunndalen
Driva
Kråkvasstind
1699
Steinbruhøa
1535
Vognill
Oppdal
Hestfjellet
1224
Jensvoll
Røros
Storvige
Slotthø
1837
Gjøra
Driva
Yset
Dalsbygda
Os
Kvernskaret
1128
Gjersjøhøgda
1229
Engan
Brattfonnhø
1676
Storskarhø
1871
Langvatnet
Snøfjellskollan
1857
Drivstua
Gråhøgda
1543
Store Korssjøen
Sørvika
Finnset
Aura
Tolga
Hodalen
Narbuvoll
Flenskampen
1292
Høg-Gia
1641
Tythøa
1773
Storskrymten
1985
Dovrefjell Nasjonalpark
Aursjøen
Svarthø
1883
Sørhellhøin
1951
Snøhetta
2286
Knutshø
1690
Dovrefjell
Telneset
Storsjøen
Buhøgda
1112
Tunna
Steinhø
1612
Savalen
Fåset
Tynset
Skittenkletten
1185
Sålekinna
1591
Gautsjøen
Storrøsta
Langsjøen
Hjerkinn
Vålåsjø
Folla
Dalholen
Moskaret
Folla
Tron
1666
Elgpiggen
1604
Glofjøken
1356
Lora
Digervarden
1780
E136
Lesja
Jori
Storhø
1708
Folldal
Grimsbu
Alvdal
Femunden
Østerdalen
Tysla
Skorsåshøgdan
1034
Lora
Dombås
Lågen
Grimsi
Solna
Isteren
Skarstind
1883
Dovre
Stygghøin
1727
Store
1827
Storhøa
1518
Barkald
Unset
Sølensjøen
Horrungen
1834
Finna
Brennhaug
Gudbrandsdalen
Sagtinden
2018
2150
2178
Gravskarhøgda
1767
Elvål
Øvre Rendal
Tangvola
1226
Sølen
1755
Blåhø
1617
Hovringen
Rondane
Rondane Nasjonalpark
Storgryta
Glomma
Ottavatn
Vågåvatn
Vågåmo
Hanestad
Femundsundet
Lomseggi
2068
Lom
Randen
Lalm
Tesse
Otta
Ottlaugkampen
947
Otnes
Engerdal
Kvitingskjølen
2066
Sjoa
Otta
Frya
Atna
Snerta
Randsverk
Muen
1424
Hirisjøhøgdene
1393
Åkerstrømmen
Mistra
Trysilelva
Glittertinden
2465
Kvam
Gråhø
1431
Vestad
Galdhøpiggen
2470
Heidalsmuen
1743
Lågen
Vinstra
Harpefoss
Famphøgdene
1320
Gråhøgda
1299
Koppang
Storhøgda
1188
Nautgardstinden
2258
Muvatn
Hundorp
Ringebu
Bekken
Hellstusutinden
2346
2368
Jotunheimen
Jotunheimen Nasjonalpark
Store Byringen
1039
Nordre Osen
Ruten
1513
Kvitfjell
Eldahøgda
1232
Tromsa
Stai
Blikfjellet
991
Heimdalshø
1843
Tjornholstinden
2330
Fåvang
Gråkampen
1212
Storsjøen
Evenstad
Jota
Espedalsvatnet
Opphus
Løset
Eidsbugarden
2165
Kalvehøgdi
2208
Gråhø
1779
Losna
Losna
Slemma
Bygdin
Strand
Sandvik
Bitihorn
1607
Skaget
1686
Jora
Løvlund
Svingvoll
Tretten
Storbekkfjellet
1123
Valmen
Gausdal
Øyer
Havfjell(Øyer)
Øvre Åstbru
Beitostølen
Segalstad
Follebu
Nevelfjell
1089
Rakskiftet
809
Havda
Ormtjernkampen Nasjonalpark
Vestre Gausdal
Fåberg
Nordsetter
Sjusjøen
Rena
Vennisfjellet
1777
Kongslia
Leine
Heggenes
Jørstadmoen
Maihaugen
Skjellbreidfjellet
1067
Rena
Vangsmjøsi
Grindaheim
Vang
Lomen
Lillehammer
Lismarka
Asta
Sør-Mesna
Åsta
Kjemn
Filefjell Skiheiser
Slidrefjord
Etna
Synnfjell
1414
Gitvola
852
Julussa
Slidre
Kjølstad
Smiugard
Hugulia
Brøttum
Åsmarka
Rustad
Glomma
Helin
Oset
Vingrom
Biristrand
Brumundsag
Fagernes
Flatøydegard
Vålhovd
Ringsrudåsen
842
Vismunda
Biri
Nærøset
Steinfjellet
760
Storfjorden
Sælegga
1137
Leira
Aurdal
Svingstad
Akselhovde
794
Moelv
Elverum
Veslebotnskarvet
1778
Valdres
Bjørgo
Robøle
Redalen
Brumunddal
Agåsen
509
Tuv
Hemsedal
Tisleifjorden
Nordsinni
Dokka
Skinnarud
Løten
Adulsbruk
Jømna
Bagn
Etna
Etna
Gjøvik
Voll
Hamar
Ilseng
Solberg
Hemsedal
Fønhus
Flubørg
Nordråk
Metubba Nasjonalpark
Nystølfjell
1295
Raufoss
Kapp
Bre
E16
Gol
Klukkerhoen
718
Hov
Lauvhøgda
722
Reinsvoll
Lena
Mjøsa
Blåenga
633
Vats
Torpo
Votna
Ål
Hallingdal
Åsli
Sørum
Ringelia
Eina
Kolbu
Skreia
Tangen
Støa
Orrkjølen
641
Hol
Dyna
1212
Nesbyen
Manfjellet
1135
Nes
Tannfjell
750
Lomsdalen
Hadeland
Einavatnet
Espa
Rasen
Brane
Blåfjellet
1157
Rødungen
Bjoneroa
Horn
Tangen
Hagkorset
757
Lygna
Hurdalsverk
Morskogen
Bromma
Sørbølfjellet
1284
Sperillen
655
Tunnhovd
Hallingdalselva
Flå
Brandbu
Jaren
Hurdal
Langset
Sand
Sagstua
Kugger
Pålsbufjorden
Gulsvik
Åmot
Samsjøberga
Gran
Gullenhaugen
759
Minnesund
Gullverket
Storsjøen
Tunnhovdfjorden
Fjellbunutun
1340
Gråfjell
1466
Ørgenvika
Krøderen
Hallingby
Randsfjorden
Rustad
Hurdalssjøen
Eidsvoll
Råholt
Vardehøgda
411
Roa
E6
E16
E136
Sunndalen
Gudbrandsdalen
Valdres
Hemsedal

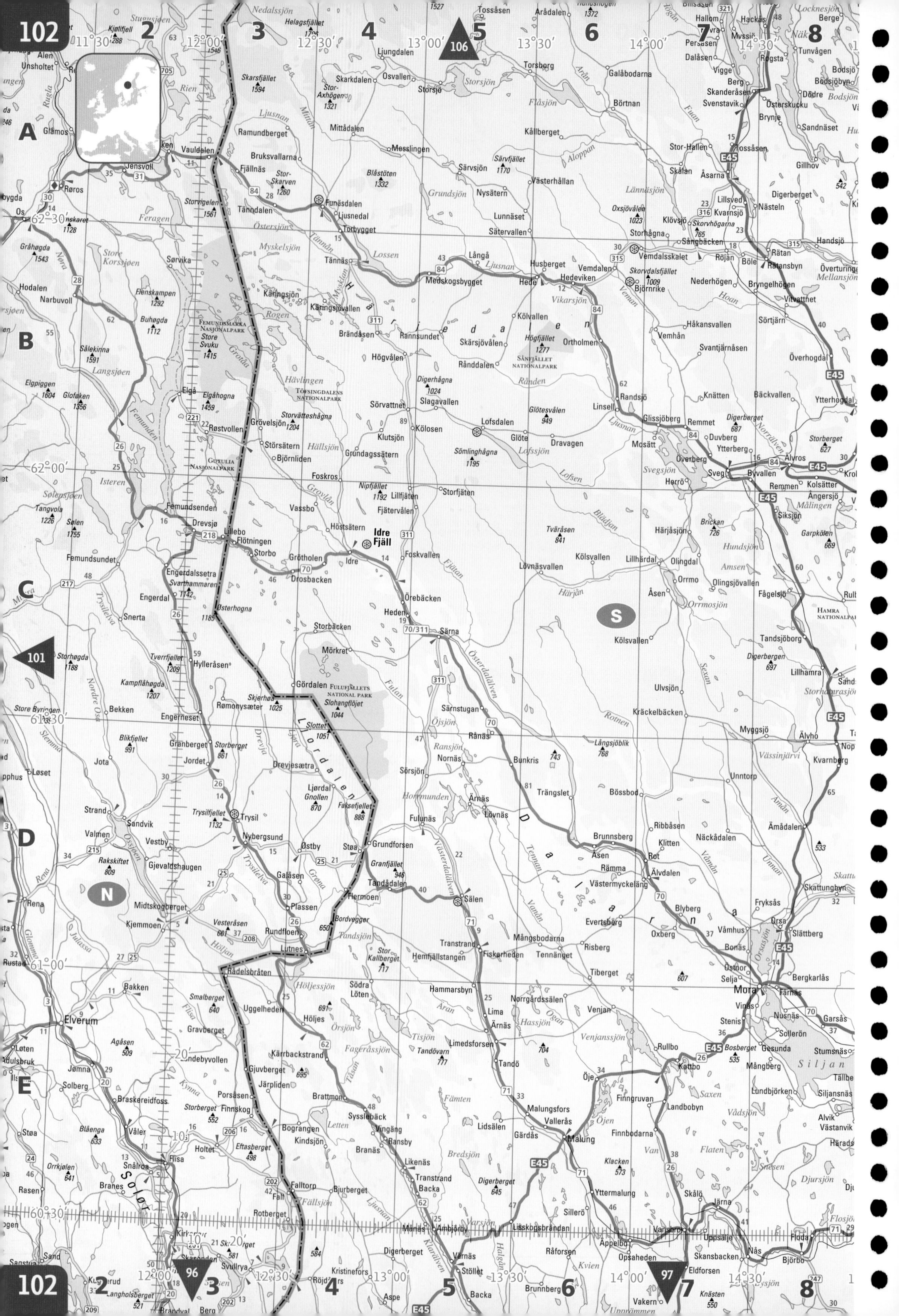

2
3
4
5
6
7
8
106
A
B
C
D
E
101
96
97
N
S
11°30′
12°00′
12°30′
13°00′
13°30′
14°00′
14°30′
62°30′
62°00′
61°30′
61°00′
60°30′
Røros
Os
Vauldalen
Fjällnäs
Tänndalen
Funäsdalen
Ljusnedal
Torbygget
Tännäs
Ljungdalen
Skarkdalen
Osvallen
Storsjö
Mittådalen
Messlingen
Bruksvallarna
Ramundberget
Särvsjön
Nysätern
Västerhållan
Lunnäset
Sätervallen
Tossåsen
Arådalen
Torsborg
Galåbodarna
Börtnan
Kållberget
Stor-Hallen
Tossåsen
Skålan
Åsarna
Klövsjö
Storhågna
Vemdalsskalet
Vemdalen
Björnrike
Hede
Hedeviken
Medskogsbygget
Långå
Rätan
Böle
Rätansbyn
Nederhögen
Bryngelhögen
Sveg
Byvallen
Remmen
Kolsätter
Härjedalen
Kölvallen
Skärsjövålen
Rånddalen
Ortholmen
Håkansvallen
Vemhån
Svantjärnåsen
Överhogdal
Ytterhogdal
Linsell
Randsjö
Glissjöberg
Remmet
Duvberg
Ytterberg
Överberg
Mosätt
Herrö
Lofsdalen
Glöte
Dravagen
Kölosen
Klutsjön
Sörvattnet
Slagavallen
Högvålen
Brändåsen
Rannsundet
Käringsjön
Käringsjövallen
FEMUNDSMARKA NASJONALPARK
TÖFSINGDALENS NATIONALPARK
GUTULIA NASJONALPARK
SÅNFJÄLLET NATIONALPARK
FULUFJÄLLETS NATIONAL PARK
HAMRA NATIONALPARK
Femunden
Elgå
Røstvollen
Grövelsjön
Störsätern
Björnliden
Foskros
Storfjäten
Lillfjäten
Fjätervålen
Idre Fjäll
Idre
Grötholen
Drosbacken
Foskvallen
Vassbo
Höstsätern
Femundsenden
Drevsjø
Lillebo
Flötningen
Storbo
Engerdalssetra
Engerdal
Snerta
Femundsundet
Hodalen
Narbuvoll
Sørvika
Örebäcken
Heden
Särna
Storbäcken
Mörkret
Gördalen
Hylleråsen
Rømonysæter
Engerneset
Bekken
Granberget
Jordet
Jota
Løset
Trysil
Nybergsund
Strand
Sandvik
Valmen
Vestby
Gjevaldshaugen
Østby
Støa
Grundforsen
Galåsen
Plassen
Tandådalen
Flermoen
Sälen
Midtskogberget
Kjemmoen
Rena
Rundfloen
Lutnes
Rådelsbråten
Södra Löten
Transtrand
Fiskarheden
Hemfjällstangen
Mångsbodarna
Tennänget
Risberg
Tiberget
Särnstugan
Rånäs
Nornäs
Sörsjön
Ärnäs
Lövnäs
Fulunäs
Bunkris
Trängslet
Bössbod
Brunnsberg
Åsen
Rot
Rämma
Älvdalen
Västermyckeläng
Evertsberg
Oxberg
Blyberg
Våmhus
Bonäs
Mora
Färnäs
Östnor
Selja
Orsa
Slättberg
Bergkarlås
Kölsvallen
Lillhärdal
Olingdal
Orrmo
Åsen
Härjåsjön
Tandsjöborg
Lillhamra
Fågelsjö
Ulvsjön
Kräckelbäcken
Myggsjö
Älvho
Kvarnberg
Unntorp
Ribbåsen
Klitten
Näckådalen
Ämådalen
Skattungbyn
Fryksås
Elverum
Bakken
Uggleheden
Höljes
Gravberget
Kärrbackstrand
Gjuvberget
Järpliden
Hammarsbyn
Lima
Ärnäs
Limedsforsen
Norrgårdssälen
Venjan
Tandö
Malungsfors
Malung
Lidsälen
Gärdås
Vallerås
Öje
Finngruvan
Landbobyn
Finnbodarna
Rullbo
Kattbo
Gesunda
Sollerön
Vinäs
Nusnäs
Stenis
Garsås
Siljan
Løten
Jømna
Solberg
Braskereidfoss
Våler
Flisa
Holtet
Finnskog
Porsåsen
Brattmon
Sysslebäck
Bograngen
Kindsjön
Vingäng
Ransby
Branäs
Likenäs
Transtrand
Backa
Falltorp
Bjurberget
Rotberget
Mornäs
Ambjörby
Lisskogsbrändan
Sillerö
Yttermalung
Skålö
Järna
Vansbro
Uppsälje
Nås
Floda
Björbo
Åppelbo
Opsaheden
Eldforsen
Skansbacken
Råforsen
Brunnberg
Digerberget
Värnäs
Stöllet
Backa
Kristinefors
Röjdåfors
Aspe
Vakern
Snåroa
Branes
Rasen
Kongsrud
Svullrya
Skasenden
E45

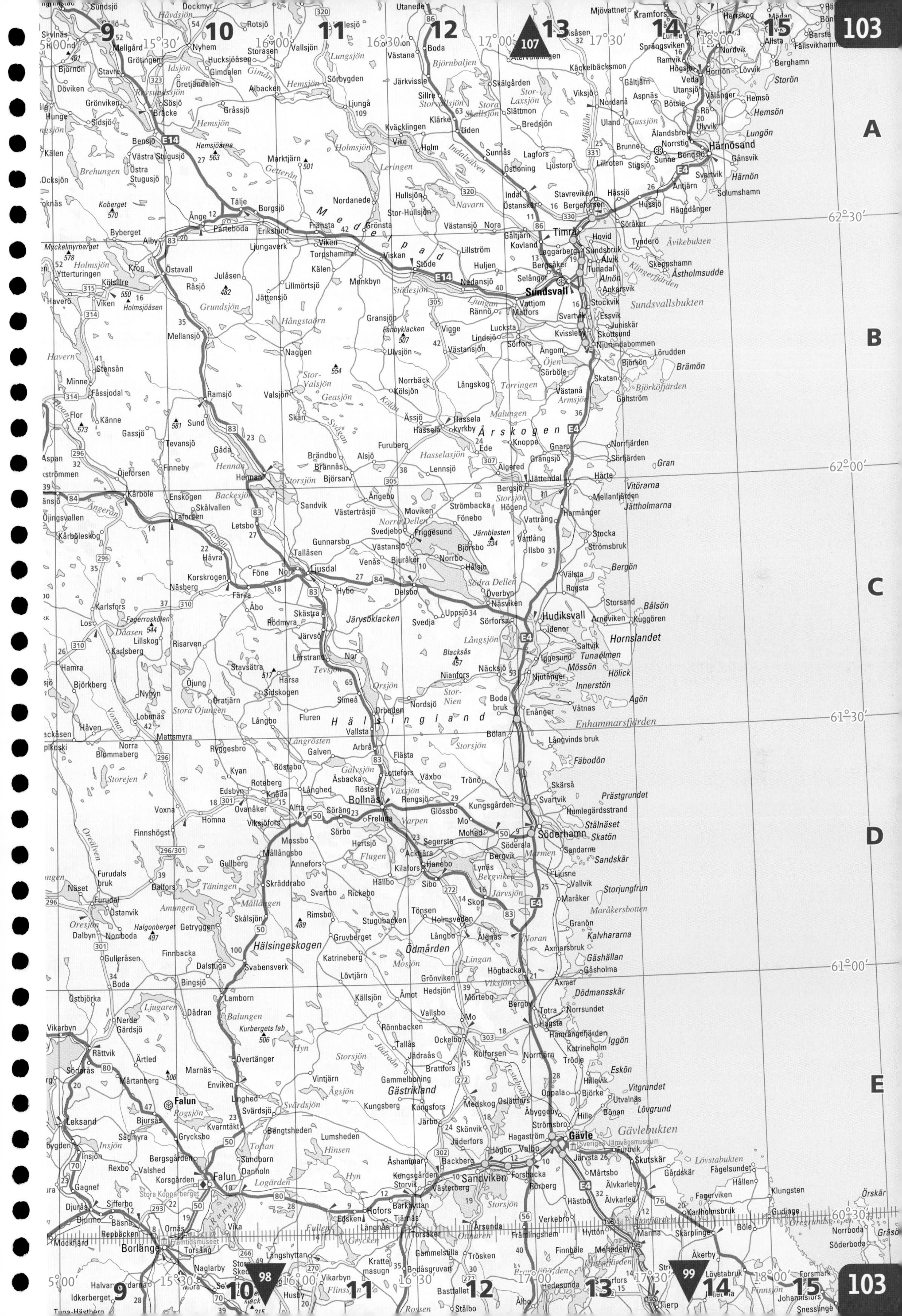
103
9
10
11
12
13
14
15
A
B
C
D
E
107
98
99
62°30′
62°00′
61°30′
61°00′
60°30′
15°30′
16°00′
16°30′
17°00′
17°30′
18°00′
Sundsjö
Dockmyr
Rotsjö
Utanede
Mjövattnet
Kramfors
Herrskog
Mellgård
Nyhem
Storåsen
Vallsjön
Boda
Västana
Sprängsviken
Nordvik
Fällsvikhamn
Grötingen
Hucksjöåsen
Gimdalen
Lungsjön
Björnön
Stavre
Idsjön
Öretjändalen
Albacken
Hemsjön
Sörbygden
Järkvissle
Björnbaljen
Skälgården
Käckelbäcksmon
Ramvik
Högsjö
Hornön
Lövvik
Berghamn
Storön
Döviken
Sösjö
Bräcke
Gråssjö
Ljungå
Sillre
Klärke
Stora Laxsjön
Slättmon
Bredsjön
Viksjö
Nordanå
Gåltjärn
Aspnäs
Utansjö
Bötsle
Välånger
Hemsö
Hemsön
Grönviken
Sidsjö
Kväcklingen
Vike
Holm
Liden
Indalsälven
Uland
Gussjön
Ålandsbro
Ulvvik
Lungön
Bensjö
E14
Västra Stugusjö
Östra Stugusjö
Hemsjöarna
Kälen
Brehungen
Marktjärn
Holmsjön
Leringen
Sunnås
Lagfors
Östloning
Ljustorp
Brunne
Norrstig
Sunne
Bondsjö
Härnösand
Gånsvik
Lillroten
Stigsjö
E4
Svartvik
Härnön
Solumshamn
Ocksjön
Koberget
Tälje
Borgsjö
Nordanede
Hullsjön
Stor-Hullsjön
Navarn
Indal
Östanskär
Stavreviken
Bergeforsen
Hässjö
Hussjö
Antjärn
Häggdånger
Ånge
Parteboda
Erikslund
Fränsta
Grönsta
Medelpad
Västansjö
Nora
Timrå
Söråker
Byberget
Alby
Ljungaverk
Viken
Torpshammar
Viskan
Lillström
Gåltjärn
Kovland
Laggarberg
Hovid
Sundsbruk
Tynderö
Åvikebukten
Myckelmyrberget
Holmsjön
Ytterturingen
Krog
Östavall
Julåsen
Kälen
Lillmörtsjö
Munkbyn
Stöde
Huljen
Bergsåker
Alvik
Tunadal
Skeppshamn
Åstholmsudde
Klingerfjärden
Kölsillre
Viken
Haverö
Holmsjöåsen
Råsjö
Jättensjö
Stödesjön
Nedansjö
Selånger
Sundsvall
Alnön
Ankarsvik
Sundsvallsbukten
Grundsjön
Ljungan
Rännö
Vattjom
Matfors
Stockvik
Svartvik
Essvik
Hångstaörn
Gransjö
Fanbyklacken
Vigge
Lucksta
Lindsjö
Sörfors
Kvissleby
Juniskär
Skottsund
Njurundabommen
Lörudden
Mellansjö
Naggen
Västansjö
Ängom
Björkön
Brämön
Havern
Stensån
Ulvsjön
Öjen
Sörböle
Skatan
Minne
Fåssjodal
Stor-Valsjön
Norrbäck
Kölsjön
Långskog
Torringen
Västanå
Armsjön
Björköfjärden
Galtström
Ramsjö
Valsjön
Geasjön
Kölån
Malungen
Flor
Känne
Sund
Skån
Ässjö
Hassela
Hasselakyrkby
Årskogen
Gassjö
Tevansjö
Svågan
Furuberg
Ede
Knoppe
Gnarp
Norrfjärden
Sörfjärden
Gran
Åspan
Gåda
Hennan
Brändbo
Alsjö
Hasselasjön
Lennsjö
Grängsjö
Älgered
Öjeforsen
Finneby
Brännås
Björsarv
Storsjön
Jättendal
Härte
Vitörarna
Kårböle
Enskogen
Backesjön
Ängebo
Strömbacka
Bergsjö
Storsjön
Högen
Mellanfjärden
Jättholmarna
Ängerån
Skålvallen
Laforsen
Sandvik
Västerträsjö
Moviken
Norra Dellen
Fönebo
Harmånger
Ljusnan
Letsbo
Svedjebo
Friggesund
Järnblasten
Vattrång
Stocka
Kårböleskog
Håvra
Tallåsen
Gunnarsbo
Västansjö
Björsbo
Vattlång
Ilsbo
Strömsbruk
Venås
Bjuråker
Norrbo
Hälsjö
Bergön
Korskrogen
Föne
Nore
Ljusdal
Södra Dellen
Välsta
Näsberg
Färila
Hybo
Delsbo
Överbyn
Näsviken
Rogsta
Storsand
Bålsön
Karlsfors
Åbo
Skästra
Uppsjö
Hudiksvall
Idenor
Arnöviken
Kuggören
Fagerroskölen
Dåasen
Los
Rödmyra
Järvsöklacken
Svedja
Sörforsa
Hornslandet
Lillskog
Risarven
Järvsö
Långsjön
Saltvik
Karlsberg
Lörstrand
Nor
Blacksås
Iggesund
Tunaölmen
Hamra
Stavsätra
Härsa
Tevsjön
Nianfors
Näcksjö
Mössön
Hölick
Björkberg
Öjung
Sidskogen
Orsjön
Njutånger
Innerstön
Nybyn
Öratjärn
Simeå
Stor-Nien
Boda bruk
Agön
Voxnan
Stora Öjungen
Nordsjö
Orbaden
Enånger
Vätnas
Lobonäs
Långbo
Fluren
Hälsingland
Håven
Vallsta
Enhammarsfjärden
Norra Blommaberg
Mattsmyra
Långrösten
Arbrå
Bölan
Långvinds bruk
Ryggesbro
Galven
Storsjön
Flästa
Fäbodön
Storejen
Kyan
Röstabo
Galvsjön
Lottefors
Växbo
Trönö
Skärså
Roteberg
Åsbacka
Edsbyn
Knåda
Länghed
Röste
Växsjön
Svartvik
Prästgrundet
Bollnäs
Rengsjö
Kungsgården
Humlegärdsstrand
Voxna
Ovanåker
Alfta
Söräng
Glössbo
Stålnäset
Homna
Viksjöfors
Freluga
Varpen
Mo
Finnshögst
Mossbo
Sörbo
Moheda
Söderhamn
Skatön
Hertsjö
Segersta
Söderala
Mållångsbo
Flugen
Ackjära
Bergvik
Sandarne
Oreälven
Gullberg
Annefors
Kilafors
Hanebo
Marmen
Lynäs
Sandskär
Furudals bruk
Dalfors
Skräddrabo
Hällbo
Sibo
Bergviken
Ljusne
Näset
Täningen
Vallvik
Storjungfrun
Furudal
Mållången
Svartbo
Rickebo
Järvsjön
Skog
Maråker
Östanvik
Amungen
Rimsbo
Tönsen
Holmsveden
Maråkersbotten
Oresjön
Halgonberget
Getryggen
Skålsjön
Stugubacken
Granön
Dalbyn
Norrboda
Hälsingeskogen
Gruvberget
Långbo
Älgnäs
Noran
Kalvhararna
Axmarsbruk
Gulleråsen
Finnbacka
Ödmården
Gåshällan
Dalstuga
Svabensverk
Katrineberg
Mosjön
Lingan
Gåsholma
Boda
Bingsjö
Lövtjärn
Högbacka
Grönviken
Viksjön
Axmar
Östbjörka
Lamborn
Källsjön
Åmot
Hedsjön
Mörtebo
Dödmansskär
Ljugaren
Dådran
Bergby
Totra
Norrsundet
Nerde Gärdsjö
Balungen
Vallsbo
Vikarbyn
Kurbergets fab
Rönnbacken
Mo
Hagsta
Hamrångefjärden
Katrineholm
Rättvik
Ärtled
Tallås
Ockelbo
Iggön
Hyn
Storsjön
Jädraån
Kolforsen
Norrtjärn
Trödje
Söderås
Marnäs
Övertänger
Jädraås
Brattfors
Eskön
Mårtanberg
Vintjärn
Gammelboning
Hillevik
Vitgrundet
Enviken
Gästrikland
Testeboån
Björke
Falun
Rogsjön
Unghed
Svärdsjö
Svärdsjön
Ågsjön
Kungsberg
Kungsfors
Medskog
Oslättfors
Åbyggeby
Utvalnäs
Lövgrund
Leksand
Bjursås
Järbo
Skönvik
Hille
Bönan
Strömsbro
Gävlebukten
Sågmyra
Kvarntäkt
Gycksbo
Bengtsheden
Lumsheden
Jäderfors
Hagaström
Gävle
Sveriges Järnvägsmuseum
Furuvik
Insjön
Insjön
Toftan
Hinsen
Högbo
Valbo
Lövstabukten
Bergsgården
Sundborn
Åshammar
Backberg
Järvsta
Skutskär
Gårdskär
Fågelsundet
Rexbo
Valshed
Danholn
Hyn
Kungsgården
Sandviken
Forsbacka
Mårtsbo
Hållen
Gagnef
Korsgården
Falun
Logärden
Storvik
Västerberg
Rörberg
Älvkarleby
Klungsten
Örskär
Stora Kopparberget
Sifferbo
Hästbo
Älvkarleö
Fagerviken
Djurås
Djurmo
Bäsna
Hofors
Barkhyttan
Tjärnäs
Storsjön
Karlholmsbruk
Gudinge
Ornäs
Vika
Runn
Fullen
Edsken
Långnäs
Verkebro
Skärplinge
Böle
Norrboda
Repbäcken
Grycken
Torsåker
Ottaren
Årsunda
Främlingshem
Hyttön
Marma
Oregrundsgrepen
Söderboda
Mockfjärd
Borlänge
Framtidsmuseet
Torsång
Långshyttan
Gammelstilla
Trösken
Finnbåle
Mehedeby
Åkerby
Forsmark
Naglarby
Kratte masugn
Bodåsgruvan
Lövstabruk
Halvarsgårdarna
Vikarbyn
Bastfället
Hedesunda
Tierp
Finnsjön
Idkerberget
Mora
Husby
Flinsjön
Albo
Johannisfors
Tuna-Hästberg
Klack
Rossen
Stålbo
Snesslinge

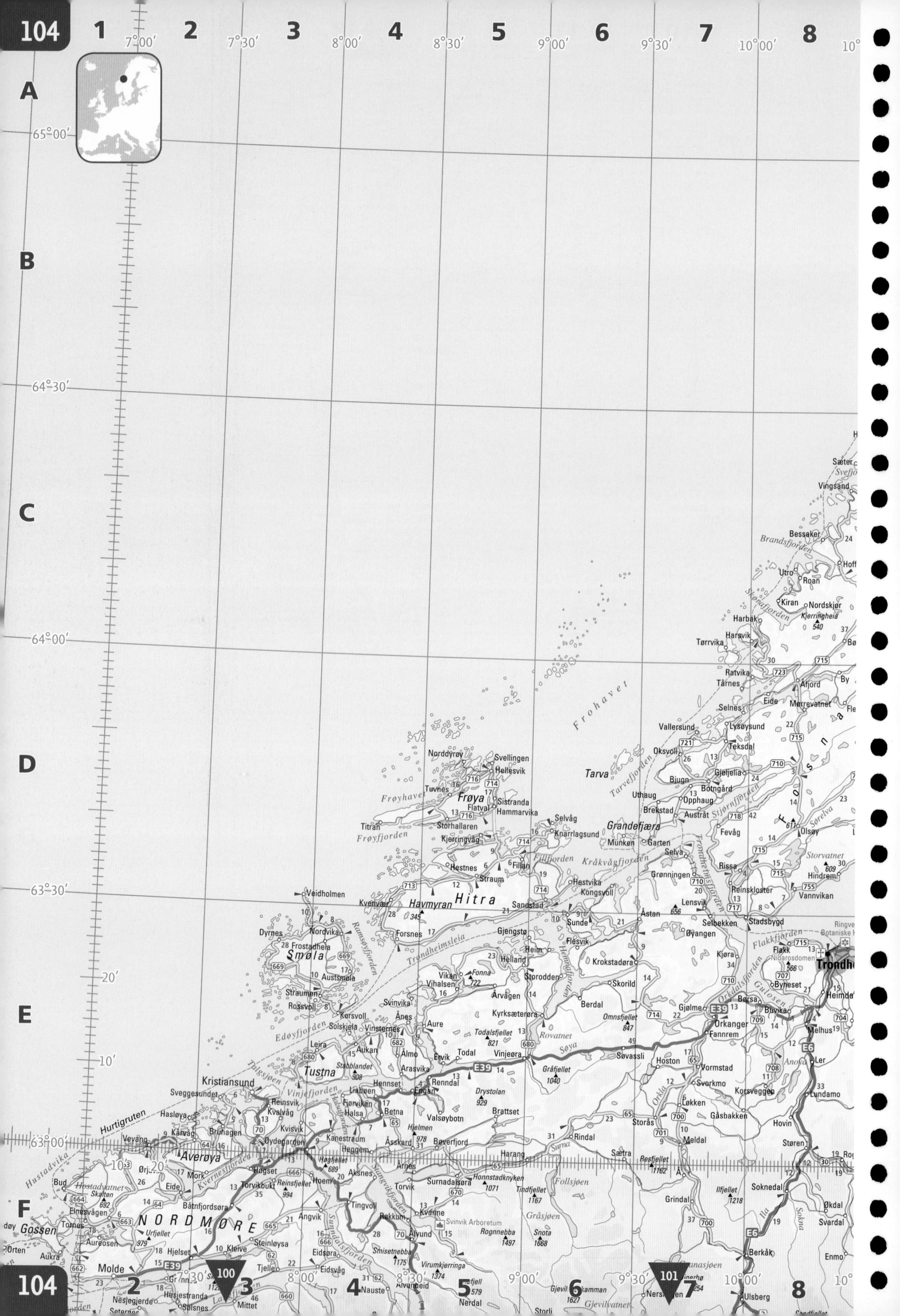

104
1 2 3 4 5 6 7 8
A B C D E F
7°00′ 7°30′ 8°00′ 8°30′ 9°00′ 9°30′ 10°00′
65°00′
64°30′
64°00′
63°30′
20′
10′
63°00′
Frohavet
Frøya
Hitra
Smøla
Tustna
Averøya
NORDMØRE
Kristiansund
Trondheim
Orkanger
Molde
Hurtigruten
Hustadvika
Trondheimsleia
Frøyhavet
Frøyfjorden
Tarva
Grandefjæra
Havmyran
Norddyrøy
Svellingen
Hellesvik
Titran
Sistranda
Hammarvika
Kjerringvåg
Hestnes
Straum
Fillan
Sandstad
Kvenvær
Veidholmen
Nordvika
Dyrnes
Edøyfjorden
Aure
Vinjeøra
Todal
Søvassli
Hemnefjorden
Melhus
Støren
Soknedal
Berkåk
Rennebu
Surnadalsøra
Sunndalsøra
Tingvoll
Eide
Bud
Elnesvågen
Aukra
Gossen
Bessaker
Roan
Åfjord
Brekstad
Uthaug
Ørland
Krokstadøra
Skorild
Lensvik
Agdenes
Selbekken
Stadsbygd
Rissa
Fosen
Vallersund
Oksvoll
Bjugn
Botngård
Opphaug
Austrått
Lysøysund
Teksdal
Gjølme
Børsa
Buvika
Ler
Lundamo
Hovin
Løkken
Meldal
Storås
Rindal
Svorkmo
Vormstad
Hoston
Fannrem
Sætra
Resfjellet
Grindal
Gjevilvatnet
Ulsberg
Storli
Nerdal
Mittet
Solsnes
Nesjegjerde
Halsa
Betna
Kanestraum
Valsøybotn
Bøverfjord
Svinvik Arboretum
Folldal
Trollheimen
E39
E6
100
101

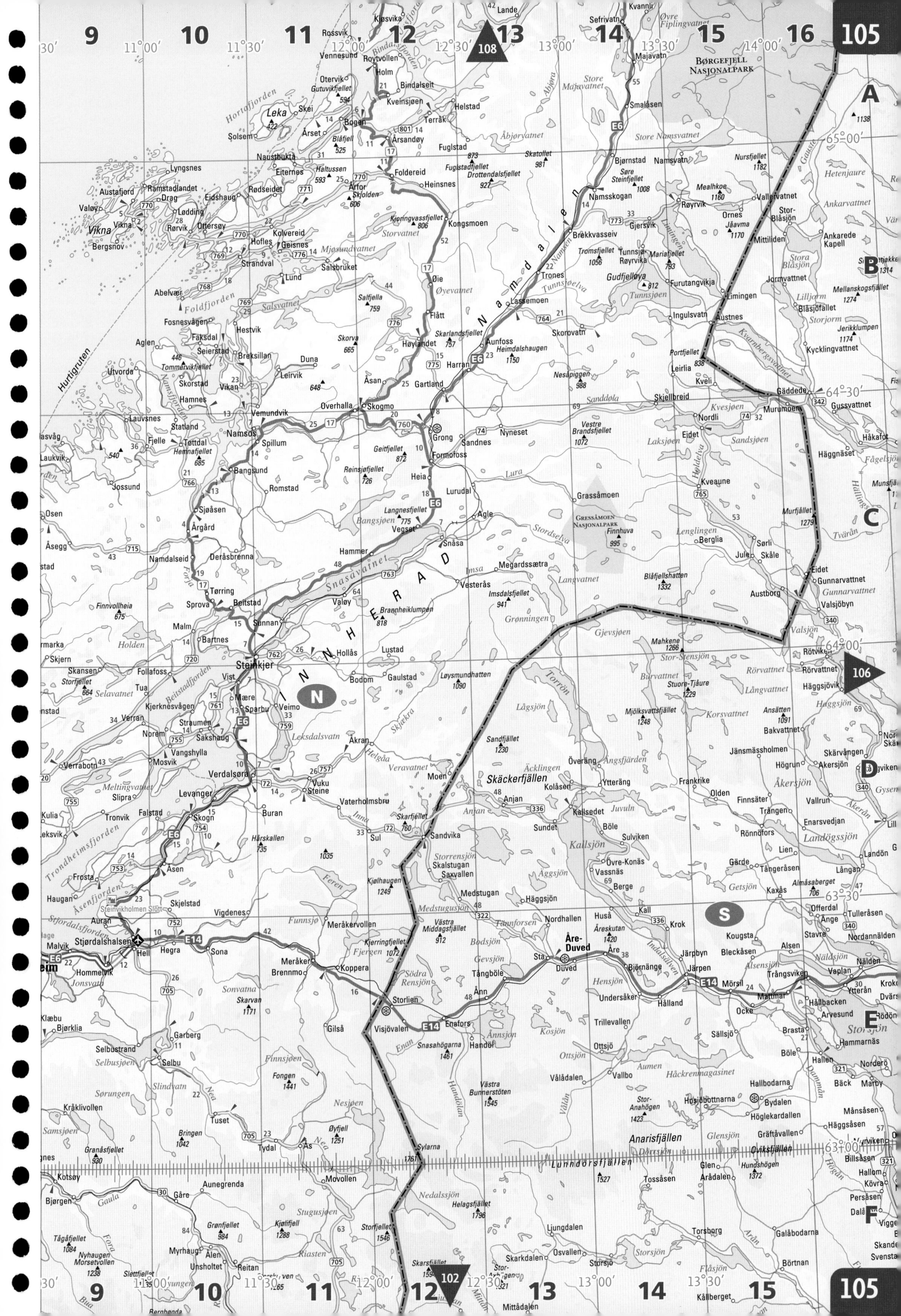
105
9
10
11
12
13
14
15
16
108
106
102
A
B
C
D
E
F
N
S
Børgefjell Nasjonalpark
Gressåmoen Nasjonalpark
Namdalen
Inn Herad
Hurtigruten
Leka
Vikna
Rørvik
Kolvereid
Foldereid
Kongsmoen
Namsskogan
Smalåsen
Majavatn
Trones
Røyrvik
Gjersvik
Tunnsjøen
Limingen
Harran
Grong
Formofoss
Namsos
Spillum
Bangsund
Overhalla
Skogmo
Høylandet
Snåsa
Snåsavatnet
Steinkjer
Sparbu
Verdalsøra
Levanger
Skogn
Åsen
Frosta
Stjørdalshalsen
Hell
Hegra
Meråker
Storlien
Vuku
Sandvika
Sul
Skäckerfjällen
Kallsjön
Åre
Duved
Järpen
Mörsil
Undersåker
Åreskutan
Anarisfjällen
Sylarna
Tydal
Selbu
Ålen
Reitan
Gäddede
Murumoen
Valsjöbyn
Hotagen
Stor-Stensjön
Ansätten
Bakvattnet
Kaxås
Offerdal
Krok
Hallen
Bydalen
Håkafot
Gaulstad
Malm
Beitstad
Lauvsnes
Osen
Jossund
Vingelen
E6
E14
Trondheimsfjorden
Gaula
Lunndörsfjällen
Helagsfjället
Storsjön
Indalsälven
Ljungdalen
Mittådalen

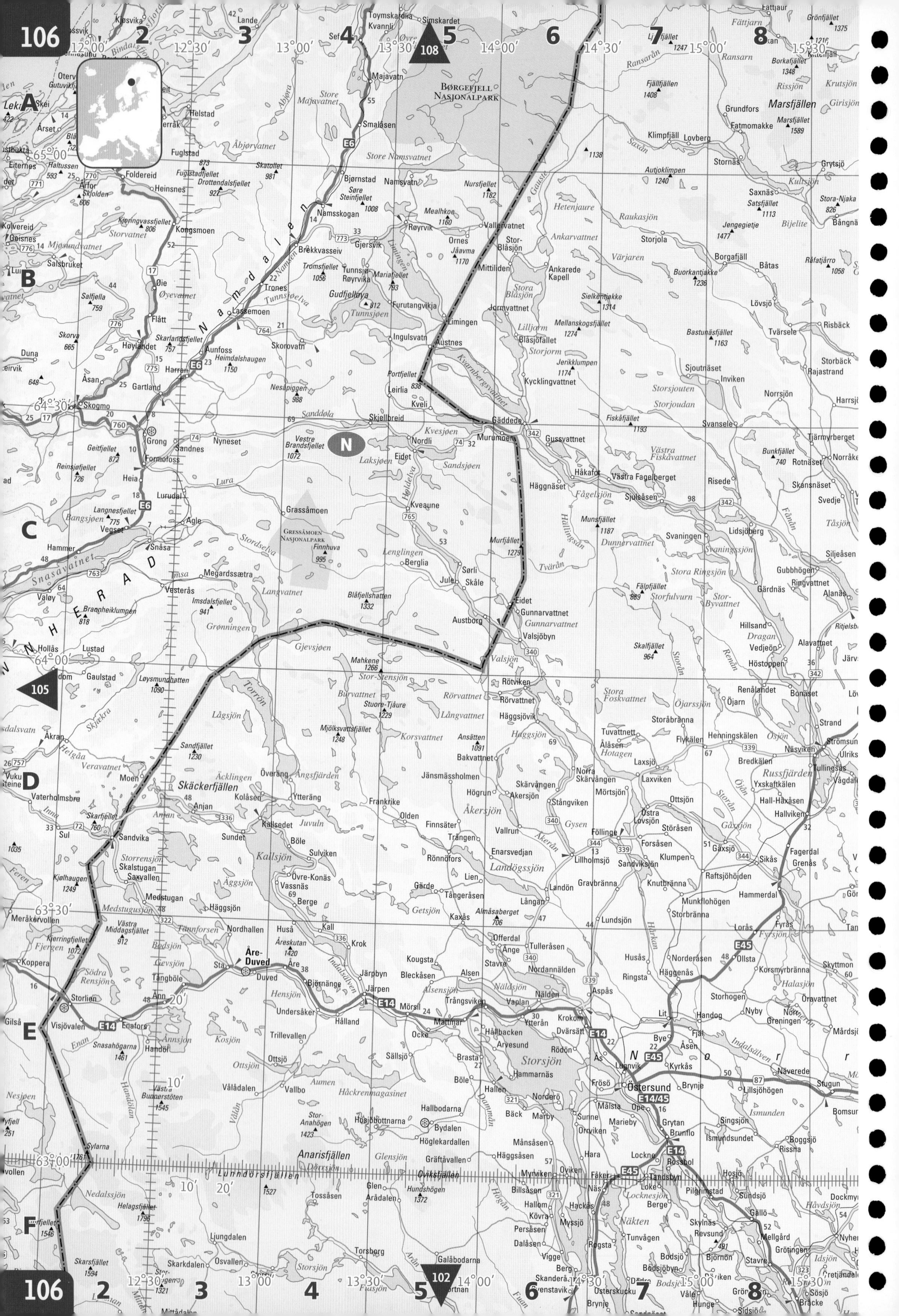
1
2
3
4
5
6
7
8
A
B
C
D
E
F
108
105
102
12°00′
12°30′
13°00′
13°30′
14°00′
14°30′
15°00′
15°30′
65°00′
64°30′
64°00′
63°30′
63°00′
Kjøsvika
Lande
Toymskardlia
Simskardet
Kvannli
Majavatn
Børgefjell Nasjonalpark
Store Majavatnet
Smalåsen
Helstad
Fuglstad
Åbjørvatnet
Store Namsvatnet
Fättjarn
Grönfjället
Ransarån
Ransarn
Fjällfjällen
Borkafjället
Rissjön
Krutsjön
Marsfjällen
Girisjön
Grundfors
Fatmomakke
Klimpfjäll
Lovberg
Saxån
Stornäs
Grytsjö
Autjoklimpen
Kultsjön
Saxnäs
Satsfjället
Stora-Njaka
Bångnäs
Bijelite
Jengegietje
Leka
Skei
Årset
Haltussen
Foldereid
Heinsnes
Årfor
Skjolden
Fuglstadfjellet
Drottendalsfjellet
Skatollet
Bjørnstad
Søre Steinfjellet
Namsvatn
Nursfjellet
Namsskogan
Mealhkoe
Røyrvik
Vallervatnet
Hetenjaure
Raukasjön
Ankarvatnet
Storjola
Kolvereid
Geisnes
Mjøsundvatnet
Salsbruket
Kjøringvassfjellet
Storvatnet
Kongsmoen
Brekkvasseiv
Gjersvik
Limingen
Ornes
Jåavma
Stor-Blåsjön
Mittilidén
Ankarede Kapell
Värjaren
Borgafjäll
Båtas
Råfatjärro
Buorkantjakke
Tromsfjellet
Tunnsjø
Røyrvika
Mariafjellet
Øie
Øyevatnet
Trones
Tunnsjøelva
Gudfjelløya
Tunnsjøen
Furutangvikja
Stora Blåsjön
Sielkentjakke
Lövsjö
Salfjella
Flått
Lassemoen
Namdalen
Jormvattnet
Mellanskogsfjället
Skorva
Høylandet
Skarlandsfjellet
Aunfoss
Heimdalshaugen
Skorovatn
Ingulsvatn
Austnes
Lilljorm
Blåsjöfallet
Storjorm
Bastunäsfjället
Tvärsele
Risbäck
Duna
Harran
Gartland
Åsan
Jerikklumpen
Kycklingvattnet
Sjoutnäset
Inviken
Storbäck
Rajastrand
Portfjellet
Leirlia
Kveli
Nesåpiggen
Kvarnbergsvattnet
Storsjouten
Storjoudan
Norrsjön
Harrsjö
Skogmo
Grong
Sanddøla
Skjellbreid
Gäddede
Fiskåfjället
Svansele
Nyneset
Sandnes
Vestre Brandsfjellet
Nordli
Kvesjøen
Murumoen
Gussvattnet
Västra Fiskåvattnet
Tjärmyrberget
Geitfjellet
Formofoss
Laksjøen
Eidet
Sandsjøen
Bunkfjället
Rotnäset
Norråker
Reinsjøfjellet
Heia
Lura
Holdelva
Håkafot
Västra Fagelberget
Häggnäset
Risede
Skansnäset
Lurudal
Fågelsjön
Sjulsåsen
Svedje
Grassåmoen
Kveaune
Munsfjället
Fånån
Tåsjön
Bangsjøen
Langnesfjellet
Vegset
Agle
Hällingsån
Lidsjöberg
Hammer
Snåsa
Stordselva
Gressåmoen Nasjonalpark
Finnhuva
Lenglingen
Berglia
Murfjället
Dunnervattnet
Svaningen
Svaningssjön
Siljeåsen
Snåsavatnet
Megardssætra
Sørli
Jule
Skåle
Tvärån
Stora Ringsjön
Gubbhögen
Ringvattnet
Valøy
Vesterås
Imsdalsfjellet
Langvatnet
Blåfjellshatten
Fälpfjället
Storfulvurn
Stor-Byvattnet
Gärdnäs
Alanäs
Brannheiklumpen
Grønningen
Eidet
Gunnarvattnet
Austborg
Valsjöbyn
Hillsand
Dragan
Vedjeön
Alavattnet
Rijelsbo
Holläs
Lustad
Gjevsjøen
Mahkene
Stor-Stensjön
Valsjön
Skalfjället
Storån
Remån
Höstoppen
Järvsjö
Gaulstad
Løysmundhatten
Torrön
Burvattnet
Stuore-Tjåure
Rörvattnet
Rötviken
Stora Foskvattnet
Öjarssjön
Öjarn
Renålandet
Bonäset
Skjækra
Lågsjön
Långvattnet
Häggsjövik
Storåbränna
Strand
Åkran
Helgåa
Mjölkvattsfjället
Korsvattnet
Ansätten
Häggsjön
Tuvattnett
Ålåsen
Hotagen
Flykälen
Henningskälen
Ösjön
Strömsund
Sandfjället
Bakvattnet
Laxsjö
Bredkälen
Näsviken
Ulriksfors
Veravatnet
Moen
Äcklingen
Överäng
Ängsfjärden
Jänsmässholmen
Norra Skärvången
Russfjärden
Tullingsås
Skäckerfjällen
Högrun
Skärvången
Akersjön
Mörtsjön
Laxviken
Yxskaftkälen
Vågdalen
Vaterholmsbru
Anjan
Kolåsen
Ytteräng
Frankrike
Stångviken
Östra Lövsjön
Ottsjön
Hall-Håxåsen
Hallviken
Skarfjellet
Kallsedet
Juvuln
Olden
Åkersjön
Finnsäter
Vallrun
Gysen
Föllinge
Storåsen
Gåxsjön
Sul
Sandvika
Sundet
Böle
Trången
Forsåsen
Gåxsjö
Sikås
Fagerdal
Grenås
Storrensjön
Skalstugan
Saxvallen
Kallsjön
Sulviken
Övre-Konäs
Vassnäs
Rönnöfors
Enarsvedjan
Landögssjön
Lillholmsjö
Sandviksjön
Klumpen
Raftsjöhöjden
Kjølhaugen
Äggsjön
Berge
Lien
Gärde
Tångeråsen
Landön
Gravbränna
Knutbränna
Medstugan
Långan
Hammerdal
Häggsjön
Getsjön
Kaxås
Almåsaberget
Munkflohögen
Storbränna
Meråkervollen
Medstugusjön
Västra Middagsfjället
Tännforsen
Nordhallen
Huså
Kall
Lundsjön
Lorås
Fyrås
Fyrsjön
Kjerringfjellet
Fjergen
Krok
Åreskutan
Offerdal
Änge
Tulleråsen
Ollsta
Skyttmon
Koppera
Södra Rensjön
Gevsjön
Bodsjön
Åre
Åre-Duved
Duved
Kougsta
Bleckåsen
Stavre
Alsen
Nordannälden
Huså
Norderåsen
Ringsta
Häggenås
Korsmyrbränna
Halasjön
Tångböle
Storlien
Ånn
Järpbyn
Björnänge
Järpen
Indalsälven
Alsensjön
Näldsjön
Nälden
Aspås
Storhogen
Öravattnet
Gilså
Visjövalen
Enafors
Enan
Hensjön
Undersåker
Mörsil
Trångsviken
Vaplan
Ytterån
Krokom
Dvärsätt
Lit
Handog
Nyby
Norr Greningen
Mårdsjö
Snasahögarna
Handöl
Annsjön
Kosjön
Trillevallen
Hålland
Mattmar
Ocke
Hållbacken
Arvesund
Bye
Fjäl
Åsen
Rödön
Ås
Lugnvik
Kyrkås
Indalsälven
Norr
Nesjøen
Ottsjö
Sällsjö
Brasta
Storsjön
Hammarnäs
Näverede
Handölan
Våldalen
Vallbo
Aumen
Håckrenmagasinet
Böle
Hallen
Frösö
Östersund
Brynje
Lillsjöhögen
Stugun
Västra Bunnerstöten
Vålån
Hallbodarna
Bydalen
Dammån
Norderö
Bäck
Marby
Målsta
Opel
Sunne
Orrviken
Marieby
Grytan
Brunflo
Singsjön
Ismunden
Ismundsundet
Bomsund
Stor-Anahögen
Hosjöbottnarna
Höglekardallen
Månsåsen
Boggsjö
Rissna
Sylarna
Anarisfjällen
Glensjön
Gräftåvallen
Häggsåsen
Hara
Lockne
Rossbol
Dörrsjön
Lunndörsfjällen
Oviksfjällen
Myrviken
Oviken
Fåker
Tandsbyn
Hosjö
Nedalssjön
Glen
Arådalen
Tossåsen
Hundshögen
Billsåsen
Näs
Loke
Locknesjön
Pilgrimstad
Sundsjö
Dockmyr
Helagsfjället
Högån
Hallom
Hackås
Berge
Gällö
Hävdsjön
Kövra
Myssjö
Nälden
Nåkten
Skylnäs
Revsund
Mellgård
Nyhem
Ljungdalen
Persåsen
Dalåsen
Tunvågen
Grötingen
Torsborg
Rogsta
Bodsjö
Björnön
Stavre
Idsjön
Skarsfjället
Skarkdalen
Osvallen
Storsjön
Galåbodarna
Vigge
Bodsjöbyn
Cretjåndalen
Berg
Skanderåsen
Svenstavik
Österkucku
Våle
Sösjö
Bräcke
Stor-Mittågen
Flåsjön
Mittådalen
Brynje
Sidsjö
Hunge
Grönan
Fruån
Svenstavik
E6
E14
E45
E14/45

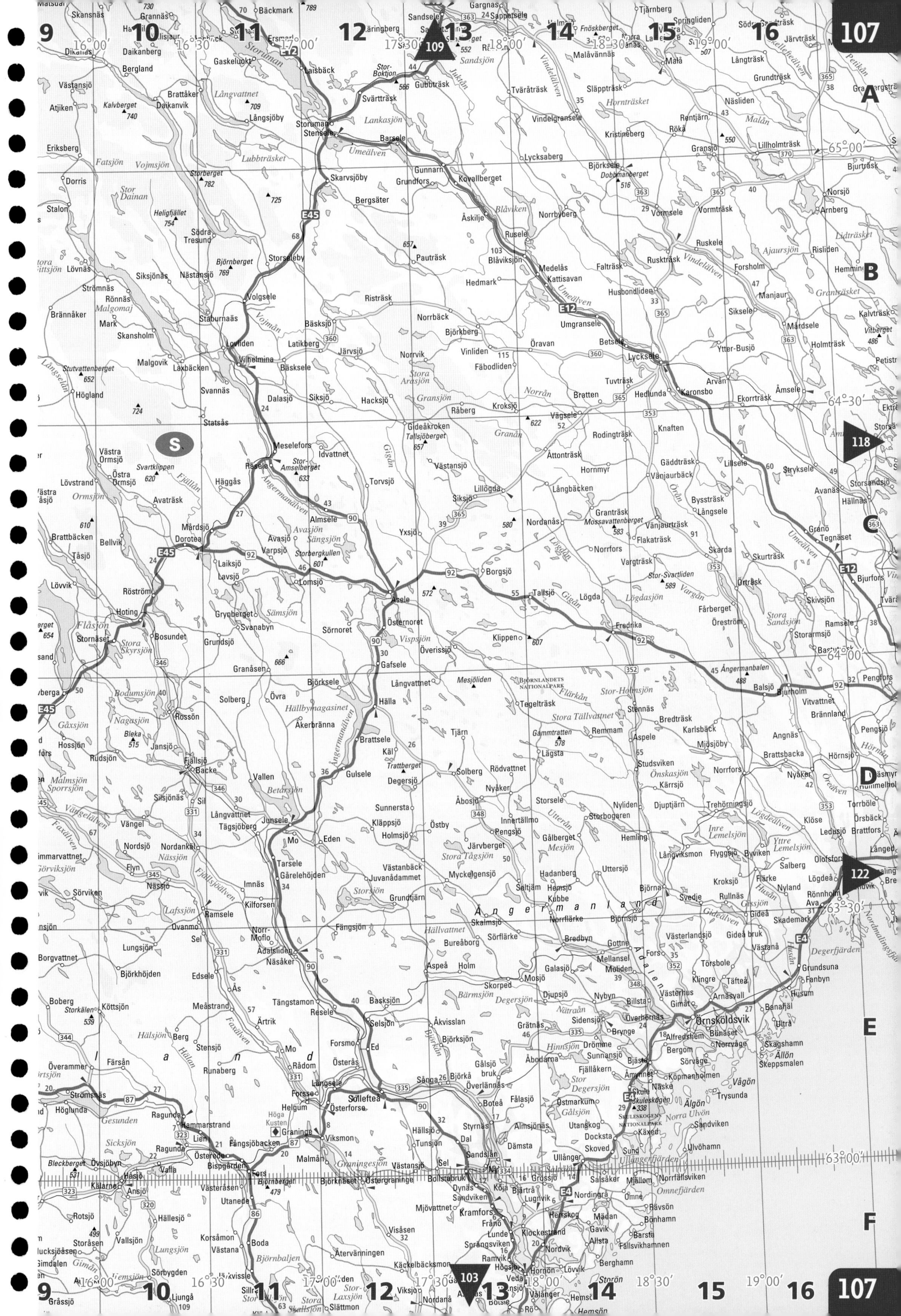
9
10
11
12
13
14
15
16
A
B
C
D
E
F
109
118
122
103
65°00'
64°30'
64°00'
63°30'
63°00'
16°00'
16°30'
17°00'
17°30'
18°00'
18°30'
19°00'
Skansnäs
Grannäs
Bäckmark
Sandsele
Gargnas
Sappetsele
Tjärnberg
Springliden
Dikanäs
Daikanberg
Gaskeluokt
Storuman
Ersmark
Laisbäck
Stor-Boktjön
Gubbträsk
Sandsjön
Juktån
Malåvännäs
Malå
Långträsk
Grundträsk
Petikån
Bergland
Västansjö
Atjiken
Kalvberget
Brattåker
Daikanvik
Långvattnet
Långsjöby
Svärtträsk
Lankasjön
Tväråträsk
Släppträsk
Hornträsket
Näsliden
Malån
Vindelgransele
Rentjärn
Röka
Vindelälven
Eriksberg
Fatsjön
Vojmsjön
Lubbträsket
Stensele
Umeälven
Barsele
Kristineberg
Gransjö
Lillholmträsk
Lycksaberg
Björksele
Dobbmanberget
Bjurträsk
Storberget
Dorris
Stor Dainan
Skarvsjöby
Gunnarn
Kovallberget
Grundfors
Bergsäter
Norsjö
Arnberg
Stalon
Heligfjället
Södra Tresund
E45
Åskilje
Blåviken
Norrbyberg
Vormsele
Vormträsk
Ruselet
Ruskele
Lidträsket
Ajaursjön
Risliden
Hemmingsmark
Pauträsk
Blåviksjön
Medelås
Kattisavan
Falträsk
Ruskträsk
Forsholm
Lövnäs
Siksjönäs
Nästansjö
Björnberget
Storseleby
Hedmark
Husbondliden
Manjaur
Granträsket
Strömnäs
Rönnäs
Malgomaj
Volgsele
Risträsk
E12
Siksele
Kalvträsk
Brännåker
Mark
Skansholm
Staburnäs
Vojmån
Bäsksjö
Norrbäck
Björkberg
Umgransele
Mårdsele
Vitberget
Malgovik
Laxbäcken
Lovliden
Vilhelmina
Latikberg
Järvsjö
Norrvik
Vinliden
Fäbodliden
Örävan
Betsele
Lycksele
Ytter-Busjö
Holmträsk
Stutvattenberget
Högland
Bäsksele
Stora Arasjön
Tuvträsk
Hedlunda
Karonsbo
Arvån
Åmsele
Svannäs
Dalasjö
Siksjö
Hacksjö
Gransjön
Kroksjö
Norrån
Bratten
Vägsele
Råberg
Ekorrträsk
Statsås
Gideåkroken
Tallsjöberget
Knaften
Rodingträsk
Granån
Meselefors
Idvattnet
Västra Ormsjö
Östra Ormsjö
Svartklippen
Fjällån
Råsele
Stor-Amselberget
Västansjö
Attonträsk
Hornmyr
Gäddträsk
Vänjaurbäck
Lillsele
Strycksele
Avanäs
Storsandsjö
Hällnäs
Lövstrand
Västra Tåsjö
Ormsjön
Häggås
Ångermanälven
Torvsjö
Gigån
Lillögda
Långbäcken
Byssträsk
Långsele
Avaträsk
Almsele
Avasjö
Sängsjön
Siksjö
Nordanås
Mossavattenberget
Granträsk
Vänjaurträsk
Flakaträsk
Granö
Tegnäset
Brattbäcken
Bellvik
Mårdsjö
Dorotea
Varpsjö
Storbergkullen
Yxsjö
Norrfors
Lögdån
Skarda
Skurträsk
Tåsjö
Laiksjö
Lavsjö
Lomsjö
Borgsjö
Vargträsk
Stor-Svartliden
Bjurfors
Lövvik
Röström
Åsele
Tallsjö
Lögda
Lögdasjön
Vargån
Örträsk
Skivsjön
Hoting
Gryberget
Sämsjön
Svanabyn
Sörnoret
Österoret
Vispsjön
Fredrika
Fårberget
Öreström
Stora Sandsjön
Ramsele
Flåsjön
Stornäset
Bosundet
Stora Skyrsjön
Grundsjö
Klippen
Överissjö
Storarmsjö
Bastuträsk
Granåsen
Gafsele
Ångermanbalen
Björksele
Långvattnet
Mesjöliden
Björnlandets nationalpark
Flärkån
Stor-Holmsjön
Balsjö
Bjurholm
Vitvattnet
Pengfors
Bodumsjön
Solberg
Övra
Hällbymagasinet
Hälla
Tegelträsk
Stora Tällvattnet
Stennäs
Brännland
Nagasjön
Rossön
Åkerbränna
Gammtratten
Remmam
Bredträsk
Karlsbäck
Pengsjö
Gåxsjön
Hossjön
Bleka
Jansjö
Brattsele
Tjärn
Lägsta
Aspele
Mjösjöby
Angnäs
Brattsbacka
Hörnsjö
Rudsjön
Fjällsjö
Backe
Kål
Trattberget
Solberg
Rödvattnet
Studsviken
Önskasjön
Norrfors
Nyåker
Malmsjön
Sporrsjön
Vallen
Betarsjön
Gulsele
Degersjö
Nyåker
Kärrsjö
Silsjönäs
Sil
Sunnersta
Åbosjö
Storsele
Nyliden
Djuptjärn
Trehörningsjö
Långvattnet
Tägsjöberg
Junsele
Kläppsjö
Innertällmo
Storbogeren
Lögdeälven
Torrböle
Örsbäck
Vängelälven
Vängel
Faxälven
Holmsjö
Östby
Pengsjö
Utterån
Inre Lemelsjön
Hemling
Klöse
Ledusjö
Brattfors
Nordsjö
Nordankäl
Mo
Eden
Järvberget
Stora Tågsjön
Gålberget
Mesjön
Långviksmon
Flyggsjö
Byviken
Yttre Lemelsjön
Olofsfors
Nässjön
Tarsele
Gärelehöjden
Västanbäck
Juvanådammet
Myckelgensjö
Hadanberg
Hemsjö
Uttersjö
Salberg
Flyn
Nässjö
Fjällsjöälven
Imnäs
Storsjön
Grundtjärn
Saltjäm
Kubbe
Björna
Svedje
Kroksjö
Flärke
Nyland
Lögdeå
Sörviken
Lafssjön
Ramsele
Kilforsen
Ångermanland
Norrflärke
Björnsjö
Rullnäs
Gissjön
Gideälven
Gideå
Rönnholm
Ava
Skademark
Ovanmo
Sel
Norr-Moflo
Fängsjön
Hällvattnet
Skalmsjö
Sörflärke
Bredbyn
Gottne
Mellansel
Västerlandsjö
Gideå bruk
Västanå
Degerfjärden
Lungsjön
Borgvattnet
Ådalsliden
Näsåker
Bureåborg
Aspeå
Holm
Galasjö
Moliden
Forsmo
Törsbole
Grundsuna
Fanbyn
Björkhöjden
Edsele
Skorped
Mosjö
Klingre
Täftea
E4
Bodberg
Storkälen
Köttsjön
Meåstrand
Ås
Tängstamon
Resele
Basksjön
Bärmsjön
Degersjön
Djupsjö
Nybyn
Billsta
Västerhus
Gimåt
Arnäsvall
Husum
Banafjäl
Ultrå
Ärtrik
Selsjön
Åkvisslan
Nätraån
Sidensjö
Överhörnäs
Örnsköldsvik
Bonäset
Norrvåge
Skagshamn
Ällön
Skeppsmalen
Hälsjön
Berg
Stensjö
Mo
Forsmo
Ed
Björksjön
Grätnäs
Hinnsjön
Drömme
Bryngé
Alfredshem
Bergom
Sörvåge
Köpmanholmen
Vågön
Överammer
Färsån
Hälan
Runaberg
Rådom
Österås
Gålsjö bruk
Åbodarna
Sunnansjö
Bjästa
Åmynnet
Näske
Trysunda
Strömsnäs
Forsse
Långsele
Sollefteå
Sånga
Björkå
Överlännäs
Fjälläkern
Stor Degersjön
Skule
Skuleskogen
Skuleskogens nationalpark
Norra Ulvön
Älgön
Höglunda
Gesunden
Ragunda
Hammarstrand
Helgum
Österforse
Höga Kusten
Graninge
Boteå
Fålasjö
Östmarkum
Gålsjön
Utanskog
Sandviken
Sicksjön
Lien
Ragunda
Östered
Fängsjöbacken
Viksmon
Hällsjö
Tunsjön
Styrnäs
Dal
Almsjönäs
Dämsta
Docksta
Skoved
Käxed
Ulvöhamn
Bleckberget
Övsjöbyn
Valla
Bispgården
Fors
Malmån
Graningesjön
Västansjö
Sandslån
Ullånger
Sund
Ullångersfjärden
Hasjö
Kälarne
Västeråsen
Björnberget
Björknäset
Östergraninge
Bollstabruk
Nyland
Gissjö
Salsåker
Mjällom
Norrfällsviken
Omnefjärden
Ansjö
Utanede
Dynäs
Sandviken
Köja
Bjärtrå
Lugnvik
Nordingrå
Omne
Rävsön
Bönhamn
Rotsjö
Hällesjö
Mjövattnet
Kramfors
Herrskog
Mädan
Gavik
Allsta
Barsta
Fällsvikhamnen
Storåsen
Vallsjön
Korsåmon
Västana
Lungsjön
Boda
Visåsen
Frånö
Lunde
Sprängsviken
Klockestrand
Nordvik
Simdalen
Gimån
Björnbaljen
Återvänningen
Käckelbäcksmon
Ramvik
Högsjö
Hornön
Lövvik
Berghamn
Sörbygden
Stornön
Ljungå
Sillre
Gålsjöröy
Viksjö
Stora Laxsjön
Slättmon
Stora Skallsjön
Nordanå
Veda
Väjänger
Hemsön
Grässjö

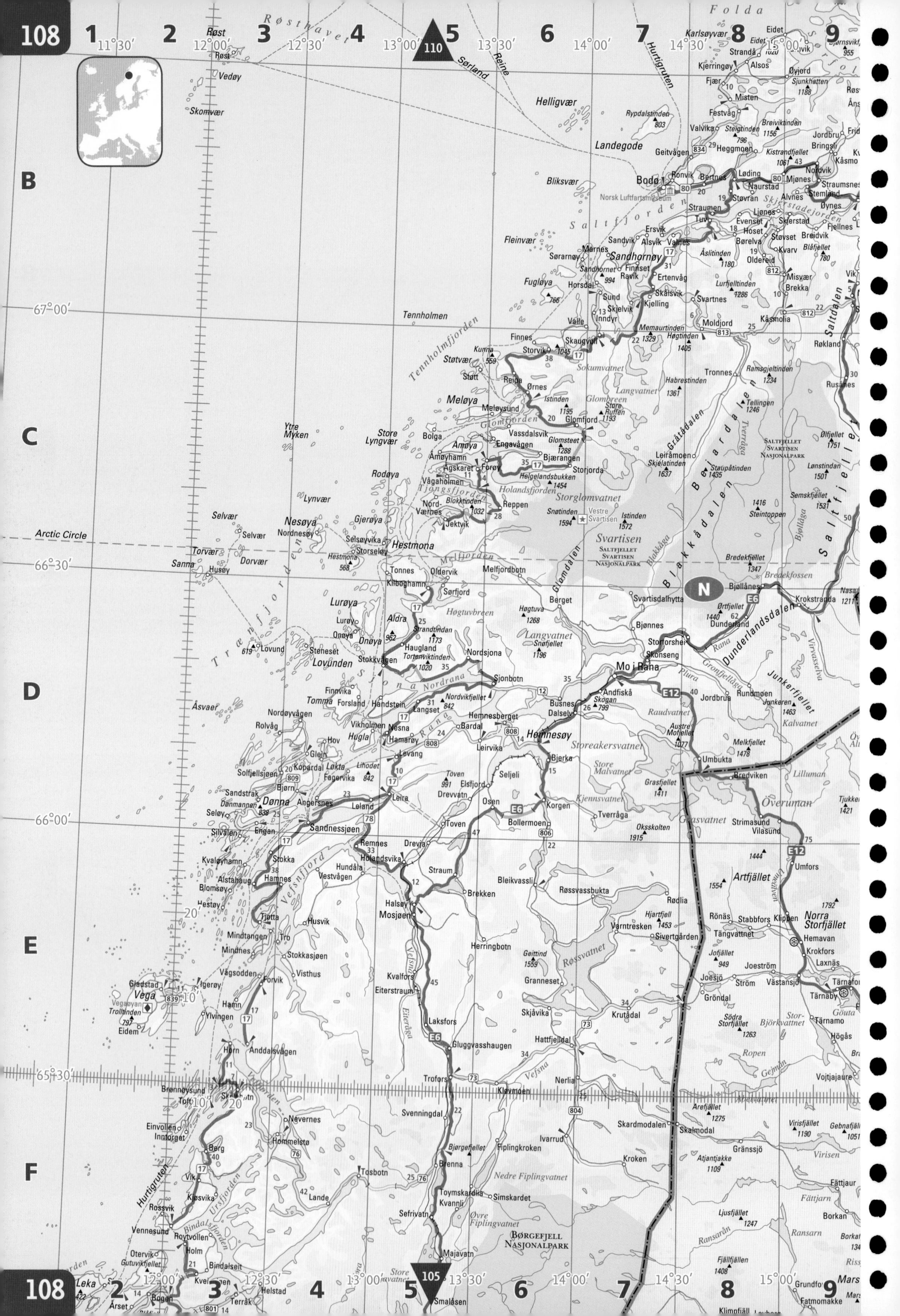

108
1
2
3
4
5
6
7
8
9
110
B
C
D
E
F
Røst
Røsthavet
Sørland
Reine
Hurtigruten
Folda
Vedøy
Skomvær
Helligvær
Landegode
Bliksvær
Bodø
Norsk Luftfartsmuseum
Saltfjorden
Fleinvær
Sandhornøy
Fugløya
Tennholmen
Tennholmfjorden
Støtvær
Meløya
Glomfjord
Glomfjorden
Ytre Myken
Store Lyngvær
Rodøya
Lynvær
Selvær
Nesøya
Gjerøya
Hestmona
Arctic Circle
Torvær
Dorvær
Sanna
Husøy
Svartisen
Saltfjellet Svartisen Nasjonalpark
Storglomvatnet
Beiardalen
Blakkådalen
Saltfjellet
Saltdalen
Lurøya
Aldra
Onøya
Lovund
Lovunden
Trænfjorden
Træna
Sjona
Nordrana
Mo i Rana
Dunderlandsdalen
Junkerfjellet
Hemnesøy
Storeakersvatnet
Store Malvatnet
Dønna
Sandnessjøen
Vefsnfjord
Mosjøen
Vega
Røssvatnet
Overuman
Artfjället
Norra Storfjället
Hemavan
Tärnaby
Gäuta
Tärnamo
Höggås
Vojtjajaure
Brønnøysund
Bindalsfjorden
Børgefjell Nasjonalpark
Nedre Fiplingvatnet
Øvre Fiplingvatnet
Hattfjelldal
Trofors
Majavatn
Smalåsen
Leka
105
66°30′
66°00′
65°30′
67°00′
11°30′
12°00′
12°30′
13°00′
13°30′
14°00′
14°30′
15°00′
E6
E12
17

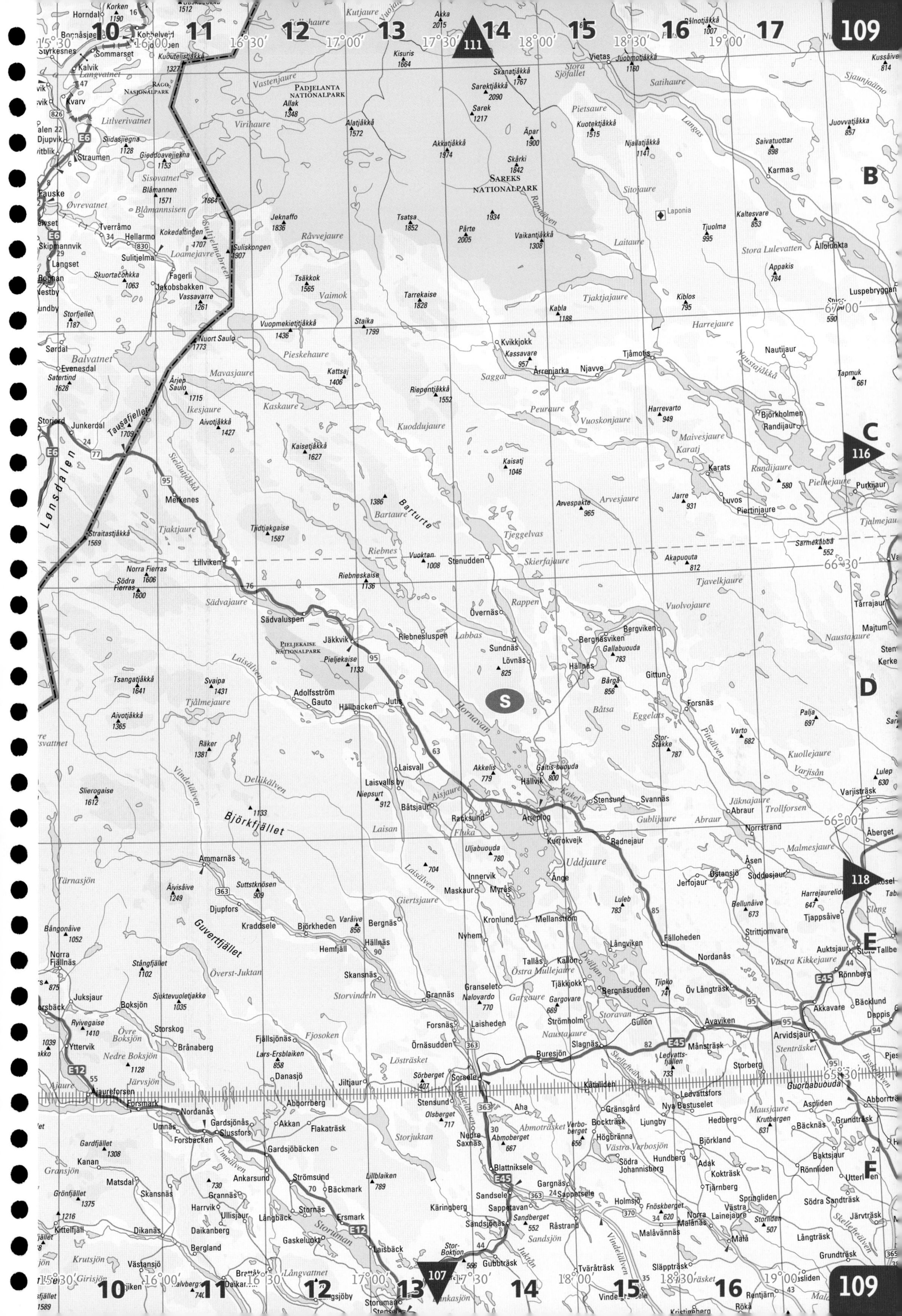

10
11
12
13
14
15
16
17
111
116
118
107
B
C
D
E
F
Padjelanta Nationalpark
Sareks Nationalpark
Rago Nasjonalpark
Pieljekaise Nationalpark
Laponia
Akka 2015
Kisuris 1664
Skanatjåkkå 1767
Sarektjåkkå 2090
Sarek 1217
Allak 1348
Alatjåkkå 1572
Akkatjåkkå 1974
Äpar 1900
Skårki 1842
Tsatsa 1852
Pårte 2005
Vaikantjåkkå 1308
Jeknaffo 1836
Tsäkkok 1565
Tarrekaise 1828
Kabla 1188
Staika 1799
Vuopmekietjtjåkkå 1436
Kvikkjokk
Kassavare 957
Årrenjarka
Njavve
Tjåmotis
Stora Sjöfallet
Vietas
Satihaure
Pietsaure
Kuotektjåkkå 1515
Njallatjåkkå 1141
Sitojaure
Laitaure
Tjaktjajaure
Stora Lulevatten
Ålloluokta
Karmas
Kiblos 795
Luspebryggan
Harrejaure
Nautijaur
Tapmuk 661
Björkholmen
Randijaur
Karats
Luvos
Piertinjaure
Purkijaur
Vastenjaure
Virihaure
Råvvejaure
Vaimok
Pieskehaure
Kaskaure
Kuoddujaure
Riepentjåkkå 1552
Kattsaj 1406
Kaisetjåkkå 1627
Barturte
Bartaure
Riebnes
Vuoktan 1008
Stenudden
Tjeggelvas
Skierfajaure
Akapuouta 812
Tjavelkjaure
Vuolvojaure
Kaisatj 1046
Arvespakte 965
Arvesjaure
Jarre 931
Harrevarto 949
Peuraure
Vuoskonjaure
Maivesjaure
Karatj
Randijaure
Pielhejaure
Tjalmejaure
Sarmekåbbå 552
Tarrajaur
Majtum
Naustajaure
66°30'
67°00'
66°00'
65°30'
Horndal
Korken 1190
Bognåsjøen
Kobbelveid
Sommarset
Kalvik
Kvarv
Litlverivatnet
Sulitjelma
Fauske
Øvrevatnet
Tverråmo
Hellarmo
Sulitjelmabreen
Loamejavre
Suliskongen 1907
Skipmannvik
Langset
Fagerli
Jakobsbakken
Vassavarre 1261
Storfjellet 1187
Nuort Saulo 1773
Sørdal
Balvatnet
Evenesdal
Satertind 1628
Mavasjaure
Ikesjaure
Årjep Saulo 1715
Aivotjåkkå 1427
Storjord
Junkerdal
Tausafjellet 1709
Lønsdalen
Sieldutjåkkå
Merkenes
Tjaktjaure
Straitastjåkkå 1569
Tjidtjakgaise 1587
Lillviken
Norra Fierras 1606
Södra Fierras 1600
Sädvajaure
Sädvaluspen
Jäkkvik
Pieljekaise 1133
Riebnesluspen
Labbas
Övernäs
Rappen
Sundnäs
Lövnäs 825
Bergnäsviken
Bergviken
Gallabuouda 783
Hällnäs
Bårgå 856
Gittun
Laisälven
Tsangatjåkkå 1641
Svaipa 1431
Tjålmejaure
Adolfsström
Gauto
Hällbacken
Jutis
Hornavan
Båtsa
Eggelats
Forsnäs
Aivotjåkkå 1365
Palja 697
Varto 682
Stor-Stakke 787
Piteälven
Kuollejaure
Varjisån
Räker 1381
Dellikälven
Laisvall
Laisvallsby
Niepsurt 912
Båtsjaur
Akkelis 779
Galtis-buouda 800
Hällvik
Kakel
Stensund
Svannäs
Jäknajaure
Abraur
Trollforsen
Lulep 630
Varjisträsk
Slierogaise 1612
Vindelälven
Björkfjället
Racksund
Arjeplog
Fluka
Gublijaure
Abraur
Norrstrand
Laisan
Kurrokvejk
Radnejaur
Åberget
Malmesjaure
Ammarnäs
Tärnasjön
Uljabuouda 780
Uddjaure
Åsen
Suddesjaur
Östansjö
Jerfojaur
Äivisåive 1249
Suttstknösen 909
Innervik
Maskaure
Myrås
Ånge
Luleb 783
Harrejaurelide 647
Tjappsåive
Bellunåive 673
Strittjomvare
Djupfors
Kraddsele
Björkheden
Varåive 856
Bergnäs
Kronlund
Mellanström
Nyhem
Fälloheden
Gierttsjaure
Guvertfjället
Hemfjäll
Hällnäs
Långviken
Nordanås
Auktsjaur
Bångonåive 1052
Norra Fjällnäs
Stångfjället 1102
Överst-Juktan
Skansnäs
Tallås
Kallön
Östra Mullejaure
Dvärjan
Tjäkkjokk
Bergnäsudden
Tjipko 741
Öv Långträsk
Västra Kikkejaure
Rönnberg
Juksjaur
Boksjön
Sjuktevuoletjakke 1035
Granselet
Nalovardo 770
Grannäs
Storvindeln
Gargaure
Gargovare 669
Strömholm
Storavan
Akkavare
Bäcklund
Deppis
Ryvigaise 1410
Övre Boksjön
Storskog
Forsnäs
Laisheden
Gullön
Avaviken
Arvidsjaur
Yttervik
Nedre Boksjön
Brånaberg
Fjällsjönäs
Fjosoken
Örnäsudden
Naustajaure
Slagnäs
Månsträsk
Stenträsket
Lars-Ersblaiken 858
Löstråsket
Buresjön
Skellefteälven
Ledvatts-fjällen 733
Storberg
Danasjö
Jiltjaur
Sörberget 407
Sorsele
Kåtaliden
Ledvattsfors
Guorbabuouda
Abborrträsk
Ajaure
Ajaureforsen
Forsmark
Nordanås
Abborrberg
Stensund
Aha
Gränsgård
Nya Bastuselet
Mausjaure
Aspliden
Krutbergen 631
Hedberg
Bäcknäs
Grundträsk
Gardsjönäs
Slussfors
Umnäs
Forsbacken
Akkan
Flakaträsk
Olsberget 717
Storjuktan
Abmotråsket
Bockträsk
Ljungby
Björkland
Verbo-berget 656
Högbränna
Västra Verbosjön
Gardfjället 1308
Gardsjöbäcken
Nedre Saxnäs
Abmoberget 667
Södra Johannisberg
Hundberg
Adak
Baktsjaur
Kokträsk
Rönnliden
Kanan
Gransjön
Umeälven
Blattniksele
Utterliden
Matsdal
Ankarsund
Strömsund
Bäckmark
Lillblaiken 789
Gargnäs
Sappetsele
Tjärnberg
Grönfjället 1375
Skansnäs
Grannäs
Harrvik
Ullisjaur
Sandsele
Sappetavan
Holmsjö
Fnösksberget 620
Springliden
Södra Sandträsk
Kittelfjäll
Stornäs
Långbäck
Ersmark
Käringberg
Sandberget 552
Råstrand
Norra Malånäs
Västra Lainejaure
Storliden 507
Järvträsk
Dikanäs
Daikanberg
Sandsjönäs
Sandsjön
Malåvännäs
Långträsk
Bergland
Gaskeluokt
Storuman
Laisbäck
Stor-Boktjon
Gubbträsk
Juktån
Vindelälven
Malå
Grundträsk
Krutsjön
Västansjö
Långvattnet
Tväråträsk
Släppträsk
Rentjärn
Röka
Kristineberg
Vindeln
Stensele
E6
E12
E45
95
363

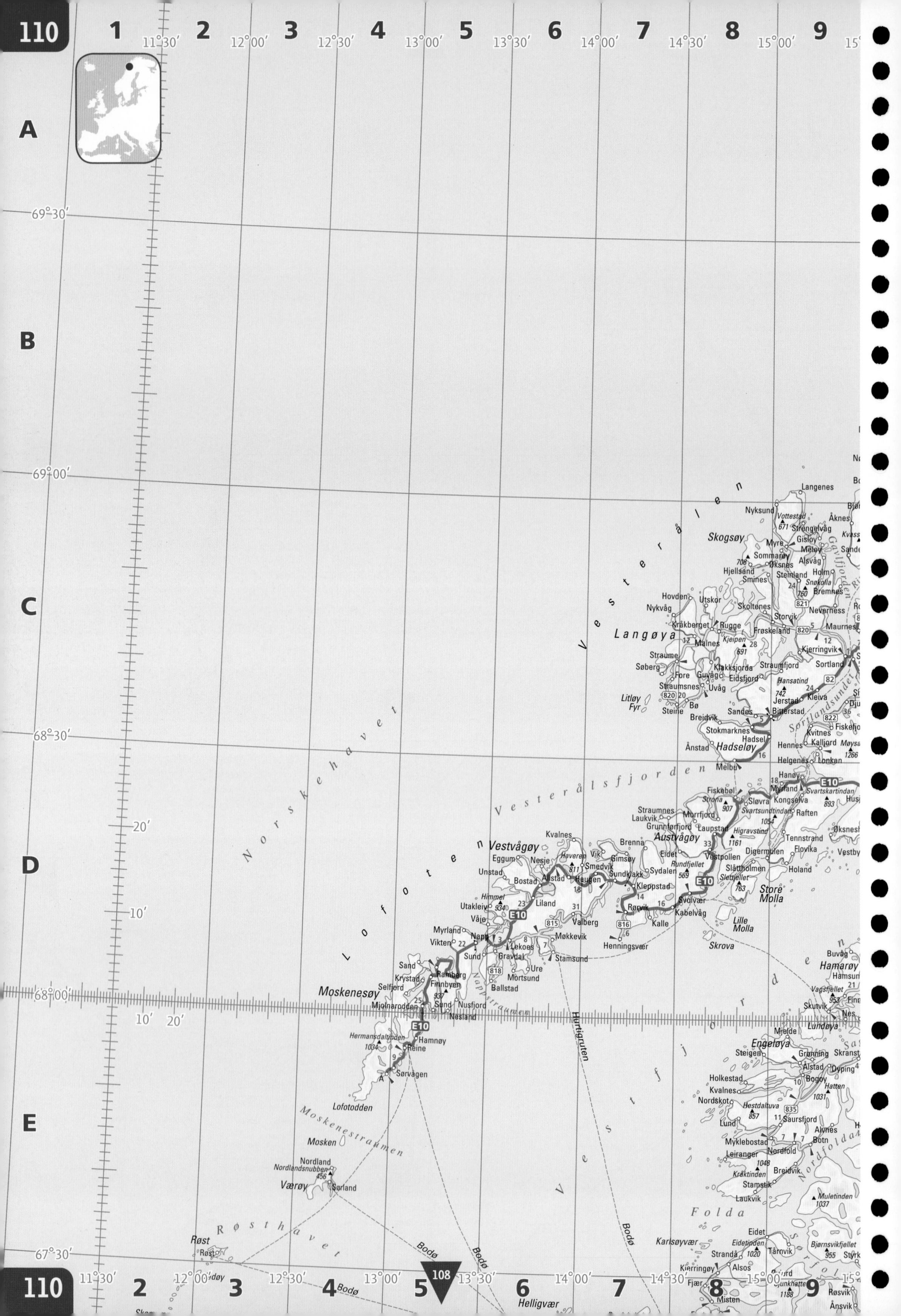
1
2
3
4
5
6
7
8
9
A
B
C
D
E
11°30′
12°00′
12°30′
13°00′
13°30′
14°00′
14°30′
15°00′
69°30′
69°00′
68°30′
68°00′
67°30′
20′
10′
Vesterålen
Norskehavet
Vesterålsfjorden
Lofoten
Vestfjorden
Røsthavet
Moskenestraumen
Nappstraumen
Folda
Sortlandsundet
Gavlfjorden
Nordfolda
Hurtigruten
Bodø
Langenes
Nyksund
Vottestad
671
Strengelvåg
Åknes
Skogsøy
Myre
Gisløy
Meløy
Sommarøy
Øksnes
Alsvåg
708
Hjellsand
Steinland
Holm
Smines
Snøkolla
760
Bremnes
Hovden
Utskor
Nykvåg
Skoltenes
Storvik
Neverness
Kråkberget
Rugge
Frøskeland
Maurnes
Langøya
Malnes
Kjeipen
691
Kjerringvik
Straume
Sortland
Søberg
Fore
Guvåg
Klakksjorda
Straumfjord
Eidsfjord
Hansatind
Straumsnes
Uvåg
742
Kleiva
Jerstad
Litløy Fyr
Bø
Steine
Breidvik
Sandes
Bitterstad
Stokmarknes
Hadsel
Kvitnes
Hennes
Kalljord
Ånstad
Hadseløy
Helgenes
Lonkan
Melbu
Hanøy
Myrland
Svartskartindan
893
Fiskebøl
Strona
907
Sløvra
Kongselva
Straumnes
Laukvik
Morrfjord
Svartsundtindan
1054
Raften
Grunnførfjord
Laupstad
Austvågøy
Higravstind
1161
Tennstrand
Kvalnes
Brenna
Vestvågøy
Eggum
Haveren
811
Vik
Gimsøy
Eidet
Vestpollen
Digermulen
Flovika
Nesje
Smedvik
Sydalen
Rundfjellet
569
Slåtholmen
Holand
Unstad
Allstad
Haugen
Sundklakk
Kleppstad
Slettjellet
763
Store Molla
Bostad
Himmel
934
Liland
Svolvær
Utakleiv
Rørvik
Kabelvåg
Våje
Valberg
Kalle
Lille Molla
Myrland
Napp
Møkkevik
Henningsvær
Skrova
Vikten
Lekoes
Sund
Gravdal
Stamsund
Sand
Krystad
Ramberg
Ure
Flimbyen
Mortsund
Selfjord
Ballstad
Moskenesøy
937
Mjølnarodden
Sund
Nusfjord
Nesland
Hermansdaltinden
1034
Hamnøy
Reine
Å
Sørvågen
Lofotodden
Mosken
Nordland
Nordlandsnubben
456
Værøy
Sørland
Røst
Buvåg
Hamarøy
Vagsfjellet
953
Skutvik
Lundøya
Mjelde
Engeløya
Steigen
Grønning
Alstad
Dyping
Holkestad
Bogøy
Kvalnes
Hatten
1031
Nordskot
Hestdaltuva
857
Lund
Saursfjord
Alvnes
Myklebostad
Botn
Leiranger
Nordfold
1048
Kråktinden
Breidvik
Stamstik
Laukvik
Muletinden
1037
Eidet
Karlsøyvær
Eidetinden
1020
Tårnvik
Bjørnsvikfjellet
955
Strandå
Kjerringøy
Alsos
Fjær
Misten
Helligvær
Røsvik
Ånsvik

108

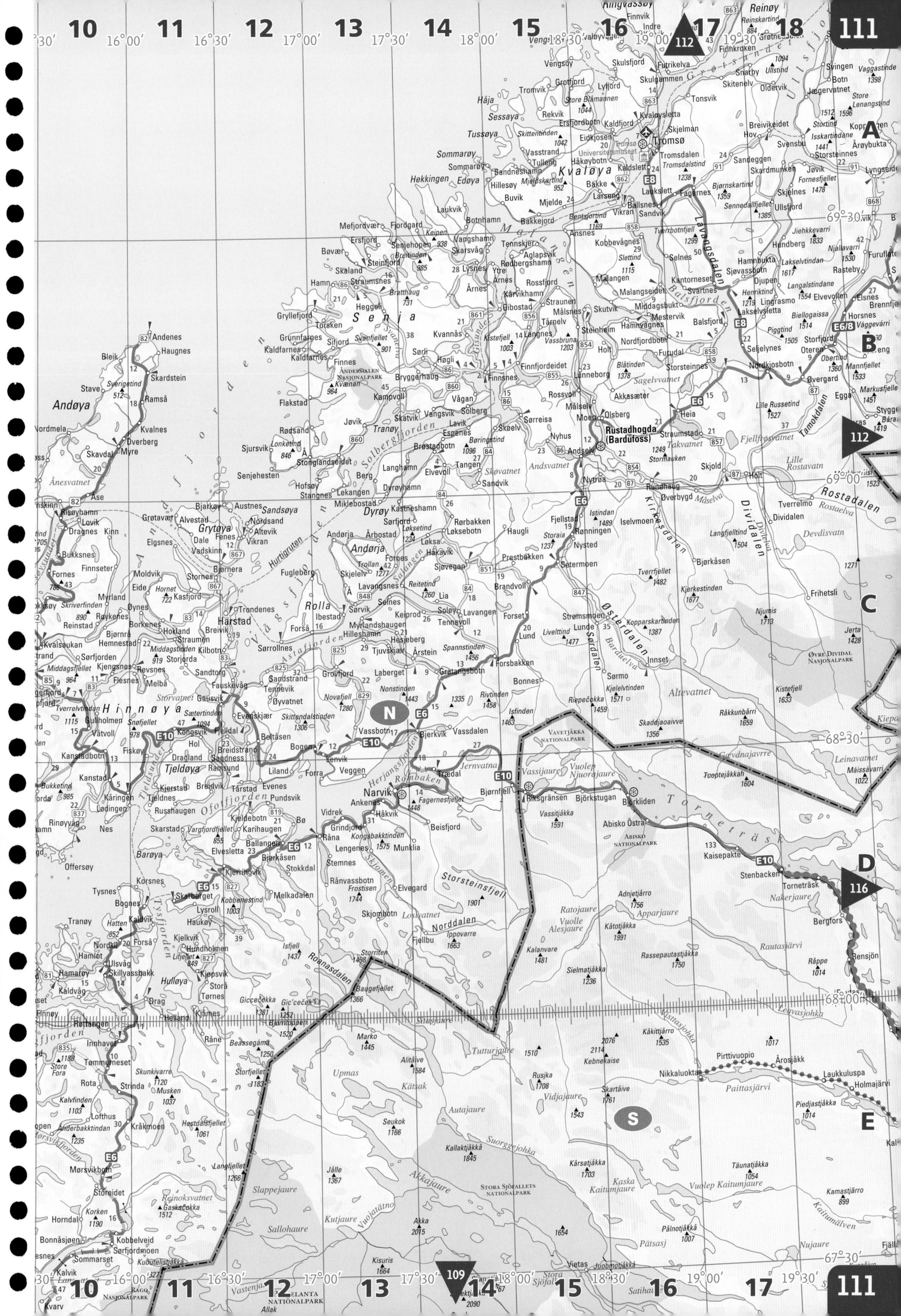
10
11
12
13
14
15
16
17
18
A
B
C
D
E
112
116
109
Tromsø
Kvaløya
Senja
Andøya
Hinnøya
Harstad
Narvik
Rustadhogda
(Bardufoss)
Finnsnes
Sjøvegan
Bjerkvik
Ballangen
Kjeldebotn
Evenes
Tjeldøya
Grytøya
Rolla
Andørja
Dyrøy
Tranøy
Lødingen
Kjøpsvik
Hamarøy
Storeidet
Kobbelveid
Sørfjordmoen
Andenes
Risøyhamn
Sortland
Riksgränsen
Björkliden
Abisko Östra
Kaisepakte
Torneträsk
Nikkaluokta
Kebnekaise
Akka
Akkajaure
Rombaken
Herjangsfjorden
Ofotfjorden
Tysfjorden
Vågsfjorden
Andfjorden
Malangen
Balsfjorden
Målselv
Dividalen
Østerdalen
Altevatnet
Ånderdalen Nasjonalpark
Øvre Dividal Nasjonalpark
Vavetjåkka Nationalpark
Abisko Nationalpark
Stora Sjöfallets Nationalpark
Padjelanta Nationalpark
Rago Nasjonalpark
N
S
E6
E8
E10
E6/8
69°30′
69°00′
68°30′
68°00′
67°30′

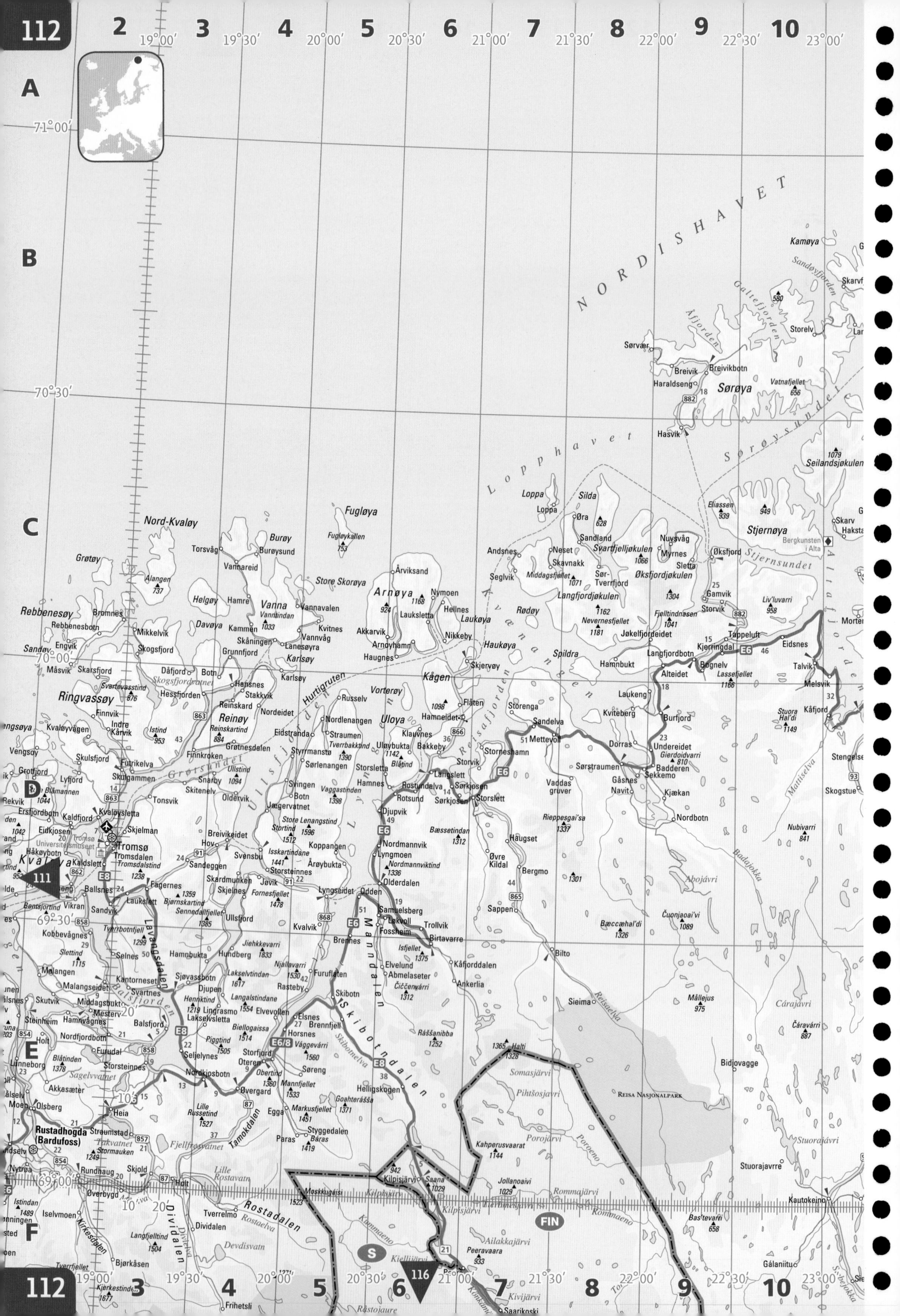

NORDISHAVET
Loppavet
Sørøysundet
Sørøya
Sørvær
Breivik
Breivikbotn
Haraldseng
Hasvik
Kamøya
Gåtefjorden
Åfjorden
Storelv
Vatnafjellet
Seilandsjøkulen
Loppa
Silda
Øra
Sandland
Svartfjelljøkulen
Nuvsvåg
Myrnes
Øksfjord
Øksfjordjøkulen
Stjernøya
Stjernsundet
Bergkunsten i Alta
Altafjorden
Andsnes
Neset
Skavnakk
Seglvik
Middagsfjellet
Sør-Tverrfjord
Langfjordjøkulen
Gamvik
Storvik
Nevernesfjellet
Fjelltindnasen
Jøkelfjordeidet
Tappeluft
Kjerringdal
Eidsnes
Langfjordbotn
Bognelv
Alteidet
Lassefjellet
Talvik
Melsvik
Kåfjord
Laukeng
Kviteberg
Burfjord
Dorras
Undereidet
Gierdoidvarri
Badderen
Sekkemo
Gåsnes
Navit
Kjækan
Nordbotn
Sørstraumen
Stengelsen
Skogstue
Mattiselva
Nubivarri
Badajokka
Abojávri
Čuonjaoai'vi
Bæccæhal'di
Bilto
Sieima
Reisaelva
Mållejus
Cárajávri
Čåravárri
Bidjovagge
Reisa Nasjonalpark
Halti
Somasjärvi
Pihtsosjärvi
Porojärvi
Poroeno
Kahperusvaarat
Jollanoaivi
Rommajärvi
Kilpisjärvi
Saana
Ailakkajärvi
Peeravaara
Kommaeno
Kautokeino
Stuorajávri
Stuorajavrre
Bas'tevarri
Gálaniitu
FIN
S
Nord-Kvaløy
Fugløya
Fugløykallen
Burøy
Burøysund
Torsvåg
Vannareid
Grøtøy
Alangen
Helgøy
Hamre
Vanna
Vannavalen
Vannøya
Store Skorøya
Arnøya
Årviksand
Nymoen
Lauksletta
Hellnes
Laukøya
Akkarvik
Arnøyhamn
Nikkeby
Haukøya
Rødøy
Spildra
Hamnbukt
Skjervøy
Kågen
Kvænangen
Reisafjorden
Flåten
Hamneidet
Storenga
Sandelva
Mettevoll
Stornesshamn
Storslett
Sørkjosen
Rotsund
Rotsundelva
Langslett
Storvik
Vaddas gruver
Rieppesgai'sa
Bæssetindan
Haugset
Øvre Kildal
Bergmo
Sappen
Rebbenesøy
Rebbenesbotn
Brømnes
Mikkelvik
Sandøy
Engvik
Måsvik
Skarsfjord
Ringvassøy
Skogsfjord
Dåfjord
Botn
Hansnes
Stakkvik
Karlsøy
Davøya
Kammen
Skåningen
Lanesøyra
Vannvåg
Kvitnes
Grunnfjord
Hessfjorden
Reinskard
Reinøy
Nordeidet
Hurtigruten
Russelv
Vorterøy
Uløya
Finnvik
Indre Kårvik
Kvaløyvågen
Vengsøy
Skulsfjord
Grøtfjord
Lyfjord
Futrikelva
Skulgammen
Finnkroken
Grøtnesdalen
Grøtsundet
Ullsfjorden
Eidstranda
Straumen
Styrmanstø
Sørlenangen
Svingen
Nordlenangen
Storsletta
Hamnes
Uløybukta
Klauvnes
Bakkeby
Djupvik
Lyngen
Nordmannvik
Lyngmoen
Olderdalen
Skitenelv
Oldervik
Tonsvik
Kvaløysletta
Kaldfjord
Eidkjosen
Ersfjordbotn
Tromsø
Skjelman
Tromsdalen
Tromsdalstind
Kaldslett
Kvaløya
Håkøybotn
Breivikeidet
Hov
Sandeggen
Svensby
Jægervatnet
Store Lenangstind
Stortind
Isskartindane
Storsteinnes
Koppangen
Årøybukta
Skardmunken
Jøvik
Skjelnes
Fornesfjellet
Lyngseidet
Odden
Samuelsberg
Løkvoll
Fossheim
Trollvik
Birtavarre
Kåfjorddalen
Isfjellet
Elvelund
Abmelaseter
Ankerlia
Fagernes
Bjørnskartind
Sennedalfjellet
Ullsfjord
Kvalvik
Brennes
Manndalen
Ballsnes
Vikran
Sandvik
Lakslett
Lavangsdalen
Tverrbotnfjell
Kobbevågnes
Slettind
Malangen
Selnes
Hambukta
Hundberg
Jiehkkevarri
Njallavarri
Furuflaten
Rasteby
Skibotn
Skibotndalen
Kantorneset
Malangseidet
Svartnes
Sjøvassbotn
Djupen
Lakselvtindan
Langalstindane
Elvevollen
Elsnes
Brennfjell
Horsnes
Čiččenvárri
Skutvik
Middagsbukt
Mestervik
Balsfjorden
Henriktind
Lingrasmo
Lakselvsletta
Steinheim
Hamnvågnes
Balsfjord
Nordfjordbotn
Biellogaissa
Piggtind
Storfjord
Oteren
Vaggevárri
Rášsanibba
Furudal
Seljelynes
Obertind
Søreng
Mannfjellet
Hellligskogen
Blåtinden
Sagelvvatnet
Storsteinnes
Nordkjosbotn
Øvergard
Lunneborg
Akkasæter
Olsberg
Moen
Heia
Tamokdalen
Lille Russetind
Egga
Markusfjellet
Goahteråšša
Styggedalen
Båras
Paras
Rustadhogda (Bardufoss)
Straumstad
Takvatnet
Stormauken
Fjellfrøsvatnet
Nytrøa
Rundhaug
Skjold
Holt
Lille Rostavatn
Øverbygd
Dividalen
Rostadalen
Rostaelva
Iselvmoen
Tverrelmo
Istindan
Kirkesdalen
Langfjelltind
Devdisvatn
Bjørkåsen
Tverrfjellet
Kjerkestinden
Frihetsli
Kilpisjärvi
Moskkugáisi
Kielljärvi
Kivijärvi
Saarikoski
Konkama
Rastojaure
Skibotnelva
E6
E8
E6/8
111
116
19°00′
19°30′
20°00′
20°30′
21°00′
21°30′
22°00′
22°30′
23°00′
71°00′
70°30′
70°00′
69°30′
69°00′
A
B
C
D
E
F

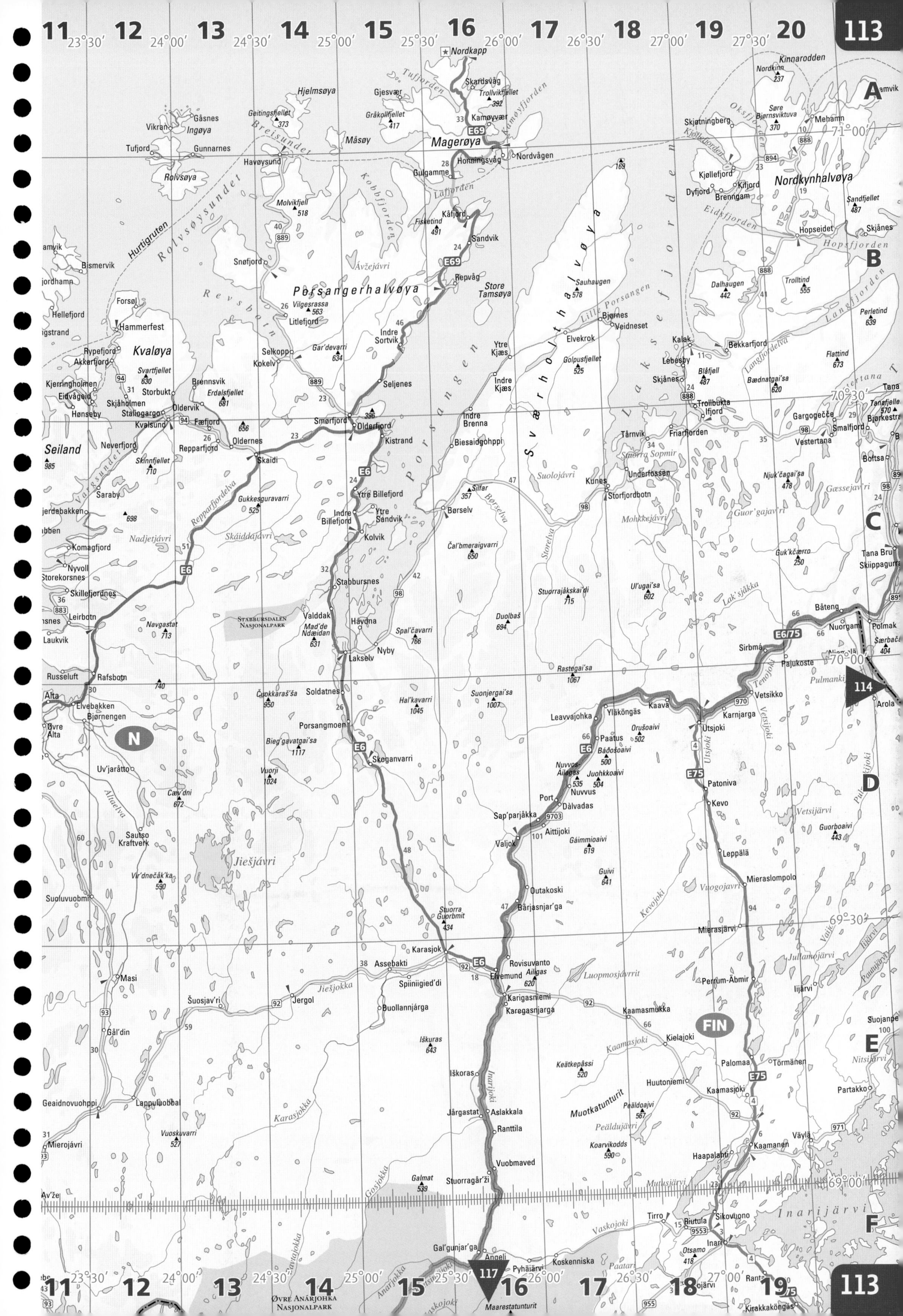
11
12
13
14
15
16
17
18
19
20
23°30′
24°00′
24°30′
25°00′
25°30′
26°00′
26°30′
27°00′
27°30′
71°00′
70°30′
70°00′
69°30′
69°00′
A
B
C
D
E
F
Nordkapp
Skarsvåg
Trollvikfjellet
392
Kamøyvær
Magerøya
E69
Honningsvåg
Nordvågen
Gjesvær
Gråkollfjellet
417
Tufjorden
Kamøyfjorden
Hjelmsøya
Måsøy
Geitingsfjellet
373
Breisundet
Gåsnes
Ingøya
Vikran
Tufjord
Gunnarnes
Havøysund
Rolvsøya
Rolvsøysundet
Hurtigruten
Gulgamme
Lafjorden
Kobbfjorden
Molvikfjell
518
Fisketind
491
Kåfjord
Sandvik
Snøfjord
Revsbotn
Ávžejávri
Repvåg
Store Tamsøya
Porsangerhalvøya
Vilgesrassa
563
Litlefjord
Indre Sortvik
Gar'devarri
634
Selkopp
Kokelv
Seljenes
Forsøl
Hammerfest
Kvaløya
Rypefjord
Akkarfjord
Svartfjellet
630
Kjerringholmen
Eidvågeid
Storbukt
Skjåholmen
Stallogargo
Hønseby
Kvalsund
Brennsvik
Erdalsfjellet
681
Olderdvik
Fæfjord
Oldernes
Repparfjord
Smørfjord
Olderfjord
Kistrand
Seiland
985
Neverfjord
Skinnfjellet
710
Skaidi
Vargsundet
Saraby
Repparfjordelva
Gukkesguravarri
525
698
Nadjetjávri
Skáiddajávri
Komagfjord
Nyvoll
Storekorsnes
Skillefjordnes
Leirbotn
Laukvik
Navgastat
713
Stabbursdalen Nasjonalpark
Valddak
Mad'de Ndæidan
631
Stabbursnes
Hávdna
Kolvik
Indre Billefjord
Ytre Billefjord
Ytre Sandvik
Lakselv
Nyby
Spal'čavarri
766
Russeluft
Rafsbotn
Alta
Elvebakken
Bjørnengen
Øvre Alta
Uv'jaråtto
Čuokkaraš'ša
950
Soldatnes
Porsangmoen
Bieg'gavatgai'sa
1117
Vuorji
1024
Skoganvarri
Cæv'dni
672
Altaelva
Sautso Kraftverk
Jiešjávri
Vir'dnečåk'ka
590
Suoluvuobmi
Masi
Šuosjav'ri
Jergol
Jiešjokka
Gål'din
Geaidnovuohppi
Lappuluobbal
Vuoskuvarri
527
Mierojávri
Av'že
Karasjokka
Gosjokka
Stuorra Guorbmit
434
Karasjok
Assebakti
Spiniigied'di
Buollannjárga
Iškuras
643
Iškoras
Jårgastat
Aslakkala
Ranttila
Vuobmaved
Galmat
539
Stuorragår'ži
Gal'gunjar'ga
Angeli
Pyhäjärvi
Koskenniska
Øvre Anárjohka Nasjonalpark
Anárjohka
Maarestatunturit
Lille Porsangen
Bjørnes
Veidneset
Elvekrok
Ytre Kjæs
Indre Kjæs
Indre Brenna
Biesaidgohppi
Porsangen
Sværholthalvøya
Sauhaugen
578
Golpusfjellet
525
169
Laksefjorden
Suolojávri
Silfar
357
Børselv
Børselva
Čal'bmeraigvarri
650
Storelva
Stuorrajåkskai'di
715
Duolbaš
694
Rastegai'sa
1067
Hal'kavarri
1045
Suonjergai'sa
1007
Kunes
Storfjordbotn
Underfossen
Stuorra Sopmir
Mohkkejávri
Tårnvik
Friarfjorden
Ul'ugai'sa
602
Lak'sjåkka
Leavvajohka
Yläköngäs
Kaava
Paatus
Orušoaivi
502
Bádošoaivi
500
Nuvvos-Áilegas
535
Juohkkoaivi
504
Nuvvus
Port
Dálvadas
Sap'parjåkka
Aittijoki
Valjok
Gáimmioaivi
619
Guivi
641
Outakoski
Bårjasnjar'ga
Rovisuvanto
Áiligas
620
Elvemund
Karigasniemi
Karegasnjarga
Luopmosjávrrit
Kaamasmukka
Kaamasjoki
Kielajoki
Keätkepässi
520
Muotkatunturit
Huutoniemi
Peäldoajvi
567
Peäldujävri
Koarvikodds
590
Inarijoki
Vaskojoki
Tirro
Riutula
Otsamo
418
Sikovuono
Inari
Rantu
Kirakkakõngäs
Paatari
Nordkinn
237
Kinnarodden
Oksfjorden
Søre Bjørnsviktuva
370
Mehamn
Skjøtningberg
Kjøllefjorden
Kjøllefjord
Dyfjord
Kifjord
Brenngam
Nordkynhalvøya
Eidsfjorden
Hopseidet
Hopsfjorden
Skjånes
Sandfjellet
487
Dalhaugen
442
Trolltind
555
Perletind
639
Langfjorden
Kalak
Bekkarfjord
Lebesby
Skjånes
Blåfjell
487
Langfjordelva
Bædnatgai'sa
620
Flattind
673
Trollbukta
Ifjord
Vestertana
Gargogečče
Smalfjord
Tana
Tanafjellet
570
Bjørkestrand
Boftsa
Njuk'čagai'sa
478
Gæssejav'ri
Guor'gajav'ri
Guk'kčærro
250
Tana Bru
Skiippagurra
Båteng
Nuorgam
Polmak
Særbačča
404
Sirbmá
Pajukoste
Tenojoki
Pulmanki
114
Vetsikko
Karnjarga
Arola
Utsjoki
Vetsijoki
Patoniva
Kevo
Vetsijärvi
Guorboaivi
443
Leppälä
Vuogojavri
Mieraslompolo
Kevojoki
Mierasjärvi
Jullamojärvi
Iijärvi
Perrum-Äbmir
FIN
N
Suojanperä
Törmänen
Nitsijärvi
Palomaa
Partakko
Haapalahti
Kaamanen
Väylä
Muddusjärvi
Inarijärvi
117
Angeli
E6
E6/75
E75

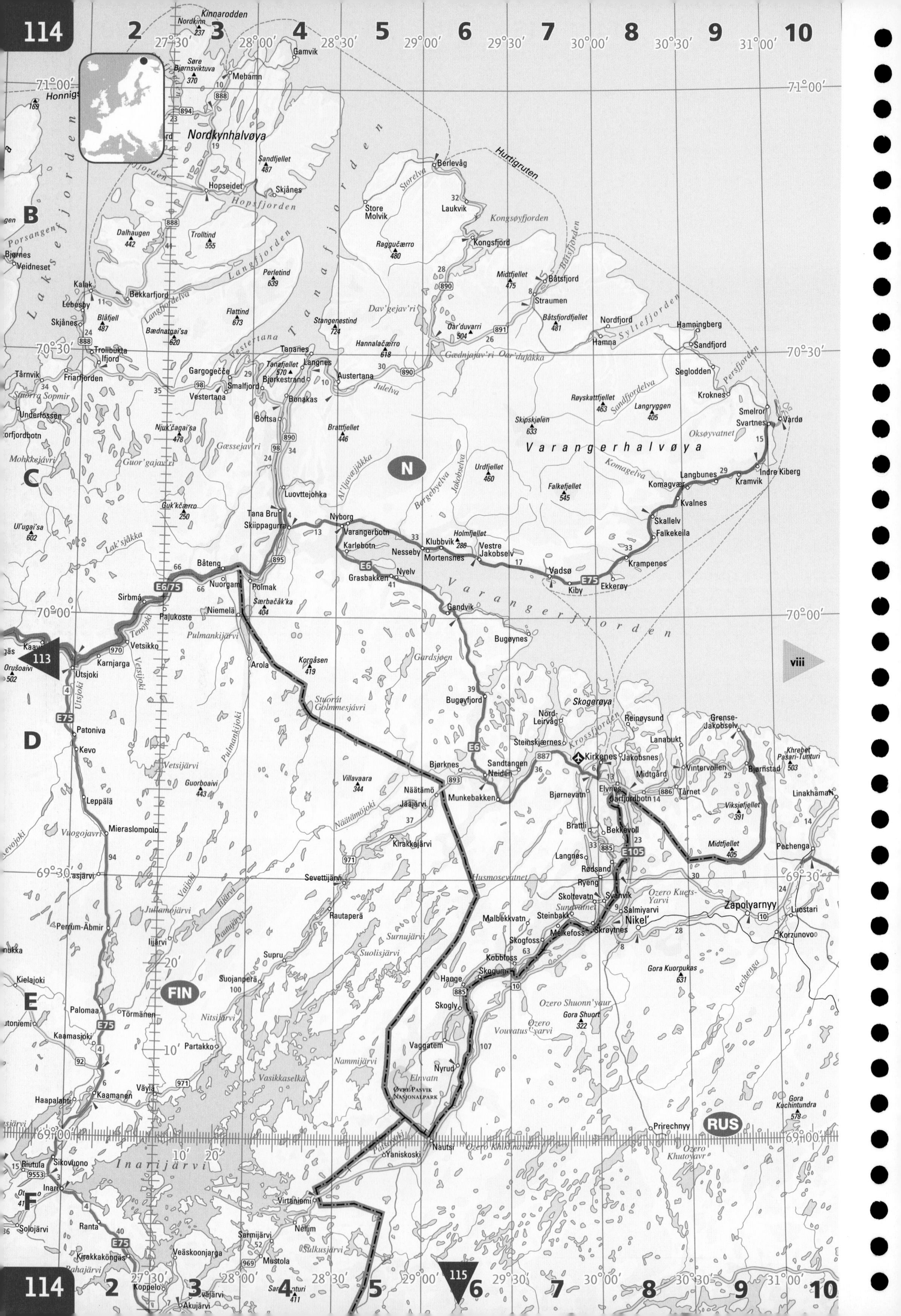

114
Kinnarodden
Nordkinn
Gamvik
Søre Bjørnsviktuva
Mehamn
Honnigs
Nordkynhalvøya
Sandfjellet
Hopseidet
Skjånes
Hopsfjorden
Laksefjorden
Porsangen
Bjørnes
Veidneset
Dalhaugen
Trolltind
Langfjorden
Perletind
Kalak
Bekkarfjord
Lebesby
Skjånes
Blåfjell
Flattind
Bædnatgai'sa
Trollbukta
Ifjord
Tårnvik
Friarfjorden
Stuorra Sopmir
Underfossen
Mohkkejávri
Gargogečče
Smalfjord
Vestertana
Tananes
Tanafjellet
Langnes
Bjørkestrand
Austertana
Bonakas
Boftsa
Tanafjorden
Berlevåg
Hurtigruten
Storelva
Store Molvik
Laukvik
Kongsøyfjorden
Kongsfjord
Raggučærro
Midtfjellet
Båtsfjord
Båtsfjorden
Straumen
Båtsfjordfjellet
Nordfjord
Hamna
Syltefjorden
Hamningberg
Sandfjord
Dav'gejav'ri
Stangenestind
Hannalačærro
Oar'duvarri
Gædnjajav'ri
Oar'dujåkka
Julelva
Seglodden
Persfjorden
Kroknes
Smelror
Svartnes
Vardø
Røyskattfjellet
Sandfjordelva
Langryggen
Skipskjølen
Oksøyvatnet
Varangerhalvøya
Komagelva
Brattfjellet
Njuk'čagai'sa
Gæssejav'ri
Guor'gajav'ri
Al'ljavæjåkka
N
Børgebyelva
Jakobselva
Urdfjellet
Falkefjellet
Langbunes
Komagvær
Indre Kiberg
Kramvik
Kvalnes
Skallelv
Falkekeila
Luovttejohka
Guk'kčærro
Tana Bru
Skiippagurra
Nyborg
Varangerbotn
Karlebotn
Klubbvik
Holmfjellet
Vestre Jakobselv
Nesseby
Mortensnes
Krampenes
Vadsø
Kiby
Ekkerøy
Ul'ugai'sa
Lak'sjåkka
Båteng
Nuorgam
Polmak
Grasbakken
Nyelv
Varangerfjorden
Sirbmá
Pajukoste
Niemelä
Særbačåk'ka
Gandvik
Tenojoki
Vetsikko
Pulmankijärvi
Bugøynes
Karnjarga
Utsjoki
Orušoaivi
Arola
Korgåsen
Gardsjøen
Utsjoki
Stuorát Golmmesjávri
Bugøyfjord
Skogerøya
Nord-Leirvåg
Reinøysund
Grense-Jakobselv
Patoniva
Kevo
Steinskjærnes
Krossfjorden
Lanabukt
Khrebet Pasari-Tunturi
Kirkenes
Jakobsnes
Vetsijärvi
Pulmankijoki
Bjørknes
Sandtangen
Neiden
Midtgård
Vintervollen
Bjørnstad
Villavaara
Guorboaivi
Näätämö
Jääjärvi
Munkebakken
Bjørnevatn
Elvenes
Hesseng
Tårnet
Linakhamari
Leppälä
Näätämöjoki
Hesseng
Viksjøfjellet
Mieraslompolo
Vuogojavri
Kirakkajärvi
Brattli
Bekkevoll
Midtfjellet
Pechenga
Langnes
Rødsand
Sevettijärvi
Husmosevatnet
Ryeng
Skoltevatn
Svanvik
Ozero Kuets-Yarvi
Salmiyarvi
Zapolyarnyy
Luostari
Julkamojärvi
Rautaperä
Malbekkvatn
Steinbakk
Melkefoss
Skrøytnes
Nikel'
Korzunovo
Perrum-Äbmir
Surnujärvi
Skogfoss
Iijärvi
Suolisjärvi
Supru
Kobbfoss
Gora Kuorpukas
Kielajoki
Suojanperä
Hange
Skogum
FIN
Pechenga
Palomaa
Törmänen
Skogly
Ozero Shuonn'yaur
Gora Shuort
Nitsijärvi
Vouvatus
Ozero Yarvi
Kaamasjoki
Partakko
Vaggatem
Nammijärvi
Nyrud
Vasikkaselkä
Elvvatn
Øvre Pasvik Nasjonalpark
Väylä
Kaamanen
Haapalahti
Gora Kuchintundra
Prirechnyy
RUS
Nautsi
Yaniskoski
Ozero Khutoyavr
Riutula
Sikovuono
Inarijärvi
Inari
Virtaniemi
Solojärvi
Ranta
Sarmijärvi
Nellim
Kirakkakongäs
Veäskoonjarga
Sulkusjärvi
Mustola
Koppelo
Akujärvi
113
115
viii

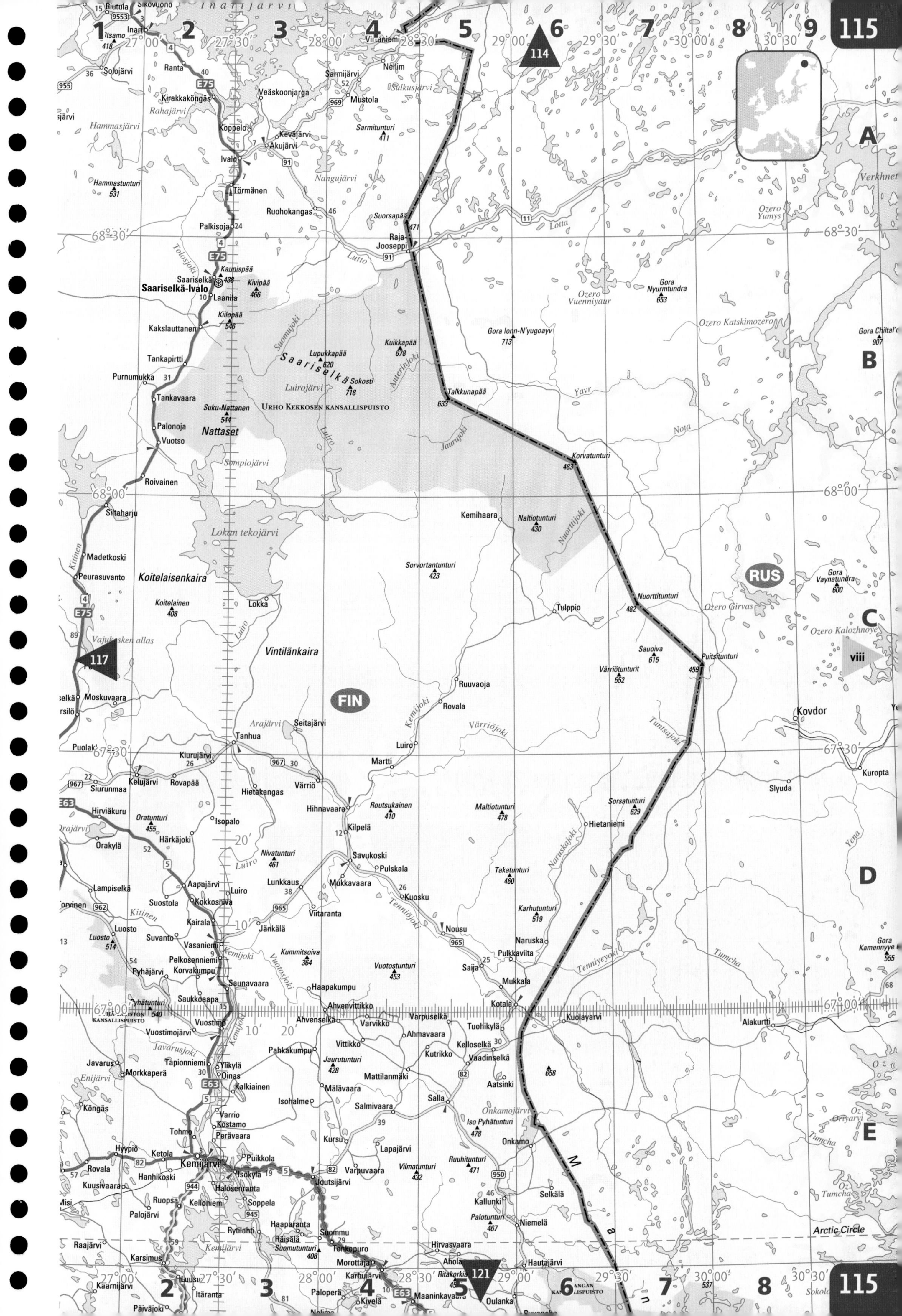
Inarijärvi
Riutula
Sikovuono
Inari
Itsamo
Ranta
Solojärvi
Kirakkakongäs
Rahajärvi
Hammasjärvi
Koppelo
Ivalo
Kevajärvi
Akujärvi
Veäskoonjarga
Sarmijärvi
Mustola
Sulkusjärvi
Nellim
Virtaniemi
Sarmitunturi
Nangujärvi
Törmänen
Hammastunturi
Ruohokangas
Palkisoja
Suorsapää
Raja-Jooseppi
Lutto
Tolosjoki
Kaunispää
Saariselkä
Saariselkä-Ivalo
Kivipää
Laanila
Kiilopää
Kakslauttanen
Tankapirtti
Purnumukka
Tankavaara
Suku-Nattanen
Nattaset
Palonoja
Vuotso
Sompiojärvi
Roivainen
Suomujoki
Saariselkä
Lupukkapää
Sokosti
Kuikkapää
Anterinjoki
Luirojärvi
Urho Kekkosen kansallispuisto
Luiro
Talkkunapää
Jaurujoki
Korvatunturi
Lotta
Ozero Vuenniyaur
Gora Nyurmtundra
Gora Ionn-N'yugoayv
Ozero Katskimozero
Gora Chiltal'c
Yavr
Nota
Verkhnet
Ozero Yumys
Siltaharju
Lokan tekojärvi
Madetkoski
Kitinen
Peurasuvanto
Koitelaisenkaira
Koitelainen
Lokka
Kemihaara
Naltiotunturi
Nuorttijoki
Sorvortantunturi
RUS
Gora Vaynatundra
Nuorttitunturi
Tulppio
Ozero Girvas
Ozero Kalozhnoye
Vajukosken allas
Vintilänkaira
Sauoiva
Värriötunturit
Puitsitunturi
Moskuvaara
Ruuvaoja
Rovala
FIN
Kemijoki
Kovdor
Arajärvi
Seitajärvi
Värriöjoki
Tuntsajoki
Tanhua
Luiro
Martti
Puolakka
Kiurujärvi
Kelujärvi
Siurunmaa
Rovapää
Hietakangas
Värriö
Kuropta
Slyuda
Hirviäkuru
Hihnavaara
Routsukainen
Maltiotunturi
Sorsatunturi
Hietaniemi
Oratunturi
Isopalo
Kilpelä
Härkäjoki
Orakylä
Nivatunturi
Savukoski
Pulskala
Naruskajoki
Yena
Takatunturi
Lampiselkä
Aapajärvi
Luiro
Lunkkaus
Mukkavaara
Kuosku
Suostola
Kokkosniva
Tenniöjoki
Karhutunturi
Torvinen
Viitaranta
Kairala
Jänkälä
Nousu
Luosto
Suvanto
Vasaniemi
Kummitsoiva
Naruska
Pelkosenniemi
Pulkkaviita
Pyhäjärvi
Korvakumpu
Vuotosjoki
Vuotostunturi
Saija
Tenniyeyoki
Tumcha
Gora Kamennyye
Saunavaara
Haapakumpu
Mukkala
Saukkoaapa
Pyhätunturi
Ahvenvittikko
Kotala
Vuostimo
Ahvenselkä
Varvikko
Varpuselkä
Tuohikylä
Kuolayarvi
Alakurtti
Vuostimojärvi
Ahmavaara
Vittikko
Kelloselkä
Javarusjoki
Tapionniemi
Pahkakumpu
Kutrikko
Vaadinselkä
Javarus
Ylikylä
Morkkaperä
Jaurutunturi
Enijärvi
Oinas
Mattilanmäki
Kalkiainen
Mälävaara
Aatsinki
Isohalme
Salla
Köngäs
Varrio
Salmivaara
Onkamojärvi
Kostamo
Iso Pyhätunturi
Tohmo
Perävaara
Kursu
Onkamo
Tumcha
Lapajärvi
Hyypiö
Ketola
Puikkola
Ruuhitunturi
Rovala
Kemijärvi
Isokylä
Varpuvaara
Vilmatunturi
Kuusivaara
Hanhikoski
Joutsijärvi
Selkälä
Halosenranta
Misi
Ruopsa
Kelloniemi
Soppela
Kallunki
Palojärvi
Palotunturi
Niemelä
Rytilahti
Haaparanta
Suommu
Arctic Circle
Raajärvi
Räisälä
Suomutunturi
Tonkopuro
Kemijärvi
Karsimus
Hirvasvaara
Morottaja
Ahola
Hautajärvi
Luusua
Kaarnijärvi
Karhujärvi
Ritakorkia
Oulangan kansallispuisto
Itäranta
Paloperä
Maaninkavaara
Oulanka
Kivelä
Päiväjoki
Sokol
Arctic Circle
114
117
121
viii

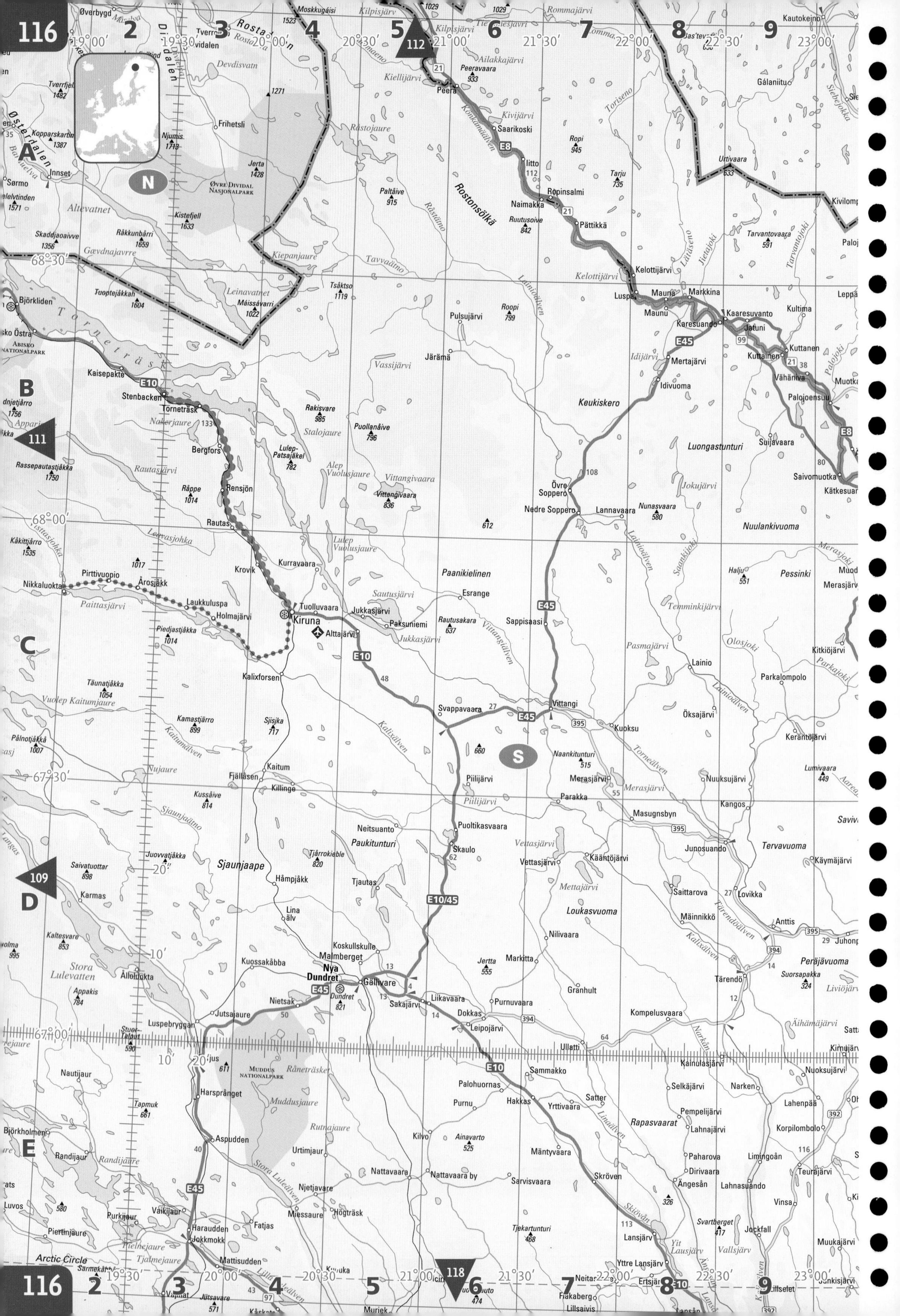
Øverbygd
Tverrfjell 1482
Kopparskardtind 1387
Østerdalen
Innset
Sørmo
Altevatnet
Skaddjaoaivve 1356
Gævdnajavrre
Tverrå
Rostadalen
Dividalen
Devdisvatn
Frihetsli
Njunis 1713
Jerta 1428
Øvre Dividal Nasjonalpark
Kistefjell 1633
Råkkunbårri 1659
Leinavatnet
Måissåvarri 1022
Tuoptejåkkah 1604
Kiepanjaure
Moskkugáisi
Kilpisjärvi
Kiellijärvi
Peera
Peeravaara 933
Ailakkajärvi
Råstojaure
Kivijärvi
Saarikoski
Konkamäeno
Ropi 945
Iitto
Ropinsalmi
Naimakka
Ruutusoive 842
Pättikkä
Tarju 735
Rostonsölkä
Paltåive 915
Råstäno
Tavvaäno
Tsåktso 1119
Kelottijärvi
Luspa
Mauna
Markkina
Maunu
Kaaresuvanto
Karesuando
Jatuni
Kultima
Kuttanen
Vähäniva
Muotka
Palojoensuu
Suijavaara
Saivomuotka
Kätkesuando
Roopi 799
Pulsujärvi
Järämä
Idijärvi
Mertajärvi
Idivuoma
Keukiskero
Luongastunturi
Jokujärvi
Nuunasvaara 580
Nuulankivuoma
Övre Soppero
Nedre Soppero
Lannavaara
Kautokeino
Gálaniitu
Urtivaara 633
Tarvantovaara 591
Kilvilompolo
Björkliden
Abisko Östra
Abisko Nationalpark
Torneträsk
Kaisepakte
Stenbacken
Nakerjaure
Bergfors
Rensjön
Rautasjärvi
Rautas
Råppe 1014
Rassepautastjåkkå 1750
Vassijärvi
Rakisvare 985
Stalojaure
Puollanåive 796
Lulep-Patsajåkel 782
Alep Vuolusjaure
Vittangivaara 836
Lulep Vuolusjaure
Kåkittjårro 1535
Nikkaluokta
Pirttivuopio
Årosjåkk
Laukkuluspa
Holmajärvi
Paittasjärvi
Piedjastjåkka 1014
Krovik
Kurravaara
Tuolluvaara
Kiruna
Alttajärvi
Jukkasjärvi
Paksuniemi
Sautusjärvi
Esrange
Paanikielinen
Rautusakara 637
Vittangiälven
Sappisaasi
Halju 551
Pessinki
Merasjärvi
Temminkijärvi
Pasmajärvi
Lainio
Kitkiöjärvi
Parkalompolo
Kalixforsen
Täunatjåkka 1054
Vuolep Kaitumjaure
Kamastjårro 899
Sjisjka 717
Svappavaara
Vittangi
Kuoksu
Öksajärvi
Keräntöjärvi
Kalixälven
Pålnotjåkkå 1007
Kaitumälven
Nujaure
Naankitunturi 515
Kaitum
Fjällåsen
Killinge
Kussåive 814
Piilijärvi
Merasjärvi
Parakka
Nuuksujärvi
Lumivaara 449
Kangos
Neitsuanto
Puoltikasvaara
Masugnsbyn
Sjaunjaape
Juovvatjåkka
Saivatuottar 898
Paukitunturi
Tjärrokieble 820
Skaulo
Vettasjärvi
Kääntöjärvi
Junosuando
Tervavuoma
Käymäjärvi
Karmas
Håmpjäkk
Tjautas
Mettajärvi
Saittarova
Lovikka
Lina älv
Loukasvuoma
Mäinnikkö
Anttis
Kaltesvare 853
Koskullskulle
Nilivaara
Juhonpieti
Stora Lulevatten
Ålloluokta
Kuossakåbba
Malmberget
Nya Dundret
Gällivare
Jertta 555
Markitta
Tärendö
Peräjävuoma
Suorsapakka 324
Appakis 784
Nietsak
Dundret 821
Liikavaara
Sakajärvi
Granhult
Purnuvaara
Dokkas
Kompelusvaara
Jutsajaure
Luspebryggan
Leipojärvi
Stuor-Tatajat 590
Äihämäjärvi
Ullatti
Kainulasjärvi
Kimujärvi
Muddus Nationalpark
Råneträsket
Sammakko
Nautijaur
Harsprånget
Muddusjaure
Palohuornas
Purnu
Hakkas
Satter
Yrttivaara
Selkäjärvi
Narken
Nuoksujärvi
Tapmuk 661
Lahenpää
Pempelijärvi
Rapasvaarat
Lahnajärvi
Korpilombolo
Björkholmen
Aspudden
Rutnajaure
Kilvo
Ainavarto 525
Urtimjaur
Mäntyvaara
Paharova
Limingoån
Teurajärvi
Randijaur
Randijaure
Stora Luleälven
Dirivaara
Ängesån
Lahnasuando
Nattavaara
Nattavaara by
Sarvisvaara
Skröven
Njetjavare
Luvos
Purkijaur
Vaikijaur
Miessaure
Högträsk
Skiövan
Vinsa
Piertinjaure
Fatjas
Harauddem
Jokkmokk
Tjekartunturi 468
Lansjärv
Svartberget 417
Jockfall
Muukajärvi
Vallsjärv
Arctic Circle
Tjalmejaure
Mattisudden
Yttre Lansjärv
Neitas
Ertsjärv
Fiskaberg
Lillsaivis
Lillselet
Junkisjärvi
Sarmekåhtie
Jutsavare 571
Muriek
Kåikato
Vajmat
Lilla Luleälven
474
Kvinuka
Lansån
Merasjoki
Olosjoki
Parkajoki
Torneälven
Lainioälven
Saankijoki
Tärendöälven
Narkån
Lindälven
Muonionälven
Lätäseno
Jietajoki
Tarvantojoki
Palojoki
Konkamäeno
Laimioälven
Leavasjohka
Sjaunjaätno
Paittasjärvi
E8
E10
E45
E10/45
21
99
395
394
392
97
111
112
109
118
N
S
A
B
C
D
E
19°00′
19°30′
20°00′
20°30′
21°00′
21°30′
22°00′
22°30′
23°00′
68°30′
68°00′
67°30′
67°00′

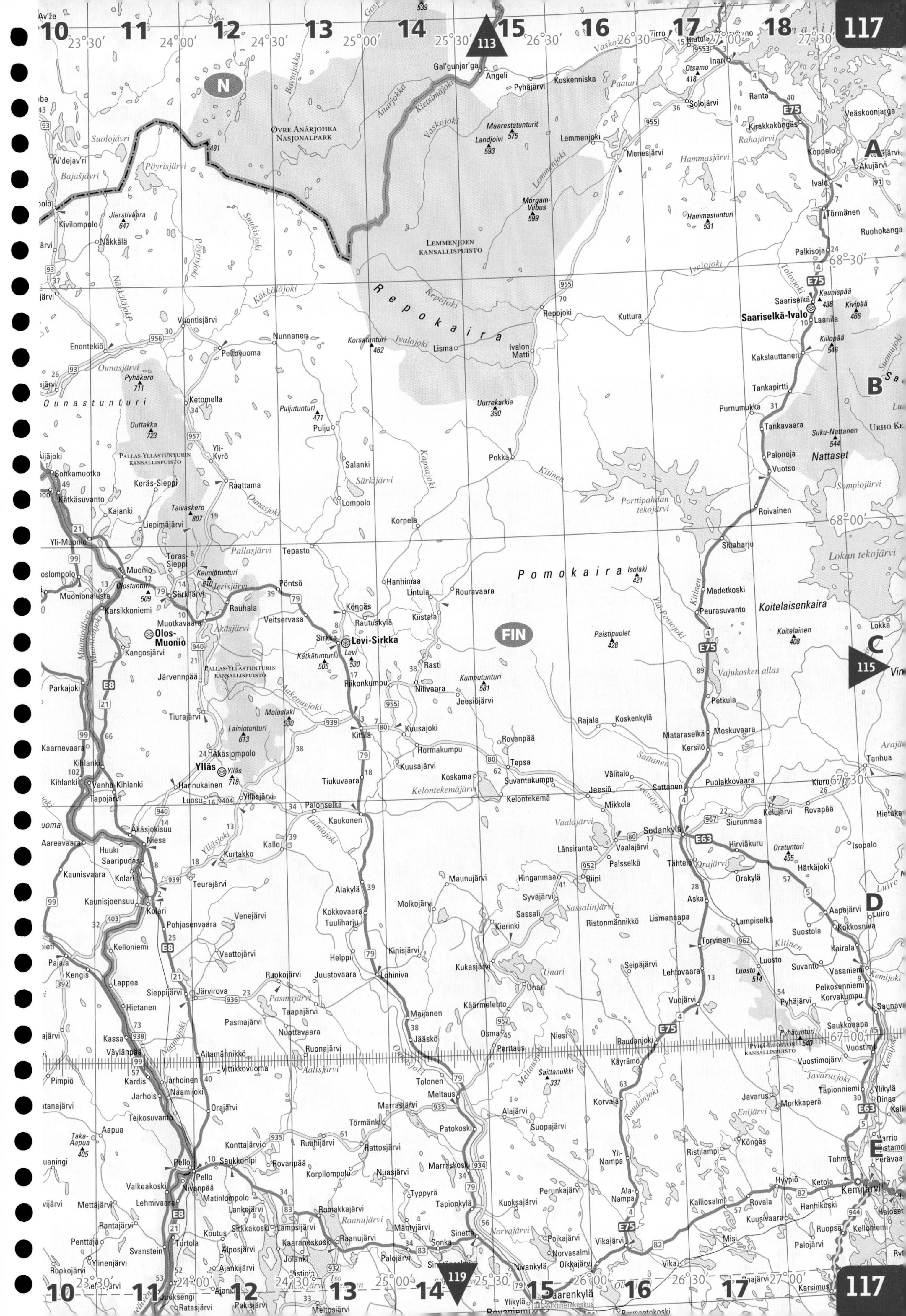
10
11
12
13
14
15
16
17
18
113
115
119
A
B
C
D
E
N
FIN
Øvre Anárjohka Nasjonalpark
Lemmenjoen kansallispuisto
Pallas-Yllästunturin kansallispuisto
Pyhä-Luoston kansallispuisto
Repokaira
Pomokaira
Ounastunturi
Koitelaisenkaira
Inari
Ivalo
Saariselkä-Ivalo
Levi-Sirkka
Olos-Muonio
Ylläs
Kittilä
Sodankylä
Muonio
Kolari
Pello
Kemijärvi
Enontekiö
Porttipahdan tekojärvi
Lokan tekojärvi
Vajukosken allas
Nattaset

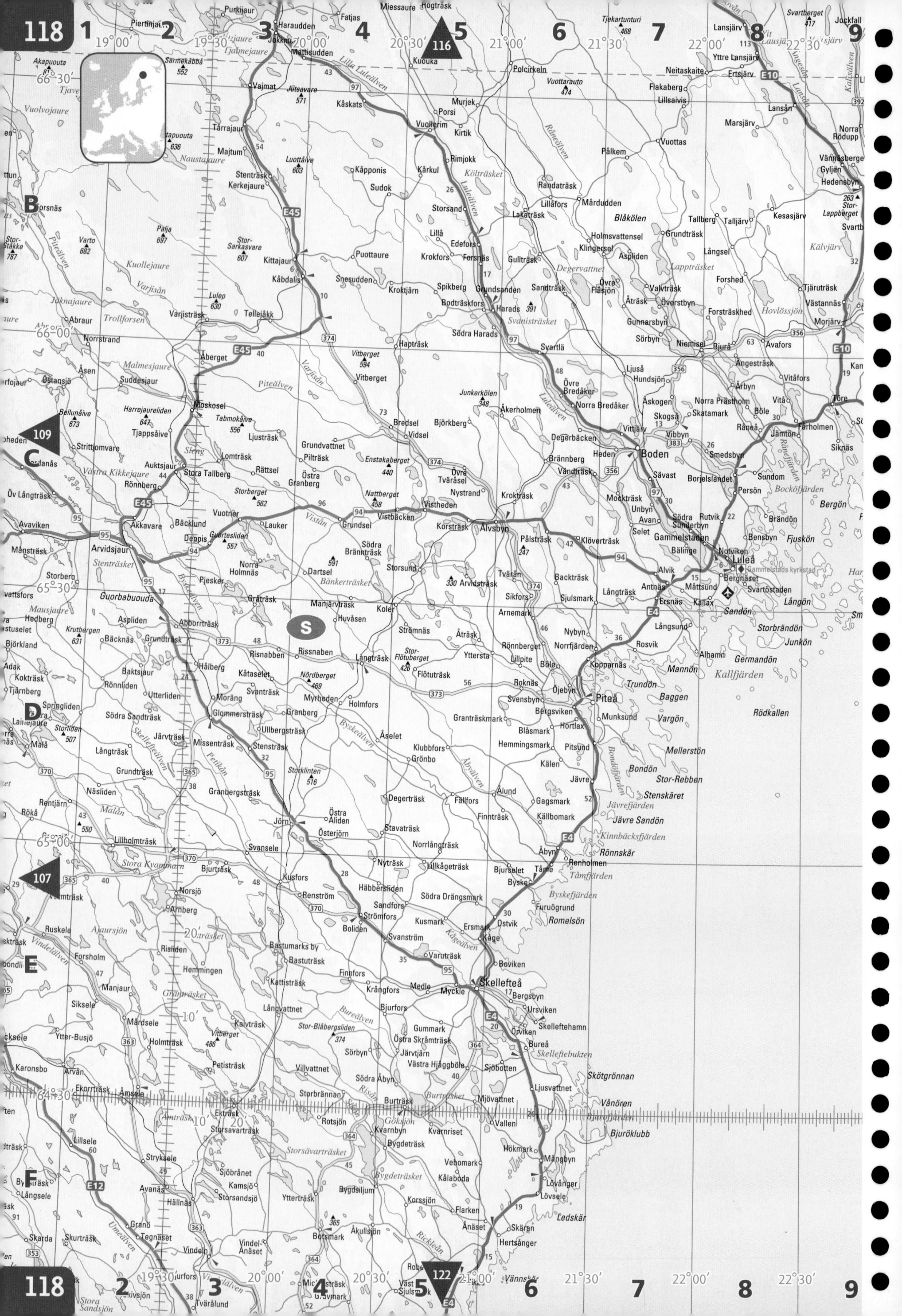

Luleå
Boden
Piteå
Skellefteå
Arvidsjaur
Älvsbyn
Moskosel
Jokkmokk
Vuollerim
Harads
Gammelstaden
Kalix
Byske
Jörn
Boliden
Norsjö
Malå
Lövånger
Kåge
Ursviken
Skelleftehamn
Hortlax
Sävast
Råneå
Storsund
Glommersträsk
Moräng
Lillpite
Vidsel
Stora Tallberg
Vindeln
Vännäs
E4
E10
E12
E45
109
107
116
122

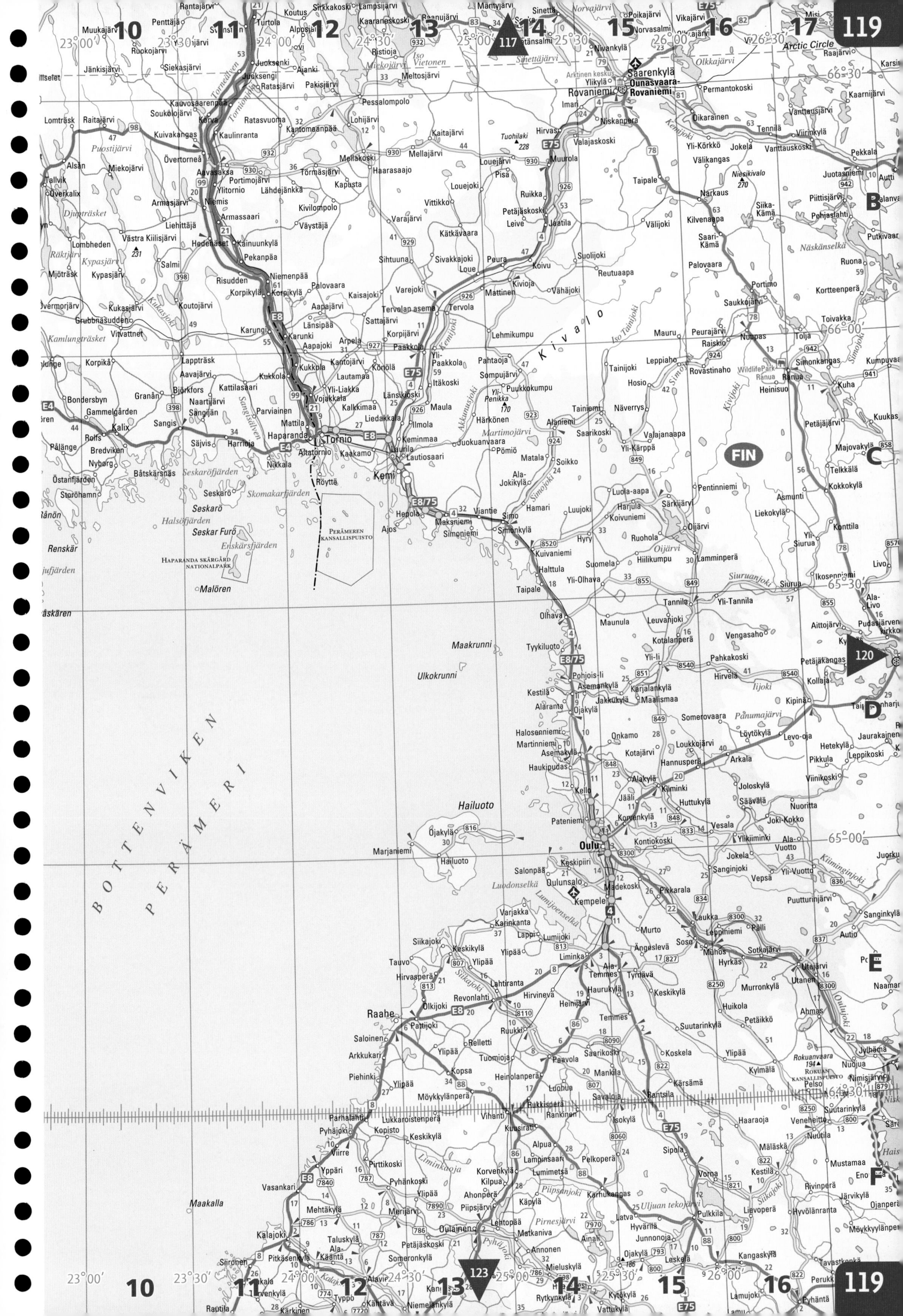

119
10
11
12
13
14
15
16
17
117
120
123
Arctic Circle
B
C
D
E
F
FIN
Rovaniemi
Saarenkylä
Ounasvaara-Rovaniemi
Tornio
Haparanda
Kemi
Kalix
Oulu
Kempele
Raahe
Kalajoki
Hailuoto
Muhos
Ranua
Kivalo
Kemijoki
Tornionjoki
Simojoki
Iijoki
Oulujoki
Siikajoki
Pyhäjoki
Kiiminginjoki
Perämeren kansallispuisto
Haparanda skärgård nationalpark
Bottenviken
Perämeri
Maakrunni
Ulkokrunni
Maakalla
Malören
Seskarö
Seskar Furö
Renskär
Oijärvi
Näskänselkä
Rokuanvaara
Rokuan kansallispuisto
Uljuan tekojärvi
Pirnesjärvi
Liminkaoja
Oulunsalo
Liminka
Kiiminki
Haukipudas
Ii
Kuivaniemi
Simo
Keminmaa
Tervola
Ylitornio
Övertorneå
Aavasaksa
Pello
Vaala
Utajärvi
Vihanti
Oulainen
Siikajoki
Lumijoki
Tyrnävä
Pyhäjoki
Alavieska
23°00′
23°30′
24°00′
24°30′
25°00′
25°30′
26°00′
26°30′
66°30′
66°00′
65°30′
65°00′
64°30′
E4
E8
E75
E8/75

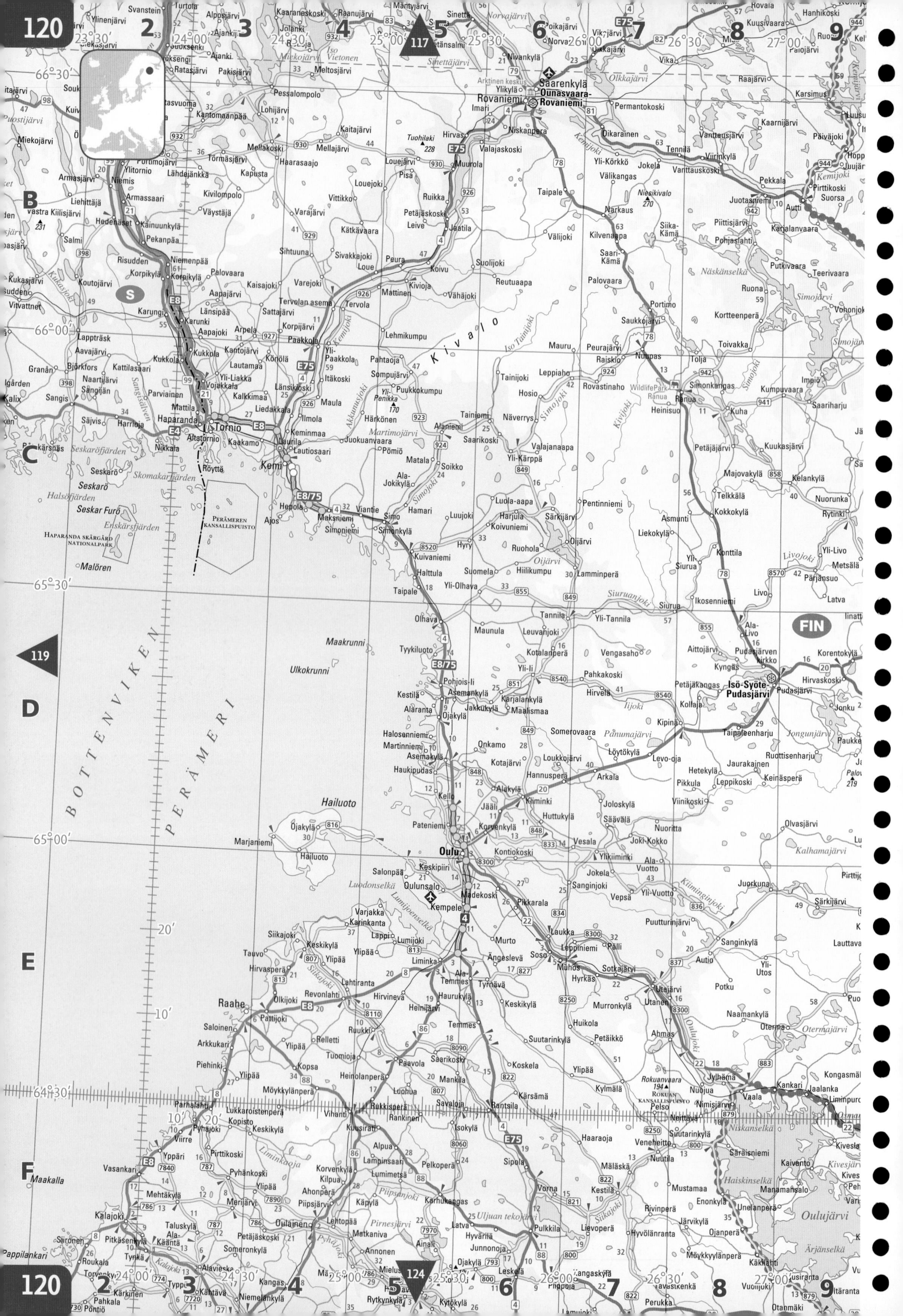

117
119
124
Rovaniemi
Ounasvaara-Rovaniemi
Saarenkylä
Arktinen keskus
Haparanda
Tornio
Kemi
Simo
Kivalo
Ranua
Wildlife Park Ranua
Isö-Syöte-Pudasjärvi
Pudasjärvi
FIN
S
BOTTENVIKEN
PERÄMERI
Maakrunni
Ulkokrunni
Hailuoto
Marjaniemi
Oulu
Oulunsalo
Kempele
Kiiminki
Haukipudas
Raahe
Liminka
Muhos
Utajärvi
Vaala
Oulujärvi
Kalajoki
Oulainen
Pyhäjoki
Seskarö
Haparanda Skärgård Nationalpark
Perämeren Kansallispuisto
Malören
Rokuanvaara 194
Rokuan Kansallispuisto
E8
E75
E8/75
E4
66°30′
66°00′
65°30′
65°00′
64°30′
23°30′
24°00′
24°30′
25°00′
25°30′
26°00′
26°30′
27°00′

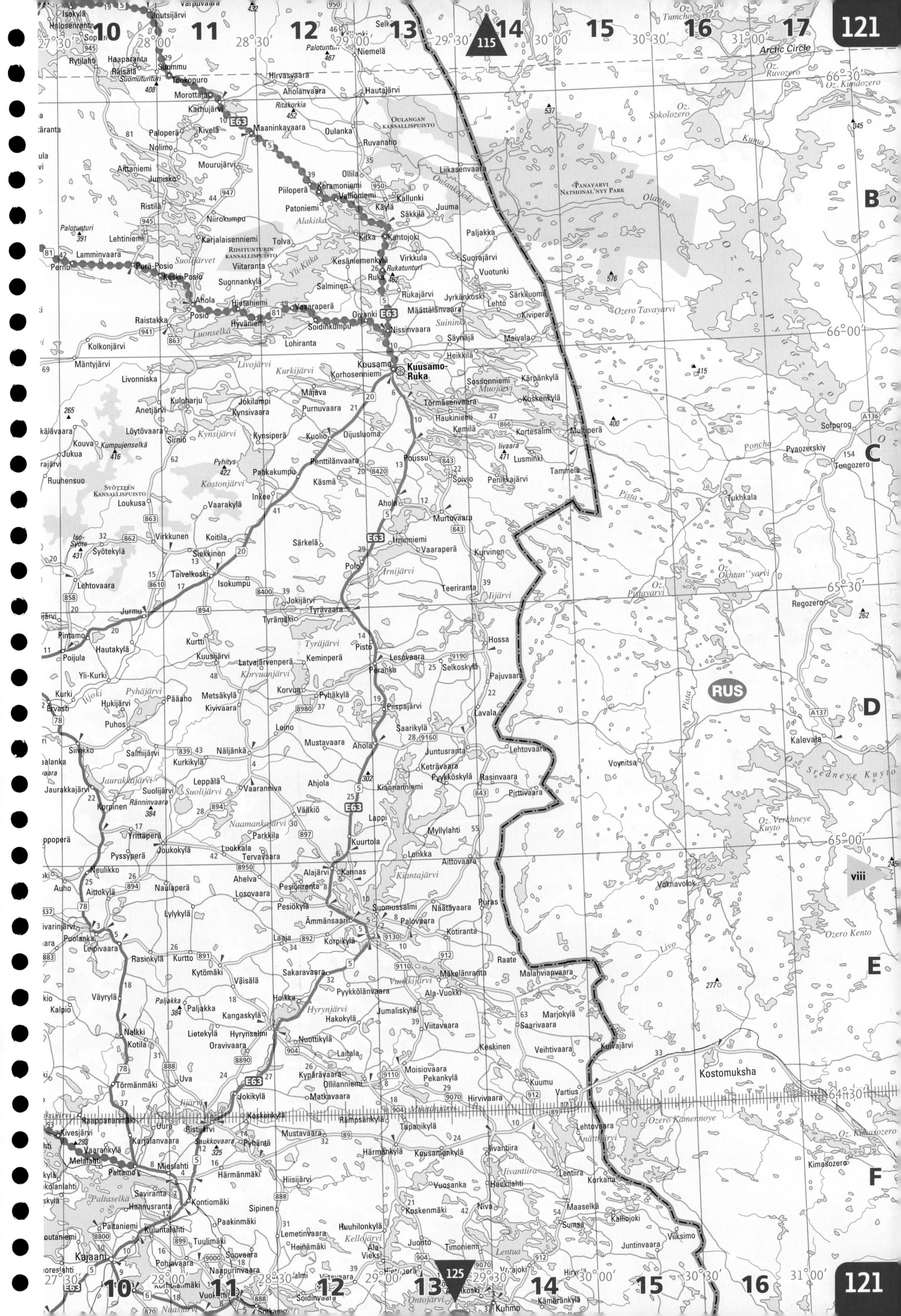

121
10
11
12
13
14
15
16
17
Arctic Circle
66°30′
66°00′
65°30′
65°00′
64°30′
27°30′
28°00′
28°30′
29°00′
29°30′
30°00′
30°30′
31°00′
115
125
viii
B
C
D
E
F
RUS
Joutsijärvi
Isokylä
Halosenranta
Rytilahti
Haaparanta
Raisälä
Suomutunturi
Suommu
Tonkopuro
Morottaja
Karhujärvi
Kivelä
Maaninkavaara
Paloperä
Nolimo
Mourujärvi
Aittaniemi
Jumisko
Ristilä
Niirokumpu
Lehtiniemi
Karjalaisenniemi
Lamminvaara
Pernu
Perä-Posio
Keski-Posio
Suolijärvet
Viitaranta
Suonnankylä
Ahola
Posio
Hietaniemi
Vasaraperä
Hyvänieni
Soidinkumpu
Raistakka
Luonselkä
Lohiranta
Kolkonjärvi
Mäntyjärvi
Hirvasvaara
Aholanvaara
Hautajärvi
Oulanka
Oulangan kansallispuisto
Ruvanaho
Niemelä
Ollila
Piiloperä
Koramoniemi
Vallioniemi
Patoniemi
Käylä
Kallunki
Säkkilä
Juuma
Alakitka
Kitka
Kantojoki
Virkkula
Kesäniemenkylä
Rukatunturi
Ruka
Rukajärvi
Salminen
Yli-Kitka
Riisitunturin kansallispuisto
Tolva
Oivanki
Nissinvaara
Määttälänvaara
Liikasenvaara
Oulankajoki
Paljakka
Suorajärvi
Vuotunki
Jyrkänkoski
Lehto
Särkiluoma
Kiviperä
Suininki
Säynäjä
Maivala
Heikkilä
Panayarvi Natsional'nyy Park
Olanga
Ozero Tavayarvi
Oz. Sokolozero
Kuma
Oz. Ruvozero
Oz. Kindozero
Oz. Tumcha
Kuusamo
Kuusamo-Ruka
Korhosenniemi
Livojärvi
Kurkijärvi
Livonniska
Majava
Purnuvaara
Sossonniemi
Muojärvi
Kärpänkylä
Koskenkylä
Törmäsenvaara
Haukiniemi
Kemilä
Kortesalmi
Multiperä
Iivaara
Lusminki
Tammela
Penikkajärvi
Soivio
Poussu
Pistа
Sofporog
Pyaozerskiy
Tungozero
Poncha
Tukhkala
Kuloharju
Anetjärvi
Jokilampi
Kynsivaara
Kynsijärvi
Kynsiperä
Kuolio
Oijusluoma
Penttilänvaara
Käsmä
Pahkakumpu
Pyhitys
Kostonjärvi
Löytövaara
Kouva
Kumpujenselkä
Jukua
Ruuhensuo
Syötteen kansallispuisto
Loukusa
Sirniö
Inkee
Vaarakylä
Ahola
Murtovaara
Iso-Syöte
Syötekylä
Virkkunen
Koitila
Siekkinen
Särkelä
Irninniemi
Vaaraperä
Kurvinen
Polo
Arnijärvi
Taivalkoski
Isokumpu
Lehtovaara
Teeriranta
Iijärvi
Oz. Okhtan''yarvi
Oz. Pistayarvi
Regozero
Jurmu
Jokijärvi
Tyrävaara
Tyrämäki
Rintamo
Hautakylä
Poijula
Kurtti
Kuusijärvi
Latvajärvenperä
Keminperä
Tyräjärvi
Pistо
Hossa
Lesovaara
Selkoskylä
Peranka
Pajuvaara
Yli-Kurki
Kurki
Iijoki
Pyhäjärvi
Korvuanjärvi
Ervasti
Hukijärvi
Pääaho
Metsäkylä
Kivivaara
Korvua
Pyhäkylä
Piispajärvi
Lavala
Puhos
Leino
Saarikylä
Mustavaara
Ahola
Siivikko
Salmijärvi
Kurkikylä
Näljänkä
Juntusranta
Lehtovaara
Voynitsa
Kalevala
Jaurakkajärvi
Leppälä
Vaaranniva
Ahjola
Keträvaara
Pyykkökylä
Kiannanniemi
Rasinvaara
Pirttivaara
Suolijärvi
Rääninvaara
Korpinen
Vääkiö
Lappi
Oz. Sredneye Kuyto
Oz. Verkhneye Kuyto
Naamankajärvi
Parkkila
Myllylahti
Yrittäperä
Joukokylä
Luokkala
Tervavaara
Kuurtola
Lonkka
Aittovaara
Pyssyperä
Neulikko
Alajärvi
Kannas
Kiantajärvi
Auho
Ahelva
Naulaperä
Pesiönranta
Aittokylä
Losovaara
Pesiökylä
Suomussalmi
Näätävaara
Puras
Voknavolok
Lylykylä
Ämmänsaari
Palovaara
Kotiranta
Ozero Kento
Puolanka
Leipivaara
Laaja
Korpikylä
Raate
Rasinkylä
Kurtto
Kytömäki
Väisälä
Sakaravaara
Mäkelänranta
Malahvianvaara
Vuokkijärvi
Ala-Vuokki
Livo
Väyrylä
Kalpio
Paljakka
Kangaskylä
Hoikka
Hyrynjärvi
Pyykkölänvaara
Jumaliskylä
Hakokylä
Marjokylä
Saarivaara
Viitavaara
Lietekylä
Hyrynsalmi
Oravivaara
Nalkki
Kotila
Nuottikylä
Laitala
Keskinen
Veihtivaara
Kuivajärvi
Kostomuksha
Uva
Törmänmäki
Kypäräyaara
Ollilanniemi
Moisiovaara
Pekankylä
Matkavaara
Hirvivaara
Kuumu
Vartius
Jokikylä
Iijärvi
Raappananmäki
Uura
Ristijärvi
Koskenkylä
Rämpsänkylä
Tapanikylä
Lehtovaara
Änättijärvi
Ozero Kamennoye
Oz. Kimasozero
Kivesjärvi
Vaarankylä
Karjalanvaara
Saukkovaara
Pyhäntä
Mustavaara
Härmänkylä
Kuusamonkylä
Iivantiira
Melalahti
Paltamo
Mieslahti
Härmänmäki
Hiisijärvi
Lentiira
Korkana
Kimasozero
Paltaselkä
Saviranta
Hannusranta
Kontiomäki
Vuosanka
Haukilahti
Sipinen
Koskenmäki
Niva
Maaselkä
Kaihojoki
Paltaniemi
Kuluntalahti
Paakinmäki
Sumsa
Viiksimo
Huuhilonkylä
Kellojärvi
Tuulimäki
Lemetinvaara
Heinämäki
Juonto
Timoniemi
Lentua
Juntinvaara
Kajaani
Pohjavaara
Suovaara
Naapurinvaara
Ala-Vieksi
Vieksi
Vorjaki
Hirvi
Kämäränkylä
Kuhmo
Ontojärvi
Soidinvaara
Sotkamo
Nuasjärvi
E63

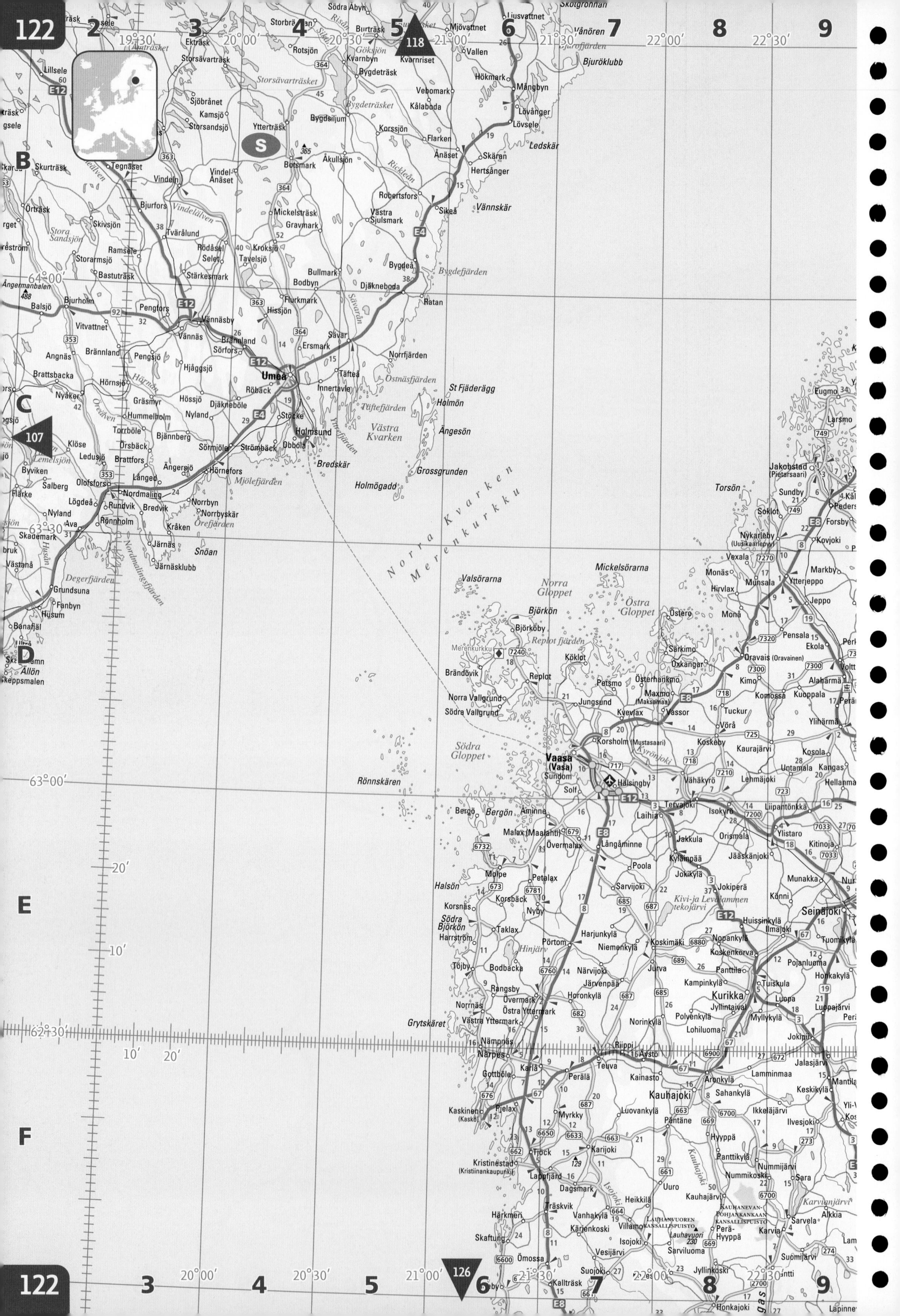

122
Umeå
Holmsund
Vännäs
Vindeln
Nordmaling
Hörnefors
Sävar
Robertsfors
Bygdeå
Ratan
Holmön
Västra Kvarken
Norra Kvarken
Merenkurkku
Valsörarna
Björkön
Replot
Vaasa (Vasa)
Korsholm (Mustasaari)
Malax (Maalahti)
Närpes
Teuva
Kauhajoki
Kristinestad (Kristiinankaupunki)
Kaskinen (Kaskö)
Seinäjoki
Kurikka
Jurva
Laihia
Isokyrö
Vöyri
Oravais (Oravainen)
Nykarleby (Uusikaarlepyy)
Jakobstad (Pietarsaari)
Ylistaro
Ilmajoki
Lauhanvuoren kansallispuisto
Rönnskären
Södra Gloppet
Norra Gloppet
Östra Gloppet
Mickelsörarna
E4
E8
E12
118
107
126

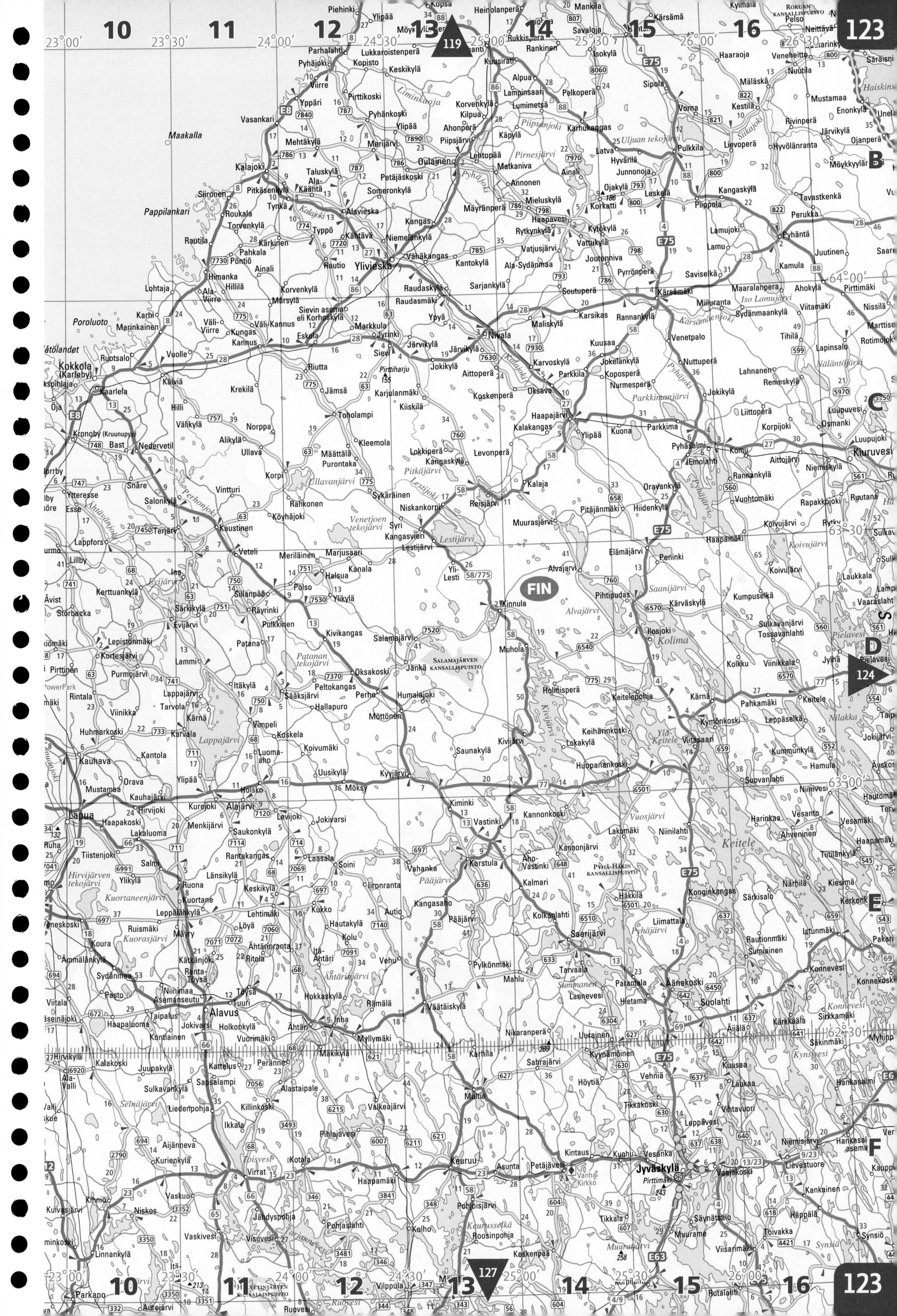

10
11
12
13
14
15
16
23°00′
23°30′
24°00′
24°30′
25°00′
25°30′
26°00′
26°30′
119
Piehinki
Ylipää
Kopsa
Heinolanperä
Mankila
Kärsämä
Kylmälä
Rokuan kansallispuisto
Pelso
Neittävä
Parhalahti
Lukkaroistenperä
Rukkisperä
Rankinen
Savaloja
Isokylä
Haaraoja
Veneheitto
Säräisni
Pyhäjoki
Kopisto
Keskikylä
Kuusirati
Nuutila
Viirre
Alpua
Pelkoperä
Sipola
Mäläskä
Haiskins
Pirttikoski
Liminkaoja
Lampinsaari
Mustamaa
Yppäri
Korvenkylä
Lumimetsä
Vorna
Kestilä
Enonkylä
Unela
Pyhänkoski
Kilpua
Vasankari
Ylipää
Ahonperä
Piipsanjoki
Karhukangas
Rivinperä
Maakalla
Mehtäkylä
Merijärvi
Piipsjärvi
Käpylä
Uljuan tekojärvi
Järvikylä
Ojanperä
Lehtopää
Pirnesjärvi
Latva
Pulkkila
Lievoperä
Hyvölänranta
Kalajoki
Taluskylä
Oulainen
Hyvärilä
Möykkyylär
B
Ala-Kääntä
Petäjäskoski
Matkaniva
Ainali
Junnonoja
Siironen
Pitkäsenkylä
Someronkylä
Pyhäjoki
Annonen
Ojakylä
Kangaskylä
Tavastkenkä
Tynkä
Alavieska
Mieluskylä
Leskelä
Piippola
Pappilankari
Roukala
Kalajoki
Kangas
Mäyränperä
Korkatti
Perukka
Torvenkylä
Typpö
Haapavesi
Lamujoki
Pyhäntä
Rautila
Kärkinen
Kähtävä
Niemelänkylä
Rytkynkylä
Kytökylä
Pahkala
Vattukylä
Lamu
Juutinen
Saare
Pöntiö
Ylivieska
Vähäkangas
Vatjusjärvi
Kantokylä
Joutenniva
Ainali
Rautio
Ala-Sydänmaa
Pyrrönperä
Saviselkä
Kamula
Himanka
Lohtaja
Hillilä
Raudaskylä
Sarjankylä
Soutuperä
Kärsämäki
Maaralanpera
Ahokylä
Pirttimäki
64°00′
Ala-Viirre
Korvenkylä
Märsylä
Raudasmäki
Miiluranta
Iso Lamujärvi
Sievin asema eli Korhoskylä
Karhi
Väli-Viirre
Väli-Kannus
Ypyä
Nivala
Maliskylä
Karsikas
Rannankylä
Sydänmaankylä
Viitamäki
Nissilä
Poroluoto
Marinkainen
Kungas
Markkula
Jyrinki
Kärsämäenjoki
Marttise
Kannus
Eskola
Järvikylä
Järvikylä
Venetpalo
Tihilä
Rotimojok
Kåtölandet
Vuolle
Sievi
Kuusaa
Ruotsalo
Riutta
Jokikylä
Karvoskylä
Jokelankylä
Nuttuperä
Lapinsalo
Näläntöjärvi
Kokkola (Karleby)
Pirttiharju
Aittoperä
Parkkila
Koposperä
Lahnanen
Kälviä
Nurmesperä
Remeskylä
Kaarlela
Krekilä
Jämsä
Karjulanmäki
Koskenperä
Oksava
Pyhäjoki
Parkkimanjärvi
Jokikylä
Kiiskilä
Haapajärvi
Liittoperä
Luupuvesi
C
Öja
Hilli
Toholampi
Kalakangas
Korpijoki
Osmanki
Välikylä
Norppa
Ylipää
Kuona
Parkkima
Kronoby (Kruunupyy)
Alikylä
Kleemola
Lokkiperä
Levonperä
Pyhäsalmi
Komu
Luupujoki
Bast
Nedervetil
Ullava
Määttälä
Kangaskylä
Aittojärvi
Kiuruvesi
Purontaka
Pitkäjärvi
Emolahti
Niemiskylä
Korpi
Kalaja
Rannankylä
Snåre
Ullavanjärvi
Sykäräinen
Lestijoki
Oravankylä
Vuohtomäki
Ytteresse
Salonkylä
Vintturi
Reisjärvi
Rapakkojoki
Ruutana
Esse
Perhonjoki
Rahkonen
Niskankorpi
Pitäjänmäki
Hiidenkylä
Ähtävänjoki
Köyhäjoki
Venetjoen tekojärvi
Muurasjärvi
Koivujärvi
Terjärv
Kaustinen
Syri
Kangasvieri
Lestijärvi
Haapamäki
63°30′
Lappfors
Lestijärvi
Elämäjärvi
Peninki
Koivujärvi
Veteli
Meriläinen
Marjusaari
Lillby
Kanala
Alvajärvi
Koivujärvi
Evijärvi
Ina
Halsua
Yli-Lesti
FIN
Laukkala
Kerttuankylä
Sillanpää
Polso
Pihtipudas
Saanijärvi
Vaaraslahti
Ylikylä
Kinnula
Kärväskylä
Kumpuselkä
Åvist
Storbacka
Särkikylä
Räyrinki
Alvajärvi
Pulkkinen
Kivikangas
Sulkavanjärvi
Evijärvi
Ilosjoki
Tossavanlahti
Lepistönmäki
Patana
Salamajärvi
Kolima
Pielavesi
Kortesjärvi
Lammi
Muhola
Pirttinen
Patanan tekojärvi
Salamajärven kansallispuisto
Kolkku
Viinikkala
Jylhä
D
Purmojärvi
Oksakoski
Jänkä
124
PowerPark
Itäkylä
Holmisperä
Keitelepohja
Rintala
Lappajärvi
Peltokangas
Perho
Humalajoki
Kärnä
Pahkamäki
Keitele
Tarvola
Sääksjärvi
Hallapuro
Viinikka
Kärnä
Keiharinkoski
Kymönkoski
Leppäselkä
Vimpeli
Möttönen
Nilakka
Huhmarkoski
Karvala
Koskela
Kivijärvi
Lokakylä
Vitasaari
Jokijärvi
Lappajärvi
Koivumäki
Ylä-Keitele
Kantola
Luoma-aho
Saunakylä
Kivijärvi
Kummunkylä
Kauhava
Uusikylä
Huopanankoski
Hamula
Orava
Mustamaa
Kyyjärvi
Äyskos
Ylipää
Suovanlahti
Möksy
Holsko
Niinivesi
63°00′
Kauhajärvi
Hautomä
Hirvijoki
Kurejoki
Alajärvi
Kiminki
Kannonkoski
Lapua
Menkijärvi
Levijoki
Jokivarsi
Vastinki
Vesanto
Vesamäki
Haapakoski
Vuosjärvi
Harinkaa
Lakaluoma
Saukonkylä
Lakomäki
Niinilahti
Ahveninen
Ruha
Tiistenjoki
Rantakangas
Laasala
Kannonjärvi
Keitele
Haapamäki
Salmi
Soini
Vahanka
Karstula
Aho-Vastinki
Tiitulankylä
Hirvijärven tekojärvi
Ylikylä
Länsikylä
Pyhä-Häkin kansallispuisto
Pääjärvi
Ruona
Iironranta
Kalmari
Närhilä
Kiesimä
Keskikylä
Kuortane
Häkkilä
Kuortaneenjärvi
Kukko
Kangasaho
Konginkangas
Särkisalo
Kerkonk
E
Leppälänkylä
Lehtimäki
Autio
Kolkanlahti
Veneskoski
Ruismäki
Löyä
Hautakylä
Pääjärvi
Liimattala
Istunmäki
Mäyry
Pyhäjärvi
Kuorasjärvi
Kolu
Saarijärvi
Rautionmäki
Pakari
Koura
Ähtärinranta
Itä-Ähtäri
Sumiainen
Ämmälänkylä
Kätkänjoki
Ritola
Vehu
Pylkönmäki
Tarvaala
Ranta-Töysä
Ähtärinjärvi
Mahlu
Äänekoski
Konnevesi
Sydänmaa
Summanen
Parantala
Konnekoski
Pasto
Niinimaa
Töysä
Hokkaskylä
Lannevesi
Heinämaa
Suolahti
Viitala
Asemanseutu
Tuuri
Rämälä
Väätäiskylä
Seinäjoki
Alavus
Haapaluoma
Taipalus
Jokivarsi
Holkonkylä
Ähtäri
Inha
Nikaranperä
Äijälä
Kärkkäälä
Sirkkamäki
62°30′
Kontiainen
Vuorimäki
Myllymäki
Uurainen
Säkinmäki
Myhinp
Hirvikylä
Mäkikylä
Karhila
Kyynämöinen
Kynsivesi
Kalakoski
Juupakylä
Kattelus
Peränne
Sahrajärvi
Ala-Valli
Kuusaa
Sapsalampi
Höytiä
Vehniä
Hankasalmi
Sulkavankylä
Alastaipale
Multia
Laukaa
Valli
Seinäjärvi
Liedenpohja
Killinkoski
Valkeajärvi
Tikkakoski
Vihtavuori
Ikkala
Leppävesi
Pihlajavesi
Aijänneva
Niemisjärvi
Hankasalmi asema
F
Kuriankylä
Töysvesi
Kotala
Kintaus
Kuohu
Vesanka
Virrat
Keuruu
Asunta
Petäjävesi
Jyväskylä
Lievestuore
Haapamäki
Vanha Kirkko
Vaajakoski
Kauppi
Kihniö
Vaskuu
Pirttimäki
Kuivasjärvi
Niskos
Jähdyspohja
Pohjoisjärvi
Kankainen
Pohjaslahti
Säynätsalo
Häppälä
Keurusselkä
Tikkala
Vaskivesi
Kolho
Roosinpohja
Muurame
Toivakka
Sinsiö
Visuvesi
Muuratjärvi
Viisarimäki
minkoski
Linnankylä
Koskenpää
Synsiä
Itä-Aure
Parkano
127
Helvetinjärven kansallispuisto
Vilppula
Ruovesi
Rutalahti
Aurejärvi
E8
E75
E63
E6

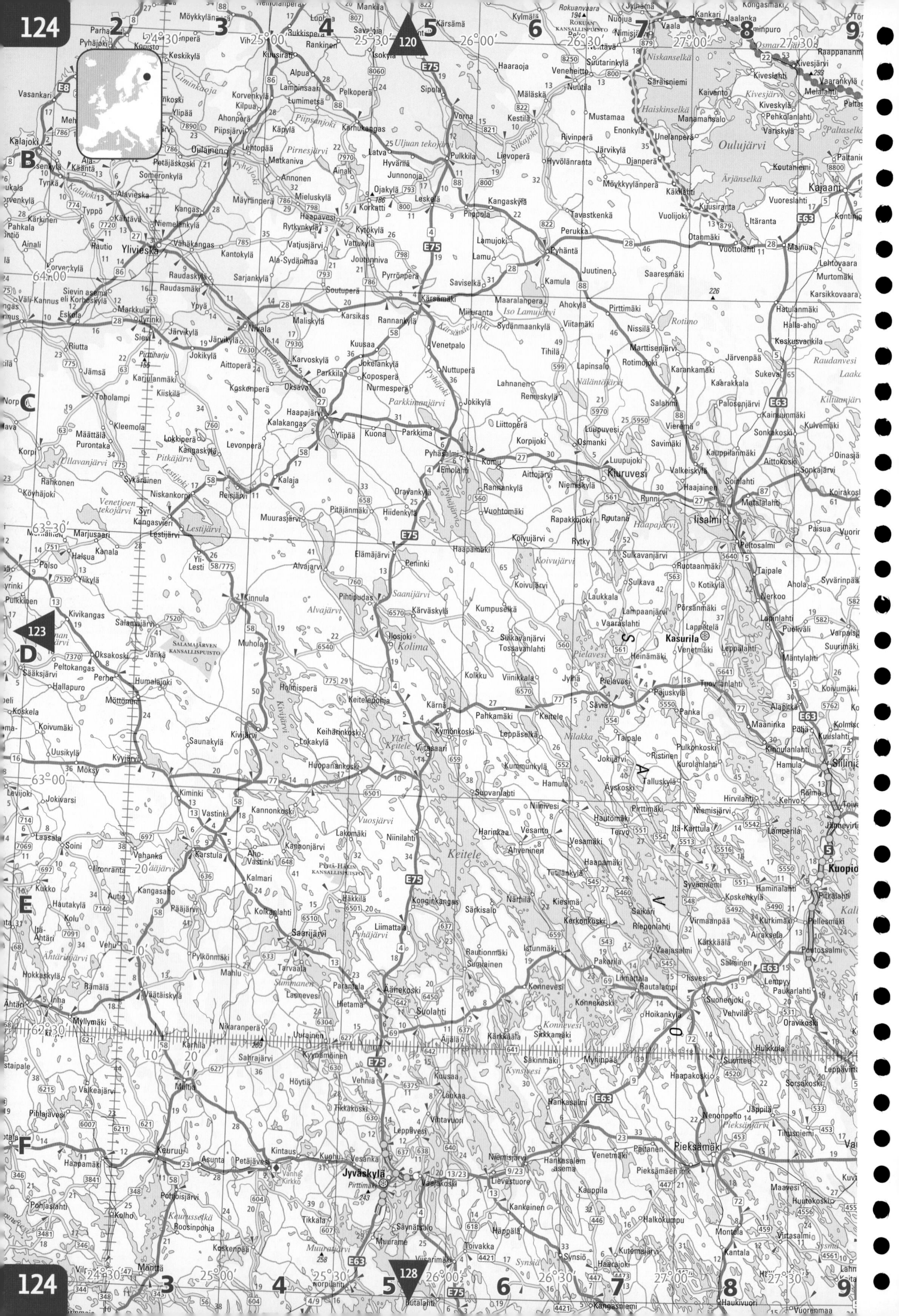
120
123
128
Kalajoki
Ylivieska
Oulainen
Haapavesi
Pyhäjoki
Kärsämäki
Nivala
Sievi
Haapajärvi
Pyhäsalmi
Pyhäntä
Kiuruvesi
Iisalmi
Kajaani
Vaala
Oulujärvi
Pyhäjärvi
Reisjärvi
Lestijärvi
Kinnula
Pihtipudas
Kolima
Viitasaari
Keitele
Pielavesi
Kasurila
Nilakka
Siilinjärvi
Kuopio
Karstula
Saarijärvi
Äänekoski
Suolahti
Konnevesi
Rautalampi
Suonenjoki
Keuruu
Multia
Petäjävesi
Jyväskylä
Laukaa
Hankasalmi
Pieksämäki
Muurame
Jämsä
Mänttä
Alavieska
Salamajärven kansallispuisto
Pyhä-Häkin kansallispuisto
Rokuan kansallispuisto
Sievin asema
Toholampi
Halsua
Perho
Kyyjärvi
Soini
Ähtäri
Vilppula
Kolho
Niskanselkä
Ärjänselkä
Uljuan tekojärvi
Kivijärvi
Alvajärvi
Vuosjärvi
Pyhäjärvi
Kynsivesi
Keurusselkä
Muuratjärvi
E8
E63
E75
63°00′
63°30′
62°30′
64°00′
24°30′
25°00′
25°30′
26°00′
26°30′
27°00′
27°30′

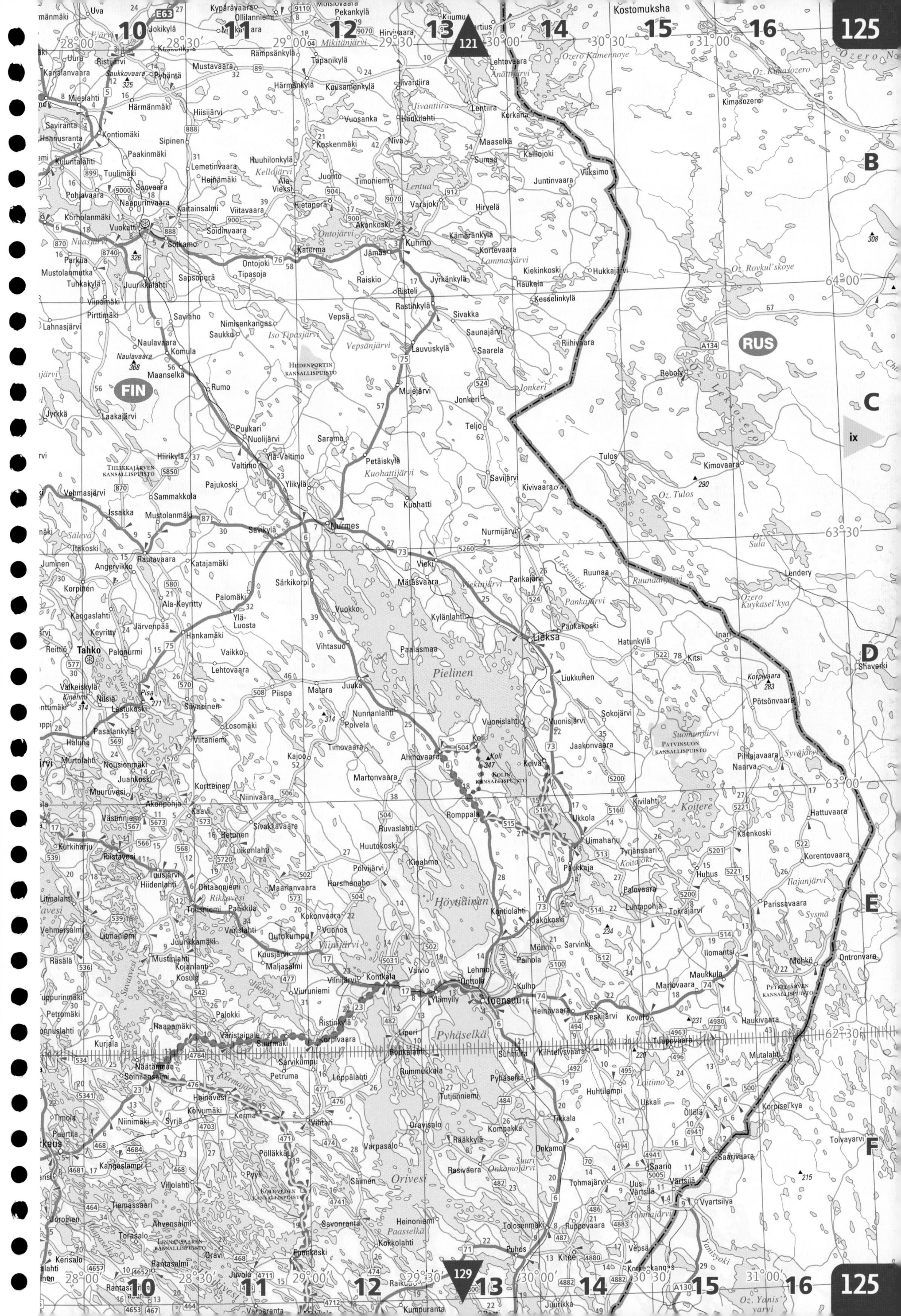
10
11
12
13
14
15
16
121
129
B
C
D
E
F
ix
FIN
RUS
Kostomuksha
Kuhmo
Sotkamo
Vuokatti
Nurmes
Lieksa
Pielinen
Höytiäinen
Joensuu
Pyhäselkä
Orivesi
Koli
Uimaharju
Ilomantsi
Outokumpu
Kitee
Tohmajärvi
Värtsilä
Vyartsilya
Tahko
Valtimo
Rautavaara
Juankoski
Kaavi
Polvijärvi
Kontiolahti
Liperi
Rääkkylä
Enonkoski
Rantasalmi
Heinävesi
Juuka
Lentiira
Hiidenportin Kansallispuisto
Tiilikkajärven Kansallispuisto
Kolin Kansallispuisto
Patvinsuon Kansallispuisto
Petkeljärven Kansallispuisto
Koloveden Kansallispuisto
Linnansaaren Kansallispuisto
Koitere
Reboly
Lendery
Oz. Lekshozero
Oz. Tulos
Kimovaara
Korpisel'kya
Tolvayarvi
Ozero Kamennoye
Oz. Kimasozero
Kimasozero
Oz. Roykul'skoye
Ozero Kuykasel'kya
Shaverki
Oz. Sula
Oz. Yanis'yarvi
64°00'
63°30'
63°00'
62°30'
28°00'
28°30'
29°00'
29°30'
30°00'
30°30'
31°00'
E63
6
73
75
76
17
74

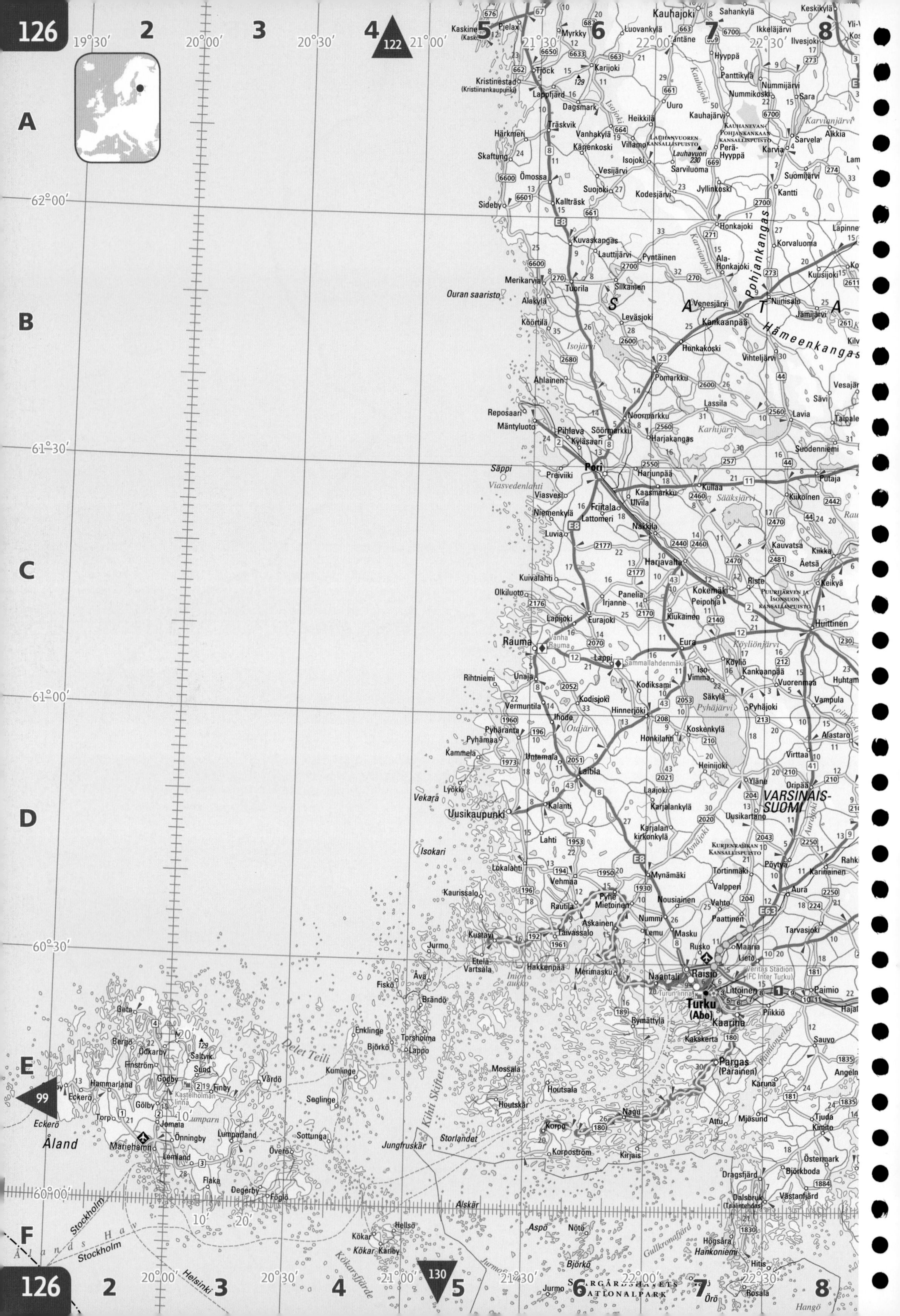
Kaskinen
Pjelax
Myrkky
Kauhajoki
Luovankylä
Sahankylä
Ikkelijärvi
Ilvesjoki
Keskikylä
Tjöck
Karijoki
Kristinestad
(Kristiinankaupunki)
Lappfjärd
Dagsmark
Isojoki
Uuro
Hyyppä
Panttikylä
Nummijärvi
Nummikoski
Sara
Kauhajärvi
Karvianjärvi
Träskvik
Härkmeri
Heikkilä
Vanhakylä
Kärjenkoski
Villamo
Lauhanvuoren kansallispuisto
Lauhavuori
Kauhanevan-Pohjankankaan kansallispuisto
Perä-Hyyppä
Sarvela
Alkkia
Karvia
Skaftung
Isojoki
Sarviluoma
Ömossa
Vesijärvi
Suomijärvi
Suojoki
Kodesjärvi
Jyllinkoski
Kantti
Sideby
Kallträsk
62° 00′
Honkajoki
Pohjankangas
Kuvaskangas
Lauttijärvi
Pyntäinen
Karvianjoki
Ala-Honkajoki
Korvaluoma
Lapinneva
Merikarvia
Tuorila
Silkainen
Kuusijoki
Ouran saaristo
Alakylä
Venesjärvi
Niinisalo
Jämijärvi
S A T A
Leväsjoki
Kankaanpää
Hämeenkangas
Köörtilä
Isojärvi
Honkakoski
Vihteljärvi
Pomarkku
Ahlainen
Lassila
Reposaari
Noormarkku
Lavia
Sävi
Mäntyluoto
Pihlava
Söörmarkku
Harjakangas
Karhijärvi
Kyläsaari
61° 30′
Suodenniemi
Säppi
Preiviiki
Pori
Harjunpää
Viasvedenlahti
Kullaa
Putaja
Viasvesi
Kaasmarkku
Ulvila
Sääksjärvi
Kiikoinen
Friitala
Lattomeri
Niemenkylä
Nakkila
Luvia
Kauvatsa
Kiikka
Harjavalta
Äetsä
Kuivalahti
Kokemäki
Riste
Keikyä
Olkiluoto
Panelia
Peipohja
Puurijärven ja Isonsuon kansallispuisto
Irjanne
Lapijoki
Eurajoki
Kiukainen
Huittinen
Rauma
Vanha Rauma
Eura
Köyliönjärvi
Lappi
Sammallahdenmäki
Köyliö
Kankaanpää
Rihtniemi
Unaja
Iso-Vimma
Vuorenmaa
Huhtamo
Kodiksami
Säkylä
Pyhäjärvi
Vampula
61° 00′
Vermuntila
Kodisjoki
Hinnerjoki
Pyhäjoki
Ihode
Otajärvi
Pyhäranta
Koskenkylä
Alastaro
Pyhämaa
Honkilahti
Kammela
Untamala
Virttaa
Heinijoki
Laitila
Lyökki
Ylöne
Oripää
Vekara
Laajoki
VARSINAIS-SUOMI
Kalanti
Karjalankylä
Uusikaupunki
Uusikartano
Lahti
Karjalan kirkonkylä
Kurjenrahkan kansallispuisto
Isokari
Mynäjoki
Pöytyä
Lokalahti
Tortinmäki
Mynämäki
Karinainen
Vehmaa
Valpperi
Kaurissalo
Pyhe
Mietoinen
Nousiainen
Aura
Rautila
Vahto
Paattinen
Askainen
Nummi
Kustavi
Lemu
Taivassalo
Masku
Tarvasjoki
Jurmo
Rusko
Maaria
60° 30′
Etelä-Vartsala
Hakkenpää
Lieto
Veritas Stadion (FC Inter Turku)
Iniön aukko
Merimasku
Naantali
Raisio
Fiskö
Åva
Turun linna
Littoinen
Paimio
Brändö
Turku
(Åbo)
Piikkiö
Geta
Rymättylä
Kaarina
Enklinge
Bergö
Ödkarby
Saltvik
Björkö
Torsholma
Kakskerta
Sauvo
Delet
Teili
Lappo
Finström
Sund
Pargas
(Parainen)
Kumlinge
Mossala
Eckerö
Hammarland
Godby
Vårdö
Kastelholman linna
Finby
Karuna
Gölby
Houtsala
Seglinge
Kihti Skiftet
Houtskär
Torp
Jomala
Lumparn
Nagu
Attu
Mjösund
Tjuda
Eckerö
Korpo
Kimito
Åland
Mariehamn
Önningby
Lumparland
Sottunga
Jungfruskär
Storlandet
Lemland
Överö
Korpoström
Kirjais
Östermark
Björkboda
Dragsfjärd
Flaka
Degerby
Föglö
Västanfjärd
60° 00′
Stockholm
Alskär
Dalsbruk
(Taalintehdas)
Ålands Hav
Stockholm
Aspö
Nötö
Gullkronafjärd
Högsåra
Kökar
Karlby
Hellsö
Kökarsfjärde
Hankoniemi
Björkö
Jurmo
Skärgårdshavets nationalpark
Hitis
Rosala
Örö
Helsinki
Hangö
19° 30′
20° 00′
20° 30′
21° 00′
21° 30′
22° 00′
22° 30′
A
B
C
D
E
F
2
3
4
5
6
7
8
122
130
99

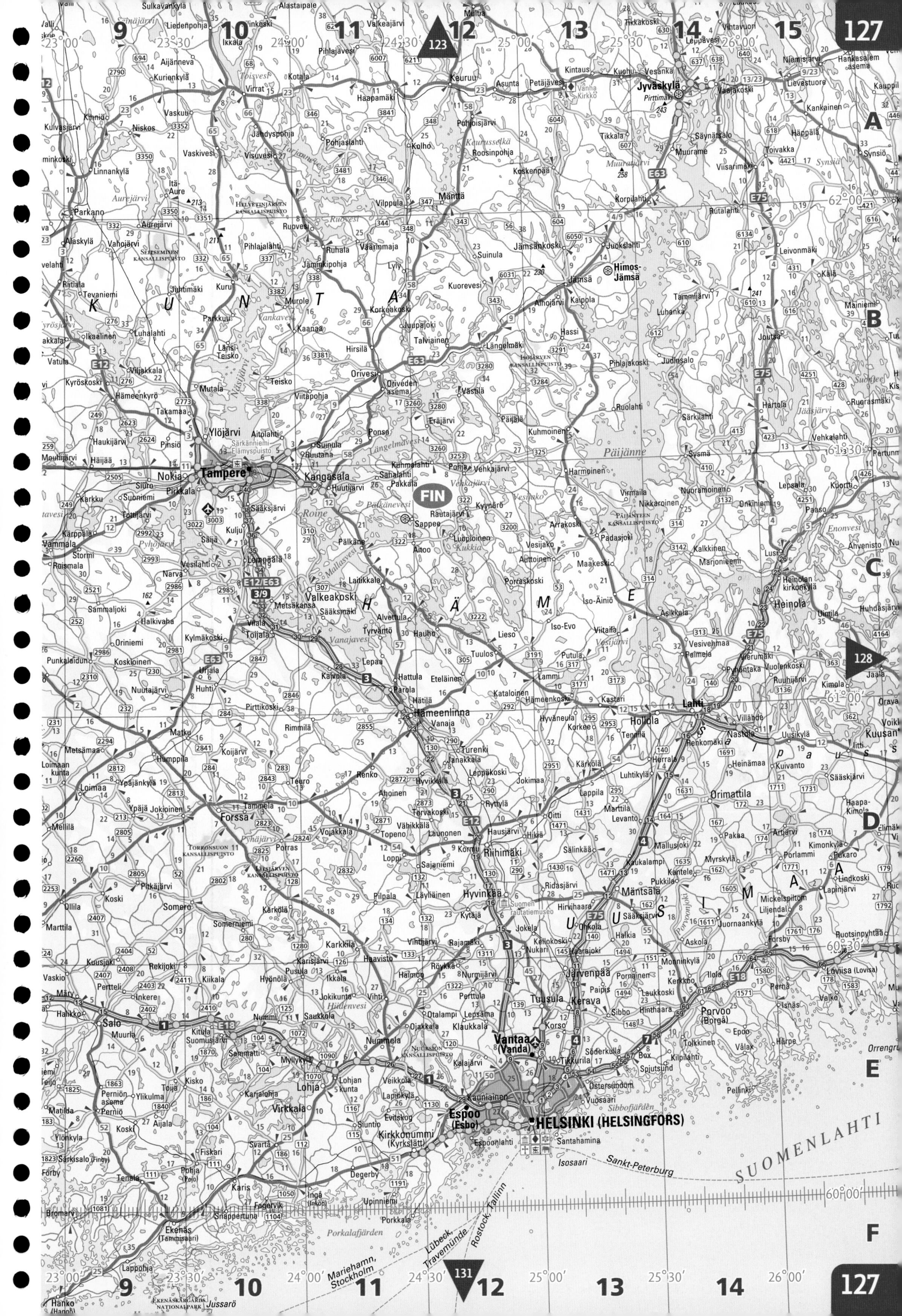
9
10
11
12
13
14
15
123
128
131
A
B
C
D
E
F
23°00′
23°30′
24°00′
24°30′
25°00′
25°30′
26°00′
62°00′
61°30′
61°00′
60°30′
60°00′
Jyväskylä
Keuruu
Virrat
Parkano
Mänttä
Jämsä
Himos-Jämsä
Orivesi
Ylöjärvi
Tampere
Nokia
Pirkkala
Kangasala
FIN
Valkeakoski
Toijala
Urjala
Hämeenlinna
Forssa
Riihimäki
Hyvinkää
Lahti
Heinola
Hollola
Nastola
Orimattila
Mäntsälä
Järvenpää
Tuusula
Kerava
Vantaa (Vanda)
Espoo (Esbo)
HELSINKI (HELSINGFORS)
Porvoo (Borgå)
Loviisa (Lovisa)
Kirkkonummi (Kyrkslätt)
Lohja
Salo
Ekenäs (Tammisaari)
Hanko (Hangö)
Karis
Päijänne
Näsijärvi
Vanajavesi
Mallasvesi
Pyhäjärvi
Hiidenvesi
Vesijärvi
K U N T A
H Ä M E
U U S I M A A
S a l p a u s s e l k ä
SUOMENLAHTI
Sankt-Peterburg
Lübeck, Travemünde
Rostock, Tallinn
Mariehamn, Stockholm
Porkalafjärden
Sibbofjärden
Santahamina
Isosaari
Jussarö
E12
E63
E75
E18
E12/E63
HELVETINJÄRVEN KANSALLISPUISTO
SEITSEMISEN KANSALLISPUISTO
ISOJÄRVEN KANSALLISPUISTO
PÄIJÄNTEEN KANSALLISPUISTO
TORRONSUON KANSALLISPUISTO
LIESJÄRVEN KANSALLISPUISTO
NUUKSION KANSALLISPUISTO
EKENÄSKÄRGÅRDS NATIONALPARK
Särkänniemi-Elämyspuisto
Suomen rautatiemuseo

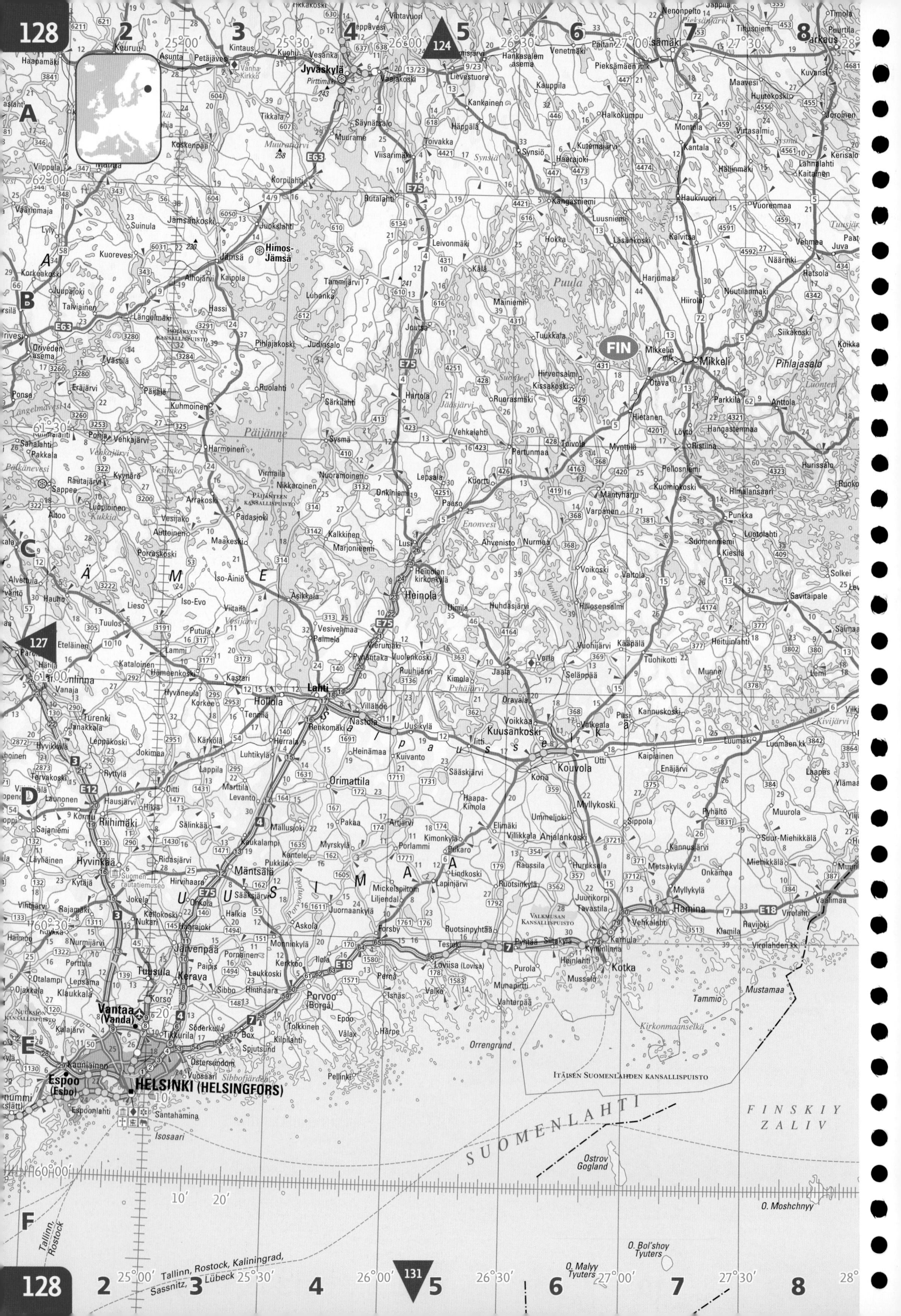

2
3
4
5
124
6
7
8
25°00′
25°30′
26°00′
26°30′
27°00′
27°30′
A
B
C
D
E
F
62°00′
61°30′
61°00′
60°30′
60°00′
Keuruu
Haapamäki
Petäjävesi
Vanha Kirkko
Jyväskylä
Vaajakoski
Säynätsalo
Muurame
Korpilahti
Jämsänkoski
Jämsä
Himos-Jämsä
Kuorevesi
Orivesi
Längelmäki
Kuhmoinen
Päijänne
Padasjoki
Asikkala
Heinola
Hartola
Sysmä
Joutsa
Leivonmäki
Toivakka
Hankasalmi asema
Pieksämäen mlk
Kangasniemi
Haukivuori
Mikkeli
FIN
Pihlajasalo
Puula
Hirvensalmi
Ristiina
Mäntyharju
Kuusankoski
Kouvola
Valkeala
Lahti
Hollola
Nastola
Orimattila
Hämeenlinna
Hyvinkää
Riihimäki
Mäntsälä
Järvenpää
Tuusula
Kerava
Vantaa (Vanda)
Espoo (Esbo)
Kauniainen
HELSINKI (HELSINGFORS)
Santahamina
Isosaari
Porvoo (Borgå)
Loviisa (Lovisa)
Pyhtää
Kotka
Karhula
Hamina
Vaalimaa
Virolahti
Savitaipale
Elimäki
Anjalankoski
Myllykoski
Sippola
Valkmusan Kansallispuisto
Itäisen Suomenlahden kansallispuisto
Päijänteen kansallispuisto
Isojärven kansallispuisto
Suomen rautatiemuseo
S A L P A U S S E L K Ä
H Ä M E
U U S I M A A
SUOMENLAHTI
FINSKIY ZALIV
Ostrov Gogland
O. Moshchnyy
O. Bol'shoy Tyuters
O. Malyy Tyuters
Tammio
Mustamaa
Orrengrund
Kirkonmaanselkä
Tallinn, Rostock
Tallinn, Rostock, Kaliningrad, Sassnitz, Lübeck
127
131
E12
E18
E63
E75

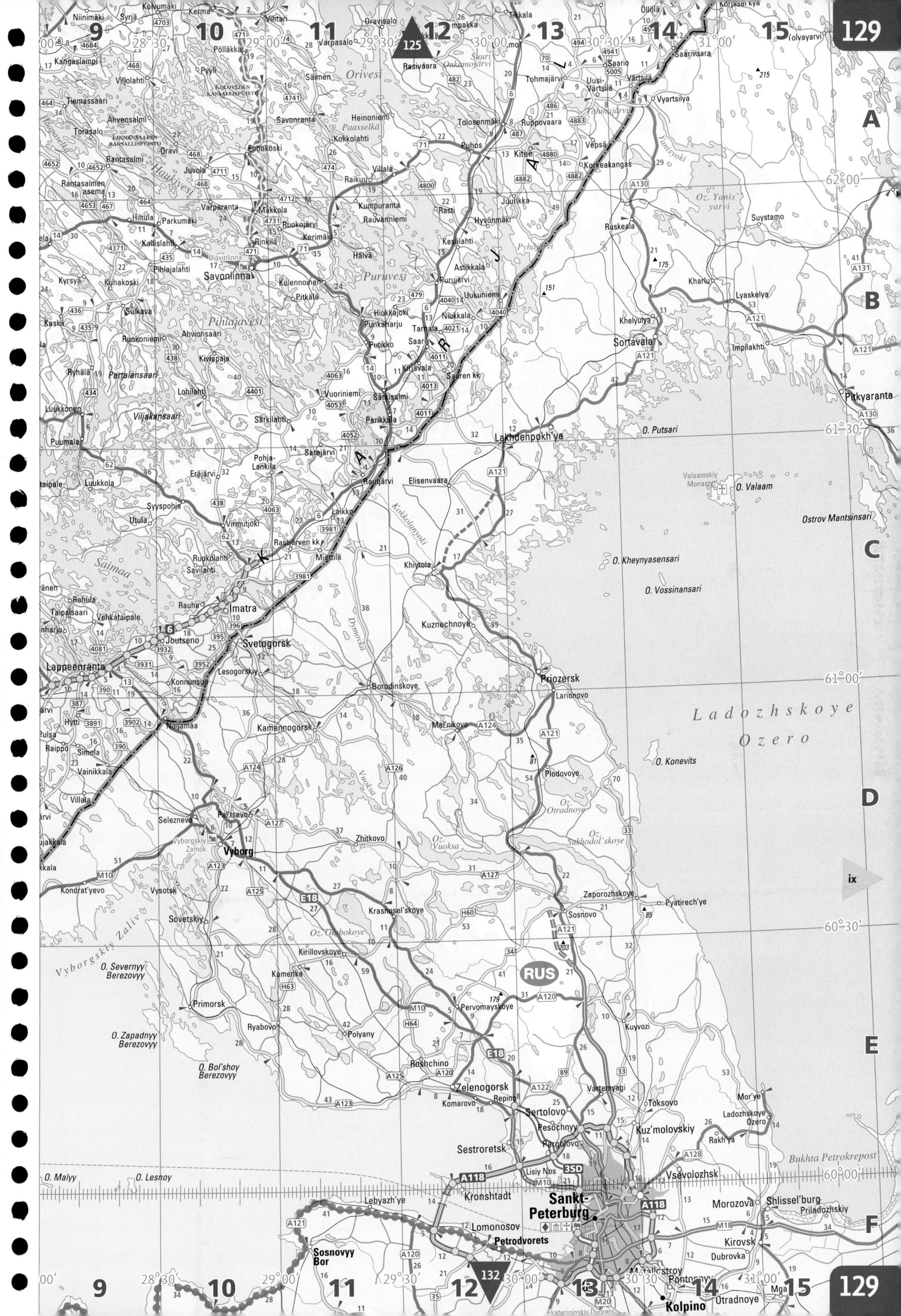
9
10
11
12
13
14
15
A
B
C
D
E
F
125
132
ix
62°00′
61°30′
61°00′
60°30′
60°00′
Niinimäki
Syrjä
Kolvumäki
Kerma
Vihtari
Oravisalo
Tikkala
Öllölä
Tolvayarvi
Varpasalo
Pölläkkä
Rasivaara
Onkamojärvi
Tohmajärvi
Saario
Värtsilä
Saarivaara
Uusi-Värtsilä
Vyartsilya
Kangaslampi
Viljolahti
Pyyli
Säimen
Orivesi
Tiemassaari
Ahvensalmi
Heinoniemi
Savonranta
Paasselkä
Tolosenmäki
Ruppovaara
Tohmajärvi
Torasalo
Kokkolahti
Puhos
Kitee
Vepsä
Oravi
Enonkoski
Haukivesi
Rantasalmi
Juvola
Villala
Raikuu
Korkeakangas
Rantasalmen asema
Varparanta
Makkola
Kumpuranta
Rauvanniemi
Rasti
Juurikka
Hyvönmäki
Oz. Yanis'yarvi
Suystamo
Ruskeala
Hiltula
Parkumäki
Ruokojärvi
Kerimäki
Kesälahti
Pyhäjärvi
Kallislahti
Rinkilä
Hälvä
Olavinlinna
Pihlajalahti
Savonlinna
Astikkala
Puruvesi
Purujärvi
Kharlu
Kyrsyä
Kuhakoski
Kulennoinen
Uukuniemi
Lyaskelya
Pitkälä
Sulkava
Hiukkajoki
Niukkala
Khelyulya
Kaskii
Pihlajavesi
Punkaharju
Tarnala
Ahvionsaari
Saari
Sortavala
Ruokoniemi
Putikko
Impilakhti
Kiviapaja
Ryhälä
Partalansaari
Kirjavala
Saaren kk
Lohilahti
Vuoriniemi
Särkisalmi
Pitkyaranta
Luukkonen
Viljakansaari
Särkilahti
Parikkala
Lakhdenpokh'ya
O. Putsari
Puumala
Sarajärvi
Pohja-Lankila
Eräjärvi
Rautjärvi
Elisenvaara
Luukkola
Valaamskiy Monastyr
O. Valaam
Syyspohja
Kokkolanyoki
Utula
Virmutjoki
Laikko
Ostrov Mantsinsaari
Rautjärven kk
Miettilä
Saimaa
Ruokolahti
Savilahti
Khiytola
O. Kheynyasensari
O. Vossinansari
Rehula
Taipalsaari
Vehkataipale
Rauha
Imatra
Dymovka
Kuznechnoye
Joutseno
Svetogorsk
Lappeenranta
Lesogorskiy
Konnunsuo
Priozersk
Larionovo
Borodinskoye
Ladozhskoye Ozero
Hytti
Nuijamaa
Kamennogorsk
Mel'nikovo
Pulsa
Raippo
Simola
O. Konevits
Vainikkala
Vuoksa
Plodovoye
Villala
Oz. Otradnoye
Seleznevo
Pal'tsevo
Vyborgskiy Zamok
Vyborg
Zhitkovo
Oz. Vuoksa
Oz. Sukhodol'skoye
Kondrat'yevo
Vysotsk
Zaporozhskoye
Pyatirech'ye
Sovetskiy
Krasnosel'skoye
Sosnovo
Oz. Glubokoye
Vyborgskiy Zaliv
O. Severnyy Berezovyy
Kirillovskoye
Kamenka
RUS
Primorsk
Pervomayskoye
Ryabovo
Polyany
Kuyvozi
O. Zapadnyy Berezovyy
O. Bol'shoy Berezovyy
Roshchino
Zelenogorsk
Komarovo
Repino
Vartemyagi
Toksovo
Mor'ye
Sertolovo
Ladozhskoye Ozero
Pesochnyy
Kuz'molovskiy
Rakh'ya
Sestroretsk
Pargolovo
Bukhta Petrokrepost
Lisiy Nos
Vsevolozhsk
O. Malyy
O. Lesnoy
Kronshtadt
Lebyazh'ye
Sankt-Peterburg
Morozova
Shlissel'burg
Priladozhskiy
Lomonosov
Petrodvorets
Kirovsk
Sosnovyy Bor
Dubrovka
Metallostroy
Pontonnyy
Otradnoye
Kolpino
Mga
E18
M10
A121
A120
A118
A124
A125
A126
A127
A123
A128
A130
A131
M18
M20

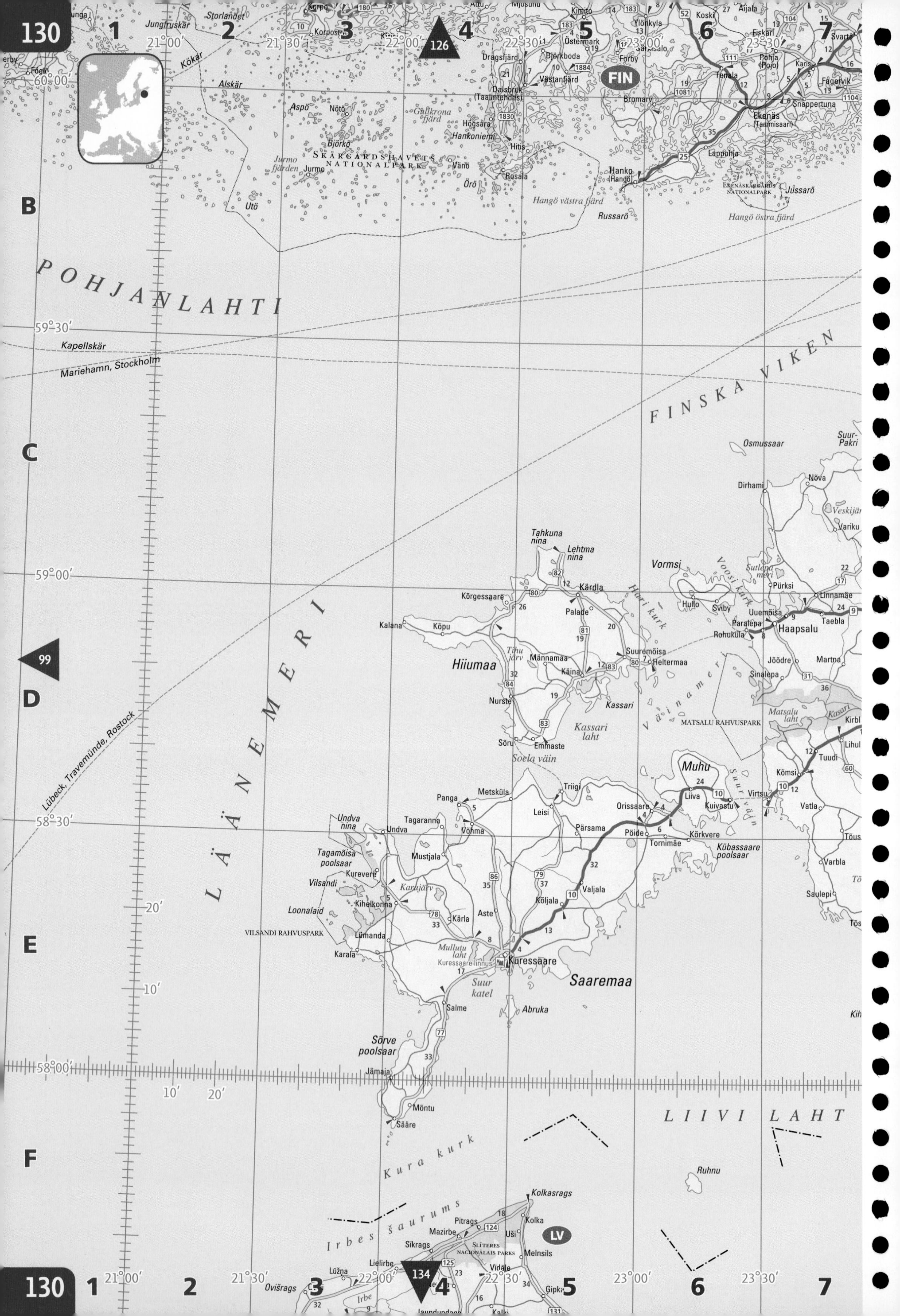
POHJANLAHTI
FINSKA VIKEN
LÄÄNEMERI
LIIVI LAHT
FIN
LV
Skärgårdshavets Nationalpark
Hiiumaa
Saaremaa
Muhu
Vormsi
Haapsalu
Kuressaare
Kärdla
Käina
Hanko (Hangö)
Ekenäs (Tammisaari)
Dragsfjärd
Dalsbruk (Taalintehdas)
Kapellskär
Mariehamn, Stockholm
Lübeck, Travemünde, Rostock
Matsalu Rahvuspark
Vilsandi Rahvuspark
Ekenäskärgårds Nationalpark
Kura kurk
Irbes šaurums
Slīteres Nacionālais Parks
Ruhnu
Osmussaar
Kolka
Kolkasrags
Sõrve poolsaar
Salme
Sääre
Möntu
Jämaja
Orissaare
Kuivastu
Virtsu
Soela väin
Kassari laht
Väinameri
Suur väin
Hari kurk
Voosi kurk

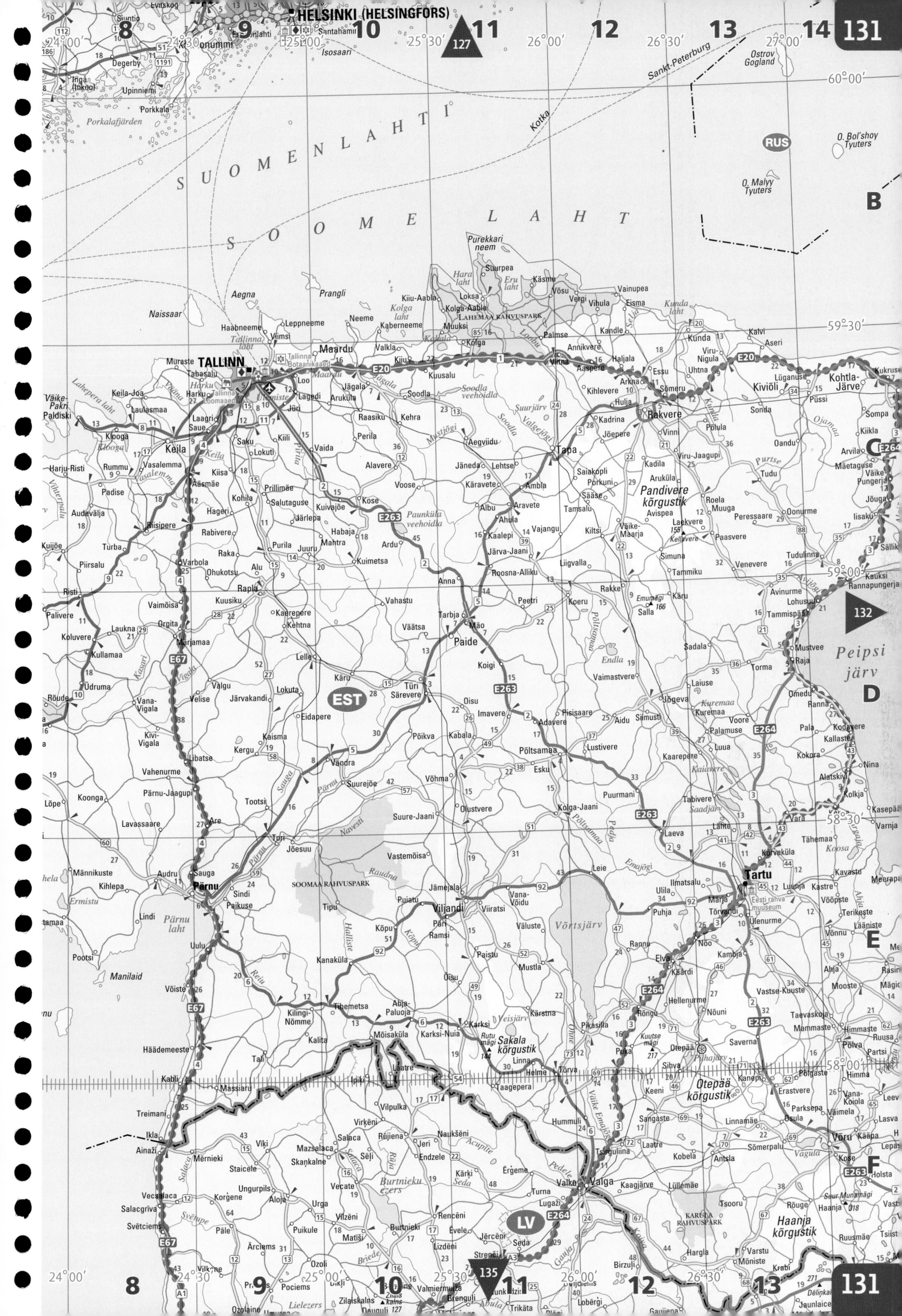
HELSINKI (HELSINGFORS)
SUOMENLAHTI
SOOME LAHT
Porkalafjärden
Porkkala
Upinniemi
Degerby
Inga (Inkoo)
Santahamina
Isosaari
Kotka
Sankt-Peterburg
Ostrov Gogland
RUS
O. Bol'shoy Tyuters
O. Malyy Tyuters
Purekkari neem
Suurpea
Hara laht
Eru laht
Käsmu
Võsu
Vergi
Vihula
Vainupea
Eisma
Kunda laht
Aegna
Prangli
Naissaar
Kolga laht
Loksa
Kolga-Aabla
Kiiu-Aabla
Lahemaa Rahvuspark
Muuksi
Kolga
Neeme
Kaberneeme
Leppneeme
Haabneeme
Viimsi
Tallinna laht
Maardu
Valkla
Kiiu
Palmse
Annikvere
Kandle
Kunda
Kalvi
Aseri
Viru-Nigula
Uhtna
E20
Kohtla-Järve
Kiviõli
Lüganuse
Sonda
Püssi
Muraste
TALLINN
Tabasalu
Harku
Tallinna Botaanikaaed
Loo
Lagedi
Jägala
Kuusalu
Soodla
Soodla veehoidla
Viitna
Aaspere
Haljala
Essu
Arkna
Kihlevere
Hulja
Sõmeru
Rakvere
Kadrina
Jõepere
Vinni
Põlula
Keila-Joa
Väike-Pakri
Paldiski
Laulasmaa
Lahepera laht
Klooga
Keila
Laagri
Saue
Saku
Kiili
Jüri
Aruküla
Raasiku
Kehra
Perila
Vaida
Alavere
Aegviidu
Suurjärv
Tapa
Lokuti
Harju-Risti
Rummu
Vasalemma
Kiisa
Äasmäe
Kohila
Prillimäe
Salutaguse
Jänedа
Lehtse
Kärавete
Ambla
Saiakopli
Porkuni
Sääse
Tamsalu
Aravete
Albu
Ahula
Kadila
Aruküla
Pandivere kõrgustik
Avispea
Roela
Muuga
Viru-Jaagupi
Tudu
Arvila
Mäetaguse
Väike-Pungerja
Jõuga
Iisaku
Oonurme
Peressaare
Padise
Audevälja
Hageri
Riisipere
Rabivere
Kose
Kuivajõe
Järlepa
Habaja
Mahtra
Paunküla veehoidla
E263
Voose
Kaalepi
Vajangu
Järva-Jaani
Kiltsi
Väike-Maarja
Laekvere
Kellavere
Paasvere
Tudulinna
Sällika
Kuijõe
Turba
Piirsalu
Raka
Purila
Juuru
Ardu
Kuimetsa
Varbola
Ohukotsu
Alu
Rapla
Roosna-Alliku
Liigvalla
Simuna
Tammiku
Venevere
Avinurme
Lohusuu
Kauksi
Rannapungerja
Risti
Palivere
Vaimõisa
Kuusiku
Kaerepere
Kehtna
Vahastu
Anna
Tarbja
Mäo
Paide
Väätsa
Peetri
Koeru
Rakke
Emumägi
Salla
Käru
Tammispää
Mustvee
Raja
Peipsi järv
Koluvere
Laukna
Orgita
Märjamaa
Kullamaa
Lelle
Koigi
Endla
Vaimastvere
Sadala
Torma
Laiuse
Kuremaa
Jõgeva
Omedu
Ranna
Kodavere
Kallaste
Kokora
Alatskivi
Nina
Kolkja
Kasepää
Varnja
Võrtsjärv
Õudruma
Rõude
Vana-Vigala
Kivi-Vigala
Valgu
Velise
Järvakandi
Lokuta
Türi
Särevere
EST
Oisu
Imavere
Adavere
Pisisaare
Aidu
Siimusti
Voore
Palamuse
Luua
Kaarepere
Eidapere
Kaisma
Kergu
Libatse
Vahenurme
Pärnu-Jaagupi
Vändra
Põikva
Kabala
Põltsamaa
Lustivere
Esku
Võhma
Olustvere
Suurejõe
Kolga-Jaani
Puurmani
Tabivere
Saadjärv
Vara
Tähemaa
Koosa
Lõpe
Koonga
Tootsi
Suure-Jaani
Lavassaare
Are
Laeva
Lähte
Kõrveküla
Männikuste
Kihlepa
Audru
Sauga
Tori
Jõesuu
Vastemõisa
Navesti
Soomaa Rahvuspark
Raudna
Jämejala
Leie
Emajõgi
Ilmatsalu
Tartu
Eesti rahva muuseum
Luunja
Kastre
Võõpste
Kavastu
Meerapalu
Terikeste
Lääniste
Vana-Võidu
Viiratsi
Viljandi
Pärnu
Sindi
Paikuse
Pärnu laht
Lindi
Tipu
Puiatu
Päri
Ramsi
Väluste
Ulila
Puhja
Märja
Tõrvandi
Ülenurme
Uulu
Pootsi
Manilaid
Kõpu
Kanaküla
Paistu
Mustla
Rannu
Nõo
Elva
Kärdi
Kambja
Võnnu
Ahja
Mooste
Vastse-Kuuste
Rasina
Võiste
Halliste
Õisu
Kärstna
Hellenurme
Nõuni
Taevaskoja
Mammaste
Himmaste
Põlva
Ruusa
Partsi
E67
Kilingi-Nõmme
Tihemetsa
Abja-Paluoja
Karksi
Karksi-Nuia
Sakala kõrgustik
Rutu mägi
Pikasilla
Rõngu
Kuutse mägi
Otepää
Pühajärv
Saverna
Häädemeeste
Kalita
Mõisaküla
Tali
Linna
Helme
Tõrva
Puka
Silva
Põlgaste
Himma
Kabli
Massiaru
Laatre
Ipiķi
Taagepera
Keeni
Otepää kõrgustik
Kanepi
Erastvere
Vana-Koiola
Parksepa
Väimela
Leevi
Lasva
Treimani
Vilpulka
Sangaste
Linnamäe
Osula
Võru
Kääpa
Ikla
Ainaži
Mērnieki
Staicele
Virķēni
Salaca
Rūjiena
Naukšēni
Jeri
Endzele
Sēļi
Ķirbi
Mazsalaca
Skankalne
Hummuli
Tsirguliina
Laatre
Kobela
Antsla
Sõmerpalu
Vagula
Kose
Holsta
Lepa
Kärķi
Ērģeme
Valka
Valga
Kaagjärve
Lüllemäe
Vecate
Ungurpils
Aloja
Burtnieku ezers
Turna
Lugaži
Tsooru
Karula Rahvuspark
Rõuge
Suur Munamägi
Haanja
Haanja kõrgustik
Ruusmäe
Vecsalaca
Korģene
Salacgrīva
Urga
Vilzēni
Rencēni
LV
E264
Svētciems
Pāle
Puikule
Matīši
Burtnieki
Ēvele
Jērcēni
Seda
Lizdēni
Strenči
Ārciems
Ozoli
Vilkene
Birzuļi
Hargla
Varstu
Mõniste
Krabi
Dēliņkalns
Jaunlaice
Pociems
Zilaiskalns
Valmiermuiža
Brenguļi
Lielezers
Ozolaine
Trikāta
Lobērgi
Gaujiena
Pēdele
Gauja
A1
A3
8
9
10
11
12
13
14
127
132
135
B
C
D
E
F
24°00'
24°30'
25°00'
25°30'
26°00'
26°30'
27°00'
60°00'
59°30'
59°00'
58°30'
58°00'

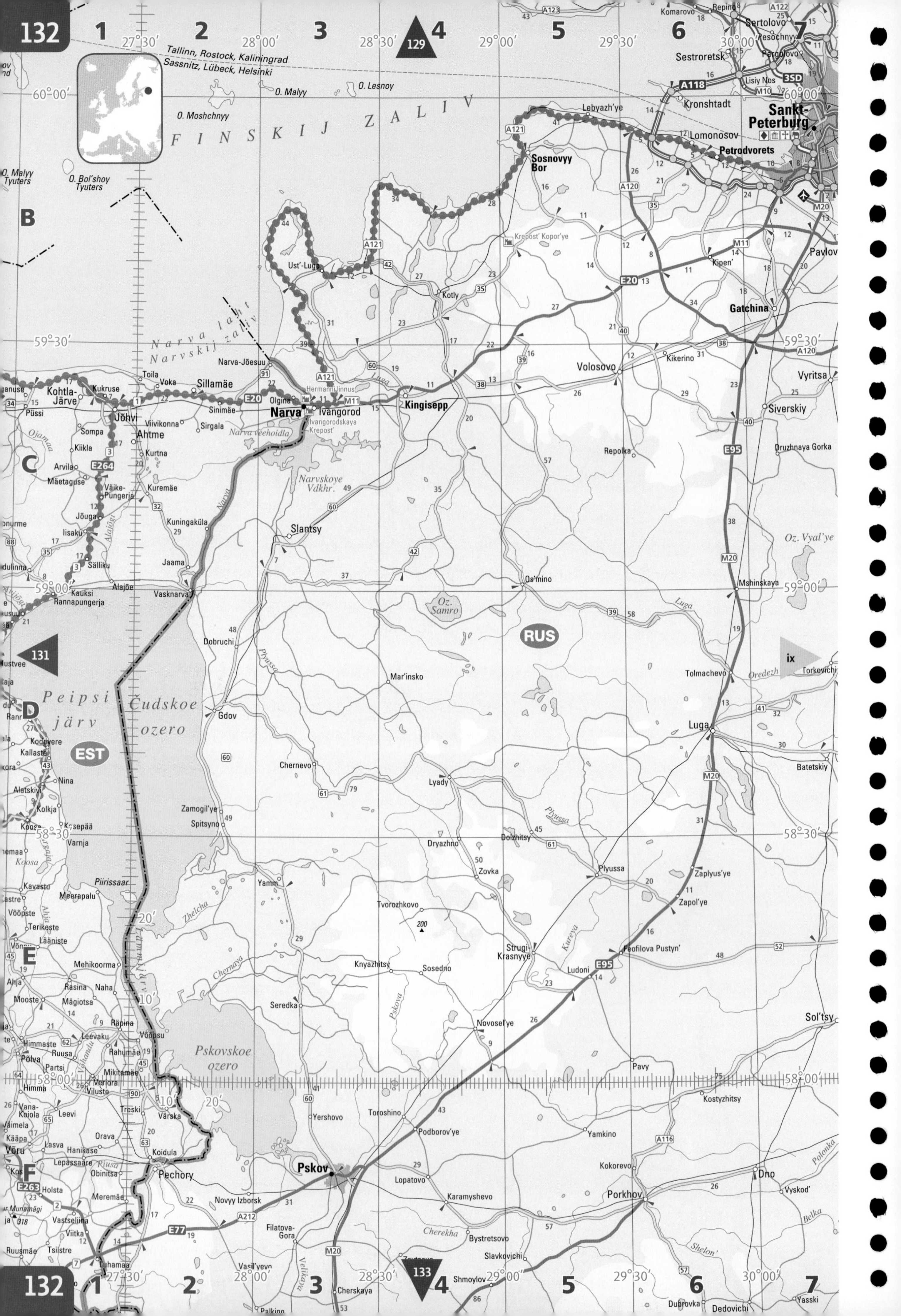
1
2
3
4
5
6
7
129
27°30′
28°00′
28°30′
29°00′
29°30′
30°00′
60°00′
59°30′
59°00′
58°30′
58°00′
Tallinn, Rostock, Kaliningrad
Sassnitz, Lübeck, Helsinki
O. Malyy
O. Lesnoy
O. Moshchnyy
O. Malyy Tyuters
O. Bol'shoy Tyuters
F I N S K I J Z A L I V
Komarovo
Repino
Sertolovo
Pesochnyy
Sestroretsk
Pargolovo
Lisiy Nos
Kronshtadt
Lebyazh'ye
Sankt-Peterburg
Lomonosov
Petrodvorets
Sosnovyy Bor
Pavlov
Krepost' Kopor'ye
Kipen'
Ust'-Luga
Kotly
Gatchina
Narva laht
Narvskij zaliv
Narva-Jõesuu
Volosovo
Kikerino
Vyritsa
Toila
Voka
Sillamäe
Kohtla-Järve
Kukruse
Püssi
Jõhvi
Sinimäe
Olgina
Narva
Ivangorod
Hermanni linnus
Ivangorodskaya Krepost'
Kingisepp
Siverskiy
Viivikonna
Sirgala
Ahtme
Narva veehoidla
Sompa
Kiikla
Kurtna
Repolka
Druzhnaya Gorka
Arvila
Mäetaguse
Väike-Pungerja
Kuremäe
Narvskoye Vdkhr.
Jõuga
Iisaku
Kuningaküla
Alajõgi
Slantsy
Oz. Vyal'ye
Sälliku
Jaama
Alajõe
Kauksi
Rannapungerja
Vasknarva
Os'mino
Oz. Samro
Mshinskaya
Luga
RUS
Dobruchi
131
ix
Plyussa
Mar'insko
Tolmachevo
Oredezh
Torkovichi
Peipsi järv
Čudskoe ozero
Gdov
Kodavere
Kallaste
EST
Chernevo
Batetskiy
Nina
Alatskivi
Kolkja
Lyady
Kasepää
Varnja
Zamogil'ye
Spitsyno
Dolzhitsy
Dryazhno
Koosa
Zovka
Plyussa
Zaplyus'ye
Piirissaar
Kavastu
Meerapalu
Yamm
Zapol'ye
Tvorozhkovo
Võõpste
Terikeste
Läänista
Zhelcha
Strugi-Krasnyye
Feofilova Pustyn'
Kureya
Mehikoorma
Knyazhitsy
Sosedno
Ludoni
Chernaya
Lämmijärv
Rasina
Naha
Mooste
Mägiotsa
Seredka
Pskova
Räpina
Novosel'ye
Sol'tsy
Himmaste
Leevaku
Võõpsu
Põlva
Ruusa
Rahumäe
Pskovskoe ozero
Partsi
Mikitamäe
Pavy
Veriora
Himmaste
Viluste
Vana-Koiola
Leevi
Treski
Värska
Yershovo
Toroshino
Kostyzhitsy
Orava
Podborov'ye
Yamkino
Kääpa
Lasva
Hanikase
Koidula
Võru
Lepassaare
Obinitsa
Pechory
Pskov
Kokorevo
Dno
Lopatovo
Holsta
Meremäe
Novyy Izborsk
Karamyshevo
Porkhov
Vyskod'
Vastseliina
Viitka
Filatova-Gora
Cherekha
Bystretsovo
Belka
Rõuge
Rusmäe
Tsiistre
Luhamaa
Slavkovichi
Shelon'
Vasil'yevo
Velikaya
133
Shmoylov
Cherskaya
Dubrovka
Dedovichi
Yasski
Palkino
E20
E95
E264
E263
E77
M11
M20
A118
A121
A120
A116
A212

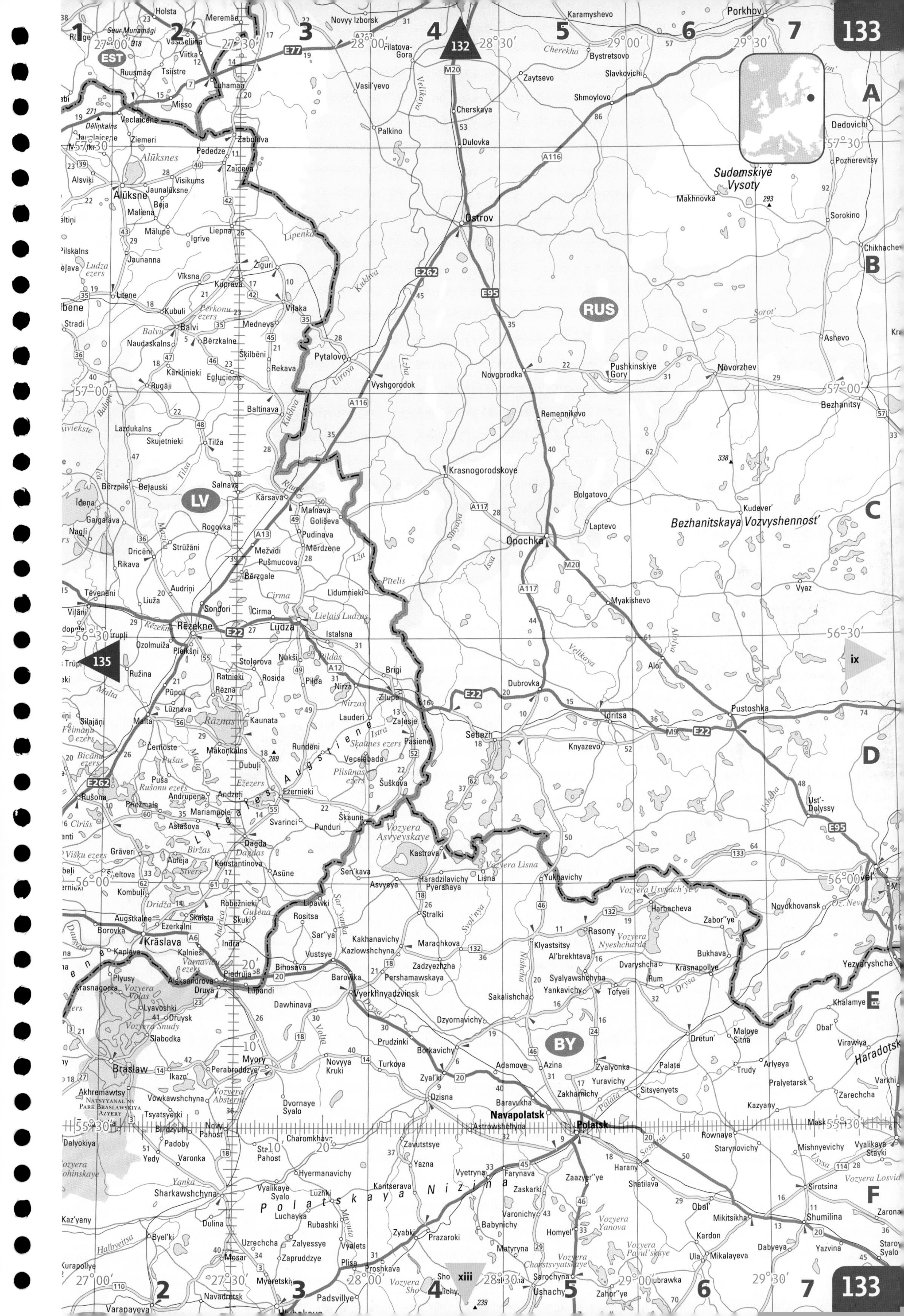
EST
LV
RUS
BY
132
135
ix
xiii
Holsta
Meremäe
Novyy Izborsk
Karamyshevo
Porkhov
Ruusmäe
Tsiistre
Luhamaa
Misso
Veclaicene
Ziemeri
Zaboļova
Pededze
Zaiceva
Alūksnes
Alūksne
Jaunalūksne
Beja
Maliena
Mālupe
Igrīve
Liepna
Jaunanna
Žīguri
Viksna
Kuprava
Litene
Kubuli
Balvi
Vīļaka
Medņeva
Naudaskalns
Bērzkalne
Šķilbēni
Rekava
Kārklinieki
Egļuciems
Rugāji
Baltinava
Lazdukalns
Skujetnieki
Tilža
Salnava
Kārsava
Malnava
Goliševa
Pudinava
Mērdzene
Bērzpils
Beļauski
Gaigalava
Nagļi
Rogovka
Strūžāni
Dricēni
Rikava
Mežvidi
Pušmucova
Bērzgale
Audriņi
Tēvenāni
Viļāni
Liuža
Sondori
Cirma
Lidumnieki
Rēzekne
Ludza
Lielais Ludzas
Istalsna
Ozolmuiža
Pleikšņi
Stoļerova
Nukši
Rosica
Pilda
Nirza
Brigi
Zilupe
Ružina
Ratnieki
Rēzna
Pūpoli
Lūznava
Malta
Rāznas
Kaunata
Lauderi
Zaļesje
Silajāņi
Čornoste
Mākoņkalns
Dubuļi
Rundēni
Vecslabada
Pasiene
Šuškova
Skaunes ezers
Plisūnas ezers
Lubāns
Rušona
Priežmale
Puša
Andzeļi
Andrupene
Ezernieki
Mariampole
Astašova
Svarinci
Punduri
Škaune
Dagda
Gravēri
Auleja
Konstantinova
Asūne
Šķeltova
Kombuļi
Robežnieki
Skaista
Skuki
Augstkalne
Ezerkalni
Borovka
Krāslava
Kaplava
Kalnieši
Indra
Piedruja
Aleksandrova
Druya
Lupandi
Plyusy
Krasnagorka
Vozyera Volas
Lyavoshki
Druysk
Vozyera Snudy
Slabodka
Braslaw
Ikazn'
Perabroddzye
Myory
Akhremawtsy
Vowkawshchyna
Vozyera Absterna
Natsyyanal'ny Park Braslawskiya Azyery
Tsyatsyerki
Bildzyuni
Novy Pahost
Padoby
Yedy
Varonka
Sharkawshchyna
Kaz'yany
Byel'ki
Halbyeitsa
Kurapollye
Mosar
Navadrutsk
Varapayeva
Dalyokiya
Stary Pahost
Charomkhava
Dvornaye Syalo
Dawhinava
Rositsa
Sar"ya
Vustsye
Bihosava
Barowka
Vyerkhnyadzvinsk
Lipawki
Sen'kava
Asvyeya
Vozyera Asvyeyskaye
Kastrova
Haradzilavichy
Pyershaya
Lisna
Vozyera Lisna
Stralki
Kakhanavichy
Kazlowshchyna
Marachkova
Zadzyezhzha
Pershamawskaya
Prudzinki
Borkavichy
Turkova
Zyal'ki
Dzisna
Novyya Kruki
Hyermanavichy
Vyalikaye Syalo
Luzhki
Luchayka
Rubashki
Polatskaya Nizina
Kantserava
Zyabki
Prazaroki
Uzrechcha
Zalyessye
Zapruddzye
Vyalets
Plisa
Proshkava
Myaretski
Padsvillye
Vozyera Sho
Shchichy
Ushachy
Sarochyna
Zahor"ye
Vozyera Charstsvyatskaye
Matyryna
Homyel'
Babynichy
Varonichy
Zaskarki
Farynava
Vyetryna
Yazna
Zavutstsye
Astrowshchyna
Navapolatsk
Baravukha
Polatsk
Adamova
Azina
Zakhamichy
Yuravichy
Zyalyonka
Sitsyenyets
Palata
Dretun'
Maloye Sitna
Trudy
Arlyeya
Pralyetarsk
Zarechcha
Kazyany
Varkhi
Haradotsk
Virawlya
Obal'
Khalamye
Yezyaryshcha
Zabor"ye
Harbacheva
Vozyera Usvyach'ye
Novokhovansk
Oz. Nevel'
Krasnapollye
Dvaryshcha
Rum
Drysa
Bukhava
Rasony
Vozyera Nyeshcharda
Klyastsitsy
Al'brekhtava
Syalyawshchyna
Yankavichy
Tofyeli
Sakalishcha
Dzyornavichy
Yukhavichy
Kardon
Mikitsikha
Shumilina
Ula
Mikalayeva
Dabyeya
Yazvina
Staroye Syalo
Zarona
Sirotsina
Obal'
Harany
Shatilava
Zaazyer"ye
Rownaye
Starynovichy
Mishnyevichy
Vyalikaya Stayki
Vozyera Losvida
Mask
Vozyera Yanova
Vozyera Pavul'skaye
Lubrawka
Filatova-Gora
Vasil'yevo
Palkino
Cherskaya
Dulovka
Velikaya
Zaytsevo
Cherekha
Bystretsovo
Slavkovichi
Shmoylovo
Dedovichi
Pozherevitsy
Sudomskiye Vysoty
Makhnovka
Sorokino
Chikhachevo
Ostrov
Kukhva
Lipenka
Pytalovo
Vyshgorodok
Utroya
Lzha
Novgorodka
Pushkinskiye Gory
Novorzhev
Ashevo
Sorot'
Bezhanitsy
Remennikovo
Krasnogorodskoye
Bolgatovo
Kudever'
Bezhanitskaya Vozvyshennost'
Laptevo
Opochka
Sinyaya
Issa
Pitelis
Lza
Myakishevo
Vyaz
Alol'
Alolya
Dubrovka
Idritsa
Pustoshka
Sebezh
Knyazevo
Ust'-Dolyssy
Ushcha
Nevel'
Istra
Latgales Augstiene
Rītupe
Ludza ezers
Balvu ezers
Pērkonu ezers
Rušonu ezers
Rāznas
Dridža
Svētes
Ezezers
Cirišs
Višku ezers
Bicāna ezers
Feimaņu ezers
Dubna
Daugava
Malta
Mazica
Tilža
Indrica
Sar"yanka
Svol'nya
Vozyera Nyeshcharda
Nishcha
Volta
Dysna
Usvyacha
Sosnitsa
Myasuta
Yanka
E77
E262
E95
E22
M20
M9
A116
A117
A13
A12
A6
20
56°30'
57°00'
57°30'
56°00'
55°30'
27°00'
27°30'
28°00'
28°30'
29°00'
29°30'
293
338
289
239
1
2
3
4
5
6
7
A
B
C
D
E
F

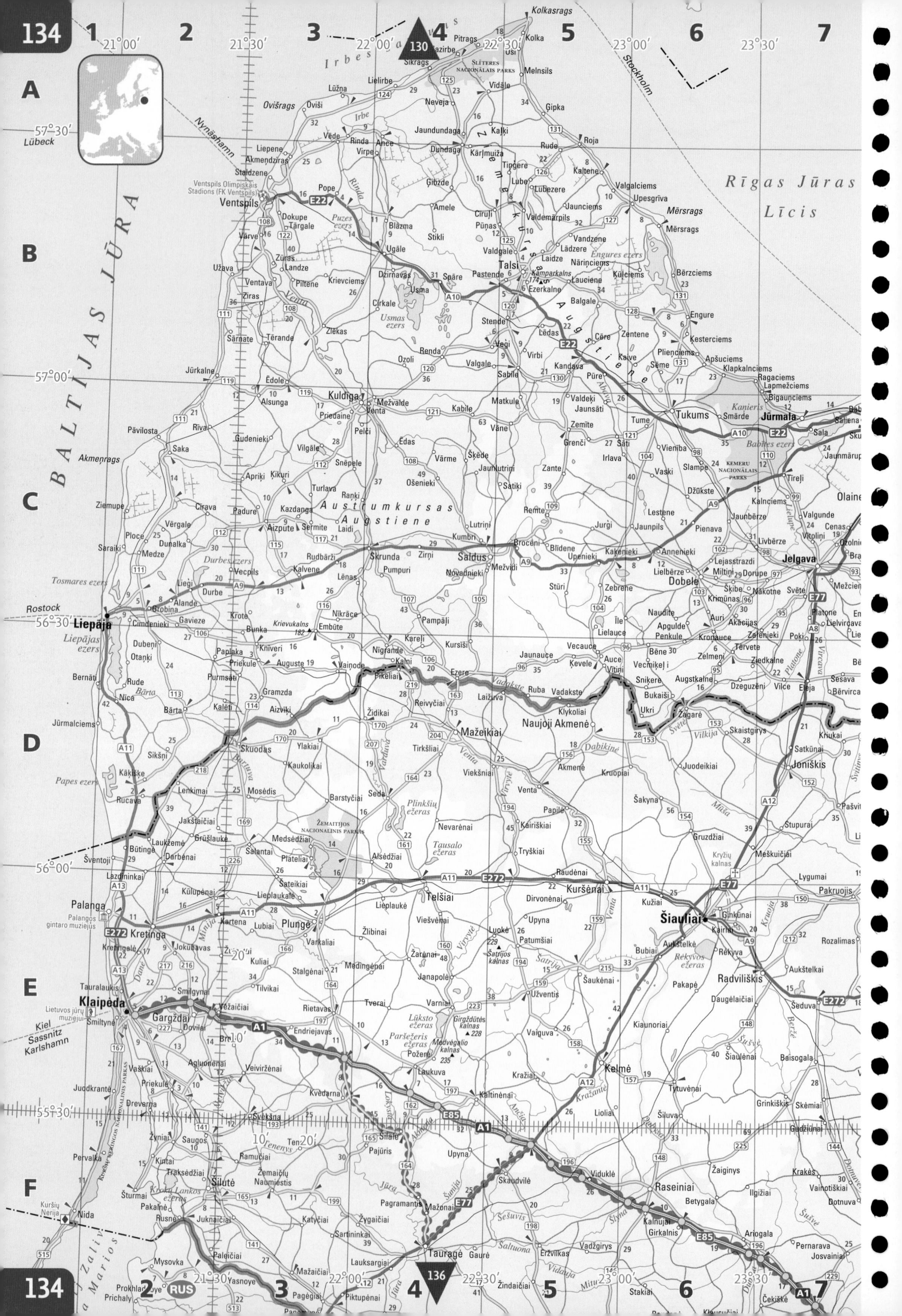
1
2
3
4
5
6
7
A
B
C
D
E
F
130
136
Kolkasrags
Irbes
Sīkrags
Mazirbe
Pitrags
Kolka
Slīteres Nacionālais Parks
Melnsils
Lielirbe
Lūžņa
Vīdāle
Ovišrags
Oviši
Neveja
Ģipka
Stockholm
Nynäshamn
Lübeck
Vēde
Rinda
Ance
Jaundundaga
Kaļķi
Roja
Irbe
Virpe
Dundaga
Kārļmuiža
Rude
Liepene
Akmeņdziras
Tingere
Kaltene
Staldzene
Ventspils Olimpiskais Stadions (FK Ventspils)
Ventspils
Pope
Lube
Lubezere
Valgalciems
Ģibzde
Upesgrīva
Rīgas Jūras Līcis
Jaunciems
Mērsrags
Amele
Ciruļi
Valdemārpils
Dokupe
Tārgale
Puzes ezers
Blāzma
Pūņas
Vandzene
Stikli
Lādzere
Vārve
Ugāle
Valdgale
Laidze
Nāriņciems
Engures ezers
Zūras
Landze
Talsi
Kamparkalns
Užava
Ventava
Piltene
Krievciems
Dzirnavas
Spāre
Pastende
Lauciene
Kūļciems
Bērzciems
Usma
Ezerkalne
Ziras
Venta
Cirkale
Balgale
Engure
Usmas ezers
Stende
Ziemeļkursas Augstiene
Sārnate
Tērande
Zlēkas
Lēdas
Cēre
Zentene
Kesterciems
Vegi
Virbi
Renda
Kaive
Plieņciems
Apšuciems
Jūrkalne
Ozoli
Valgale
Kandava
Sēme
Klapkalnciems
Sabile
Pūre
Ragaciems
Lapmežciems
Ēdole
Bigauņciems
Kuldīga
Matkule
Valdeķi
Abava
Alsunga
Mežvalde
Venta
Jaunsāti
Kanieris
Priedaine
Kabile
Tukums
Smārde
Jūrmala
Tume
Rīva
Pāvilosta
Vāne
Zemīte
Sloka
Gudenieki
Pelči
Ēdas
Grenči
Sāti
Babītes ezers
Saka
Vilgāle
Vārme
Šķēde
Irlava
Vienība
Akmeņrags
Snēpele
Jaunlutriņi
Zante
Vaski
Slampe
Ķemeru Nacionālais Parks
Tīreļi
Apriķi
Ķikuri
Ošenieki
Satiķi
Džūkste
Olaine
Turlava
Raņķi
Kalnciems
Ziemupe
Cirava
Kazdanga
Austrumkursas Augstiene
Remte
Lestene
Jaunbērze
Valgunde
Padure
Aizpute
Laidi
Sermite
Lutriņi
Jurģi
Jaunpils
Pienava
Vērgale
Kumbri
Līvbērze
Ploce
Dunalka
Broceni
Blīdene
Kakenieki
Annenieki
Saraiķi
Medze
Rudbārži
Skrunda
Zirņi
Saldus
Upenieki
Jelgava
Durbes ezers
Vecpils
Kalvene
Pumpuri
Mežvidi
Lejasstrazdi
Tosmares ezers
Lēnas
Novadnieki
Stūri
Lielbērze
Dobele
Dorupe
Lieģi
Durbe
Zebrene
Krimūnas
Nākotne
Svēte
Rostock
Alande
Grobiņa
Nīkrāce
Pampāļi
Naudīte
Liepāja
Cimdenieki
Gavieze
Krote
Bunka
Krievukalns
Embūte
Īle
Auri
Akacijas
Platone
Liepājas ezers
Lielauce
Apgulde
Dubeņi
Kniveri
Kareļi
Kursīši
Vecauce
Penkule
Krona uce
Zaļenieki
Otaņķi
Paplaka
Nīgrande
Jaunauce
Bēne
Tērvete
Priekule
Kalni
Auce
Vecmiķeļi
Zelmeņi
Ziedkalne
Bernāti
Purmsāti
Auguste
Vaiņode
Pikeliai
Ezere
Ķevele
Vītiņi
Sniķere
Augstkalne
Sesava
Rude
Nīca
Bārta
Gramzda
Reivyčiai
Laižuva
Ruba
Vadakstė
Bukaiši
Dzeguzēni
Vilce
Eleja
Bērvirca
Bārta
Kalēti
Aizviķi
Židikai
Klykoliai
Ukri
Žagarė
Jūrmalciems
Mažeikiai
Naujoji Akmenė
Skaistgirys
Kriukai
Skuodas
Ylakiai
Tirkšliai
Dabikinė
Vilkija
Sikšņi
Kaukolikai
Venta
Viekšniai
Akmenė
Kruopiai
Juodeikiai
Satkūnai
Joniškis
Papes ezers
Lenkimai
Mosėdis
Seda
Venta
Barstyčiai
Plinkšių ežeras
Šakyna
Rucava
Papilė
Jakštaičiai
Žemaitijos Nacionalinis Parkas
Nevarėnai
Kairiškiai
Stupurai
Laukžemė
Grūšlaukė
Gruzdžiai
Būtingė
Salantai
Medsėdžiai
Tausalo ežeras
Tryškiai
Mūša
Šventoji
Darbėnai
Plateliai
Alsėdžiai
Kryžių kalnas
Meškuičiai
Lazdininkai
Sateikiai
Raudėnai
Lygumai
Palanga
Kūlupėnai
Lieplaukalė
Telšiai
Kuršėnai
Dirvonėnai
Kužiai
Pakruojis
Palangos gintaro muziejus
Kartena
Lieplaukė
Upyna
Kretinga
Lubiai
Plungė
Žlibinai
Viešvėnai
Šiauliai
Ginkūnai
Kairiai
Kruoja
Rozalimas
Jokūbavas
Varkaliai
Luokė
Patumšiai
Kretingalė
Žarėnai
Šatrijos kalnas
Bubiai
Aukštelkė
Rėkyva
Rėkyvos ežeras
Aukštelkai
Kuliai
Stalgėnai
Medingėnai
Dane
Minija
Janapolė
Šatrija
Šaukėnai
Radviliškis
Tauralaukis
Tilvikai
Užventis
Pakapė
Klaipėda
Smilgyniai
Rietavas
Tverai
Varniai
Daugėlaičiai
Lietuvos jūrų muziejus
Smiltynė
Gargždai
Vėžaičiai
Dovilai
Endriejavas
Lūksto ežeras
Girgždūtės kalnas
Šeduva
Kiel
Sassnitz
Karlshamn
Paršežeris ežeras
Medvėgalio kalnas
Kiaunoriai
Vaiguva
Beržė
Agluonėnai
Veiviržėnai
Požerė
Šušvė
Šiaulėnai
Baisogala
Vaškiai
Laukuva
Kražiai
Kelmė
Priekulė
Kvėdarna
Kaltinėnai
Tytuvėnai
Juodkrantė
Dreverna
Kražantė
Liolai
Grinkiškis
Skėmiai
Švėkšna
Šilalė
Šiluva
Gudžiūnai
Žyniai
Saugos
Ramučiai
Akmena
Upyna
Dubysa
Kuršių Nerijos Nacionalinis Parkas
Pervalka
Pajūris
Kintai
Traksėdžiai
Žemaičių Naumiestis
Skaudvilė
Viduklė
Žaiginys
Krakės
Šilutė
Jūra
Raseiniai
Vainotiškiai
Šturmai
Kuršių Nerija
Kintai
Rusnė
Juknaičiai
Pagramantis
Mažonai
Šešuvis
Betygala
Ilgižiai
Dotnuva
Pakalnė
Katyčiai
Žygaičiai
Kalnujai
Girkalnis
Nida
Sartininkai
Šiluva
Ariogala
Šušvė
Kuršių Zalivas
Marios
Paleičiai
Tauragė
Gaurė
Saltuona
Eržvilkas
Vadžgirys
Pernarava
Josvainiai
Mysovka
Mažaičiai
Lauksargiai
Jūra
Vidaugа
Mituva
Dubysa
Prokhladnoye
Prichaly
Yasnoye
RUS
Pagėgiai
Piktupėnai
Žindaičiai
Stakiai
Čekiškė
Baltijas Jūra
E22
E77
E85
E272
A1
A8
A9
A10
A11
A12
A13
21°00′
21°30′
22°00′
22°30′
23°00′
23°30′
57°30′
57°00′
56°30′
56°00′
55°30′

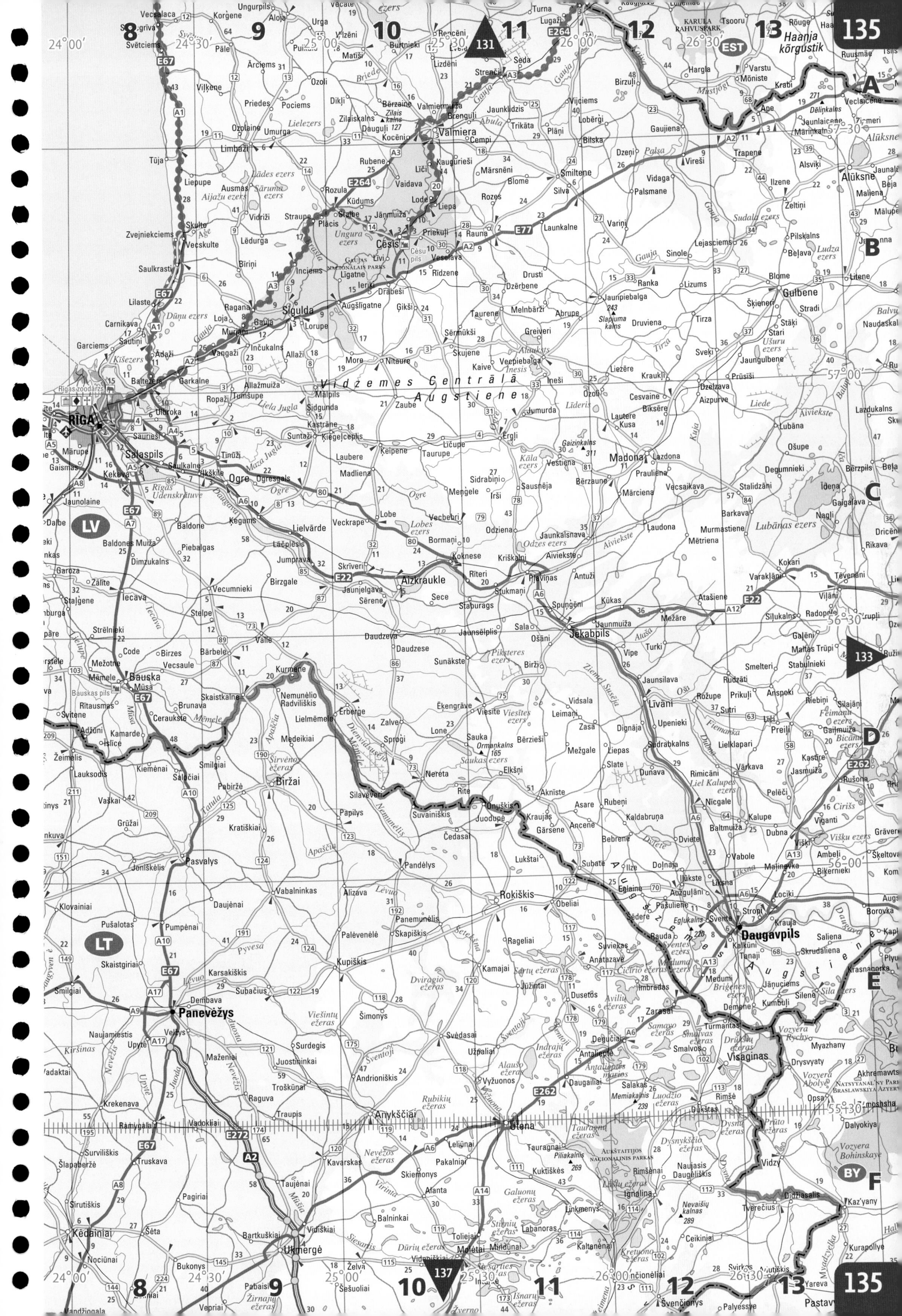
135
8
9
10
11
12
13
131
137
133
A
B
C
D
E
F
EST
LV
LT
BY
24°00'
24°30'
25°00'
25°30'
26°00'
26°30'
57°00'
56°30'
56°00'
55°30'
Vecsalaca
Korgene
Ungurpils
Aloja
Urga
Vilzēni
Rencēni
Burtnieki
Turna
Lugaži
Karula Rahvuspark
Tsooru
Rõuge
Haanja kõrgustik
Ruusmäe
Salacgrīva
Svētciems
Pāle
Ārciems
Matīši
Lizdēni
Sēda
Strenči
Birzuļi
Hargla
Varstu
Mõniste
Krabi
Veclaicene
Dēliņkalns
Jaunlaicene
Mārinkalns
Vilķene
Priedes
Pociems
Ozoli
Dikļi
Bērzaine
Zilaiskalns
Valmiermuiža
Jaunklidzis
Vijciems
Lobērģi
Ape
Gaujiena
Dauguļi
Kocēni
Brenguļi
Valmiera
Cempi
Trikāta
Plāņi
Bilska
Dzeņi
Vireši
Trapene
Alsviķi
Alūksne
Jaunalūksne
Limbaži
Umurga
Ozolaine
Lielezers
Tūja
Rubene
Vaidava
Liči
Kauguri
Kaugurieši
Mārsnēni
Smiltene
Silva
Blome
Palsmane
Vidaga
Ilzene
Zeltiņi
Maliena
Liepupe
Ausmas
Aijažu ezers
Lādes ezers
Rozula
Kūdums
Lode
Liepa
Rozes
Stalbe
Jānmuiža
Straupe
Plācis
Vidriži
Skulte
Vecskulte
Zvejniekciems
Lēdurga
Ungura ezers
Cēsis
Cēsu pils
Priekuļi
Rauna
Launkalne
Variņi
Sudala ezers
Pilskalns
Beļava
Lejasciems
Sinole
Bīriņi
Saulkrasti
Gaujas Nacionālais parks
Līvi
Līgatne
Inciems
Veselava
Rīdzene
Drusti
Ranka
Lizums
Blome
Litene
Gulbene
Lilaste
Ieriķi
Drabeši
Dzērbene
Jaunpiebalga
Šķieneri
Stradi
Naudaskalns
Carnikava
Ragana
Loja
Dūņu ezers
Sigulda
Augšlīgatne
Ģikši
Taurene
Melnbārži
Abrupe
Slapjuma kalns
Druviena
Tirza
Stāķi
Stari
Ūsuru ezers
Garciems
Sautiņi
Adaži
Murjāņi
Gauja
Lorupe
Inčukalns
Vangaži
Allaži
Sērmūkši
Greiveri
More
Nītaure
Skujene
Kaive
Vecpiebalga
Inesis
Alauksts
Liezēre
Sveķi
Jaungulbene
Kišezers
Baltezers
Garkalne
Rīgas zoodārzs
Allažmuiža
Mālpils
Vidzemes Centrālā Augstiene
Ineši
Krauklī
Prūšiši
Ozoli
Cesvaine
Dzelzava
Aizpurve
Rīga
Ropaži
Tumšupe
Lielā Jugla
Sidgunda
Zaube
Jumurda
Lauteres
Kusa
Bikšere
Liede
Lubāna
Aiviekste
Lazdukalns
Ulbroka
Kastrāne
Kiegeļceplis
Suntaži
Ērgļi
Līčupe
Taurupe
Gaiziņkalns
Mārupe
Sauriesi
Salaspils
Tinūži
Keipene
Laubere
Madona
Lazdona
Praulienа
Ošupe
Bērzpils
Gaismas
Kekava
Saulkalne
Ikšķile
Ogre
Ogresgals
Madliena
Sidrabiņi
Kāla ezers
Vestiena
Bērzaune
Degumnieki
Rīgas Ūdenskrātuve
Jaunolaine
Mengele
Irši
Sausnēja
Mārciena
Vecsaikava
Stalidzāni
Idena
Gaigalava
Dalbe
Baldone
Ķegums
Lielvārde
Veckrape
Lobe
Vecbebri
Odziena
Jaunkalsnava
Barkava
Murmastiene
Lubānas ezers
Nagļi
Baldones Muiža
Piebalgas
Lāčplēsis
Lobes ezers
Bormaņi
Odzes ezers
Laudona
Mētriena
Dricēni
Rikava
Dimzukalns
Jumprava
Skrīveri
Koknese
Krīškalni
Aiviekste
Kokari
Garoza
Zālīte
Birzgale
Aizkraukle
Riteri
Pļaviņas
Antuži
Varakļāni
Tevenāni
Staļģene
Iecava
Vecumnieki
Jaunjelgava
Sērene
Sece
Stukmaņi
Spuņģēni
Kūkas
Atašiene
Viļāni
Staburags
Jaunmuiža
Mežāre
Siļukalns
Radopole
Strēlnieki
Stelpe
Valle
Daudzeva
Jaunsēlpils
Sala
Ošāni
Jēkabpils
Galēni
Maltas Trūpi
Code
Birzes
Bārbele
Daudzese
Sunākste
Pikšteres ezers
Birži
Turki
Vīpe
Smelteri
Stabulnieki
Mežotne
Vecsaule
Mēmele
Bauska
Bauskas pils
Mūsa
Kurmene
Jaunsilava
Rudzāti
Ritausmas
Skaistkalne
Brunava
Ceraukste
Nemunėlio Radviliškis
Erberģe
Dienvidsusēja
Ēķengrāve
Viesīte
Viesītes ezers
Vidsala
Leimaņi
Līvāni
Rožupe
Prikuļi
Anspoki
Svitene
Adžūni
Kamarde
Īslīce
Lielmēmele
Zalve
Sprogi
Lone
Sauka
Zasa
Dignāja
Upenieki
Sutri
Līči
Preiļi
Riebiņi
Feimaņu ezers
Gaiļmuiža
Bicānu ezers
Žeimelis
Medeikiai
Ormankalns
Saukas ezers
Bērzieši
Mežgale
Sudrabkalns
Lielklapari
Kastīre
Jasmuiža
Lauksodis
Kiemėnai
Smilgiai
Salociai
Širvėnos ežeras
Nereta
Elkšņi
Liepas
Slate
Dunava
Vārkava
Rimicāni
Liel Kalupes ezers
Rušona
Pabiržė
Biržai
Rite
Silavėveri
Akniste
Asare
Rubeņi
Nīcgale
Pelēči
Ciriša
Vaškai
Tatula
Papilys
Suvainiškis
Onuškis
Juodupė
Kraujas
Gārsene
Ancene
Kaldabruņa
Kalupe
Viganti
Grūžai
Kratiškiai
Apaščia
Čedasai
Bebrene
Baltmuiža
Dubna
Višķi
Višķu ezers
Grāveri
Pasvalys
Joniškėlis
Pandėlys
Lukštai
Subate
Ilze
Doļnaja
Vabole
Ambeļi
Šķeltova
Malinovka
Biķernieki
Vabalninkas
Alizava
Rokiškis
Obeliai
Eglaine
Augšzemes Augstiene
Ilūkste
Auzgulāni
Liksna
Lociki
Klovainiai
Daujėnai
Panemunėlis
Sēdere
Pašulienе
Eglukalns
Svente
Stropi
Krauja
Daugavpils
Borovka
Pušalotas
Pumpėnai
Palėvenėlė
Skapiškis
Rageliai
Rauda
Sventes ezers
Kalkūni
Tanaji
Saliena
Skrudaliena
Latgales Augstiene
Krasnagorka
Skaistgiriai
Pyvesa
Kupiškis
Suvieķas
Anatazave
Medumu ezers
Medumi
Jānuciems
Silene
Sila ezers
Karsakiškis
Dviragio ežeras
Kamajai
Sartų ežeras
Čičirio ežeras
Imbradas
Smilgiai
Dembava
Subačius
Juzintai
Dusetos
Avilių ežeras
Zarasai
Demene
Kumbuli
Panevėžys
Viešintų ežeras
Šimonys
Samavo ežeras
Smalvų ežeras
Turmantas
Vozyera Rychy
Naujamiestis
Upytė
Velžys
Surdegis
Svėdasai
Užpaliai
Indrajų ežeras
Degučiai
Antalieptė
Drūkšių ežeras
Smalvos
Visaginas
Myazhany
Kiršinas
Maženiai
Juostininkai
Šventoji
Drysvyaty
Akhremawtsy
Vadaktai
Troškūnai
Andrioniškis
Vyžuonos
Alauso ežeras
Daugailiai
Salakas
Memiakalnis
Luodžio ežeras
Rimšė
Vozyera Abolye
Natsyyanal'ny Park Braslawskiya Azyery
Opsa
Krekenava
Raguva
Traupis
Rubikių ežeras
Dūkštas
Dalyokiya
Ramygala
Vadokliai
Anykščiai
Utena
Tauragnų ežeras
Dysnų ežeras
Prūto ežeras
Surviliškis
Truskava
Nevėžos ežeras
Leliūnai
Kavarskas
Pakalniai
Tauragnai
Piliakalnis
Aukštaitijos Nacionalinis Parkas
Dysnykščio ežeras
Vozyera Bohinskaye
Šlapaberžė
Skiemonys
Kuktiškės
Rimšėnai
Naujasis Daugėliškis
Vidzy
Taujėnai
Alanta
Galuonų ežeras
Lūšių ežeras
Ignalina
Didžiasalis
Sirutiškis
Pagiriai
Virintа
Nevaišių kalnas
Kaz'yany
Balninkai
Linkmenys
Tverečius
Kėdainiai
Šėta
Bartkuškiai
Vidiškiai
Tolieja
Stirnių ežeras
Labanoras
Kaltanėnai
Ceikiniai
Nociūnai
Ukmergė
Siesartis
Dūrių ežeras
Molėtai
Mindūnai
Kretuono ežeras
Kurapollye
Bukonys
Želva
Videniškiai
Svirkos
Ančioneliai
Yareva
Pabaiskas
Šešuoliai
Žirnajų ežeras
Išnaru ežeras
Švenčionys
Pastavy
Vepriai
Žverno
Palyessye
Jandžiogala
Mūša
Nevėžis
Šventoji
Daugava
Gauja
Aiviekste
Dubna
Oša
Ogre
Iecava
E67
E77
E22
E262
E264
E272
A1
A2
A3
A4
A5
A6
A7
A8
A9
A10
A12
A13
A14
A17

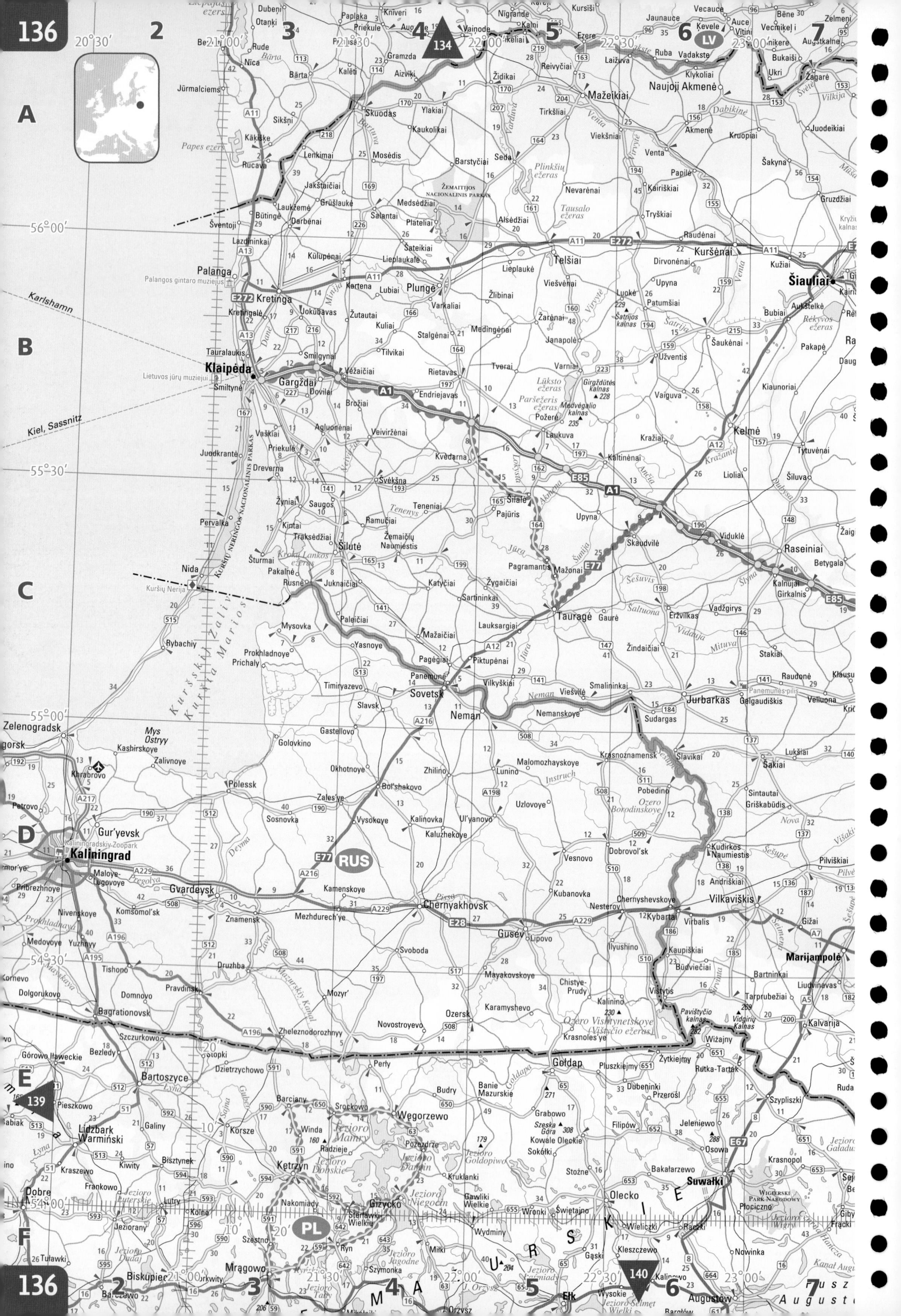

134
LV
RUS
PL
139
140
Skuodas
Mažeikiai
Naujoji Akmenė
Akmenė
Venta
Seda
Žagarė
Joniškis
Palanga
Palangos gintaro muziejus
Kretinga
Plungė
Telšiai
Kuršėnai
Šiauliai
Klaipėda
Lietuvos jūrų muziejus
Smiltynė
Gargždai
Rietavas
Varniai
Kelmė
Raseiniai
Tytuvėnai
Šilalė
Šilutė
Rusnė
Nida
Kuršių Nerija
Juodkrantė
Pervalka
Preila
Tauragė
Skaudvilė
Jurbarkas
Panemunės pilis
Pagėgiai
Sovetsk
Neman
Slavsk
Zelenogradsk
Khrabrovo
Polessk
Gur'yevsk
Kaliningrad
Kaliningradskiy Zoopark
Gvardeysk
Chernyakhovsk
Gusev
Nesterov
Kybartai
Vilkaviškis
Marijampolė
Kalvarija
Šakiai
Kudirkos Naumiestis
Krasnoznamensk
Dobrovol'sk
Ozero Vishtynetskoye
Vištytis
Pravdinsk
Bagrationovsk
Ozersk
Zheleznodorozhnyy
Bartoszyce
Lidzbark Warmiński
Kętrzyn
Węgorzewo
Giżycko
Gołdap
Olecko
Suwałki
Wigierski Park Narodowy
Ełk
Augustów
Mrągowo
Biskupiec
Ryn
Sejny
Puszcza Augustowska
Kurshskiy Zaliv
Kuršių Marios
Kuršių Nerijos Nacionalinis Parkas
Žemaitijos Nacionalinis Parkas
Plateliai
Karlshamn
Kiel, Sassnitz
Mys Ostryy
E28
E67
E77
E85
E272
A1
A11
A12
A229
55°00′
55°30′
56°00′
54°30′
54°00′
21°00′
21°30′
22°00′
22°30′
23°00′
20°30′
A
B
C
D
E
F
2
3
4
5
6
7

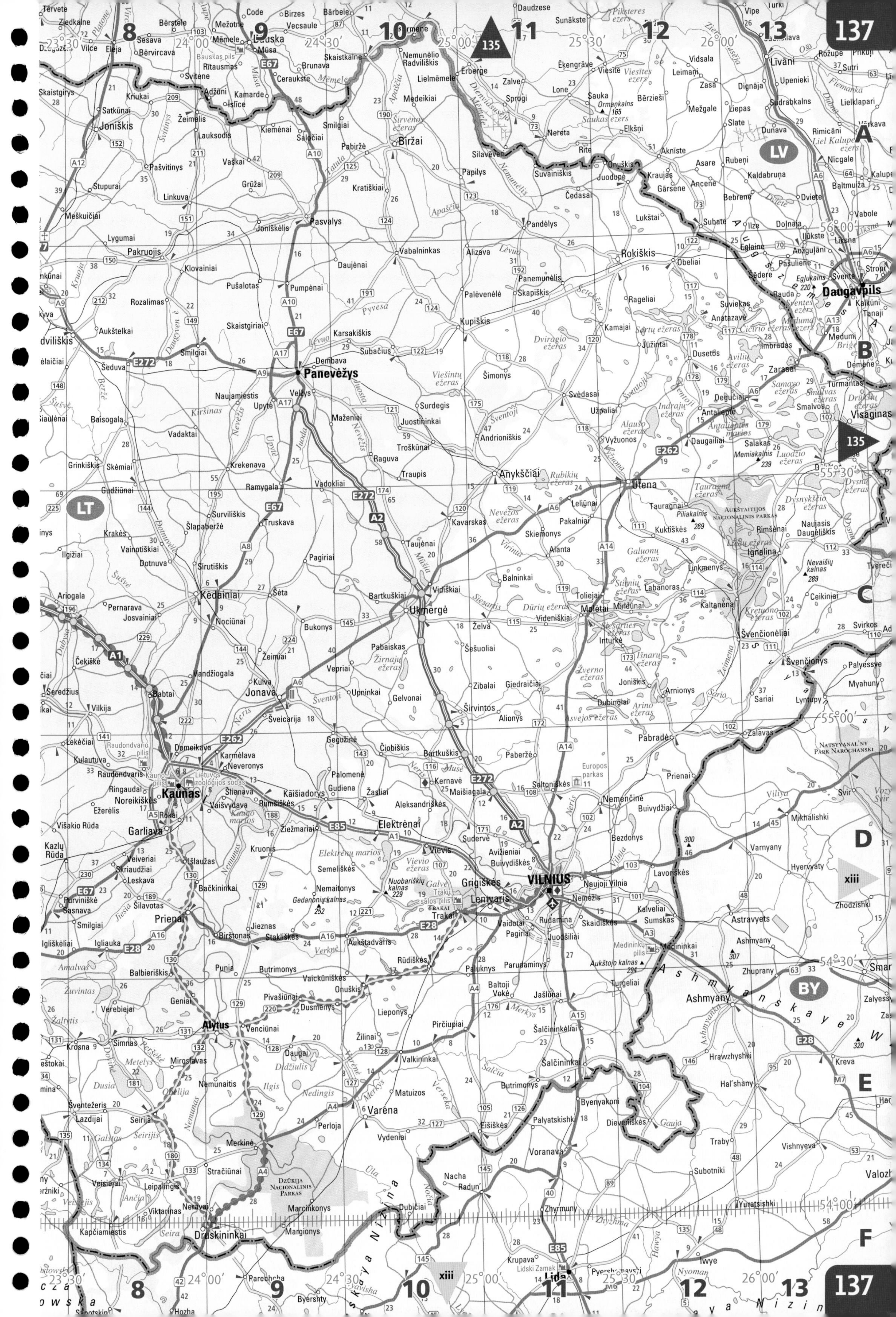
135
LV
LT
BY
A
B
C
D
E
F
8
9
10
11
12
13
23°30′
24°00′
24°30′
25°00′
25°30′
26°00′
56°00′
55°30′
55°00′
54°30′
54°00′
Bauska
Bauskas pils
Mūsa
Ritausmas
Eleja
Vecsaule
Bārbele
Skaistkalne
Brunava
Ceraukste
Code
Birzes
Mežotne
Mēmele
Bērstele
Sesava
Vilce
Ziedkalne
Tervete
Daudzese
Sunākste
Piksteres ezers
Vipe
Līvāni
Ēkengrāve
Viesīte
Viesītes ezers
Vidsala
Leimaņi
Zasa
Dignāja
Upenieki
Sauka
Ormankalns 165
Saukas ezers
Bērzieši
Mežgale
Liepas
Sudrabkalns
Slate
Dunava
Elkšņi
Nereta
Rite
Akniste
Asare
Rubeņi
Kaldabruņa
Nīcgale
Rimicāni
Liel Kalupe ezers
Kalupe
Baltmuiža
Dviete
Vabole
Dolnaja
Subate
Ilūkste
Līksna
Eglaine
Aužgulāni
Pašuliene
Daugavpils
Eglukalns 220
Svente
Sēdere
Rauda
Kalkūni
Tanaji
Medumi
Demene
Aug Ž Ž eme
Erberģe
Zalve
Sprogi
Lone
Jonišķis
Satkūnai
Kriukai
Adžūni
Islīce
Kamarde
Žeimelis
Lauksodis
Kiemėnai
Saločiai
Pabiržė
Biržai
Širvėnos ežeras
Medeikiai
Smilgiai
Lielmēmele
Nemunėlio Radviliškis
Kirmėne
Skaistgirys
Pašvitinys
Vaškai
Grūžai
Stupurai
Linkuva
Meškuičiai
Joniškėlis
Pasvalys
Lygumai
Pakruojis
Klovainiai
Pušalotas
Pumpėnai
Daujėnai
Vabalninkas
Kratiškiai
Papilys
Silaeveri
Suvainiškis
Onuškis
Juodupė
Kraujas
Gārsene
Ancene
Bebrene
Čedasai
Pandėlys
Lukštai
Rokiškis
Obeliai
Alizava
Panemunėlis
Skapiškis
Palėvenėlė
Rageliai
Suviekas
Anatazave
Kamajai
Juzintai
Dusetos
Zarasai
Imbradas
Turmantas
Visaginas
Smalvos
Salakas
Memiakalnis 239
Luodžio ežeras
Degučiai
Antalieptė
Daugailiai
Utena
Radviliškis
Aukštelkai
Šeduva
Rozalimas
Skaistgiriai
Smilgiai
Panevėžys
Dembava
Karsakiškis
Subačius
Kupiškis
Dviragio ežeras
Šimonys
Viešintų ežeras
Svėdasai
Užpaliai
Vyžuonos
Alaušo ežeras
Baisogala
Naujamiestis
Upytė
Velžys
Maženiai
Surdegis
Juostininkai
Andrioniškis
Troškūnai
Raguva
Traupis
Vadaktai
Grinkiškis
Skėmiai
Krekenava
Ramygala
Vadokliai
Anykščiai
Rubikių ežeras
Gudžiūnai
Surviliškis
Šlapaberžė
Truskava
Kavarskas
Nevėžos ežeras
Leliūnai
Pakalniai
Tauragnai
Tauragnų ežeras
Piliakalnis 269
Aukštaitijos Nacionalinis Parkas
Kuktiškės
Rimšėnai
Naujasis Daugėliškis
Ignalina
Nevaišių kalnas 289
Tverečius
Krakės
Vainotiškiai
Dotnuva
Ilgižiai
Sirutiškis
Taujėnai
Pagiriai
Skiemonys
Alanta
Galuonų ežeras
Linkmenys
Balninkai
Ariogala
Pernarava
Josvainiai
Kėdainiai
Šėta
Nociūnai
Bartkušiai
Vidiškiai
Ukmergė
Toliejai
Molėtai
Mindūnai
Labanoras
Kaltanėnai
Ceikiniai
Dūrių ežeras
Videniškiai
Inturkė
Švenčionėliai
Svirkos
Čekiškė
Bukonys
Želva
Pabiskas
Žirnajų ežeras
Šešuoliai
Švenčionys
Palyessye
Seredžius
Vilkija
Babtai
Vandžiogala
Kulva
Jonava
Upninkai
Gelvonai
Vepriai
Zibalai
Giedraičiai
Joniškis
Arnionys
Saria
Sariai
Lyntupy
Myahuny
Širvintos
Alionys
Dubingiai
Asvejos ežeras
Šveicarija
Lekėčiai
Raudondvario pilis
Kulautuva
Raudondvaris
Domeikava
Karmėlava
Neveronys
Gegužinė
Čiobiškis
Bartkuškis
Paberžė
Pabradė
Zalavas
Europos parkas
Kernavė
Maišiagala
Paloménė
Gudiena
Kaišiadorys
Žasliai
Aleksandriškės
Kaunas
Kauno pilis
Lietuvos zoologijos sodas
Ringaudai
Noreikiškės
Ežerėlis
Šlienava
Vaišvydava
Kauno marios
Rumšiškės
Elektrėnai
Nemenčinė
Buivydžiai
Prienai
Natsyyanal'ny Park Narochanski
Svir
Mikhalishki
Viliya
Garliava
Rokai
Višakio Rūda
Kazlų Rūda
Veiveriai
Skriaudžiai
Leskava
Išlaužas
Žiežmariai
Kruonis
Elektrėnų marios
Vievis
Vievio ežeras
Semeliškės
Sudervė
Avižieniai
Buivydiškės
Bezdonys
Varnyany
Hyervyaty
Vilnius
Naujoji Vilnia
Lavoriškės
Bačkininkai
Nemaitonys
Nuobariškių kalnas 229
Gedanonių kalnas 252
Galvė
Trakų salos pilis
Trakai
Grigiškės
Lentvaris
Nemėžis
Kalveliai
Sumskas
Astravyets
Zhodzishki
Purviniškė
Sasnava
Smilgiai
Šilavotas
Prienai
Jieznas
Birštonas
Stakliškės
Aukštadvaris
Vaidotai
Pagiriai
Rudamina
Skaidiškės
Juodšiliai
Medininkai
Medininkų pilis
Ashmyany
Aukštojo kalnas 294
Igliškėliai
Igliauka
Amalvas
Balbieriškis
Punia
Rūdiškės
Butrimonys
Vaickūniškės
Paluknys
Parudaminys
Zhuprany
Smarhon
Turgeliai
Ashmyanskaye Wzvyshsha
Žuvintas
Verebiejai
Genial
Pivašiūnai
Dusmenys
Onuškis
Lieponys
Baltoji Vokė
Jašiūnai
Merkys
Zalyessye
Alytus
Venciūnai
Pirčiupiai
Šalčininkėliai
Kreva
Krosna
Simnas
Metelys
Miroslavas
Daugai
Žilinai
Valkininkai
Šalčininkai
Hrawzhyshki
Hal'shany
Nemunaitis
Dusia
Obelija
Ilgis
Didžiulis
Nedingis
Matuizos
Salčia
Butrimonys
Šventežeris
Lazdijai
Seirijai
Varėna
Perloja
Eišiškės
Byenyakoni
Dieveniškės
Gauja
Palyatskishki
Galstas
Merkinė
Vydeniai
Voranava
Traby
Vishnyeva
Veisiejai
Leipalingis
Stračiūnai
Dzūkijos Nacionalinis Parkas
Ūla
Nacha
Radun'
Subotniki
Valozhyn
Ančia
Viktarinas
Neravai
Marcinkonys
Dubičiai
Zhyrmuny
Yuratsishki
Kapčiamiestis
Seira
Druskininkai
Margionys
Krupava
Lidski Zamak
Lida
Pyershamayski
Iwye
Nyoman
Parechcha
Byershty
Hozha
Sapotskin
E67
E272
E262
E85
E28
A1
A2
A4
A5
A6
A8
A9
A10
A12
A13
A14
A15
A16
A17
M7
xiii

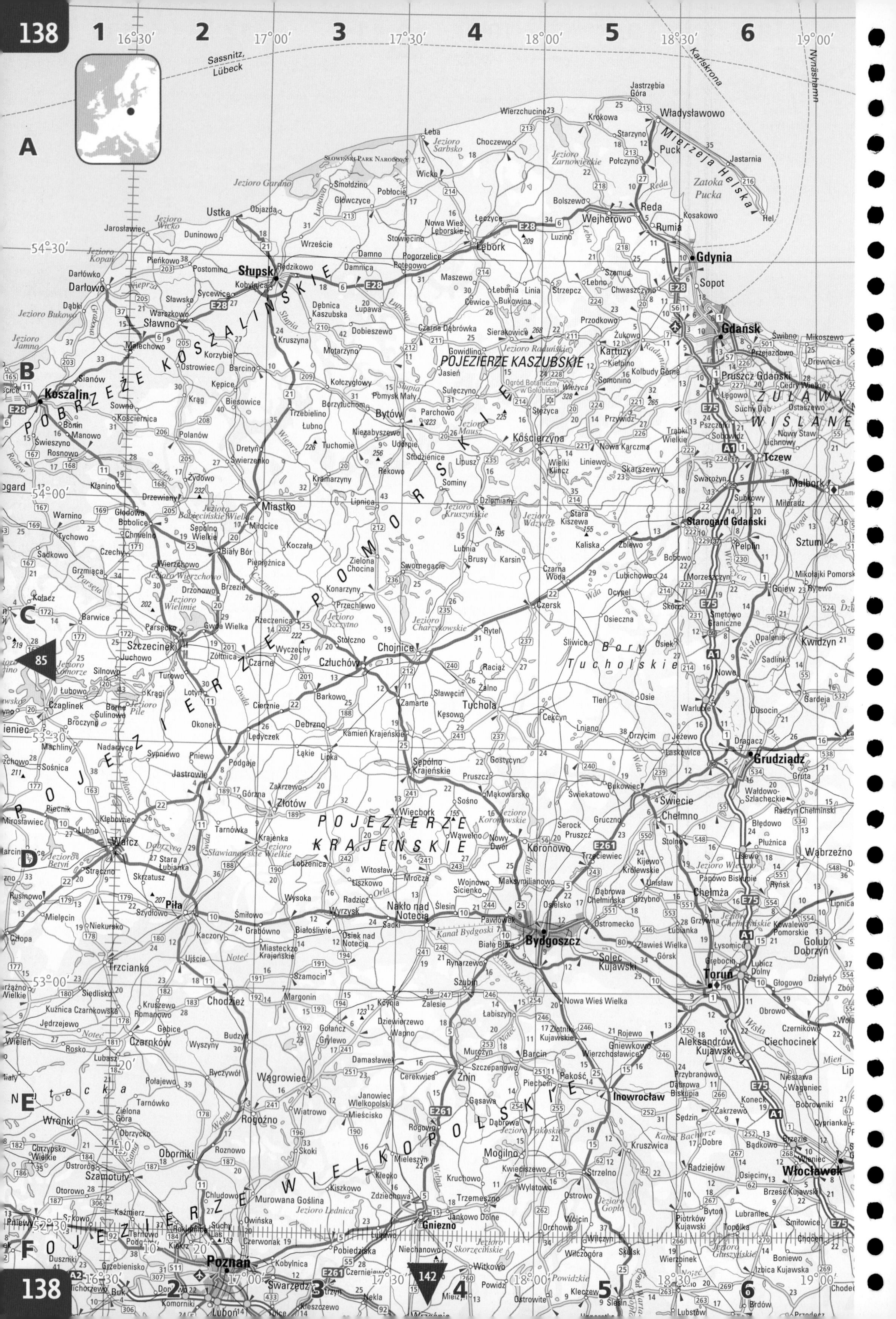
1
2
3
4
5
6
16°30′
17°00′
17°30′
18°00′
18°30′
19°00′
A
B
C
D
E
F
54°30′
54°00′
53°30′
53°00′
52°30′
Sassnitz, Lübeck
Karlskrona
Nynäshamn
Władysławowo
Jastrzębia Góra
Mierzeja Helska
Zatoka Pucka
Jastarnia
Hel
Puck
Reda
Rumia
Gdynia
Sopot
Gdańsk
Wejherowo
Lębork
Łeba
Jezioro Sarbsko
Słowiński Park Narodowy
Jezioro Gardno
Jezioro Łebsko
Smołdzino
Ustka
Słupsk
Darłowo
Sławno
Koszalin
Pobrzeże Koszalińskie
Pojezierze Kaszubskie
Kartuzy
Kościerzyna
Bytów
Miastko
Pruszcz Gdański
Żuławy Wiślane
Tczew
Malbork
Starogard Gdański
Pojezierze Pomorskie
Czersk
Chojnice
Człuchów
Szczecinek
Bory Tucholskie
Tuchola
Kwidzyn
Grudziądz
Świecie
Chełmno
Pojezierze Krajeńskie
Złotów
Wałcz
Piła
Nakło nad Notecią
Bydgoszcz
Toruń
Chełmża
Wąbrzeźno
Golub Dobrzyń
Solec Kujawski
Trzcianka
Chodzież
Wągrowiec
Żnin
Inowrocław
Aleksandrów Kujawski
Ciechocinek
Włocławek
Mogilno
Strzelno
Kruszwica
Radziejów
Jezioro Gopło
Gniezno
Pojezierze Wielkopolskie
Oborniki
Szamotuły
Rogoźno
Czarnków
Wronki
Notecka
Poznań
Swarzędz
Luboń
Września
Kanał Bydgoski
85
142

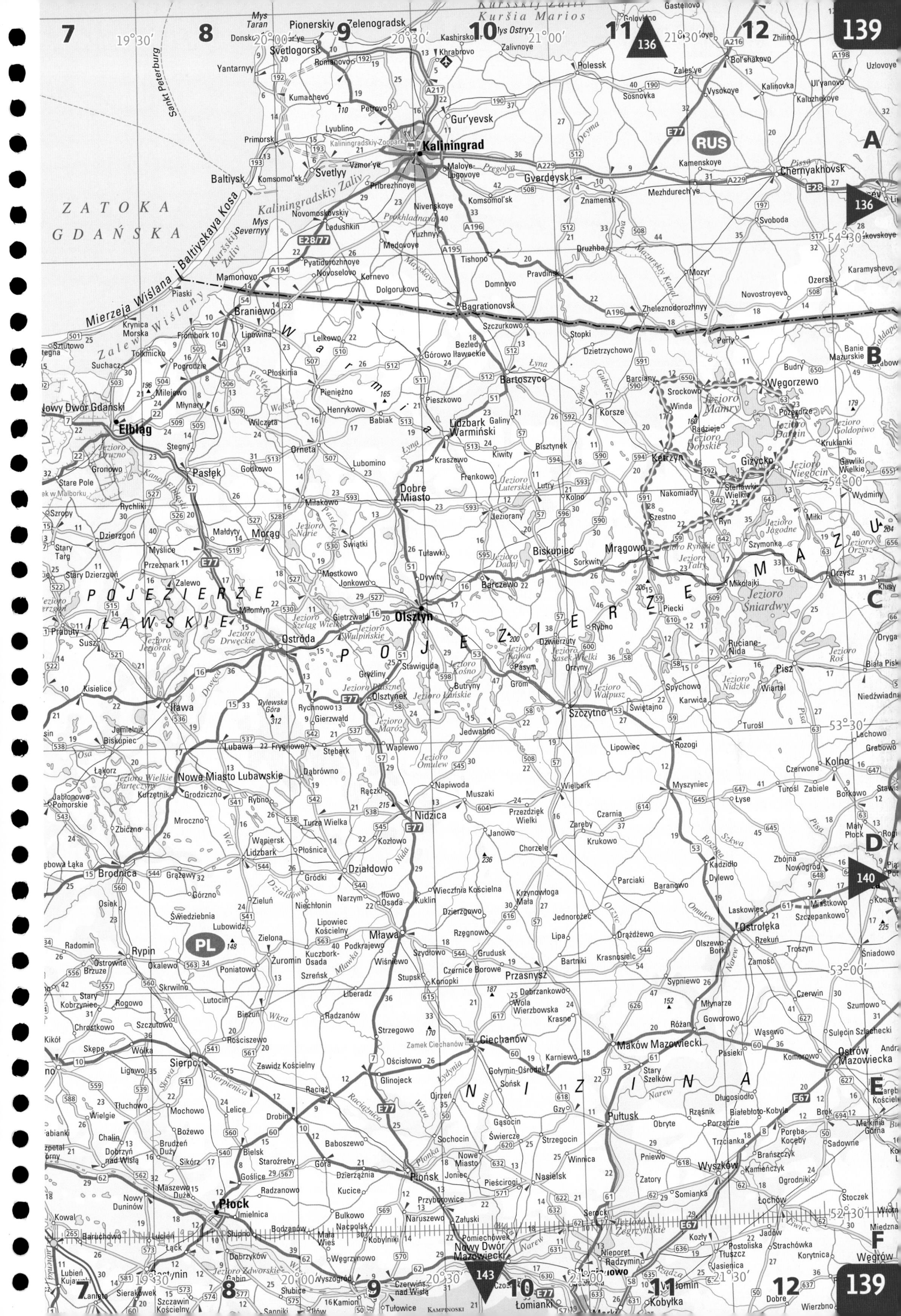
7
8
9
10
11
12
A
B
C
D
E
F
136
140
143
RUS
PL
ZATOKA
GDAŃSKA
Kurśia Marios
Kaliningradskiy Zaliv
Mierzeja Wiślana / Baltiyskaya Kosa
Zalew Wiślany
Warmia
POJEZIERZE IŁAWSKIE
POJEZIERZE MAZURSKIE
NIZINA
Sankt Peterburg
Kaliningrad
Svetlogorsk
Pionerskiy
Zelenogradsk
Yantarnyy
Primorsk
Baltiysk
Svetlyy
Gur'yevsk
Polessk
Gvardeysk
Chernyakhovsk
Znamensk
Bagrationovsk
Mamonovo
Pravdinsk
Zheleznodorozhnyy
Ozersk
Braniewo
Frombork
Elbląg
Nowy Dwór Gdański
Pasłęk
Orneta
Lidzbark Warmiński
Bartoszyce
Górowo Iławeckie
Kętrzyn
Węgorzewo
Giżycko
Jezioro Mamry
Jezioro Niegocin
Jezioro Śniardwy
Mrągowo
Biskupiec
Dobre Miasto
Morąg
Olsztyn
Ostróda
Iława
Olsztynek
Szczytno
Mikołajki
Orzysz
Pisz
Ruciane-Nida
Barczewo
Pasym
Nidzica
Lubawa
Nowe Miasto Lubawskie
Działdowo
Brodnica
Lidzbark
Mława
Przasnysz
Ostrołęka
Kolno
Rozogi
Myszyniec
Ciechanów
Maków Mazowiecki
Różan
Ostrów Mazowiecka
Pułtusk
Wyszków
Płońsk
Sierpc
Rypin
Żuromin
Płock
Raciąż
Nowy Dwór Mazowiecki
Serock
Radzymin
Łomianki
Kobyłka
Węgrów
E28
E28/77
E77
E67
A229
A196
19°30′
20°00′
20°30′
21°00′
21°30′
54°30′
54°00′
53°30′
53°00′
52°30′

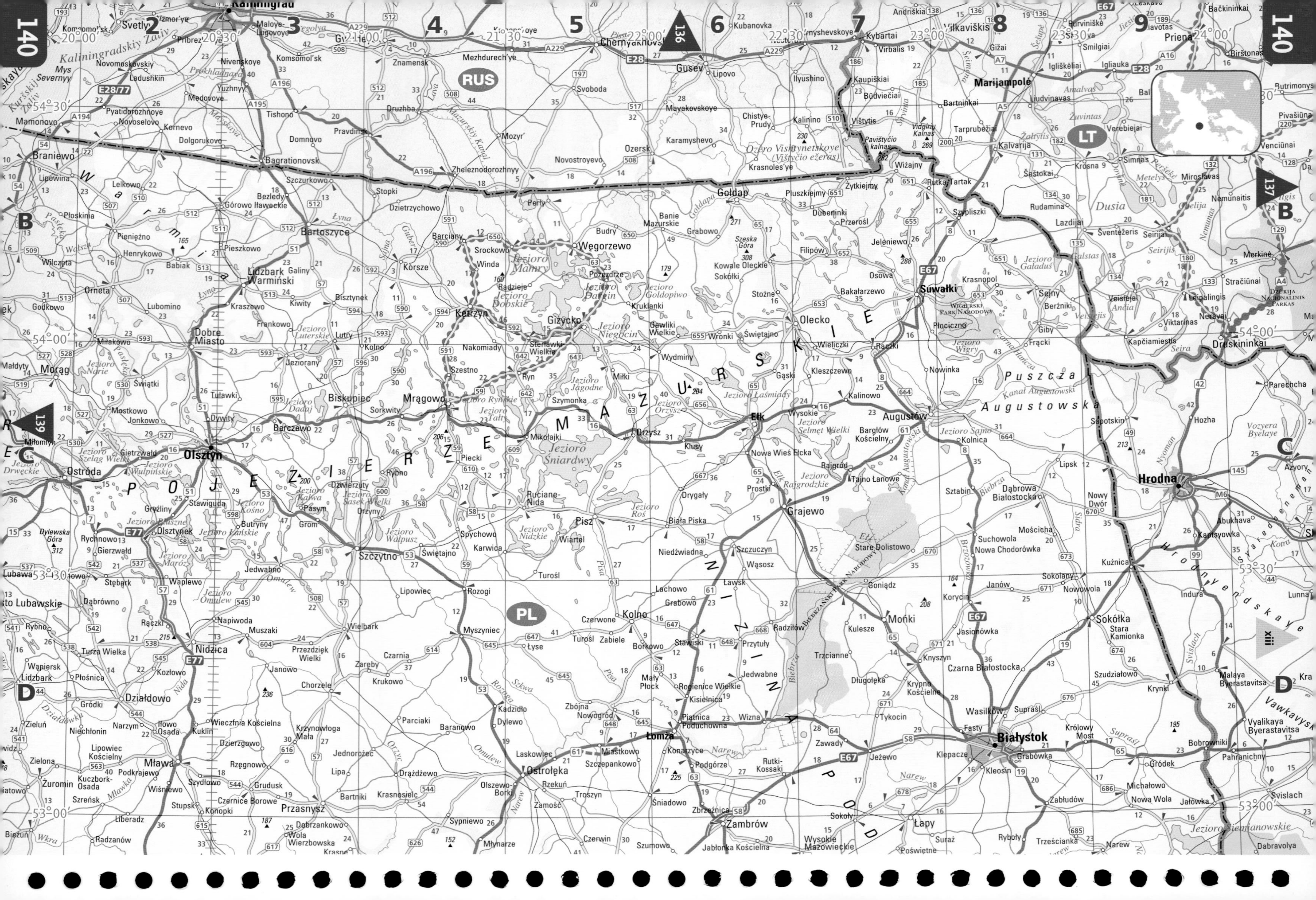

136
137
139
LT
RUS
PL
Kaliningrad
Marijampolė
Vilkaviškis
Prienai
Druskininkai
Hrodna
Sokółka
Białystok
Suwałki
Augustów
Ełk
Olecko
Gołdap
Węgorzewo
Giżycko
Kętrzyn
Mrągowo
Pisz
Grajewo
Mońki
Łomża
Kolno
Ostrołęka
Szczytno
Olsztyn
Ostróda
Nidzica
Działdowo
Mława
Przasnysz
Bartoszyce
Lidzbark Warmiński
Braniewo
Mamonovo
Bagrationovsk
Chernyakhovsk
Gusev
Zambrów
Puszcza Augustowska
Hrodnyenskaye
Jezioro Śniardwy
Jezioro Mamry
E28
E67
E77

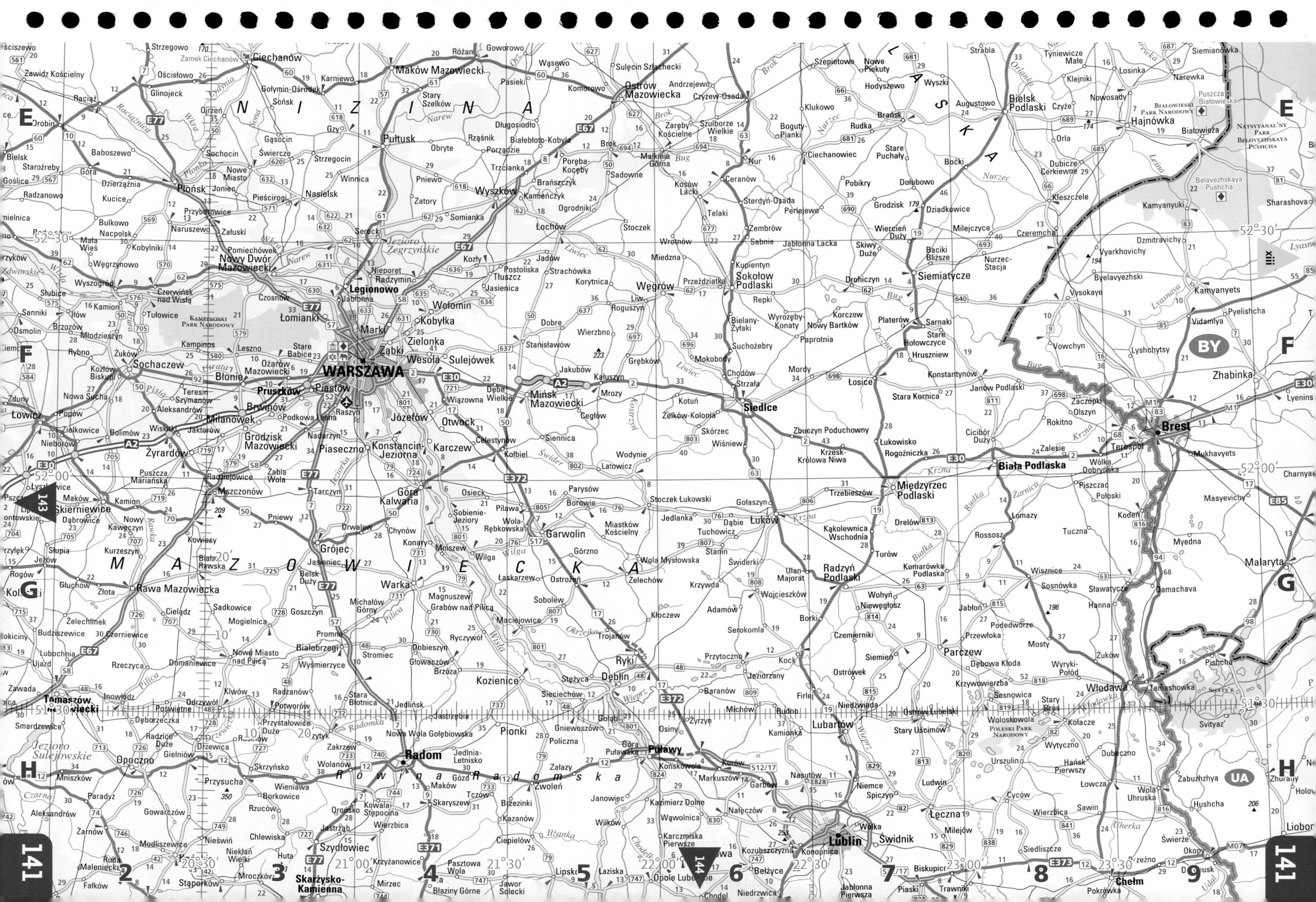
WARSZAWA
Brest
Biała Podlaska
Międzyrzec Podlaski
Siedlce
Lublin
Radom
Puławy
Łęczna
Świdnik
Chełm
Włodawa
Parczew
Radzyń Podlaski
Łuków
Garwolin
Mińsk Mazowiecki
Węgrów
Sokołów Podlaski
Siemiatycze
Bielsk Podlaski
Hajnówka
Białowieża
Ostrów Mazowiecka
Wyszków
Pułtusk
Maków Mazowiecki
Ciechanów
Płońsk
Nowy Dwór Mazowiecki
Legionowo
Łomianki
Pruszków
Piaseczno
Otwock
Grójec
Grodzisk Mazowiecki
Żyrardów
Sochaczew
Skierniewice
Rawa Mazowiecka
Tomaszów Mazowiecki
Opoczno
Szydłowiec
Skarżysko-Kamienna
Kozienice
Dęblin
Ryki
Lubartów
Łosice
Terespol
Kamyanyets
Zhabinka
Malaryta
Lowicz
N I Z I N A
M A Z O W I E C K A
R ó w i n a R a d o m s k a
BY
UA
E
F
G
H
143
144

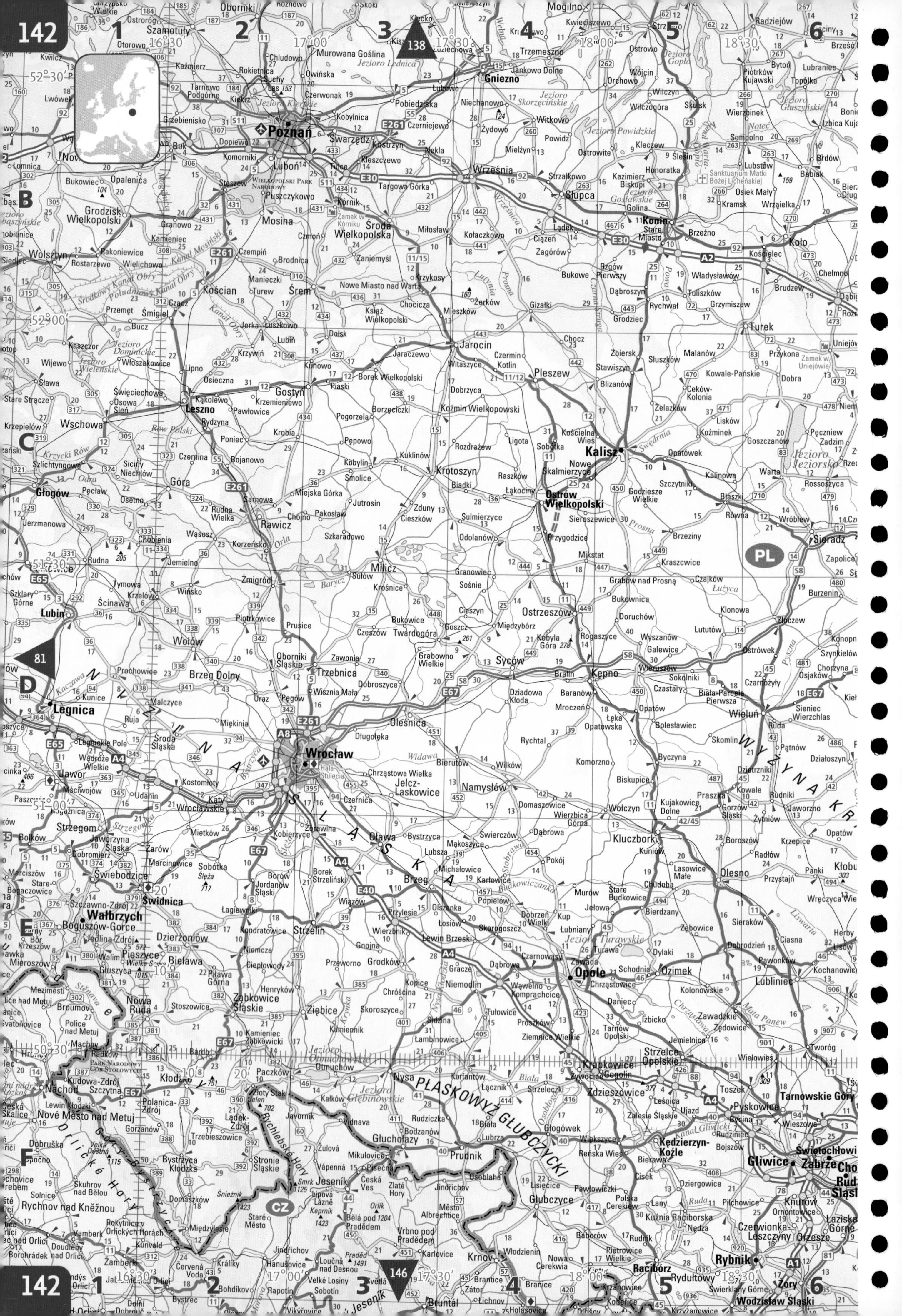

1
2
3
4
5
6
138
146
81
B
C
D
E
F
PL
CZ
Poznań
Gniezno
Września
Konin
Koło
Turek
Jarocin
Pleszew
Kalisz
Ostrów Wielkopolski
Leszno
Gostyń
Krotoszyn
Milicz
Rawicz
Głogów
Lubin
Legnica
Wrocław
Oleśnica
Oława
Brzeg
Namysłów
Kępno
Wieluń
Sieradz
Kluczbork
Olesno
Opole
Lubliniec
Świdnica
Wałbrzych
Dzierżoniów
Nysa
Prudnik
Kędzierzyn-Koźle
Gliwice
Zabrze
Racibórz
Rybnik
Wodzisław Śląski
Tarnowskie Góry
Strzelce Opolskie
Kłodzko
Náchod
Jeseník
Krnov
Środa Wielkopolska
Śrem
Kościan
Wolsztyn
Grodzisk Wielkopolski
Wschowa
Słupca
Trzebnica
Oborniki Śląskie
Sycyn
Ostrzeszów
NIZINA ŚLĄSKA
WYŻYNA KRAKOWSKO
PŁASKOWYŻ GŁUBCZYCKI
Góry Bystrzyckie
Orlické Hory
Rychlebské Hory

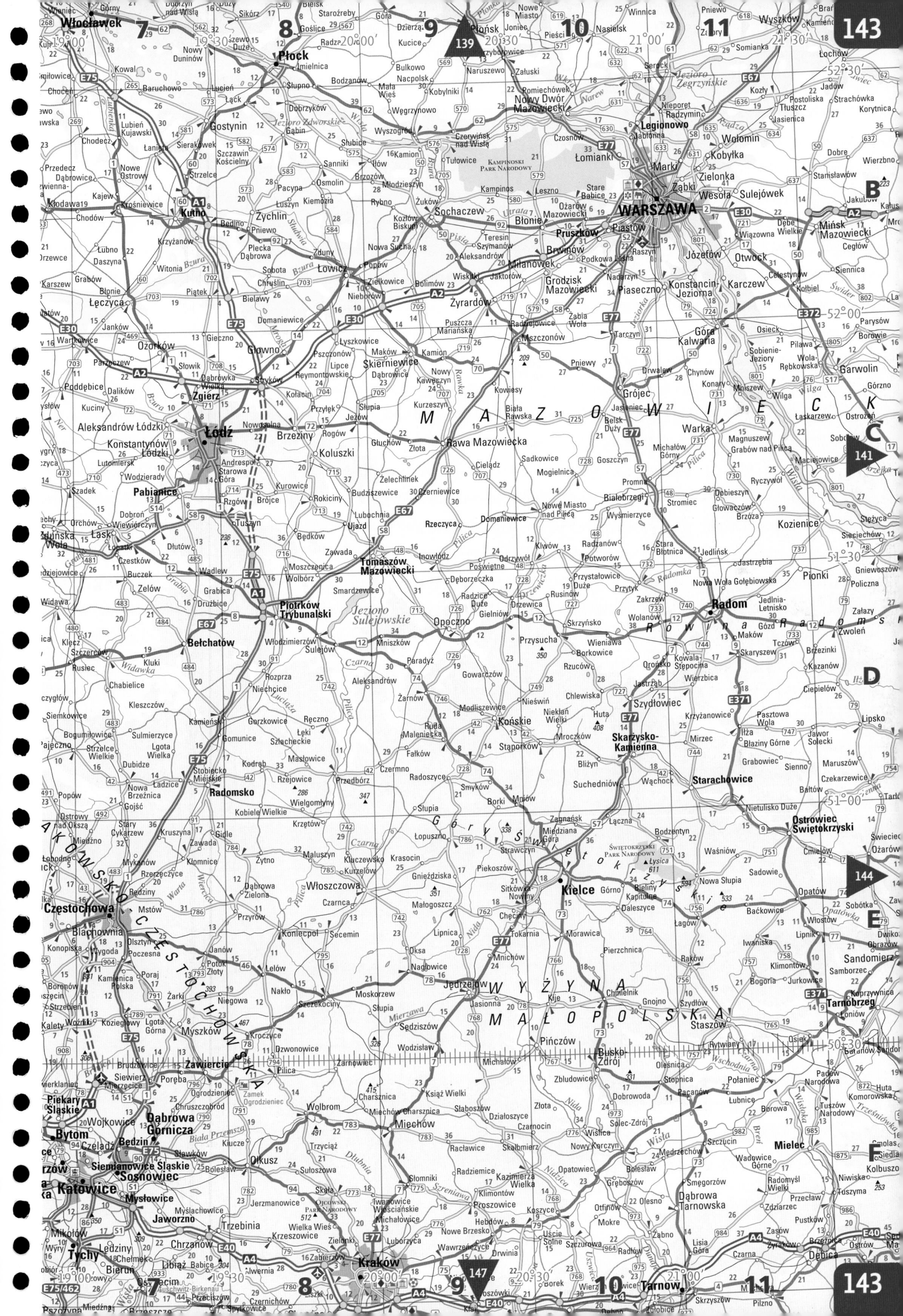
Włocławek
Płock
Płońsk
Wyszków
Nowy Dwór Mazowiecki
Legionowo
Gostynin
Kutno
Łowicz
Sochaczew
Łomianki
WARSZAWA
Pruszków
Błonie
Grodzisk Mazowiecki
Żyrardów
Skierniewice
Piaseczno
Otwock
Mińsk Mazowiecki
Łęczyca
Zgierz
Łódź
Pabianice
Koluszki
Brzeziny
Rawa Mazowiecka
Grójec
Warka
Garwolin
Łask
Tomaszów Mazowiecki
Piotrków Trybunalski
Bełchatów
Opoczno
Radom
Kozienice
Zwoleń
Pionki
Końskie
Skarżysko-Kamienna
Starachowice
Radomsko
Kielce
Ostrowiec Świętokrzyski
Włoszczowa
Jędrzejów
Częstochowa
Zawiercie
Miechów
Busko-Zdrój
Staszów
Sandomierz
Tarnobrzeg
Mielec
Dąbrowa Górnicza
Będzin
Bytom
Sosnowiec
Katowice
Mysłowice
Jaworzno
Tychy
Olkusz
Chrzanów
Kraków
Tarnów
Dębica
M A Z O W I E C K
R ó w i n a R a d o m s
W Y Ż Y N A
M A Ł O P O L S K A
KAMPINOSKI PARK NARODOWY
ŚWIĘTOKRZYSKI PARK NARODOWY
OJCOWSKI PARK NARODOWY
Jezioro Sulejowskie
139
141
144
147
B
C
D
E
F
7
8
9
10
11

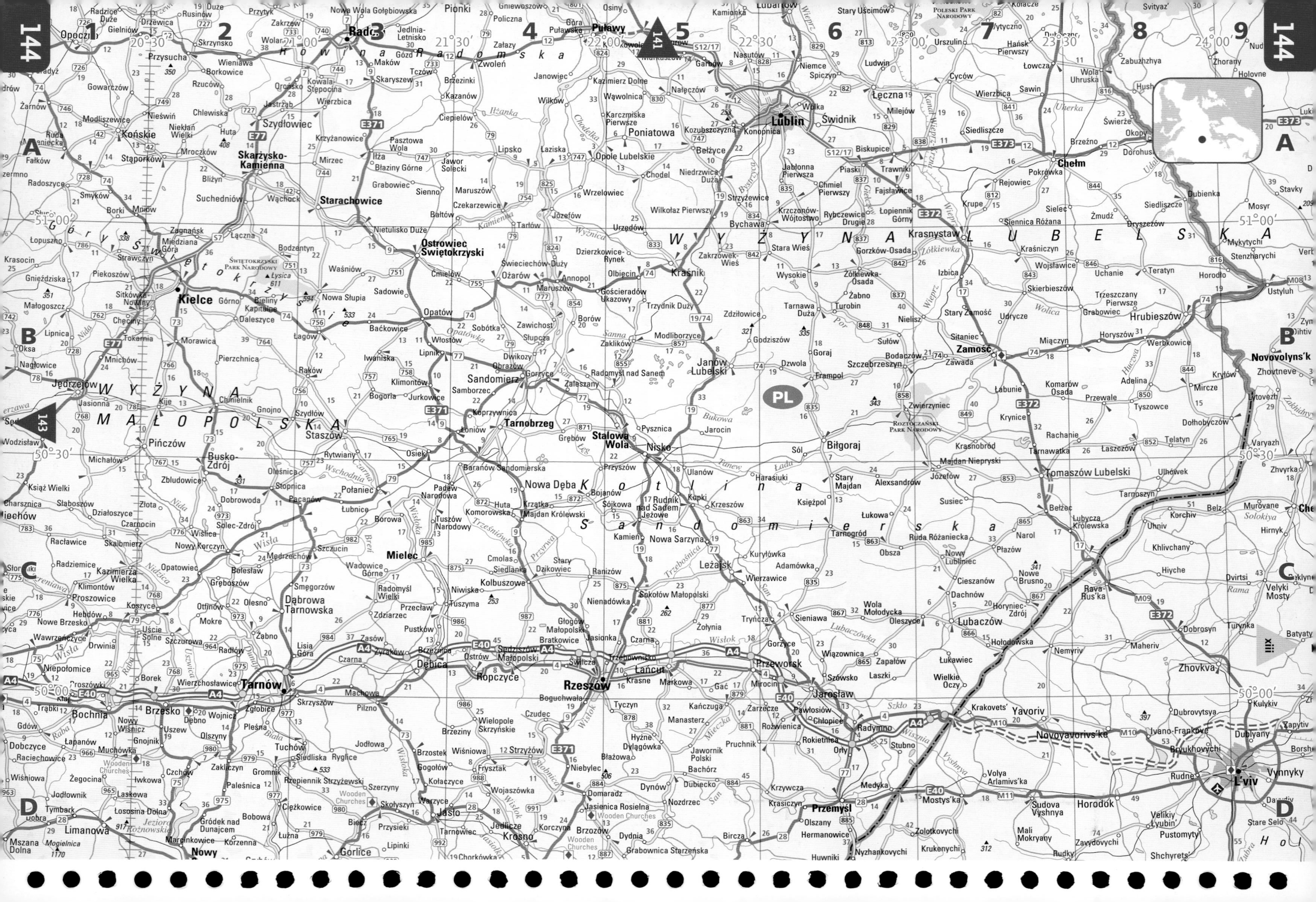
144
1
2
3
4
5
6
7
8
9
A
B
C
D
Lublin
Chełm
Zamość
Hrubieszów
Krasnystaw
Biłgoraj
Kraśnik
Puławy
Radom
Kielce
Skarżysko-Kamienna
Starachowice
Ostrowiec Świętokrzyski
Sandomierz
Tarnobrzeg
Stalowa Wola
Nisko
Mielec
Dębica
Tarnów
Rzeszów
Łańcut
Przeworsk
Jarosław
Przemyśl
Krosno
Jasło
Gorlice
Bochnia
Brzesko
Limanowa
Nowy
Busko-Zdrój
Pińczów
Jędrzejów
Końskie
Opoczno
Szydłowiec
Staszów
Kolbuszowa
Ropczyce
Leżajsk
Lubaczów
Tomaszów Lubelski
Janów Lubelski
Świdnik
Łęczna
Poniatowa
L'viv
Yavoriv
Zhovkva
Horodok
Novovolyns'k
PL
W Y Ż Y N A L U B E L S K A
W Y Ż Y N A M A Ł O P O L S K A
K o t l i n a S a n d o m i e r s k a
R ó w n i n a R a d o m s k a
G ó r y Ś w i ę t o k r z y s k i e
Świętokrzyski Park Narodowy
Roztoczański Park Narodowy
Poleski Park Narodowy
Wooden Churches
Wisła
San
Wieprz
E40
E371
E372
E373
E77
A4
141
143
xiii

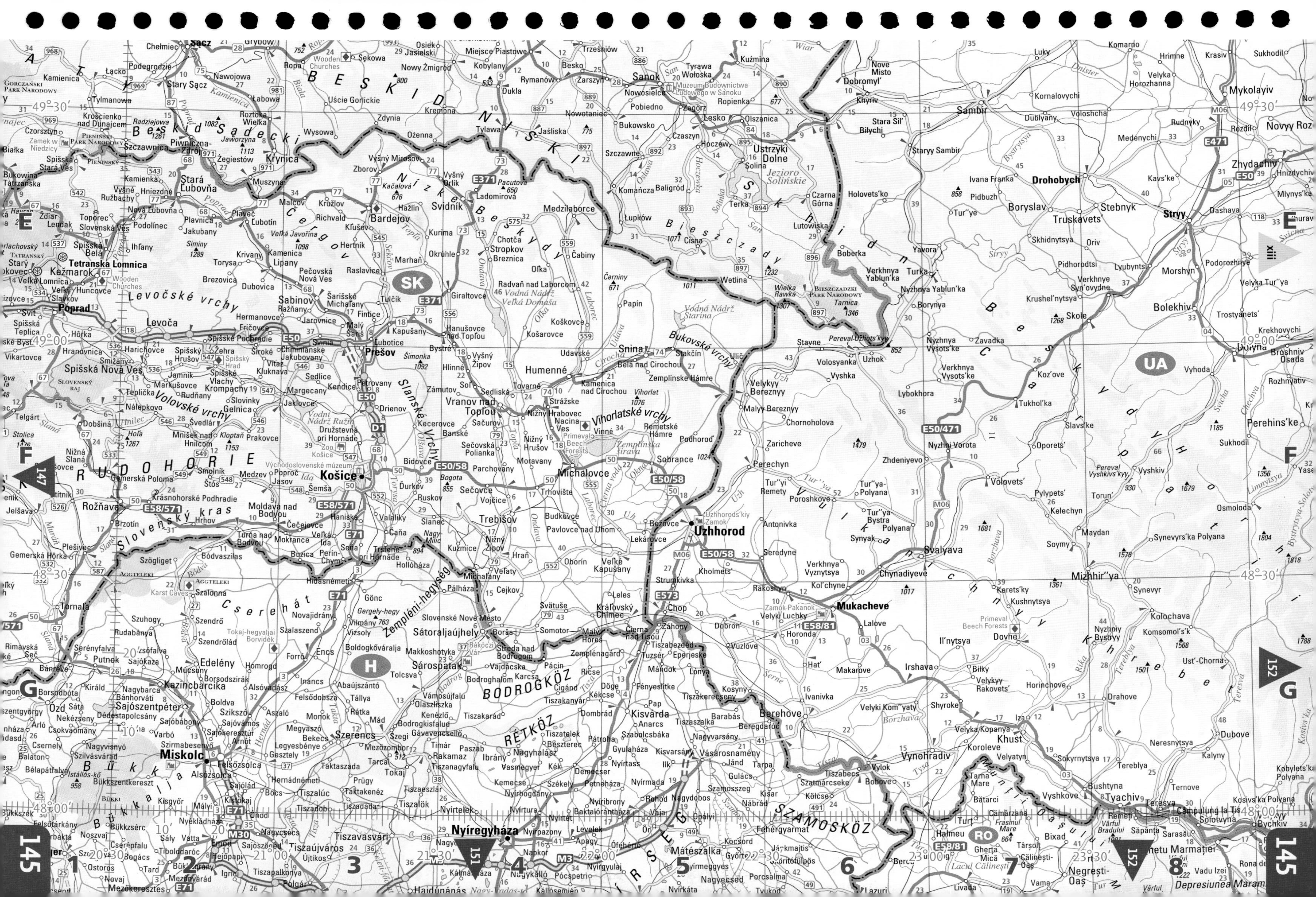
UA
SK
H
RO
152
147
151
xiii
Mykolayiv
Stryy
Drohobych
Truskavets'
Boryslav
Sambir
Skole
Morshyn
Bolekhiv
Stebnyk
Mizhhir''ya
Svalyava
Mukacheve
Uzhhorod
Chop
Berehove
Vynohradiv
Khust
Tyachiv
Dovhe
Irshava
Perechyn
Velykyy Bereznyy
Nyzhni Vorota
Sanok
Ustrzyki Dolne
Lesko
Krynica
Stary Sącz
Muszyna
Bardejov
Svidník
Stropkov
Medzilaborce
Humenné
Snina
Michalovce
Vranov nad Topľou
Trebišov
Prešov
Sabinov
Košice
Levoča
Poprad
Kežmarok
Tetranska Lomnica
Stará Ľubovňa
Spišská Nová Ves
Rožňava
Moldava nad Bodvou
Sátoraljaújhely
Sárospatak
Tokaj
Szerencs
Miskolc
Nyíregyháza
Kisvárda
Mátészalka
Tiszaújváros
Tiszavasvári
Edelény
Kazincbarcika
Ózd
Fehérgyarmat
Vásárosnamény
B e s k y d y
K a r p a t y
B i e s z c z a d y
N í z k e B e s k y d y
Č e r g o v
B E S K I D N I S K I
B e s k i d S ą d e c k i
L e v o č s k é v r c h y
V o l o v s k é v r c h y
S l o v e n s k ý k r a s
R U D O H O R I E
Slanské Vrchy
Vihorlatské vrchy
Bukovské vrchy
Zempléni-hegység
C s e r e h á t
B ü k k
BODROGKÖZ
RÉTKÖZ
SZAMOSKÖZ
Primeval Beech Forests
Wooden Churches
E50
E71
E58/81
E50/58
E371
E573
E471
E50/471
D1
M3
M06
M30

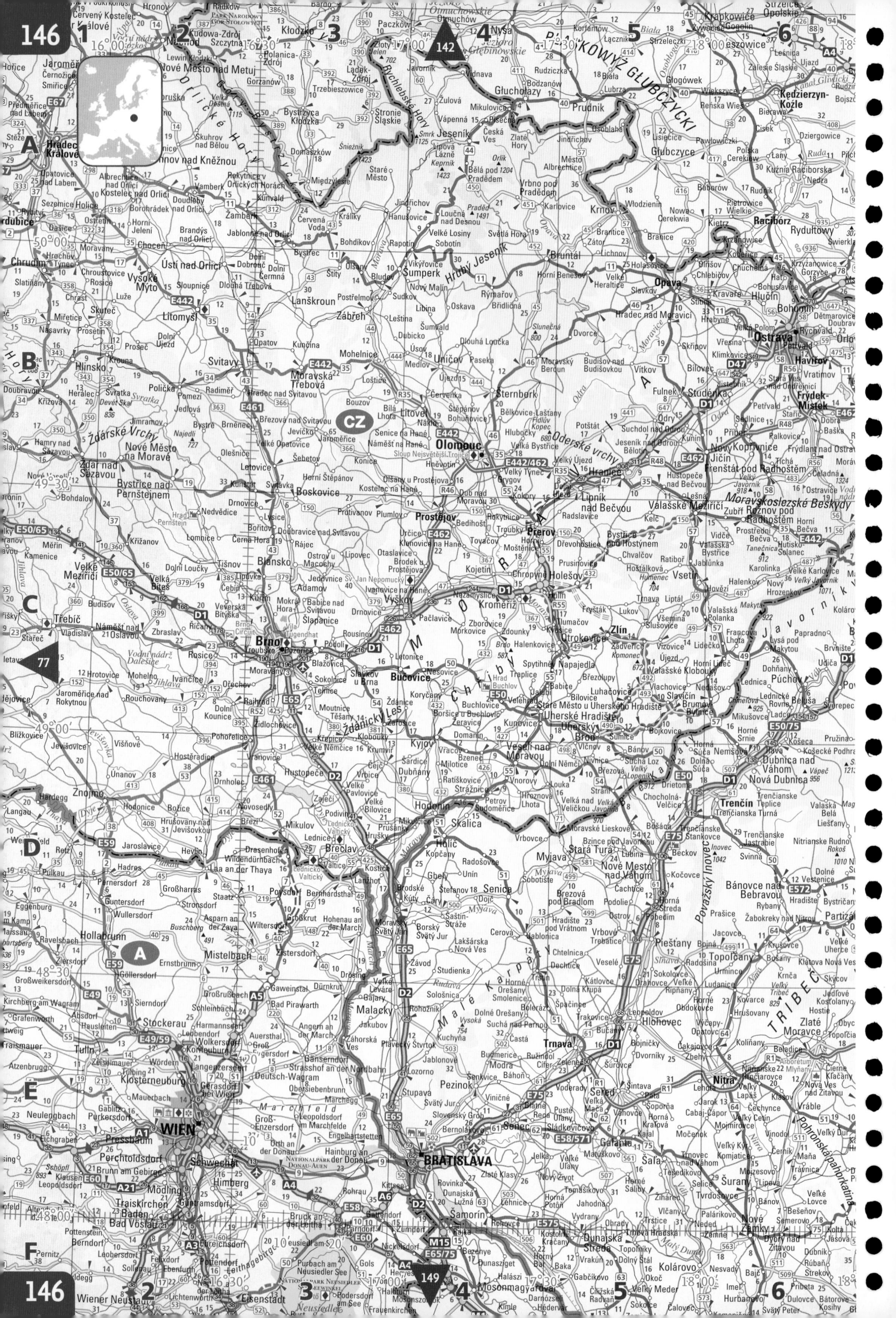
142
149
77
CZ
A
Hradec Králové
Nové Město nad Metují
Náchod
Kłodzko
Nysa
Prudnik
Głuchołazy
Jeseník
Krnov
Opava
Ostrava
Havířov
Frýdek-Místek
Racibórz
Kędzierzyn-Koźle
Hlučín
Bohumín
Pardubice
Chrudim
Ústí nad Orlicí
Litomyšl
Svitavy
Šumperk
Lanškroun
Zábřeh
Mohelnice
Uničov
Šternberk
Olomouc
Prostějov
Přerov
Hranice
Lipník nad Bečvou
Nový Jičín
Frenštát pod Radhoštěm
Valašské Meziříčí
Rožnov pod Radhoštěm
Vsetín
Holešov
Kroměříž
Zlín
Otrokovice
Vyškov
Blansko
Boskovice
Brno
Třebíč
Velké Meziříčí
Žďár nad Sázavou
Nové Město na Moravě
Bystřice nad Pernštejnem
Polička
Moravská Třebová
Jihlava
Znojmo
Mikulov
Břeclav
Hodonín
Uherské Hradiště
Uherský Brod
Veselí nad Moravou
Kyjov
Bučovice
Hustopeče
Trenčín
Púchov
Dubnica nad Váhom
Nová Dubnica
Myjava
Senica
Skalica
Holíč
Malacky
Piešťany
Hlohovec
Topoľčany
Trnava
Pezinok
Senec
Galanta
Šaľa
Nitra
Nové Zámky
Šurany
Dunajská Streda
Šamorín
BRATISLAVA
WIEN
Schwechat
Mödling
Baden
Bad Vöslau
Wiener Neustadt
Eisenstadt
Stockerau
Korneuburg
Klosterneuburg
Tulln
Hollabrunn
Mistelbach
Laa an der Thaya
Poysdorf
Zistersdorf
Gänserndorf
Deutsch-Wagram
Bruck an der Leitha
Hainburg an der Donau
Neusiedler See
Mosonmagyaróvár
Hrubý Jeseník
Oderské vrchy
Moravskoslezské Beskydy
Javorníky
Chřiby
Ždánický Les
Malé Karpaty
Biele Karpaty
Považský Inovec
Tribeč
Pohronská pahorkatina
Žďárské Vrchy
Orlické Hory
Rychlebské Hory
Płaskowyż Głubczycki
Marchfeld
E50
E65
E75
E442
E461
E462
E49
E59
E60
E58
E575
E571
E572
D1
D2
A1
A4
A5
A6
A21
A3
1
2
3
4
5
6
A
B
C
D
E
F

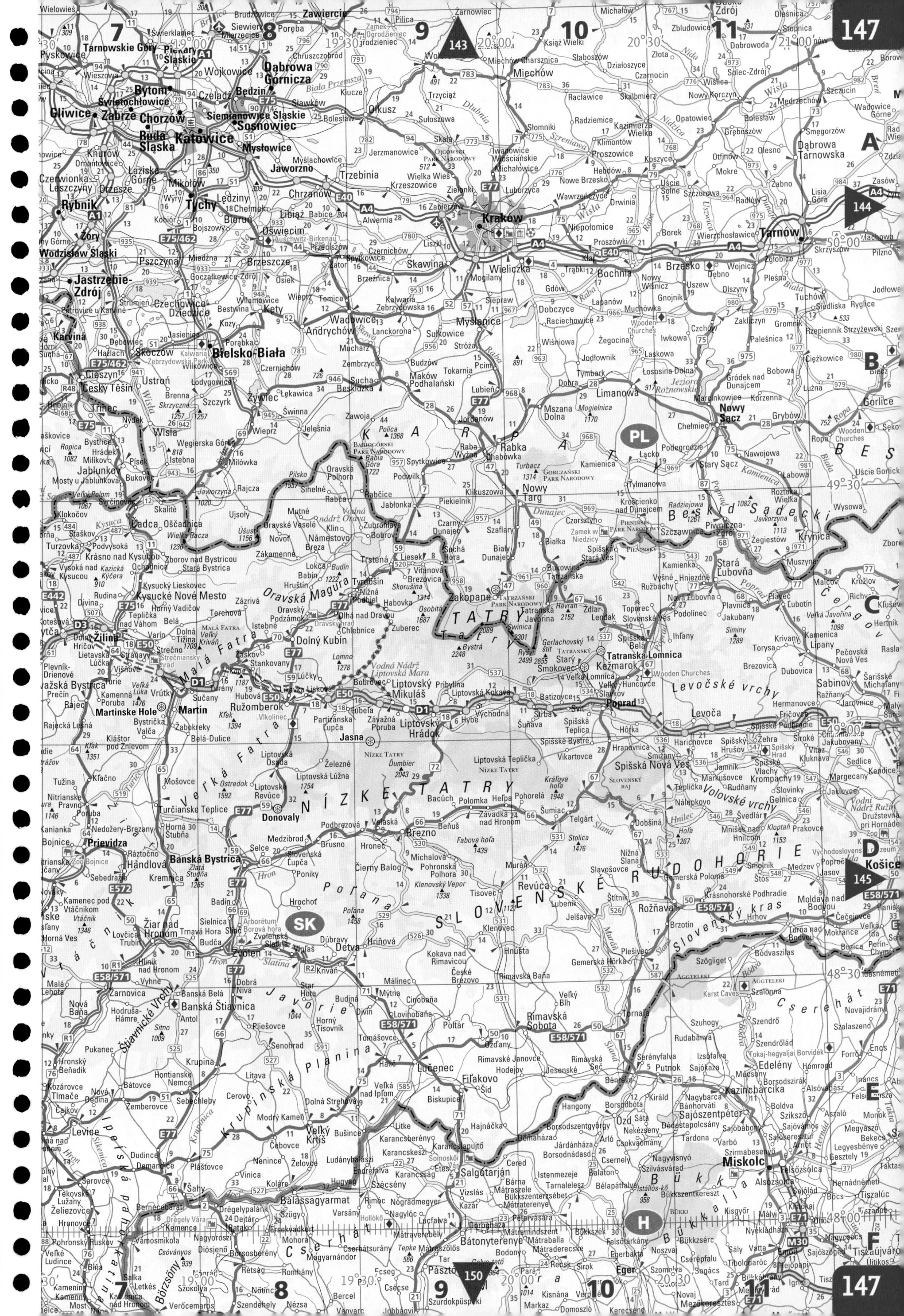
7
8
9
10
11
143
144
145
150
A
B
C
D
E
F
PL
SK
H
Tarnowskie Góry
Zawiercie
Dąbrowa Górnicza
Bytom
Gliwice
Zabrze
Chorzów
Katowice
Sosnowiec
Ruda Śląska
Mysłowice
Jaworzno
Rybnik
Tychy
Żory
Wodzisław Śląski
Jastrzębie-Zdrój
Karviná
Cieszyn
Český Těšín
Třinec
Bielsko-Biała
Oświęcim
Olkusz
Miechów
Kraków
Wieliczka
Bochnia
Tarnów
Myślenice
Wadowice
Andrychów
Żywiec
Nowy Sącz
Limanowa
Nowy Targ
Zakopane
Gorlice
Krynica
Čadca
Žilina
Martin
Ružomberok
Dolný Kubín
Liptovský Mikuláš
Poprad
Kežmarok
Levoča
Sabinov
Košice
Banská Bystrica
Zvolen
Brezno
Rožňava
Lučenec
Rimavská Sobota
Prievidza
Levice
Banská Štiavnica
Balassagyarmat
Salgótarján
Miskolc
Eger
K A R P A T Y
TATRY
NÍZKE TATRY
Malá Fatra
Veľká Fatra
Oravská Magura
Beskid Sądecki
SLOVENSKÉ RUDOHORIE
Poľana
Javorie
Krupinská Planina
Cserhát
Bükk
Slovenský kras
Levočské vrchy
Volovské vrchy
Čergov
Wisła
Dunajec
Poprad
Hron
Ipeľ
E40
E50
E58/571
E75
E77
A1
A4
D1
19°00'
19°30'
20°00'
20°30'
21°00'
50°00'
49°30'
49°00'
48°30'
48°00'

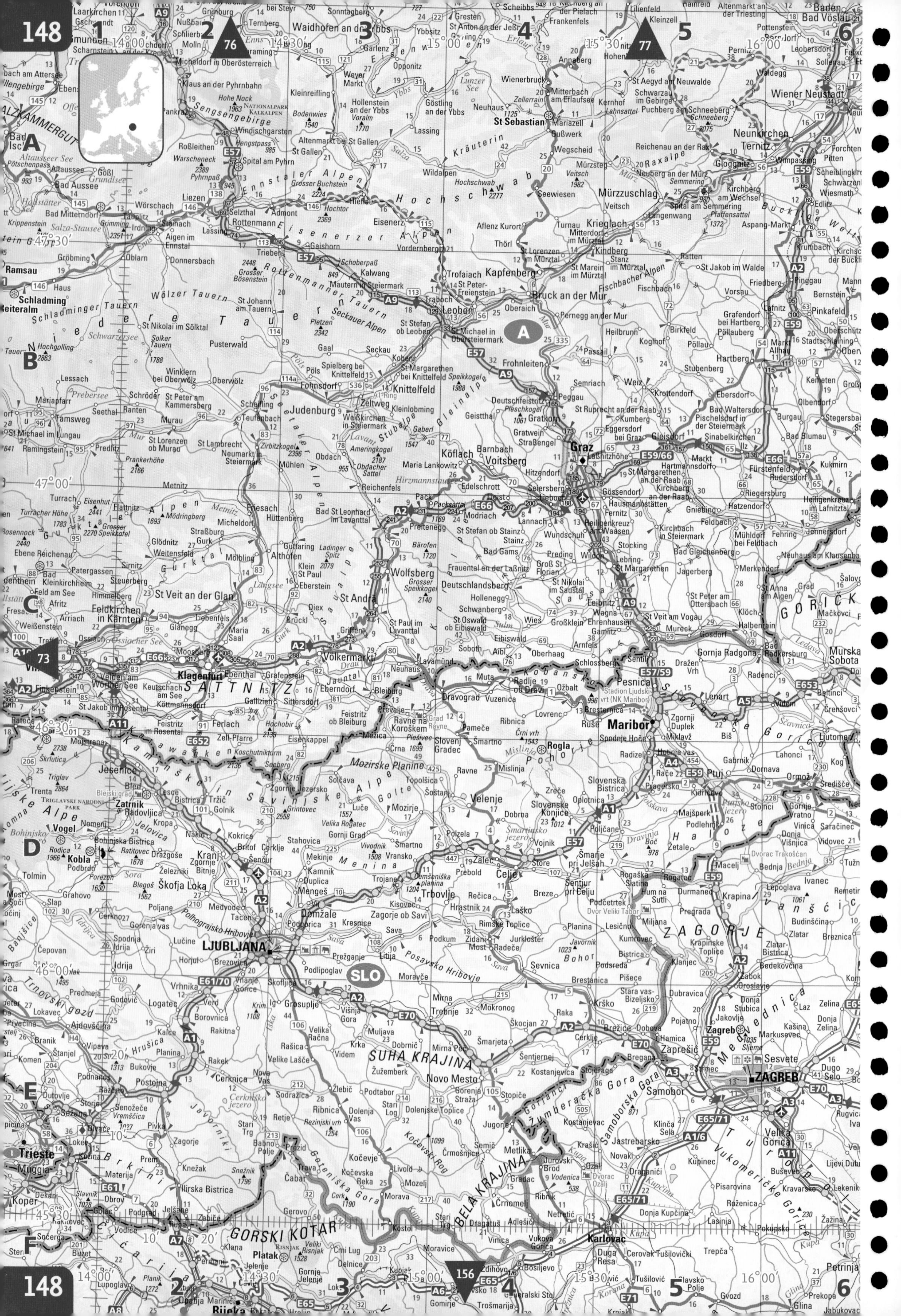
76
77
Waidhofen an der Ybbs
St Sebastian
Mariazell
Wiener Neustadt
Neunkirchen
Mürzzuschlag
Liezen
Bad Aussee
Schladming
Leoben
Kapfenberg
Bruck an der Mur
Niedere Tauern
A
Knittelfeld
Judenburg
Graz
Voitsberg
Köflach
Wolfsberg
Deutschlandsberg
St Veit an der Glan
Feldkirchen in Kärnten
Klagenfurt
Völkermarkt
Villach
73
Maribor
Rogla
Ptuj
Celje
Velenje
Kranj
Ljubljana
SLO
Jesenice
Bled
Vogel
Kobla
Novo Mesto
Trieste
Koper
Rijeka
Karlovac
Zagreb
ZAGREB
Krapina
Samobor
Gorski Kotar
156
Murska Sobota
Velika Gorica

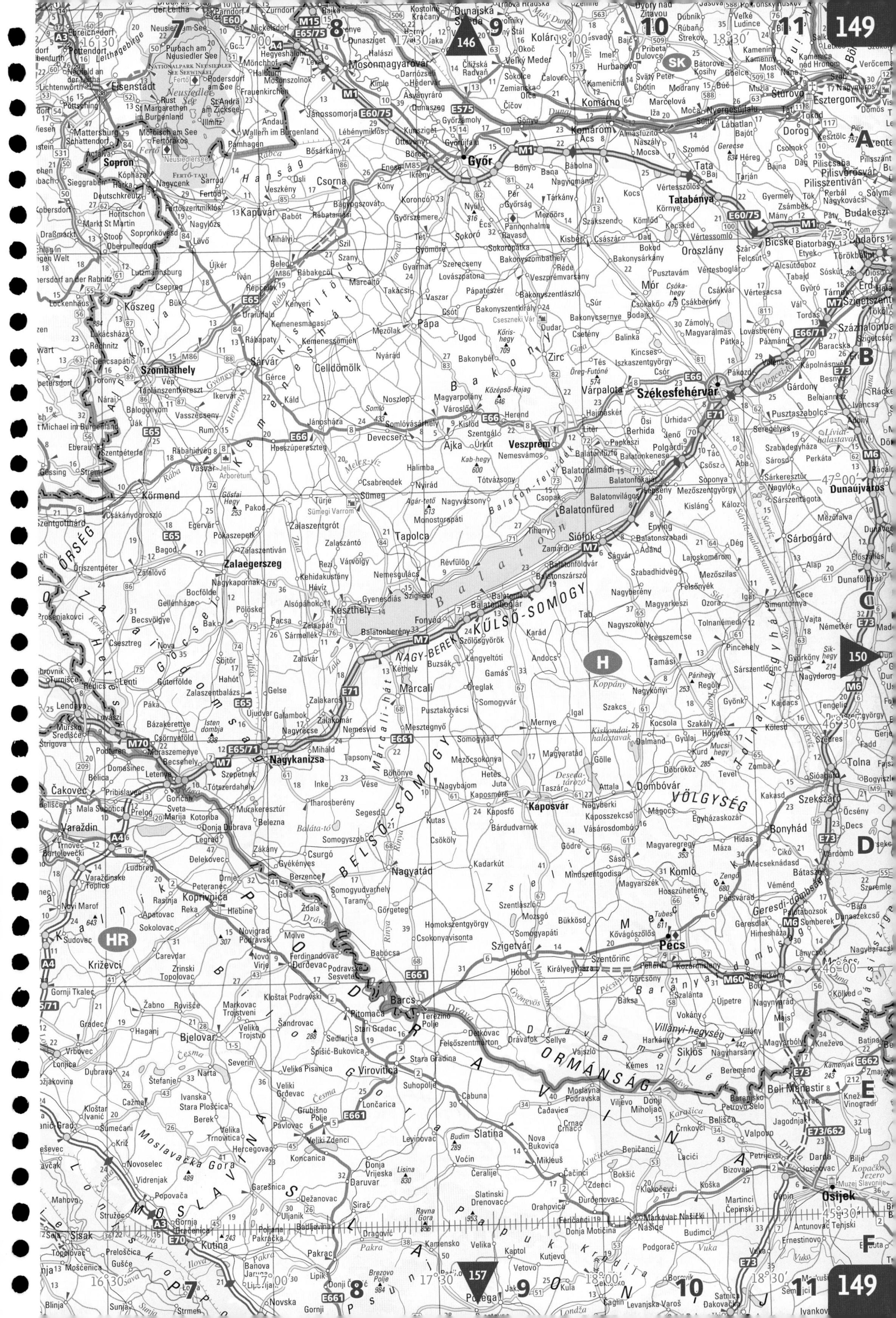
7
8
9
10
11
146
150
157
A
B
C
D
E
F
SK
H
HR
Sopron
Eisenstadt
Neusiedler See
Győr
Mosonmagyaróvár
Komárno
Komárom
Tata
Tatabánya
Štúrovo
Esztergom
Kapuvár
Csorna
Pápa
Szombathely
Kőszeg
Sárvár
Celldömölk
Körmend
Zalaegerszeg
Veszprém
Székesfehérvár
Várpalota
Mór
Oroszlány
Bicske
Budaörs
Érd
Százhalombatta
Balatonfüred
Siófok
Tapolca
Keszthely
Hévíz
Sümeg
Ajka
Dunaújváros
Sárbogárd
Paks
Tolna
Szekszárd
Bonyhád
Kaposvár
Pécs
Szigetvár
Dombóvár
Komló
Nagykanizsa
Marcali
Nagyatád
Barcs
Siklós
Mohács
Osijek
Beli Manastir
Virovitica
Slatina
Koprivnica
Križevci
Bjelovar
Varaždin
Čakovec
Daruvar
Kutina
Sisak
Požega
Kisalföld
Bakony
Balaton
Külső-Somogy
Belső-Somogy
Zselic
Völgység
Ormánság
Dráva
Duna
Mecsek
Bilo gora
Papuk
Moslavačka Gora

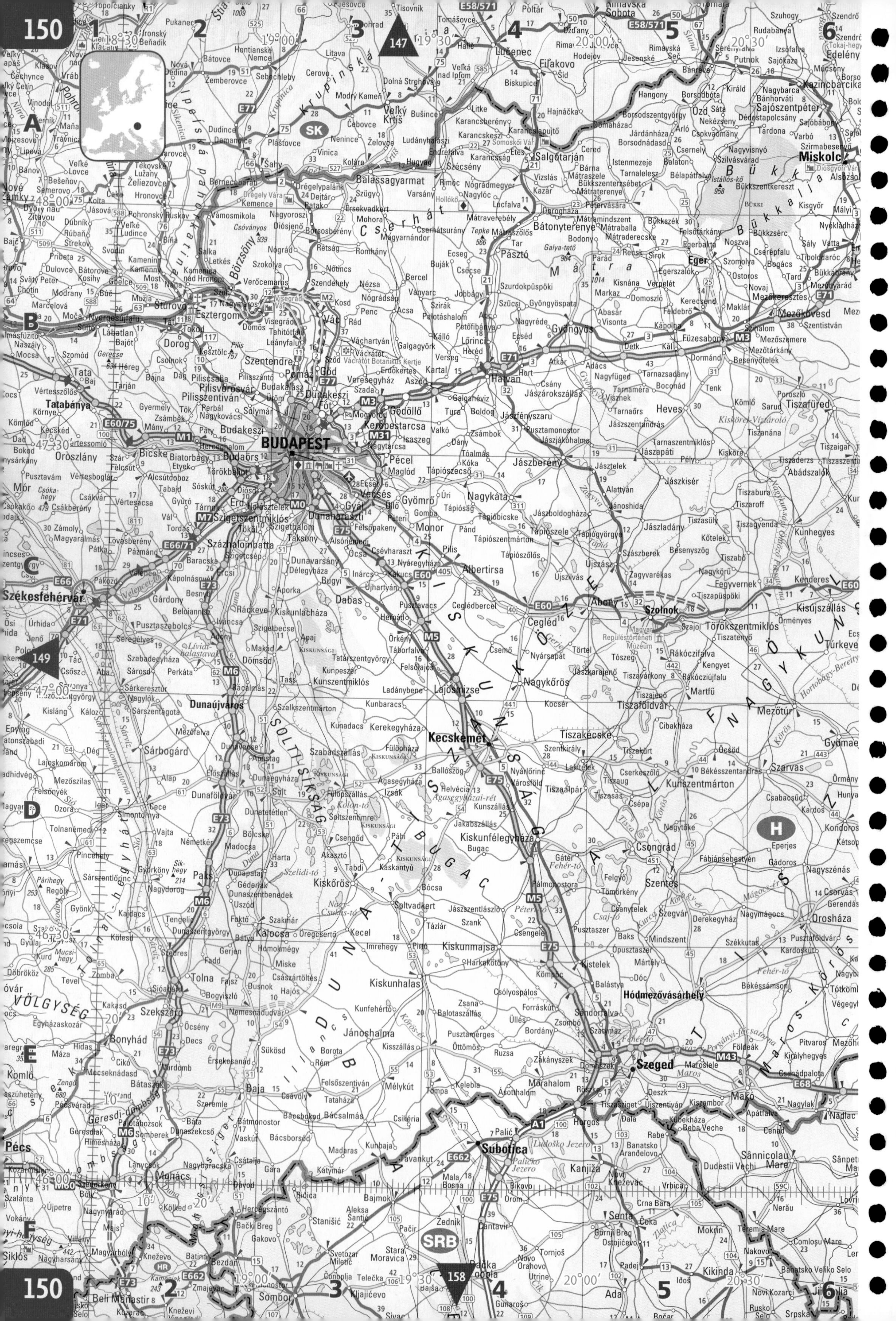

147
149
158
SK
SRB
HR
H
BUDAPEST
Miskolc
Eger
Szolnok
Kecskemét
Szeged
Hódmezővásárhely
Székesfehérvár
Tatabánya
Subotica
Pécs
Salgótarján
Balassagyarmat
Lučenec
Rimavská Sobota
Gyöngyös
Hatvan
Jászberény
Cegléd
Nagykőrös
Dunaújváros
Paks
Kalocsa
Baja
Mohács
Szekszárd
Kiskunhalas
Kiskunfélegyháza
Csongrád
Szentes
Orosháza
Makó
Kiskőrös
Esztergom
Vác
Gödöllő
Mezőkövesd
Ózd
Kazincbarcika
Tiszafüred
Mezőtúr
Szarvas
Štúrovo
Mátra
Bükk
Cserhát
Börzsöny
Krupinská planina
DUNA-TISZA KÖZE
KISKUNSÁG
NAGYKUNSÁG
BUGAC
SOLTI SÍKSÁG
VÖLGYSÉG
Tolna

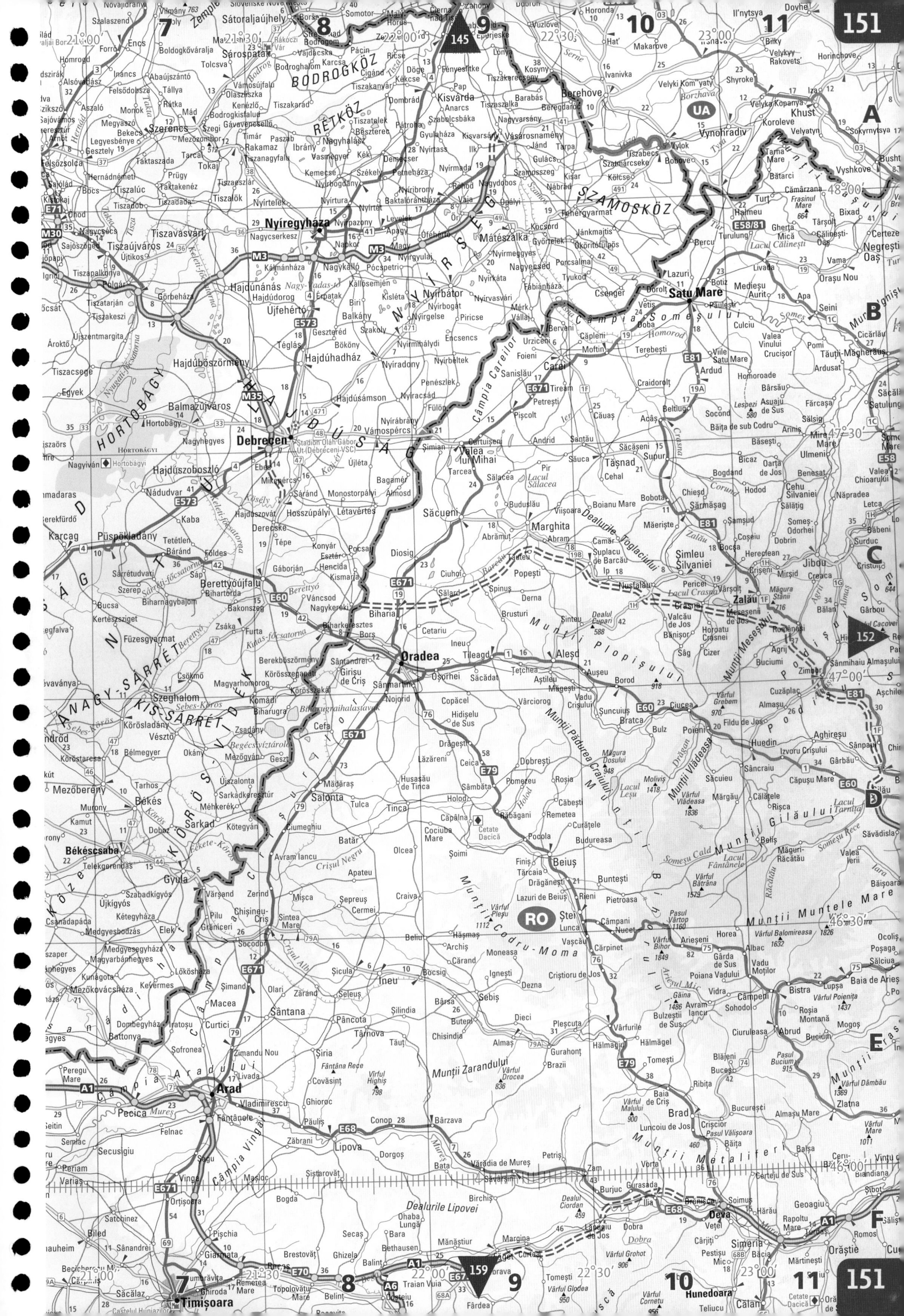

Sátoraljaújhely
Sárospatak
BODROGKÖZ
Tolcsva
Szerencs
Tokaj
RÉTKÖZ
Kisvárda
Berehove
Vynohradiv
Khust
UA
Nyíregyháza
Vásárosnamény
SZAMOSKÖZ
Fehérgyarmat
Mátészalka
Nagyecsed
Csenger
Satu Mare
Tiszavasvári
Tiszaújváros
Polgár
Hajdúnánás
Hajdúdorog
Újfehértó
Nagykálló
Nyírbátor
Hajdúböszörmény
Hajdúhadház
Carei
Câmpia Careilor
Câmpia Someşului
HORTOBÁGY
Balmazújváros
Hortobágy
Debrecen
HAJDÚSÁG
NYÍRSÉG
Vámospércs
Valea lui Mihai
Tăşnad
Hajdúszoboszló
Sacueni
Marghita
Püspökladány
Karcag
Berettyóújfalu
Şimleu Silvaniei
Zalău
Jibou
Oradea
Aleşd
Munţii Plopişului
Munţii Meseşului
Szeghalom
NAGY-SÁRRÉT
KIS-SÁRRÉT
KÖRÖS-VIDÉK
Huedin
Munţii Pădurea Craiului
Munţii Vlădeasa
Salonta
Beiuş
Békés
Békéscsaba
Gyula
Munţii Bihor
RO
Ştei
Munţii Codru-Moma
Munţii Gilăului
Chişineu-Criş
Ineu
Sebiş
Câmpia Aradului
Arad
Munţii Zarandului
Brad
Pecica
Lipova
Munţii Metaliferi
Deva
Dealurile Lipovei
Timişoara
Hunedoara
Orăştie
Câmpia Vingăi
A
B
C
D
E
F
7
8
9
10
11
145
152
159

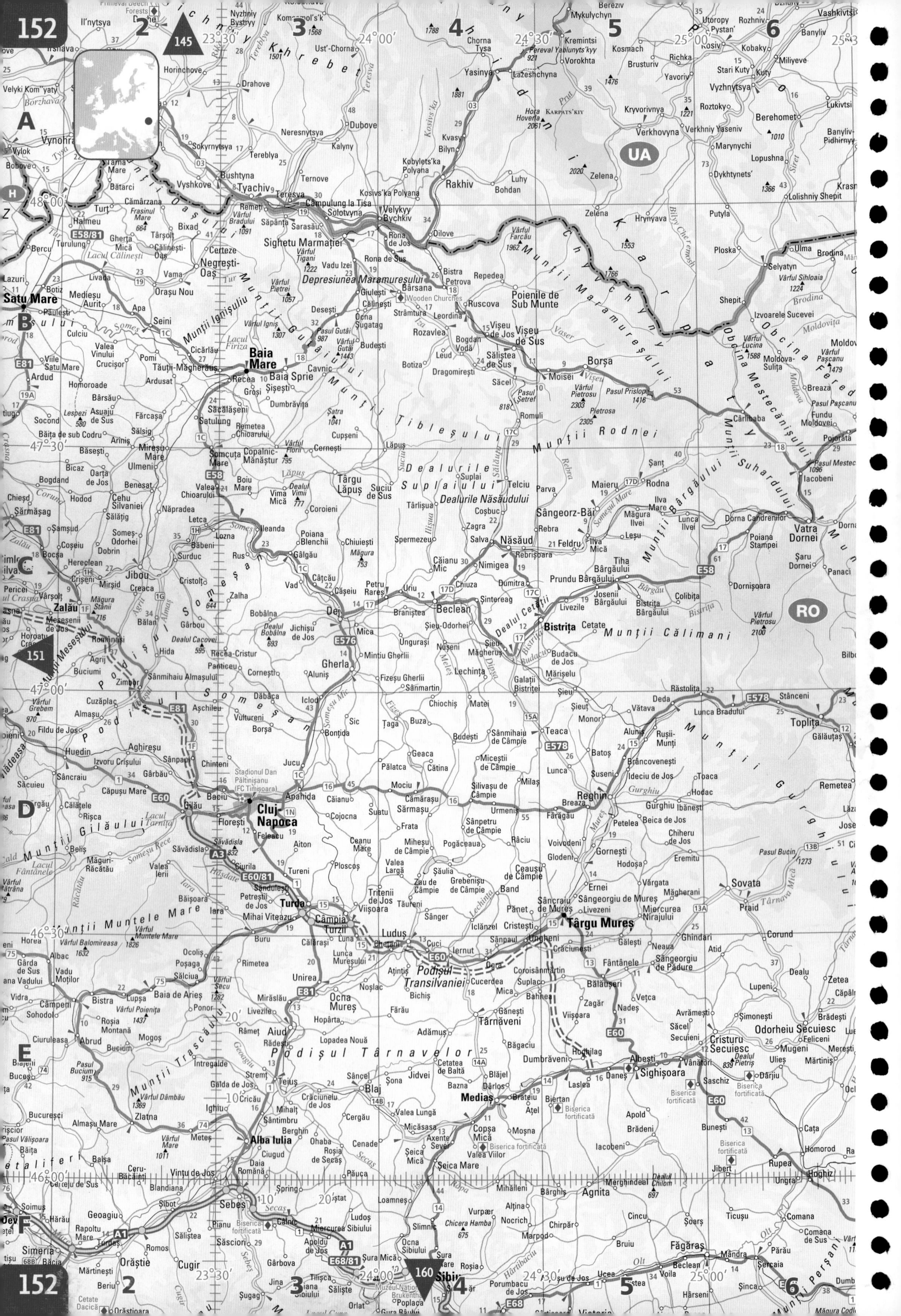

152
UA
RO
H
Satu Mare
Baia Mare
Sighetu Marmației
Negrești-Oaș
Rakhiv
Tyachiv
Yasinya
Verkhovyna
Vyzhnytsya
Borșa
Vișeu de Sus
Năsăud
Bistrița
Dej
Gherla
Beclean
Zalău
Jibou
Cluj-Napoca
Huedin
Turda
Câmpia Turzii
Luduș
Târgu Mureș
Reghin
Toplița
Vatra Dornei
Sovata
Sighișoara
Mediaș
Blaj
Alba Iulia
Aiud
Sebeș
Sibiu
Făgăraș
Odorheiu Secuiesc
Cristuru Secuiesc
Agnita
Rupea
Orăștie
Simeria
Târnăveni
Zlatna
Munții Rodnei
Munții Călimani
Munții Gurghiului
Munții Gilăului
Munții Trascăului
Munții Muntele Mare
Podișul Transilvaniei
Podișul Târnavelor
Depresiunea Maramureșului
Dealurile Năsăudului
Munții Țibleșului
Munții Maramureșului
Munții Suhardului
Munții Bârgăului
Obcina Mestecănișului
Hora Hoverla 2061
E58
E81
E60
E576
E578
A1
A3
151
145
160
47°30′
47°00′
46°30′
46°00′
23°30′
24°00′
24°30′
25°00′

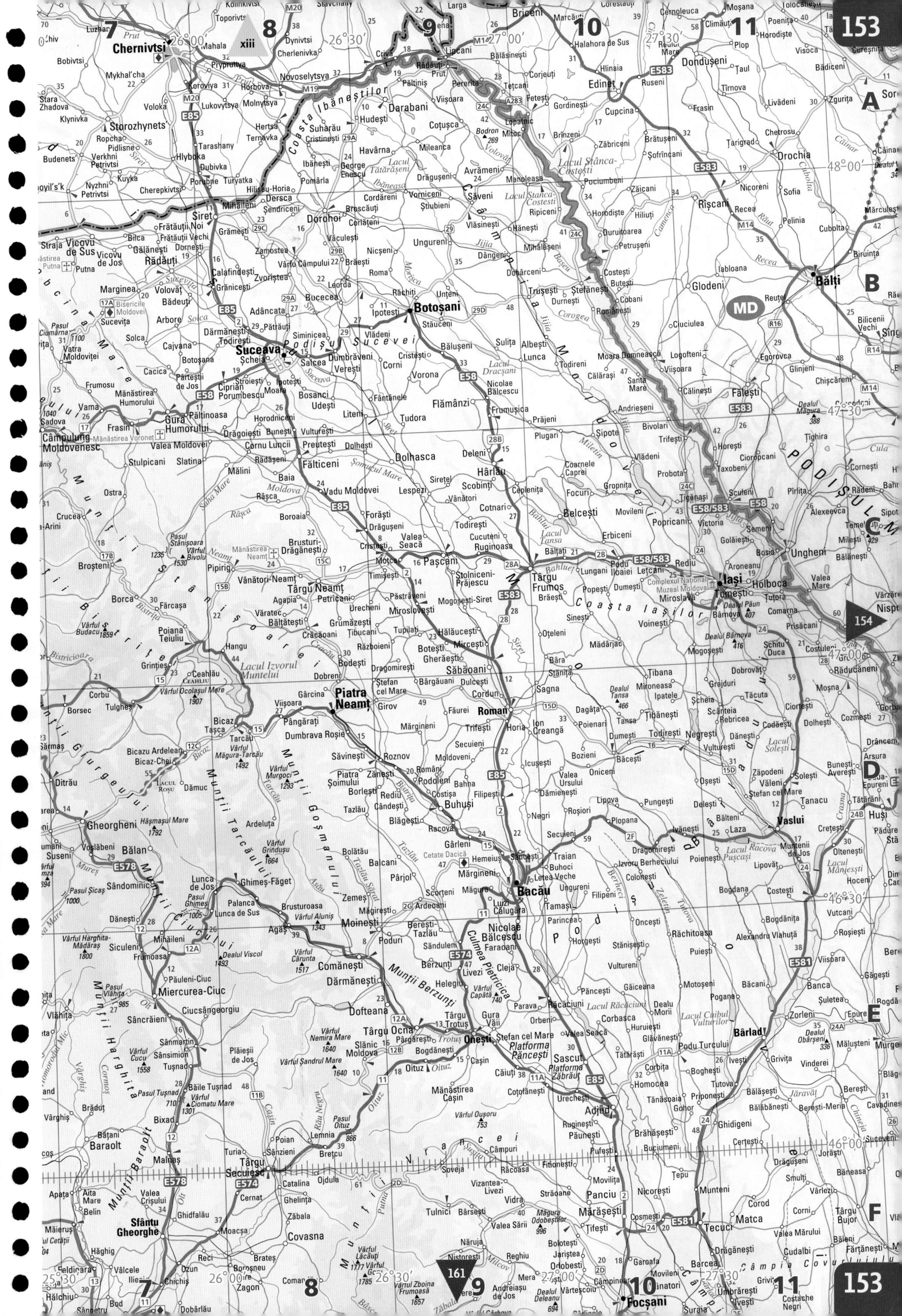
153
7
8
9
10
11
Chernivtsi
Storozhynets'
Siret
Rădăuți
Suceava
Botoșani
Dorohoi
Darabani
Săveni
Edineț
Dondușeni
Drochia
Rîșcani
Bălți
Glodeni
Fălești
MD
Ungheni
Iași
Târgu Frumos
Pașcani
Fălticeni
Gura Humorului
Câmpulung Moldovenesc
Vatra Moldoviței
Târgu Neamț
Piatra Neamț
Roman
Hârlău
Bicaz
Ceahlău
Lacul Izvorul Muntelui
Gheorgheni
Miercurea-Ciuc
Sfântu Gheorghe
Baraolt
Covasna
Târgu Secuiesc
Târgu Ocna
Onești
Moinești
Comănești
Bacău
Buhuși
Vaslui
Huși
Bârlad
Adjud
Tecuci
Mărășești
Focșani
Podișul Sucevei
Câmpia Jijiei
Coasta Iașilor
Podișul Central Moldovenesc
Podișul Bârladului
Munții Stânișoarei
Munții Tarcăului
Munții Goșmanului
Munții Ciucului
Munții Harghita
Munții Vrancei
Munții Berzunți
Culmea Pietricica
E58
E85
E583
E574
E578
E581
A
B
C
D
E
F
154
161
48°00'
47°30'
47°00'
46°30'
46°00'
26°00'
26°30'
27°00'
27°30'

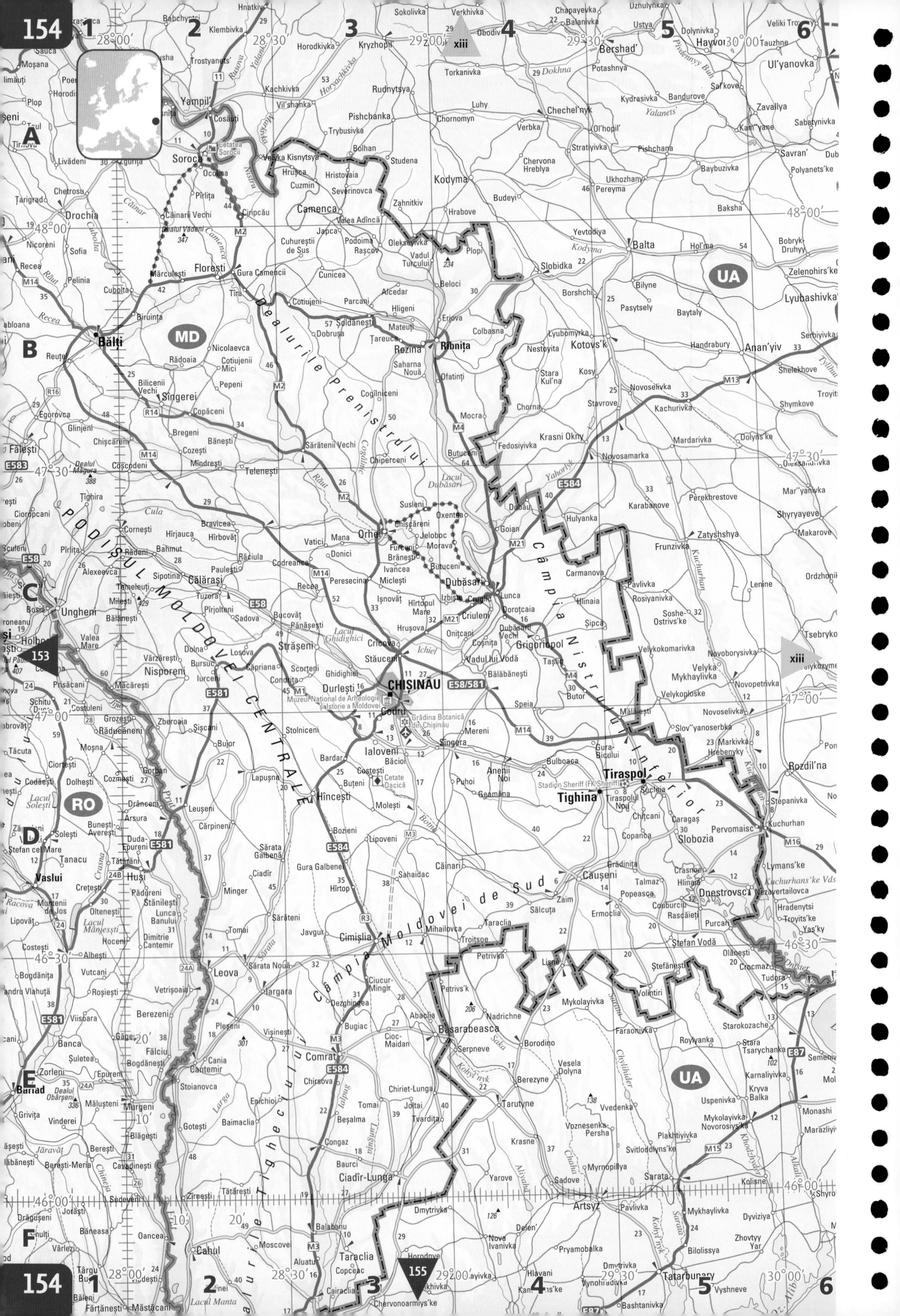

MD
UA
RO
Bălți
Soroca
Florești
Drochia
Sîngerei
Fălești
Ungheni
Nisporeni
Călărași
Orhei
Rezina
Rîbnița
Dubăsari
Grigoriopol
CHIȘINĂU
Strășeni
Ialoveni
Hîncești
Anenii Noi
Tiraspol
Tighina
Slobozia
Căușeni
Ștefan Vodă
Cimișlia
Leova
Basarabeasca
Comrat
Ciadîr-Lunga
Taraclia
Cahul
Cantemir
Huși
Vaslui
Bârlad
Kodyma
Balta
Kotovs'k
Bershad'
Yampil'
Anan'yiv
Rozdil'na
Artsyz
Tatarbunary
Dealurile Prenistrului
PODIȘUL MOLDOVEI CENTRALE
Câmpia Nistrului Inferior
Câmpia Moldovei de Sud
Dealurile Tigheciului
Lacul Dubăsari
Muzeul Național de Arheologie și Istorie a Moldovei
Grădina Botanică din Chișinău
Stadion Sheriff (FK Sheriff)
Cetate Dacică
Cetatea Sorocii
153
155
xiii
28°00'
28°30'
29°00'
29°30'
30°00'
48°00'
47°30'
47°00'
46°30'
46°00'

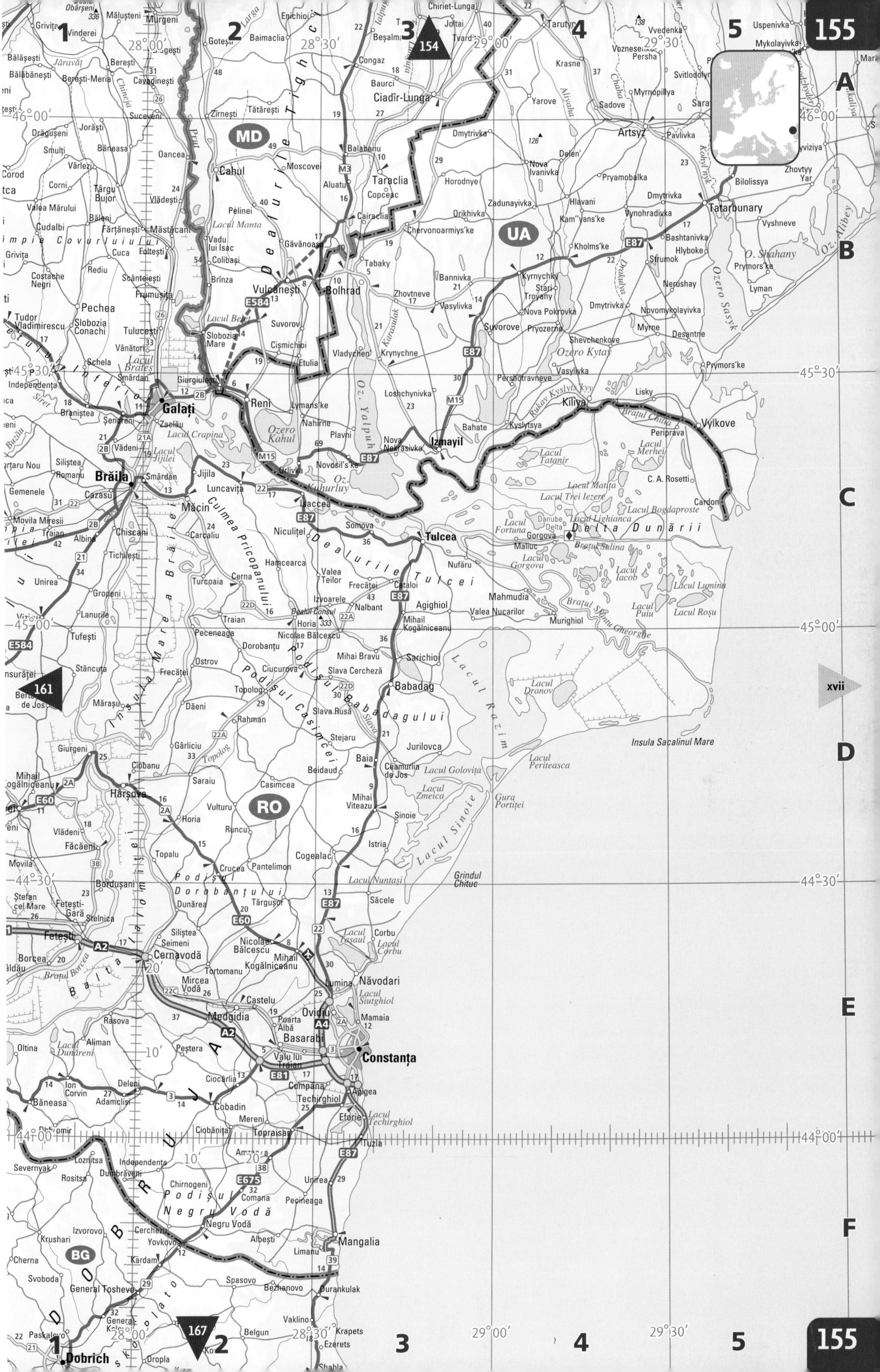
1
2
3
4
5
A
B
C
D
E
F
154
161
167
xvii
MD
UA
RO
BG
28°00′
28°30′
29°00′
29°30′
46°00′
45°30′
45°00′
44°30′
44°00′
Obârșeni
Mălușteni
Murgeni
Grivița
Vinderei
Gotești
Baimaclia
Enichioi
Beșalma
Chiriet-Lunga
Joltai
Tvardița
Tarutyno
Vvedenka
Uspenivka
Mykolayivka
Bălăști
Bălăbănești
Berești
Berești-Meria
Cavadinești
Congaz
Baurci
Ciadîr-Lunga
Krasne
Vozneseńka
Persha
Svitlodolyns'ke
Yarove
Sadove
Myrnopillya
Artsyz
Pavlivka
Zîrnești
Tătărești
Suceveni
Drăgușeni
Jorăști
Smulți
Băneasa
Oancea
Cahul
Moscovei
Balabanu
Taraclia
Copceac
Aluatu
Dmytrivka
Nova Ivanivka
Delen'
Pryamobalka
Horodnyye
Zadunayivka
Hlavani
Vynohradivka
Tatarbunary
Dmytrivka
Bilolissya
Zhovtyy Yar
Corod
Corni
Târgu Bujor
Vlădești
Valea Mărului
Cudalbi
Băleni
Fârțănești
Măstăcani
Pelinei
Lacul Manta
Cairaclia
Chervonoarmiys'ke
Orikhivka
Kam"yans'ke
Vyshneve
Bashtanivka
Hlyboke
O. Shahany
Prymors'ke
Grivița
Cuca
Folteşti
Vadu lui Isac
Colibași
Găvănoasa
Tabaky
Kholms'ke
Strumok
Rediu
Costache Negri
Scânteiești
Frumușița
Brînza
Vulcănești
Bolhrad
Bannivka
Vasylivka
Zhovtneve
Kyrnychky
Stari Troyany
Nova Pokrovka
Dmytrivka
Nerushay
Lyman
Pechea
Tudor Vladimirescu
Slobozia Conachi
Tulucești
Vânători
Lacul Beleu
Slobozia Mare
Suvorov
Cișmichioi
Etulia
Vladychen'
Krynychne
Suvorove
Pryozerne
Shevchenkove
Myrne
Desantne
Novomykolayivka
Ozero Sasyk
Ozero Kytay
Schela
Lacul Brateș
Smârdan
Independența
Giurgiulești
Galați
Reni
Lymans'ke
Nahirne
Ozero Kahul
Oz. Yalpuh
Loshchynivka
Pershotravneve
Vasylivka
Prymors'ke
Kiliya
Lisky
Vylkove
Periprava
Brănistea
Șendreni
Zaclău
Lacul Crapina
Plavni
Nova Nekrasivka
Izmayil
Bahate
Kyslytsya
Brațul Chilia
Lacul Merhei
Lacul Tatanir
C. A. Rosetti
Cardon
Văden i
Lacul Jijilei
Silistea
Romanu
Brăila
Smârdan
Jijila
Luncavița
Isaccea
Orlivka
Novosil's'ke
Oz. Kuhurluy
Lacul Matița
Lacul Trei Iezere
Lacul Bogdaproste
Gemenele
Cazasu
Măcin
Culmea Pricopanului
Lacul Fortuna
Danube Delta
Lacul Lighianca
Delta Dunării
Gorgova
Movila Miresii
Traian
Albina
Chiscani
Carcaliu
Niculițel
Somova
Tulcea
Dealurile Tulcei
Malluc
Brațul Sulina
Lacul Gorgova
Tichilești
Unirea
Gropeni
Hamcearca
Valea Teilor
Frecăței
Cataloi
Nufăru
Lacul Iacob
Lacul Lumina
Turcoaia
Cerna
Izvoarele
Nalbant
Agighiol
Mahmudia
Valea Nucarilor
Brațul Sfântu Gheorghe
Lacul Puiu
Lacul Roșu
Lanurile
Traian
Dealul Consul
Horia
Mihai Kogălniceanu
Murighiol
Tufești
Peceneaga
Dorobanțu
Nicolae Bălcescu
Mihai Bravu
Sarichioi
Insula Mare a Brăilei
Ostrov
Ciucurova
Slava Cercheză
Babadag
Lacul Razim
Lacul Dranov
Stăncuța
Frecăței
Topolog
Podișul Babadagului
Slava Rusă
Podișul Casimcei
Mărașu
Dăeni
Rahman
Stejaru
Jurilovca
Insula Sacalinul Mare
Giurgeni
Gârliciu
Baia
Ceamurlia de Jos
Lacul Golovița
Lacul Periteasca
Mihail Kogălniceanu
Ciobanu
Saraiu
Beidaud
Casimcea
Lacul Zmeica
Gura Portiței
Hârșova
Vulturu
Mihai Viteazu
Sinoie
Vlădeni
Horia
Runcu
Lacul Sinoie
Făcăeni
Istria
Movila
Topalu
Cogealac
Crucea
Pantelimon
Lacul Nuntași
Grindul Chituc
Bordușani
Podișul Dorobanțului
Săcele
Ștefan cel Mare
Fetești-Gară
Dunărea
Târgușor
Stelnica
Siliștea
Seimeni
Lacul Tașaul
Corbu
Lacul Corbu
Fetești
Nicolae Bălcescu
Mihail Kogălniceanu
Cernavodă
Borcea
Brațul Borcea
Balta Ialomiței
Tortomanu
Lumina
Năvodari
Mircea Vodă
Lacul Siutghiol
Castelu
Medgidia
Poarta Albă
Ovidiu
Mamaia
Rasova
Basarabi
Aliman
Lacul Dunăreni
Oltina
Peștera
Valu lui Traian
Constanța
Ciocârlia
Cumpăna
Agigea
Ion Corvin
Deleni
Adamclisi
Băneasa
Cobadin
Techirghiol
Mereni
Eforie
Lacul Techirghiol
Dobromir
Ciobănița
Topraisar
Tuzla
Loznitsa
Independenta
Dumbrăveni
Severnyak
Rositsa
Amzacea
Chirnogeni
Podișul Negru Vodă
Comana
Pecineaga
Negru Vodă
Krushari
Izvorovo
Cerchezu
Yovkovo
Albești
Mangalia
Limanu
Cherna
Kardam
Svoboda
General Toshevo
Spasovo
Bezhanovo
Durankulak
Dobrudja
General Kolevo
Vaklino
Paskalevo
Belgun
Krapets
Ezerets
Dobrich
Dropla
Shabla
E87
E584
E60
E675
E81
M3
M15
A2
A4

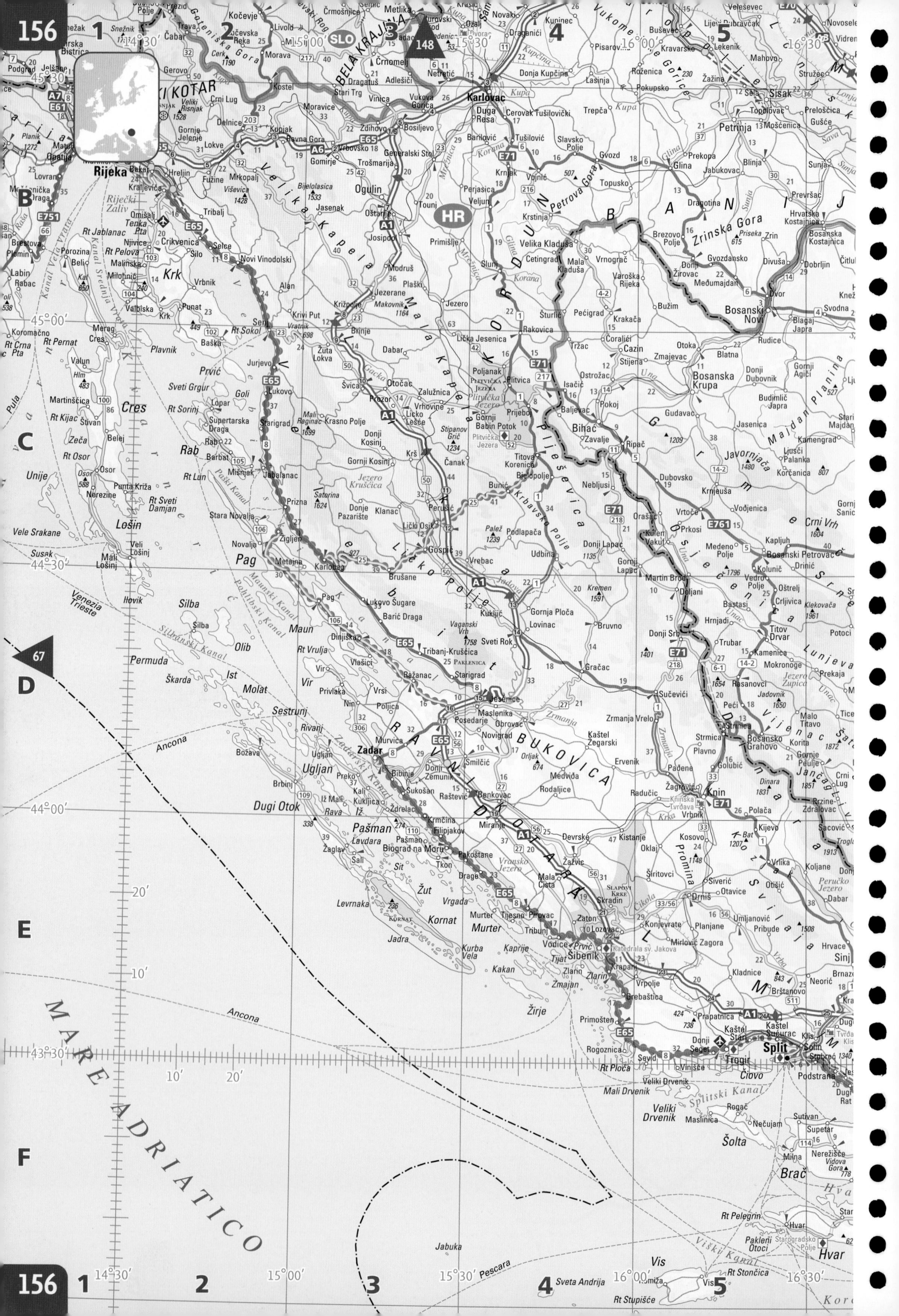
1
2
3
4
5
B
C
D
E
F
148
67
SLO
HR
14°30′
15°00′
15°30′
16°00′
16°30′
45°30′
45°00′
44°30′
44°00′
43°30′
20′
10′
MARE ADRIATICO
Venezia Trieste
Ancona
Pescara
Rijeka
Karlovac
Sisak
Petrinja
Glina
Ogulin
Duga Resa
Delnice
Čabar
Kočevje
Črnomelj
Metlika
Netretić
Vinica
Vukova Gorica
Bosiljevo
Vrbovsko
Ravna Gora
Gomirje
Generalski Stol
Trošmarija
Josipdol
Oštarije
Tounj
Slunj
Veljun
Vojnić
Krnjak
Topusko
Gvozd
Lasinja
Pokupsko
Kravarsko
Velika Kladuša
Cetingrad
Mala Kladuša
Vrnograč
Bužim
Bosanski Novi
Dvor
Bosanska Kostajnica
Hrvatska Kostajnica
Dobrljin
Rakovica
Cazin
Bosanska Krupa
Bihać
Ripač
Zavalje
Plitvice
Plitvička Jezera
Korenica
Bjelopolje
Udbina
Donji Lapac
Martin Brod
Kulen Vakuf
Drvar
Bosansko Grahovo
Knin
Drniš
Sinj
Split
Trogir
Kaštel Stari
Kaštel Sućurac
Solin
Podstrana
Primošten
Rogoznica
Šibenik
Skradin
Vodice
Pirovac
Tisno
Murter
Drage
Pakoštane
Biograd na Moru
Pašman
Benkovac
Obrovac
Zadar
Nin
Vir
Privlaka
Posedarje
Maslenica
Jasenice
Starigrad
Karlobag
Gospić
Perušić
Otočac
Brinje
Senj
Novi Vinodolski
Crikvenica
Kraljevica
Bakar
Opatija
Krk
Cres
Lošinj
Mali Lošinj
Veli Lošinj
Rab
Pag
Novalja
Silba
Olib
Ist
Molat
Ugljan
Dugi Otok
Kornat
Žut
Kaprije
Žirje
Zlarin
Čiovo
Šolta
Brač
Hvar
Vis
Jabuka
Sveta Andrija
Krka
Una
Kupa
Korana
Zrmanja
Velika Kapela
Mala Kapela
Kordun
Ravni Kotari
Bukovica
Lika
Ličko Polje
Krbavsko polje
Plješevica
Velebit
Dinara
Gorski Kotar
Zrinska Gora
Petrova Gora
Grmeč
Kvarner
Kvarnerić
Riječki Zaliv
Paški Kanal
Velebitski Kanal
Zadarski Kanal
Splitski Kanal
Viški Kanal
Katedrala sv. Jakova
Kninska Tvrđava
Paklenica
E65
E71
E61
E751
E761
A1
A6
A7

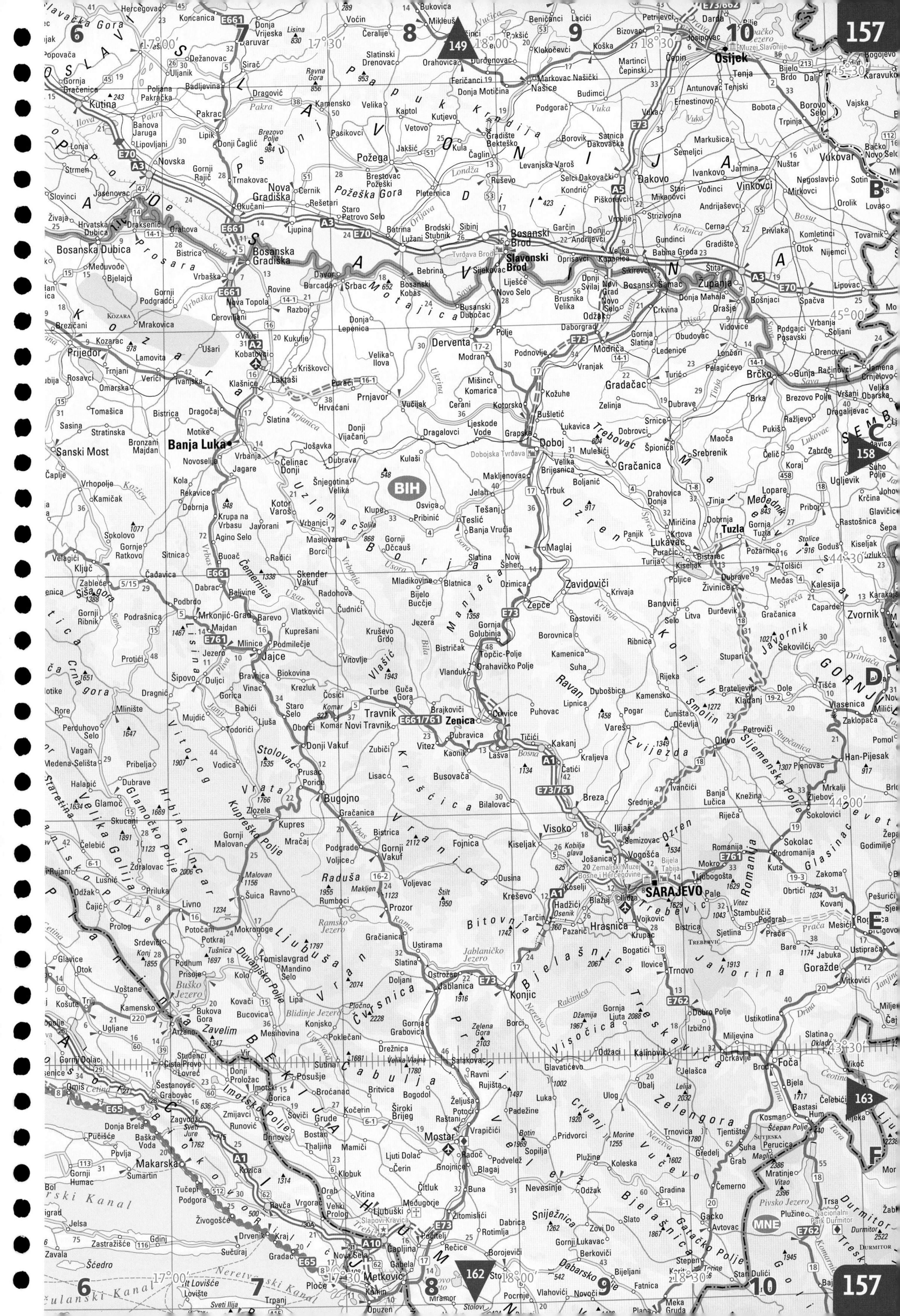
Osijek
Vukovar
Vinkovci
Đakovo
Našice
Požega
Nova Gradiška
Slavonski Brod
Bosanski Brod
Bosanska Gradiška
Bosanska Dubica
Kutina
Daruvar
Pakrac
Novska
Županja
Bosanski Šamac
Derventa
Doboj
Prijedor
Banja Luka
Sanski Most
Gradačac
Brčko
Tuzla
Zvornik
Zavidovići
Teslić
Jajce
Travnik
Zenica
Kakanj
Visoko
SARAJEVO
Hrasnica
Bugojno
Kupres
Livno
Tomislavgrad
Jablanica
Konjic
Mostar
Čapljina
Metković
Ploče
Makarska
Omiš
Imotski
Posušje
Široki Brijeg
Ljubuški
Međugorje
Nevesinje
Gacko
Foča
Goražde
Višegrad
Vlasenica
Kladanj
Olovo
Srebrenik
Maglaj
Lukavac
Vareš
Breza
Bijeljina
Bosnia
BIH
MNE
S L A V O N I J A
P o s a v i n a
D a l m a c i j a
Durmitor
Dobojska Tvrđava
Zemaljski Muzej Bosne i Hercegovine
Muzej Slavonije
E73
E661
E70
E65
E761
E762
A1
A3
A5
6
7
8
9
10
B
C
D
E
F
149
158
162
163
17°00'
17°30'
18°00'
18°30'
45°30'
45°00'
44°30'
44°00'
43°30'

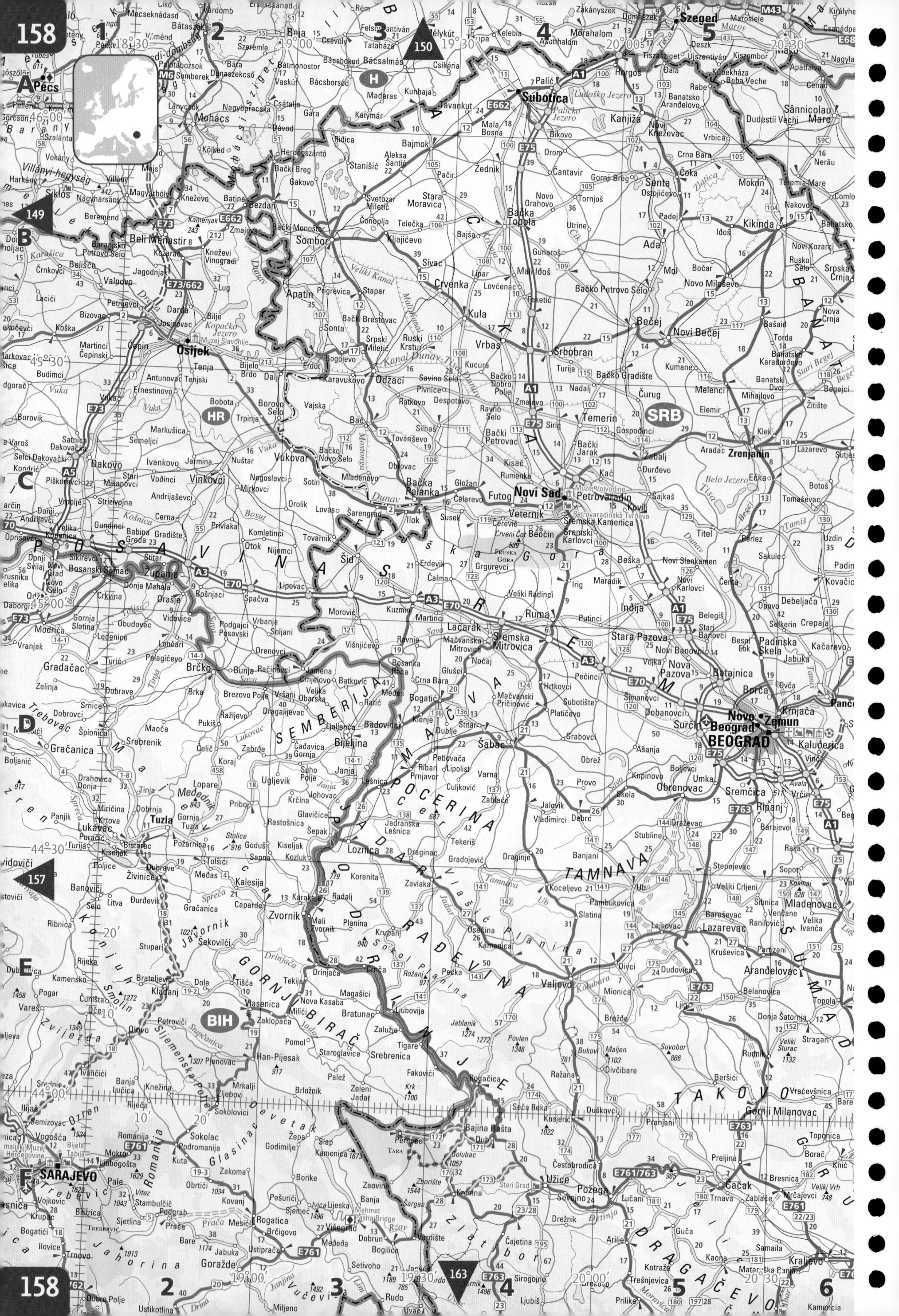

Pécs
Mohács
Szeged
Baja
Subotica
Sombor
Apatin
Osijek
Beli Manastir
Vukovar
Vinkovci
Đakovo
Bačka Topola
Kula
Vrbas
Srbobran
Bečej
Novi Bečej
Senta
Ada
Kikinda
Zrenjanin
Temerin
Novi Sad
Petrovaradin
Sremski Karlovci
Bačka Palanka
Ilok
Šid
Ruma
Inđija
Sremska Mitrovica
Stara Pazova
Nova Pazova
Batajnica
Novo Beograd
Zemun
BEOGRAD
Obrenovac
Šabac
Bijeljina
Brčko
Tuzla
Lukavac
Gračanica
Zvornik
Loznica
Valjevo
Lazarevac
Mladenovac
Aranđelovac
Ub
Ljubovija
Srebrenica
Bajina Bašta
Užice
Požega
Čačak
Kraljevo
Gornji Milanovac
Višegrad
Rogatica
Goražde
SARAJEVO
Vlasenica
Kladanj
Olovo
HR
BIH
SRB
H
POSAVINA
SEMBERIJA
MAČVA
POCERINA
JADAR
PODRINJE
RAĐEVINA
GORNJI BIRAČ
TAMNAVA
TAKOVO
ŠUMADIJA
DRAGAČEVO
BANAT
BAČKA
SREM
Fruška Gora
Dunav
Sava
Drina
Tisa
A1
A3
E70
E75
E73
E662
E761
E763
149
150
157
163

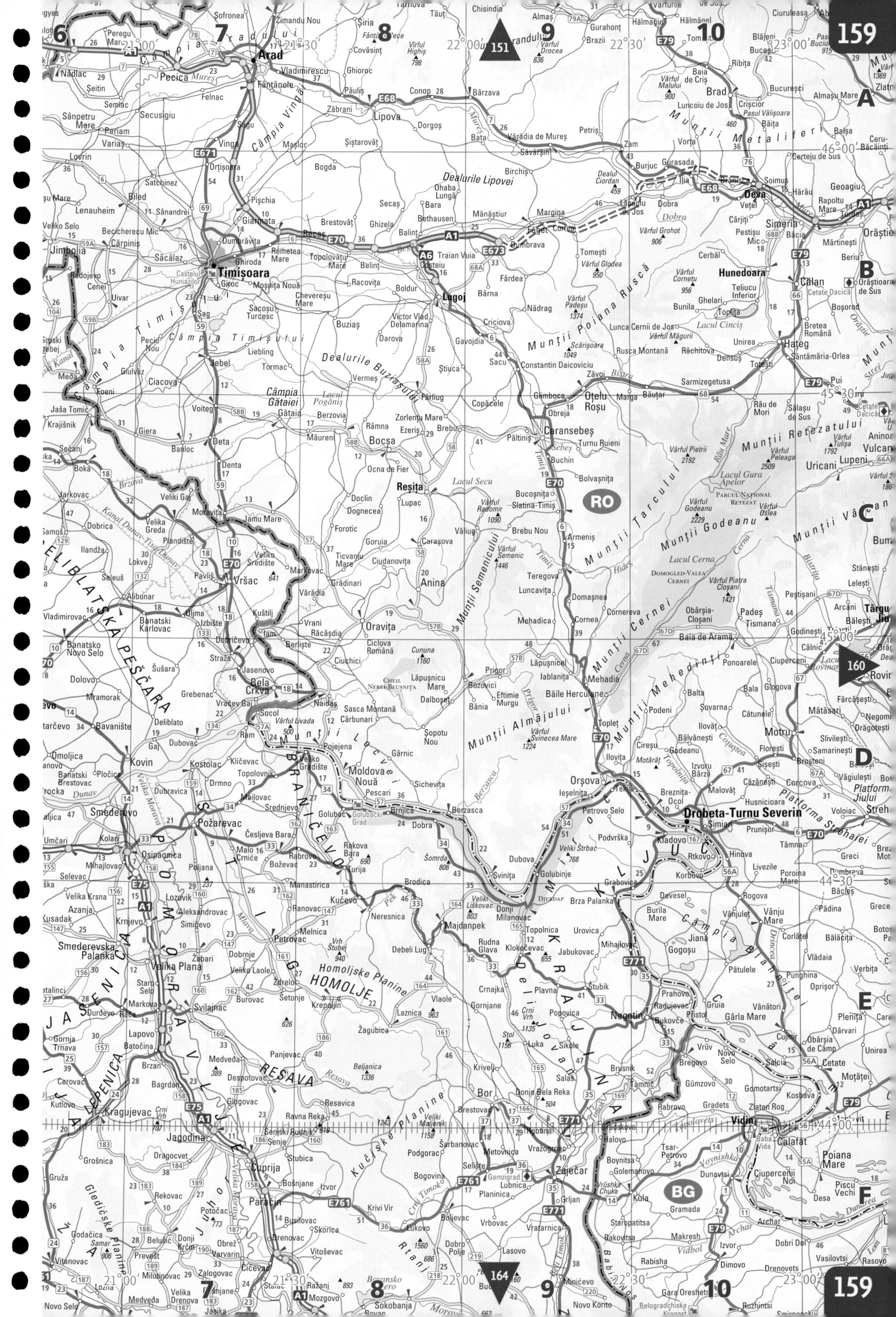

151
160
164
6
7
8
9
10
A
B
C
D
E
F
RO
BG
Arad
Timișoara
Lipova
Lugoj
Deva
Hunedoara
Brad
Simeria
Orăștie
Hațeg
Caransebeș
Reșița
Oravița
Anina
Bocșa
Orșova
Drobeta-Turnu Severin
Vršac
Bela Crkva
Kovin
Smederevo
Požarevac
Veliko Gradište
Moldova Nouă
Golubac
Majdanpek
Negotin
Kladovo
Zaječar
Bor
Paraćin
Ćuprija
Jagodina
Kragujevac
Velika Plana
Smederevska Palanka
Vidin
Calafat
Kula
Băile Herculane
Mehadia
Oțelu Roșu
Făget
Jimbolia
Sânnicolau Mare
Pecica
Munții Poiana Ruscă
Munții Țarcului
Munții Godeanu
Munții Retezatului
Munții Cernei
Munții Mehedinți
Munții Almăjului
Munții Semenicului
Munții Locvei
Munții Metaliferi
Dealurile Lipovei
Dealurile Buziașului
Câmpia Timișului
Câmpia Vingăi
Câmpia Aradului
Câmpia Blahniței
Platforma Strehaiei
Deliblatska Peščara
Homoljske Planine
Kučajske Planine
Braničevo
Ključ
Krajina
Homolje
Resava
Pomoravlje
Lepenica
Jasenica
Lacul Secu
Lacul Cerna
Lacul Gura Apelor
Lacul Cinciș
Parcul Național Retezat
Domogled-Valea Cernei
Cheile Nerei-Beușnița
Djerdap

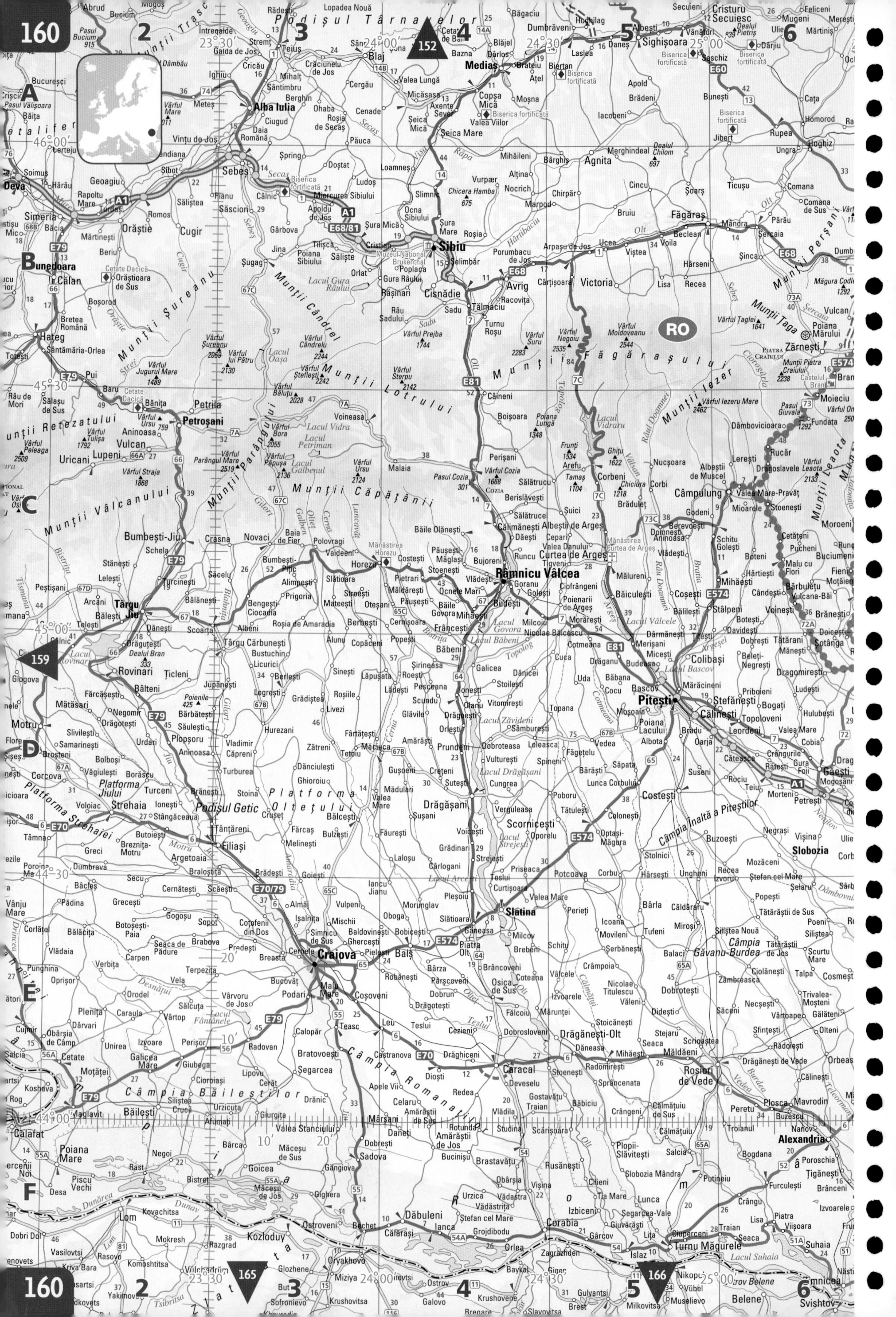
Munţii Trascău
Podişul Târnavelor
Alba Iulia
Blaj
Mediaş
Sighişoara
Deva
Simeria
Hunedoara
Orăştie
Sebeş
Cugir
Sibiu
Cisnădie
Avrig
Făgăraş
Victoria
Agnita
Rupea
Hoghiz
Zărneşti
Haţeg
Petroşani
Petrila
Vulcan
Lupeni
Uricani
Munţii Şureanu
Munţii Cândrel
Munţii Lotrului
Munţii Făgăraşului
Munţii Iezer
Munţii Perşani
Munţii Leaota
Munţii Retezatului
Munţii Vâlcanului
Munţii Parângului
Munţii Căpăţânii
Vârful Moldoveanu 2544
Vârful Negoiu 2535
RO
Câmpulung
Curtea de Argeş
Râmnicu Vâlcea
Horezu
Novaci
Bumbeşti-Jiu
Târgu Jiu
Rovinari
Motru
Piteşti
Mioveni
Găeşti
Costeşti
Drăgăşani
Slatina
Balş
Craiova
Filiaşi
Podişul Getic
Platforma Olteţului
Platforma Jiului
Platforma Strehaiei
Strehaia
Câmpia Înaltă a Piteştilor
Câmpia Găvanu-Burdea
Câmpia Romanaţiului
Câmpia Băileştilor
Băileşti
Calafat
Caracal
Drăgăneşti-Olt
Roşiori de Vede
Alexandria
Corabia
Turnu Măgurele
Dăbuleni
Lom
Kozloduy
Oryakhovo
Nikopol
Belene
Svishtov
Dunărea
Dunav
A1
E68
E79
E81
E574
E70
Biserica fortificată

152
159
165
166

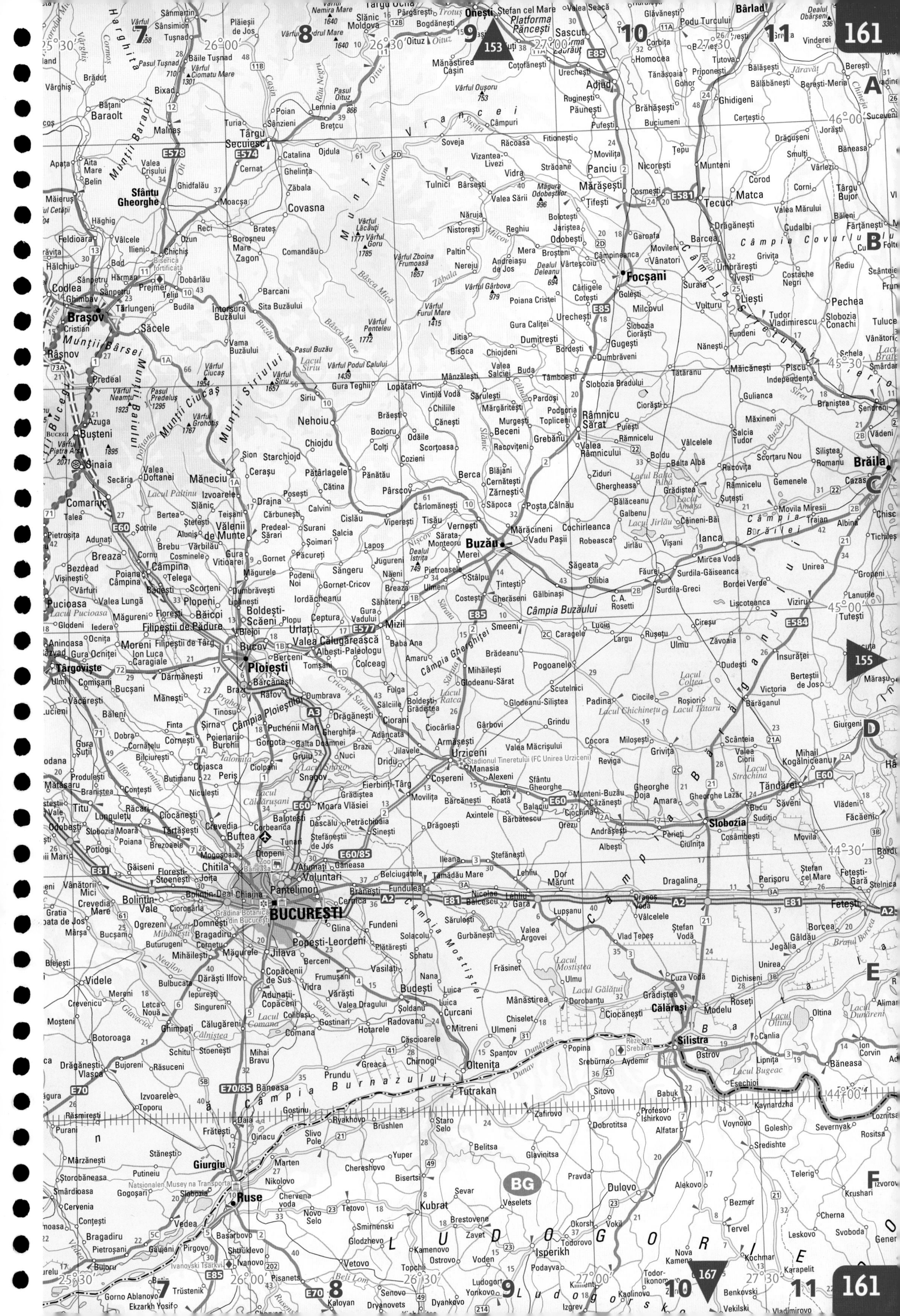

153
155
167
Brașov
Sfântu Gheorghe
Târgu Secuiesc
Covasna
Onești
Adjud
Focșani
Mărășești
Tecuci
Bârlad
Râmnicu Sărat
Buzău
Brăila
Ploiești
Câmpina
Vălenii de Munte
Mizil
Urziceni
Slobozia
Țăndărei
Fetești
Călărași
Silistra
Oltenița
Tutrakan
Giurgiu
Ruse
BUCUREȘTI
Târgoviște
Sinaia
Bușteni
Predeal
Râșnov
Codlea
Pucioasa
Titu
Budești
Fundulea
Lehliu Gara
Făurei
Ianca
Pogoanele
Dulovo
Kubrat
Isperikh
Kaynardzha
BG
Munții Vrancei
Munții Siriului
Munții Ciucaș
Munții Baiului
Munții Bârsei
Munții Baraolt
Harghita
Bucegi
Câmpia Covurlui
Câmpia Siretului Inferior
Câmpia Brăilei
Câmpia Bărăganului
Câmpia Buzăului
Câmpia Ploieștilor
Câmpia Gherghiței
Câmpia Mostiștei
Câmpia Burnazului
Balta Ialomiței
Ludogorie
Ludogorsko
Dunărea
Dunav
E85
E60
E81
E70
E577
E578
E574
E581
E584
A2
A3
7
8
9
10
11
25°30'
26°00'
26°30'
27°00'
27°30'
46°00'
45°30'
45°00'
44°30'
44°00'
A
B
C
D
E
F

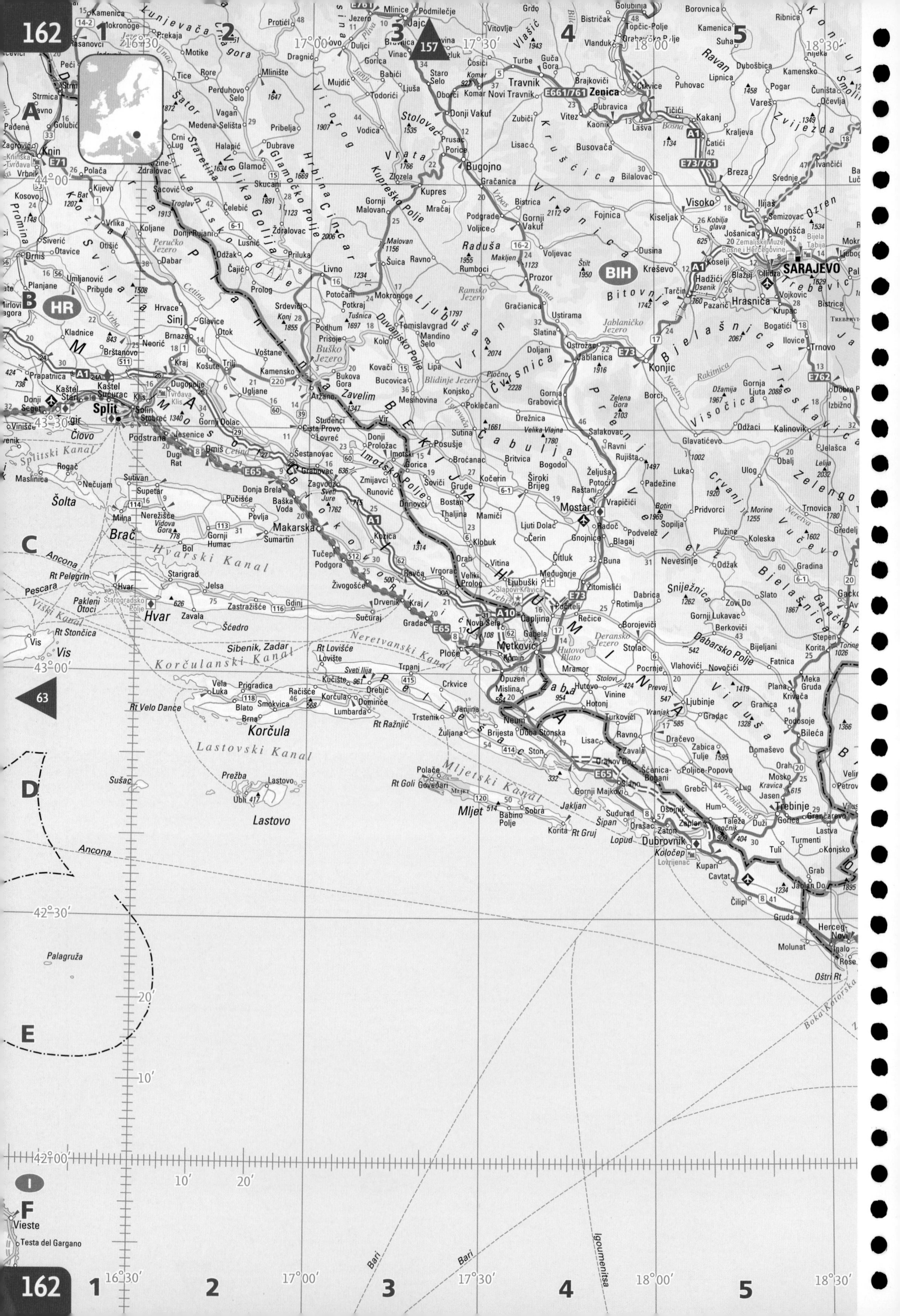

1
2
3
4
5
A
B
C
D
E
F
157
63
HR
BIH
I
16°30′
17°00′
17°30′
18°00′
18°30′
44°00′
43°30′
43°00′
42°30′
42°00′
Kamenica
Mokronoge
Prekaja
Rasanovci
Peći
Strmica
Ravno
Golubić
Knin
Kninska Tvrđava
Vrbnik
Polača
Kijevo
Kosovo
Promina
Siverić
Otavice
Drniš
Planjane
Umljanović
Pribude
Kladnice
Bršt anovo
Prapatnica
Kaštel Stari
Kaštel Sućurac
Donji Seget
Split
Solin
Stobreč
Klis
Tvrđava Klis
Dugopolje
Podstrana
Jesenice
Dugi Rat
Omiš
Čiovo
Splitski Kanal
Rogač
Nečujam
Maslinica
Šolta
Sutivan
Supetar
Pučišće
Milna
Nerežišće
Brač
Bol
Gornji Humac
Hvarski Kanal
Ancona
Rt Pelegrin
Pescara
Hvar
Pakleni Otoci
Starogradsko Polje
Starigrad
Jelsa
Zavala
Zastražišće
Gdinj
Šćedro
Viški Kanal
Rt Stončica
Vis
Korčulanski Kanal
Sibenik, Zadar
Vela Luka
Prigradica
Blato
Smokvica
Račišće
Korčula
Lumbarda
Brna
Rt Velo Dance
Lastovski Kanal
Sušac
Prežba
Lastovo
Ubli
Palagruža
Vieste
Testa del Gargano
Cetina
Sinj
Hrvace
Glavice
Otok
Neorić
Brnaze
Trilj
Košute
Kraj
Ugljane
Gornji Dolac
Lovreć
Studenci
Cista Provo
Šestanovac
Grabovac
Zagvozd
Sveti Jure
Baška Voda
Donja Brela
Makarska
Tučepi
Podgora
Živogošće
Drvenik
Sućuraj
Gradac
Kozica
Ravča
Vrgorac
Imotski
Runović
Zmijavci
Proložac
Posušje
Grude
Drinovci
Vir
Zavelim
Aržano
Kamensko
Voštane
Bukova Gora
Kovači
Bucovica
Mesihovina
Konjsko
Lipa
Tomislavgrad
Mandino Selo
Duvanjsko Polje
Buško Jezero
Prisoje
Podhum
Livno
Potočani
Potkraj
Tušnica
Mokronoge
Ravno
Šuica
Kupres
Zlosela
Vrata
Gornji Malovan
Kupreško Polje
Glamoč
Skucani
Dubrave
Pribelja
Medena-Selišta
Halapić
Vagan
Perduhovo Selo
Motike
Tice
Rore
Mliništa
Dragnić
Protići
Šator
Crni Lug
Grkovci
Zdralovac
Sacović
Troglav
Čelebić
Koljane
Donji Rujani
Lusnić
Odžak
Čajić
Peručko Jezero
Dabar
Prolog
Priluka
Ždralovac
Livanjsko Polje
Staretina
Cincar
Hrbina
Glamočko Polje
Velika Golija
Vitorog
Jezero
Duljci
Mlinice
Podmilečje
Jajce
Vinac
Gorica
Babići
Mujdić
Todorići
Ljuša
Vodica
Staro Selo
Oborci
Donji Vakuf
Stolovac
Prusac
Bugojno
Gračanica
Vrbas
Podgrade
Voljice
Gornji Vakuf
Bistrica
Raduša
Makljen
Rumboci
Prozor
Ramsko Jezero
Gračianica
Ustirama
Slatina
Doljani
Ostrožac
Jablanica
Jablaničko Jezero
Konjic
Čvrsnica
Vran
Ljubuša
Blidinje Jezero
Plocno
Pokleani
Drežnica
Gornja Grabovica
Čabulja
Sutina
Britvica
Bogodol
Široki Brijeg
Kočerin
Broćanac
Soviči
Bostan
Thaljina
Mamiči
Klobuk
Orah
Vitina
Ljubuški
Međugorje
Čitluk
Ljuti Dolac
Čerin
Gnojnica
Mostar
Radoč
Blagaj
Buna
Žitomislići
Počitelj
Čapljina
Nova Sela
Gabela
Metković
Komin
Ploče
Hutovo Blato
Opuzen
Mislina
Rečice
Rotimlja
Dabrica
Stolac
Deransko Jezero
Pocrnje
Mramor
Hutovo
Vinine
Hotonj
Neum
Duba Stonska
Brijesta
Janjina
Trstenik
Žuljana
Pelješac
Orebić
Dominče
Kučište
Lovište
Rt Lovišće
Trpanj
Crkvice
Rt Ražnjić
Neretvanski Kanal
Ston
Lisac
Ravno
Zavala
Turkovići
Slano
Dračevo
Zabica
Tulje
Poljice-Popovo
Šćenica-Bobani
Gornji Majkovi
Mljetski Kanal
Polače
Rt Goli
Goveđari
Mljet
Babino Polje
Sobra
Korita
Rt Gruj
Jakljan
Šipan
Lopud
Sudurad
Orašac
Zaton
Osojnik
Dubrovnik
Koločep
Lovrijenac
Kupari
Cavtat
Čilipi
Gruda
Molunat
Herceg Novi
Igalo
Rose
Oštri Rt
Boka Kotorska
Trebinje
Jasen
Mosko
Orah
Duži
Taleža
Hum
Grebci
Lug
Zaplanik
Lastva
Turmenti
Konjsko
Tuli
Grab
Jablan Do
Domaševo
Bileća
Podosoje
Granica
Gradac
Ljubinje
Vidoša
Kriváča
Plana
Meka Gruda
Fatnica
Bijeljani
Berkovići
Gornji Lukavac
Zovi Do
Slato
Dabarsko Polje
Vlahovići
Novčići
Borojevići
Nevesinje
Odžak
Pridvorci
Sopilja
Podveležje
Velež
Pluzine
Koleska
Gradina
Bjelašnica
Gatačko Polje
Snježnica
Trnovica
Crvanj
Zelengora
Ulog
Obalj
Jelašca
Kalinovik
Odžaci
Glavatičevo
Luka
Padežine
Borci
Visočica
Treskavica
Izbično
Dobro Polje
Trnovo
Ilovice
Bogatići
Rakitnica
Bjelašnica
Džamija
Gornja Ljuta
Krupac
Vojkovic
Hrasnica
Pazarić
Tarčin
Hadžići
Koselji
Blažuj
Ilidža
SARAJEVO
Trebević
Bistrica
Kiseljak
Kobilja glava
Jošanica
Vogošća
Ilijaš
Semizovac
Visoko
Ozren
Bijela Tabija
Zemaljski Muzej Bosne i Hercegovine
Kreševo
Dusina
Fojnica
Bitovnja
Vranica
Voljevac
Štilt
Bilalovac
Busovača
Breza
Srednje
Kaonik
Lašva
Kakanj
Bosna
Tičići
Kraljeva
Čatići
Zvijezda
Vareš
Pogar
Lipnica
Dubošbica
Kamensko
Čunište
Očevlja
Puhovac
Čakvice
Dubravica
Vitez
Zenica
Brajkovići
Zubići
Lisac
Kruščica
Travnik
Novi Travnik
Komar
Turbe
Guča Gora
Čosići
Vlašić
Vitovlje
Grdo
Bistričak
Golubinja
Topčić-Polje
Vlanduk
Borovnica
Kamenica
Suha
Ribnica
Ravan
Konjuh
Ivančići
Moštre
Bari
Igoumenitsa
E65
E71
E73
E73/761
E661/761
E762
A1
A10

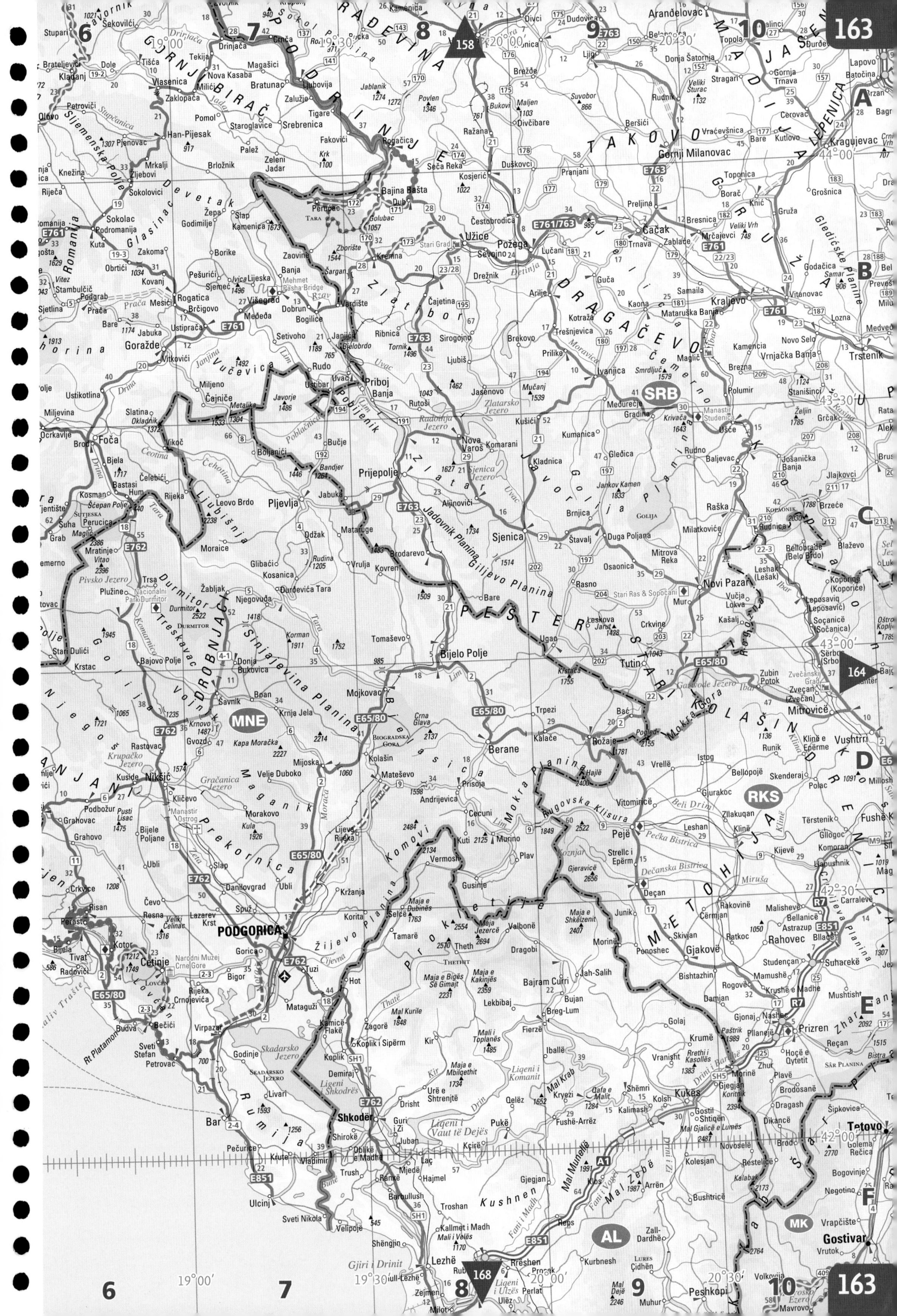
6
7
8
9
10
A
B
C
D
E
F
158
164
168
19°00'
19°30'
20°00'
20°30'
44°00'
43°30'
43°00'
42°30'
42°00'
SRB
MNE
RKS
AL
MK
PODGORICA
Šavornik
Šekovići
Stupari
Kladanj
Olovo
Vlasenica
Milići
Nova Kasaba
Bratunac
Ljubovija
Srebrenica
Drinjača
Zvornik
Krupanj
Kamenica
Divci
Dudovica
Aranđelovac
Topola
Batočina
Lapovo
Kragujevac
Ljig
Rudnik
Gornji Milanovac
Takovo
Šumadija
Jasenica
Lepenica
Gornja Trnava
Stragari
Vraćevšnica
Kutlovo
Bare
Cerovac
Toponica
Grošnica
Knić
Gruža
Borač
Čačak
Preljina
Trnava
Zablaće
Mrčajevci
Kraljevo
Vitanovac
Lozna
Samaila
Mataruška Banja
Kaona
Guča
Arilje
Lučani
Požega
Užice
Kosjerić
Čestobrodica
Sevojno
Drežnik
Dragačevo
Ivanjica
Prilike
Čemerno
Maglič
Brezna
Polumir
Vrnjačka Banja
Novo Selo
Trstenik
Stanišinci
Grčak
Međurečje
Gradina
Manastir Studenica
Ušće
Baljevac
Rudno
Raška
Jošanička Banja
Jlajkovci
Brzeće
Kušići
Kumanica
Gleđica
Golija
Sjenica
Štavalj
Duga Poljana
Mitrova Reka
Osaonica
Novi Pazar
Leshak (Lešak)
Bellobradë (Belo Brdo)
Blaževo
Koporiqë (Koporiće)
Leposaviq (Leposavić)
Soçanicë (Sočanica)
Rasna
Stari Ras & Sopoćani
Mur
Vučja Lokva
Kašalj
Crkvine
Leskova Jaruga
Ugao
Tutin
Pešter
Stari Kolašin
Zubin Potok
Zveçan (Zvečan)
Mitrovicë
Vushtrri
Runik
Klinë e Epërme
Skenderaj
Polac
Istog
Vrellë
Bellopojë
Gjurakoc
Vitomiricë
Pejë
Zllakuqan
Leshan
Klinë
Tërstenik
Fushë Kosova
Glllogoc
Komoran
Llapushnik
Kijevë
Strellc i Epërm
Deçan
Rakovinë
Malishevë
Carralevë
Bellanicë
Astrazup
Çermjan
Junik
Skivjan
Ponoshec
Gjakovë
Ratkoc
Rahovec
Bllacë
Studençan
Suharekë
Mamushë
Bishtazhin
Rogovë
Krushë e Madhe
Mushtisht
Gjonaj
Nashec
Prizren
Planejë
Pastrik
Reçan
Hoçë e Qytetit
Zhur
Plavë
Brodosanë
Dragash
Šipkovica
Tetovo
Dikancë
Brod
Golema Rečica
Restelicë
Bogovinje
Negotino
Gostivar
Vrapčište
Vrutok
Novosele
Kolesjan
Bushtricë
Krumë
Vranisht
Morinë
Gjegjan
Kukës
Kolsh
Shëmri
Kalimash
Gostil
Shtiqën
Kruje
Arrën
Zall-Dardhë
Çidhën
Kurbnesh
Peshkopi
Volkovija
Mavrovo
Muhur
Fushë-Arrëz
Qelëz
Pukë
Kryezi
Mal Munellë
Mal Zebë
Klos
Reps
Rrëshen
Kushnen
Gjegjan
Troshan
Kallmet i Madh
Lezhë
Zejmen
Milot
Ulëz
Perlat
Shëngjin
Velipojë
Barbullush
Hajmel
Mjedë
Ranxë
Laç
Trush
Shkodër
Shirokë
Guri i Zi
Juban
Kçirë
Drisht
Urë e Shtrenjtë
Vau i Dejës
Koplik
Koplik i Sipërm
Demiraj
Kamicë-Flakë
Zagorë
Kir
Iballë
Fierzë
Golaj
Breg-Lum
Bujan
Bajram Curri
Jah-Salih
Lekbibaj
Dragobi
Valbonë
Theth
Tamarë
Selcë
Korita
Hot
Tuzi
Mataguži
Vladimir
Krute
Ulcinj
Sveti Nikola
Pečurice
Bar
Rumija
Virpazar
Godinje
Livari
Skadarsko Jezero
Petrovac
Sveti Stefan
Budva
Bečići
Rijeka Crnojevića
Cetinje
Lovćen
Kotor
Tivat
Radovići
Bijela
Perast
Risan
Crkvice
Grahovo
Grahovac
Podbožur
Nikšić
Kuside
Rastovac
Krnovo
Gvozd
Šavnik
Boan
Krnja Jela
Mojkovac
Kolašin
Mateševo
Andrijevica
Berane
Prisoja
Murino
Plav
Gusinje
Vermosh
Komovi
Prokletije
Mokra Planina
Rugovska Klisura
Rožaje
Kalače
Trpezi
Bać
Bijelo Polje
Tomaševo
Pljevlja
Prijepolje
Jabuka
Mataruge
Brodarevo
Vrulja
Kovren
Odžak
Glibaći
Kosanica
Đurđevića Tara
Žabljak
Njegovuđa
Durmitor
Pluzine
Trsa
Vitao
Šćepan Polje
Foča
Bjela
Čelebići
Bastasi
Rijeka
Leovo Brdo
Ljubišnja
Moraice
Mratinje
Suha
Kosman
Miljevina
Brod
Ustikolina
Goražde
Vitkovići
Jabuka
Ustiprača
Međeđa
Dobrun
Višegrad
Rogatica
Mesići
Brčigovo
Sjemeć
Pešurići
Kovanj
Prača
Sokolac
Podromanija
Romanija
Glasinac
Kuta
Obrtići
Han-Pijesak
Pjenovac
Knežina
Žljebovi
Sokolovici
Mrkalji
Žepa
Godimilje
Kamenica
Slap
Borike
Zaovine
Banja
Šargan
Kremna
Mokra Gora
Bajina Bašta
Perućac
Rogačica
Zlatibor
Čajetina
Sirogojno
Ljubiš
Rutoši
Priboj
Banja
Uvac
Rudo
Ustibar
Pobijenik
Bučje
Bandjer
Boljanići
Nova Varoš
Komarani
Aljinovići
Zlatar
Jadovnik Planina
Giljevo Planina
Javor
Jasenovo
Rudnik
Slatina
Čajniče
Miljeno
Vučevica
Metaljka
Javorje
Sinjajevina Planina
Drobnjaci
Treskavac
Bajovo Polje
Donja Bukovica
Golija
Njegoš
Krstac
Stari Dulići
Vojnik
Kapa Moračka
Bjelasica
Maganik
Prekornica
Morakovo
Velje Duboko
Mijoska
Danilovgrad
Spuž
Lazarev Krst
Ubli
Gorica
Bigor
Kržanja
Žijevo
Čevo
Resna
Bijele Poljane
Ubli
Slap
Klično
Krstac
Lijeva Rijeka
Kuti
Cecuni
Rt Platamon
Gjiri i Drinit
Mal Dejë
Lures
Tara
Drina
Lim
Ibar
Morača
Drin
Zeta
Bune

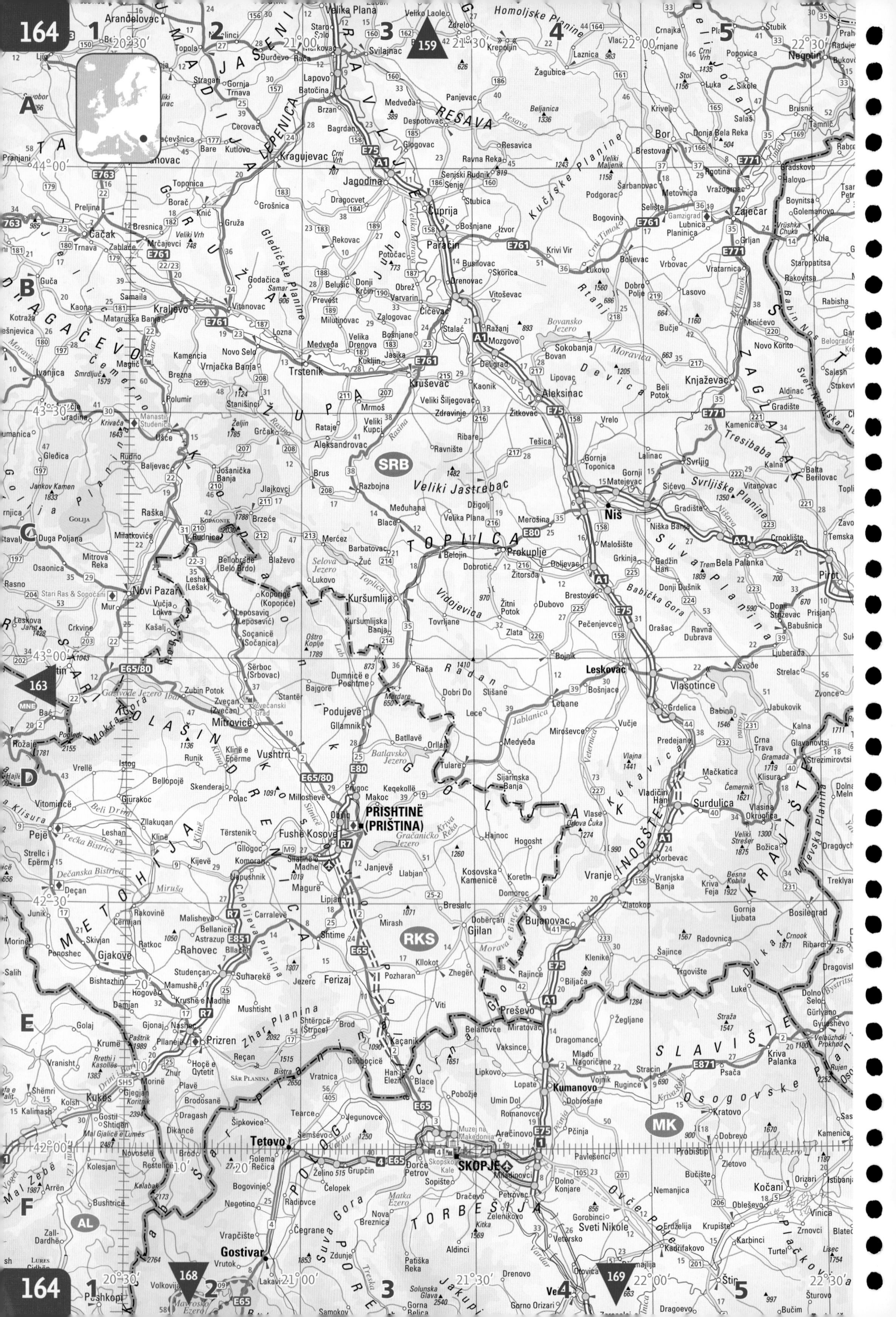

Aranđelovac
Topola
Velika Plana
Svilajnac
Homoljske Planine
Krepoljin
Žagubica
Crnajka
Štubik
Negotin
Kragujevac
Jagodina
Ćuprija
Paraćin
Despotovac
Resava
Resavica
Bor
Zaječar
Gamzigrad
Knjaževac
Čačak
Kraljevo
Vrnjačka Banja
Trstenik
Kruševac
Aleksinac
Sokobanja
Ivanjica
Novi Pazar
Raška
Kopaonik
Brus
Blace
Prokuplje
Niš
Niška Banja
Bela Palanka
Pirot
Kuršumlija
Toplica
Veliki Jastrebac
Leskovac
Vlasotince
Lebane
Medveđa
Surdulica
Vranje
Bujanovac
Preševo
Mitrovicë
Vushtrri
Podujevë
Prishtinë (Priština)
Fushë Kosovë
Gjilan
Ferizaj
Pejë
Deçan
Gjakovë
Rahovec
Suharekë
Prizren
Kukës
Tetovo
Gostivar
Skopje
Kumanovo
Kratovo
Kriva Palanka
Kočani
Sveti Nikole
Štip
Veles
Rožaje
Peshkopi
SRB
RKS
MK
MNE
AL
E75
E80
E761
E763
E771
E65
E65/80
E851
E871
A1
A4
R7
20°30′
21°00′
21°30′
22°00′
22°30′
44°00′
43°30′
43°00′
42°30′
42°00′
1
2
3
4
5
A
B
C
D
E
F
159
163
168
169

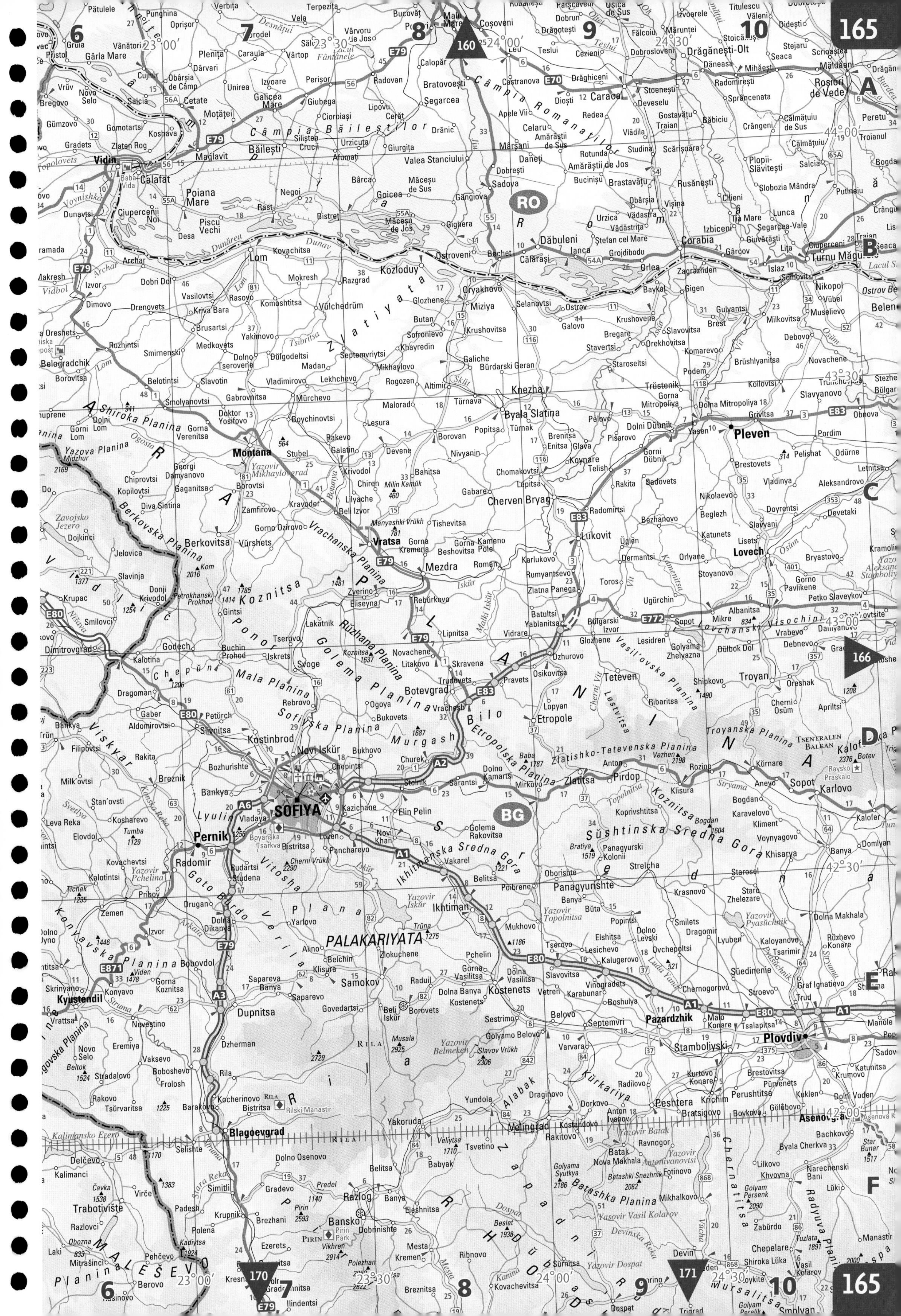

6
7
8
9
10
160
166
170
171
A
B
C
D
E
F
RO
BG
Vidin
Calafat
Băileşti
Caracal
Drăgăneşti-Olt
Roşiori de Vede
Turnu Măgurele
Corabia
Dăbuleni
Lom
Kozloduy
Oryakhovo
Nikopol
Knezha
Byala Slatina
Pleven
Montana
Vratsa
Mezdra
Cherven Bryag
Lukovit
Lovech
Troyan
Teteven
Etropole
Botevgrad
Berkovitsa
Belogradchik
Dimitrovgrad
SOFIYA
Pernik
Radomir
Kostinbrod
Novi Iskŭr
Zlatitsa
Pirdop
Karlovo
Sopot
Samokov
Ikhtiman
Kostenets
Dupnitsa
Kyustendil
Rila
Blagoevgrad
Simitli
Razlog
Bansko
Velingrad
Pazardzhik
Plovdiv
Stamboliyski
Peshtera
Asenovgrad
Panagyurishte
Câmpia Băileştilor
Câmpia Romanaţilor
Zlatiyata
Dunărea
Dunav
Stara Planina
Vrachanska Planina
Koznitsa
Murgash
Etropolska Planina
Zlatishko-Tetevenska Planina
Troyanska Planina
Sŭshtinska Sredna Gora
Ikhtimanska Sredna Gora
Vitosha
Verila
Rila
Pirin
Zapadni Rodopi
Batashka Planina
PALAKARIYATA
Musala 2925
Botev 2376
E79
E70
E83
E80
E871
E772
A1
A2
A3
A6
23°00′
23°30′
24°00′
24°30′
44°00′
43°30′
43°00′
42°30′
42°00′

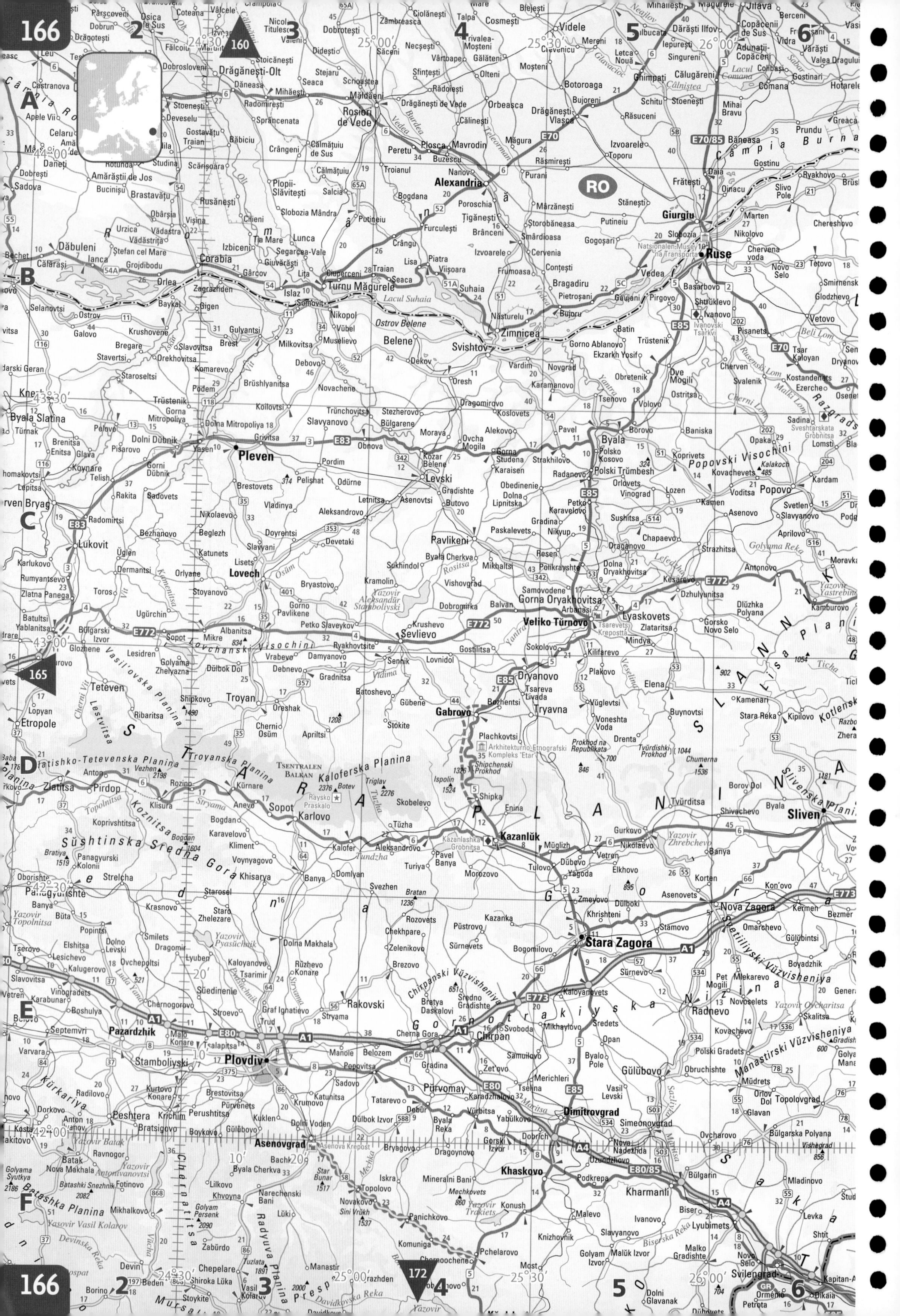
166
RO
Drăgănești-Olt
Roșiori de Vede
Alexandria
Videle
Corabia
Turnu Măgurele
Zimnicea
Giurgiu
Ruse
Nikopol
Svishtov
Belene
Pleven
Levski
Byala
Lovech
Pavlikeni
Gorna Oryakhovitsa
Veliko Tŭrnovo
Lyaskovets
Sevlievo
Troyan
Teteven
Etropole
Gabrovo
Dryanovo
Tryavna
Elena
Lukovit
Cherven Bryag
Popovo
Kazanlŭk
Karlovo
Sopot
Pirdop
Zlatitsa
Shipka
Sliven
Nova Zagora
Stara Zagora
Chirpan
Radnevo
Pazardzhik
Plovdiv
Stamboliyski
Asenovgrad
Peshtera
Rakovski
Pŭrvomay
Dimitrovgrad
Khaskovo
Kharmanli
Simeonovgrad
Svilengrad
Lyubimets
Septemvri
Velingrad
Stara Planina
Sredna Gora
Troyanska Planina
Kaloferska Planina
Zlatishko-Tetevenska Planina
Sŭshtinska Sredna Gora
Chirpanski Vŭzvisheniya
Gornotrakiyska Nizina
Popovski Visochini
Lovchanski Visochini
Manastirski Vŭzvisheniya
Svetiiliyski Vŭzvisheniya
Batashka Planina
Rhodopi
Câmpia Burnas
Câmpia Română
Ostrov Belene
Yazovir Batak
Yazovir Koprinka
Natsionalen Muzey na Transporta
Arkhitekturno-Etnografski Kompleks 'Etar'
Ivanovski Tsarkvi
Asenova Krepost
Tsarevets Krepostta
E70
E83
E85
E772
E773
E80
E80/85
A1
A4
165
160
172
GR
2
3
4
5
6
A
B
C
D
E
F

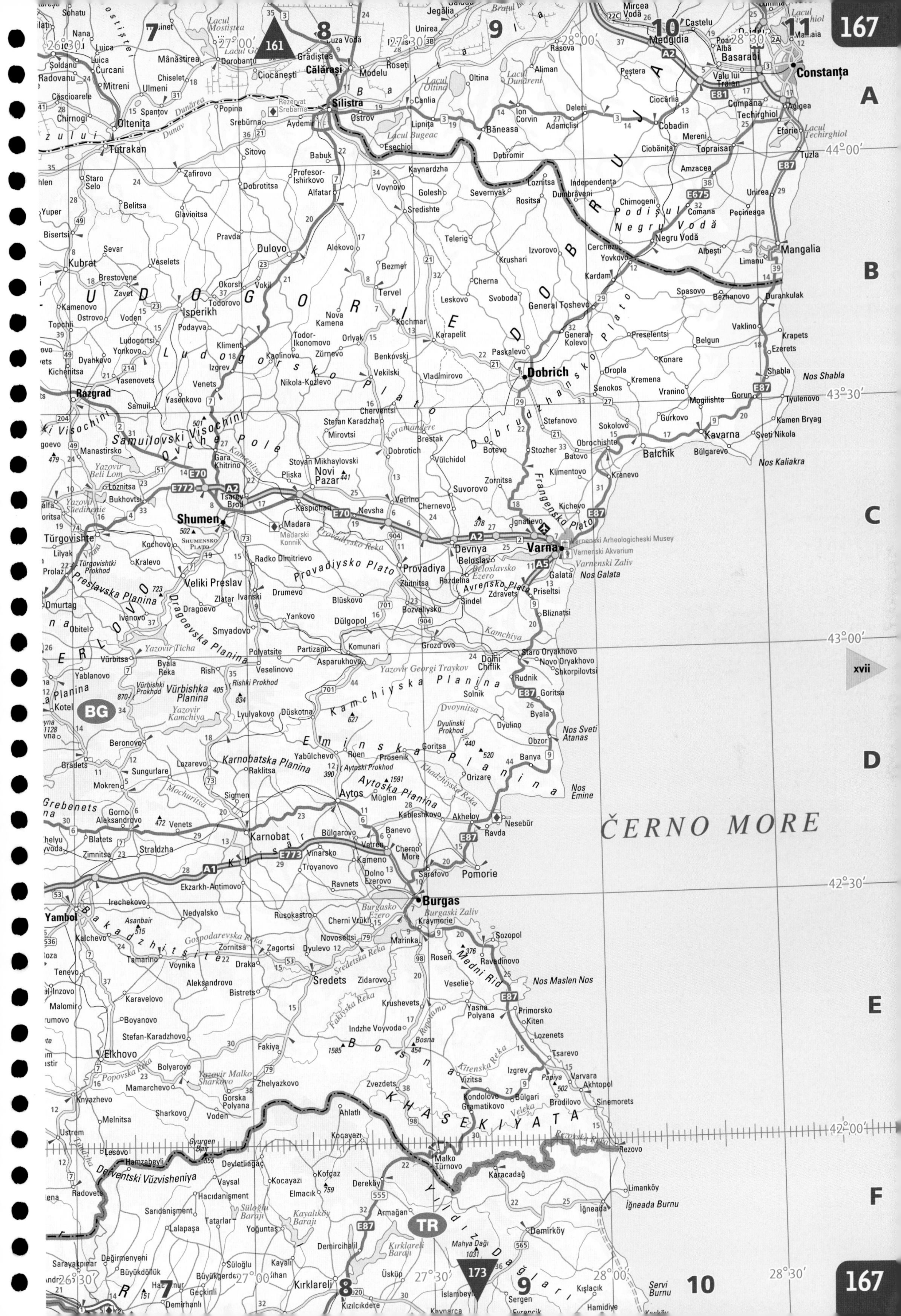

ČERNO MORE
DOBRUJA
LUDOGORIE
Ludogorsko Plato
Provadiysko Plato
Dobrudzhansko Plato
Frangensko Plato
Samuilovski Visochini
Ovche Pole
Preslavska Planina
Dragoevska Planina
Vŭrbishka Planina
Kamchiyska Planina
Eminska Planina
Karnobatska Planina
Aytoska Planina
Bakadzhitsite
Medni Rid
Strandzha
KHASEKIYATA
Dervenstki Vŭzvisheniya
Yıldız Dağları
Podișul Negru Vodă
Constanța
Medgidia
Mangalia
Negru Vodă
Călărași
Silistra
Oltenița
Tutrakan
Dulovo
Isperikh
Razgrad
Kubrat
Tervel
Dobrich
General Toshevo
Balchik
Kavarna
Shabla
Varna
Varnenski Zaliv
Devnya
Provadiya
Shumen
Novi Pazar
Tŭrgovishte
Veliki Preslav
Omurtag
Kotel
Byala
Obzor
Nesebŭr
Pomorie
Aytos
Karnobat
Burgas
Burgaski Zaliv
Sozopol
Sredets
Primorsko
Tsarevo
Akhtopol
Sinemorets
Rezovo
Malko Tŭrnovo
Yambol
Elkhovo
Kırklareli
İğneada
Demirköy
Nos Shabla
Nos Kaliakra
Nos Galata
Nos Sveti Atanas
Nos Emine
Nos Maslen Nos
BG
TR
44°00′
43°30′
43°00′
42°30′
42°00′
26°30′
27°00′
27°30′
28°00′
28°30′
A
B
C
D
E
F
7
8
9
10
11
161
173
xvii

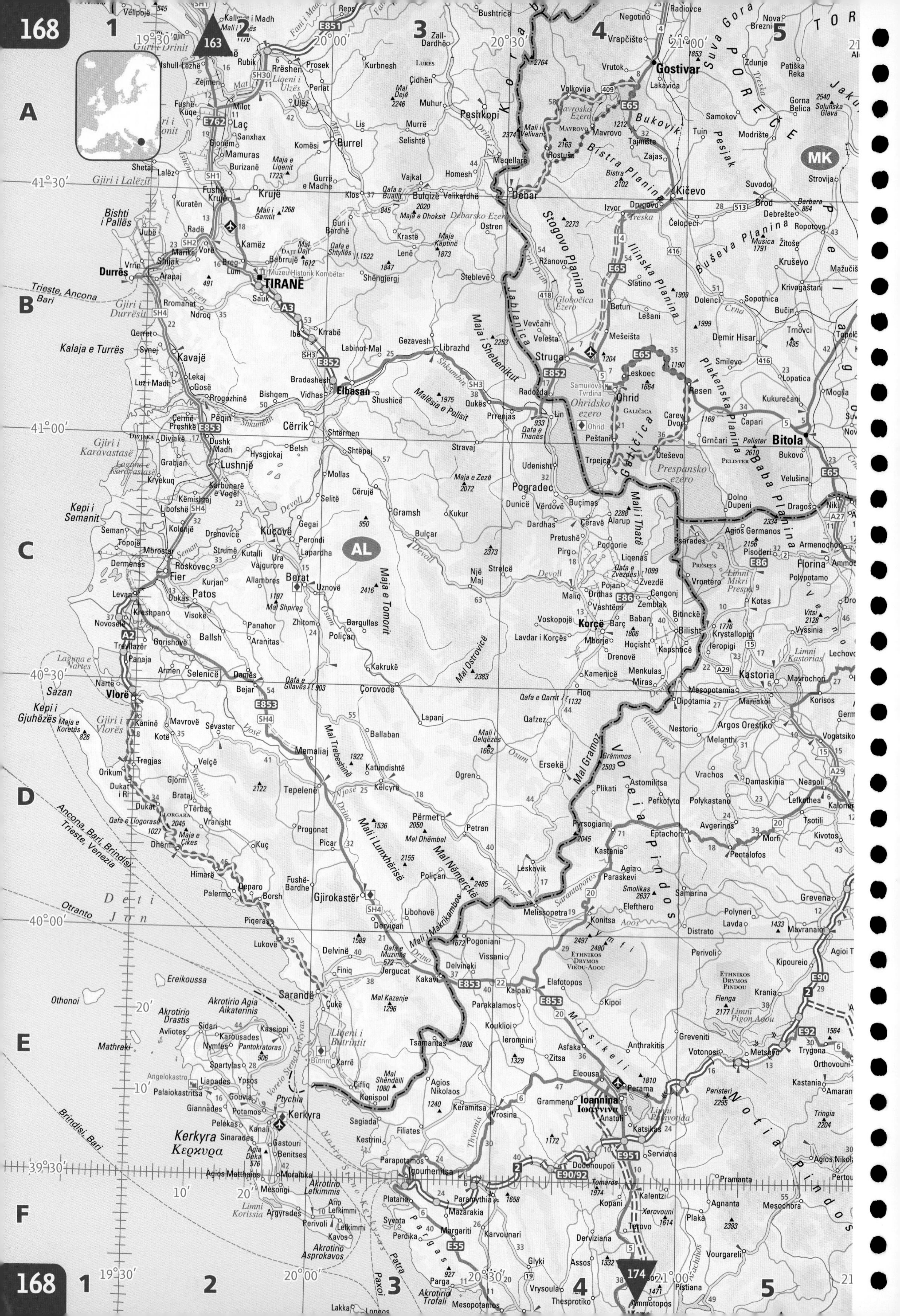
1
2
3
4
5
A
B
C
D
E
F
163
174
MK
AL
TIRANË
Durrës
Kavajë
Elbasan
Librazhd
Lushnjë
Fier
Patos
Berat
Kuçovë
Vlorë
Tepelenë
Gjirokastër
Sarandë
Himarë
Delvinë
Konispol
Kerkyra
Κερκυρα
Igoumenitsa
Ioannina
Ιωαννινα
Konitsa
Korçë
Pogradec
Bilisht
Ersekë
Leskovik
Përmet
Kastoria
Florina
Bitola
Resen
Ohrid
Struga
Debar
Kičevo
Gostivar
Mavrovo
Peshkopi
Burrel
Krujë
Laç
Lezhë
Shëngjergj
Gramsh
Çorovodë
Ballsh
Selenicë
Memaliaj
Kelcyrë
Libohovë
Metsovo
Grevena
Kalpaki
Paramythia
Parga
Margariti
Filiates
Sazan
Othonoi
Ereikoussa
Mathraki
Paxoi
Deti Jon
Ohridsko ezero
Prespansko ezero
Limni Mikri Prespa
Limni Kastorias
Limni Pamvotida
Liqeni i Butrintit
Maja e Tomorit
Mali i Thatë
Mal Gramoz
Vo re i a Pindos
Notia Pindos
Baba Planina
Galičica
Stogovo Planina
Ilinska Planina
Bistra Planina
Plakenska Planina
Suva Gora
Poreče
Jablanica
Korab
Mitsikeli
Grámmos 2503
Smolikas 2637
Trieste, Ancona Bari
Ancona, Bari, Brindisi Trieste, Venezia
Otranto
Brindisi, Bari
Patra
E65
E852
E853
E86
E90
E92
E951
E55
E762
E851
A2
A3
SH1
SH4
19°30′
20°00′
20°30′
21°00′
41°30′
41°00′
40°30′
40°00′
39°30′

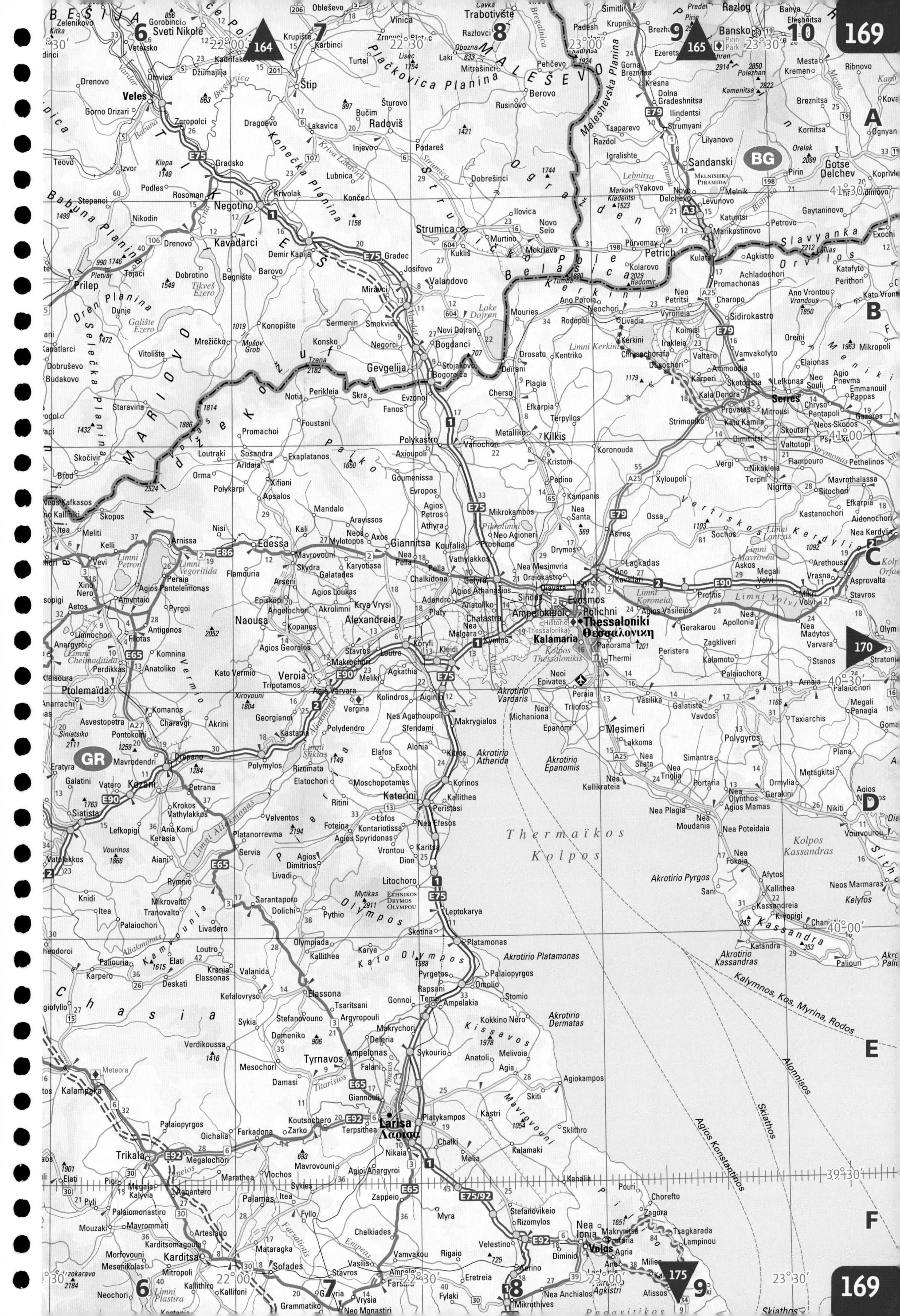
6
7
8
9
10
164
165
170
175
A
B
C
D
E
F
BG
GR
Veleš
Sveti Nikole
Štip
Radoviš
Strumica
Berovo
Pehčevo
Razlog
Bansko
Sandanski
Gotse Delchev
Melnik
Petrich
Kulata
Negotino
Kavadarci
Demir Kapija
Prilep
Valandovo
Gevgelija
Bogdanci
Dojran
Sidirokastro
Serres
Kilkis
Polykastro
Edessa
Giannitsa
Naousa
Alexandreia
Veroia
Ptolemaïda
Kozani
Siatista
Thessaloniki
Θεσσαλονικη
Kalamaria
Ampelokipoi
Evosmos
Polichni
Sindos
Katerini
Litochoro
Elassona
Tyrnavos
Larisa
Λαρισα
Trikala
Kalampaka
Karditsa
Farsala
Volos
Nea Ionia
Almyros
Nea Moudania
Polygyros
Thermi
Lagkadas
Nigrita
Plačkovica Planina
Maleševo
Ogražden
Belasica
Kerkini
Slavyanka
Orvilos
Babuna Planina
Tikveš Ezero
Konečka Planina
Dren Planina
Selečka Planina
Mariovo
Nidže
Kožuf
Paiko
Vermio
Vertiskos
Kerdyli
Limni Kerkini
Lake Dojran
Limni Koroneia
Limni Volvi
Limni Vegoritida
Limni Petron
Thermaïkos Kolpos
Kolpos Thessalonikis
Kolpos Kassandras
Kassandra
Olympos
Kato Olympos
Kissavos
Mavrovouni
Kamvounia
Chasia
Pieria
Meteora
Akrotirio Platamonas
Akrotirio Dermatas
Akrotirio Pyrgos
Akrotirio Kassandras
Akrotirio Epanomis
Akrotirio Atherida
Akrotirio Vardaris
Kalymnos, Kos, Myrina, Rodos
Alonnisos
Skiathos
Agios Konstantinos
E75
E79
E86
E90
E65
E92
E75/92
A25
A27
A3
22°00′
22°30′
23°00′
23°30′
41°30′
41°00′
40°30′
40°00′
39°30′

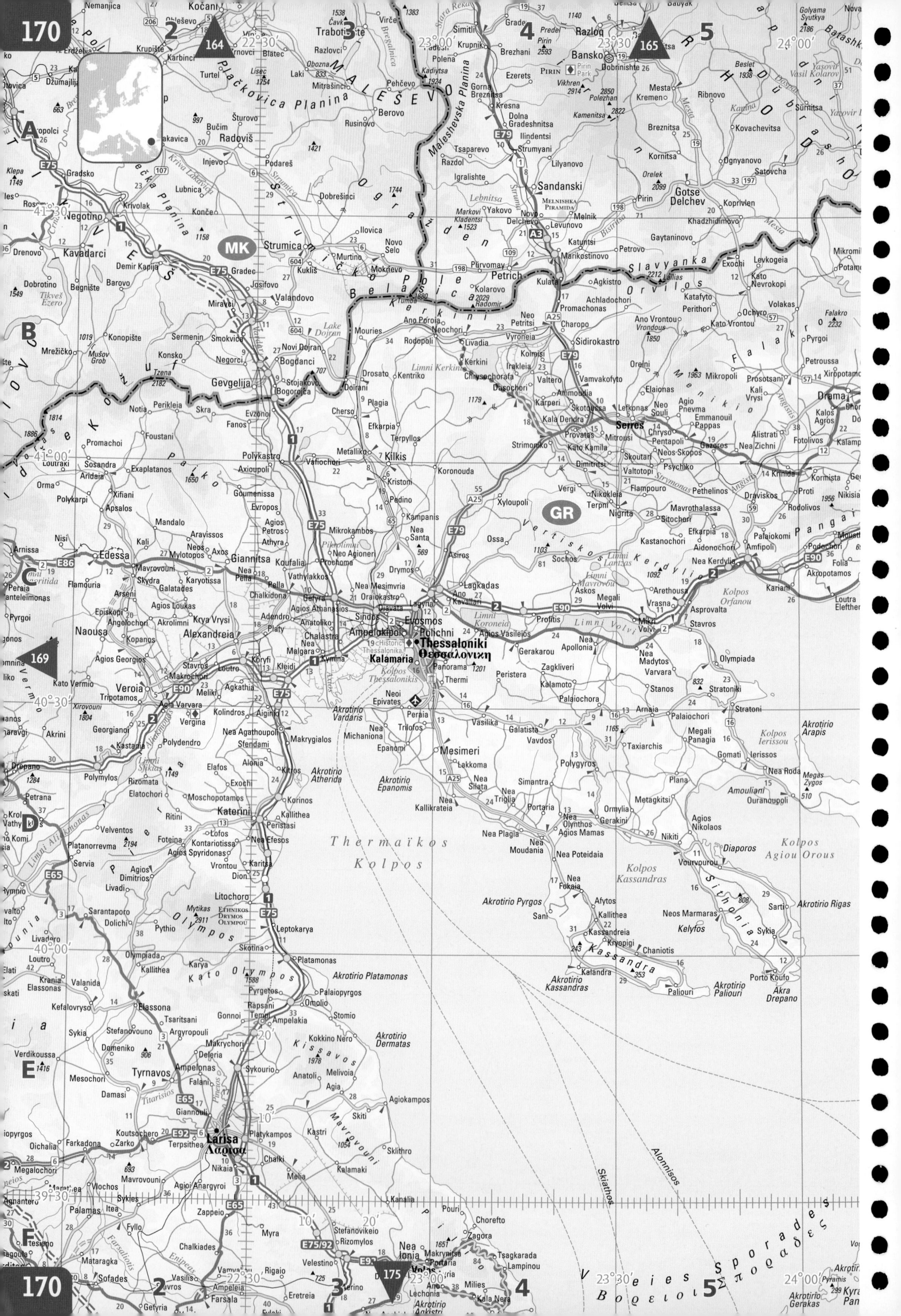
164
165
169
175
MK
GR
Thessaloniki
Θεσσαλονικη
Kalamaria
Larisa
Λαρισα
Serres
Drama
Veroia
Naousa
Edessa
Giannitsa
Katerini
Kilkis
Strumica
Gevgelija
Kavadarci
Negotino
Radoviš
Sandanski
Petrich
Gotse Delchev
Bansko
Razlog
Kočani
Tyrnavos
Elassona
Volos
Nea Ionia
Nea Moudania
Polygyros
Thermaïkos Kolpos
Kolpos Kassandras
Kolpos Agiou Orous
Kolpos Ierissou
Kolpos Orfanou
Kassandra
Sithonia
Olympos
Kissavos
Mavrovouni
Pirin
Slavyanka
Orvilos
Belasica
Kerkini
Vertiskos
Kerdylio
Pangaio
Vermio
Paiko
Limni Kerkini
Limni Koroneia
Limni Volvi
Lake Dojran
Akrotirio Kassandras
Akrotirio Paliouri
Akrotirio Pyrgos
Akrotirio Platamonas
Akrotirio Epanomis
Akrotirio Atherida
Akrotirio Dermatas
Akrotirio Rigas
Akrotirio Arapis
Vories Sporades
Βορειοι Σποραδες
Skiathos
Alonnisos
E75
E79
E90
E86
E65
E92
A25
41°30'
41°00'
40°30'
40°00'
39°30'
22°30'
23°00'
23°30'
24°00'

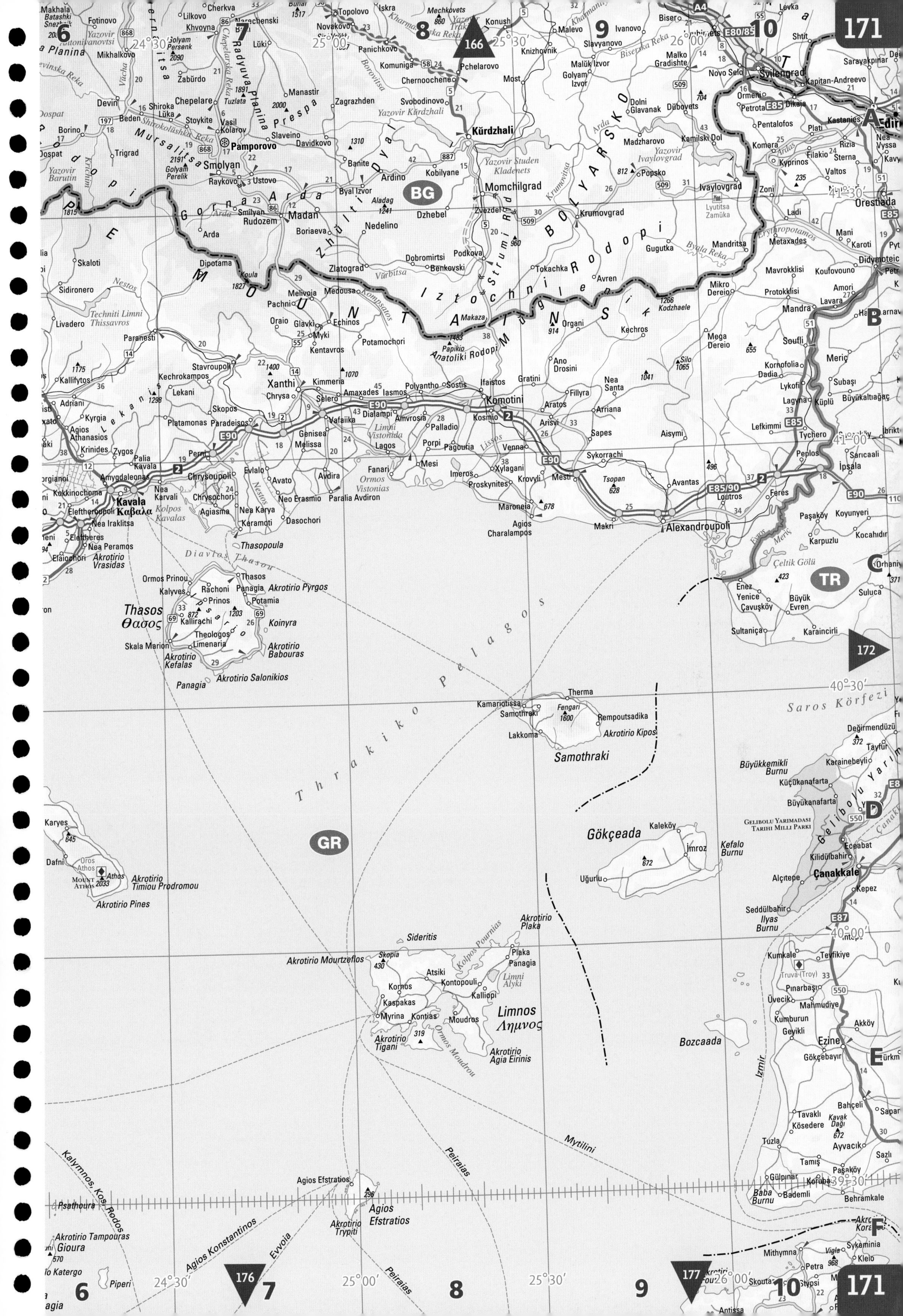
6
7
8
9
10
166
Makhala
Batashki Snezhi
Fotinovo
Yazovir Antonivanovtsi
Planina
Mikhalkovo
Cherkva
Lilkovo
Khvoyna
Narechenski
Golyam Persenk
2090
Lŭki
Topolovo
Iskra
Novakovo
Panichkovo
Mechkovets
860
Konush
Komuniga
Chernoocheno
Pchelarovo
Malevo
Ivanovo
Slavyanovo
Knizhovnik
Malŭk Izvor
Golyam Izvor
Most
Biser
Malko Gradishte
Novo Selo
Svilengrad
Kapitan-Andreevo
Shtit
Sarayakpınar
Lyubimets
A4
E80/85
Zabŭrdo
Manastir
Tuzlata
1891
2000
Prespa
Devin
Shiroka Lŭka
Chepelare
Stoykite
Vasil Kolarov
Pamporovo
Smolyan
Dospat
Borino
Beden
Trigrad
Mursalitsa
Slaveino
Davidkovo
Zagrazhden
Svobodinovo
Yazovir Kŭrdzhali
Kŭrdzhali
1310
Banite
Ardino
Kobilyane
887
Yazovir Studen Kladenets
Momchilgrad
Dyal
Zhŭlti
BG
Dolni Glavanak
Dŭbovets
704
Madzharovo
Kamilski Dol
Yazovir Ivaylovgrad
Popsko
812
Ivaylovgrad
Lyutitsa Zamŭka
BOLYARSKO
Ormeni
Petrota
Dikaia
Pentalofos
Plati
Kastanies
Edirne
Komara
Rizia
Nea Vyssa
Kyprinos
Filakio
Sterna
Kavyli
Valtos
235
Zoni
Orestiada
Ladi
Mani
Karoti
Metaxades
Didymoteicho
Yazovir Barutin
Golyam Perelik
2191
Raykovo
Ustovo
1815
Gorna Arda
Smilyan
Rudozem
Madan
Byal Izvor
Aladag
1241
Dzhebel
Zvezdel
Krumovgrad
Boriaeva
Nedelino
Arda
Dobromirtsi
Benkovski
Podkova
960
Strumi
Tokachka
Avren
Gugutka
Mandritsa
Byala Reka
Iztochni Rodopi
Mŭglenik
Zlatograd
Vŭrbitsa
Skaloti
Dipotama
Koula
1827
Sidironero
Nestos
Melivoia
Medousa
Pachni
Oraio
Glavki
Echinos
Myki
Kentavros
Makaza
1483
Papikio
Anatoliki Rodopi
914
Organi
Kechros
1266
Kodzhaele
Mikro Dereio
Mega Dereio
655
Mavrokklisi
Koufovouno
Amori
Protokklisi
Lavara
Mandra
Soufli
Meriç
Kornofolia
Dadia
Lykofi
Subaşı
Lagyna
Küplü
Büyükaltıağaç
Livadero
Techniti Limni Thissavros
Paranesti
Potamochori
1175
Kallifytos
Stavroupoli
1400
Xanthi
Kimmeria
1070
Polyantho
Sostis
Ifaistos
Gratini
Ano Drosini
Nea Santa
1041
Silo
1065
Kechrokampos
Lekani
1298
Chrysa
Selero
Amaxades
Iasmos
Komotini
Fillyra
Aratos
Arriana
Lefkimmi
Tychero
Adriani
Kyrgia
Agios Athanasios
Krinides
Zygos
Skopos
Platamonas
Paradeisos
Vafaiika
Dialampi
Amvrosia
Palladio
Kosmio
Arisvi
Sapes
Aisymi
Limni Vistonida
Genisea
Melissa
Lagos
Porpi
Pagouria
Venna
Sykorrachi
Peplos
Sarıcaali
İpsala
Palia Kavala
Perni
Amygdaleonas
Chrysoupoli
Evlalo
Avato
Avdira
Fanari
Mesi
Imeros
Xylagani
Proskynites
Krovyli
Mesti
Tsopan
628
Avantas
496
Loutros
Feres
Kokkinochoma
Kavala Καβάλα
Nea Karvali
Chrysochori
Agiasma
Neo Erasmio
Paralia Avdiron
Ormos Vistonias
Maroneia
678
Agios Charalampos
Makri
Alexandroupoli
Paşaköy
Koyunyeri
Karpuzlu
Kocahıdır
Eleftheroupoli
Nea Iraklitsa
Kolpos Kavalas
Nea Karya
Keramoti
Dasochori
Eleftheres
Nea Peramos
Elaiochori
Akrotirio Vrasidas
Thasopoula
Diavlos Thasou
Çeltik Gölü
423
TR
Orhaniye
Enez
Yenice
Çavuşköy
Büyük Evren
Suluca
Sultaniça
Karaincirli
172
Ormos Prinou
Rachoni
Thasos
Panagia
Akrotirio Pyrgos
Kalyves
Prinos
Potamia
Thasos Θάσος
872
1203
Kallirachi
Ipsario
Koinyra
Theologos
Limenaria
Skala Marion
Akrotirio Kefalas
Akrotirio Babouras
Panagia
Akrotirio Salonikios
Thrakiko Pelagos
Therma
Kamariotissa
Samothraki
Fengari
1600
Rempoutsadika
Lakkoma
Akrotirio Kipos
Samothraki
Saros Körfezi
Değirmendüzü
372
Tayfur
Büyükkemikli Burnu
Karainebeyli
Küçükanafarta
Büyükanafarta
Gelibolu Yarımadası Tarihi Milli Parkı
550
Gökçeada
Kaleköy
İmroz
Kefalo Burnu
672
Uğurlu
Eceabat
Kilidülbahir
Çanakkale
Alçıtepe
Kepez
Seddülbahir
Ilyas Burnu
E87
GR
Karyes
645
Dafni
Oros Athos
Mount Athos
2033
Akrotirio Timiou Prodromou
Akrotirio Pines
Akrotirio Plaka
Sideritis
Kolpos Pournias
Plaka
Panagia
Akrotirio Mourtzeflos
Skopia
430
Atsiki
Kontopouli
Limni Alyki
Kalliopi
Kornos
Kaspakas
Myrina
Kontias
Moudros
Limnos Λήμνος
Akrotirio Tigani
319
Ormos Moudrou
Akrotirio Agia Eirinis
Kumkale
Tevfikiye
Truva (Troy)
Pınarbaşı
Üvecik
Mahmudiye
Kumburun
Geyikli
Akköy
Ezine
Gökçebayır
Bozcaada
Izmir
Tavaklı
Kösedere
Kavak Dağı
672
Bahçeli
Ayvacık
Tuzla
Tamış
Paşaköy
Sazlı
Gülpınar
Koruoba
Baba Burnu
Bademli
Behramkale
Mytilini
Peiraias
Kalymnos, Kos, Rodos
Agios Efstratios
296
Agios Efstratios
Akrotirio Trypiti
Psathoura
Agios Konstantinos
Evvoia
Akrotirio Tampouras
Gioura
570
Katergo
Piperi
Mithymna
Vigla
968
Sykaminia
Klei
Petra
Stypsi
Skoutari
Antissa
176
177
24°30′
25°00′
25°30′
26°00′
41°30′
41°00′
40°30′
40°00′
39°30′
A
B
C
D
E
F

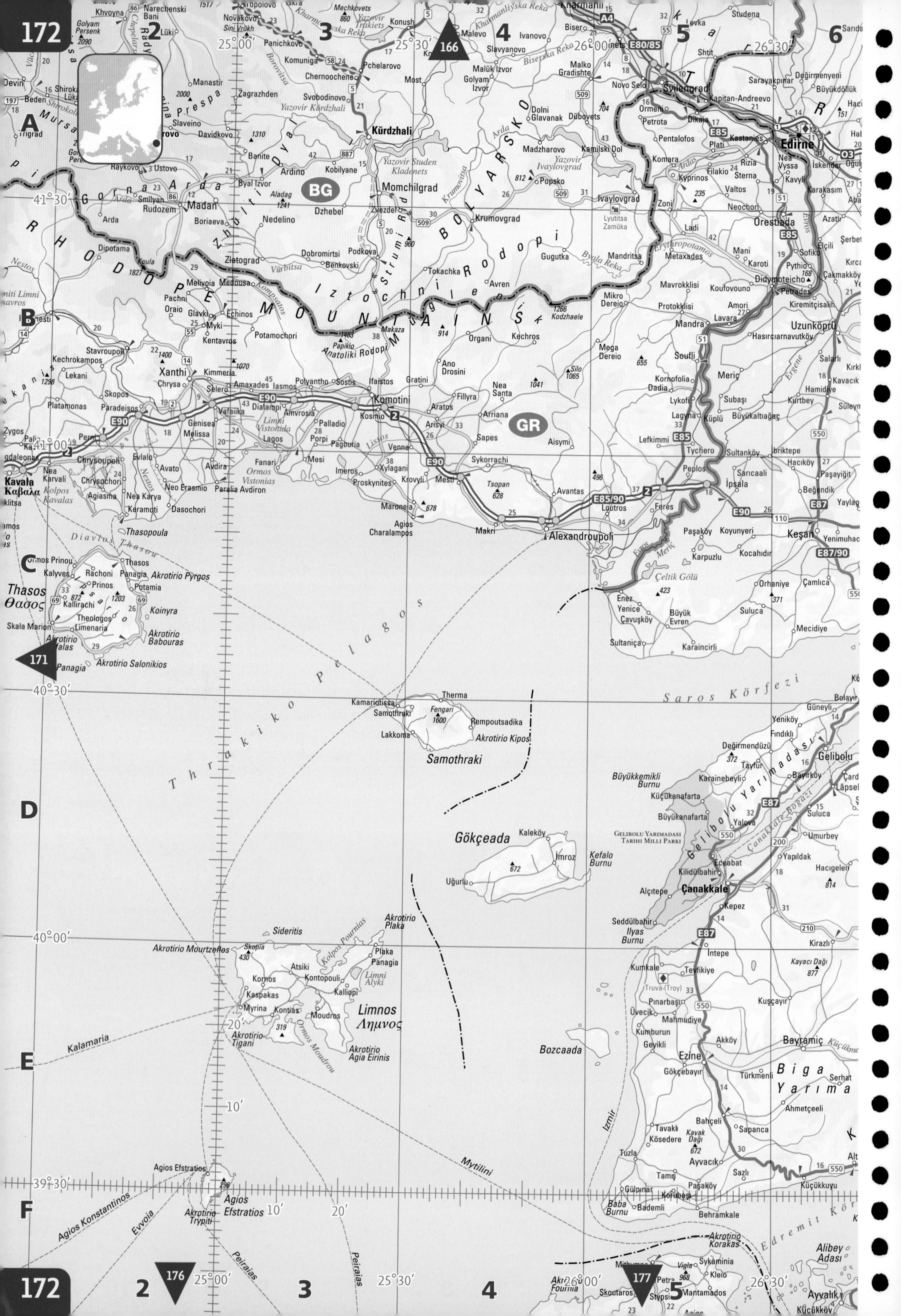
Kürdzhali
Momchilgrad
Krumovgrad
Ivaylovgrad
Svilengrad
Edirne
Madan
Smilyan
Rudozem
Zlatograd
Dzhebel
Kirkovo
BG
GR
Iztochni Rodopi
RHODOPE MOUNTAINS
Xanthi
Komotini
Alexandroupoli
Kavala
Καβαλα
Orestiada
Didymoteicho
Soufli
Feres
Uzunköprü
İpsala
Keşan
Thasos
Θασος
Samothraki
Gökçeada
Thrakiko Pelagos
Saros Körfezi
Gelibolu
Çanakkale
Eceabat
Kilitbahir
Gelibolu Yarımadası
Gelibolu Yarımadası Tarihi Milli Parkı
Çanakkale Boğazı
Limnos
Λημνος
Myrina
Moudros
Bozcaada
Ezine
Ayvacık
Bayramiç
Biga Yarımadası
Agios Efstratios
Truva (Troy)
Ayvalık
Mytilini
Peiraias
Evvoia
Kalamaria
Nestos
Arda
E90
E85
E87
41°30′
41°00′
40°30′
40°00′
39°30′
25°00′
25°30′
26°00′
26°30′
166
171
176
177

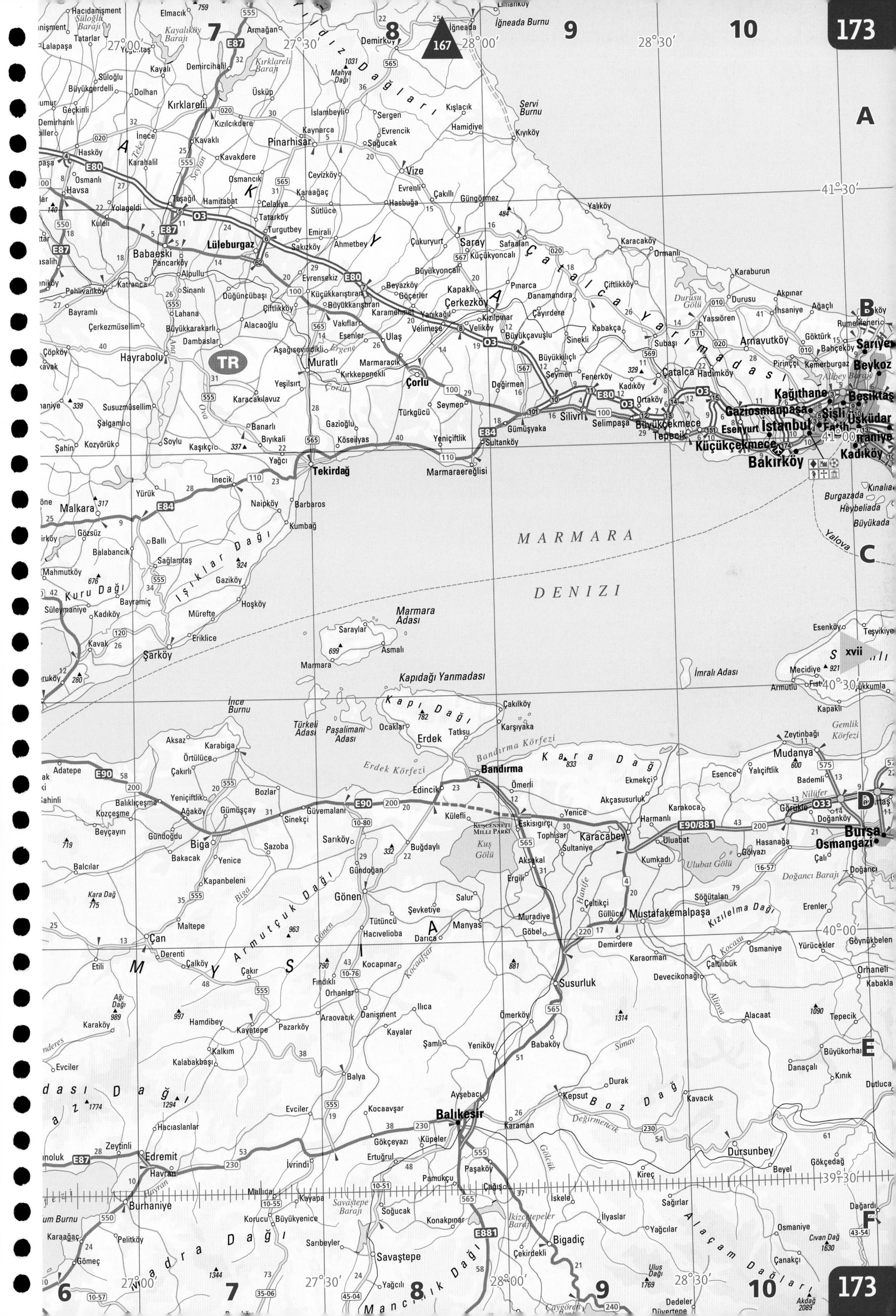
7
8
9
10
167
A
B
C
D
E
F
27°00′
27°30′
28°00′
28°30′
41°30′
41°00′
40°30′
40°00′
39°30′
Hacıdanişment
Süloğlu Barajı
Lalapaşa
Tatarlar
Elmacık
Kayalıköy Barajı
Armağan
Yıldız Dağları
İğneada
İğneada Burnu
Limanköy
Demirköy
Mahya Dağı
1031
Kayalı
Demircihalil
Kırklareli Barajı
Süloğlu
Büyükgerdelli
Dolhan
Üsküp
Geçkinli
Demirhanlı
Kırklareli
Kızılcıkdere
İslambeyli
Sergen
Kışlacık
Hamidiye
Servi Burnu
Kıyıköy
İnece
Kavaklı
Kaynarca
Evrencik
Soğucak
Pınarhisar
Hasköy
Karahalil
Kavakdere
Vize
Osmanlı
Havsa
Osmancık
Cevizköy
Karaağaç
Evrenli
Çakıllı
Taşağıl
Hamitabat
Celaliye
Hasbuğa
Güngörmez
Yolageldi
Sütlüce
Yalıköy
Kuleli
Tatarköy
Turgutbey
Emirali
Lüleburgaz
Sakızköy
Ahmetbey
Çukuryurt
Saray
Safaalan
Küçükyoncalı
Karacaköy
Ormanlı
Babaeski
Pancarköy
Alpullu
Büyükyoncalı
Evrensekiz
Çatalca Yarımadası
Karaburun
Pehlivanköy
Katranca
Sinanlı
Düğüncübaşı
Beyazköy
Göçerler
Kapaklı
Pınarca
Danamandıra
Çiftlikköy
Küçükkarıştıran
Büyükkarıştıran
Çerkezköy
Kızılpınar
Durusu Gölü
Durusu
Akpınar
İhsaniye
Ağaçlı
Bayramlı
Lahana
Çiftlikköy
Karamehmet
Yanıkağıl
Çayırdere
Yassıören
Rumelifeneri
Çerkezmüselllim
Büyükkarakarlı
Alacaoğlu
Vakıflar
Velimeşe
Veliköy
Büyükçavuşlu
Kabakça
Dambaslar
Esenler
Ulaş
Subaşı
Arnavutköy
Göktürk
Bahçeköy
Sarıyer
Çöpköy
Hayrabolu
TR
Aşağısevindikli
Sinekli
Büyükkılıçlı
Pirinççi
Kemerburgaz
Beykoz
Muratlı
Marmaracık
Kırkkepenekli
Seymen
Fenerköy
Çatalca
Hadımköy
Kağıthane
Beşiktaş
Yeşilsırt
Çorlu
Değirmen
Kadıköy
Ortaköy
Gaziosmanpaşa
Şişli
Üsküdar
Susuzmüsellim
Karacakılavuz
Seymen
Silivri
Selimpaşa
Büyükçekmece
Tepecik
Esenyurt
İstanbul
Fatih
Şalgamlı
Gazioğlu
Türkgücü
Gümüşyaka
Küçükçekmece
Ümraniye
Banarlı
Bıyıkalı
Köseilyas
Yeniçiftlik
Sultanköy
Kadıköy
Şahin
Kozyörük
Soylu
Kaşıkçı
Yağcı
Tekirdağ
Marmaraereğlisi
Bakırköy
İnecik
Yürük
Naipköy
Barbaros
Kınalıada
Burgazada
Heybeliada
Büyükada
Malkara
Kumbağ
Gözsüz
Ballı
Balabancık
MARMARA
DENİZİ
Yalova
Mahmutköy
Sağlamtaş
Işıklar Dağı
Kuru Dağı
Gaziköy
Bayramiç
Süleymaniye
Kadıköy
Hoşköy
Mürefte
Marmara Adası
Saraylar
Esenköy
Teşvikiye
Eriklice
Kavak
Asmalı
Şarköy
Marmara
Kapıdağı Yanmadası
İmralı Adası
Mecidiye
Armutlu
Fıstıklı
Kapaklı
İnce Burnu
Kapı Dağı
Çakılköy
Karşıyaka
Türkeli Adası
Paşalimanı Adası
Ocaklar
Erdek
Tatlısu
Zeytinbağı
Gemlik Körfezi
Aksaz
Karabiga
Bandırma Körfezi
Kara Dağ
Mudanya
Örtülüce
Erdek Körfezi
Bandırma
Adatepe
Çakırlı
Ömerli
Ekmekçi
Esence
Yalıçiftlik
Bademli
Yeniçiftlik
Bozlar
Edincik
Akçasusurluk
Nilüfer
Balıklıçeşme
Ağaköy
Gümüşçay
Güvemalanı
Yenice
Karakoca
Görükle
Bursa
Kozçeşme
Sinekçi
Külefli
Kuşcenneti Milli Parkı
Eskisığırcı
Harmanlı
Doğanköy
Beyçayırı
Gündoğdu
Sarıköy
Tophisar
Karacabey
Uluabat
Hasanağa
Osmangazi
Biga
Sazoba
Buğdaylı
Kuş Gölü
Sultaniye
Gölyazı
Balcılar
Bakacak
Yenice
Gündoğan
Aksakal
Kumkadı
Uluabat Gölü
Çalı
Doğancı
Kapanbeleni
Ergili
Doğancı Barajı
Kara Dağ
Armutçuk Dağı
Gönen
Salur
Çeltikçi
Söğütalan
Erenler
Şevketiye
Güllüce
Mustafakemalpaşa
Kızılelma Dağı
Maltepe
Tütüncü
Hacıvelioba
Manyas
Muradiye
Göbel
Çan
Darıca
Demirdere
Osmaniye
Yürücekler
Göynükbelen
Derenti
Çalköy
Karaorman
Çaltılıbük
Etili
Çakır
Kocapınar
Devecikonağı
Orhaneli
Fındıklı
Susurluk
Kabakla
Orhanlar
Ağı Dağı
Hamdibey
Kayatepe
Pazarköy
Aravacık
Danişment
Ilıca
Ömerköy
Alacaat
Tepecik
Karaköy
Kayalar
Kalkım
Şamlı
Yeniköy
Babaköy
Simav
Büyükorhan
Kalabakbaşı
Evciler
Balya
Durak
Danaçalı
Kınık
Dutluca
Ayşebacı
Kepsut
Boz Dağ
Kavacık
Evciler
Kocaavşar
Balıkesir
Hacıaslanlar
Gökçeyazı
Küpeler
Karaman
Değirmencik
Dursunbey
Zeytinli
Edremit
Ertuğrul
Havran
İvrindi
Paşaköy
Gölcük
Kireç
Beyel
Gökçedağ
Pamukçu
Çağış
Burhaniye
Mallıca
Kayapa
Savaştepe Barajı
İskele
Sağırlar
Dağardı
Soğucak
Büyükyenice
Konakpınar
İkizcetepeler Barajı
İlyaslar
Korucu
Yağcılar
Osmaniye
Civan Dağ
Pelitköy
Madra Dağı
Sarıbeyler
Bigadiç
Alaçam Dağları
Gömeç
Savaştepe
Çekirdekli
Ulus Dağı
Çanakçı
Yağcılı
Mancılık Dağı
Dedeler
Düvertepe
Akdağ
Çaygören

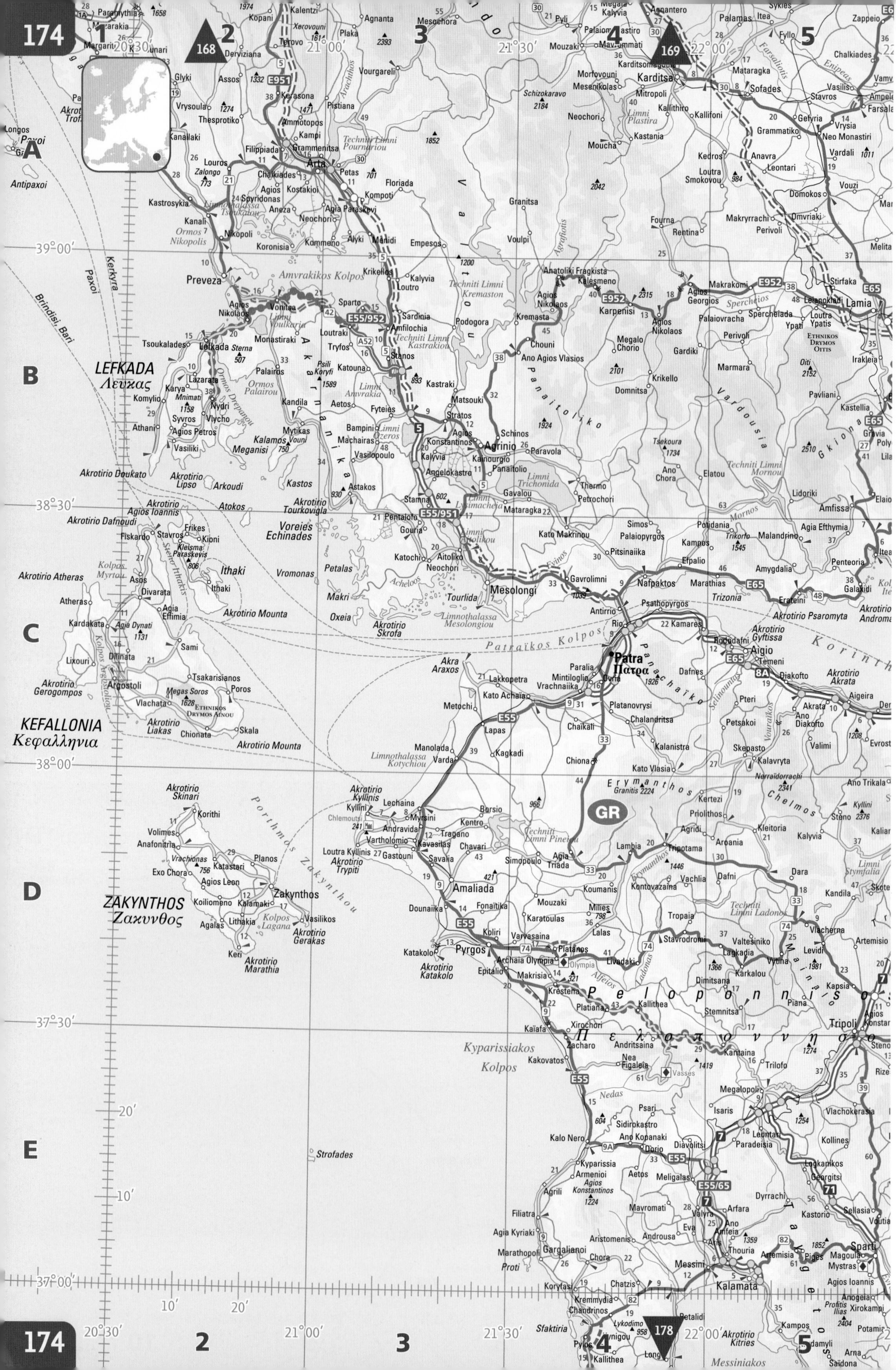

168
169
178
GR
LEFKADA
Λευκας
KEFALLONIA
Κεφαλληνια
ZAKYNTHOS
Ζακυνθος
Ithaki
Paxoi
Antipaxoi
Preveza
Arta
Karditsa
Lamia
Agrinio
Mesolongi
Nafpaktos
Patra
Πατρα
Pyrgos
Amaliada
Tripoli
Kalamata
Sparti
Megalopoli
Kyparissia
Filippiada
Amfilochia
Vonitsa
Lefkada
Karpenisi
Amfissa
Galaxidi
Aigio
Kalavryta
Argostoli
Lixouri
Sami
Zakynthos
Gastouni
Andravida
Kyllini
Olympia
Archaia Olympia
Zacharo
Filiatra
Gargalianoi
Messini
Pylos
Sofades
Farsala
Domokos
Amvrakikos Kolpos
Patraïkos Kolpos
Kyparissiakos Kolpos
Messiniakos
Porthmos Zakynthou
Kolpos Myrtou
Limni Trichonida
Techniti Limni Kremaston
Techniti Limni Kastrakiou
Techniti Limni Mornou
Techniti Limni Ladonos
Limni Plastira
Pelopnnisos
Πελοποννησος
Akarnanika
Panaitoliko
Vardousia
Gkiona
Erymanthos
Chelmos
Taygetos
Strofades
Sfaktiria
Proti
Akrotirio Araxos
Akrotirio Katakolo
Akrotirio Skinari
Akrotirio Marathia
Akrotirio Gerakas
Akrotirio Doukato
Akrotirio Atheras
Akrotirio Dafnoudi
Akrotirio Mounta
Akrotirio Psaromyta
Akrotirio Kitries
Voreies Echinades
Kastos
Kalamos
Meganisi
Atokos
Arkoudi
Oxeia
Petalas
Vromonas
Makri
Brindisi, Bari
Kerkyra
E55
E65
E951
E952
E55/952
E55/951
E55/65
39°00′
38°30′
38°00′
37°30′
37°00′
20°30′
21°00′
21°30′
22°00′
A
B
C
D
E
1
2
3
4
5

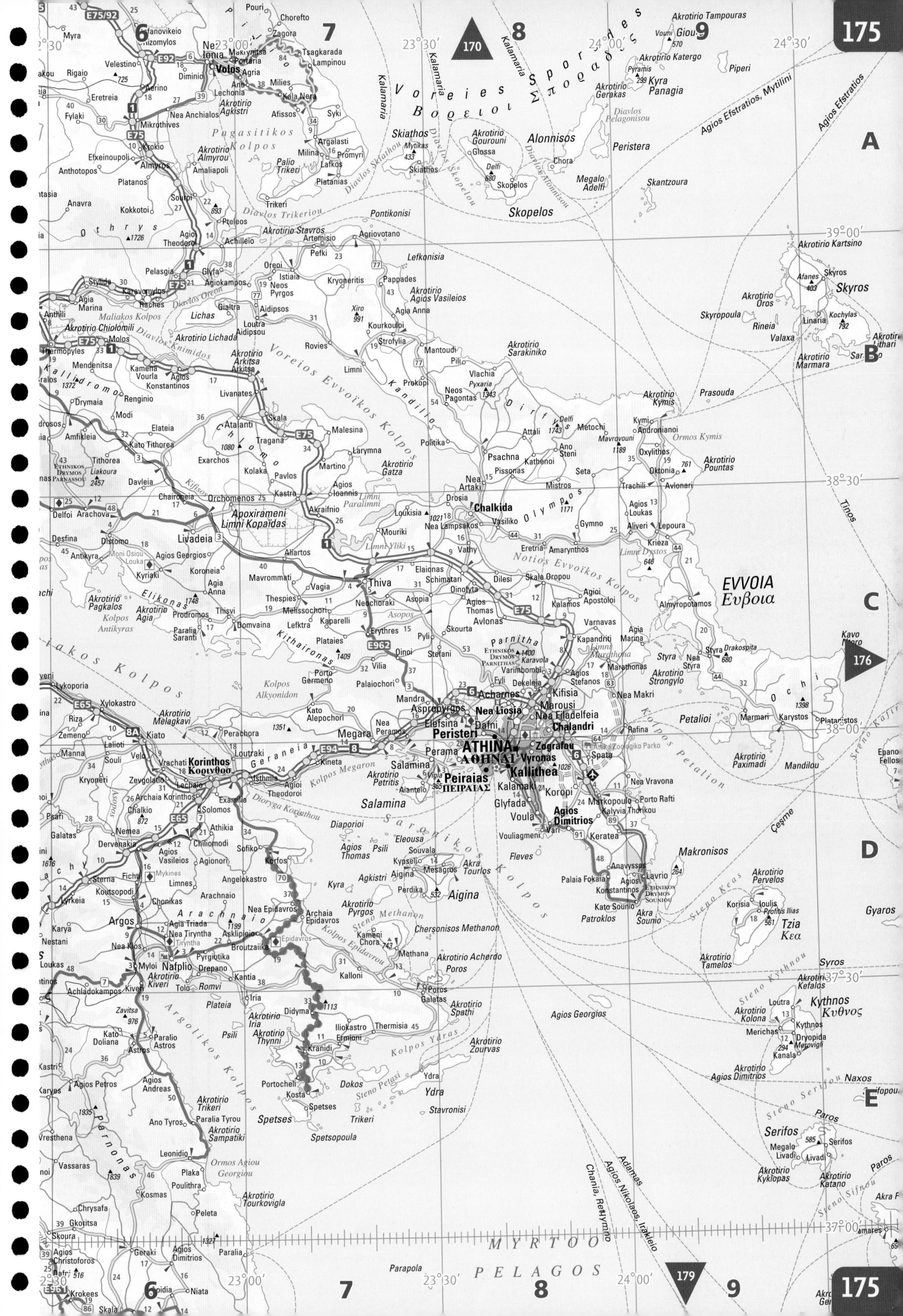

170
176
179
Voreies Sporades
Βορειοι Σποραδες
Skiathos
Skopelos
Alonnisos
Kyra Panagia
Peristera
Megalo Adelfi
Skantzoura
Piperi
Gioura
Akrotirio Tampouras
Akrotirio Katergo
Diavlos Pelagonisou
Agios Efstratios, Mytilini
Agios Efstratios
Kalamaria
Pagasitikos Kolpos
Volos
Nea Ionia
Velestino
Almyros
Trikeri
Palio Trikeri
Argalasti
Milina
Platanias
Diavlos Trikeriou
Diavlos Skiathou
Diavlos Skopelou
Diavlos Alonnisou
Pontikonisi
Akrotirio Stavros
Artemisio
Agriovotano
Pefki
Lefkonisia
Istiaia
Oreoi
Neos Pyrgos
Pappades
Akrotirio Agios Vasileios
Agia Anna
Aidipsos
Loutra Aidipsou
Lichas
Akrotirio Lichada
Maliakos Kolpos
Stylida
Lamia
Agia Marina
Akrotirio Chiolomili
Diavlos Knimidos
Thermopyles
Molos
Kamena Vourla
Agios Konstantinos
Voreios Evvoikos Kolpos
Kandilio
Dirfys
Mantoudi
Prokopi
Limni
Rovies
Strofylia
Kourkoulpi
Akrotirio Sarakiniko
Neos Pagontas
Pyxaria
Akrotirio Kymis
Kymi
Andronianoi
Ormos Kymis
Prasouda
Skyros
Skyropoula
Akrotirio Kartsino
Akrotirio Lithari
Akrotirio Marmara
Valaxa
Rineia
Linaria
Atalanti
Chlomo
Larymna
Malesina
Akrotirio Gatza
Martino
Kastro
Orchomenos
Livadeia
Apoxirameni Limni Kopaidas
Delfoi
Arachova
Limni Yliki
Limni Paralimni
Chalkida
Psachna
Nea Artaki
Olympos
Eretria
Amarynthos
Aliveri
Gymno
Lepoura
Limni Dystos
Kriezas
EVVOIA
Ευβοια
Almyropotamos
Notios Evvoikos Kolpos
Thiva
Elikonas
Kolpos Antikyras
Akrotirio Pagkalos
Kithaironas
Kolpos Alkyonidon
Parnitha
Ethnikos Drymos Parnithas
Oinofyta
Skala Oropou
Kapandriti
Limni Marathona
Marathonas
Varnavas
Styra
Akrotirio Strongylo
Nea Styra
Marmari
Karystos
Petalioi
Ochi
Kavo Ntoro
Korinthiakos Kolpos
Lykoporia
Xylokastro
Kiato
Akrotirio Melagkavi
Perachora
Loutraki
Geraneia
Megara
Nea Peramos
Elefsina
Aspropyrgos
Mandra
Acharnes
Nea Liosia
Peristeri
Dafni
Marousi
Kifisia
Nea Filadelfeia
Chalandri
Nea Makri
Rafina
ATHINA
ΑΘΗΝΑΙ
Zografou
Vyronas
Kallithea
Peiraias
ΠΕΙΡΑΙΑΣ
Perama
Salamina
Kalamaki
Glyfada
Voula
Vouliagmeni
Vari
Koropi
Markopoulo
Spata
Porto Rafti
Kalyvia Thorikou
Keratea
Agios Dimitrios
Anavyssos
Palaia Fokaia
Lavrio
Akra Sounio
Patroklos
Makronisos
Kolpos Petalion
Akrotirio Paximadi
Mandilou
Korinthos
Κορινθος
Isthmia
Diorygа Korinthou
Kolpos Megaron
Saronikos Kolpos
Aigina
Agkistri
Methana
Kolpos Epidavrou
Chersonisos Methanon
Poros
Akrotirio Spathi
Akrotirio Zourvas
Ydra
Dokos
Spetses
Spetsopoula
Kranidi
Ermioni
Thermisia
Kolpos Ydras
Steno Petasi
Stavronisi
Trikeri
Nemea
Argos
Nafplio
Mykines
Tiryntha
Epidavros
Arachnaio
Argolikos Kolpos
Akrotirio Kiveri
Tolo
Parnonas
Leonidio
Ormos Agiou Georgiou
Akrotirio Tourkovigla
Kyparissi
Akrotirio Trikeri
Paralia Tyrou
Akrotirio Sampatiki
Tzia
Κεα
Ioulis
Korisia
Steno Keas
Akrotirio Tamelos
Gyaros
Syros
Kythnos
Κυθνος
Steno Kythnou
Loutra
Dryopida
Merichas
Kanala
Akrotirio Kefalos
Akrotirio Kolona
Serifos
Livadi
Steno Serifou
Paros
Naxos
Steno Sifnou
Akrotirio Kyklopas
Akrotirio Katano
Agios Georgios
Chania, Rethymno
Agios Nikolaos, Irakleio
Adamas
Tinos
Çeşme
MYRTOO PELAGOS
Parapola
Skoura
Geraki
Kosmas
Krokees
23°00′
23°30′
24°00′
24°30′
39°00′
38°30′
38°00′
37°30′
37°00′

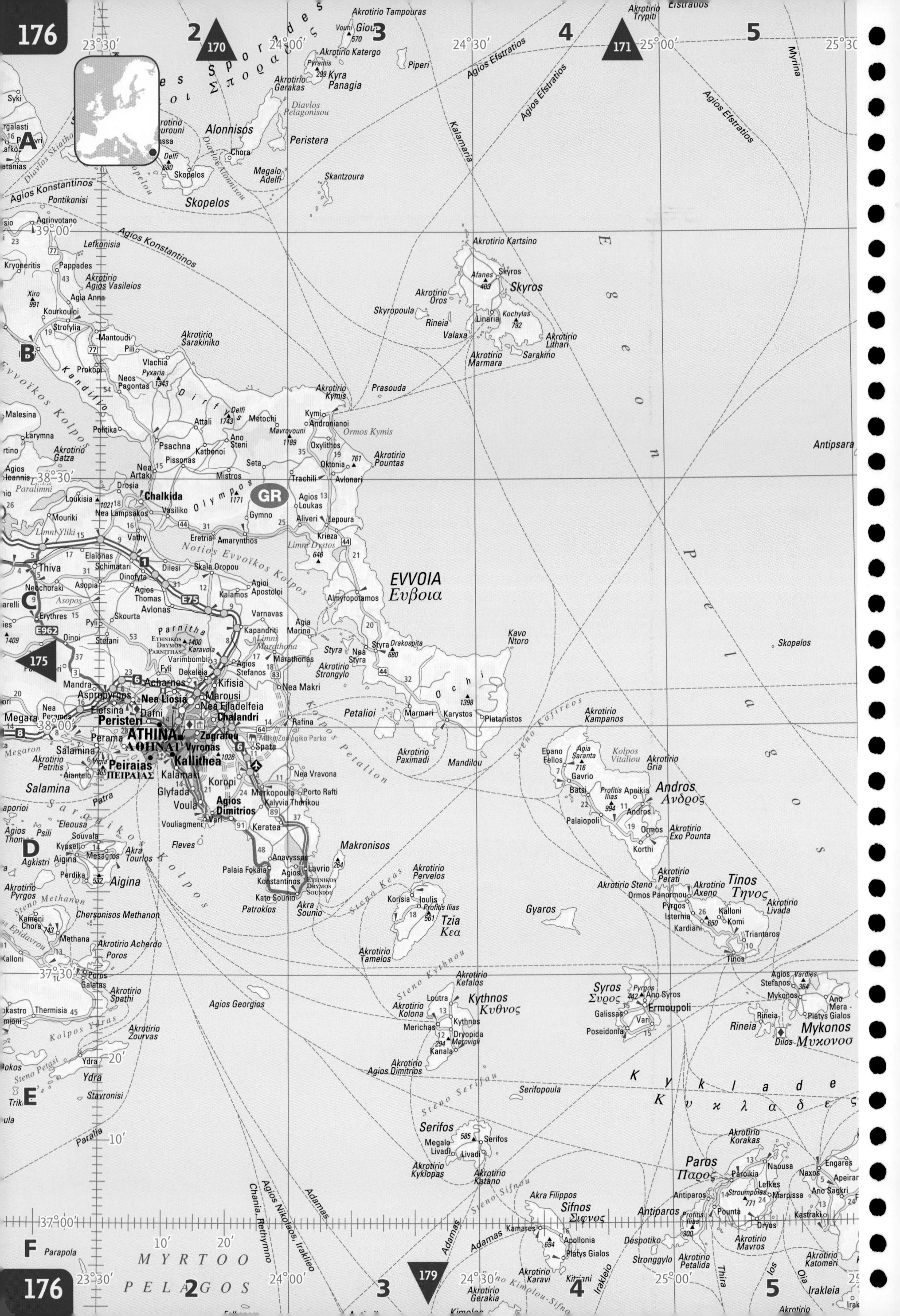
176
23°30′
24°00′
24°30′
25°00′
25°30′
170
171
Akrotirio Tampouras
Vouni Giou 570
Akrotirio Trypiti
Efstratios
Akrotirio Katergo
Pyramis 299
Kyra Panagia
Piperi
Akrotirio Gerakas
Diavlos Pelagonisou
Alonnisos
Chora
Peristera
Delfi 680
Skopelos
Megalo Adelfi
Skantzoura
Skopelos
Agios Konstantinos
Pontikonisi
Agios Efstratios
Kalamaria
Myrina
39°00′
Lefkonisia
Kryoneritis
Pappades
Akrotirio Agios Vasileios
Xiro 991
Agia Anna
Kourkoulοi
Strofylia
Mantoudi
Pili
Akrotirio Sarakiniko
Vlachia
Prokopi
Neos Pagontas
Pyxaria 1343
Akrotirio Kartsino
Afanes 403
Skyros
Akrotirio Oros
Skyropoula
Rineia
Kochylas 792
Linaria
Valaxa
Akrotirio Lithari
Akrotirio Marmara
Sarakino
Akrotirio Kymis
Prasouda
Malesina
Larymna
Politika
Delfi 1743
Metochi
Attali
Kymi
Andronianoi
Mavrovouni 1189
Ormos Kymis
Psachna
Ano Steni
Kathenoi
Pissonas
Oxylithos
Akrotirio Gatza
Oktonia
761
Akrotirio Pountas
Antipsara
Nea Artaki
Mistros
Trachili
Avlonari
38°30′
Drosia
Chalkida
Olympos 1171
GR
Agios Loukas
Loukisia
Nea Lampsakos
Vasiliko
Gymno
Mouriki
Vathy
Eretria
Amarynthos
Aliveri
Lepoura
Krieza
Limni Dystos
646
Thiva
Elaionas
Schimatari
Dilesi
Skala Oropou
Oinofyta
Notios Evvoïkos Kolpos
EVVOIA
Ευβοια
Neochoraki
Asopia
Agios Thomas
Kalamos
Agioi Apostoloi
Almyropotamos
Avlonas
Erythres
Skourta
Varnavas
Agia Marina
Parnitha
Kapandriti
Oinoi
Stefani
E962
E75
175
Varimbombi
Marathonas
Agios Stefanos
Styra
Nea Styra
Drakospita 680
Akrotirio Strongylo
Kavo Ntoro
Skopelos
Dekeleia
Mandra
Acharnes
Kifisia
Nea Makri
Aspropyrgos
Nea Liosia
Marousi
Ochi 1398
Nea Peramos
Elefsina
Dafni
Nea Filadelfeia
Chalandri
Petalioi
Marmari
Karystos
Platanistos
Megara
38°00′
Peristeri
Rafina
ATHINA
ΑΘΗΝΑΙ
Zografou
Spata
Megaron
Salamina
Vyronas
Kallithea
Peiraias
ΠΕΙΡΑΙΑΣ
Akrotirio Petritis
Aianteio
Kalamaki
Koropi
Nea Vravona
Kolpos Petalion
Akrotirio Paximadi
Mandilou
Salamina
Glyfada
Markopoulo
Porto Rafti
Voula
Agios Dimitrios
Kalyvia Thorikou
Vari
Vouliagmeni
Keratea
Akrotirio Kampanos
Epano Fellos
Agia Saranta 716
Gavrio
Kolpos Vitaliou
Akrotirio Gria
Batsi
Profitis Ilias 994
Apoikia
Andros
Ανδρος
Palaiopoli
Andros
Ormos
Akrotirio Exo Pounta
Korthi
Eleousa
Souvala
Kypseli
Mesagros
Aigina
Akra Tourlos
Fleves
Makronisos
Agkistri
Perdika
532
Aigina
Palaia Fokaia
Anavyssos
Agios Konstantinos
Lavrio
264
Akrotirio Pervelos
Akrotirio Perati
Tinos
Τηνος
Akrotirio Steno
Ormos Panormou
Akrotirio Axeno
Akrotirio Livada
Akrotirio Pyrgos
Steno Methanon
Chersonisos Methanon
Kato Sounio
Patroklos
Akra Sounio
Korisia
Ioulis
Profitis Ilias 561
Tzia
Κεα
Gyaros
Pyrgos
Isternia
650
Kalloni
Komi
Kardiani
Triantaros
Kameni Chora 743
Methana
Akrotirio Acherdo
Poros
Kalloni
Akrotirio Tamelos
Tinos
37°30′
Poros
Galatas
Akrotirio Spathi
Akrotirio Kefalos
Syros
Συρος
Pyrgos 442
Ano Syros
Ermoupoli
Agios Stefanos
Vardies 364
Mykonos
Ano Mera
Platys Gialos
Agios Georgios
Loutra
Akrotirio Kolona
Kythnos
Κυθνος
Merichas
Dryopida
Merovigli
294
Kanala
Galissas
Poseidonia
Vari
Rineia
Dilos
Mykonos
Μυκονοσ
Thermisia
Kolpos Ydras
Akrotirio Zourvas
Ydra
Ydra
Steno Petasi
Stavronisi
20′
Akrotirio Agios Dimitrios
Steno Serifou
Serifopoula
Kyklades
Κυκλαδες
Paralia
10′
Serifos
585
Serifos
Megalo Livadi
Livadi
Akrotirio Kyklopas
Akrotirio Katano
Akrotirio Korakas
Paros
Παρος
Paroikia
Naousa
Lefkes
Naxos
Engares
Apeiranthos
Antiparos
Stroumpolas 771
Marpissa
Ano Sagkri
Akra Filippos
Sifnos
Σιφνος
Steno Sifnou
Antiparos
Profitis Ilias 300
Pounta
Kastraki
Dryos
37°00′
Chania, Rethymno
Agios Nikolaos, Irakleio
Adamas
Kamares
Apollonia
694
Platys Gialos
Despotiko
Stronggylo
Akrotirio Petalida
Akrotirio Mavros
Akrotirio Katomeri
Parapola
MYRTOO PELAGOS
179
Akrotirio Karavi
Kitriani
Akrotirio Gerakia
Kimolos
Steno Kimolou-Sifnou
Irakleio
Thira
Ios
Oia
Irakleia
Egeon Pelagos
A
B
C
D
E
F
2
3
4
5
176

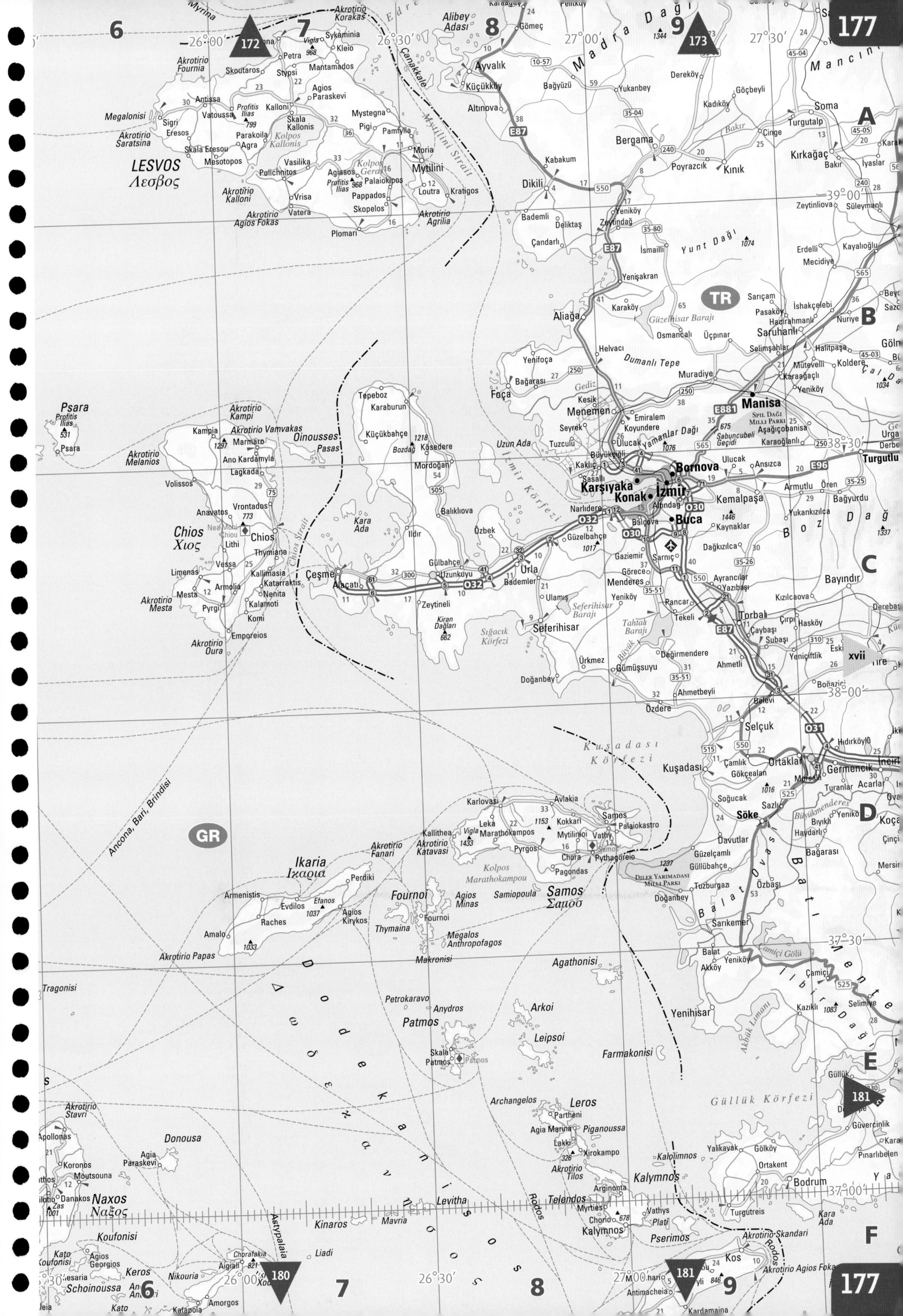
177
6
7
8
9
172
173
26°00′
26°30′
27°00′
27°30′
Akrotirio Korakas
Sykaminia
Vigla 968
Kleio
Petra
Stypsi
Mantamados
Akrotirio Fournia
Skoutaros
Agios Paraskevi
Antissa
Kalloni
Megalonisi
Sigri
Vatoussa
Profitis Ilias 799
Skala Kallonis
Mystegna
Pigi
Pamfylla
Eresos
Parakoila
Agra
Kolpos Kallonis
Akrotirio Saratsina
Skala Eresou
Mesotopos
Moria
Mytilini
LESVOS
Λεσβος
Vasilika
Polichnitos
Agiasos
Kolpos Geras
Profitis Ilias 968
Palaiokipos
Loutra
Kratigos
Akrotirio Kalloni
Vrisa
Pappados
Skopelos
Akrotirio Agios Fokas
Vatera
Akrotirio Agrilia
Plomari
Çanakkale
Mytilini Strait
Edremit
Alibey Adası
Gömeç
Ayvalık
Küçükköy
Altınova
E87
Madra Dağı
1344
Bağyüzü
Yukanbey
Dereköy
Göçbeyli
Kadıköy
Soma
Manca
Bakır
Turgutalp
Çinge
Bergama
Kırkağaç
Bakır
İyaslar
Kabakum
Poyrazcık
Kınık
Dikili
Yeniköy
Zeytindağ
Bademli
Deliktaş
Çandarlı
İsmailli
Yunt Dağı
1074
Zeytinliova
Süleymanlı
Erdelli
Kayalıoğlu
Mecidiye
39°00′
Yenişakran
TR
Sarıçam
İshakçelebi
Aliağa
Karaköy
Güzelhisar Barajı
Pasaköy
Hacırahmanlı
Nuriye
Osmancalı
Üçpınar
Saruhanlı
Selimşahlar
Halitpaşa
Helvacı
Dumanlı Tepe
Yenifoça
Mütevelli
Koldere
Karaağaçlı
Muradiye
Yeniköy
Bağarası
Foça
Gediz
Kesik
Manisa
Spil Dağı Milli Parkı
Menemen
Emiralem
Koyundere
Yamanlar Dağı
1076
Sabuncubeli Geçidi
Aşağıçobanisa
Karaoğlanlı
Urganlı
Seyrek
Tuzçullu
Uzun Ada
Ulucak
38°30′
Turgutlu
Büyükçiğli
Kaklıç
Sasallı
Bornova
Ulucak
Ansızca
Karşıyaka
Konak
İzmir
Altındağ
Kemalpaşa
Armutlu
Ören
Bağyurdu
Narlıdere
Yukarıkızılca
Boz Dağ
1337
Balçova
Buca
Kaynaklar
1446
Güzelbahçe
1017
Dağkızılca
Gaziemir
Sarnıç
Görece
Menderes
Ayrancılar
Yazıbaşı
Bayındır
Kızılcaova
Torbalı
Derebaşı
Çırpı
Hasköy
Çaybaşı
Subaşı
Yeniçiftlik
Eski
xvii
Tire
İzmir Körfezi
Psara
Profitis Ilias 531
Akrotirio Kampi
Kampia
Akrotirio Vamvakas
Oinousses
Pasas
1297
Marmaro
Akrotirio Melanios
Ano Kardamyla
Lagkada
Volissos
Vrontados
Anavatos
773
Nea Moni Chiou
Chios
Χιος
Lithi
Thymiana
Vessa
Limenas
Kallimasia
Katarraktis
Armolia
Nenita
Mesta
Pyrgi
Kalamoti
Akrotirio Mesta
Komi
Emporeios
Akrotirio Oura
Chios Strait
Tepeboz
Karaburun
Küçükbahçe
1218
Bozdağ
Kösedere
Mordoğan
Balıklıova
Kara Ada
Ildır
Özbek
Çeşme
Alaçatı
Gülbahçe
Uzunkuyu
Urla
Bademler
Zeytineli
Ulamış
Seferihisar Barajı
Kiran Dağları 662
Sığacık Körfezi
Seferihisar
Yeniköy
Pancar
Tekeli
Tahtalı Barajı
Değirmendere
Ürkmez
Gümüşsuyu
Ahmetli
Doğanbey
Ahmetbeyli
Boğaziçi
38°00′
Özdere
Belevi
Selçuk
Hıdırköylü
Kuşadası Körfezi
Kuşadası
Çamlık
Gökçealan
Ortaklar
Germencik
İncirliova
1016
Turanlar
Acarlar
Soğucak
Sazlı
Büyükmenderes
Söke
Yeniköy
Bıyıklı
Haydarlı
Koçarlı
Çinçin
Bağarası
Davutlar
Güzelçamlı
Güllübahçe
Dilek Yarımadası Milli Parkı
Tuzburgaz
Özbaşı
Mersin
Doğanbey
Balat Ovası
Batı Menteşe
Sarıkemer
Camiçi Gölü
37°30′
Balat
Yeniköy
Akköy
Çamiçi
Kazıklı
1083
Selimiye
İlbır Dağı
Akbük Limanı
Yenihisar
GR
Ancona, Bari, Brindisi
Karlovasi
Avlakia
Samos
Palaiokastro
Leka
Kokkari
1153
Vigla 1433
Kallithea
Marathokampos
Mytilinioi
Vathy
Akrotirio Katavasi
Pyrgos
Chora
Pythagoreio
Akrotirio Fanari
Pagondas
Kolpos Marathokampou
Samiopoula
Samos
Σαμος
Ikaria
Ικαρια
Perdiki
Armenistis
Evdilos
Efanos 1037
Agios Kirykos
Raches
Fournoi
Agios Minas
Thymaina
Megalos Anthropofagos
Amalo
1033
Akrotirio Papas
Makronisi
Agathonisi
Tragonisi
Dodekanisos
Δωδεκανησος
Petrokaravo
Anydros
Arkoi
Patmos
Leipsoi
Skala
Farmakonisi
E
181
Güllük Körfezi
Güvercinlik
Akrotirio Stavri
Archangelos
Leros
Partheni
Agia Marina
Piganoussa
Apollonas
Donousa
Agia Paraskevi
Lakki
Xirokampo
Kalolimnos
Yalıkavak
Gölköy
Koronos
Moutsouna
Akrotirio Tilos
Ortakent
Danakos
Naxos
Ναξος
Zas 1001
Kalymnos
Bodrum
37°00′
Arginonta
Telendos
Levitha
Myrties
Vathys
Platí
Turgutreis
Kara Ada
Chorio
Kalymnos
Koufonisi
Kinaros
Mavria
Pserimos
F
Akrotirio Skandari
Rodos
Astypalaia
Liadi
Kato Koufonisi
Agios Georgios
Chorafakia 821
Aigiali
Kos
Akrotirio Agios Fokas
Keros
Nikouria
Schoinoussa
180
Antimacheia
Kardamaina
Amorgos
Katapola
Kato
177

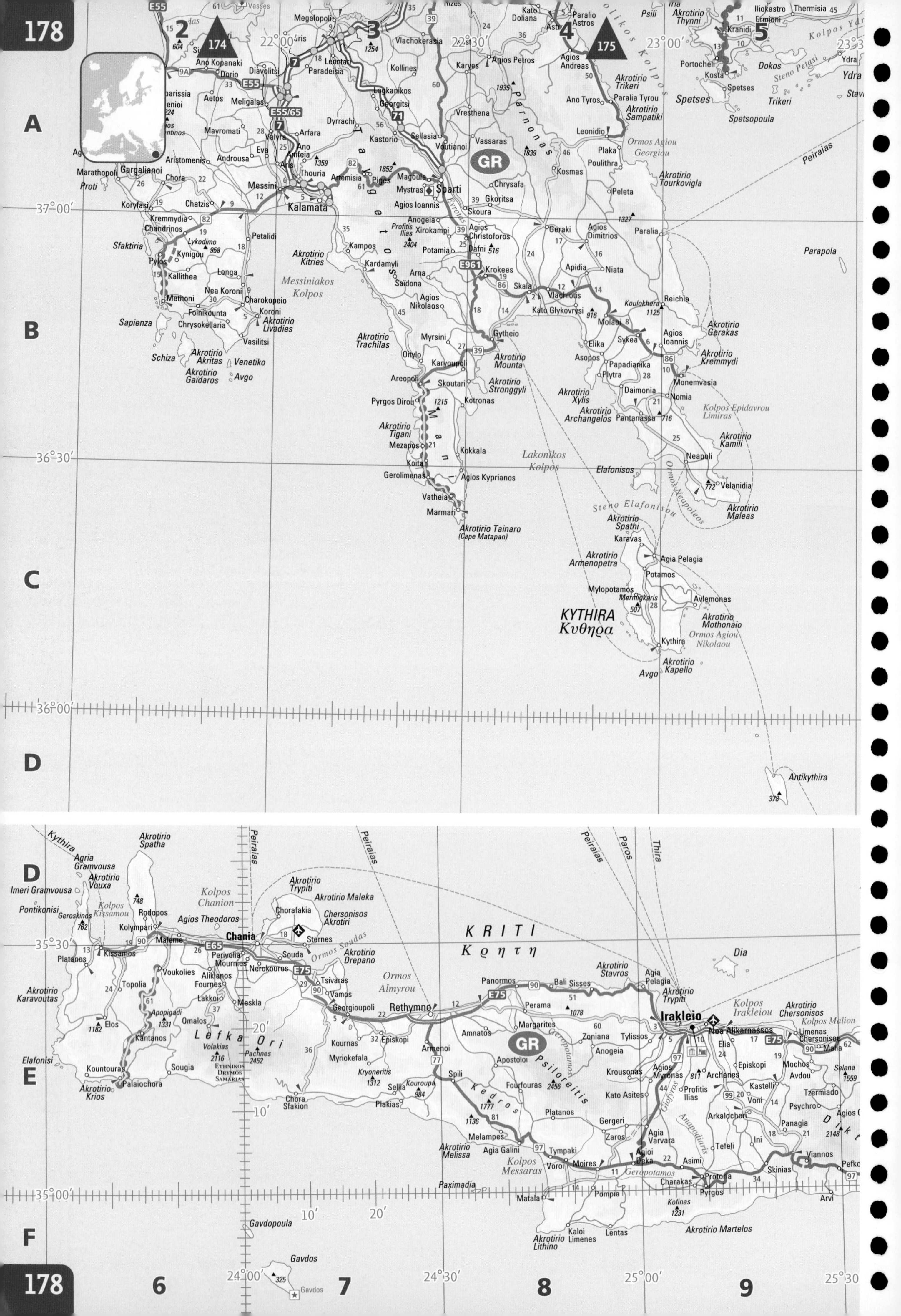

178
A
B
C
D
E
F
6
7
8
9
174
175
GR
Kalamata
Sparti
Mystras
Messini
Gargalianoi
Marathopoli
Proti
Koryfasi
Chatzis
Kremmydia
Chandrinos
Sfaktiria
Pylos
Kynigou
Lykodimo
Kallithea
Longa
Methoni
Nea Koroni
Charokopeio
Foinikounta
Koroni
Chrysokellaria
Vasilitsi
Sapienza
Schiza
Akrotirio Akritas
Akrotirio Gaidaros
Venetiko
Avgo
Akrotirio Livadies
Petalidi
Messiniakos Kolpos
Akrotirio Kitries
Kampos
Kardamyli
Saidona
Arna
Agios Nikolaos
Akrotirio Trachilas
Myrsini
Oitylo
Karyoupoli
Areopoli
Pyrgos Dirou
Skoutari
Kotronas
Akrotirio Tigani
Mezapos
Mani
Kokkala
Koita
Gerolimenas
Agios Kyprianos
Vatheia
Marmari
Akrotirio Tainaro
(Cape Matapan)
Gytheio
Akrotirio Mounta
Akrotirio Stronggyli
Taygetos
Profitis Ilias
Xirokampi
Anogeia
Potamia
Dafni
Krokees
Agios Christoforos
Agios Ioannis
Magoula
Piges
Artemisia
Thouria
Aris
Ano Amfeia
Arfara
Valyra
Eva
Androusa
Aristomenis
Chora
Mavromati
Dyrrachi
Meligalas
Aetos
Diavolitsi
Dorio
Ano Kopanaki
Megalopoli
Leontari
Paradeisia
Vlachokerasia
Kollines
Longkanikos
Georgitsi
Kastorio
Sellasia
Voutianoi
Vresthena
Karyes
Agios Petros
Vassaras
Parnonas
Chrysafa
Gkoritsa
Skoura
Kosmas
Geraki
Agios Dimitrios
Apidia
Niata
Skala
Vlachiotis
Kato Glykovrysi
Molaoi
Sykea
Elika
Asopos
Papadianika
Plytra
Daimonia
Pantanassa
Akrotirio Xylis
Akrotirio Archangelos
Lakonikos Kolpos
Elafonisos
Neapoli
Velanidia
Akrotirio Maleas
Ormos Neapoleos
Kolpos Epidavrou Limiras
Akrotirio Kamili
Nomia
Monemvasia
Akrotirio Kremmydi
Agios Ioannis
Akrotirio Gerakas
Reichia
Koulokhera
Paralia
Parapola
Akrotirio Tourkovigla
Peleta
Poulithra
Plaka
Leonidio
Ormos Agiou Georgiou
Akrotirio Sampatiki
Paralia Tyrou
Ano Tyros
Akrotirio Trikeri
Agios Andreas
Paralio Astros
Kato Doliana
Astros
Akrotirio Thynni
Psili
Portocheli
Kosta
Spetses
Spetsopoula
Kranidi
Iliokastro
Thermisia
Ermioni
Dokos
Trikeri
Ydra
Steno Petasi
Peiraias
Steno Elafonisou
Akrotirio Spathi
Karavas
Agia Pelagia
Potamos
Akrotirio Armenopetra
Mylopotamos
Mermigkaris
Avlemonas
KYTHIRA
Κυθηρα
Akrotirio Mothonaio
Ormos Agiou Nikolaou
Kythira
Akrotirio Kapello
Avgo
Antikythira
Kythira
Akrotirio Spatha
Agria Gramvousa
Akrotirio Vouxa
Imeri Gramvousa
Kolpos Kissamou
Pontikonisi
Geroskinos
Rodopos
Kolympari
Agios Theodoros
Kolpos Chanion
Akrotirio Trypiti
Akrotirio Maleka
Chorafakia
Chersonisos Akrotiri
Sternes
Chania
Maleme
Platanos
Kissamos
Perivolia
Mournies
Souda
Ormos Soudas
Akrotirio Drepano
Nerokouros
Tsivaras
Vamos
Alikianos
Fournes
Voukolies
Topolia
Akrotirio Karavoutas
Lakkoi
Meskla
Apopigadi
Omalos
Elos
Kantanos
Lefka Ori
Volakias
Pachnes
Ethnikos Drymos Samarias
Sougia
Elafonisi
Kountouras
Palaiochora
Akrotirio Krios
Georgioupoli
Ormos Almyrou
Rethymno
Kournas
Episkopi
Myriokefala
Kryoneritis
Sellia
Kouroupa
Plakias
Chora Sfakion
Gavdopoula
Gavdos
KRITI
Κρητη
Panormos
Bali
Sisses
Akrotirio Stavros
Agia Pelagia
Akrotirio Trypiti
Perama
Margarites
Amnatos
Armenoi
Apostoloi
Zoniana
Tylissos
Anogeia
Psiloreitis
Spili
Kedros
Fourfouras
Krousonas
Agios Myronas
Kato Asites
Platanos
Gergeri
Zaros
Agia Varvara
Melampes
Akrotirio Melissa
Agia Galini
Tympaki
Kolpos Messaras
Voroi
Moires
Agioi Deka
Geropotamos
Paximadia
Matala
Pompia
Kaloi Limenes
Lentas
Akrotirio Lithino
Kofinas
Charakas
Pyrgos
Protoria
Asimi
Tefeli
Anapodiaris
Akrotirio Martelos
Irakleio
Kolpos Irakleiou
Nea Alikarnassos
Dia
Elia
Archanes
Profitis Ilias
Episkopi
Voni
Kastelli
Arkalochori
Ini
Panagia
Viannos
Skinias
Arvi
Pefko
Mochos
Avdou
Tzermiado
Psychro
Agios
Akrotirio Chersonisos
Limenas Chersonisou
Kolpos Malion
Malia
Selena
Dikti
Paros
Thira
37°00′
36°30′
36°00′
35°30′
35°00′
22°00′
22°30′
23°00′
24°00′
24°30′
25°00′
25°30′

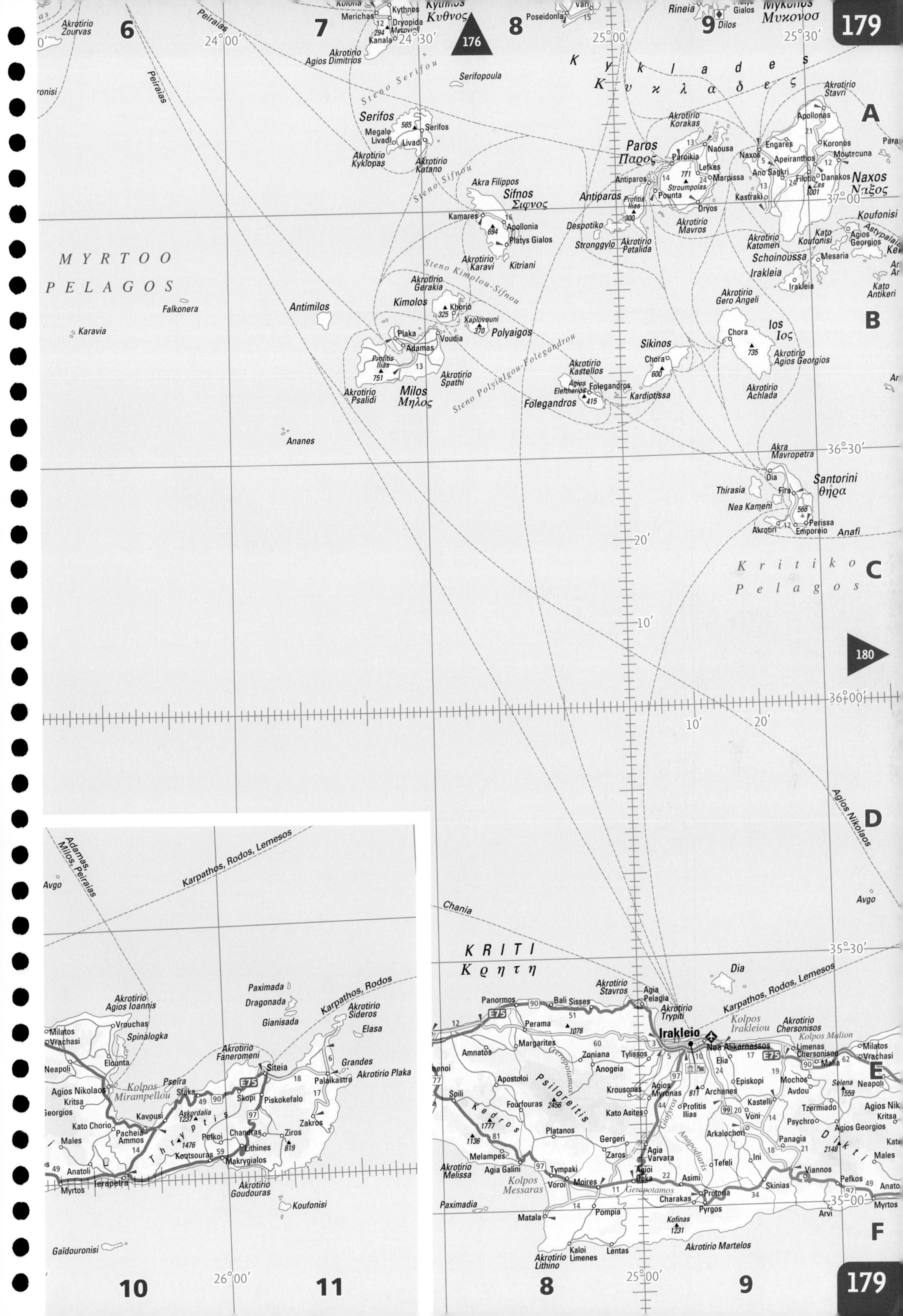

Kyklades
Κυκλαδες
MYRTOO PELAGOS
Kritiko Pelagos
KRITI
Κρητη
Serifos
Sifnos
Σιφνος
Paros
Παρος
Naxos
Ναξος
Antiparos
Kimolos
Milos
Μηλος
Polyaigos
Antimilos
Folegandros
Sikinos
Ios
Ιος
Santorini
Θηρα
Thirasia
Anafi
Irakleia
Schoinoussa
Koufonisi
Despotiko
Ananes
Falkonera
Karavia
Serifopoula
Mykonos
Μυκονος
Kythnos
Κυθνος
Dilos
Rineia
Dia
Irakleio
Kolpos Irakleiou
Kolpos Messaras
Kolpos Mirampellou
Psiloreitis
Kedros
Dikti
Thryptis
Agios Nikolaos
Siteia
Ierapetra
Chersonisos
Malia
Arkalochori
Moires
Matala
Paximadia
Koufonisi
Gaidouronisi
Karpathos, Rodos, Lemesos
Chania
Peiraias
Adamas, Milos, Peiraias
Steno Serifou
Steno Sifnou
Steno Kimolou-Sifnou
Steno Polyaigou-Folegandrou
176
180

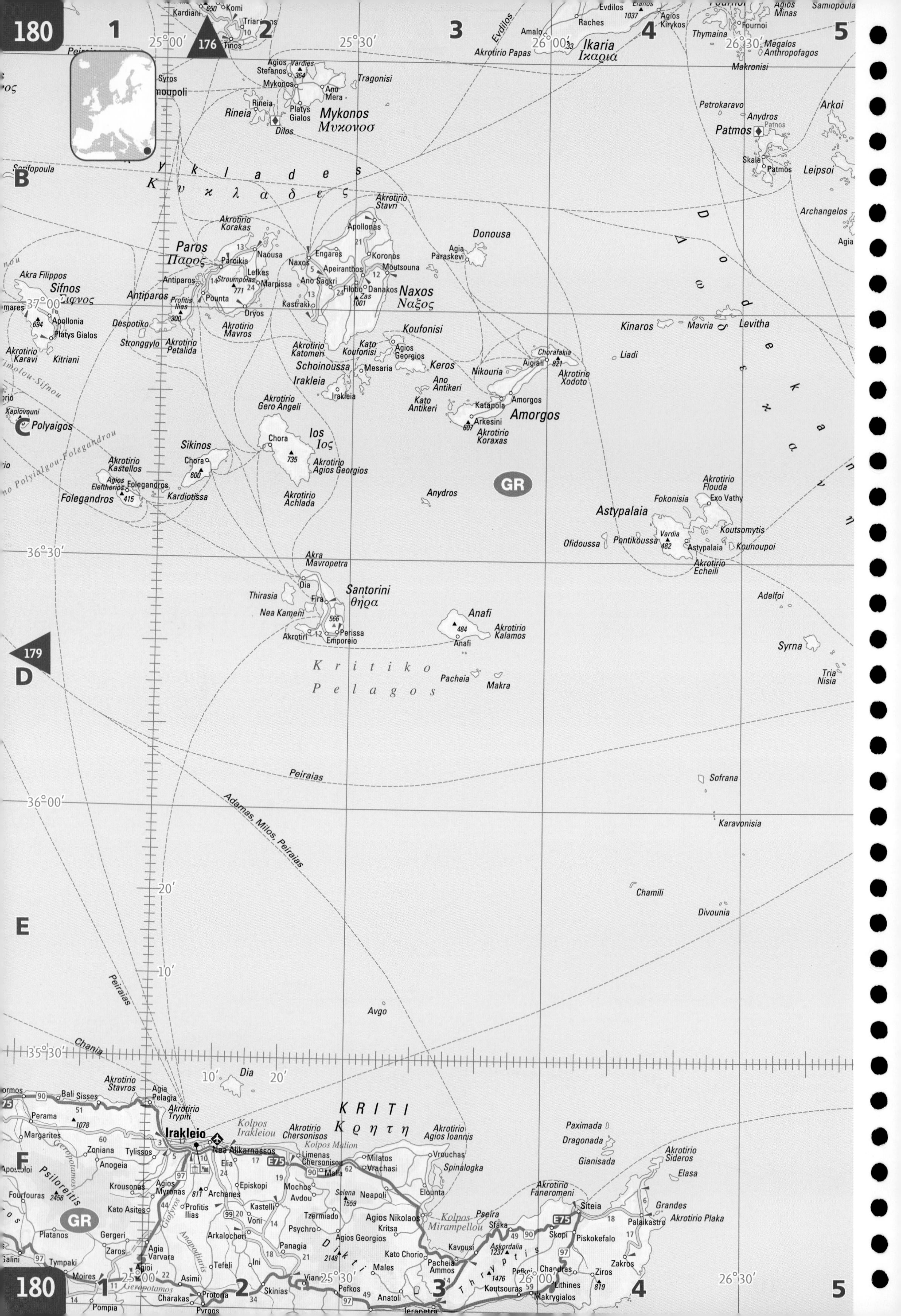

Kyklades
Κυκλαδες
Mykonos
Μυκονοσ
Naxos
Ναξος
Paros
Παρος
Sifnos
Σιφνος
Ios
Ιος
Santorini
θηρα
Amorgos
Astypalaia
Anafi
Ikaria
Ικαρια
Patmos
Kritiko Pelagos
KRITI
Κρητη
Irakleio
GR
Dodekanisa
Δωδεκανησα
36°30′
36°00′
35°30′
25°00′
25°30′
26°00′
26°30′

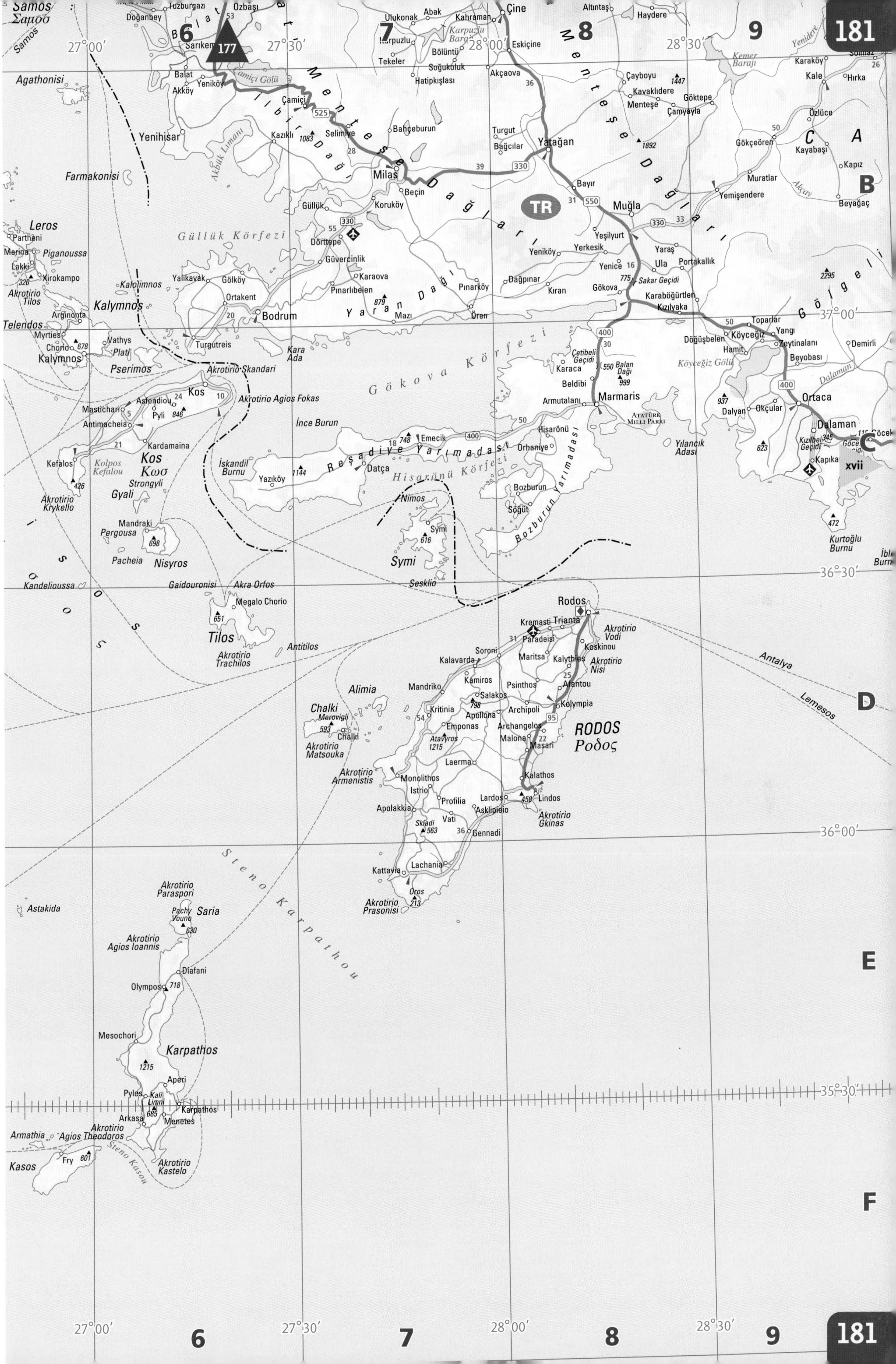

Samos
Σαμος
Agathonisi
Farmakonisi
Leros
Partheni
Lakki
Xirokampo
Kalolimnos
Kalymnos
Telendos
Myrties
Vathys
Platí
Kalymnos
Pserimos
Kos
Κως
Asfendiou
Pyli
Mastichari
Antimacheia
Kardamaina
Kefalos
Kolpos Kefalou
Strongyli
Gyali
Akrotirio Krykello
Mandraki
Pergousa
Pacheia
Nisyros
Kandelioussa
Gaidouronisi
Akra Orfos
Megalo Chorio
Tilos
Akrotirio Trachilos
Antitilos
Alimia
Chalki
Akrotirio Matsouka
Akrotirio Armenistis
Rodos
Ροδος
RODOS
Kremasti
Trianta
Paradeisi
Kalavarda
Soroni
Maritsa
Kalythies
Koskinou
Akrotirio Vodi
Akrotirio Nisi
Kamiros
Mandriko
Psinthos
Afantou
Salakos
Kritinia
Apollona
Archipoli
Kolympia
Emponas
Archangelos
Atavyros
Malona
Masari
Laerma
Kalathos
Monolithos
Istrio
Profilia
Lardos
Lindos
Apolakkia
Asklipieio
Akrotirio Gkinas
Vati
Gennadi
Lachania
Kattavia
Akrotirio Prasonisi
Steno Karpathou
Astakida
Akrotirio Paraspori
Saria
Akrotirio Agios Ioannis
Diafani
Olympos
Mesochori
Karpathos
Aperi
Pyles
Kali Limni
Karpathos
Arkasa
Menetes
Armathia
Akrotirio Agios Theodoros
Kasos
Fry
Steno Kasou
Akrotirio Kastelo
Bodrum
Turgutreis
Yalıkavak
Gölköy
Ortakent
Kara Ada
Akrotirio Skandari
Akrotirio Agios Fokas
İnce Burun
İskandil Burnu
Yazıköy
Datça
Reşadiye Yarımadası
Hisarönü Körfezi
Gökova Körfezi
Güllük Körfezi
Güllük
Dörttepe
Güvercinlik
Karaova
Pınarlıbelen
Yaran Dağı
Mazı
Ören
Pınarköy
Milas
Beçin
Koruköy
Selimiye
Kazıklı
Çamiçi
Çamiçi Gölü
Bahçeburun
Yenihisar
Akbük Limanı
Menteşe Dağları
İlbir Dağı
Balat
Akköy
Yeniköy
Sarıkemer
Doğanbey
Tuzburgazı
Özbaşı
Ulukonak
Abak
Kahraman
Çine
Karpuzlu
Karpuzlu Barajı
Bölüntü
Tekeler
Soğukoluk
Hatipkışlası
Eskiçine
Akçaova
Turgut
Bağcılar
Yatağan
Bayır
Muğla
Yeşilyurt
Yeniköy
Yerkesik
Yenice
Dağpınar
Kıran
Gökova
Sakar Geçidi
Ula
Yaraş
Portakallık
Karaböğürtlen
Kızılyaka
Çetibeli Geçidi
Karaca
Balan Dağı
Beldibi
Marmaris
Armutalanı
Atatürk Milli Parkı
Hisarönü
Orhaniye
Bozburun
Bozburun Yarımadası
Söğüt
Emecik
Nimos
Symi
Seskio
Altıntaş
Haydere
Çayboyu
Kavaklıdere
Menteşe
Göktepe
Çamyayla
Kemer Barajı
Yenidere
Karaköy
Kale
Hırka
Özlüce
Gökçeören
Kayabaşı
Kapız
Muratlar
Yemişendere
Beyağaç
Akçay
Gölgeli Dağları
Toparlar
Yangı
Döğüşbelen
Köyceğiz
Hamit
Zeytinalanı
Beyobası
Demirli
Köyceğiz Gölü
Dalaman
Dalyan
Okçular
Ortaca
Kızılbel Geçidi
Kapıkaya
Yılancık Adası
Kurtoğlu Burnu
Antalya
Lemesos
TR
27°00′
27°30′
28°00′
28°30′
37°00′
36°30′
36°00′
35°30′
6
7
8
9
A
B
C
D
E
F
177
xvii

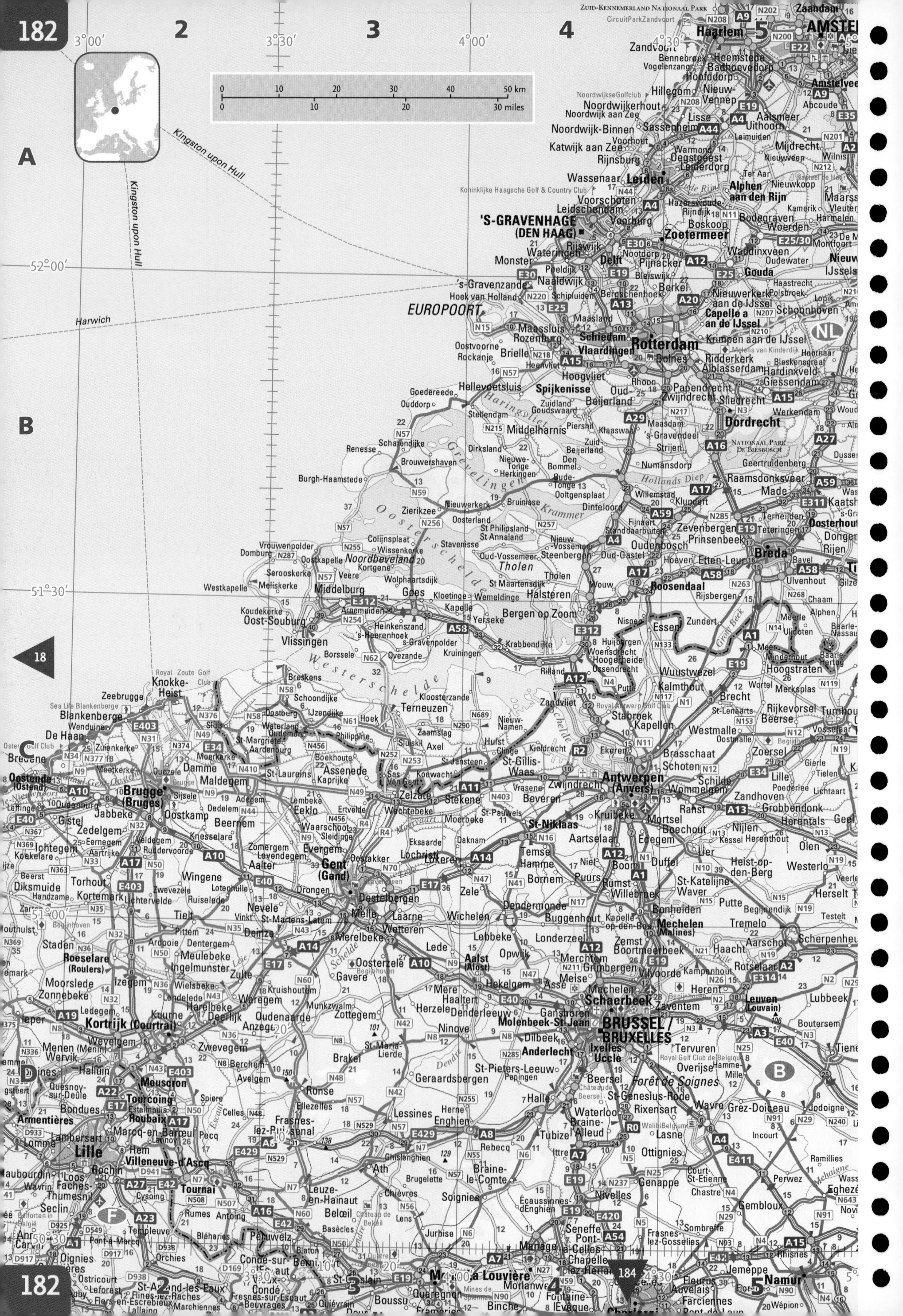

3°00′
2
3°30′
3
4°00′
4
4°30′
5
A
B
C
D
0 10 20 30 40 50 km
0 10 20 30 miles
Kingston upon Hull
Harwich
52°00′
51°30′
51°00′
50°30′
18
184
NL
B
F
Zuid-Kennemerland Nationaal Park
CircuitParkZandvoort
Haarlem
AMSTERDAM
Zandvoort
Bennebroek
Heemstede
Vogelenzang
Badhoevedorp
Hoofddorp
Hillegom
Nieuw-Vennep
Noordwijkerhout
Noordwijk aan Zee
Lisse
Aalsmeer
Uithoorn
Amstelveen
Abcoude
Noordwijk-Binnen
Sassenheim
Voorhout
Katwijk aan Zee
Warmond
Oegstgeest
Leiderdorp
Rijnsburg
Mijdrecht
Wilnis
Wassenaar
Leiden
Ter Aar
Nieuwkoop
Alphen aan den Rijn
Koninklijke Haagsche Golf & Country Club
Voorschoten
Leidschendam
Hazerswoude-Rijndijk
Bodegraven
Boskoop
Woerden
Kamerik
Harmelen
Vleuten
Maarssen
'S-GRAVENHAGE (DEN HAAG)
Voorburg
Zoetermeer
Rijswijk
Wateringen
Monster
Poeldijk
Naaldwijk
Delft
Nootdorp
Pijnacker
Bleiswijk
Waddinxveen
Oudewater
Gouda
Haastrecht
Berkel
Bergschenhoek
Schipluiden
's-Gravenzande
Hoek van Holland
EUROPOORT
Nieuwerkerk aan de IJssel
Capelle a an de IJssel
Schoonhoven
Lopik
Maassluis
Maasland
Rozenburg
Schiedam
Vlaardingen
Rotterdam
Krimpen aan de IJssel
Molens van Kinderdijk
Oostvoorne
Rockanje
Brielle
Heenvliet
Hoogvliet
Bolnes
Ridderkerk
Alblasserdam
Bleskensgraaf
Hardinxveld-Giessendam
Goedereede
Ouddorp
Hellevoetsluis
Spijkenisse
Oud-Beijerland
Rhoon
Papendrecht
Zwijndrecht
Sliedrecht
Werkendam
Haringvliet
Stellendam
Zuidland
Goudswaard
Piershil
Middelharnis
Klaaswaal
Maasdam
's-Gravendeel
Strijen
Dordrecht
Nationaal Park De Biesbosch
Renesse
Scharendijke
Dirksland
Nieuwe-Tonge
Herkingen
Zuid-Beijerland
Den Bommel
Ooltgensplaat
Numansdorp
Hollands Diep
Geertruidenberg
Dussen
Brouwershaven
Grevelingen
Burgh-Haamstede
Oude-Tonge
Willemstad
Klundert
Raamsdonksveer
Made
Kaatsheuvel
Zierikzee
Nieuwerkerk
Bruinisse
Krammer
Dinteloord
Oosterhout
Terheijden
Teteringen
Oosterland
Oosterschelde
St Philipsland
St Annaland
Fijnaart
Standdaarbuiten
Zevenbergen
Prinsenbeek
Dongen
Rijen
Colijnsplaat
Wissenkerke
Stavenisse
Nieuw-Vossemeer
Oudenbosch
Breda
Vrouwenpolder
Domburg
Oostkapelle
Noordbeveland
Kortgene
Oud-Vossemeer
Tholen
Steenbergen
Oud-Gastel
Hoeven
Etten-Leur
Bavel
Ulvenhout
Gilze
Serooskerke
Veere
Wolphaartsdijk
Westkapelle
Meliskerke
Middelburg
Goes
Kloetinge
Wemeldinge
St Maartensdijk
Halsteren
Wouw
Roosendaal
Rijsbergen
Chaam
Koudekerke
Oost-Souburg
Arnemuiden
Kapelle
Yerseke
Bergen op Zoom
Nispen
Essen
Zundert
Alphen
Baarle-Nassau
Vlissingen
Heinkenszand
's-Heerenhoek
's-Gravenpolder
Krabbendijke
Huijbergen
Woensdrecht
Hoogerheide
Ossendrecht
Meer
Minderhout
Baarle-Hertog
Hoogstraten
Borssele
Ovezande
Kruiningen
Westerschelde
Rilland
Wuustwezel
Wortel
Merksplas
Royal Zoute Golf Club
Knokke-Heist
Breskens
Schoondijke
Kloosterzande
Putte
Kalmthout
Brecht
Zeebrugge
Sea Life Blankenberge
Blankenberge
Wenduine
Terneuzen
IJzendijke
Oostburg
Waterland-Oudeman
Hoek
Zaamslag
Nieuw-Namen
Zandvliet
Royal Antwerp Golf Club
Stabroek
Kapellen
St-Lenaarts
Rijkevorsel
Turnhout
Beerse
Vosselaar
De Haan
Zuienkerke
Sluis
St-Margriete
Aardenburg
Philippine
Sluiskil
Axel
Hulst
Clinge
Kieldrecht
Ekeren
Westmalle
Oostmalle
Zoersel
Gierle
Tielen
Bredene
Moerkerke
Damme
Boekhoute
Assenede
Kaprijke
St Jansteen
Koewacht
St-Gillis-Waas
Brasschaat
Schoten
Schilde
Lille
Poederlee
Lichtaart
Oostende (Ostend)
Meetkerke
Oudzele
Brugge (Bruges)
Maldegem
St-Laureins
Sas van Gent
Zelzate
Stekene
Zwijndrecht
Antwerpen (Anvers)
Wommelgem
Zandhoven
Grobbendonk
Oudenburg
Sijsele
Jabbeke
Oedelem
Adegem
Eeklo
Ertvelde
Wachtebeke
Vrasene
Beveren
Ranst
Herentals
Leffinge
Gistel
Oostkamp
Beernem
Lembeke
Waarschoot
Sleidinge
Moerbeke
St-Pauwels
St-Niklaas
Kruibeke
Mortsel
Boechout
Nijlen
Zedelgem
Knesselare
Eksaarde
Daknam
Aartselaar
Edegem
Kessel
Herenthout
Olen
Ichtegem
Eernegem
Aartrijke
Veldegem
Ruddervoorde
Zomergem
Lovendegem
Evergem
Temse
Hamme
Niel
Boom
Lier
Koekelare
Wingene
Aalter
Gent (Gand)
Oostakker
Lochristi
Lokeren
Duffel
Heist-op-den-Berg
Westerlo
Diksmuide
Torhout
Lotenhulle
Bornem
Puurs
Rumst
St-Katelijne-Waver
Kortemark
Lichtervelde
Zwevezele
Ruiselede
Drongen
Destelbergen
Zele
Willebroek
Putte
Veerle
Herselt
Tielt
Nevele
Vinkt
St-Martens-Latem
Melle
Laarne
Wichelen
Dendermonde
Buggenhout
Kapelle-op-den-Bos
Bonheiden
Mechelen (Malines)
Begijnendijk
Testelt
Pittem
Dentergem
Deinze
Merelbeke
Wetteren
Lebbeke
Londerzeel
Tremelo
Aarschot
Scherpenheuvel
Staden
Ardooie
Lede
Zemst
Boortmeerbeek
Haacht
Roeselare (Roulers)
Meulebeke
Ingelmunster
Oosterzele
Aalst (Alost)
Opwijk
Merchtem
Grimbergen
Vilvoorde
Kampenhout
Rotselaar
Moorslede
Izegem
Zulte
Gavere
Meise
Asse
Herent
Zonnebeke
Wielsbeke
Lendelede
Harelbeke
Waregem
Kruishoutem
Munkzwalm
Mere
Haaltert
Hekelgem
Machelen
Schaerbeek
Zaventem
Leuven (Louvain)
Lubbeek
Ieper
Ledegem
Kuurne
Deerlijk
Oudenaarde
Zottegem
Herzele
Denderleeuw
Ganshoren
Molenbeek-St-Jean
BRUSSEL / BRUXELLES
Kortrijk (Courtrai)
Anzegem
Ninove
Boutersem
Tienen
Menen (Menin)
Wevelgem
Wervik
Zwevegem
St-Maria-Lierde
Dilbeek
Ixelles
Uccle
Tervuren
Anderlecht
Royal Golf Club de Belgique
Overijse
Hamme-Mille
Halluin
Mouscron
Berchem
Avelgem
Brakel
St-Pieters-Leeuw
Pepingen
Beersel
Forêt de Soignes
Quesnoy-sur-Deûle
Ronse
Geraardsbergen
Dendre
Armentières
Bondues
Tourcoing
Roubaix
Spiere
Celles
Ellezelles
Lessines
Herne
Enghien
Halle
St-Genesius-Rode
Rixensart
Wavre
Grez-Doiceau
Jodoigne
Lambersart
Lomme
Lille
Marcq-en-Barœul
Pecq
Hem
Villeneuve-d'Ascq
Frasnes-lez-Buissenal
Ghislenghien
Tubize
Braine-l'Alleud
Waterloo
Lasne
Incourt
Ramillies
Haubourdin
Loos
Faches-Thumesnil
Wavrin
Seclin
Templeuve
Rochin
Tournai
Cysoing
Rumes
Antoing
Ath
Leuze-en-Hainaut
Brugelette
Chièvres
Beloeil
Lens
Soignies
Rebecq
Braine-le-Comte
Ittre
Ottignies
Court-St-Étienne
Chastre
Genappe
Nivelles
Perwez
Eghezée
Gembloux
Écaussinnes-d'Enghien
Orchies
Bléharies
Péruwelz
Basècles
Jurbise
Seneffe
Pont-à-Celles
Fraslies-lez-Gosselies
Sombreffe
Rhisnes
Carvin
Oignies
Ostricourt
Leforest
Flers-en-Escrebieux
Lallaing
Pont-à-Marcq
Condé-sur-l'Escaut
Fresnes-sur-Escaut
St-Amand-les-Eaux
Flines-lez-Raches
Marchiennes
Beuvrages
Bernissart
St-Ghislain
Quiévrain
Boussu
Mons
Quaregnon
Frameries
La Louvière
Morlanwelz
Binche
Manage
Chapelle-lez-Herlaimont
Fontaine-l'Évêque
Charleroi
Fleurus
Auvelais
Farciennes
Jemeppe
Floreffe
Namur
Wépion

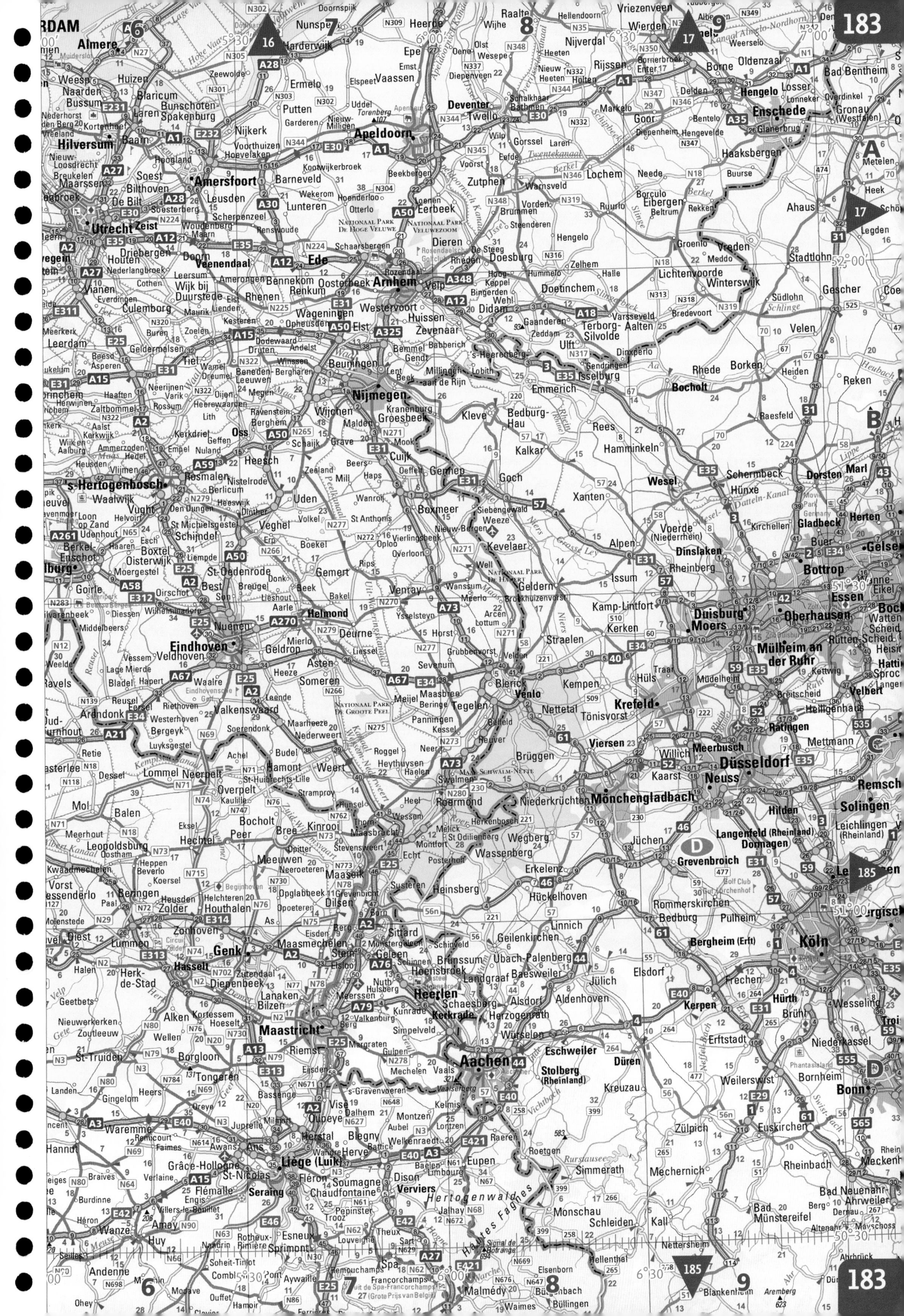
183
Almere
Harderwijk
Nunspeet
Heerde
Raalte
Wijhe
Nijverdal
Wierden
Hellendoorn
Vriezenveen
Weesp
Huizen
Naarden
Bussum
Blaricum
Bunschoten-Spakenburg
Ermelo
Putten
Vaassen
Epe
Deventer
Twello
Rijssen
Borne
Oldenzaal
Hengelo
Enschede
Bad Bentheim
Gronau (Westfalen)
Losser
Hilversum
Baarn
Nijkerk
Apeldoorn
Gorssel
Markelo
Goor
Haaksbergen
Soest
Amersfoort
Barneveld
Zutphen
Lochem
Neede
Eibergen
Ahaus
Bilthoven
De Bilt
Utrecht
Zeist
Leusden
Lunteren
Otterlo
Eerbeek
Vorden
Ruurlo
Borculo
Veenendaal
Ede
Dieren
Doesburg
Groenlo
Vreden
Stadtlohn
Houten
Driebergen
Doorn
Wijk bij Duurstede
Rhenen
Bennekom
Renkum
Oosterbeek
Arnhem
Velp
Doetinchem
Lichtenvoorde
Winterswijk
Südlohn
Gescher
Vianen
Culemborg
Wageningen
Westervoort
Huissen
Zevenaar
Didam
Terborg-Silvolde
Aalten
Velen
Leerdam
Tiel
Elst
Bemmel
Ulft
Dinxperlo
Isselburg
Emmerich
Rhede
Borken
Bocholt
Reken
Beuningen
Nijmegen
Wijchen
Groesbeek
Kranenburg
Kleve
Bedburg-Hau
Rees
Kalkar
Hamminkeln
Raesfeld
Zaltbommel
Oss
Grave
Cuijk
Gennep
Goch
Wesel
Schermbeck
Dorsten
Marl
's-Hertogenbosch
Rosmalen
Heesch
Uden
Boxmeer
Weeze
Xanten
Hünxe
Gladbeck
Herten
Gelsenkirchen
Waalwijk
Vught
Veghel
Schijndel
Boxtel
Oisterwijk
Kevelaer
Alpen
Voerde (Niederrhein)
Dinslaken
Bottrop
Goirle
Best
St-Oedenrode
Gemert
Venray
Geldern
Issum
Rheinberg
Essen
Helmond
Deurne
Horst
Kamp-Lintfort
Duisburg
Moers
Oberhausen
Eindhoven
Nuenen
Veldhoven
Geldrop
Asten
Someren
Straelen
Kerken
Mülheim an der Ruhr
Waalre
Valkenswaard
Blerick
Venlo
Tegelen
Kempen
Krefeld
Hüls
Velbert
Ratingen
Heiligenhaus
Tönisvorst
Nettetal
Viersen
Meerbusch
Düsseldorf
Neuss
Willich
Kaarst
Mettmann
Weert
Roggel
Brüggen
Lommel
Neerpelt
Overpelt
Mol
Balen
Roermond
Niederkrüchten
Mönchengladbach
Hilden
Solingen
Remscheid
Bocholt
Bree
Kinrooi
Peer
Hechtel
Leopoldsburg
Wegberg
Wassenberg
Jüchen
Grevenbroich
Langenfeld (Rheinland)
Dormagen
Leichlingen (Rheinland)
Meeuwen
Maaseik
Echt
Erkelenz
Heinsberg
Hückelhoven
Beringen
Zolder
Houthalen
Dilsen
Rommerskirchen
Bedburg
Pulheim
Diest
Zonhoven
Genk
Sittard
Geleen
Linnich
Geilenkirchen
Bergheim (Erft)
Köln
Lummen
Hasselt
Maasmechelen
Brunssum
Hoensbroek
Ubach-Palenberg
Baesweiler
Landgraaf
Herk-de-Stad
Diepenbeek
Lanaken
Bilzen
Heerlen
Kerkrade
Alsdorf
Herzogenrath
Jülich
Aldenhoven
Elsdorf
Frechen
Kerpen
Hürth
Brühl
Wesseling
Maastricht
Würselen
Eschweiler
Düren
Erftstadt
Niederkassel
Sint-Truiden
Tongeren
Borgloon
Riemst
Aachen
Stolberg (Rheinland)
Kreuzau
Weilerswist
Bornheim
Bonn
Visé
Oupeye
Herstal
Blegny
Zülpich
Euskirchen
Waremme
Ans
Liège (Luik)
Herve
Eupen
Roetgen
Simmerath
Mechernich
Rheinbach
Seraing
Flémalle
Fléron
Soumagne
Chaudfontaine
Dison
Verviers
Monschau
Schleiden
Kall
Bad Neuenahr-Ahrweiler
Bad Münstereifel
Amay
Wanze
Huy
Esneux
Theux
Spa
Andenne
Malmédy
Büllingen
Hellenthal
Nettersheim
Blankenheim
Hertogenwald
Hautes Fagnes
Nationaal Park De Hoge Veluwe
Nationaal Park Veluwezoom
Nationaal Park De Maasduinen
Nationaal Park De Groote Peel
Maas-Schwalm-Nette
183

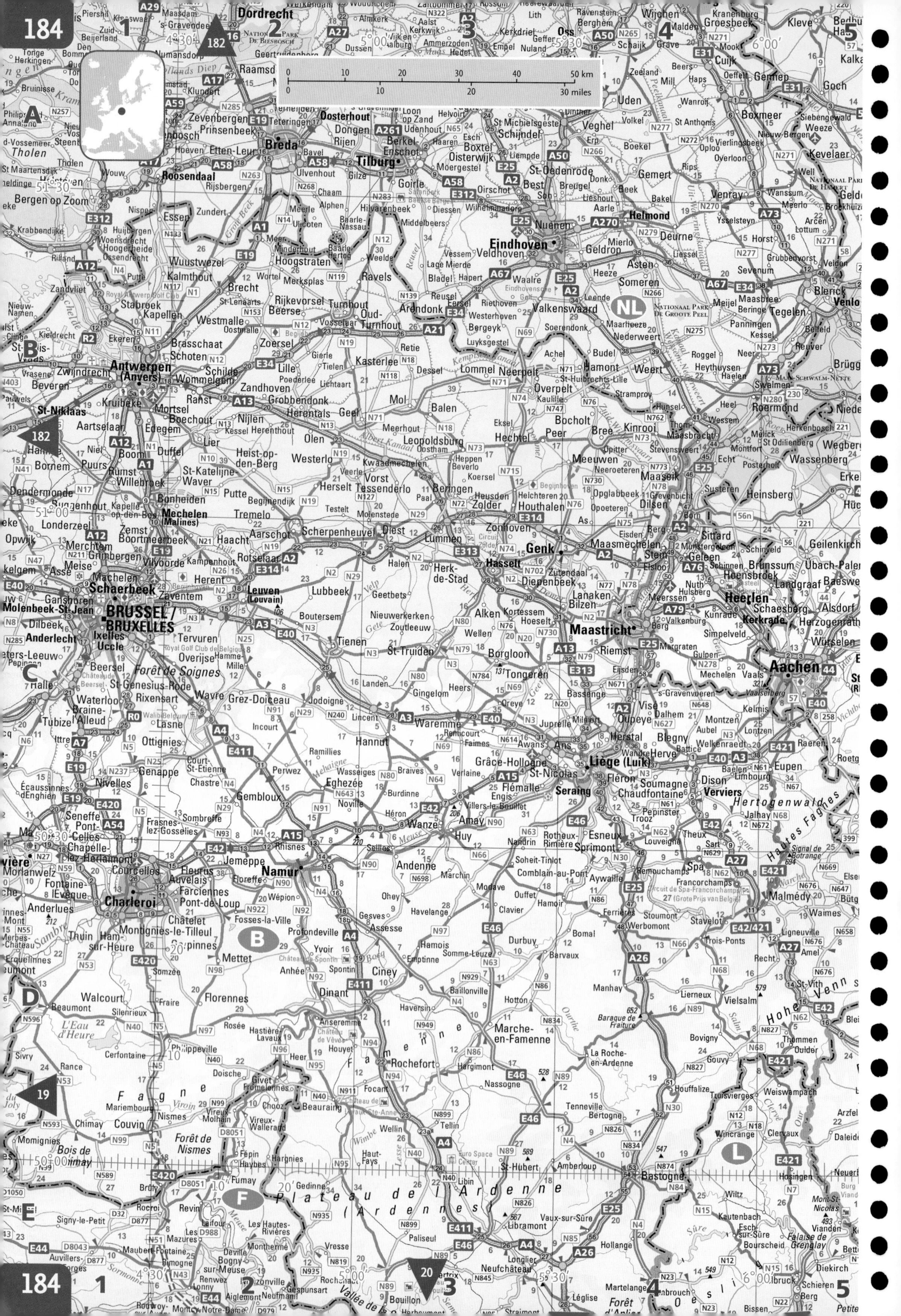

0 10 20 30 40 50 km
0 10 20 30 miles
182
19
20
NL
B
F
L
Dordrecht
Breda
Tilburg
Oosterhout
Roosendaal
Bergen op Zoom
Eindhoven
Helmond
Venlo
Roermond
Weert
Antwerpen (Anvers)
St-Niklaas
Mechelen (Malines)
Turnhout
Geel
Mol
Lommel
Neerpelt
Overpelt
Hasselt
Genk
Maastricht
Sittard
Geleen
Heerlen
Kerkrade
Aachen
Leuven (Louvain)
Schaerbeek
BRUSSEL / BRUXELLES
Anderlecht
Uccle
Tienen
St-Truiden
Tongeren
Liège (Luik)
Seraing
Verviers
Eupen
Spa
Malmédy
Namur
Charleroi
Huy
Dinant
Ciney
Rochefort
Marche-en-Famenne
La Roche-en-Ardenne
Bastogne
St-Hubert
Libramont
Neufchâtel
Bouillon
Nivelles
Wavre
Gembloux
Waremme
Hannut
Jodoigne
Philippeville
Couvin
Chimay
Fumay
Givet
Rocroi
Hertogenwald
Hautes Fagnes
Hohe Venn
Forêt de Soignes
Plateau de l'Ardenne (Ardennes)
Fagne
Famenne
Oesling
184 1 2 3 4 5
A B C D E

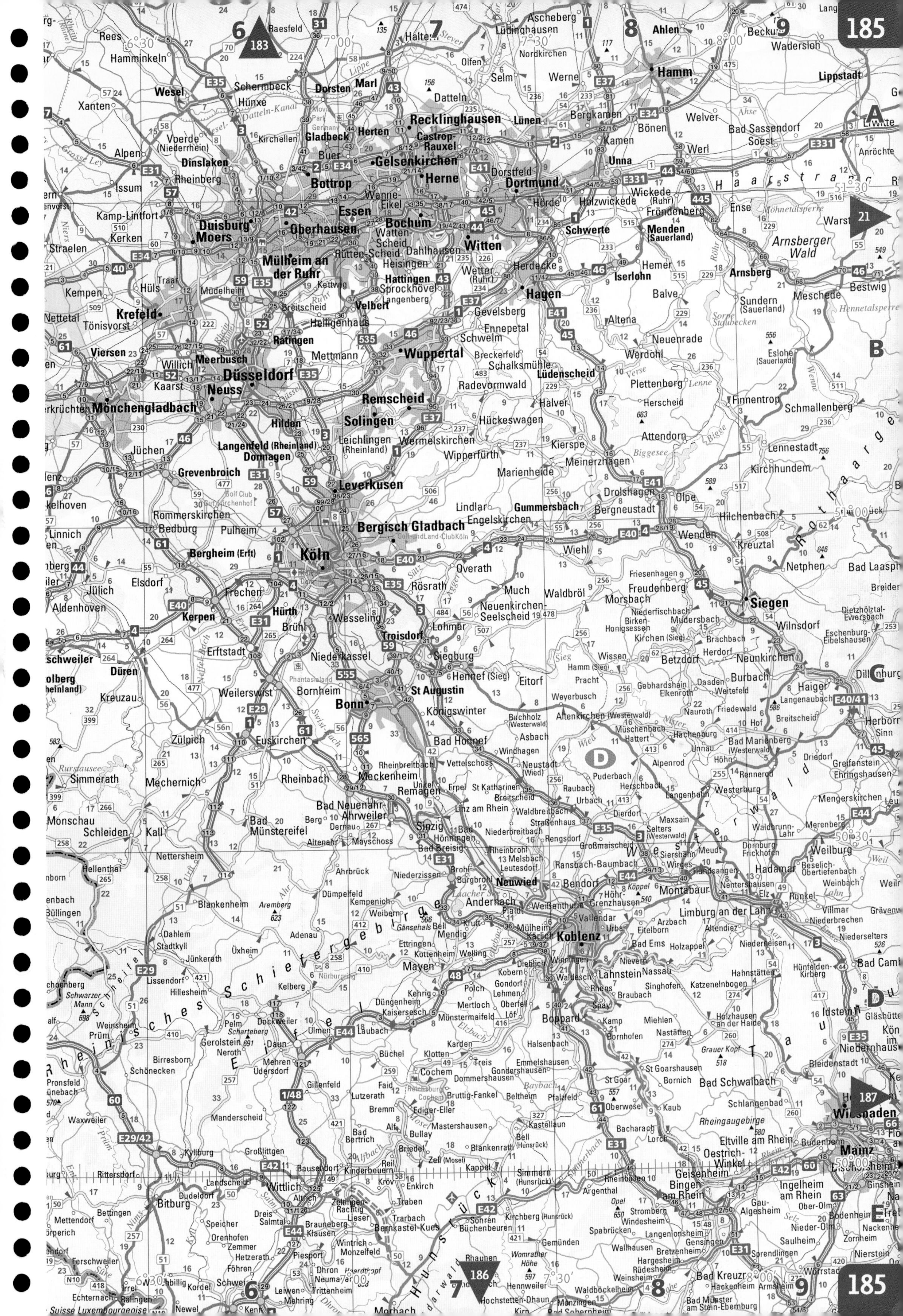
Rees
Hamminkeln
Raesfeld
Haltern
Ascheberg
Lüdinghausen
Nordkirchen
Ahlen
Beckum
Wadersloh
Wesel
Schermbeck
Dorsten
Marl
Olfen
Selm
Werne
Hamm
Lippstadt
Xanten
Hünxe
Datteln
Recklinghausen
Lünen
Bergkamen
Welver
Bad Sassendorf
Soest
Voerde (Niederrhein)
Kirchhellen
Gladbeck
Herten
Castrop-Rauxel
Kamen
Bönen
Werl
Alpen
Dinslaken
Buer
Gelsenkirchen
Dorstfeld
Unna
Rheinberg
Bottrop
Herne
Dortmund
Wickede (Ruhr)
Haarstrang
Issum
Wanne-Eikel
Hörde
Holzwickede
Fröndenberg
Ense
Möhnetalsperre
Kamp-Lintfort
Duisburg
Moers
Essen
Oberhausen
Bochum
Schwerte
Menden (Sauerland)
Warstein
Kerken
Straelen
Watten-Scheid
Rütten-Scheid
Dahlhausen
Witten
Arnsberger Wald
Mülheim an der Ruhr
Heisingen
Herdecke
Hemer
Iserlohn
Arnsberg
Meschede
Bestwig
Kempen
Hüls
Mündelheim
Kettwig
Hattingen
Sprockhövel
Wetter (Ruhr)
Hagen
Balve
Sundern (Sauerland)
Nettetal
Krefeld
Tönisvorst
Breitscheid
Langenberg
Velbert
Gevelsberg
Altena
Heiligenhaus
Ennepetal
Schwelm
Neuenrade
Viersen
Ratingen
Wuppertal
Eslohe (Sauerland)
Willich
Meerbusch
Mettmann
Breckerfeld
Werdohl
Düsseldorf
Kaarst
Neuss
Schalksmühle
Lüdenscheid
Plettenberg
Radevormwald
Mönchengladbach
Remscheid
Halver
Finnentrop
Schmallenberg
Hilden
Solingen
Hückeswagen
Herscheid
Langenfeld (Rheinland)
Dormagen
Leichlingen (Rheinland)
Wermelskirchen
Attendorn
Biggesee
Jüchen
Wipperfürth
Kierspe
Meinerzhagen
Lennestadt
Grevenbroich
Marienheide
Kirchhundem
Leverkusen
Drolshagen
Olpe
Kelhoven
Rommerskirchen
Lindlar
Gummersbach
Bergneustadt
Hilchenbach
Bedburg
Pulheim
Bergisch Gladbach
Engelskirchen
Wenden
Kreuztal
Linnich
Bergheim (Erft)
Köln
Wiehl
Netphen
Bad Laasphe
Elsdorf
Overath
Friesenhagen
Jülich
Frechen
Much
Waldbröl
Freudenberg
Siegen
Aldenhoven
Kerpen
Hürth
Wesseling
Rösrath
Neuenkirchen-Seelscheid
Morsbach
Lohmar
Mudersbach
Wilnsdorf
Brühl
Troisdorf
Erftstadt
Niederkassel
Siegburg
Wissen
Betzdorf
Herdorf
Neunkirchen
Düren
Hennef (Sieg)
Eitorf
Burbach
Dillenburg
Weilerswist
Bornheim
St Augustin
Haiger
Kreuzau
Bonn
Königswinter
Altenkirchen (Westerwald)
Herborn
Hachenburg
Zülpich
Euskirchen
Bad Honnef
Asbach
Bad Marienberg
Rheinbreitbach
Neustadt (Wied)
Puderbach
Simmerath
Mechernich
Rheinbach
Meckenheim
Remagen
Westerburg
Bad Neuenahr-Ahrweiler
Linz am Rhein
Monschau
Schleiden
Kall
Bad Münstereifel
Sinzig
Bad Hönningen
Bad Breisig
Maxsain
Selters (Westerwald)
Westerwald
Weilburg
Nettersheim
Ahrbrück
Andernach
Neuwied
Bendorf
Montabaur
Hadamar
Blankenheim
Mayen
Koblenz
Vallendar
Limburg an der Lahn
Bad Ems
Lahnstein
Nassau
Stadtkyll
Gerolstein
Daun
Boppard
Nastätten
Idstein
Prüm
Ulmen
Cochem
St Goar
Taunus
Bad Schwalbach
Wiesbaden
Kastellaun
Bacharach
Eltville am Rhein
Mainz
Bitburg
Wittlich
Simmern (Hunsrück)
Bingen am Rhein
Ingelheim am Rhein
Bernkastel-Kues
Kirchberg (Hunsrück)
Morbach
Bad Kreuznach
Hunsrück
Eifel
Rheinisches Schiefergebirge
Rothaargebirge
Sauerland

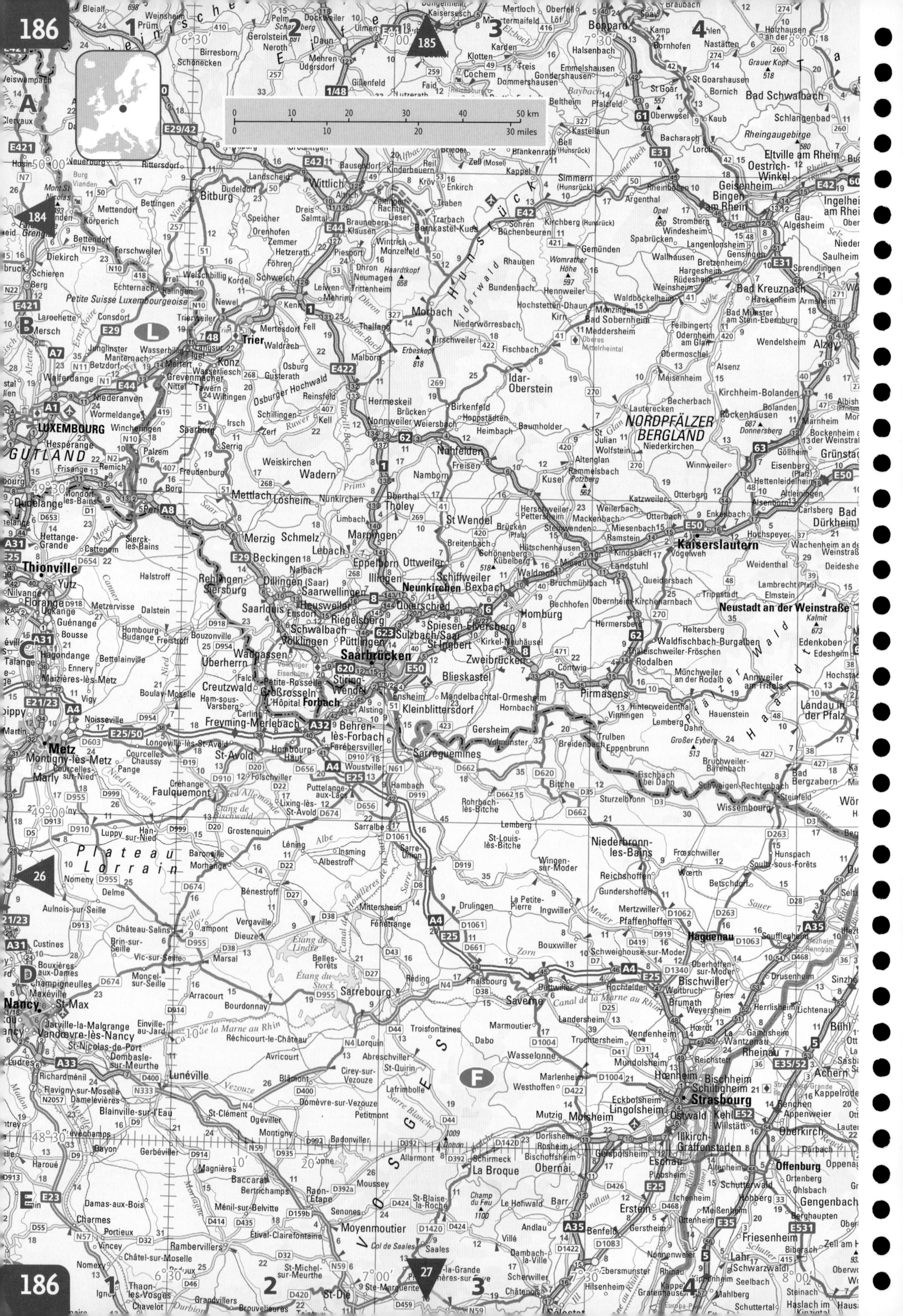
185
184
26
27
0 10 20 30 40 50 km
0 10 20 30 miles
L
F
LUXEMBOURG
GUTLAND
Petite Suisse Luxembourgeoise
Trier
Bitburg
Wittlich
Eifel
Hunsrück
Idar-Oberstein
NORDPFÄLZER BERGLAND
Pfälzer Wald
Haardt
Kaiserslautern
Neustadt an der Weinstraße
Landau in der Pfalz
Bad Kreuznach
Bingen am Rhein
Bad Schwalbach
Boppard
Simmern (Hunsrück)
Cochem
Bernkastel-Kues
Saarbrücken
Neunkirchen
Homburg
Zweibrücken
Pirmasens
St Wendel
Merzig
Saarlouis
Völklingen
Forbach
Sarreguemines
Bitche
Wissembourg
Haguenau
Strasbourg
Kehl
Offenburg
Lahr (Schwarzwald)
Obernai
Molsheim
Saverne
Sarrebourg
Lunéville
Nancy
Metz
Thionville
St-Avold
Faulquemont
Plateau Lorrain
Vosges
Baccarat
Raon-l'Étape
St-Dié
Schirmeck
La Broque
Achern
Bühl
Rastatt
Alzey
Kusel
Mettlach
Luxembourg

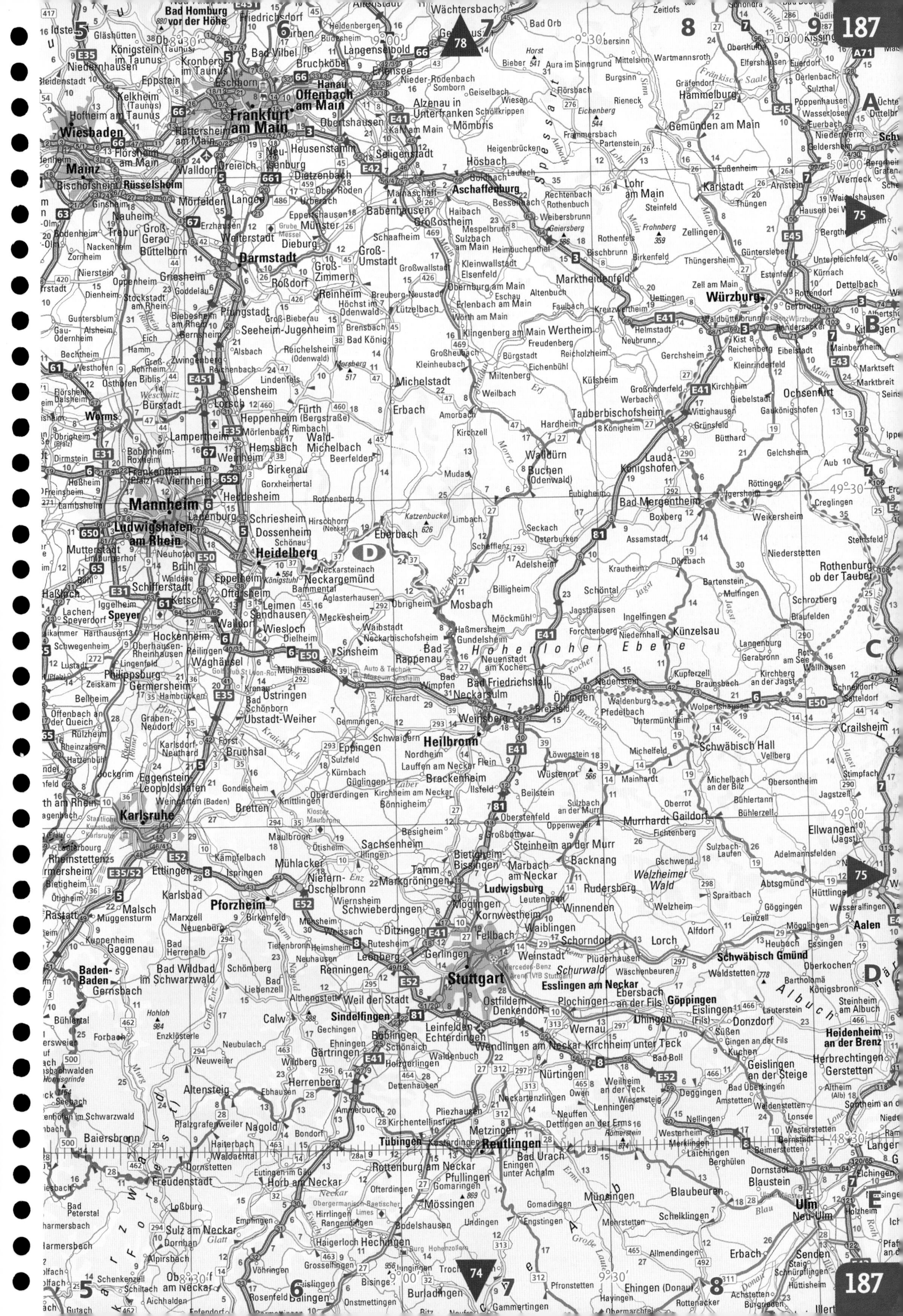

Bad Homburg vor der Höhe
Wächtersbach
Bad Orb
Königstein im Taunus
Bad Vilbel
Langenselbold
Hammelburg
Frankfurt am Main
Offenbach am Main
Hanau
Alzenau in Unterfranken
Gemünden am Main
Wiesbaden
Mainz
Rüsselsheim
Seligenstadt
Aschaffenburg
Lohr am Main
Karlstadt
Darmstadt
Dieburg
Marktheidenfeld
Würzburg
Kitzingen
Worms
Bensheim
Michelstadt
Erbach
Wertheim
Tauberbischofsheim
Ochsenfurt
Mannheim
Ludwigshafen am Rhein
Heidelberg
Eberbach
Walldürn
Buchen (Odenwald)
Bad Mergentheim
Rothenburg ob der Tauber
Speyer
Mosbach
Künzelsau
Sinsheim
Bad Friedrichshall
Neckarsulm
Öhringen
Crailsheim
Heilbronn
Schwäbisch Hall
Bruchsal
Karlsruhe
Ellwangen (Jagst)
Pforzheim
Ludwigsburg
Backnang
Aalen
Stuttgart
Esslingen am Neckar
Schwäbisch Gmünd
Göppingen
Baden-Baden
Sindelfingen
Böblingen
Heidenheim an der Brenz
Calw
Nürtingen
Geislingen an der Steige
Nagold
Tübingen
Reutlingen
Freudenstadt
Rottenburg am Neckar
Ulm
Neu-Ulm
Hechingen
Ehingen (Donau)
Balingen

A

Aachen D 183 D8
Aalen D 187 D9
Aalsmeer NL 182 A5
Aalst B 182 D4
Aalst NL 183 B6
Aalten NL 183 B9
Aalter B 182 C2
Aardenburg NL 182 C2
Aarle NL 183 C7
Aarschot B 182 D5
Aartrijke B 182 C2
Aartselaar B 182 C4
Abcoude NL 182 A5
Abreschviller F 186 D3
Abtsgmünd D 187 D8
Achel B 183 C6
Achern D 186 D5
Achstetten D 187 E8
Adegem B 182 C2
Adelmannsfelden D 187 D8
Adelsheim D 187 C7
Adenau D 185 D6
Aglasterhausen D 187 C6
Ahaus D 183 A10
Ahlen D 185 A8
Ahrbrück D 183 E9
Aichhalden D 187 E5
Aiglemont F 184 E2
Albergen NL 183 A9
Albertshofen D 187 B9
Albestroff F 186 D2
Albisheim (Pfrimm) D 186 B5
Alblasserdam NL 182 B5
Aldenhoven D 183 D8
Alf D 185 D7
Alfdorf D 187 D8
Alken B 183 D6
Allarmont F 186 E3
Allmendingen D 187 E8
Almelo NL 183 A9
Almere NL 183 A6
Almkerk NL 182 B5
Alost B 182 D4
Alpen D 183 B9
Alpenrod D 185 C8
Alphen NL 182 C5
Alphen aan den Rijn NL 182 A5
Alpirsbach D 187 E5
Alsbach D 187 B6
Alsdorf D 183 D8
Alsenborn D 186 C4
Alsenz D 186 B4
Alsheim D 185 E9
Alsting F 186 C2
Altena D 185 B8
Altenahr D 183 D9
Altenbuch D 187 B7
Altendiez D 185 D8
Altenglan D 186 B3
Altenheim D 186 E4
Altenkirchen (Westerwald) D 185 C8
Altenstadt D 187 A6
Altensteig D 187 D6
Altheim (Alb) D 187 D9
Althengstett D 187 D6
Altleiningen D 186 B5
Altrich D 185 E6
Alzenau in Unterfranken D 187 A7
Alzey D 186 B5
Amay B 183 D6
Amberloup B 184 D4
Ameide NL 182 B5
Amel B 184 D5
Amerongen NL 183 B6
Amersfoort NL 183 A6
Ammerbuch D 187 D6
Ammerzoden NL 183 B6
Amnéville F 186 C1
Amorbach D 187 B7
Amstelveen NL 182 A5
Amsterdam NL 182 A5
Amstetten D 187 D8
Andelst NL 183 B7
Andenne B 183 E6
Anderlecht B 182 D4
Anderlues B 182 E4
Andernach D 185 D7
Andlau F 186 E3
Anhée B 184 D2
Annœullin F 182 D1
Annweiler am Trifels D 186 C4
Anröchte D 185 A9
Ans B 183 D7
Anseremme B 184 D2
Antoing B 182 D2
Antwerpen B 182 C4
Anvers B 182 C4
Anzegem B 182 D2
Apeldoorn NL 183 A7
Appenweier D 186 D4
Arcen NL 183 C8
Ardooie B 182 D2
Arendonk B 183 C6
Argenthal D 185 E8
Armentières F 182 D1
Armsheim D 185 E9
Arnemuiden NL 182 C3
Arnhem NL 183 B7
Arnsberg D 185 B9
Arnstein D 187 B8
Arracourt F 186 D2
Arry F 186 C1
Arzbach D 185 D8
Arzfeld D 185 D5
As B 183 C7
Asbach D 185 C7
Aschaffenburg D 187 B7
Ascheberg D 185 A8
Asperen NL 183 B6
Assamstadt D 187 C8
Asse B 182 D4
Assenede B 182 C3
Assesse B 184 D3
Asten NL 183 C7
Ath B 182 D3
Attendorn D 185 B8
Aub D 187 B9
Aubel B 183 D7
Aubenton F 184 E1
Auby F 182 E2
Aulnois sur-Seille F 186 D1
Aura im Sinngrund D 187 A8
Auvelais B 182 E5
Auvillers-les-Forges F 184 E1
Avelgem B 182 D2
Avricourt F 186 D2
Awans B 183 D6
Axel NL 182 C3
Aywaille B 183 E7

B

Baarle-Hertog B 182 C5
Baarle-Nassau NL 182 C5
Baarn NL 183 A6
Babberich NL 183 B8
Babenhausen D 187 B6
Baccarat F 186 E2
Bacharach D 185 D8
Backnang D 187 D7
Bad Bentheim D 183 A10
Bad Bergzabern D 186 C4
Bad Berleburg D 185 B9
Bad Bertrich D 185 D7
Bad Boll D 187 D8
Bad Breisig D 185 D7
Bad Camberg D 185 D9
Bad Dürkheim D 187 C5
Bad Ems D 185 D8
Baden-Baden D 187 D5
Bad Friedrichshall D 187 C7
Bad Herrenalb D 187 D5
Badhoevedorp NL 182 A5
Bad Homburg vor der Höhe D 187 A6
Bad Honnef D 185 C7
Bad Hönningen D 185 C7
Bad Kissingen D 187 A9
Bad König D 187 B7
Bad Kreuznach D 185 E8
Bad Laasphe D 185 C9
Bad Liebenzell D 187 D6
Bad Marienberg (Westerwald) D 185 C8
Bad Mergentheim D 187 C8
Bad Münstereifel D 183 D9
Bad Neuenahr-Ahrweiler D 183 D10
Badonviller F 186 D2
Bad Orb D 187 A7
Bad Peterstal D 187 E5
Bad Rappenau D 187 C7
Bad Sassendorf D 185 A9
Bad Schönborn D 187 C6
Bad Schwalbach D 185 D9
Bad Sobernheim D 185 E8
Bad Überkingen D 187 D8
Bad Urach D 187 E7
Bad Vilbel D 187 A6
Bad Wildbad im Schwarzwald D 187 D6
Bad Wimpfen D 187 C7
Baelen B 183 D7
Baesweiler D 183 D8
Baiersbronn D 187 D5
Baillonville B 184 D3
Bakel NL 183 C7
Balen B 183 C6
Balingen D 187 E6
Balve D 185 B8
Bammental D 187 C6
Barneveld NL 183 A7
Baronville F 186 D2
Barr F 186 E3
Bartenstein D 187 C8
Bartholomä D 187 D8
Barvaux B 184 D3
Basècles B 182 D3
Bassenge B 183 D7
Bastogne B 184 D4
Bathmen NL 183 A8
Battice B 183 D7
Baumholder D 186 B3
Bausendorf D 185 D6
Bavel NL 182 B5
Bayon F 186 E1
Beaumont B 184 D1
Beauraing B 184 D2
Becherbach D 186 B4
Bechhofen D 186 C3
Bechtheim D 187 B5
Beckingen D 186 C2
Beckum D 185 A9
Bedburg D 183 D9
Bedburg-Hau D 183 B8
Beek NL 183 B7
Beek NL 183 B7
Beekbergen NL 183 A7
Beerfelden D 187 B6
Beernem B 182 C2
Beers NL 183 B7
Beerse B 182 C5
Beersel B 182 D4
Beerst B 182 C1
Beesd NL 183 B6
Begijnendijk B 182 C5
Behren-lès-Forbach F 186 C2
Beilstein D 187 C7
Beimerstetten D 187 E8
Belfeld NL 183 C8
Bell D 185 D7
Bell (Hunsrück) D 185 D7
Bellenberg D 187 E9
Belles-Forêts F 186 D2
Bellheim D 187 C5
Belœil B 182 D3
Beltheim D 185 D7
Beltrum NL 183 A9
Bemmel NL 183 B7
Bendorf D 185 D8
Beneden-Leeuwen NL 183 B6
Bénestroff F 186 D2
Benfeld F 186 E4
Bennebroek NL 182 A5
Bennekom NL 183 A7
Bensheim D 187 B6
Bentelo NL 183 A9
Berchem B 182 D3
Berg D 183 D9
Berg L 184 E5
Berg NL 183 D7
Berg NL 183 D7
Berg (Pfalz) D 187 D5
Bergen op Zoom NL 182 C4
Bergeyk NL 183 C6
Bergharen NL 183 B7
Berghaupten D 186 E4
Bergheim (Erft) D 183 D9
Berghem NL 183 B7
Berghülen D 187 E8
Bergisch Gladbach D 183 D10
Bergkamen D 185 A8
Bergneustadt D 185 B8
Bergschenhoek NL 182 B5
Bergtheim D 187 B9
Beringe NL 183 C7
Beringen B 183 C6
Berkel NL 182 B4
Berkel-Enschot NL 183 B6
Berlicum NL 183 B6
Bernissart B 182 E3
Bernkastel-Kues D 185 E7
Bernstadt D 187 D9
Bertogne B 184 D4
Bertrange L 186 B1
Bertrichamps F 186 E2
Bertrix B 184 E3
Beselich-Obertiefenbach D 185 D9
Besigheim D 187 D7
Bessenbach D 187 B7
Best NL 183 B6
Bestwig D 185 B9
Betschdorf F 186 D4
Bettelainville F 186 C1
Bettembourg L 186 B1
Bettendorf L 184 E5
Bettingen D 185 E5
Betzdorf D 185 C8
Betzdorf L 186 B1
Beuningen NL 183 B7
Beuvrages F 182 E2
Beveren B 182 C4
Beverlo B 183 C6
Bexbach D 186 C3
Biberach D 186 E5
Biblis D 187 B5
Bieber D 187 A7
Biebesheim am Rhein D 187 B5
Bietigheim D 187 D5
Bietigheim-Bissingen D 187 D7
Bièvre B 184 E3
Billigheim D 187 C7
Bilthoven NL 183 A6
Bilzen B 183 D7
Binche B 182 E4
Bingen am Rhein D 185 E8
Bingerden NL 183 B8
Birkenau D 187 B6
Birkenfeld D 186 B3
Birkenfeld D 187 B8
Birkenfeld D 187 D6
Birken-Honigsessen D 185 C8
Birresborn D 185 D6
Bischbrunn D 187 B7
Bischheim F 186 D4
Bischoffsheim F 186 E3
Bischofsheim D 185 E9
Bischwiller F 186 D4
Bisingen D 187 E6
Bissen L 184 E5
Bitburg D 185 E6
Bitche F 186 C3
Bladel NL 183 C6
Blainville-sur-l'Eau F 186 D1
Blâmont F 186 D2
Blankenberge B 182 C2
Blankenheim D 183 E9
Blankenrath D 185 D7
Blaricum NL 183 A6
Blaton B 182 D3
Blaubeuren D 187 E8
Blaufelden D 187 C8
Blaustein D 187 E8
Blegny B 183 D7
Bléharies B 182 D2
Bleialf D 185 D5
Bleidenstadt D 185 D9
Bleiswijk NL 182 A5
Blerick NL 183 C8
Bleskensgraaf NL 182 B5
Blieskastel D 186 C3
Bobenheim-Roxheim D 187 B5
Böblingen D 187 D7
Bocholt B 183 C7
Bocholt D 183 B9
Bochum D 185 B7
Bockenheim an der Weinstraße D 187 B5
Bodegraven NL 182 A5
Bodelshausen D 187 E6
Bodenheim D 185 E9
Boechout B 182 C4
Boekel NL 183 B7
Boekhoute B 182 C3
Bogny-sur-Meuse F 184 E2
Böhl D 187 C5
Bolanden D 186 B5
Bolnes NL 182 B5
Bomal B 184 D4
Bondorf D 187 D6
Bondues F 182 D2
Bönen D 185 A8
Bonheiden B 182 C5
Bonn D 183 D10
Bönnigheim D 187 C7
Boom B 182 C4
Boortmeerbeek B 182 D5
Boppard D 185 D8
Borculo NL 183 A9
Borg D 186 B1
Borgloon B 183 D6
Borken D 183 B9
Born NL 183 C7
Borne NL 183 A9
Bornem B 182 C4
Bornerbroek NL 183 A9
Bornheim D 183 D9
Bornhofen D 185 D8
Bornich D 185 D8
Borssele NL 182 C3
Boskoop NL 182 A5
Bottrop D 183 B9
Bouillon B 184 E3
Boulay-Moselle F 186 C1
Bourdonnay F 186 D2
Bourscheid L 184 E5
Bousse F 186 C1
Boussu B 182 E3
Boutersem B 182 D5
Bouxières-aux-Dames F 186 D1
Bouxwiller F 186 D3
Bouzonville F 186 C2
Bovigny B 184 D4
Boxberg D 187 C8
Boxmeer NL 183 B7
Boxtel NL 183 B6
Brachbach D 185 C8
Brackenheim D 187 C7
Braine-l'Alleud B 182 D4
Braine-le-Comte B 182 D4
Braives B 183 D6
Brakel B 182 D3
Brasschaat B 182 C4
Braubach D 185 D8
Brauneberg D 185 E6
Braunfels D 185 C9
Braunsbach D 187 C8
Brecht B 182 C5
Breckerfeld D 185 B7
Breda NL 182 B5
Bredene B 182 C1
Bredevoort NL 183 B9
Bree B 183 C7
Breidenbach F 186 C3
Breitenbach D 186 C3
Breitscheid D 183 C9
Breitscheid D 185 C7
Breitscheid D 185 C9
Bremm D 185 D7
Brensbach D 187 B6
Breskens NL 182 C3
Bretten D 187 C6
Bretzenheim D 185 E8
Bretzfeld D 187 C7
Breuberg-Neustadt D 187 B7
Breugel NL 183 B7
Breukelen NL 183 A6
Briedel D 185 D7
Brielle NL 182 B4
Brin-sur-Seille F 186 D1
Broekhuizenvorst NL 183 C8
Brohl D 185 D7
Brouvelieures F 186 E2
Brouwershaven NL 182 B3
Bruchköbel D 187 A6
Bruchmühlbach D 186 C3
Bruchsal D 187 C6
Bruchweiler-Bärenbach D 186 C4
Brücken D 186 B3
Brücken (Pfalz) D 186 C3
Brugelette B 182 D3
Bruges B 182 C2
Brugge B 182 C2
Brüggen D 183 C8
Brühl D 183 D9
Brühl D 187 C6
Bruinisse NL 182 B4
Brûly B 184 E2
Brumath F 186 D4
Brummen NL 183 A8
Brunehamel F 184 E1
Brunssum NL 183 D7
Brussel/Bruxelles B 182 D4
Bruttig-Fankel D 185 D7
Bruxelles B 182 D4
Büchel D 185 D7
Buchen (Odenwald) D 187 B7
Büchenbeuren D 185 E7
Buchholz (Westerwald) D 185 C7
Budel NL 183 C7
Budenheim D 185 D9
Büdesheim D 187 A6
Buer D 183 B10
Buggenhout B 182 C4
Bühl D 186 D5
Bühlertal D 187 D5
Bühlertann D 187 C8
Bühlerzell D 187 C8
Bullay D 185 D7
Büllingen B 183 E8
Bundenbach D 185 E7
Bunschoten-Spakenburg NL 183 A6
Burbach D 185 C9
Burdinne B 183 D6
Buren NL 183 B6
Burgbrohl D 185 D7
Burgh-Haamstede NL 182 B3
Burgsinn D 187 A8
Bürgstadt D 187 B7
Burladingen D 187 E7
Bürstadt D 187 B5
Bussum NL 183 A6
Bütgenbach B 183 E8
Büttelborn D 187 B6
Bütthard D 187 B8
Buurse NL 183 A9

C

Calw D 187 D6
Capelle aan de IJssel NL 182 B5
Carling F 186 C2
Carlsberg D 186 C5
Carvin F 182 E1
Castrop-Rauxel D 185 A7
Cattenom F 186 C1
Ceintrey F 186 D1
Celles B 182 D2
Cerfontaine B 184 D1
Chaam NL 182 C5
Chaligny F 186 D1
Champigneulles F 186 D1
Chapelle-lez-Herlaimont B 182 E4
Charleroi B 182 E4
Charmes F 186 E1
Chastre B 182 D5
Château-Salins F 186 D2
Châtelet B 184 D2
Châtel-sur-Moselle F 186 E1
Châtenois F 186 E3
Chaudfontaine B 183 D7
Chavelot F 186 E1
Chièvres B 182 D3
Chimay B 184 D1
Chooz F 184 D2
Ciney B 184 D3
Cirey-sur-Vezouze F 186 D2
Clavier B 183 E6
Clervaux L 184 D5
Clinge NL 182 C4
Cochem D 185 D7
Coesfeld D 183 B10
Colijnsplaat NL 182 B3
Colroy-la-Grande F 186 E3
Comblain-au-Pont B 183 E7
Comines B 182 D1
Condé-sur-l'Escaut F 182 E3
Consdorf L 186 B1
Contwig D 186 C3
Cothen NL 183 A6
Courcelles B 182 E4
Courcelles-Chaussy F 186 C1
Courcelles-sur-Nied F 186 C1
Courrières F 182 E1
Courtrai B 182 D2
Court-St-Étienne B 182 D5
Couvin B 184 D2
Crailsheim D 187 C9
Creglingen D 187 C9
Créhange F 186 C2
Creutzwald F 186 C2
Crévéchamps F 186 D1
Cuijk NL 183 B7
Culemborg NL 183 B6
Custines F 186 D1
Cysoing F 182 D2

D

Daaden D 185 C8
Dabo F 186 D3
Dahlem D 185 D6
Dahlhausen D 183 C10
Dahn D 186 C4
Daknam B 182 C3
Daleiden D 184 D5
Dalhem B 183 D7
Dalstein F 186 C1
Damas-aux-Bois F 186 E1
Dambach-la-Ville F 186 E3
Damelevières F 186 D1
Damme B 182 C2
Darmstadt D 187 B6
Datteln D 185 A7
Daun D 185 D6
De Bilt NL 183 A6
Deerlijk B 182 D2
Deggingen D 187 D8
De Haan B 182 C2
Deidesheim D 187 C5
Deinze B 182 D3
Delden NL 183 A9
Delft NL 182 A4
Delme F 186 D1
De Meern NL 183 A6
Den Bommel NL 182 B4
Denderleeuw B 182 D4
Dendermonde B 182 C4
Den Dungen NL 183 B6
Denekamp NL 183 A10
Den Haag NL 182 A4
Denkendorf D 187 D7
Dentergem B 182 D2
Dernau D 183 D10
Dessel B 183 C6
De Steeg NL 183 A8
Destelbergen B 182 C3
Dettelbach D 187 B9
Dettenhausen D 187 D7
Dettingen an der Erms D 187 D7
Dettwiller F 186 D3
Deurne NL 183 C7
Deventer NL 183 A8
Deville F 184 E2
Dhron D 185 E6
Didam NL 183 B8
Dieblich D 185 D7
Dieburg D 187 B6
Diekirch L 184 E5
Dielheim D 187 C6
Diemen NL 182 A5
Dienheim D 185 E9
Diepenbeek B 183 D6
Diepenheim NL 183 A9
Diepenveen NL 183 A8
Dierdorf D 185 C8
Dieren NL 183 A8
Diessen NL 183 C6
Diest B 183 D6
Dietzenbach D 187 A6
Dietzhölztal-Ewersbach D 185 C9
Dieuze F 186 D2
Dikkebus B 182 D1
Diksmuide B 182 C1
Dilbeek B 182 D4
Dillenburg D 185 C9
Dillingen (Saar) D 186 C2
Dilsen B 183 C7
Dinant B 184 D2
Dinslaken D 183 B9
Dinteloord NL 182 B4
Dinther NL 183 B6
Dinxperlo NL 183 B8
Dirksland NL 182 B4
Dirmstein D 187 B5
Dison B 183 D7
Ditzingen D 187 D7
Dockweiler D 185 D6
Dodewaard NL 183 B7
Doesburg NL 183 A8
Doetinchem NL 183 B8
Doische B 184 D2
Dombasle-sur-Meurthe F 186 D1
Domburg NL 182 B3
Domèvre-sur-Vezouze F 186 D2
Dommershausen D 185 D7
Dongen NL 182 B5
Donk NL 183 B7
Donzdorf D 187 D8
Doorn NL 183 A6
Doornspijk NL 183 A7
Dordrecht NL 182 B5
Dorlisheim F 186 D3
Dormagen D 183 C9
Dornburg-Frickhofen D 185 C9
Dornhan D 187 E6
Dornstadt D 187 E8
Dornstetten D 187 E5
Dorsten D 183 B9
Dorstfeld D 185 A7
Dortmund D 185 A7
Dörzbach D 187 C8
Dossenheim D 187 C6
Dreieich D 187 A6
Dreis D 185 E6
Drensteinfurt D 185 A8
Dreumel NL 183 B6
Driebergen NL 183 A6
Driedorf D 185 C9
Drolshagen D 185 B8
Drongen B 182 C3
Drulingen F 186 D3
Drusenheim F 186 D4
Druten NL 183 B7
Dudelange L 186 C1
Dudeldorf D 185 E6
Duffel B 182 C5
Duisburg D 183 C9
Dümpelfeld D 183 E9
Düngenheim D 185 D7
Durbach D 186 D5
Durbuy B 184 D3
Düren D 183 D8
Durmersheim D 187 D5
Düsseldorf D 183 C9
Dussen NL 182 B5

E

Eberbach D 187 C6
Ebersbach an der Fils D 187 D8
Ebersmunster F 186 E4
Ebhausen D 187 D6
Écaussinnes-d'Enghien B 182 D4
Echt NL 183 C7
Echternach L 185 E5
Eckbolsheim F 186 D4
Ede NL 183 A7
Edegem B 182 C4
Edenkoben D 186 C5
Edesheim D 186 C5
Ediger-Eller D 185 D7
Eefde NL 183 A8
Eeklo B 182 C3
Eerbeek NL 183 A8
Eernegem B 182 C2
Eersel NL 183 C6
Eggenstein-Leopoldshafen D 187 C5
Eghezée B 182 D5
Ehingen (Donau) D 187 E8
Ehningen D 187 D6
Ehringshausen D 185 C9
Eibelstadt D 187 B9
Eibergen NL 183 A9
Eich D 187 B5
Eichenbühl D 187 B7
Eijsden NL 183 D7
Eindhoven NL 183 C6
Einville-au-Jard F 186 D1
Eisden B 183 D7
Eisenberg (Pfalz) D 186 B5
Eislingen (Fils) D 187 D8
Eitelborn D 185 D8
Eitorf D 185 C7
Ekeren B 182 C4
Eksaarde B 182 C3
Eksel B 183 C6
Elchingen D 187 E9
Elferhausen D 187 A8
Elkenroth D 185 C8
Ellenberg D 187 C9
Ellezelles B 182 D3
Ellwangen (Jagst) D 187 D9
Elsdorf D 183 D9
Elsenborn B 183 E8
Elsenfeld D 187 B7
Elsloo NL 183 D7
Elspeet NL 183 A7
Elst NL 183 B6
Elst NL 183 B7
Eltville am Rhein D 185 D9
Elz D 185 D9
Emmelshausen D 185 D8
Emmerich D 183 B8
Empel NL 183 B6
Empfingen D 187 E6
Emptinne B 184 D3
Emst NL 183 A7
Engden D 183 A10
Engelskirchen D 185 C7
Enghien B 182 D4
Engis B 183 D6
Engstingen D 187 E7
Eningen unter Achalm D 187 E7
Enkenbach D 186 C4
Enkirch D 185 E7
Ennepetal D 185 B7
Ennery F 186 C1
Enschede NL 183 A9
Ensdorf D 186 C2
Ense D 185 B9
Ensheim D 186 C3
Enter NL 183 A9
Enzklösterle D 187 D5
Epe NL 183 A7
Epfendorf D 187 E6
Eppelborn D 186 C2
Eppelheim D 187 C6
Eppenbrunn D 186 C4
Eppertshausen D 187 B6
Eppingen D 187 C6
Eppstein D 187 A5
Erbach D 187 B7
Erbach D 187 E8
Erftstadt D 183 D9
Erkelenz D 183 C8
Erlenbach am Main D 187 B7
Ermelo NL 183 A7
Erndtebrück D 185 C9
Erp NL 183 B7
Erpel D 185 C7
Erquelinnes B 184 D1
Erstein F 186 E4
Ertvelde B 182 C3
Erwitte D 185 A9
Erzhausen D 187 B6
Esch NL 183 B6
Eschau D 187 B7
Eschau F 186 E4
Eschborn D 187 A6
Eschenburg-Eibelshausen D 185 C9
Esch-sur-Sûre L 184 E4
Eschweiler D 183 D8
Eslohe (Sauerland) D 185 B9
Esneux B 183 D7
Essen B 182 C4
Essen D 183 C10
Essingen D 187 D9
Esslingen am Neckar D 187 D7
Estaimpuis B 182 D2
Estenfeld D 187 B9
Étival-Clairefontaine F 186 E2
Ettelbruck L 184 E5
Ettenheim D 186 E4
Etten-Leur NL 182 B5
Ettlingen D 187 D5
Ettringen D 185 D7
Eubigheim D 187 B8
Euerdorf D 187 A9
Eupen B 183 D8
Euskirchen D 183 D9
Eußenheim D 187 A8
Eutingen im Gäu D 187 E6
Everdingen NL 183 B6
Evergem B 182 C3

F

Faches-Thumesnil F 182 D2
Faid D 185 D7
Faimes B 183 D6
Falck F 186 C2
Fameck F 186 C1
Farciennes B 182 E5
Farébersviller F 186 C2
Faulbach D 187 B7
Faulquemont F 186 C2
Feilbingert D 185 E8
Fell D 186 B2
Fellbach D 187 D7
Fénétrange F 186 D3
Fépin F 184 D2
Ferrières B 183 E7
Ferschweiler D 185 E5
Fichtenberg D 187 D8
Fijnaart NL 182 B4
Finnentrop D 185 B8
Fischbach D 186 B3
Fischbach bei Dahn D 186 C4
Flavigny-sur-Moselle F 186 D1
Flein D 187 C7
Flémalle B 183 D6
Fléron B 183 D7
Flers-en-Escrebieux F 182 E2
Fleurus B 182 E5
Flines-lez-Raches F 182 E2
Florange F 186 C1
Floreffe B 182 E5
Florennes B 184 D2
Flörsbach D 187 A7
Flörsheim am Main D 187 A5
Flörsheim-Dalsheim D 187 B5
Focant B 184 D3
Föhren D 185 E6
Folschviller F 186 C2
Fontaine-l'Évêque B 182 E4
Forbach D 187 D5
Forbach F 186 C2
Forchtenberg D 187 C8
Forst D 187 C6
Fosses-la-Ville B 184 D2
Fraire B 184 D2
Frameries B 182 E3
Frammersbach D 187 A7
Francorchamps B 183 E7
Frankenthal (Pfalz) D 187 B5
Frankfurt am Main D 187 A6
Frasnes-lez-Buissenal B 182 D3
Frasnes-lez-Gosselies B 182 D4
Frechen D 183 D9
Freinsheim D 187 B5
Freisen D 186 B3
Freistroff F 186 C1
Fresnes-sur-Escaut F 182 E3
Freudenberg D 185 C8
Freudenberg D 187 B7
Freudenburg D 186 B2
Freudenstadt D 187 E5
Freyming-Merlebach F 186 C2
Friedewald D 185 C8
Friedrichsdorf D 187 A6
Friesenhagen D 185 C8
Friesenheim D 186 E4
Frisange L 186 B1
Frœschwiller F 186 D4
Fromelennes F 184 D2
Fröndenberg D 185 B8
Frouard F 186 D1
Fumay F 184 E2
Fürth D 187 B6

G

Gaanderen NL 183 B8
Gaggenau D 187 D5
Gaildorf D 187 D8
Gambsheim F 186 D4
Gammertingen D 187 E7
Gand B 182 C3
Ganshoren B 182 D4
Garderen NL 183 A7
Gärtringen D 187 D6
Gau-Algesheim D 185 E9
Gaukönigshofen D 187 B8
Gau-Odernheim D 185 E9
Gavere B 182 D3
Gebhardshain D 185 C8
Gechingen D 187 D6
Gedinne B 184 E2
Geel B 183 C6
Geertruidenberg NL 182 B5
Geesteren NL 183 A9
Geetbets B 183 D6
Geffen NL 183 B6
Geilenkirchen D 183 D8
Geiselbach D 187 A7
Geisenheim D 185 E8
Geislingen D 187 E6
Geislingen an der Steige D 187 D8
Geispolsheim F 186 D4
Gelchsheim D 187 B9
Geldermalsen NL 183 B6
Geldern D 183 B8
Geldersheim D 187 A9
Geldrop NL 183 C7
Geleen NL 183 D7
Gelnhausen D 187 A7
Gelsenkirchen D 183 B10
Gembloux B 182 D5
Gemert NL 183 B7
Gemmingen D 187 C6
Gemünden D 185 E7
Gemünden am Main D 187 A8
Genappe B 182 D4
Gendringen NL 183 B8
Gendt NL 183 B7
Gengenbach D 186 E5
Genk B 183 D7
Gennep NL 183 B7
Gensingen D 185 E8
Gent B 182 C3
Geraardsbergen B 182 D3
Gerabronn D 187 C8
Gerbéviller F 186 E2
Gerbrunn D 187 B8
Gerchsheim D 187 B8
Gerlingen D 187 D7
Germersheim D 187 C5
Gernsbach D 187 D5
Gernsheim D 187 B5
Gerolstein D 185 D6
Gerpinnes B 184 D2
Gersheim D 186 C3
Gerstetten D 187 D9
Gerstheim F 186 E4
Gescher D 183 B10
Gespunsart F 184 E2
Gesves B 184 D3
Gevelsberg D 185 B7
Ghislenghien B 182 D3
Giebelstadt D 187 B8
Gierle B 182 C5
Gillenfeld D 185 D6
Gilze NL 182 B5
Gingelom B 183 D6
Gingen an der Fils D 187 D8
Ginsheim D 185 E9
Gistel B 182 C1
Givet F 184 D2
Gladbeck D 183 B9
Glanerbrug NL 183 A9
Gläshütten D 187 A5
Goch D 183 B8

Nettetal D 183 C8
Neubrunn D 187 B8
Neubulach D 187 D6
Neuenbürg D 187 D6
Neuenkirchen-Seelscheid D 185 C7
Neuenrade D 185 B8
Neuenstadt am Kocher D 187 C7
Neuenstein D 187 C8
Neuerburg D 185 D5
Neufchâteau B 184 E3
Neuffen D 187 D7
Neufmanil F 184 E2
Neufra D 187 E7
Neuhausen D 187 D6
Neuhofen D 187 C5
Neu-Isenburg D 187 A6
Neuler D 187 D9
Neumagen D 185 E6
Neunkirchen D 185 C9
Neunkirchen D 186 C3
Neuss D 183 C9
Neustadt (Wied) D 185 C7
Neustadt an der Weinstraße D 186 C5
Neu-Ulm D 187 E9
Neuves-Maisons F 186 D1
Neuweiler D 187 D6
Neuwied D 185 D7
Nevele B 182 C3
Newel D 185 E6
Niederanven L 186 B1
Niederbrechen D 185 D9
Niederbreitbach D 185 C7
Niederbronn-les-Bains F 186 D4
Niederfischbach D 185 C8
Niederkassel D 183 D10
Niederkirchen D 186 B4
Niederkrüchten D 183 C8
Niederneisen D 185 D9
Niedernhall D 187 C8
Niedernhausen D 185 D9
Nieder-Olm D 185 E9
Nieder-Rodenbach D 187 A7
Niederselters D 185 D9
Niederstetten D 187 C8
Niederwerrn D 187 A9
Niederwörresbach D 186 B3
Niederzissen D 185 D7
Niefern-Öschelbronn D 187 D6
Niel B 182 C4
Nierstein D 185 E9
Nieuw-Bergen NL 183 B8
Nieuwegein NL 183 A6
Nieuwerkerk NL 182 B4
Nieuwerkerk aan de IJssel NL 182 B5
Nieuwerkerken B 183 D6
Nieuwe-Tonge NL 182 B4
Nieuw-Heeten NL 183 A8
Nieuwkoop NL 182 A5
Nieuw-Loosdrecht NL 183 A6
Nieuw-Milligen NL 183 A7
Nieuw-Namen NL 182 C4
Nieuwveen NL 182 A5
Nieuw-Vennep NL 182 A5
Nieuw-Vossemeer NL 182 B4
Nievern D 185 D8
Nijkerk NL 183 A6
Nijlen B 182 C5
Nijmegen NL 183 B7
Nijverdal NL 183 A8
Nilvange F 186 C1
Ninove B 182 D4
Nismes B 184 D2
Nispen NL 182 C4
Nistelrode NL 183 B7
Nittel D 186 B1
Nivelles B 182 D4
Nohfelden D 186 B3
Noisseville F 186 C1
Nomeny F 186 D1
Nomexy F 186 E1
Nonnenweier D 186 E4
Nonnweiler D 186 B2
Noordwijk aan Zee NL 182 A4
Noordwijk-Binnen NL 182 A4
Noordwijkerhout NL 182 A5
Nootdorp NL 182 A4
Nordheim D 187 C7
Nordkirchen D 185 A8
Nouzonville F 184 E2
Noville B 182 D5
Nüdlingen D 187 A9
Nuenen NL 183 C7
Nuland NL 183 B6
Numansdorp NL 182 B4
Nunkirchen D 186 C2
Nunspeet NL 183 A7
Nürtingen D 187 D7
Nuth NL 183 D7

O

Oberderdingen D 187 C6
Oberfell D 185 D7
Oberharmersbach D 186 E5
Oberhausen D 183 C9
Oberhausen-Rheinhausen D 187 C5
Oberhoffen-sur-Moder F 186 D4
Oberkirch D 186 D5
Oberkochen D 187 D9
Obermoschel D 186 B4
Obernai F 186 E3
Obernburg am Main D 187 B7
Oberndorf am Neckar D 187 E6
Obernheim-Kirchenarnbach D 186 C4
Ober-Olm D 185 E9
Ober-Roden D 187 B6
Oberrot D 187 C8
Obersinn D 187 A8
Obersontheim D 187 C8
Oberstenfeld D 187 C7
Oberthal D 186 B3
Oberthulba D 187 A8
Obertshausen D 187 A6
Oberursel (Taunus) D 187 A6
Oberwesel D 185 D8
Oberwolfach D 187 E5
Obrigheim D 187 C7
Obrigheim (Pfalz) D 187 B5
Ochsenfurt D 187 B9
Ochtrup D 183 A10
Odernheim am Glan D 186 B4
Oedelem B 182 C2
Oeffelt NL 183 B7
Oegstgeest NL 182 A5
Oene NL 183 A8
Oerlenbach D 187 A9
Oestrich-Winkel D 185 D8
Offenbach am Main D 187 A6
Offenbach an der Queich D 187 C5
Offenburg D 186 E4
Ofterdingen D 187 E7
Oftersheim D 187 C6
Ogéviller F 186 D2
Ohey B 183 E6
Ohlsbach D 186 E4
Öhringen D 187 C7
Oignies F 182 E1
Oijen NL 183 B6
Oirschot NL 183 B6
Oisterwijk NL 183 B6
Oldenzaal NL 183 A9
Olen B 182 C5
Olfen D 185 A7
Olpe D 185 B8
Olst NL 183 A8
Onstmettingen D 187 E6
Ooltgensplaat NL 182 B4
Oostakker B 182 C3
Oostburg NL 182 C2
Oostende B 182 C1
Oosterbeek NL 183 B7
Oosterhout NL 182 B5
Oosterland NL 182 B4
Oosterzele B 182 D3
Oostham B 183 C6
Oostkamp B 182 C2
Oostkapelle NL 182 B3
Oostmalle B 182 C5
Oost-Souburg NL 182 C3
Oostvoorne NL 182 B4
Ootmarsum NL 183 A9
Opglabbeek B 183 C7
Opheusden NL 183 B7
Opitter B 183 C7
Oploo NL 183 B7
Opoeteren B 183 C7
Oppenau D 187 E5
Oppenheim D 185 E9
Oppenweiler D 187 D7
Opwijk B 182 D4
Orchies F 182 E2
Orenhofen D 185 E6
Oreye B 183 D6
Ortenberg D 186 E4
Osburg D 186 B2
Oss NL 183 B7
Ossendrecht NL 182 C4
Ostend B 182 C1
Osterburken D 187 C7
Ostfildern D 187 D7
Osthofen D 187 B5
Ostricourt F 182 E2
Östringen D 187 C6
Ostwald F 186 D4
Ötigheim D 187 D5
Ötisheim D 187 D6
Ottenheim D 186 E4
Ottenhöfen im Schwarzwald D 187 D5
Otterbach D 186 C4
Otterberg D 186 B4
Otterlo NL 183 A7
Ottersweier D 186 D5
Ottignies B 182 D5
Ottweiler D 186 C3
Oud-Beijerland NL 182 B4
Ouddorp NL 182 B3
Oudenaarde B 182 D3
Oudenbosch NL 182 B5
Oudenburg B 182 C2
Oude-Tonge NL 182 B4
Oudewater NL 182 A5
Oud-Gastel NL 182 B4
Oud-Turnhout B 182 C5
Oud-Vossemeer NL 182 B4
Oudzele B 182 C2
Ouffet B 183 E6
Oulder B 184 D5
Oupeye B 183 D7
Overath D 185 C7
Overdinkel NL 183 A10
Overijse B 182 D5
Overloon NL 183 B7
Overpelt B 183 C6
Ovezande NL 182 C3
Owen D 187 D7

P

Paal B 183 C6
Padoux F 186 E2
Paliseul B 184 E3
Palzem D 186 B1
Pange F 186 C1
Panningen NL 183 C7
Papendrecht NL 182 B5
Partenstein D 187 A8
Pâturages B 182 E3
Pecq B 182 D2
Peer B 183 C6
Pelm D 185 D6
Pepingen B 182 D4
Pepinster B 183 D7
Perl D 186 C1
Péruwelz B 182 D3
Perwez B 182 D5
Petite-Rosselle F 186 C2
Petitmont F 186 D2
Pexonne F 186 E2
Pfaffenhofen an der Roth D 187 E9
Pfaffenhoffen F 186 D4
Pfalzfeld D 185 D8
Pfalzgrafenweiler D 187 D6
Pfedelbach D 187 C7
Pforzheim D 187 D6
Pfronstetten D 187 E7
Pfullingen D 187 E7
Pfungstadt D 187 B6
Phalsbourg F 186 D3
Philippeville B 184 D2
Philippine NL 182 C3
Philippsburg D 187 C5
Piershil NL 182 B4
Piesport D 185 E6
Pijnacker NL 182 A4
Pirmasens D 186 C4
Pittem B 182 D2
Plaidt D 185 D7
Plettenberg D 185 B8
Pliezhausen D 187 D7
Plobsheim F 186 E4
Plochingen D 187 D7
Ploegsteert B 182 D1
Plüderhausen D 187 D8
Poederlee B 182 C5
Polch D 185 D7
Polsbroek NL 182 B5
Pompey F 186 D1
Pont-à-Celles B 182 D4
Pont-à-Marcq F 182 D2
Pont-de-Loup B 182 E5
Poppenhausen D 187 A9
Portieux F 186 E1
Posterholt NL 183 C8
Poussay F 186 E1
Pracht D 185 C8
Prinsenbeek NL 182 B5
Profondeville B 184 D2
Pronsfeld D 185 D5
Provenchères-sur-Fave F 186 E3
Prüm D 185 D5
Puderbach D 185 C8
Pulheim D 183 C9
Putte B 182 C5
Putte NL 182 C4
Puttelange-aux-Lacs F 186 C2
Putten NL 183 A7
Püttlingen D 186 C2
Puurs B 182 C4

Q

Quaregnon B 182 E3
Queidersbach D 186 C4
Quendorf D 183 A10
Quesnoy-sur-Deûle F 182 D2
Quierschied D 186 C3
Quiévrain B 182 E3
Quiévrechain F 182 E3

R

Raalte NL 183 A8
Raamsdonksveer NL 182 B5
Radevormwald D 185 B7
Raeren B 183 D8
Raesfeld D 183 B9
Ralingen D 185 E6
Rambervillers F 186 E2
Rambrouch L 184 E4
Ramillies B 182 D5
Rammelsbach D 186 B3
Rammingen D 187 D9
Ramstein D 186 C4
Rance B 184 D1
Randersacker D 187 B8
Rangendingen D 187 E6
Ransbach-Baumbach D 185 D8
Ranst B 182 C5
Raon-l'Étape F 186 E2
Rastatt D 187 D5
Ratingen D 183 C9
Raubach D 185 C8
Ravels B 182 C5
Ravenstein NL 183 B7
Rebecq B 182 D4
Réchicourt-le-Château F 186 D2
Recht B 184 D5
Rechtenbach D 187 B8
Recklinghausen D 183 B10
Réding F 186 D3
Rees D 183 B8
Rehlingen-Siersburg D 186 C2
Reichelsheim (Odenwald) D 187 B6
Reichenbach D 187 B6
Reichenberg D 187 B8
Reicholzheim D 187 B8
Reichshoffen F 186 D4
Reichstett F 186 D4
Reil D 185 D7
Reilingen D 187 C6
Reinheim D 187 B6
Reinsfeld D 186 B2
Reken D 183 B10
Rekken NL 183 A9
Remagen D 185 C7
Remich L 186 B1
Remicourt B 183 D6
Remouchamps B 183 E7
Remscheid D 183 C10
Renchen D 186 D5
Renesse NL 182 B3
Rengsdorf D 185 C7
Renkum NL 183 B7
Rennerod D 185 C9
Renningen D 187 D6
Renswoude NL 183 A7
Renwez F 184 E2
Retie B 183 C6
Reusel NL 183 C6
Reutlingen D 187 E7
Reuver NL 183 C8
Revin F 184 E2
Rhaunen D 185 E7
Rhede D 183 B9
Rheden NL 183 A8
Rheinau D 186 D4
Rheinbach D 183 D9
Rheinberg D 183 B9
Rheinböllen D 185 E8
Rheinbreitbach D 185 C7
Rheinbrohl D 185 D7
Rheinstetten D 187 D5
Rheinzabern D 187 C5
Rhenen NL 183 B7
Rhens D 185 D8
Rhinau F 186 E4
Rhisnes B 182 D5
Rhoon NL 182 B4
Richardménil F 186 D1
Ridderkerk NL 182 B5
Riegelsberg D 186 C2
Riemst B 183 D7
Rieneck D 187 A8
Riethoven NL 183 C6
Rijen NL 182 B5
Rijkevorsel B 182 C5
Rijnsburg NL 182 A4
Rijsbergen NL 182 B5
Rijsel F 182 D2
Rijssen NL 183 A9
Rijswijk NL 182 A4
Rilland NL 182 C4
Rimbach D 187 B6
Rimogne F 184 E2
Rips NL 183 B7
Rittersdorf D 185 D5
Rixensart B 182 D5
Rochefort B 184 D3
Rochehaut B 184 E3
Rochin F 182 D2
Rockanje NL 182 B4
Rockenhausen D 186 B4
Rocroi F 184 E2
Rodalben D 186 C4
Roermond NL 183 C7
Roeselare B 182 D2
Roetgen D 183 D8
Roggel NL 183 C7
Röhlingen D 187 D9
Rohrbach-lès-Bitche F 186 C3
Rombas F 186 C1
Rommerskirchen D 183 C9
Ronse B 182 D3
Roosendaal NL 182 B4
Rosée B 184 D2
Rosenfeld D 187 E6
Rosheim F 186 D3
Rosmalen NL 183 B6
Rösrath D 185 C7
Roßdorf D 187 B6
Rossum NL 183 B6
Rot am See D 187 C9
Rothenberg D 187 B6
Rothenbuch D 187 B7
Rothenburg ob der Tauber D 187 C9
Rothenfels D 187 B8
Rotheux-Rimière B 183 D6
Rotselaar B 182 D5
Rottenacker D 187 E8
Rottenburg am Neckar D 187 E6
Rottendorf D 187 B9
Rotterdam NL 182 B5
Röttingen D 187 B8
Roubaix F 182 D2
Roulers B 182 D2
Rouvroy F 182 E1
Rouvroy-sur-Audry F 184 E2
Rozenburg NL 182 B4
Rozendaal NL 183 A7
Ruddervoorde B 182 C2
Rudersberg D 187 D8
Rüdesheim D 185 E8
Ruiselede B 182 C2
Rülzheim D 187 C5
Rumes B 182 D2
Rumigny F 184 E1
Rumst B 182 C4
Runkel D 185 D9
Rüsselsheim D 187 A5
Rutesheim D 187 D6
Rüthen D 185 B9
Rütten-Scheid D 183 C9
Ruurlo NL 183 A8

S

Saales F 186 E3
Saarbrücken D 186 C2
Saarburg D 186 B2
Saarlouis D 186 C2
Saarwellingen D 186 C2
Sachsenheim D 187 D7
St-Amand-les-Eaux F 182 E2
St-Avold F 186 C2
St-Blaise-la-Roche F 186 E3
St-Clément F 186 D2
St-Dié F 186 E2
Ste-Marguerite F 186 E2
Ste-Marie-aux-Mines F 186 E3
St-Firmin F 186 E1
St-Ghislain B 182 E3
St-Hubert B 184 D3
St-Louis-lès-Bitche F 186 D3
St-Max F 186 D1
St-Michel F 184 E1
St-Michel-sur-Meurthe F 186 E2
St-Nicolas B 183 D7
St-Nicolas-de-Port F 186 D1
St-Oedenrode NL 183 B6
St-Quirin F 186 D3
St-Vith B 184 D5
Salmtal D 185 E6
Sandhausen D 187 C6
Sankt Augustin D 185 C7
Sankt Goar D 185 D8
Sankt Goarshausen D 185 D8
Sankt Ingbert D 186 C3
Sankt Julian D 186 B4
Sankt Katharinen D 185 C7
Sankt Wendel D 186 C3
Santpoort NL 182 A5
Sarralbe F 186 D3
Sarrebourg F 186 D3
Sarreguemines F 186 C3
Sarre-Union F 186 D3
Sart B 183 D7
Sasbach D 186 D5
Sasbachwalden D 186 D5
Sassenheim NL 182 A5
Sas Van Gent NL 182 C3
Satteldorf D 187 C9
Saulheim D 185 E9
Saverne F 186 D3
Schaafheim D 187 B7
Schaarsbergen NL 183 A7
Schaerbeek B 182 D4
Schaesberg NL 183 D8
Schaijk NL 183 B7
Schalkhaar NL 183 A8
Schalksmühle D 185 B8
Scharendijke NL 182 B3
Schebheim D 187 B9
Schefflenz D 187 C7
Schelklingen D 187 E8
Schenkenzell D 187 E5
Schermbeck D 183 B9
Scherpenheuvel B 182 D5
Scherpenzeel NL 183 A6
Scherwiller F 186 E3
Schiedam NL 182 B4
Schieren L 184 E5
Schifferstadt D 187 C5
Schiffweiler D 186 C3
Schijndel NL 183 B6
Schilde B 182 C5
Schillingen D 186 B2
Schiltach D 187 E5
Schiltigheim F 186 D4
Schinnen NL 183 D7
Schinveld NL 183 D7
Schipluiden NL 182 B4
Schirmeck F 186 E3
Schlangenbad D 185 D9
Schleiden D 183 D8
Schmallenberg D 185 B9
Schmelz D 186 C2
Schnelldorf D 187 C9
Schnürpflingen D 187 E8
Schoenberg B 185 D5
Schöllkrippen D 187 A7
Schömberg D 187 D6
Schönaich D 187 D7
Schondra D 187 A8
Schönecken D 185 D5
Schönenberg-Kübelberg D 186 C3
Schöntal D 187 C8
Schoondijke NL 182 C3
Schoonhoven NL 182 B5
Schorndorf D 187 D8
Schoten B 182 C4
Schriesheim D 187 C6
Schrozberg D 187 C8
Schuttertal D 186 E4
Schutterwald D 186 E4
Schüttorf D 183 A10
Schwäbisch Gmünd D 187 D8
Schwäbisch Hall D 187 C8
Schwaigern D 187 C7
Schwalbach D 186 C2
Schwegenheim D 187 C5
Schweich D 185 E6
Schweigen-Rechtenbach D 186 C4
Schweighouse-sur-Moder F 186 D4
Schweinfurt D 187 A9
Schwelm D 185 B7
Schwerte D 185 B8
Schwieberdingen D 187 D7
Seckach D 187 C7
Seclin F 182 D2
Seebach D 187 D5
Seeheim-Jugenheim D 187 B6
Seilles B 183 E6
Seinsheim D 187 B9
Sélestat F 186 E3
Seligenstadt D 187 A6
Selm D 185 A7
Selters (Westerwald) D 185 C8
Seltz F 186 D5
Senden D 187 E9
Seneffe B 182 D4
Senones F 186 E2
Seraing B 183 D7
Serooskerke NL 182 B3
Serrig D 186 B2
Sevenum NL 183 C8
's-Gravendeel NL 182 B5
's-Gravenhage NL 182 A4
's-Gravenmoer NL 182 B5
's-Gravenpolder NL 182 C3
's-Gravenvoeren B 183 D7
's-Gravenzande NL 182 B4
's-Heerenberg NL 183 B8
's-Heerenhoek NL 182 C3
's-Hertogenbosch NL 183 B6
Siebengewald NL 183 B8
Siegburg D 185 C7
Siegen D 185 C9
Sierck-les-Bains F 186 C1
Siershahn D 185 D8
Signy-le-Petit F 184 E1
Sijsele B 182 C2
Silenrieux B 184 D1
Simmerath D 183 D8
Simmern (Hunsrück) D 185 E8
Simpelveld NL 183 D7
Sindelfingen D 187 D6
Singhofen D 185 D8
Sinn D 185 C9
Sinsheim D 187 C6
Sint Annaland NL 182 B4
Sint Anthonis NL 183 B7
Sint-Genesius-Rode B 182 D4
Sint-Gillis-Waas B 182 C4
Sint-Huibrechts-Lille B 183 C6
Sint Jansteen NL 182 C4
Sint-Katelijne-Waver B 182 C5
Sint-Laureins B 182 C3
Sint-Lenaarts B 182 C5
Sint Maartensdijk NL 182 B4
Sint-Margriete B 182 C3
Sint-Maria-Lierde B 182 D3
Sint-Martens-Latem B 182 C3
Sint Michielsgestel NL 183 B6
Sint-Niklaas B 182 C4
Sint Odilienberg NL 183 C8
Sint-Pauwels B 182 C4
Sint Philipsland NL 182 B4
Sint-Pieters-Leeuw B 182 D4
Sint-Truiden B 183 D6
Sinzheim D 187 D5
Sinzig D 185 C7
Sittard NL 183 D7
Sivry B 184 D1
Sleidinge B 182 C3
Sliedrecht NL 182 B5
Sluis NL 182 C2
Sluiskil NL 182 C3
Soerendonk NL 183 C7
Soest D 185 A9
Soest NL 183 A6
Soesterberg NL 183 A6
Soheit-Tinlot B 183 E6
Sohren D 185 E7
Soignies B 182 D4
Solingen D 183 C10
Sombreffe B 182 D5
Someren NL 183 C7
Somme-Leuze B 184 D3
Somzée B 184 D1
Son NL 183 B6
Soufflenheim F 186 D4
Soultz-sous-Forêts F 186 D4
Soumagne B 183 D7
Spa B 183 E7
Spabrücken D 185 E8
Spay D 185 D8
Speicher D 185 E6
Speyer D 187 C5
Spiere B 182 D2
Spiesen-Elversberg D 186 C3
Spijkenisse NL 182 B4
Spontin B 184 D3
Spraitbach D 187 D8
Sprendlingen D 185 E8
Sprimont B 183 D7
Sprockhövel D 185 B7
Stabroek B 182 C4
Staden B 182 D2
Stadtkyll D 185 D6
Stadtlohn D 183 B9
Staig D 187 E8
Standdaarbuiten NL 182 B5
Stavelot B 184 D4
Stavenisse NL 182 B4
Steenbergen NL 182 B4
Steenderen NL 183 A8
Stein NL 183 D7
Steinach D 186 E5
Steinfeld D 186 C5
Steinfeld D 187 B8
Steinheim am Albuch D 187 D9
Steinheim an der Murr D 187 D7
Steinsfeld D 187 C9
Steinwenden D 186 C4
Stekene B 182 C4
Stellendam NL 182 B4
Stevensweert NL 183 C7
Stimpfach D 187 C9
Stiring-Wendel F 186 C2
Stockstadt am Rhein D 187 B5
Stolberg (Rheinland) D 183 D8
Stoumont B 183 E7
Straelen D 183 C8
Straimont B 184 E3
Stramproy NL 183 C7
Strasbourg F 186 D4
Strassen L 186 B1
Straßenhaus D 185 C8
Strijen NL 182 B5
Stromberg D 185 E8
Sturzelbronn F 186 C4
Stuttgart D 187 D7
Suddendorf D 183 A10
Südlohn D 183 B9
Sulz am Neckar D 187 E6
Sulzbach am Main D 187 B7
Sulzbach an der Murr D 187 C7
Sulzbach-Laufen D 187 D8
Sulzbach/Saar D 186 C3
Sulzfeld D 187 C6
Sulzthal D 187 A9
Sundern (Sauerland) D 185 B9
Susteren NL 183 C7
Swalmen NL 183 C8

T

Taintrux F 186 E2
Talange F 186 C1
Tamm D 187 D7
Tantonville F 186 E1
Tauberbischofsheim D 187 B8
Tawern D 186 B2
Tegelen NL 183 C8
Tellin B 184 D3
Templeuve F 182 D2
Temse B 182 C4
Tenneville B 184 D4
Ter Aar NL 182 A5
Terborg-Silvolde NL 183 B8
Terheijden NL 182 B5
Terneuzen NL 182 C3
Tervuren B 182 D5
Tessenderlo B 183 C6
Testelt B 182 C5
Teteringen NL 182 B5
Thaleischweiler-Fröschen D 186 C4
Thalfang D 186 B2
Thaon-les-Vosges F 186 E1
't Harde NL 183 A7
Theux B 183 D7
Thionville F 186 C1
Tholen NL 182 B4
Tholey D 186 C3
Thommen B 184 D5
Thorn NL 183 C7
Thuin B 184 D1
Thüngen D 187 B8
Thüngersheim D 187 B8
Tiefenbronn D 187 D6
Tiel NL 183 B6
Tielen B 182 C5
Tielt B 182 D2
Tienen B 182 D5
Tilburg NL 183 B6
Tongeren B 183 D6
Tönisvorst D 183 C8
Torhout B 182 C2
Tourcoing F 182 D2
Tournai B 182 D2
Traar D 183 C9
Traben D 185 E7
Trarbach D 185 E7
Trebur D 187 B5
Treis D 185 D7
Tremelo B 182 D5
Trier D 186 B2
Trierweiler D 186 B2
Trippstadt D 186 C4
Trittenheim D 185 E6
Trochtelfingen D 187 E7
Troisdorf D 183 D10
Troisfontaines F 186 D3
Trois-Ponts B 184 D4
Troisvierges L 184 D5
Trooz B 183 D7
Truchtersheim F 186 D4
Trulben D 186 C4
Tubbergen NL 183 A9
Tübingen D 187 D7
Tubize B 182 D4
Turnhout B 182 C5
Twello NL 183 A8

U

Übach-Palenberg D 183 D8
Überherrn D 186 C2
Ubstadt-Weiher D 187 C6
Uccle B 182 D4
Üchtelhausen D 187 A9
Uckange F 186 C1
Uddel NL 183 A7
Uden NL 183 B7
Udenhout NL 183 B6
Üdersdorf D 185 D6
Uettingen D 187 B8
Uffenheim D 187 B9
Uhingen D 187 D8
Uithoorn NL 182 A5
Ulft NL 183 B8
Ulicoten NL 182 C5
Ulm D 187 E8
Ulmen D 185 D6
Ulvenhout NL 182 B5
Undingen D 187 E7
Unkel D 185 C7
Unna D 185 A8
Unnau D 185 C8
Untermünkheim D 187 C8
Unterpleichfeld D 187 B9
Urbach D 185 C8
Urbar D 185 D8
Urberach D 187 B6
Utrecht NL 183 A6
Üxheim D 185 D6

V

Vaals NL 183 D8
Vaassen NL 183 A7
Valkenburg NL 183 D7
Valkenswaard NL 183 C6
Vallendar D 185 D8
Vandœuvre-lès-Nancy F 186 D1
Varik NL 183 B6
Varsseveld NL 183 B8
Vaux-sur-Sûre B 184 E4
Veenendaal NL 183 A7
Veere NL 182 B3
Veerle B 182 C5
Veghel NL 183 B7
Velbert D 183 C10
Veldegem B 182 C2
Velden NL 183 C8
Veldhoven NL 183 C6
Velen D 183 B9
Vellberg D 187 C8
Velp NL 183 B7
Vendenheim F 186 D4
Venlo NL 183 C8
Venray NL 183 B7
Vergaville F 186 D2
Verlaine B 183 D6
Verny F 186 C1
Verviers B 183 D7
Vessem NL 183 C6
Vettelschoss D 185 C7
Vianden L 184 E5
Vianen NL 183 B6
Vic-sur-Seille F 186 D2
Vielsalm B 184 D4
Vierlingsbeek NL 183 B7
Viernheim D 187 B6
Viersen D 183 C8
Vieux-Condé F 182 E3
Vigy F 186 C1
Villé F 186 E3
Villeneuve-d'Ascq F 182 D2
Villers-le-Bouillet B 183 D6
Villers-lès-Nancy F 186 D1
Villmar D 185 D9
Vilvoorde B 182 D4
Vincey F 186 E1
Vinkt B 182 C2
Vinningen D 186 C4
Vireux-Molhain F 184 D2
Vireux-Wallerand F 184 D2
Visé B 183 D7
Vlaardingen NL 182 B4
Vleuten NL 183 A6
Vlijmen NL 183 B6
Vlissingen NL 182 C3
Voerde (Niederrhein) D 183 B9
Vogelenzang NL 182 A5
Vogelweh D 186 C4
Vöhringen D 187 E6
Vöhringen D 187 E9
Volkach D 187 B9
Volkel NL 183 B7
Völklingen D 186 C2
Volmunster F 186 C3
Voorburg NL 182 A4
Voorhout NL 182 A4
Voorschoten NL 182 A4
Voorst NL 183 A8
Voorthuizen NL 183 A7
Vorden NL 183 A8
Vorst B 183 C6
Vosselaar B 182 C5
Vrasene B 182 C4
Vreden D 183 A9
Vreeland NL 183 A6
Vresse B 184 E2
Vriezenveen NL 183 A9
Vrouwenpolder NL 182 B3
Vught NL 183 B6

W

Waalre NL 183 C6
Waalwijk NL 183 B6
Waarschoot B 182 C3
Wachenheim an der Weinstraße D 187 C5
Wachtebeke B 182 C3
Wächtersbach D 187 A7
Waddinxveen NL 182 A5
Wadern D 186 B2
Wadersloh D 185 A9
Wadgassen D 186 C2
Wageningen NL 183 B7
Waghäusel D 187 C6
Waiblingen D 187 D7
Waibstadt D 187 C6
Waigolshausen D 187 B9
Waimes B 183 E8
Walcourt B 184 D1
Waldachtal D 187 E6
Waldböckelheim D 185 E8
Waldbreitbach D 185 C7
Waldbröl D 185 C8
Waldbrunn-Lahr D 185 C9
Waldbüttelbrunn D 187 B8
Waldenbuch D 187 D7
Waldenburg D 187 C8
Waldesch D 185 D8
Waldfischbach-Burgalben D 186 C4
Wald-Michelbach D 187 B6
Waldmohr D 186 C3
Waldrach D 186 B2
Waldsee D 187 C5
Waldstetten D 187 D8
Walferdange L 186 B1
Walldorf D 187 A6
Walldorf D 187 C6
Walldürn D 187 B7
Wallhausen D 185 E8
Wallhausen D 187 C9
Wamel NL 183 B6
Wandre B 183 D7
Wanne-Eikel D 183 B10
Wanroij NL 183 B7
Wanssum NL 183 B8
Wanze B 183 D6
Wapenveld NL 183 A8
Waregem B 182 D2
Waremme B 183 D6
Warmond NL 182 A5
Warnsveld NL 183 A8
Warstein D 185 B9
Wartmannsroth D 187 A8
Wäschenbeuren D 187 D8
Waspik NL 182 B5
Wasseiges B 183 D6
Wasselonne F 186 D3

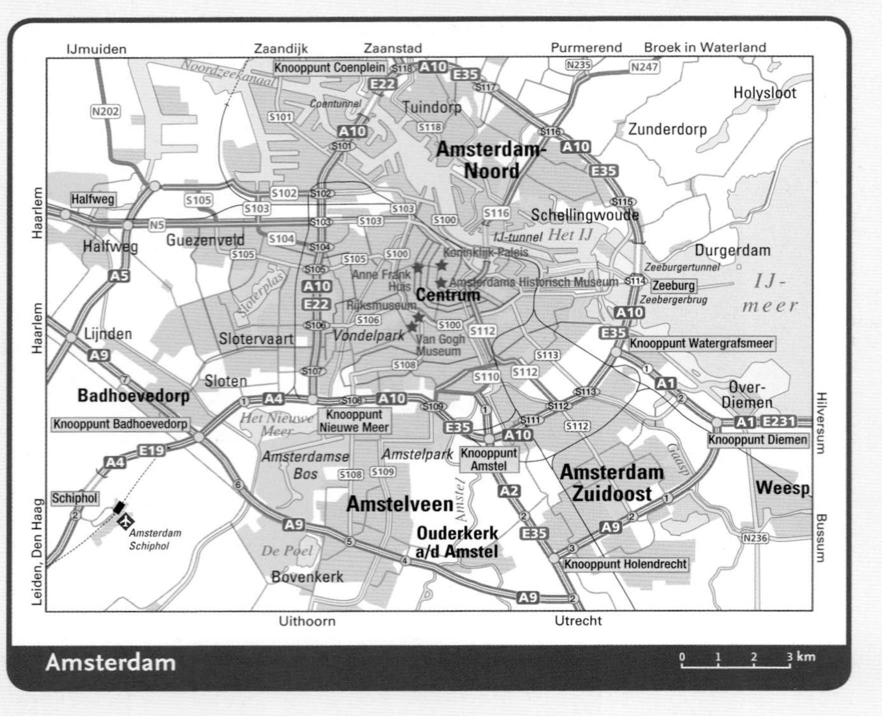
Amsterdam
IJmuiden
Zaandijk
Zaanstad
Purmerend
Broek in Waterland
Holysloot
Zunderdorp
Tuindorp
Amsterdam-Noord
Schellingwoude
Durgerdam
IJ-meer
Halfweg
Guezenveld
Centrum
Zeeburg
Lijnden
Slotervaart
Vondelpark
Badhoevedorp
Sloten
Over-Diemen
Amstelveen
Amsterdam Zuidoost
Weesp
Schiphol
Ouderkerk a/d Amstel
Bovenkerk
Uithoorn
Utrecht
Hilversum
Bussum
Haarlem
Leiden, Den Haag

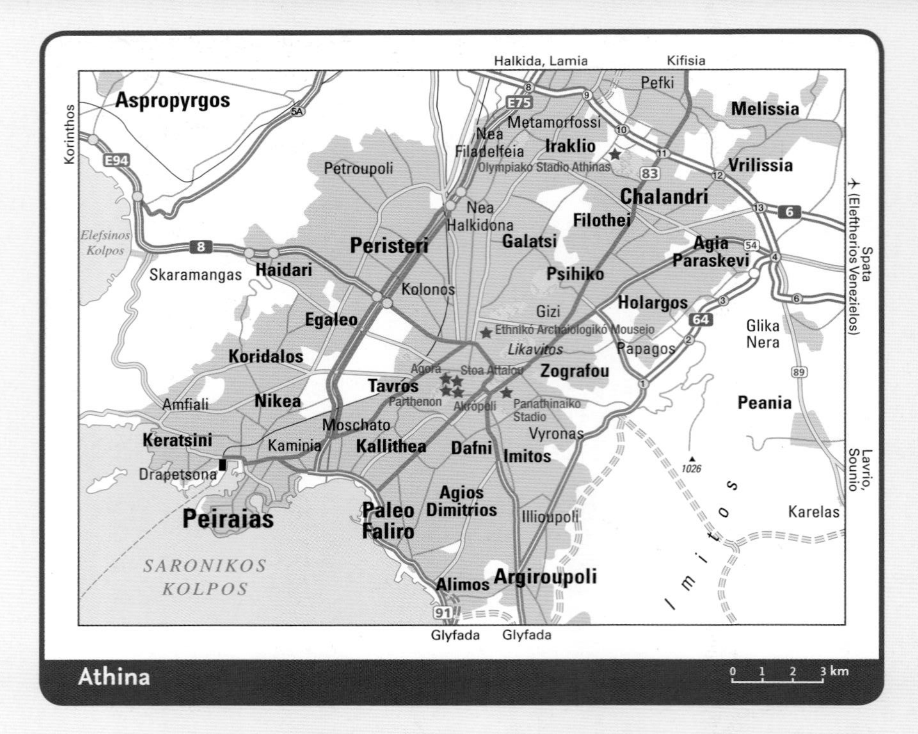
Athina
Halkida, Lamia
Kifisia
Aspropyrgos
Pefki
Melissia
Metamorfossi
Nea Filadelfeia
Iraklio
Vrilissia
Petroupoli
Chalandri
Nea Halkidona
Filothei
Peristeri
Galatsi
Agia Paraskevi
Skaramangas
Haidari
Psihiko
Kolonos
Holargos
Glika Nera
Egaleo
Gizi
Papagos
Koridalos
Likavitos
Zografou
Tavros
Peania
Amfiali
Nikea
Moschato
Vyronas
Keratsini
Kaminia
Kallithea
Dafni
Imitos
Drapetsona
Agios Dimitrios
Peiraias
Paleo Faliro
Illioupoli
Karelas
SARONIKOS KOLPOS
Alimos
Argiroupoli
Glyfada
Korinthos
Spata (Eleftherios Venezielos)
Lavrio, Sounio

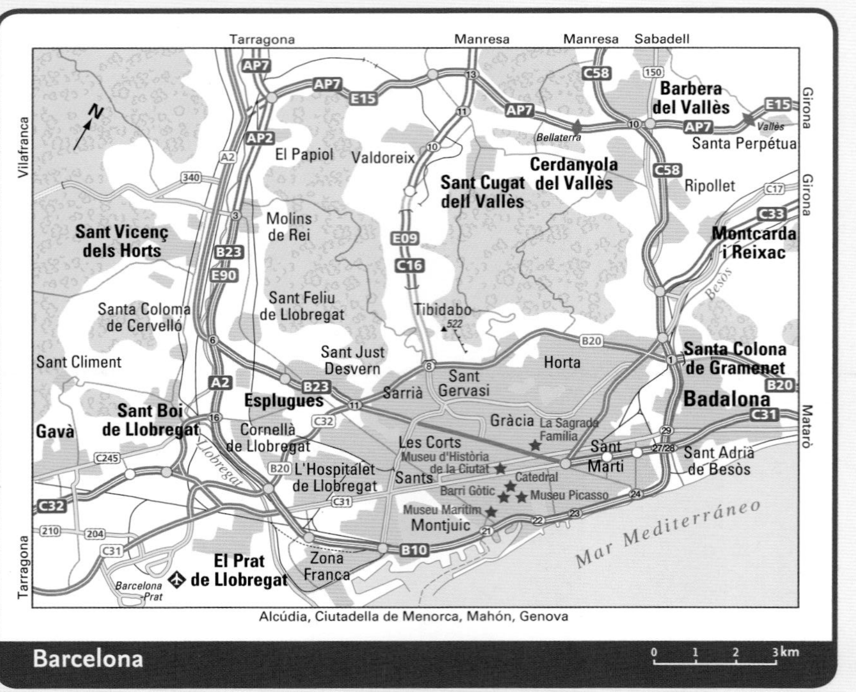
Barcelona
Tarragona
Manresa
Sabadell
Barbera del Vallès
Santa Perpètua
El Papiol
Valdoreix
Cerdanyola del Vallès
Sant Cugat dell Vallès
Ripollet
Sant Vicenç dels Horts
Molins de Rei
Montcarda i Reixac
Santa Coloma de Cervelló
Sant Feliu de Llobregat
Tibidabo
Sant Climent
Sant Just Desvern
Horta
Santa Colona de Gramenet
Badalona
Gavà
Sant Boi de Llobregat
Esplugues
Sarrià
Sant Gervasi
Gràcia
Cornellà de Llobregat
Les Corts
Sant Martí
Sant Adrià de Besòs
L'Hospitalet de Llobregat
Sants
Montjuïc
El Prat de Llobregat
Zona Franca
Mar Mediterráneo
Alcúdia, Ciutadella de Menorca, Mahón, Genova
Vilafranca
Girona
Mataró

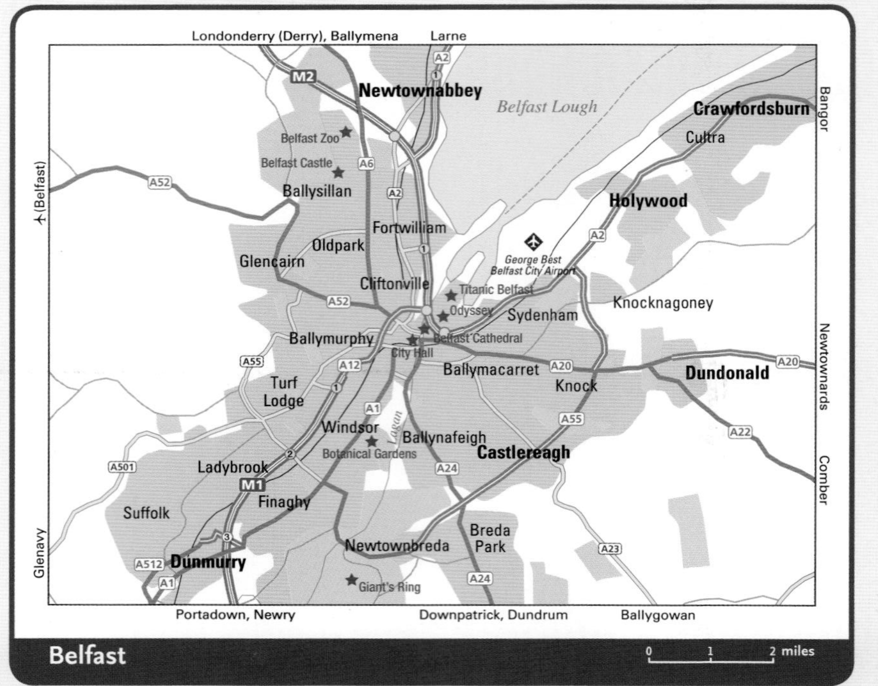
Belfast
Londonderry (Derry), Ballymena
Larne
Newtownabbey
Belfast Lough
Crawfordsburn
Cultra
Ballysillan
Holywood
Fortwilliam
Oldpark
Glencairn
Cliftonville
Knocknagoney
Sydenham
Ballymurphy
Turf Lodge
Ballymacarret
Knock
Dundonald
Windsor
Ballynafeigh
Castlereagh
Ladybrook
Finaghy
Suffolk
Newtownbreda
Breda Park
Dunmurry
Portadown, Newry
Downpatrick, Dundrum
Ballygowan
Glenavy
Bangor
Newtownards
Comber

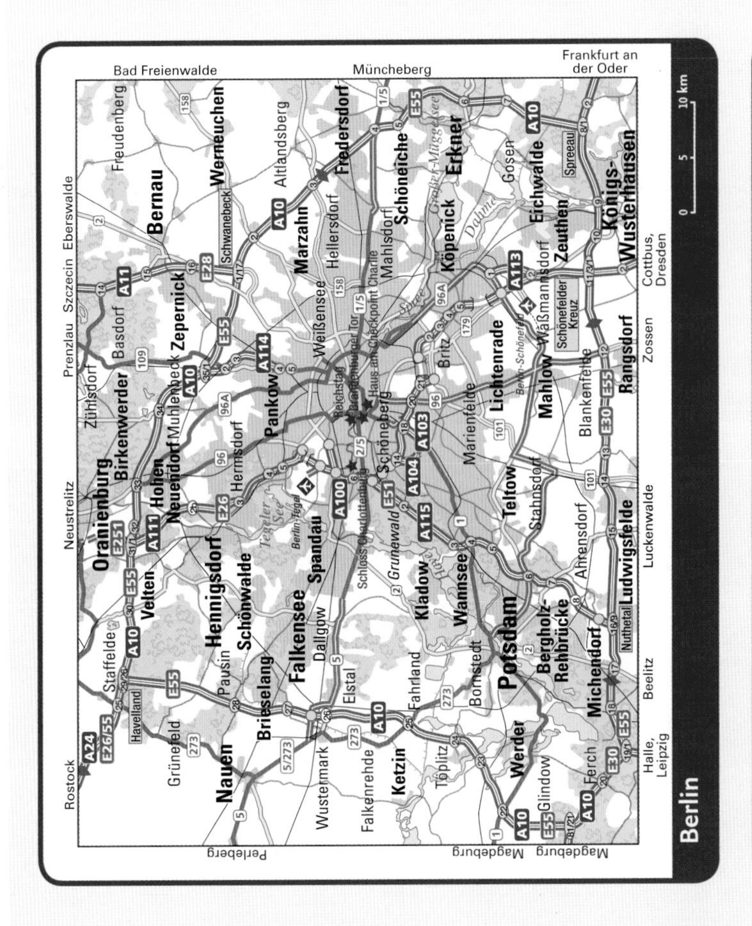

Berlin

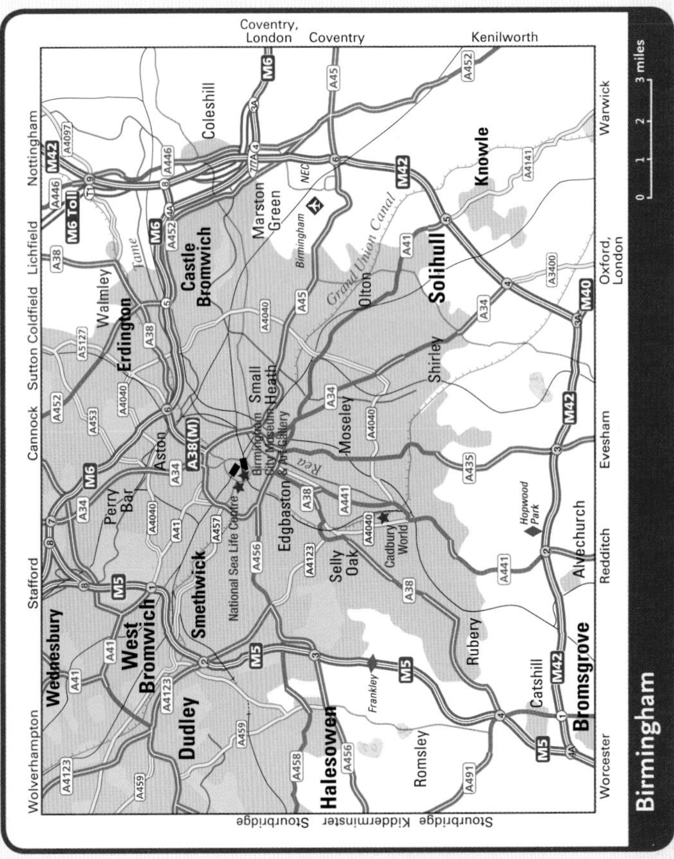

Birmingham

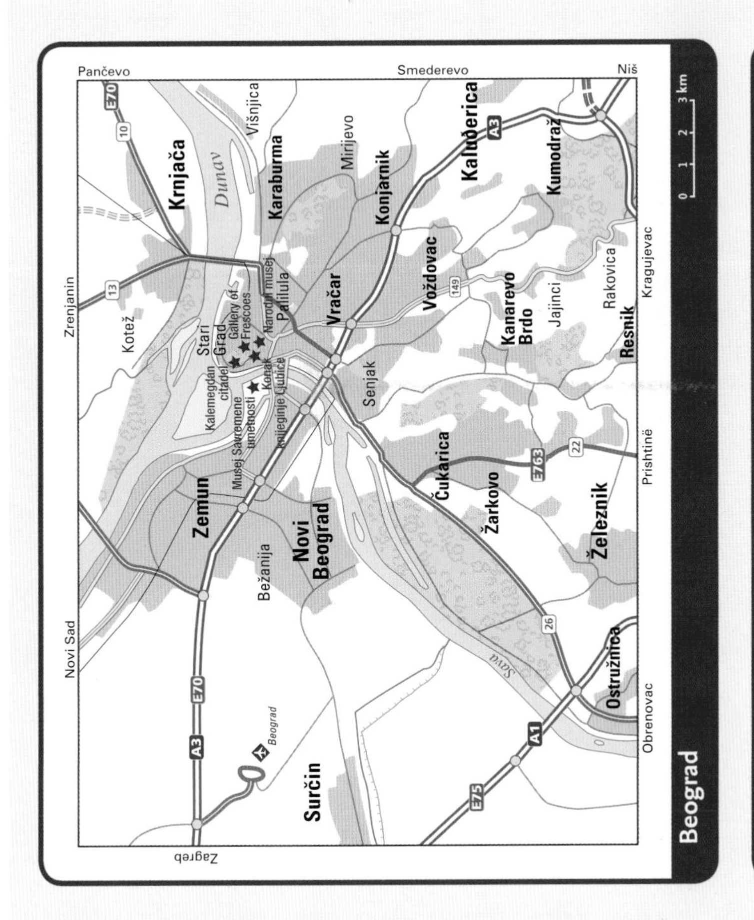

Beograd

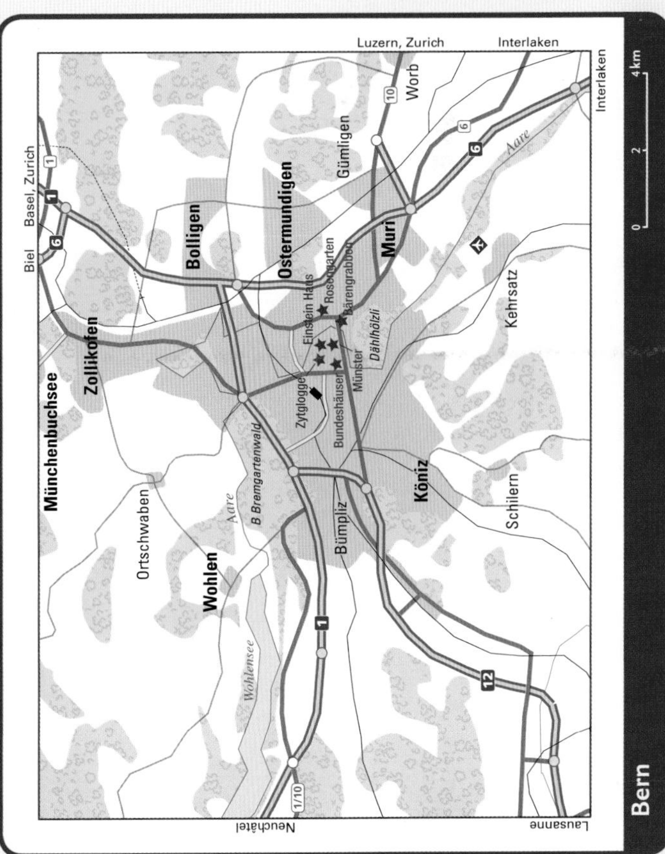

Bern

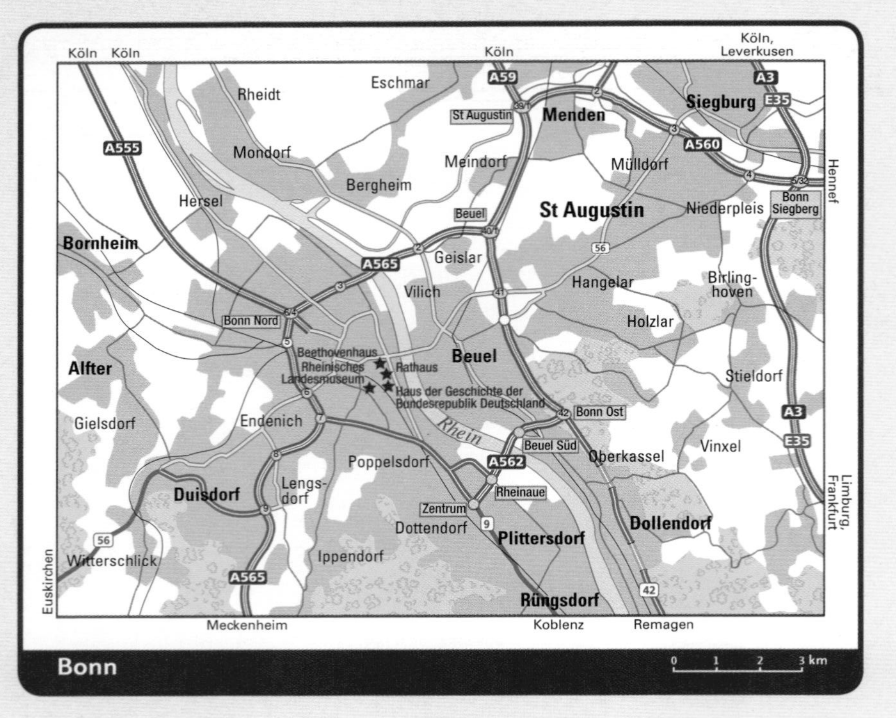
Köln Köln
Köln
Köln, Leverkusen
Hennef
Limburg, Frankfurt
Euskirchen
Meckenheim
Koblenz
Remagen
Rheidt
Eschmar
Menden
Siegburg
Mondorf
Bergheim
Meindorf
Mülldorf
St Augustin
Niederpleis
Hersel
Bornheim
Geislar
Vilich
Hangelar
Birling-hoven
Holzlar
Beuel
Alfter
Beethovenhaus
Rheinisches Landesmuseum
Rathaus
Haus der Geschichte der Bundesrepublik Deutschland
Stieldorf
Gielsdorf
Endenich
Rhein
Oberkassel
Vinxel
Duisdorf
Lengs-dorf
Poppelsdorf
Dottendorf
Plittersdorf
Dollendorf
Witterschlick
Ippendorf
Rüngsdorf
Bonn
0 1 2 3 km

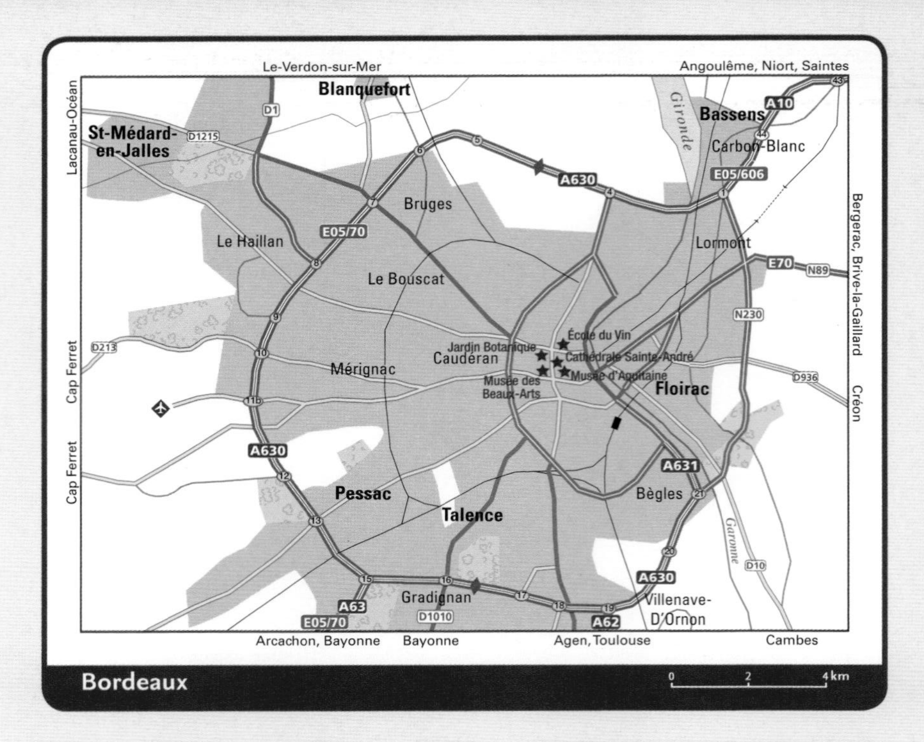
Le-Verdon-sur-Mer
Angoulême, Niort, Saintes
Lacanau-Océan
Bergerac, Brive-la-Gaillard
Créon
Cap Ferret
Cap Ferret
Arcachon, Bayonne
Bayonne
Agen, Toulouse
Cambes
Blanquefort
St-Médard-en-Jalles
Gironde
Bassens
Carbon-Blanc
Bruges
Le Haillan
Lormont
Le Bouscat
École du Vin
Jardin Botanique
Cauderan
Cathédrale Sainte-André
Musée des Beaux-Arts
Musée d'Aquitaine
Mérignac
Floirac
Pessac
Talence
Bègles
Garonne
Gradignan
Villenave-D'Ornon
Bordeaux
0 2 4 km

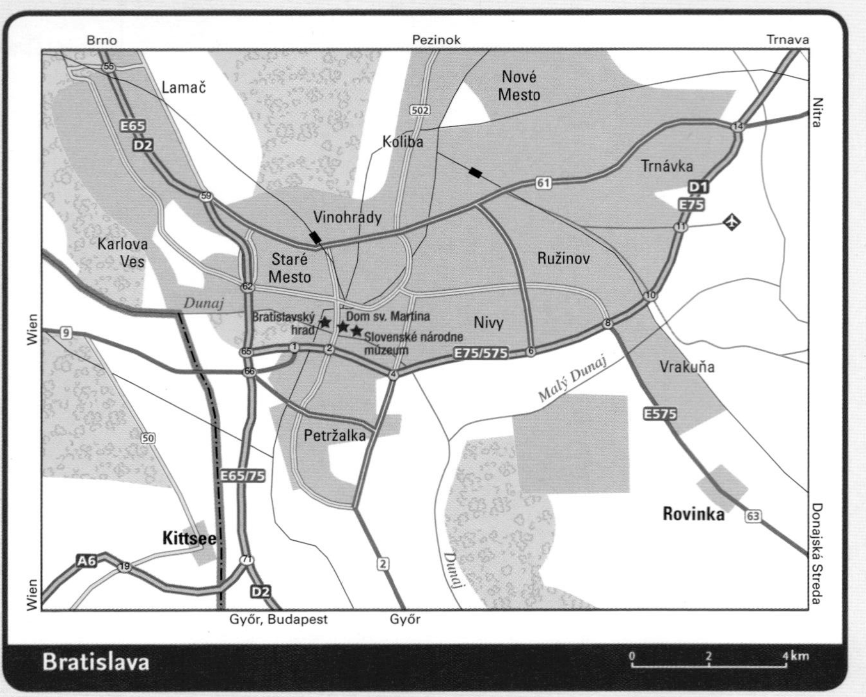
Brno
Pezinok
Trnava
Nitra
Wien
Wien
Donajská Streda
Győr, Budapest
Győr
Lamač
Nové Mesto
Koliba
Trnávka
Vinohrady
Karlova Ves
Staré Mesto
Ružinov
Dunaj
Bratislavský hrad
Dom sv. Martina
Slovenské národne múzeum
Nivy
Malý Dunaj
Vrakuňa
Petržalka
Rovinka
Kittsee
Bratislava
0 2 4 km

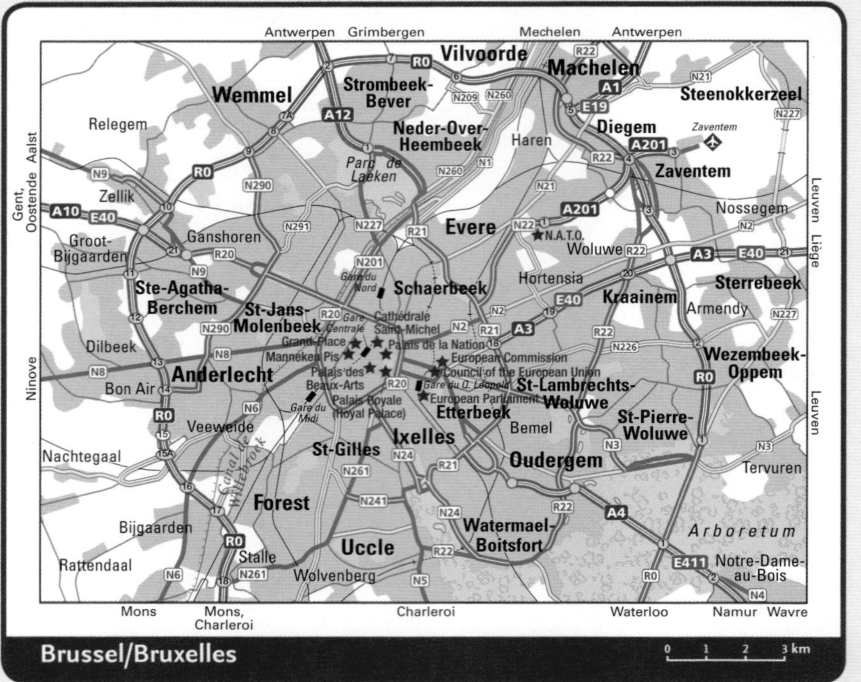
Antwerpen
Grimbergen
Mechelen
Antwerpen
Gent, Oostende
Aalst
Ninove
Leuven
Liège
Leuven
Mons
Mons, Charleroi
Charleroi
Waterloo
Namur
Wavre
Vilvoorde
Machelen
Wemmel
Strombeek-Bever
Steenokkerzeel
Relegem
Neder-Over-Heembeek
Haren
Diegem
Zaventem
Parc de Laeken
Zellik
Evere
Nossegem
Ganshoren
N.A.T.O.
Woluwe
Groot-Bijgaarden
Hortensia
Schaerbeek
Sterrebeek
Ste-Agatha-Berchem
St-Jans-Molenbeek
Cathédrale Saint-Michel
Kraainem
Armendy
Grand-Place
Palais de la Nation
Dilbeek
Manneken Pis
European Commission
Wezembeek-Oppem
Palais des Beaux-Arts
Council of the European Union
Anderlecht
St-Lambrechts-Woluwe
European Parliament
Bon Air
Palais Royale (Royal Palace)
Etterbeek
Veeweide
Bemel
St-Pierre-Woluwe
Ixelles
St-Gilles
Nachtegaal
Oudergem
Tervuren
Forest
Bijgaarden
Watermael-Boitsfort
Arboretum
Stalle
Uccle
Rattendaal
Wolvenberg
Notre-Dame-au-Bois
Brussel/Bruxelles
0 1 2 3 km

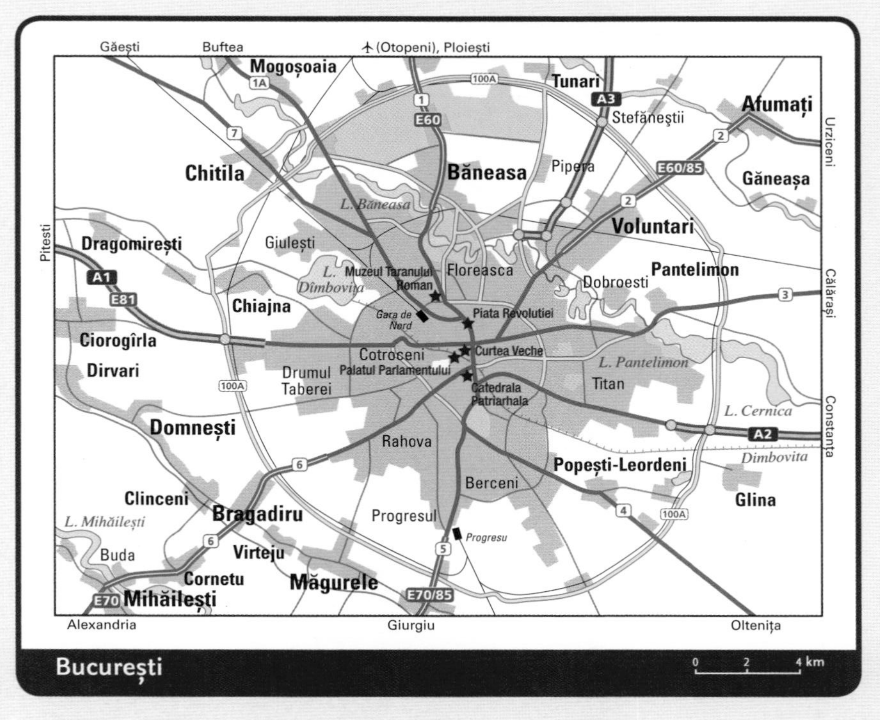

Budapest

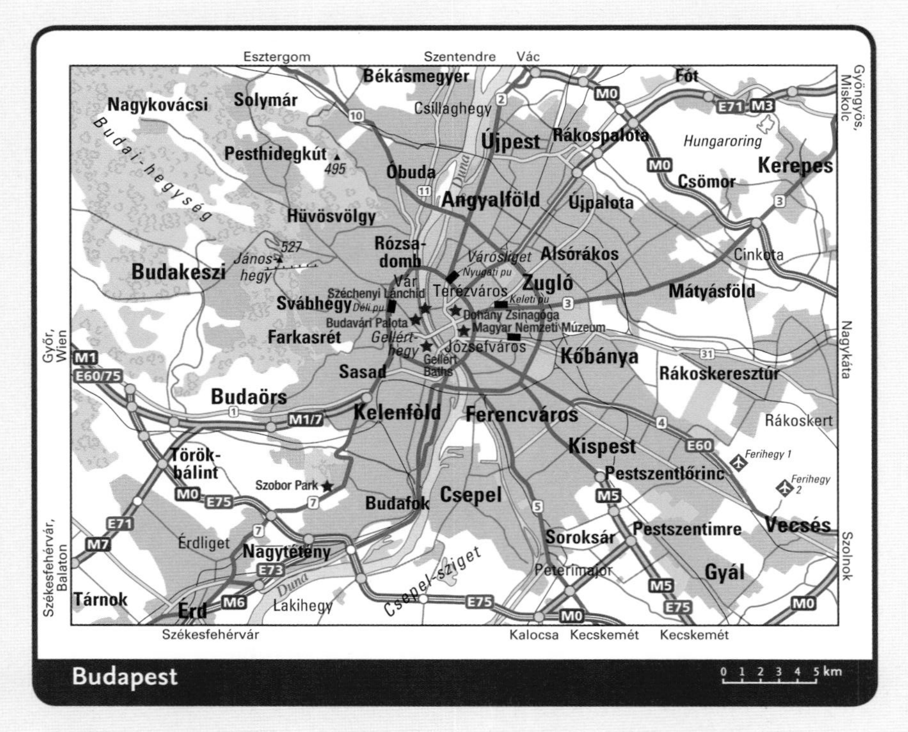

Chișinău

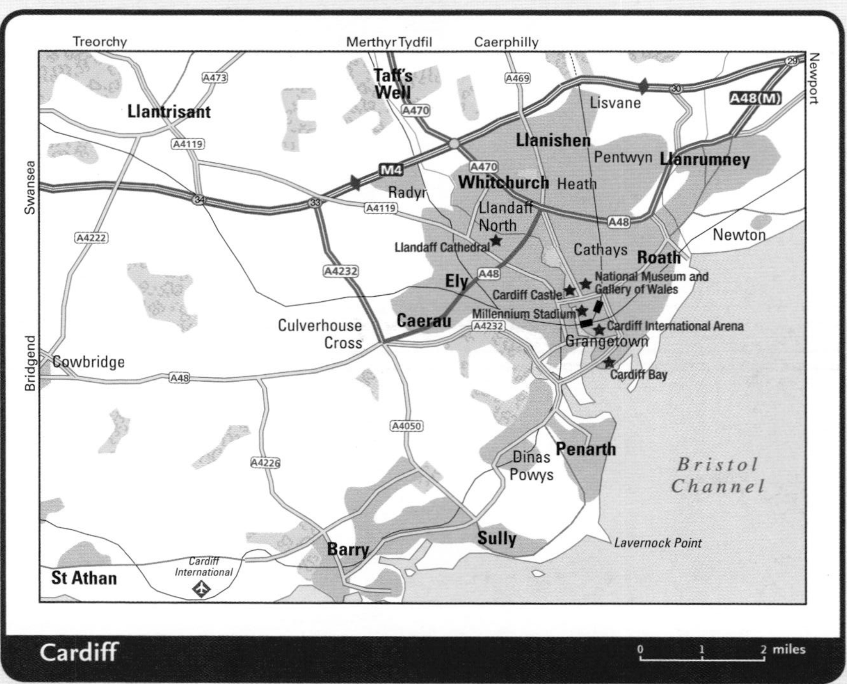

București

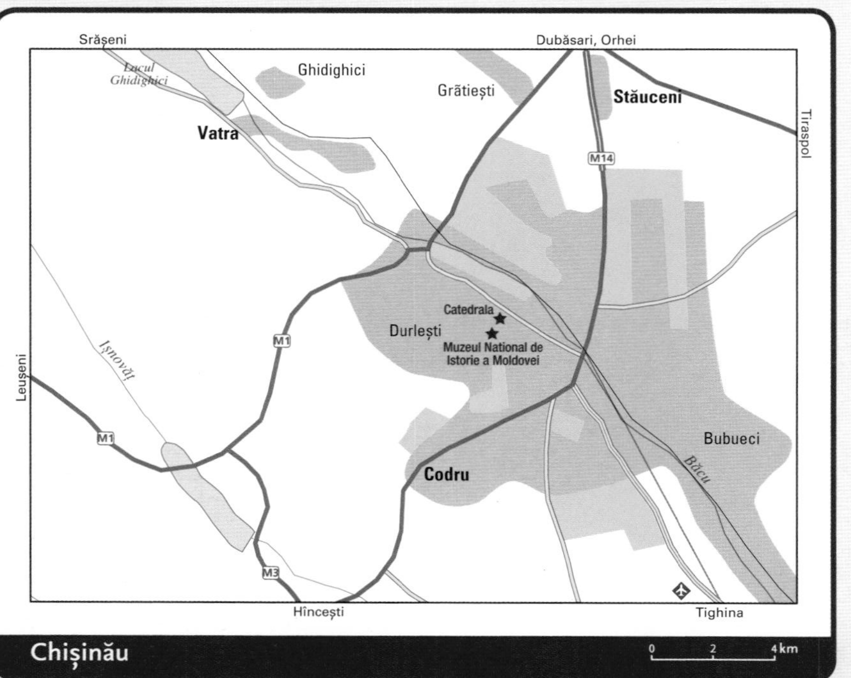

Cardiff

Bucureşti
Băneasa
Voluntari
Pantelimon
Chitila
Chiajna
Domneşti
Măgurele
Popeşti-Leordeni
Glina
Afumaţi
Mogoşoaia
Bragadiru
Tunari
Dragomireşti
Cornetu
Mihăileşti
Újpest
Angyalföld
Zugló
Ferencváros
Kelenföld
Csepel
Kispest
Kőbánya
Óbuda
Budaörs
Budakeszi
Érd
Vecsés
Gyál
Kerepes
Fót
Soroksár
Budafok
Newport
Bristol Channel
Penarth
Barry
Sully
Llanishen
Whitchurch
Roath
Ely
Caerau
Llantrisant
St Athan
Cowbridge
Llanrumney
Lisvane
Radyr
Taff's Well
Chişinău
Tiraspol
Stăuceni
Codru
Durleşti
Vatra
Bubueci
Ghidighici
Grătieşti

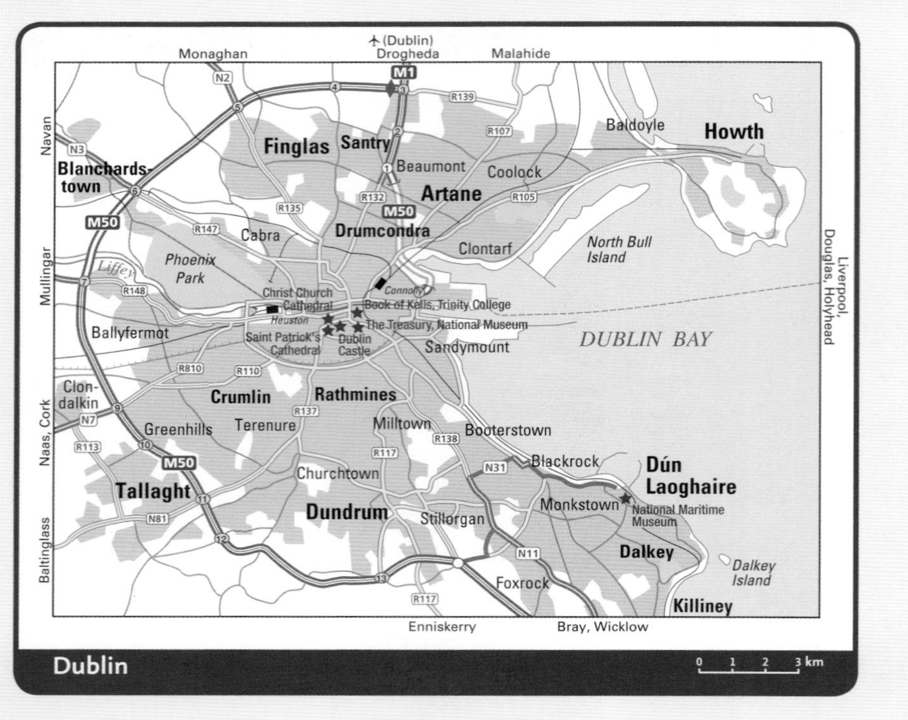
Dublin
DUBLIN BAY
Howth
Baldoyle
North Bull Island
Finglas
Santry
Beaumont
Coolock
Artane
Drumcondra
Clontarf
Cabra
Phoenix Park
Blanchardstown
Ballyfermot
Clondalkin
Greenhills
Crumlin
Terenure
Rathmines
Milltown
Booterstown
Sandymount
Blackrock
Dún Laoghaire
National Maritime Museum
Monkstown
Dalkey
Dalkey Island
Killiney
Foxrock
Stillorgan
Dundrum
Churchtown
Tallaght
Christ Church Cathedral
Book of Kells, Trinity College
The Treasury, National Museum
Saint Patrick's Cathedral
Dublin Castle
Connolly
Heuston
Monaghan
Drogheda
Malahide
Liverpool, Douglas, Holyhead
Enniskerry
Bray, Wicklow
Navan
Mullingar
Naas, Cork
Baltinglass

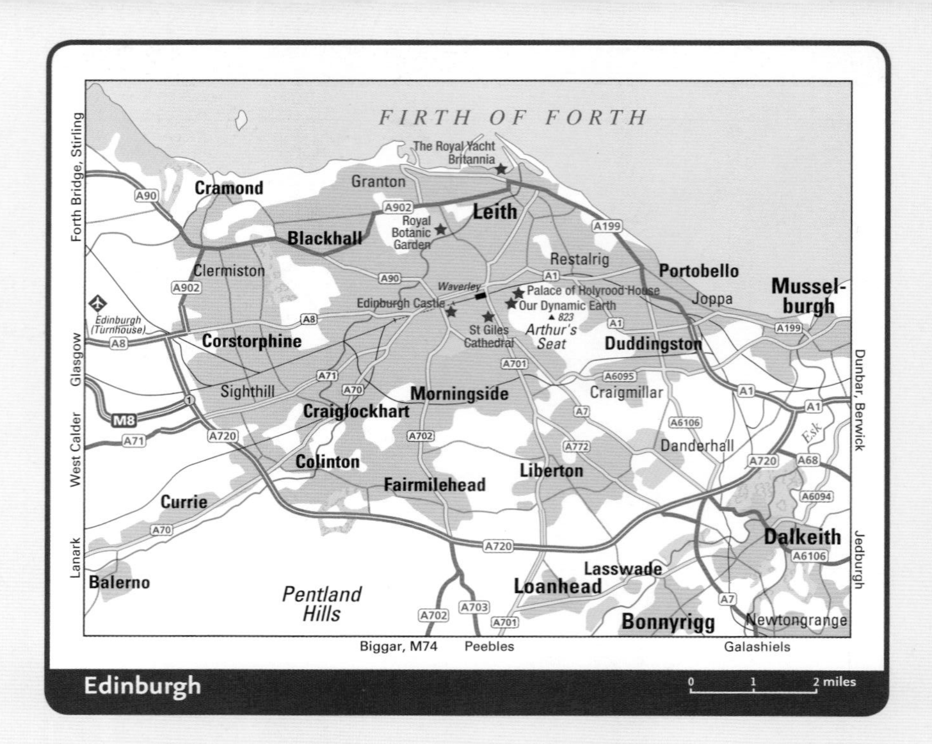
Edinburgh
FIRTH OF FORTH
The Royal Yacht Britannia
Granton
Cramond
Leith
Royal Botanic Garden
Blackhall
Clermiston
Restalrig
Portobello
Joppa
Musselburgh
Palace of Holyrood House
Our Dynamic Earth
Arthur's Seat
Edinburgh Castle
Waverley
St Giles Cathedral
Corstorphine
Duddingston
Sighthill
Morningside
Craigmillar
Craiglockhart
Colinton
Fairmilehead
Liberton
Danderhall
Currie
Dalkeith
Lasswade
Loanhead
Bonnyrigg
Newtongrange
Balerno
Pentland Hills
Edinburgh (Turnhouse)
Forth Bridge, Stirling
Glasgow
West Calder
Lanark
Biggar, M74
Peebles
Galashiels
Dunbar, Berwick
Jedburgh

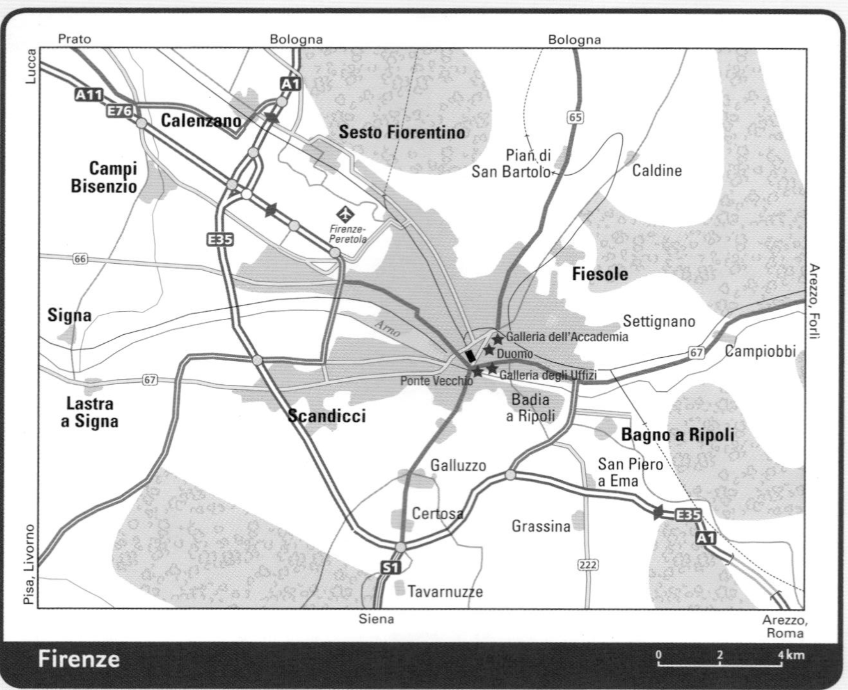
Firenze
Calenzano
Sesto Fiorentino
Campi Bisenzio
Firenze-Peretola
Pian di San Bartolo
Caldine
Fiesole
Settignano
Campiobbi
Signa
Lastra a Signa
Scandicci
Galleria dell'Accademia
Duomo
Galleria degli Uffizi
Ponte Vecchio
Badia a Ripoli
Bagno a Ripoli
Galluzzo
San Piero a Ema
Certosa
Grassina
Tavarnuzze
Prato
Bologna
Lucca
Pisa, Livorno
Siena
Arezzo, Roma
Arezzo, Forlì

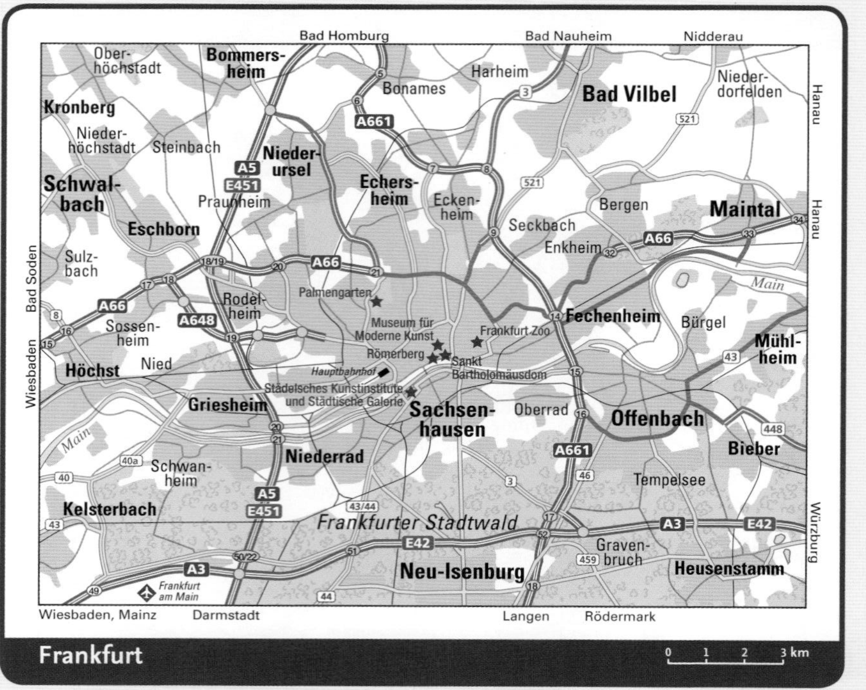
Frankfurt
Oberhöchstadt
Bommersheim
Bonames
Harheim
Bad Vilbel
Niederdorfelden
Kronberg
Niederhöchstadt
Steinbach
Niederursel
Eschersheim
Eckenheim
Schwalbach
Praunheim
Eschborn
Seckbach
Bergen
Enkheim
Maintal
Sulzbach
Rödelheim
Palmengarten
Fechenheim
Bürgel
Sossenheim
Museum für Moderne Kunst
Römerberg
Frankfurt Zoo
Sankt Bartholomäusdom
Mühlheim
Höchst
Nied
Hauptbahnhof
Städelsches Kunstinstitute und Städtische Galerie
Griesheim
Sachsenhausen
Oberrad
Offenbach
Bieber
Niederrad
Schwanheim
Tempelsee
Kelsterbach
Frankfurter Stadtwald
Neu-Isenburg
Gravenbruch
Heusenstamm
Frankfurt am Main
Bad Homburg
Bad Nauheim
Nidderau
Hanau
Bad Soden
Wiesbaden
Wiesbaden, Mainz
Darmstadt
Langen
Rödermark
Würzburg

196

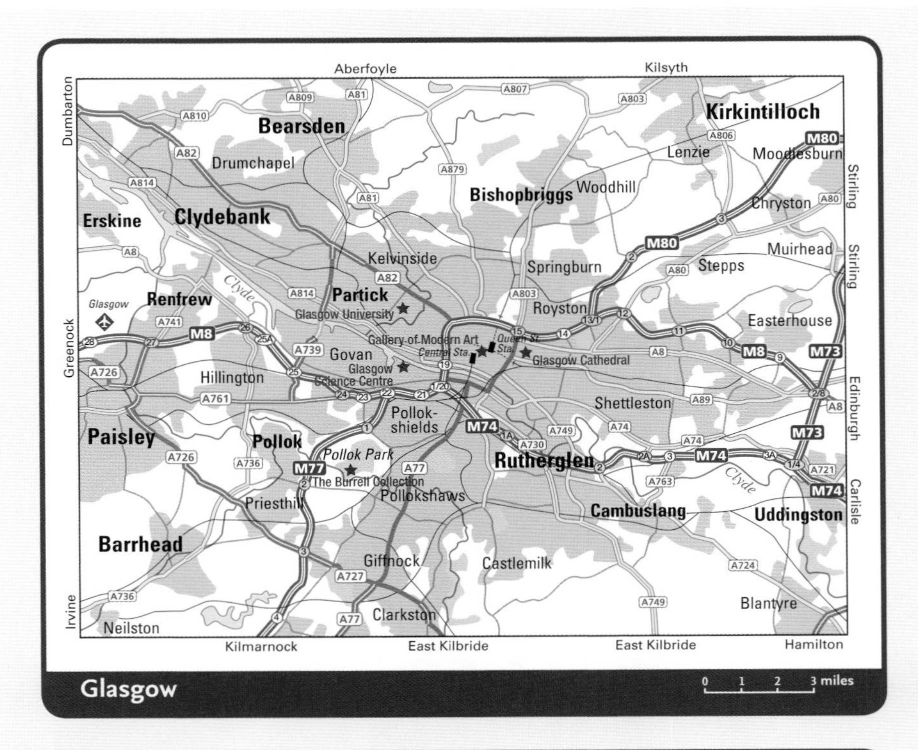
Glasgow
Aberfoyle
Kilsyth
Dumbarton
Greenock
Irvine
Stirling
Edinburgh
Carlisle
Kilmarnock
East Kilbride
Hamilton
Bearsden
Kirkintilloch
Lenzie
Moodiesburn
Drumchapel
Bishopbriggs
Woodhill
Chryston
Erskine
Clydebank
Muirhead
Kelvinside
Springburn
Stepps
Renfrew
Partick
Glasgow University
Royston
Easterhouse
Gallery of Modern Art
Glasgow Cathedral
Govan
Glasgow Science Centre
Hillington
Shettleston
Pollokshields
Paisley
Pollok
Pollok Park
The Burrell Collection
Pollokshaws
Rutherglen
Priesthill
Cambuslang
Uddingston
Barrhead
Giffnock
Castlemilk
Blantyre
Clarkston
Neilston
Clyde
0 1 2 3 miles

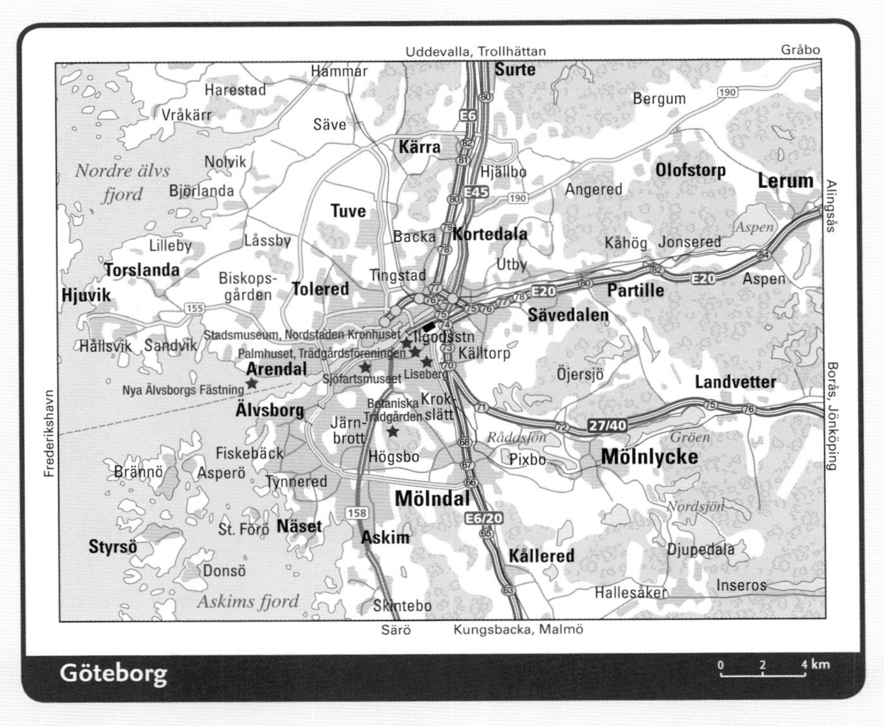
Göteborg
Uddevalla, Trollhättan
Gråbo
Alingsås
Borås, Jönköping
Frederikshavn
Särö
Kungsbacka, Malmö
Hammar
Surte
Harestad
Vråkärr
Säve
Bergum
Kärra
Nordre älvs fjord
Nolvik
Björlanda
Hjällbo
Angered
Olofstorp
Lerum
Tuve
Backa
Kortedala
Lilleby
Lässby
Kåhög
Jonsered
Aspen
Torslanda
Biskopsgården
Tolered
Tingstad
Utby
Partille
Hjuvik
Sävedalen
Hällsvik
Sandvik
Stadsmuseum, Nordstaden Kronhuset
Palmhuset, Trädgårdsföreningen
Kålltorp
Arendal
Sjöfartsmuseet
Liseberg
Öjersjö
Landvetter
Nya Älvsborgs Fästning
Älvsborg
Botaniska Trädgården
Krokslätt
Järnbrott
Rådasjön
Pixbo
Mölnlycke
Fiskebäck
Högsbo
Brännö
Asperö
Tynnered
Mölndal
St. Förö
Näset
Askim
Nordsjön
Styrsö
Kållered
Djupedala
Donsö
Hallesåker
Inseros
Askims fjord
Skintebo
0 2 4 km

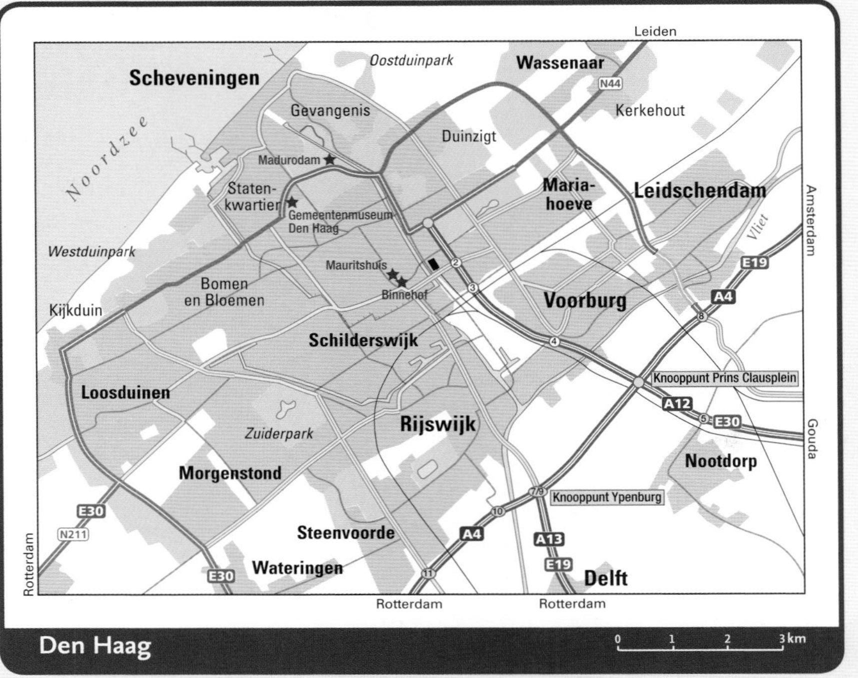
Den Haag
Leiden
Amsterdam
Gouda
Rotterdam
Scheveningen
Oostduinpark
Wassenaar
Gevangenis
Kerkehout
Duinzigt
Noordzee
Madurodam
Statenkwartier
Gemeentemuseum Den Haag
Mariahoeve
Leidschendam
Westduinpark
Mauritshuis
Binnenhof
Vliet
Bomen en Bloemen
Voorburg
Kijkduin
Schilderswijk
Knooppunt Prins Clausplein
Loosduinen
Zuiderpark
Rijswijk
Nootdorp
Morgenstond
Knooppunt Ypenburg
Steenvoorde
Wateringen
Delft
0 1 2 3 km

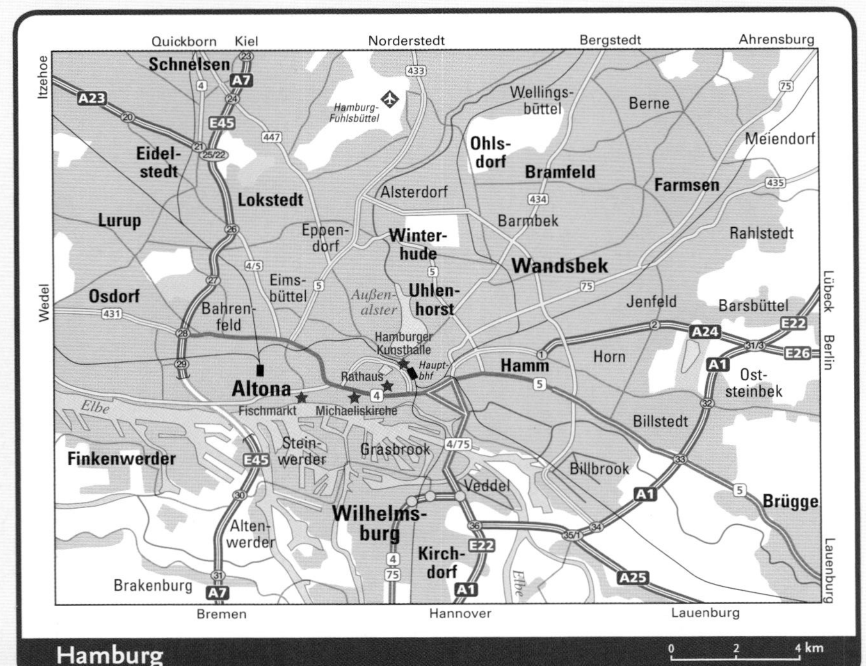
Hamburg
Quickborn
Kiel
Norderstedt
Bergstedt
Ahrensburg
Itzehoe
Wedel
Lübeck
Berlin
Lauenburg
Bremen
Hannover
Schnelsen
Hamburg-Fuhlsbüttel
Wellingsbüttel
Berne
Meiendorf
Eidelstedt
Ohlsdorf
Bramfeld
Farmsen
Lokstedt
Alsterdorf
Lurup
Eppendorf
Winterhude
Barmbek
Rahlstedt
Wandsbek
Eimsbüttel
Außenalster
Uhlenhorst
Osdorf
Jenfeld
Barsbüttel
Bahrenfeld
Hamburger Kunsthalle
Hauptbhf
Rathaus
Hamm
Horn
Oststeinbek
Altona
Fischmarkt
Michaeliskirche
Elbe
Billstedt
Steinwerder
Grasbrook
Finkenwerder
Billbrook
Veddel
Brügge
Wilhelmsburg
Altenwerder
Kirchdorf
Brakenburg
0 2 4 km

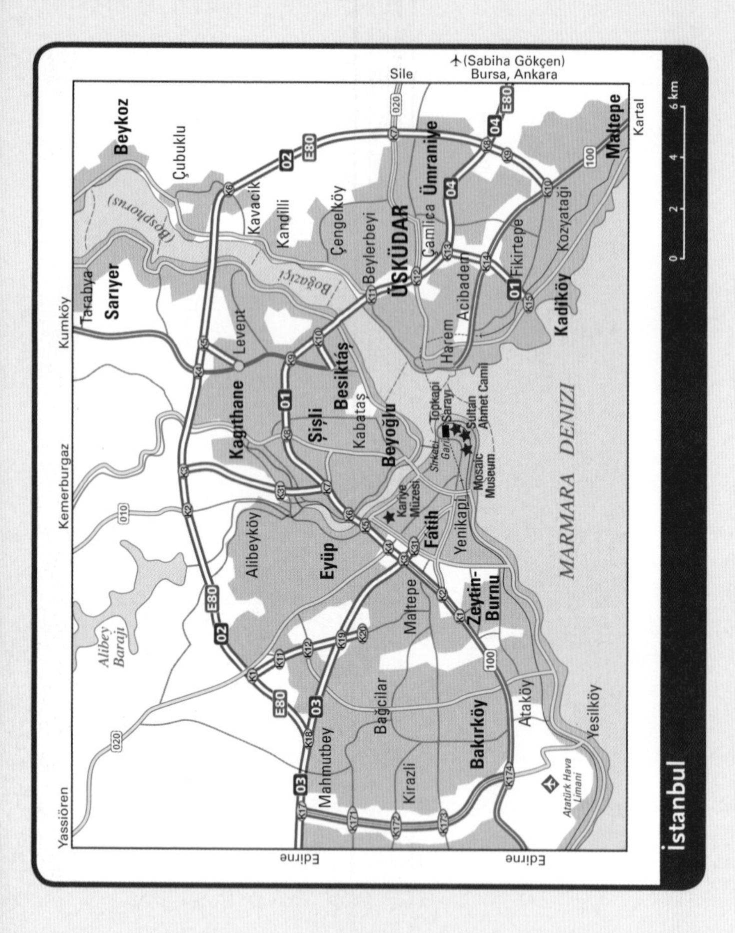
İstanbul
Beykoz
Çubuklu
Sarıyer
Tarabya
Kavacık
Kandilli
Çengelköy
Beylerbeyi
ÜSKÜDAR
Ümraniye
Çamlıca
Acıbadem
Fikirtepe
Kozyatağı
Kadıköy
Maltepe
Kartal
Levent
Kağıthane
Beşiktaş
Şişli
Kabataş
Beyoğlu
Harem
Topkapı Sarayı
Sultan Ahmet Camii
Mosaic Museum
Kariye Müzesi
Fatih
Yenikapı
Eyüp
Alibeyköy
Zeytinburnu
Maltepe
Bağcılar
Kirazlı
Mahmutbey
Bakırköy
Ataköy
Yeşilköy
Atatürk Hava Limanı
MARMARA DENIZI
Alibey Barajı
Boğaziçi
(Bosphorus)
Şile
(Sabiha Gökçen) Bursa, Ankara
Kumköy
Kemerburgaz
Yassiören
Edirne

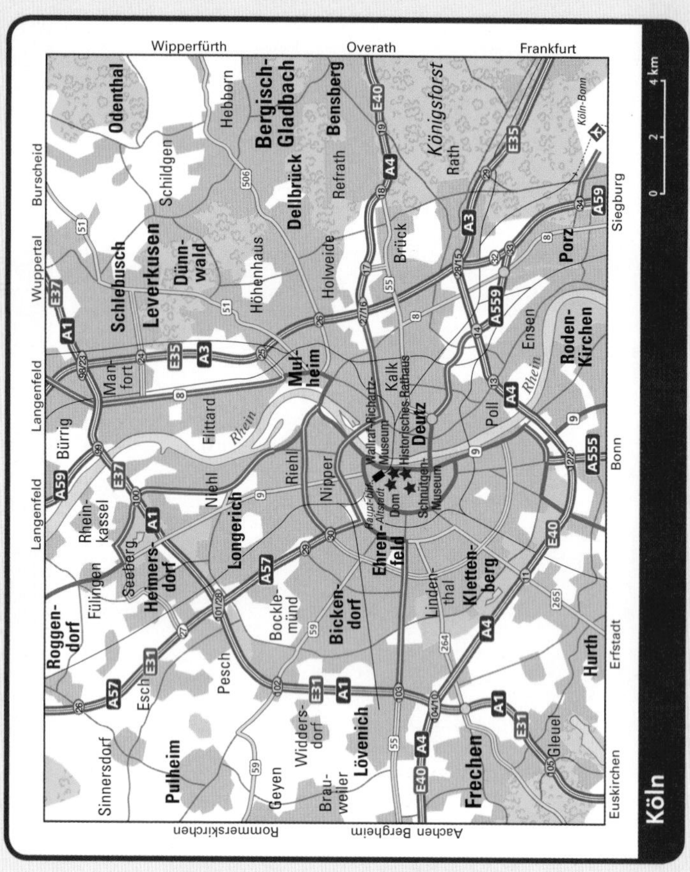
Köln
Wipperfürth
Overath
Frankfurt
Odenthal
Hebborn
Bergisch-Gladbach
Bensberg
Königsforst
Rath
Schildgen
Dellbrück
Refrath
Leverkusen
Schlebusch
Dünnwald
Höhenhaus
Holweide
Brück
Porz
Mülheim
Kalk
Deutz
Flittard
Rhein
Riehl
Nippes
Dom
Schnütgen-Museum
Historisches Rathaus
Ehrenfeld
Niehl
Longerich
Bürrig
Rheinkassel
Merkenich
Fühlingen
Seeberg
Heimersdorf
Roggendorf
Bocklemünd
Bickendorf
Lindenthal
Klettenberg
Pesch
Esch
Widdersdorf
Lövenich
Weiden
Frechen
Hürth
Gleuel
Pulheim
Sinnersdorf
Geyen
Brauweiler
Poll
Ensen
Rodenkirchen
Siegburg
Bonn
Erftstadt
Euskirchen
Aachen Bergheim
Rommerskirchen
Langenfeld
Wuppertal
Burscheid

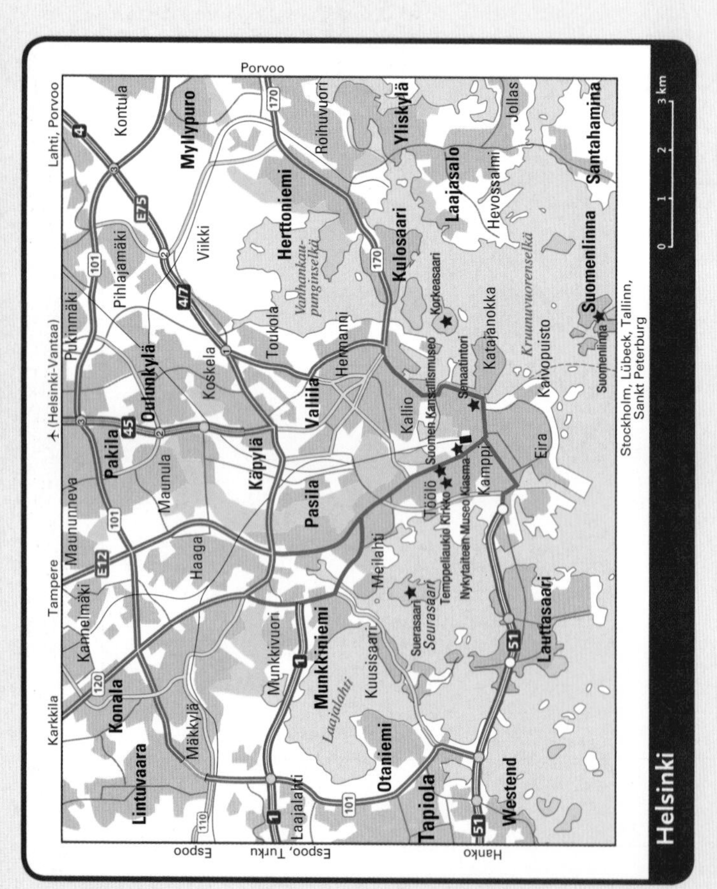
Helsinki
Porvoo
Lahti, Porvoo
Kontula
Myllypuro
Roihuvuori
Yliskylä
Jollas
Laajasalo
Santahamina
Herttoniemi
Viikki
Kulosaari
Korkeasaari
Hevossalmi
Suomenlinna
Pihlajamäki
Pukinmäki
Toukola
Hermanni
Vallila
Katajanokka
Kaivopuisto
Oulunkylä
Koskela
Käpylä
Pakila
Maunula
Pasila
Kallio
Kamppi
Eira
Töölö
Kiasma
Haaga
Meilahti
Munkkiniemi
Munkkivuori
Kuusisaari
Lauttasaari
Konala
Kannelmäki
Malminkartano
Mäkkylä
Lintuvaara
Otaniemi
Tapiola
Westend
Laajalahti
Seurasaari
Stockholm, Lübeck, Tallinn, Sankt Peterburg
Espoo, Turku
Espoo
Hanko
Karkkila
Tampere
Helsinki-Vantaa

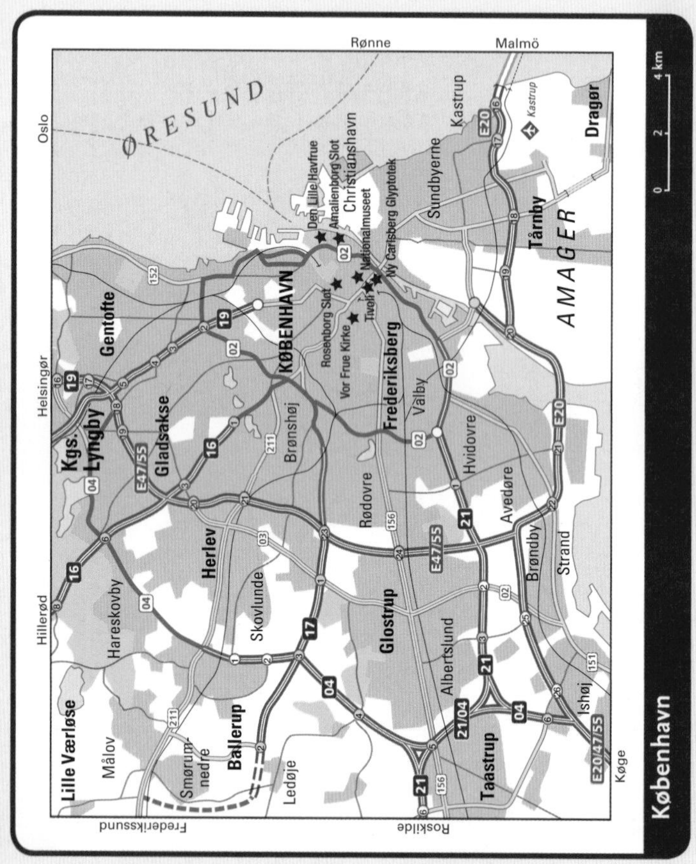
København
ØRESUND
Rønne
Malmö
Oslo
Helsingør
Hillerød
Kastrup
Dragør
Tårnby
AMAGER
Sundbyerne
Christianshavn
Den Lille Havfrue
Amalienborg Slot
Nationalmuseet
Ny Carlsberg Glyptotek
Tivoli
Rosenborg Slot
Vor Frue Kirke
KØBENHAVN
Frederiksberg
Valby
Hvidovre
Avedøre
Brøndby
Strand
Ishøj
Gentofte
Kgs. Lyngby
Gladsakse
Brønshøj
Rødovre
Herlev
Glostrup
Albertslund
Taastrup
Skovlunde
Hareskovby
Ballerup
Smørumnedre
Måløv
Ledøje
Lille Værløse
Køge
Roskilde
Frederikssund

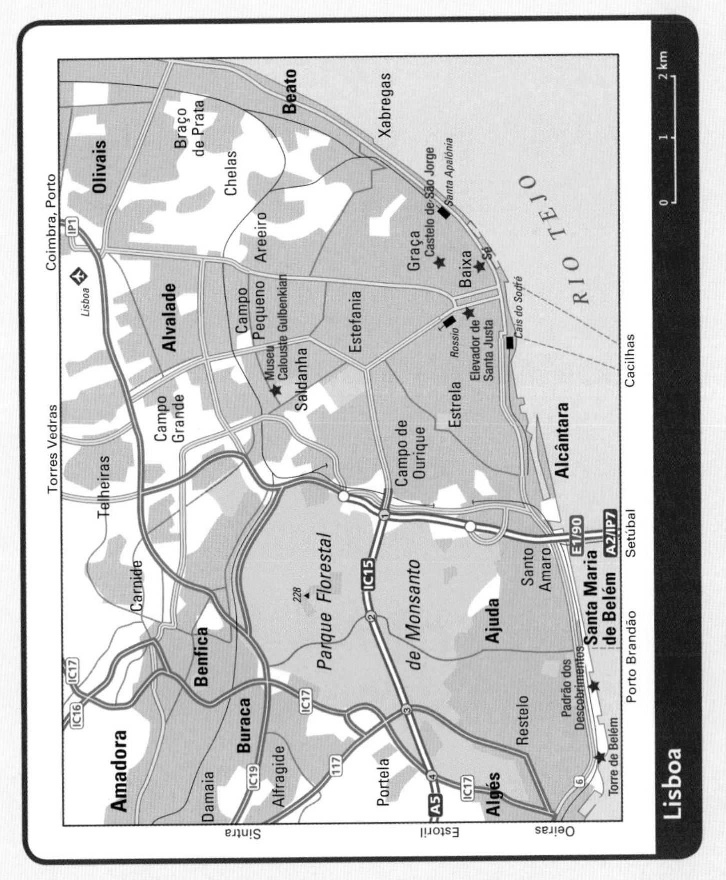
Lisboa
Amadora
Benfica
Buraca
Alfragide
Damaia
Carnide
Telheiras
Alvalade
Olivais
Campo Grande
Campo Pequeno
Areeiro
Chelas
Braço de Prata
Beato
Xabregas
Saldanha
Estefania
Graça
Castelo de São Jorge
Baixa
Sé
Rossio
Elevador de Santa Justa
Cais do Sodré
Estrela
Campo de Ourique
Alcântara
Parque Florestal de Monsanto
Ajuda
Santo Amaro
Santa Maria de Belém
Padrão dos Descobrimentos
Torre de Belém
Restelo
Portela
Algés
RIO TEJO
Museu Calouste Gulbenkian
Lisboa
Torres Vedras
Coimbra, Porto
Sintra
Estoril
Oeiras
Porto Brandão
Setúbal
Cacilhas
0 1 2 km

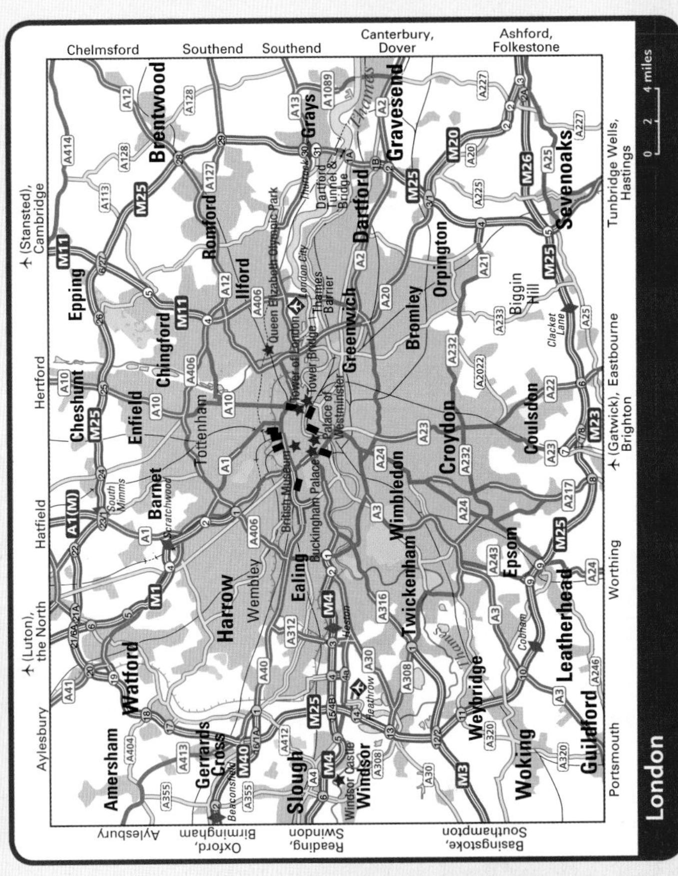
London
Chelmsford
Southend
Southend
Canterbury, Dover
Ashford, Folkestone
Brentwood
Grays
Gravesend
Dartford
Romford
Ilford
Epping
Cheshunt
Enfield
Chingford
Tottenham
Barnet
Harrow
Wembley
Ealing
Watford
Amersham
Gerrards Cross
Slough
Windsor
Heathrow
Twickenham
Wimbledon
Croydon
Bromley
Orpington
Greenwich
Biggin Hill
Sevenoaks
Coulsdon
Epsom
Leatherhead
Weybridge
Woking
Guildford
Tower of London
Tower Bridge
Palace of Westminster
Buckingham Palace
British Museum
Queen Elizabeth Olympic Park
Thames Barrier
(Stansted), Cambridge
(Luton), the North
(Gatwick), Eastbourne, Brighton
Tunbridge Wells, Hastings
Hertford
Hatfield
Aylesbury
Oxford, Birmingham
Reading, Swindon
Basingstoke, Southampton
Portsmouth
Worthing
0 2 4 miles

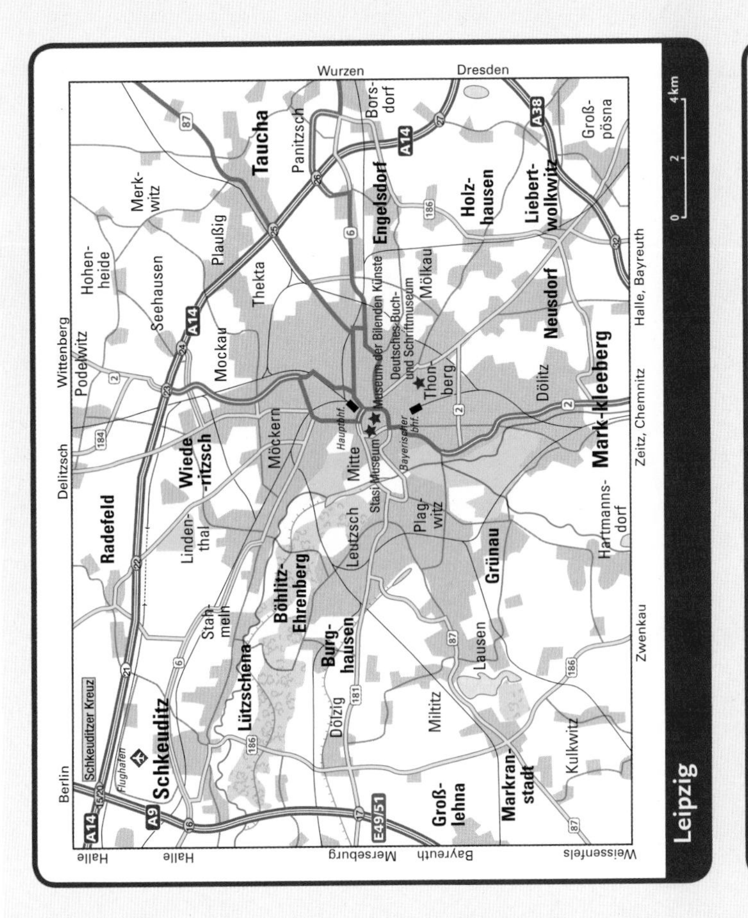
Leipzig
Schkeuditz
Radefeld
Wiederitzsch
Lindenthal
Möckern
Mitte
Taucha
Engelsdorf
Holzhausen
Liebertwolkwitz
Markkleeberg
Großlehna
Markranstädt
Grünau
Lützschena
Böhlitz-Ehrenberg
Burghausen
Leutzsch
Plagwitz
Connewitz
Probstheida
Stötteritz
Paunsdorf
Schönefeld
Thekla
Mockau
Seehausen
Podelwitz
Miltitz
Kulkwitz
Hauptbahnhof
Museum der Bildenden Künste
Deutsches Buch- und Schriftmuseum
Stasi Museum
Berlin
Wittenberg
Delitzsch
Wurzen
Dresden
Halle
Merseburg
Bayreuth
Weissenfels
Zeitz, Chemnitz
Halle, Bayreuth
0 2 4km

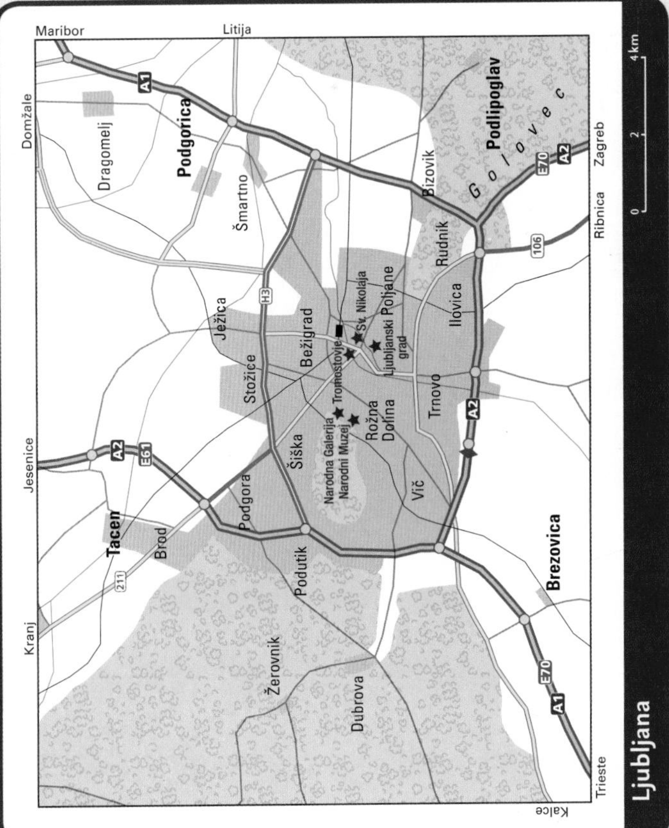
Ljubljana
Tacen
Podgorica
Dragomelj
Šmartno
Ježica
Stožice
Bežigrad
Šiška
Podgora
Brod
Podutik
Žerovnik
Dubrova
Narodna Galerija
Narodni Muzej
Tromostovje
Sv. Nikolaja
Ljubljanski Poljane grad
Rožna Dolina
Vič
Trnovo
Ilovica
Rudnik
Bizovik
Golovec
Podlipoglav
Brezovica
Maribor
Litija
Domžale
Jesenice
Kranj
Trieste
Kalce
Ribnica
Zagreb
0 2 4km

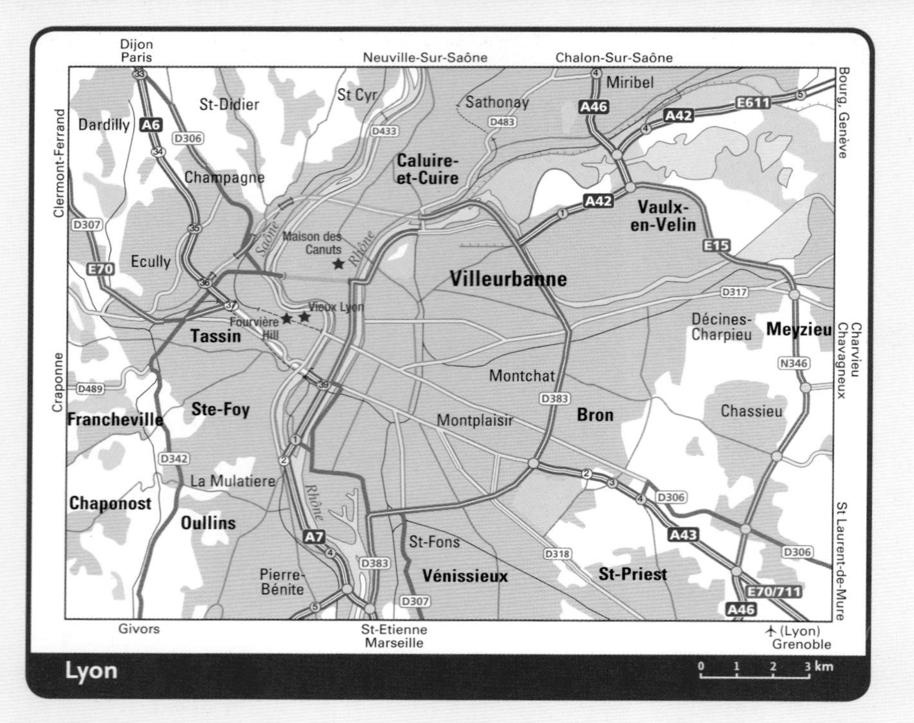
Lyon
Dijon Paris
Neuville-Sur-Saône
Chalon-Sur-Saône
Bourg, Genève
Charvieu Chavagneux
St Laurent-de-Mure
Clermont-Ferrand
Craponne
Givors
St-Etienne Marseille
(Lyon) Grenoble
Miribel
Sathonay
St Cyr
St-Didier
Dardilly
Champagne
Caluire-et-Cuire
Vaulx-en-Velin
Ecully
Maison des Canuts
Villeurbanne
Décines-Charpieu
Meyzieu
Vieux Lyon
Fourvière Hill
Tassin
Montchat
Bron
Chassieu
Francheville
Ste-Foy
Montplaisir
La Mulatière
Chaponost
Oullins
St-Fons
Vénissieux
St-Priest
Pierre-Bénite
Rhône
Saône
0 1 2 3 km

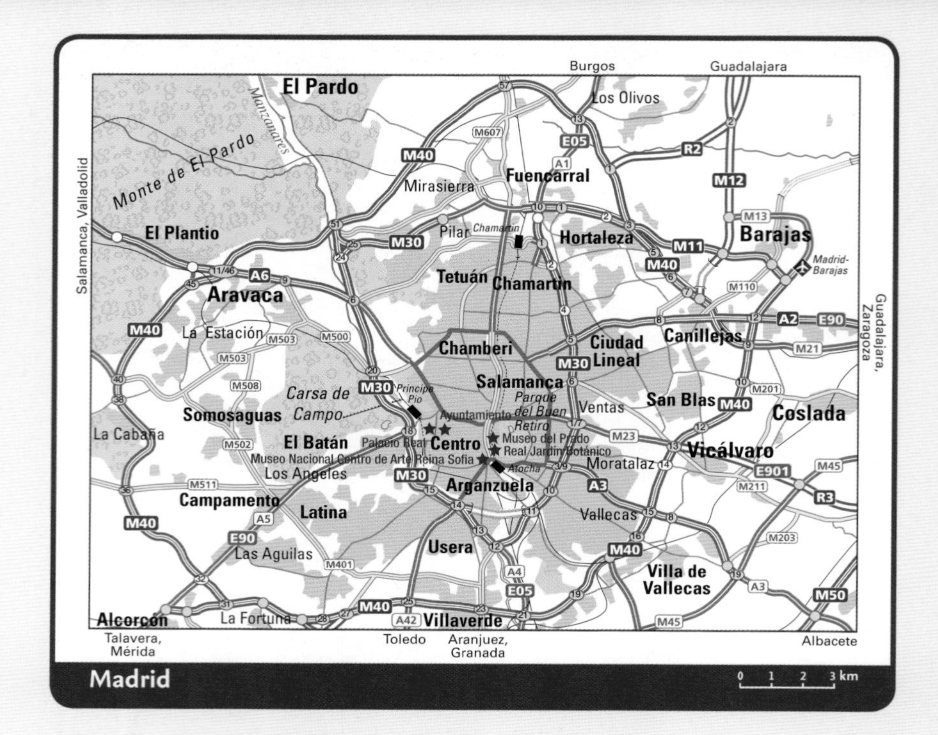
Madrid
Burgos
Guadalajara
Guadalajara, Zaragoza
Salamanca, Valladolid
Albacete
Talavera, Mérida
Toledo
Aranjuez, Granada
El Pardo
Los Olivos
Monte de El Pardo
Manzanares
Mirasierra
Fuencarral
El Plantío
Pilar
Hortaleza
Barajas
Madrid-Barajas
Aravaca
Tetuán
Chamartín
La Estación
Chamberí
Ciudad Lineal
Canillejas
Salamanca
Carsa de Campo
Príncipe Pío
Somosaguas
Ayuntamiento
Parque del Buen Retiro
Ventas
San Blas
Coslada
La Cabaña
El Batán
Palacio Real
Centro
Museo del Prado
Real Jardín Botánico
Vicálvaro
Museo Nacional Centro de Arte Reina Sofía
Los Angeles
Atocha
Moratalaz
Arganzuela
Campamento
Latina
Vallecas
Las Aguilas
Usera
Villa de Vallecas
Alcorcón
La Fortuna
Villaverde
0 1 2 3 km

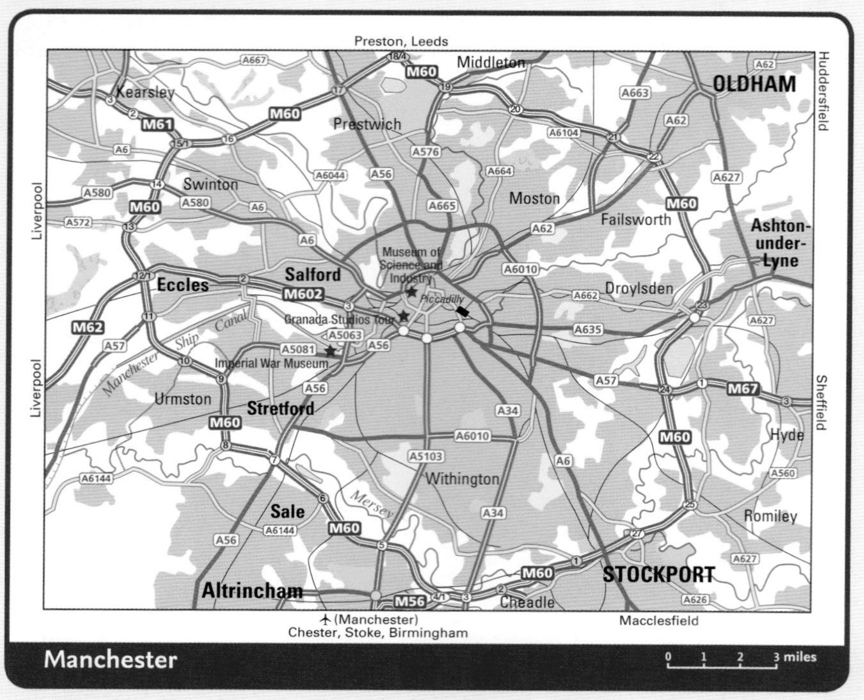
Manchester
Preston, Leeds
Huddersfield
Liverpool
Sheffield
Macclesfield
(Manchester) Chester, Stoke, Birmingham
Middleton
OLDHAM
Kearsley
Prestwich
Swinton
Moston
Failsworth
Ashton-under-Lyne
Museum of Science and Industry
Eccles
Salford
Piccadilly
Droylsden
Granada Studios Tour
Imperial War Museum
Manchester Ship Canal
Urmston
Stretford
Hyde
Withington
Sale
Mersey
Romiley
Altrincham
Cheadle
STOCKPORT
0 1 2 3 miles

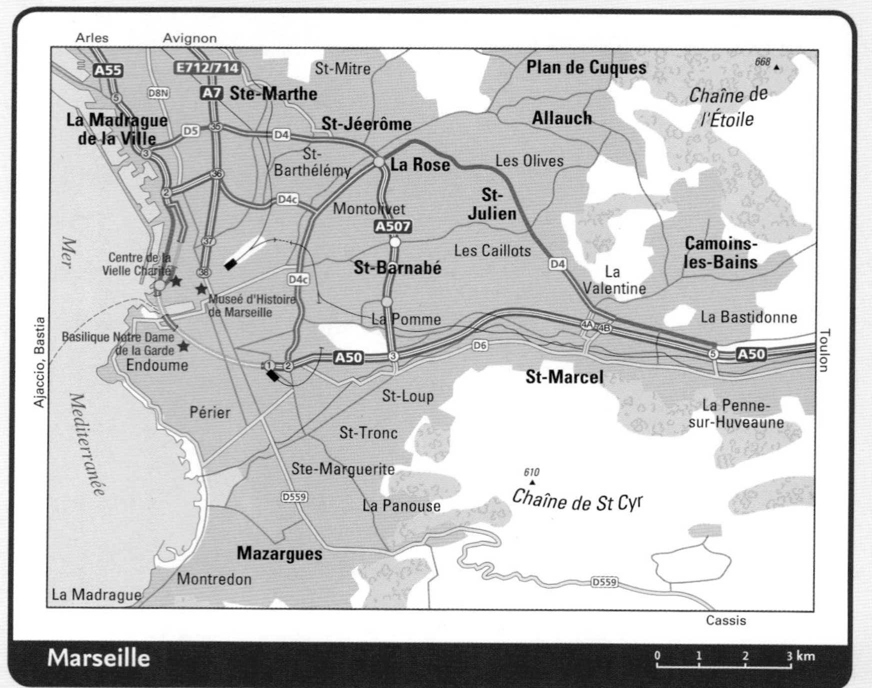
Marseille
Arles
Avignon
Toulon
Ajaccio, Bastia
Cassis
St-Mitre
Ste-Marthe
Plan de Cuques
Chaîne de l'Étoile
La Madrague de la Ville
St-Jéerôme
Allauch
St-Barthélémy
La Rose
Les Olives
St-Julien
Montolivet
Camoins-les-Bains
Les Caillols
Centre de la Vieille Charité
St-Barnabé
La Valentine
Mer
Musée d'Histoire de Marseille
La Pomme
La Bastidonne
Basilique Notre Dame de la Garde
Endoume
St-Marcel
St-Loup
Périer
La Penne-sur-Huveaune
Méditerranée
St-Tronc
Ste-Marguerite
Chaîne de St Cyr
La Panouse
Mazargues
Montredon
La Madrague
0 1 2 3 km

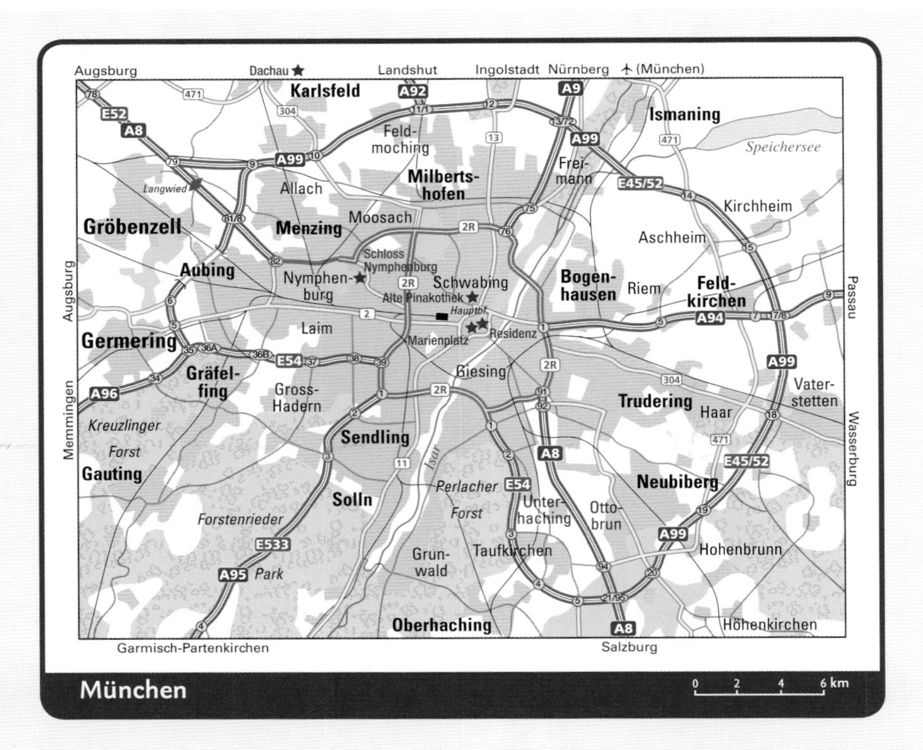
München
Passau
Wasserburg
Augsburg
Ingolstadt
Nürnberg
(München)
Landshut
Dachau
Salzburg
Garmisch-Partenkirchen
Memmingen
Ismaning
Karlsfeld
Feld-moching
Milberts-hofen
Frei-mann
Bogen-hausen
Feld-kirchen
Kirchheim
Aschheim
Riem
Trudering
Haar
Vater-stetten
Neubiberg
Otto-brunn
Unter-haching
Taufkirchen
Oberhaching
Perlacher Forst
Grün-wald
Giesing
Schwabing
Residenz
Alte Pinakothek
Marienplatz
Schloss Nymphenburg
Nymphen-burg
Moosach
Allach
Menzing
Laim
Gross-Hadern
Sendling
Solln
Forstenrieder Park
Aubing
Gräfel-fing
Gröbenzell
Germering
Kreuzlinger Forst
Gauting
Langwied
Speichersee
Isar
Höhenkirchen
Hohenbrunn

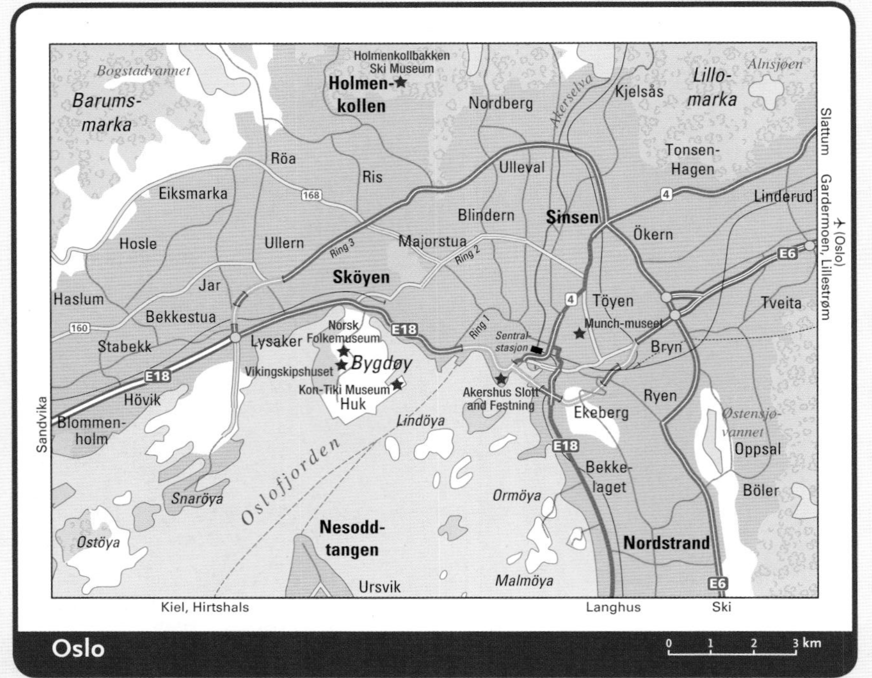
Oslo
Slattum
(Oslo)
Gardermoen, Lillestrøm
Langhus
Ski
Kiel, Hirtshals
Sandvika
Lillo-marka
Alnsjøen
Kjelsås
Tonsen-Hagen
Linderud
Tveita
Økern
Oppsal
Bøler
Østensjø-vannet
Bryn
Ryen
Töyen
Munch-museet
Sinsen
Ekeberg
Bekke-laget
Nordstrand
Nordberg
Ullevål
Blindern
Sentral-stasjon
Akershus Slott and Festning
Ormøya
Malmøya
Majorstua
Holmenkollbakken Ski Museum
Holmen-kollen
Ris
Skøyen
Bygdøy
Norsk Folkemuseum
Vikingskipshuset
Kon-Tiki Museum
Huk
Lindøya
Oslofjorden
Nesodd-tangen
Ursvik
Røa
Ullern
Lysaker
Eiksmarka
Jar
Bekkestua
Hosle
Stabekk
Høvik
Snarøya
Østøya
Barums-marka
Bogstadvannet
Haslum
Blommen-holm
Akerselva

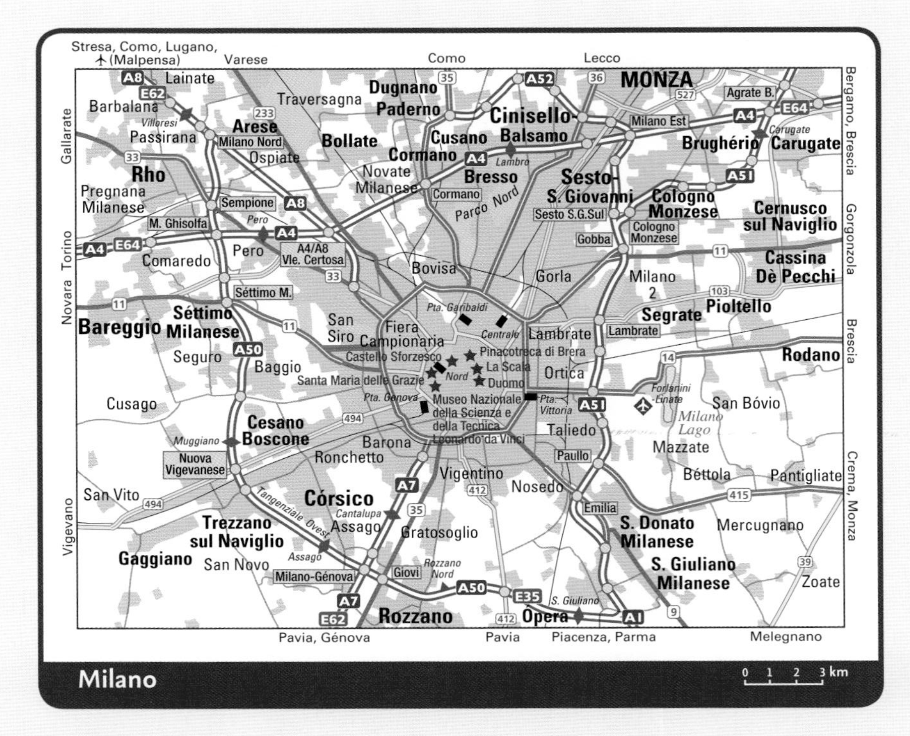
Milano
Bergamo, Brescia
Gorgonzola
Brescia
Crema, Monza
Melegnano
Piacenza, Parma
Pavia
Pavia, Genova
Vigevano
Novara
Torino
Gallarate
Stresa, Como, Lugano, (Malpensa)
Varese
Como
Lecco
MONZA
Agrate B.
Carugate
Brugherio
Cernusco sul Naviglio
Cassina De Pecchi
Rodano
Pioltello
Segrate
Cologno Monzese
Milano 2
Sesto S. Giovanni
Cinisello Balsamo
Cusano
Bresso
Cormano
Paderno Dugnano
Bollate
Novate Milanese
Parco Nord
Niguarda
Lambrate
Ortica
Taliedo
Linate
Lago
San Bóvio
Mazzate
Bettola
Pantigliate
Mercugnano
Zoate
Donato Milanese
S. Giuliano Milanese
Nosedo
Vigentino
Pinacoteca di Brera
La Scala
Duomo
Castello Sforzesco
Santa Maria delle Grazie
Museo Nazionale della Scienza e della Tecnologia da Vinci
Fiera Campionaria
Bovisa
Gorla
San Siro
Baggio
Barona
Ronchetto
Corsico
Gratosoglio
Rozzano
Assago
Opera
Cesano Boscone
Trezzano sul Naviglio
Gaggiano
San Vito
Cusago
Seguro
Settimo Milanese
Baggio
Bareggio
Rho
Pero
Arese
Lainate
Barbalana
Passirana
Pregnana Milanese
Comaredo
Ospiate
Traversagna

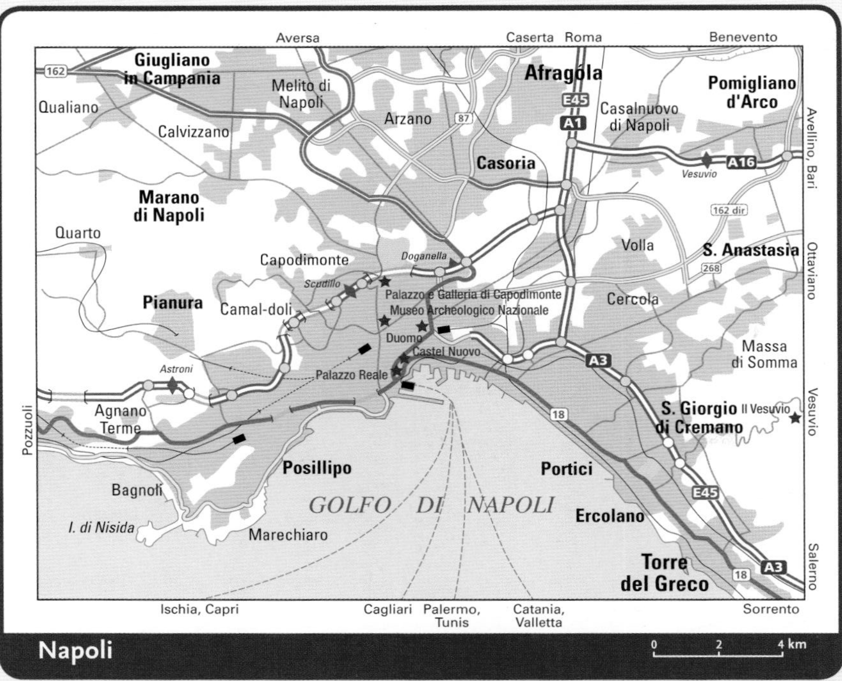
Napoli
Avellino, Bari
Ottaviano
Vesuvio
Salerno
Sorrento
Catania, Valletta
Cagliari
Palermo, Tunis
Ischia, Capri
Pozzuoli
Aversa
Caserta
Roma
Benevento
Pomigliano d'Arco
S. Anastasia
Massa di Somma
Vesuvio
S. Giorgio a Cremano
Torre del Greco
Ercolano
Portici
Cercola
Volla
Casalnuovo di Napoli
Afragola
Casoria
Arzano
Melito di Napoli
Capodimonte
Palazzo e Galleria di Capodimonte
Museo Archeologico Nazionale
Duomo
Castel Nuovo
Palazzo Reale
GOLFO DI NAPOLI
Posillipo
Marechiaro
Camaldoli
Pianura
Marano di Napoli
Calvizzano
Giugliano in Campania
Qualiano
Quarto
Agnano Terme
Astroni
Bagnoli
I. di Nisida

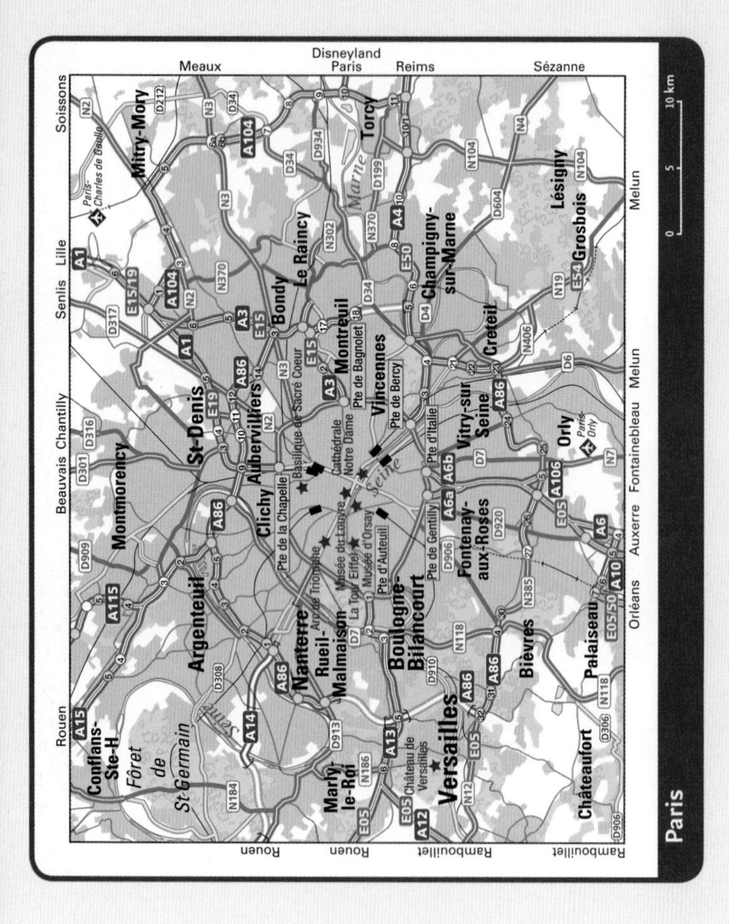
Paris
Meaux
Disneyland Paris
Reims
Sézanne
Soissons
Senlis
Lille
Beauvais
Chantilly
Rouen
Melun
Fontainebleau
Auxerre
Orléans
Rambouillet
Mitry-Mory
Torcy
Le Raincy
Bondy
Montreuil
Vincennes
Champigny-sur-Marne
Créteil
Lesigny
Grosbois
St-Denis
Aubervilliers
Montmorency
Argenteuil
Clichy
Nanterre
Rueil-Malmaison
Boulogne-Billancourt
Vitry-sur-Seine
Fontenay-aux-Roses
Orly
Versailles
Bièvres
Palaiseau
Châteaufort
Marly-le-Roi
Conflans-Ste-H
Fôret de St Germain
Basilique du Sacré Coeur
Cathédrale Notre Dame
Musée du Louvre
La Tour Eiffel
Musée d'Orsay
Château de Versailles
Seine
Marne
0 5 10 km

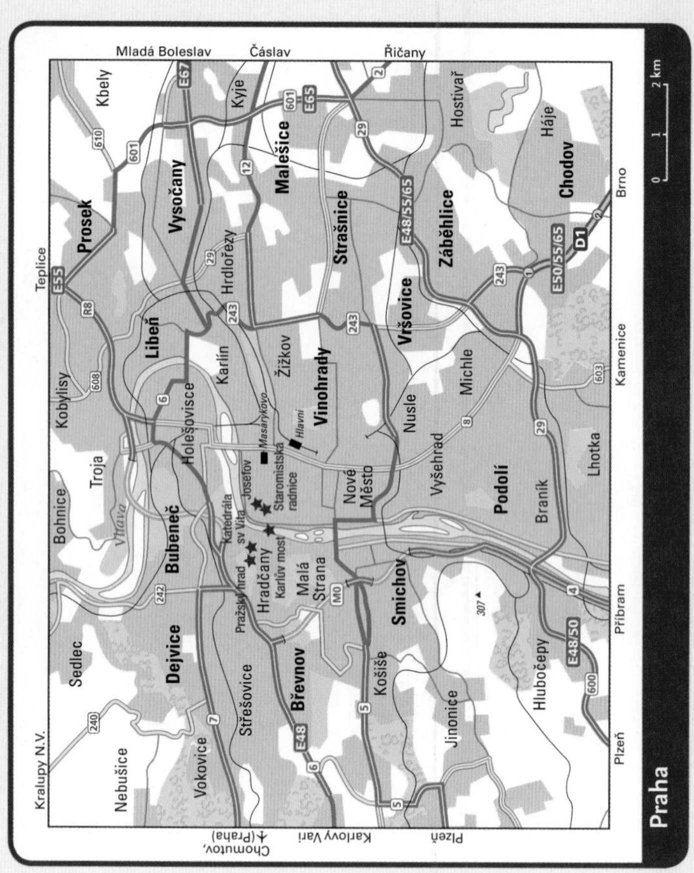
Praha
Mladá Boleslav
Čáslav
Říčany
Teplice
Kralupy N.V.
Kamenice
Brno
Příbram
Plzeň
Karlovy Vari
Chomutov, (Praha)
Kbely
Prosek
Vysočany
Kyje
Malešice
Hostivař
Háje
Chodov
Strašnice
Záběhlice
Hrdlořezy
Libeň
Karlín
Žižkov
Vinohrady
Vršovice
Michle
Nusle
Kobylisy
Troja
Bohnice
Holešovice
Bubeneč
Vyšehrad
Nové Město
Podolí
Braník
Lhotka
Malá Strana
Hradčany
Dejvice
Smíchov
Sedlec
Střešovice
Břevnov
Košíře
Vokovice
Nebušice
Jinonice
Hlubočepy
Vltava
Pražský hrad
Katedrála sv Víta
Karlův most
Staroměstská radnice
Josefov
Masarykovo
Hlavní
0 1 2 km

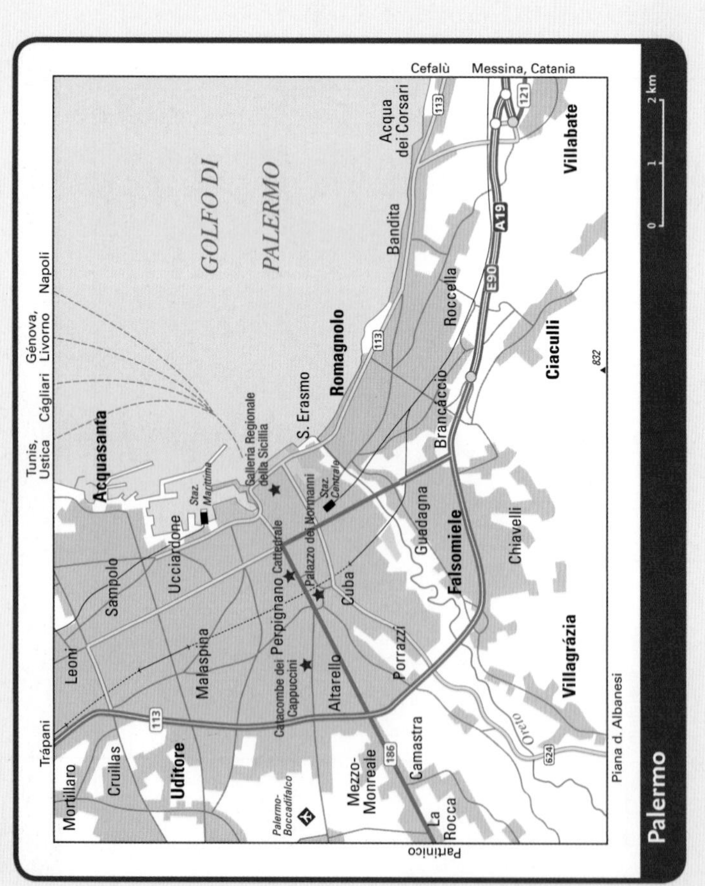
Palermo
GOLFO DI PALERMO
Tunis, Ustica
Cágliari
Génova, Livorno
Napoli
Trápani
Cefalù
Messina, Catania
Piana d. Albanesi
Partinico
Mondello
Acquasanta
Sampolo
Ucciardone
S. Erasmo
Romagnolo
Acqua dei Corsari
Bandita
Roccella
Villabate
Ciaculli
Brancaccio
Falsomiele
Guadagna
Chiavelli
Villagrázia
Porrazzi
Cuba
Altarello
Mezzo-Monreale
La Rocca
Camastra
Malaspina
Leoni
Uditore
Cruillas
Mortillaro
Palermo-Boccadifalco
Galleria Regionale della Sicilia
Palazzo dei Normanni
Cattedrale
Perpignano
Catacombe dei Cappuccini
Staz. Marittima
Staz. Centrale
Oreto
0 1 2 km

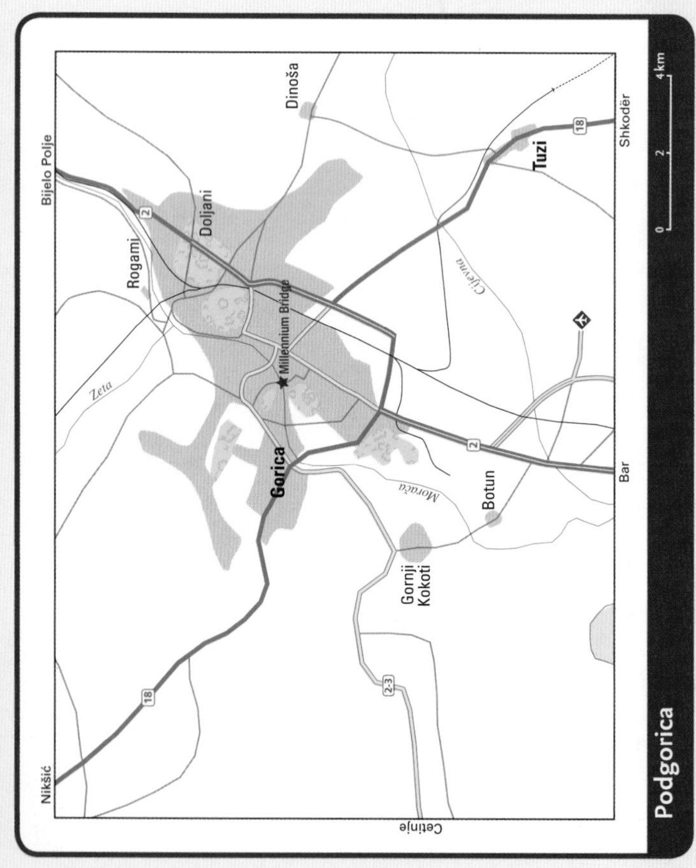
Podgorica
Bijelo Polje
Dinoša
Shkodër
Tuzi
Bar
Cetinje
Nikšić
Rogami
Doljani
Millennium Bridge
Gorica
Botun
Gornji Kokoti
Zeta
Morača
Cijevna
0 2 4 km

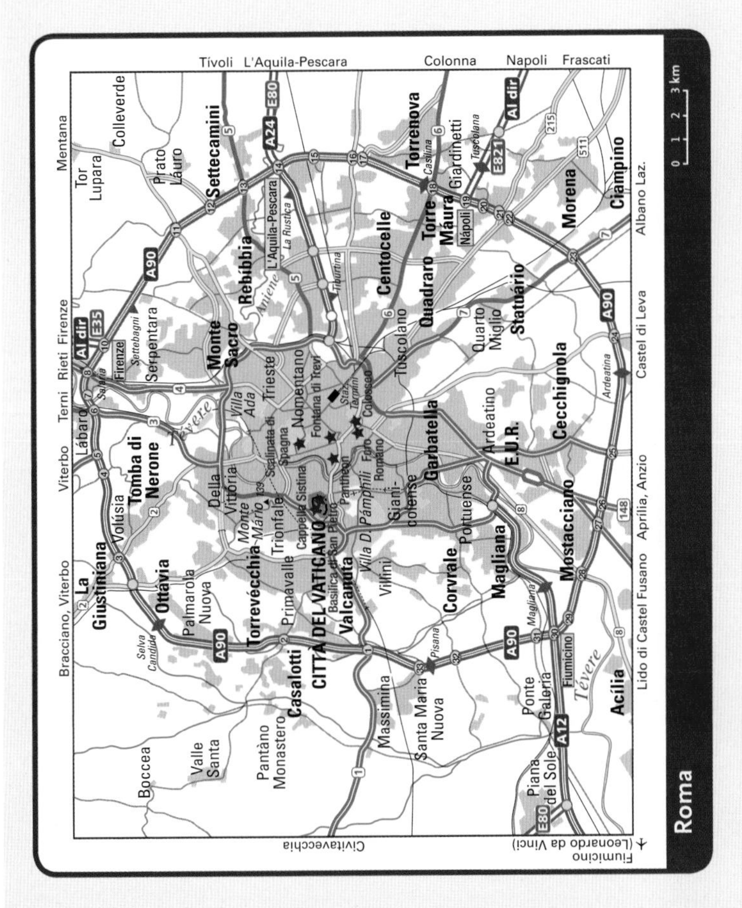
Roma
Tívoli
L'Aquila-Pescara
Colonna
Napoli
Frascati
Mentana
Viterbo
Terni
Rieti
Firenze
Bracciano, Viterbo
Civitavecchia
Fiumicino (Leonardo da Vinci)
Lido di Castel Fusano
Aprilia, Anzio
Castel di Leva
Albano Laz.
Settecamini
Torrenova
Ciampino
Morena
Centocelle
Quadraro
Monte Sacro
Tomba di Nerone
La Giustiniana
Ottavia
Torrevecchia
Valcanuta
CITTÀ DEL VATICANO
Casalotti
Corviale
Magliana
Garbatella
E.U.R.
Cecchignola
Mostacciano
Acilia
Massimina
Boccea
Valle Santa
Ponte Galeria
Piana del Sole
Santa Maria Nuova
Statuario
Colleverde
Tor Lupara
Prato Lauro
Rebibbia
Tiburtino
Tuscolano
Ardeatino
Portuense
Vitinia
Primavalle
Palmarola Nuova
Volùsia
Lábaro
Serpentara
Nomentano
Trieste
Fontana di Trevi
Colosseo
Pantheon
Cappella Sistina
Basilica di San Pietro
0 1 2 3 km

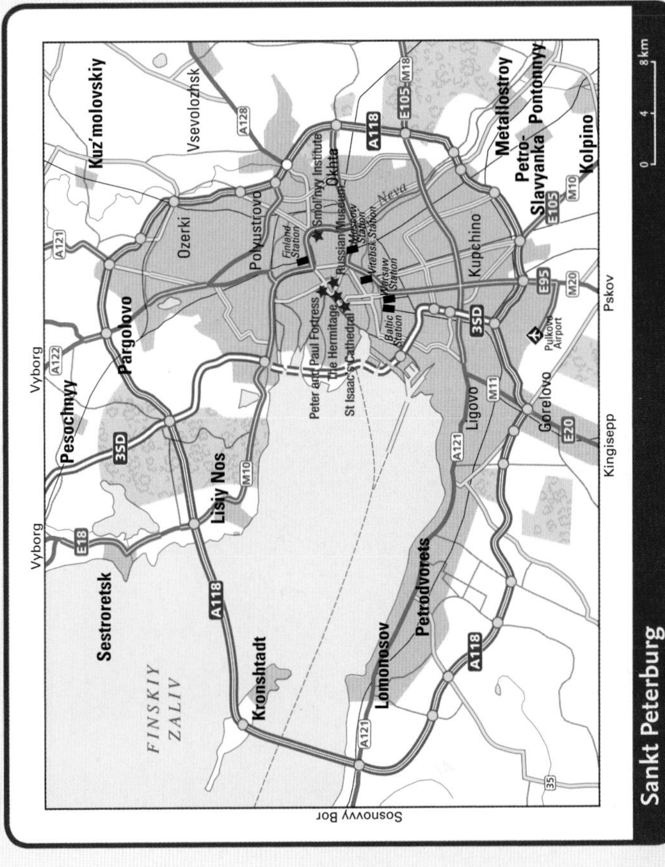
Sankt Peterburg
Kuz'molovskiy
Vsevolozhsk
Metallostroy
Petro-Slavyanka
Pontonnyy
Kolpino
Ozerki
Polyustrovo
Kupchino
Pargolovo
Pesochnyy
Lisiy Nos
Sestroretsk
Kronshtadt
Lomonosov
Petrodvorets
Ligovo
Gorelovo
Pulkovo Airport
Vyborg
Pskov
Kingisepp
Sosnovyy Bor
FINSKIY ZALIV
Neva
Smol'nyy Institute
Russian Museum
Peter and Paul Fortress
The Hermitage
St Isaac's Cathedral
Finland Station
Moscow Station
Vitebsk Station
Warsaw Station
Baltic Station
A118
A121
E18
E20
E95
E105
M10
M11
M18
M20
0 4 8 km

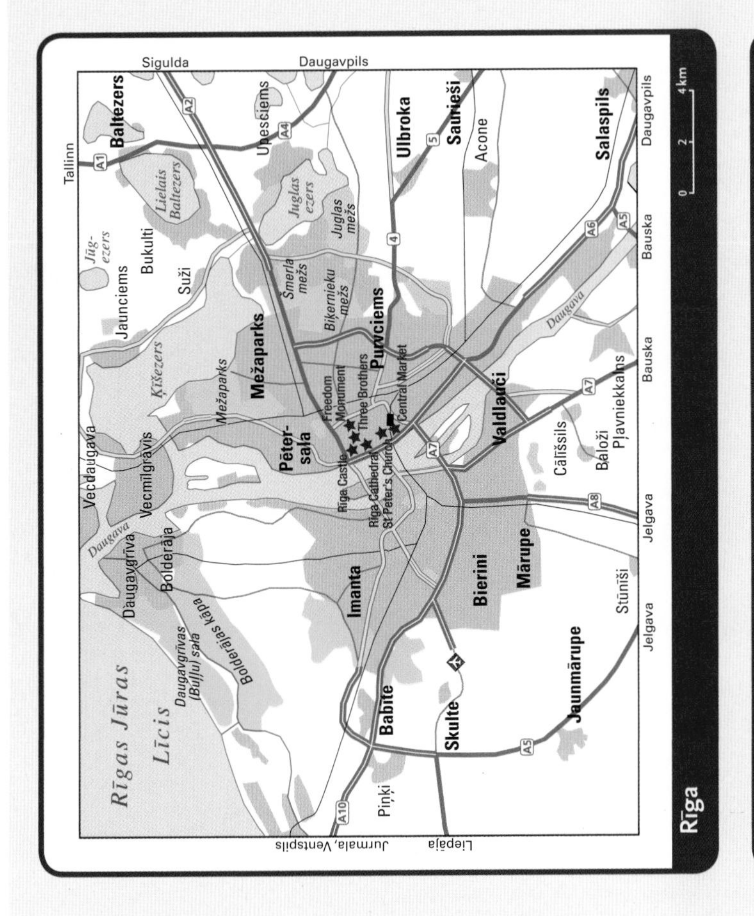
Rīga
Sigulda
Daugavpils
Tallinn
Bauska
Jelgava
Liepāja
Jurmala, Ventspils
Baltezers
Ulbroka
Saurieši
Salaspils
Acone
Upesciems
Bukulti
Jaunciems
Suži
Mežaparks
Purvciems
Pētersala
Vecdaugava
Vecmilgrāvis
Daugavgrīva
Bolderāja
Imanta
Bierini
Mārupe
Valdlauči
Cēlšsils
Baloži
Pļavnieki
Stūnīši
Babīte
Skulte
Jaunmārupe
Piņķi
Rīgas Jūras Līcis
Juglas ezers
Ķīšezers
Daugava
Freedom Monument
Three Brothers
Central Market
Riga Castle
Riga Cathedral
St Peter's Church
0 2 4 km

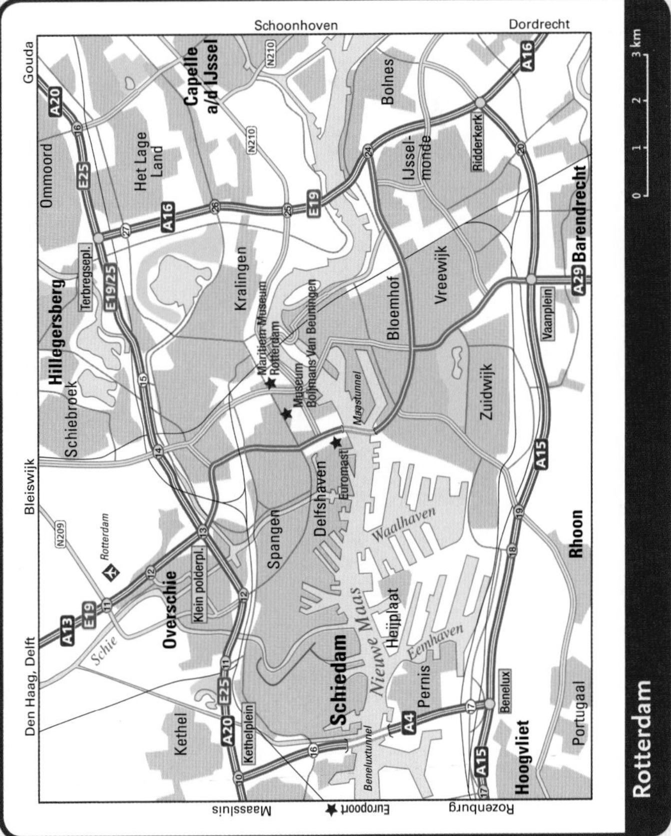
Rotterdam
Schoonhoven
Dordrecht
Gouda
Den Haag, Delft
Bleiswijk
Maassluis
Europoort
Rozenburg
Capelle a/d IJssel
Bolnes
IJsselmonde
Ommoord
Het Lage Land
Kralingen
Hillegersberg
Schiebroek
Bloemhof
Vreewijk
Barendrecht
Zuidwijk
Rhoon
Overschie
Spangen
Delfshaven
Schiedam
Kethel
Pernis
Hoogvliet
Portugaal
Nieuwe Maas
Waalhaven
Eemhaven
Maritiem Museum Rotterdam
Museum Boijmans Van Beuningen
Euromast
0 1 2 3 km

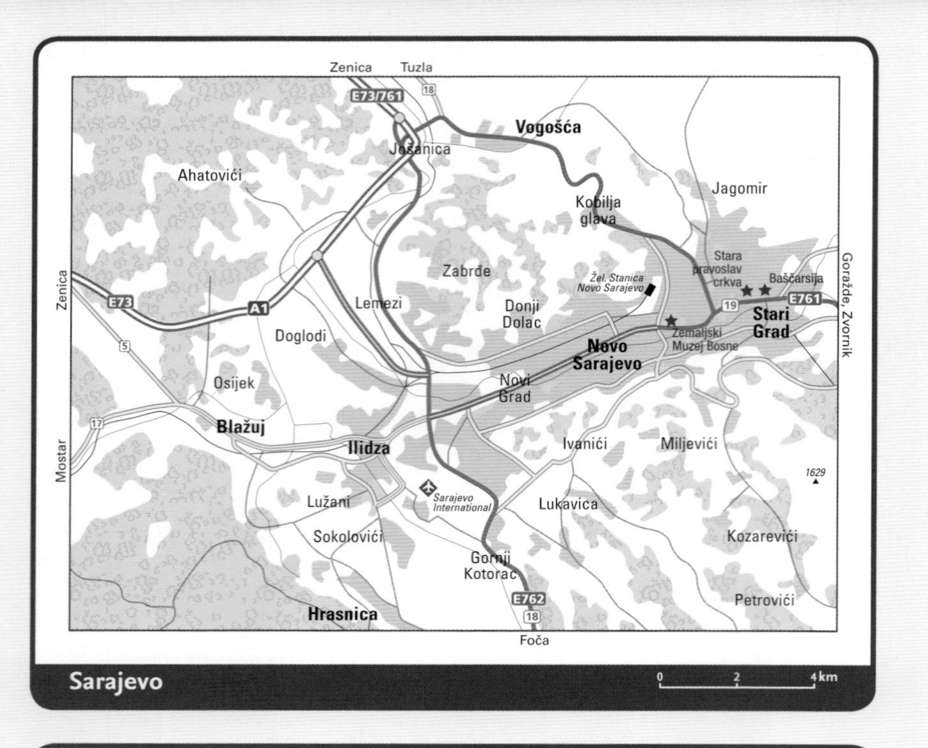
Sarajevo
Goražde, Zvornik
Zenica
Tuzla
Jagomir
Stara Pravoslav crkva
Baščaršija
Stari Grad
Zemaljski Muzej Bosne
Kobilja glava
Žel. Stanica Novo Sarajevo
Novo Sarajevo
Miljevići
Kozarevići
Petrovići
Vogošća
Donji Dolac
Novi Grad
Ivanići
Lukavica
Zabrđe
Sarajevo International
Gornji Kotorac
Foča
Jošanica
Lemezi
Ilidža
Lužani
Sokolovići
Hrasnica
Ahatovići
Doglodi
Osijek
Blažuj
Mostar
0 2 4 km

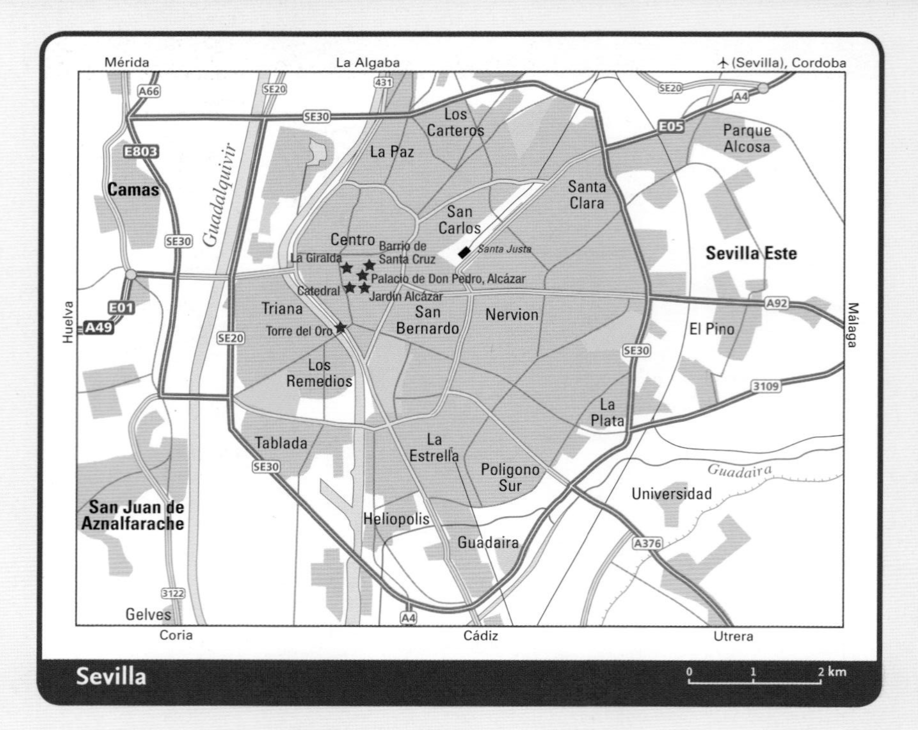
Sevilla
Málaga
Huelva
Mérida
La Algaba
Cádiz
Utrera
Coria
(Sevilla), Cordoba
Parque Alcosa
Sevilla Este
El Pino
Universidad
Santa Clara
La Plata
Los Carteros
San Carlos
Santa Justa
Nervion
Poligono Sur
La Paz
Barrio de Santa Cruz
Palacio de Don Pedro, Alcázar
Jardin Alcázar
San Bernardo
La Estrella
Guadaira
Centro
La Giralda
Catedral
Torre del Oro
Los Remedios
Heliopolis
Triana
Tablada
Guadalquivir
Camas
San Juan de Aznalfarache
Gelves
0 1 2 km

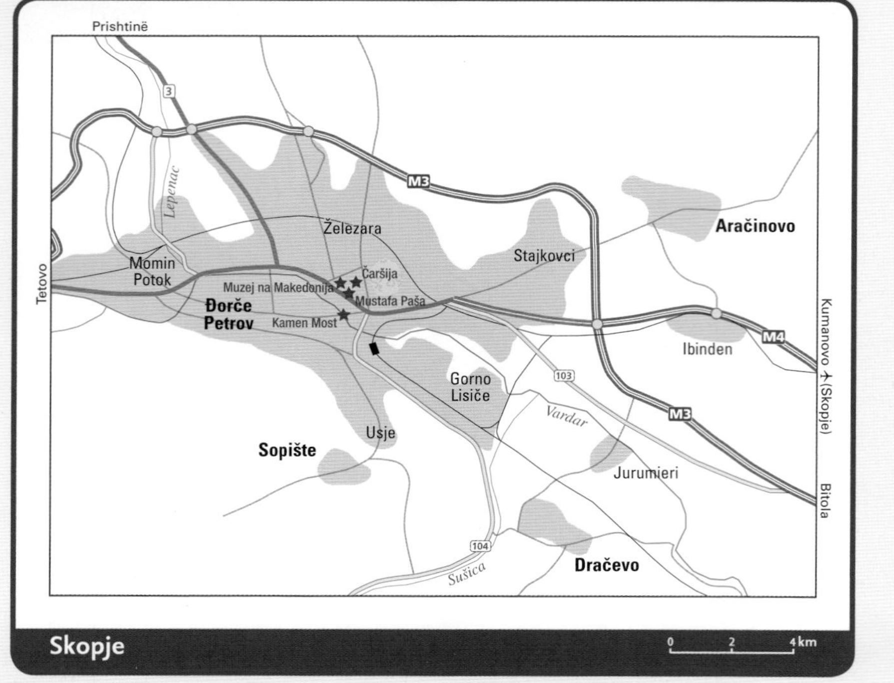
Skopje
Kumanovo (Skopje)
Bitola
Aračinovo
Ibinden
Jurumieri
Dračevo
Stajkovci
Vardar
Gorno Lisiče
Šarsija
Mustafa Paša
Železara
Kamen Most
Muzej na Makedonija
Ušje
Sopište
Đorče Petrov
Lepenac
Momin Potok
Prishtinë
Tetovo
0 2 4 km

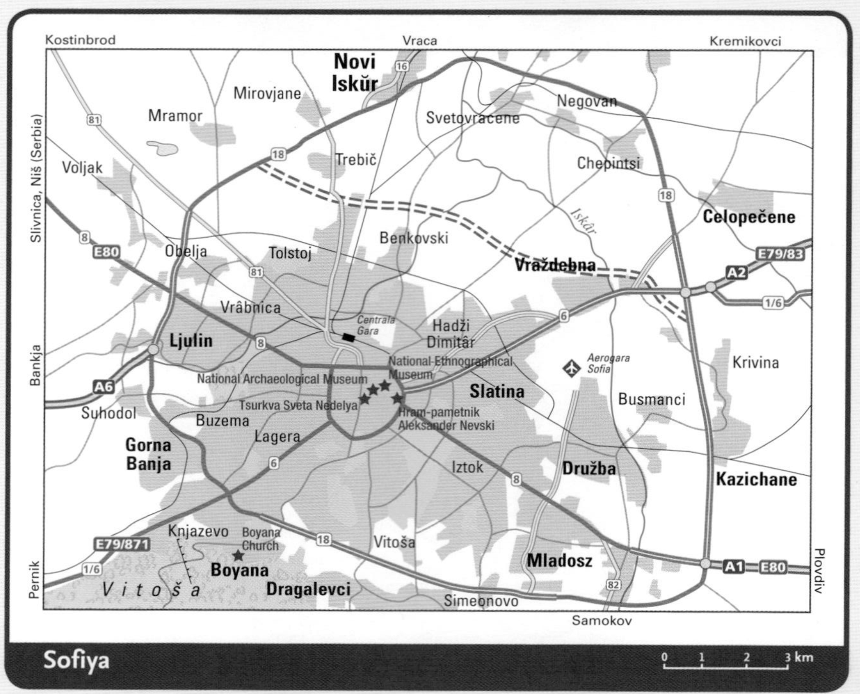
Sofiya
Plovdiv
Kremikovci
Celopečene
Krivina
Kazichane
Busmanci
Aerogara Sofia
Družba
Mladosz
Samokov
Negovan
Chepintsi
Iskăr
Vraždebna
Svetovraćene
Slatina
Iztok
Simeonovo
Vraca
Novi Iskŭr
Benkovski
Hadži Dimităr
National Ethnographical Museum
Hram-pametnik Aleksandăr Nevski
Vitoša
Trebič
Centralna Gara
National Archaeological Museum
Tsurkva Sveta Nedelya
Dragalevci
Mirovjane
Tolstoj
Vrăbnica
Lagera
Buzema
Boyana Church
Boyana
Mramor
Obelja
Ljulin
Gorna Banja
Knjazevo
Kostinbrod
Voljak
Suhodol
Slivnica, Niš (Serbia)
Bankja
Pernik
0 1 2 3 km

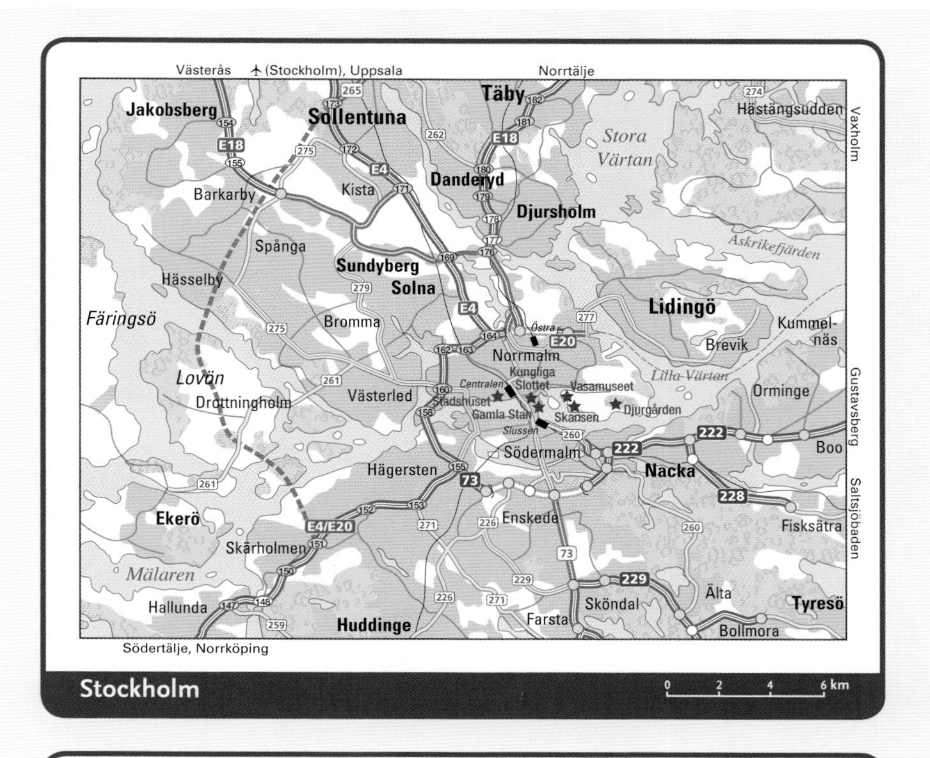
Västerås
(Stockholm), Uppsala
Norrtälje
Vaxholm
Gustavsberg
Saltsjöbaden
Södertälje, Norrköping
Jakobsberg
Sollentuna
Täby
Hästängsudden
Stora Värtan
Danderyd
Djursholm
Kista
Barkarby
Spånga
Sundyberg
Solna
Hässelby
Färingsö
Bromma
Lidingö
Askrikefjärden
Kummelnäs
Brevik
Lovön
Drottningholm
Västerled
Norrmalm
Kungliga Slottet
Vasamuseet
Skansen
Djurgården
Stadshuset
Gamla Stan
Slussen
Lilla Värtan
Orminge
Boo
Södermalm
Hägersten
Nacka
Ekerö
Skärholmen
Enskede
Fisksätra
Mälaren
Hallunda
Huddinge
Farsta
Sköndal
Älta
Tyresö
Bollmora
Stockholm
0 2 4 6 km

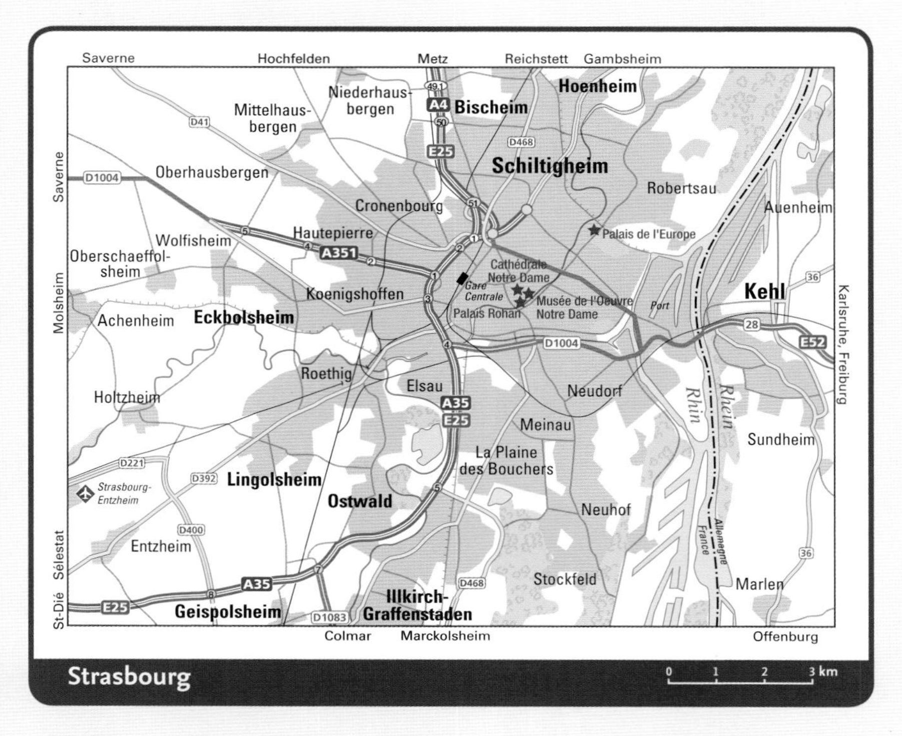
Saverne
Hochfelden
Metz
Reichstett
Gambsheim
Karlsruhe, Freiburg
Molsheim
Sélestat
St-Dié
Colmar
Marckolsheim
Offenburg
Mittelhausbergen
Niederhausbergen
Bischeim
Hoenheim
Schiltigheim
Oberhausbergen
Robertsau
Auenheim
Cronenbourg
Palais de l'Europe
Wolfisheim
Hautepierre
Oberschaeffolsheim
Cathédrale Notre Dame
Gare Centrale
Musée de l'Oeuvre Notre Dame
Palais Rohan
Koenigshoffen
Kehl
Achenheim
Eckbolsheim
Rhin
Rhein
Roethig
Holtzheim
Elsau
Neudorf
Meinau
Sundheim
La Plaine des Bouchers
Strasbourg-Entzheim
Lingolsheim
Ostwald
Neuhof
Entzheim
Stockfeld
Marlen
Allemagne
France
Geispolsheim
Illkirch-Graffenstaden
Strasbourg
0 1 2 3 km

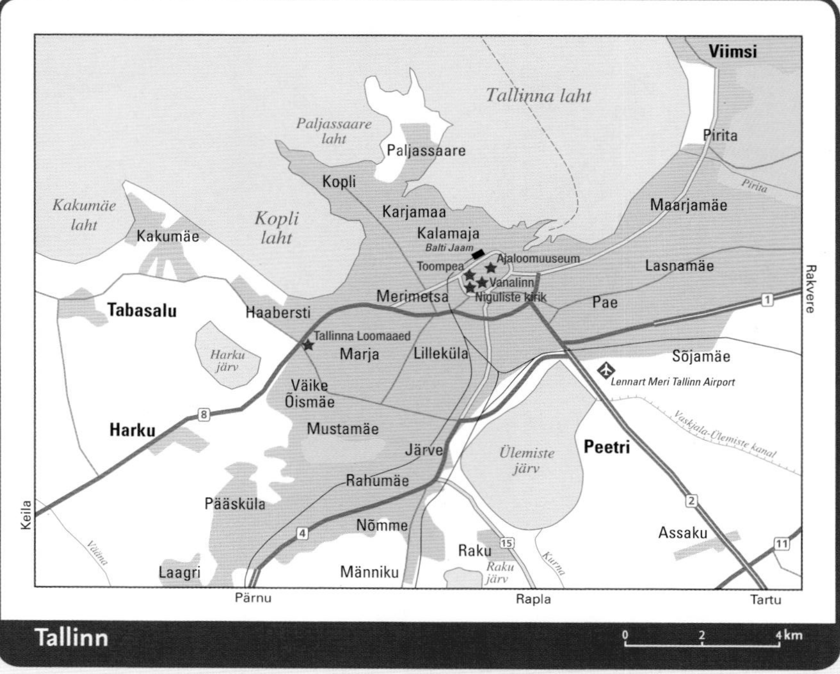
Viimsi
Tallinna laht
Paljassaare laht
Paljassaare
Pirita
Kopli
Kakumäe laht
Kakumäe
Kopli laht
Karjamaa
Kalamaja
Maarjamäe
Balti Jaam
Ajaloomuuseum
Toompea
Vanalinn
Niguliste Kirik
Lasnamäe
Merimetsa
Tabasalu
Haabersti
Pae
Rakvere
Tallinna Loomaaed
Harku järv
Marja
Lilleküla
Sõjamäe
Lennart Meri Tallinn Airport
Väike Õismäe
Harku
Mustamäe
Järve
Ülemiste järv
Peetri
Pääsküla
Rahumäe
Nõmme
Raku
Assaku
Keila
Laagri
Männiku
Pärnu
Rapla
Tartu
Tallinn
0 2 4 km

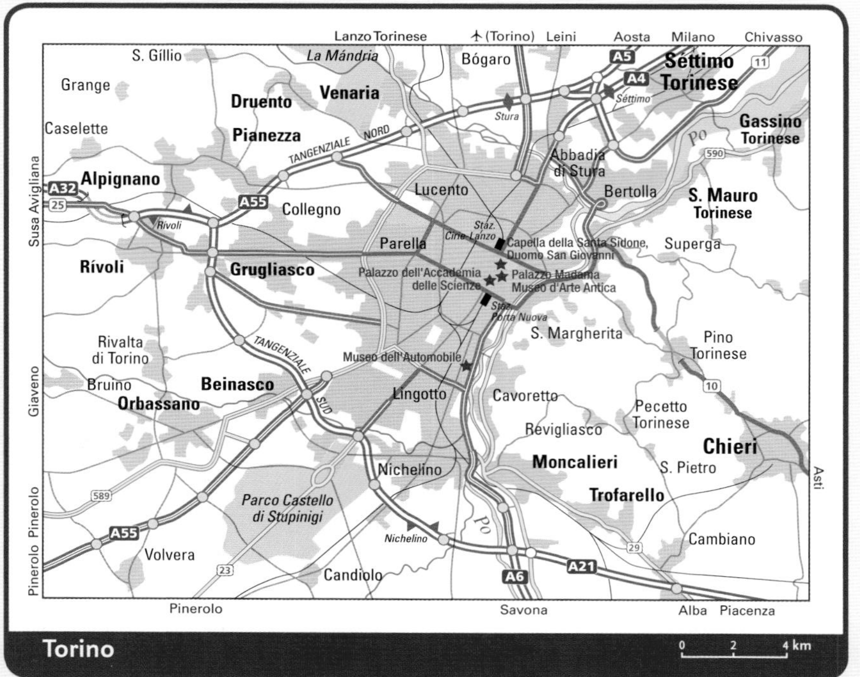
Lanzo Torinese
(Torino)
Leini
Aosta
Milano
Chivasso
S. Gillio
La Mándria
Bógaro
Settimo Torinese
Grange
Druento
Venaria
Caselette
Pianezza
Stura
Gassino Torinese
Abbadia di Stura
Alpignano
Lucento
Bertolla
S. Mauro Torinese
Susa Avigliana
Collegno
Rivoli
Parella
Capella della Santa Sidone, Duomo San Giovanni
Superga
Grugliasco
Palazzo dell'Accademia delle Scienze
Palazzo Madama Museo d'Arte Antica
Porta Nuova
Rivalta di Torino
S. Margherita
Pino Torinese
Museo dell'Automobile
Giaveno
Bruino
Beinasco
Orbassano
Lingotto
Cavoretto
Pecetto Torinese
Revigliasco
Chieri
Nichelino
Moncalieri
S. Pietro
Asti
Parco Castello di Stupinigi
Trofarello
Pinerolo
Volvera
Cambiano
Candiolo
Savona
Alba
Piacenza
Torino
0 2 4 km

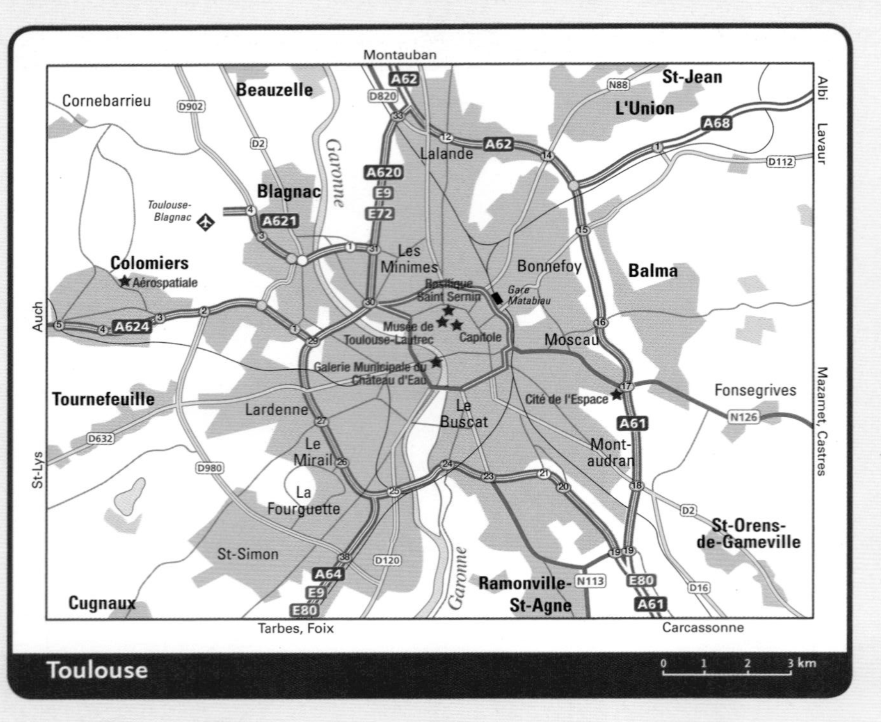
Montauban
Albi
Lavaur
Mazamet, Castres
Carcassonne
Tarbes, Foix
St-Lys
Auch
Cornebarrieu
Beauzelle
St-Jean
L'Union
Blagnac
Toulouse-Blagnac
Lalande
Garonne
Colomiers
Aérospatiale
Les Minimes
Bonnefoy
Balma
Basilique Saint Sernin
Gare Matabiau
Musée de Toulouse-Lautrec
Capitole
Moscou
Galerie Municipale du Château d'Eau
Tournefeuille
Lardenne
Le Buscat
Cité de l'Espace
Fonsegrives
Le Mirail
La Fourguette
Mont-audran
St-Orens-de-Gameville
St-Simon
Ramonville-St-Agne
Cugnaux
Toulouse
0 1 2 3 km

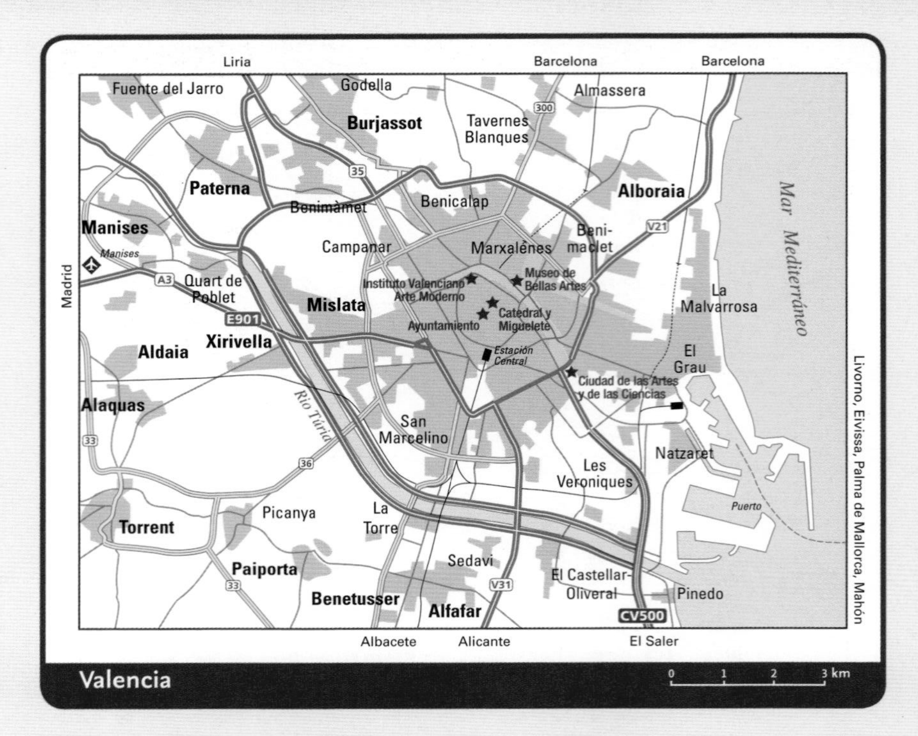
Liria
Barcelona
Madrid
Livorno, Eivissa, Palma de Mallorca, Mahón
Albacete
Alicante
El Saler
Fuente del Jarro
Godella
Almassera
Burjassot
Tavernes Blanques
Paterna
Benimàmet
Benicalap
Alboraia
Manises
Campanar
Marxalenes
Beni-maclet
Mar Mediterráneo
Quart de Poblet
Instituto Valenciano Arte Moderno
Museo de Bellas Artes
Mislata
Catedral y Miguelete
Ayuntamiento
La Malvarrosa
Aldaia
Xirivella
Estación Central
El Grau
Ciudad de las Artes y de las Ciencias
Alaquas
Río Turia
San Marcelino
Natzaret
Les Veroniques
Torrent
Picanya
La Torre
Puerto
Paiporta
Sedaví
Benetusser
El Castellar-Oliveral
Alfafar
Pinedo
Valencia
0 1 2 3 km

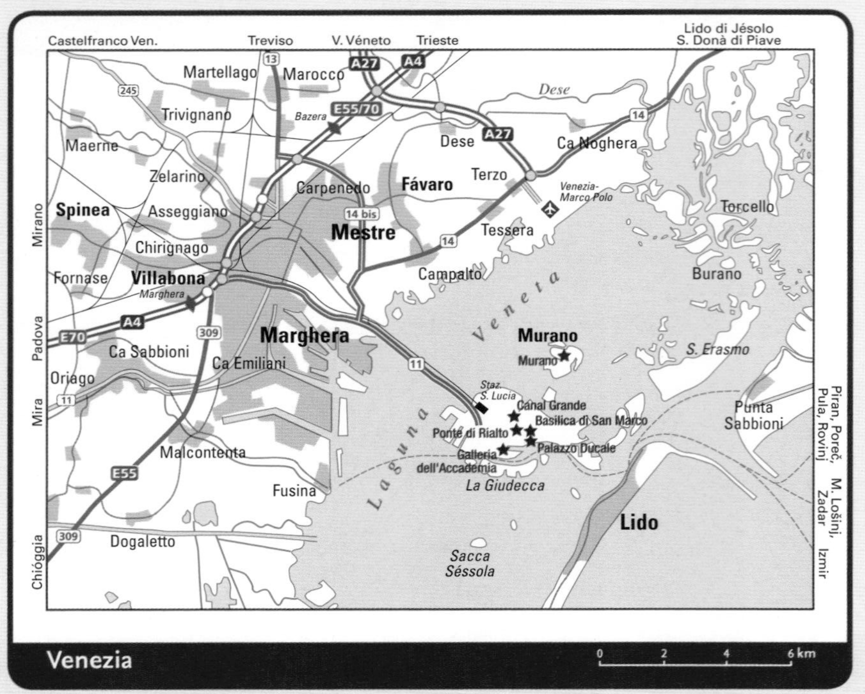
Castelfranco Ven.
Treviso
V. Véneto
Trieste
Lido di Jésolo
S. Donà di Piave
Mirano
Padova
Mira
Chióggia
Piran, Poreč, Pula, Rovinj
M. Lošinj, Zadar
Izmir
Martellago
Marocco
Trivignano
Bazera
Dese
Maerne
Dese
Ca Noghera
Zelarino
Carpenedo
Fávaro
Terzo
Venezia-Marco Polo
Spinea
Asseggiano
Mestre
Tessera
Torcello
Chirignago
Campalto
Burano
Fornase
Villabona
Marghera
Veneta
Murano
Ca Sabbioni
Marghera
S. Erasmo
Oriago
Ca Emiliani
Staz. S. Lucia
Canal Grande
Punta Sabbioni
Ponte di Rialto
Basilica di San Marco
Malcontenta
Galleria dell'Accademia
Palazzo Ducale
Laguna
Fusina
La Giudecca
Lido
Dogaletto
Sacca Sèssola
Venezia
0 2 4 6 km

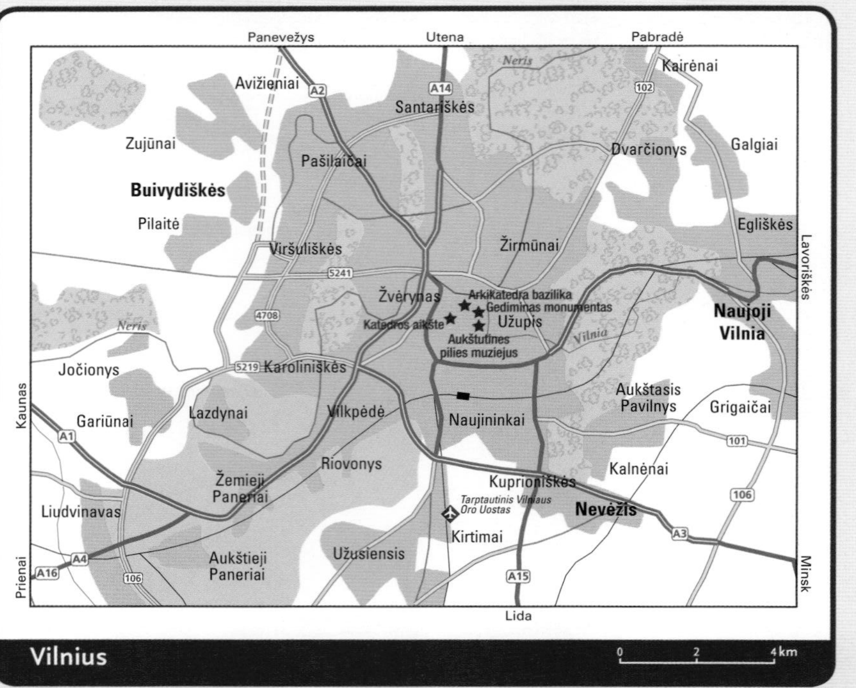
Panevėžys
Utena
Pabradė
Kaunas
Prienai
Lavoriškės
Minsk
Lida
Avižieniai
Santariškės
Kairėnai
Zujūnai
Pašilaičiai
Dvarčionys
Galgiai
Buivydiškės
Pilaitė
Viršuliškės
Žirmūnai
Egliškės
Neris
Žvėrynas
Arkikatedra bazilika
Gedimino monumentas
Užupis
Katedros aikštė
Aukštutinės pilies muziejus
Vilnia
Naujoji Vilnia
Jočionys
Karoliniškės
Aukštasis Pavilnys
Gariūnai
Lazdynai
Vilkpėdė
Naujininkai
Grigaičiai
Riovonys
Kalnėnai
Žemieji Paneriai
Kuprioniškės
Tarptautinis Vilniaus Oro Uostas
Liudvinavas
Nevėžis
Kirtimai
Aukštieji Paneriai
Užusienis
Vilnius
0 2 4 km

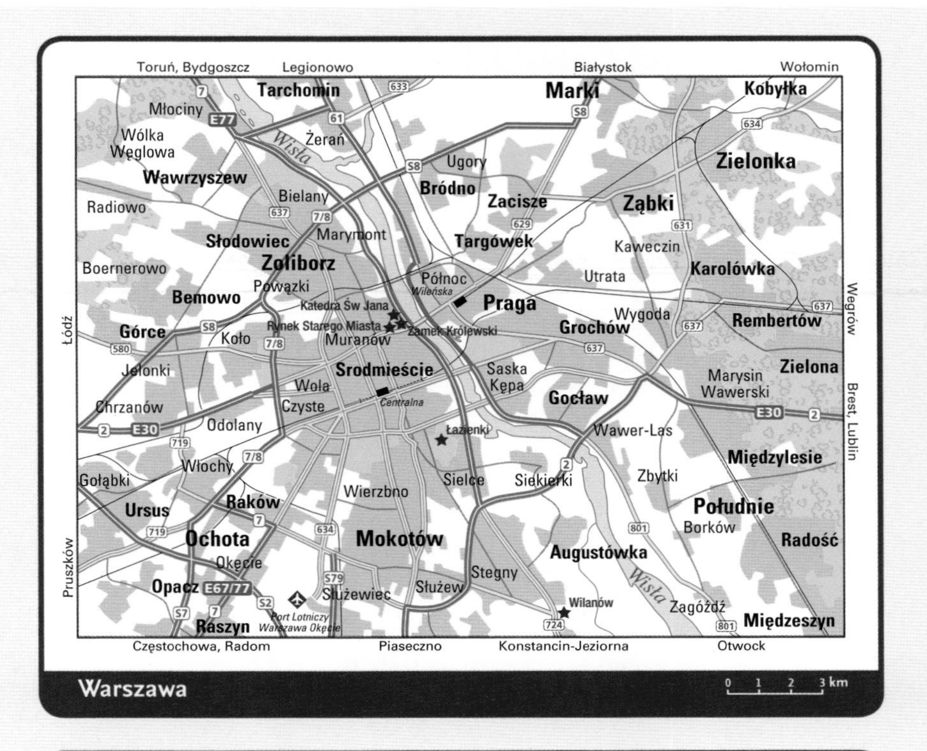
Toruń, Bydgoszcz
Legionowo
Białystok
Wołomin
Łódź
Pruszków
Węgrów
Brest, Lublin
Częstochowa, Radom
Piaseczno
Konstancin-Jeziorna
Otwock
Tarchomin
Marki
Kobyłka
Zielonka
Ząbki
Żerań
Wawrzyszew
Bielany
Bródno
Zacisze
Targówek
Słodowiec
Żoliborz
Bemowo
Praga
Karolówka
Rembertów
Grochów
Górce
Śródmieście
Wola
Saska Kępa
Gocław
Zielona
Marysin Wawerski
Wawer-Las
Międzylesie
Ochota
Mokotów
Augustówka
Południe
Radość
Ursus
Okęcie
Opacz
Raszyn
Wilanów
Międzeszyn
Wisła
Warszawa
0 1 2 3 km

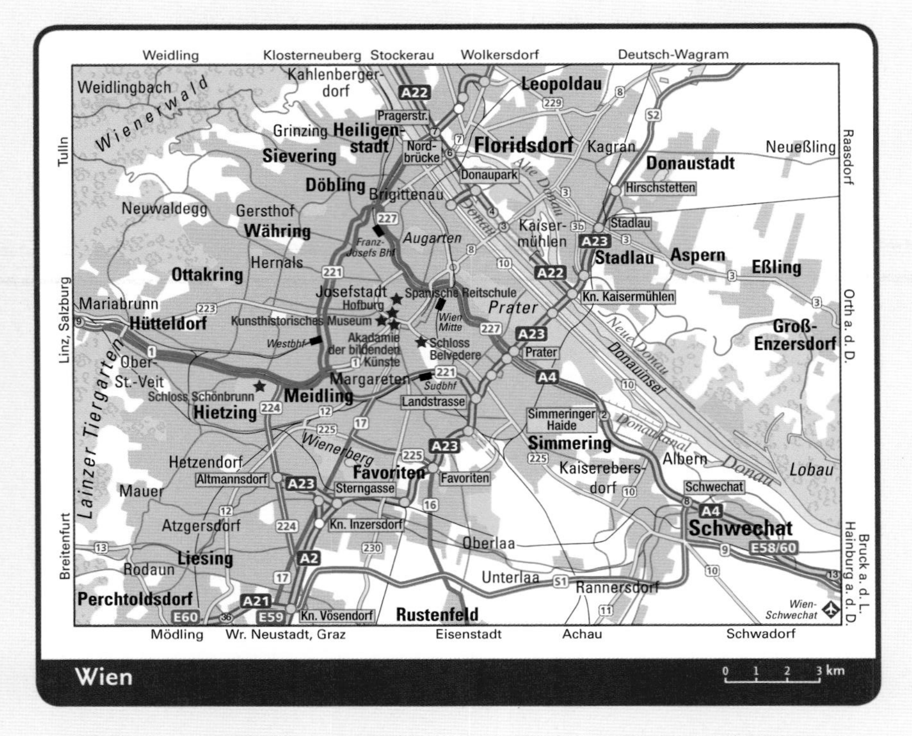
Weidling
Klosterneuberg
Stockerau
Wolkersdorf
Deutsch-Wagram
Tulln
Linz, Salzburg
Breitenfurt
Raasdorf
Orth a. d. D.
Bruck a. d. L.
Hainburg a. d. D.
Mödling
Wr. Neustadt, Graz
Eisenstadt
Achau
Schwadorf
Leopoldau
Floridsdorf
Kagran
Donaustadt
Neueßling
Heiligenstadt
Sievering
Döbling
Brigittenau
Währing
Ottakring
Hernals
Stadlau
Aspern
Eßling
Groß-Enzersdorf
Josefstadt
Prater
Hütteldorf
Meidling
Hietzing
Margareten
Simmering
Favoriten
Liesing
Perchtoldsdorf
Rustenfeld
Schwechat
Lobau
Lainzer Tiergarten
Wienerwald
Wien
0 1 2 3 km

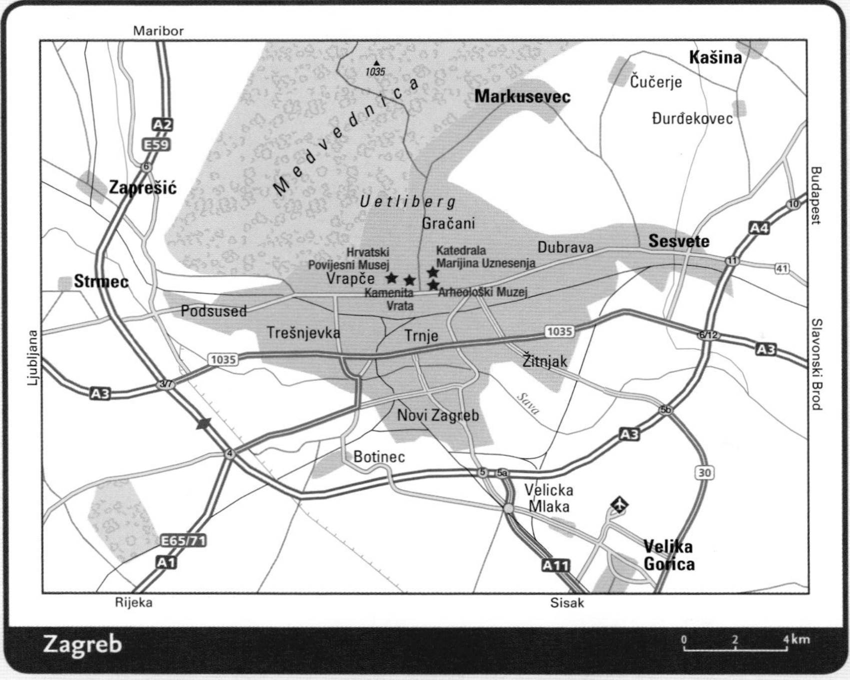
Maribor
Ljubljana
Budapest
Slavonski Brod
Rijeka
Sisak
Kašina
Čučerje
Đurđekovec
Markuševec
Medvednica
Uetliberg
Gračani
Dubrava
Sesvete
Zaprešić
Strmec
Podsused
Vrapče
Trešnjevka
Trnje
Žitnjak
Novi Zagreb
Botinec
Velicka Mlaka
Velika Gorica
Sava
Zagreb
0 2 4 km

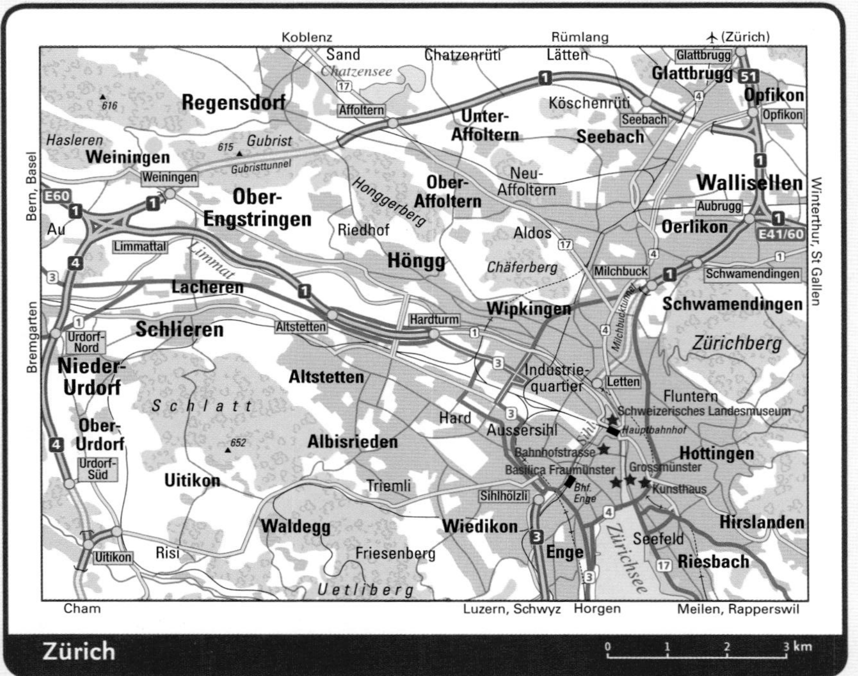
Koblenz
Rümlang
(Zürich)
Bern, Basel
Bremgarten
Winterthur, St Gallen
Cham
Luzern, Schwyz
Horgen
Meilen, Rapperswil
Regensdorf
Glattbrugg
Opfikon
Unter-Affoltern
Seebach
Weiningen
Ober-Engstringen
Ober-Affoltern
Wallisellen
Oerlikon
Höngg
Schwamendingen
Zürichberg
Wipkingen
Schlieren
Nieder-Urdorf
Ober-Urdorf
Altstetten
Albisrieden
Hottingen
Uitikon
Waldegg
Wiedikon
Enge
Hirslanden
Riesbach
Zürichsee
Uetliberg
Zürich
0 1 2 3 km

Amsterdam Athina Berlin Bern

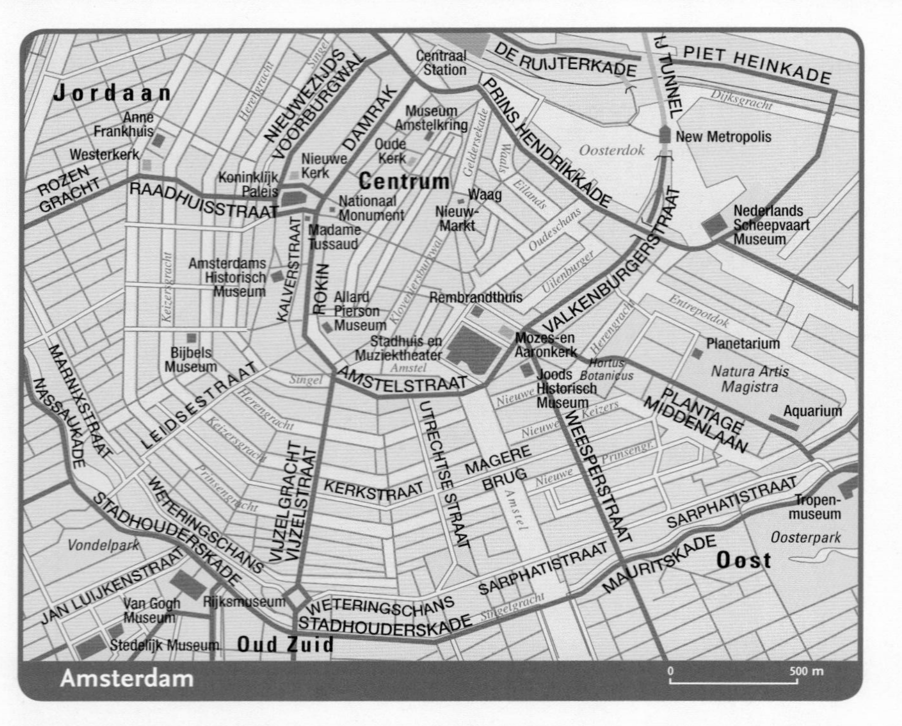
Amsterdam
500 m
Jordaan
Centrum
Oost
Oud Zuid
Centraal Station
New Metropolis
Nederlands Scheepvaart Museum
Anne Frankhuis
Westerkerk
Koninklijk Paleis
Nieuwe Kerk
Oude Kerk
Museum Amstelkring
Nationaal Monument
Madame Tussaud
Waag
Nieuw-Markt
Amsterdams Historisch Museum
Rembrandthuis
Allard Pierson Museum
Stadhuis en Muziektheater
Mozes-en Aäronkerk
Joods Historisch Museum
Bijbels Museum
Planetarium
Natura Artis Magistra
Aquarium
Tropen-museum
Oosterpark
Vondelpark
Van Gogh Museum
Rijksmuseum
Stedelijk Museum
DE RUIJTERKADE
PIET HEINKADE
IJ TUNNEL
PRINS HENDRIKKADE
DAMRAK
NIEUWEZIJDS VOORBURGWAL
RAADHUISSTRAAT
ROZENGRACHT
KALVERSTRAAT
ROKIN
VALKENBURGERSTRAAT
AMSTELSTRAAT
PLANTAGE MIDDENLAAN
LEIDSESTRAAT
UTRECHTSE STRAAT
KERKSTRAAT
MAGERE BRUG
WEESPERSTRAAT
VIJZELGRACHT
VIJZELSTRAAT
WETERINGSCHANS
STADHOUDERSKADE
SARPHATISTRAAT
MAURITSKADE
MARNIXSTRAAT
NASSAUKADE
JAN LUIJKENSTRAAT

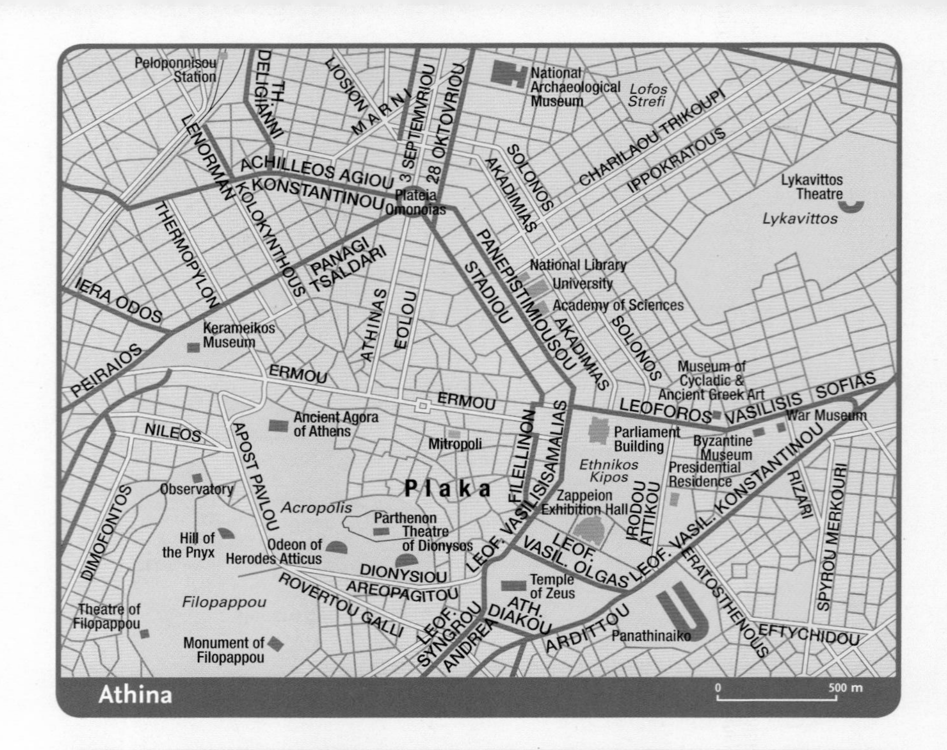
Athina
500 m
Peloponnisou Station
National Archaeological Museum
Lofos Strefi
Lykavittos Theatre
Lykavittos
Plateia Omonoias
National Library
University
Academy of Sciences
Museum of Cycladic & Ancient Greek Art
War Museum
Kerameikos Museum
Ancient Agora of Athens
Mitropoli
Parliament Building
Ethnikos Kipos
Byzantine Museum
Presidential Residence
Zappeion Exhibition Hall
Plaka
Acropolis
Observatory
Parthenon
Theatre of Dionysos
Hill of the Pnyx
Odeon of Herodes Atticus
Temple of Zeus
Panathinaiko
Filopappou
Theatre of Filopappou
Monument of Filopappou
ACHILLEOS AGIOU KONSTANTINOU
3 SEPTEMVRIOU
28 OKTOVRIOU
SOLONOS
AKADIMIAS
PANEPISTIMIOU
STADIOU
ERMOU
ATHINAS
EOLOU
LEOFOROS VASILISIS SOFIAS
FILELLINON
DIONYSIOU AREOPAGITOU
APOST PAVLOU
PEIRAIOS
IERA ODOS

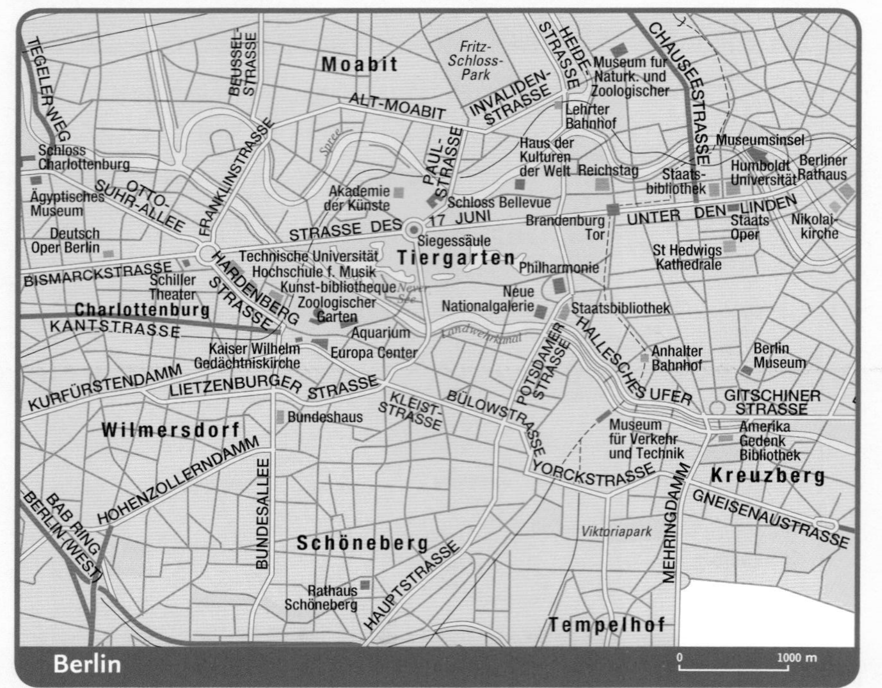
Berlin
1000 m
Moabit
Tiergarten
Charlottenburg
Wilmersdorf
Schöneberg
Kreuzberg
Tempelhof
Schloss Charlottenburg
Ägyptisches Museum
Deutsch Oper Berlin
Fritz-Schloss-Park
Museum für Naturk. und Zoologischer
Lehrter Bahnhof
Haus der Kulturen der Welt
Reichstag
Museumsinsel
Humboldt Universität
Berliner Rathaus
Staats-bibliothek
Staats Oper
Nikolai-kirche
Akademie der Künste
Schloss Bellevue
Siegessäule
Brandenburg Tor
St Hedwigs Kathedrale
Technische Universität
Hochschule f. Musik
Zoologischer Garten
Philharmonie
Neue Nationalgalerie
Staatsbibliothek
Aquarium
Europa Center
Kaiser Wilhelm Gedächtniskirche
Anhalter Bahnhof
Berlin Museum
Bundeshaus
Museum für Verkehr und Technik
Amerika Gedenk Bibliothek
Rathaus Schöneberg
Viktoriapark
UNTER DEN LINDEN
STRASSE DES 17. JUNI
KURFÜRSTENDAMM
KANTSTRASSE
CHAUSSEESTRASSE
GNEISENAUSTRASSE
MEHRINGDAMM

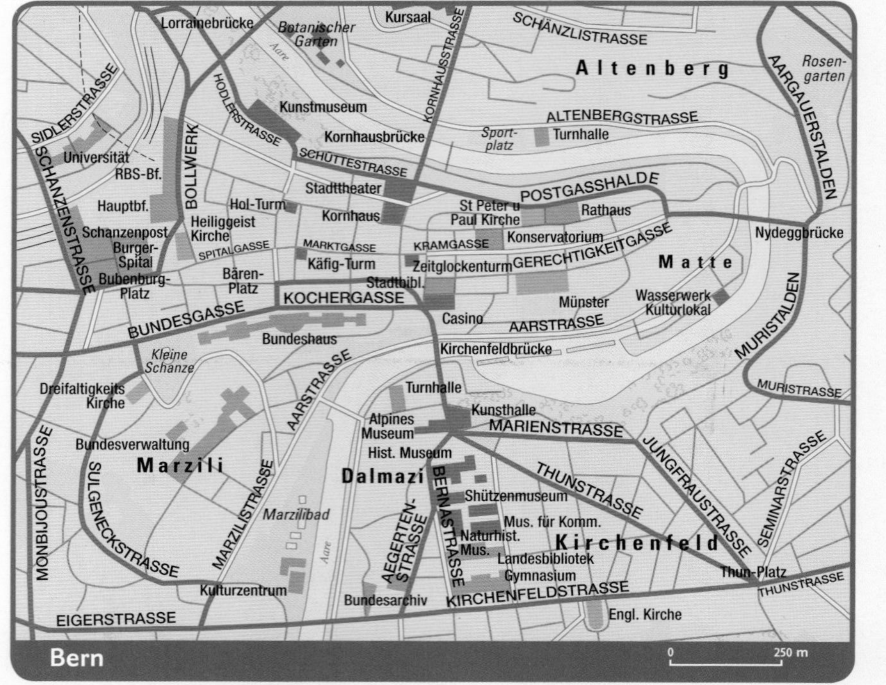
Bern
250 m
Altenberg
Matte
Marzili
Dalmazi
Kirchenfeld
Lorrainebrücke
Botanischer Garten
Kursaal
Rosen-garten
Kunstmuseum
Kornhausbrücke
Universität
RBS-Bf.
Hauptbf.
Stadttheater
Kornhaus
Rathaus
Hol-Turm
Heiliggeist Kirche
Käfig-Turm
Zeitglockenturm
Konservatorium
Münster
Wasserwerk Kulturlokal
Nydeggbrücke
Bundeshaus
Casino
Kirchenfeldbrücke
Kunsthalle
Alpines Museum
Hist. Museum
Bundesarchiv
Marzilibad
Dreifaltigkeits Kirche
Bundesverwaltung
Kulturzentrum
Engl. Kirche
SCHANZENSTRASSE
BUNDESGASSE
KOCHERGASSE
POSTGASSHALDE
AARSTRASSE
MARIENSTRASSE
THUNSTRASSE
KIRCHENFELDSTRASSE
EIGERSTRASSE
MONBIJOUSTRASSE
SULGENECKSTRASSE

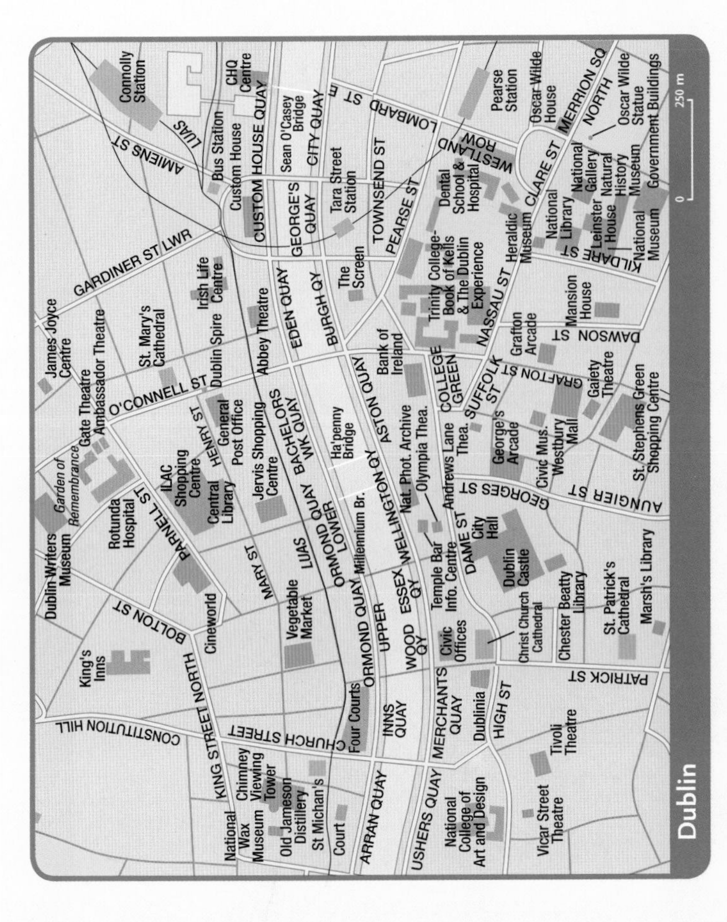
Dublin
250 m
Connolly Station
CHQ Centre
Bus Station
Custom House
CUSTOM HOUSE QUAY
Sean O'Casey Bridge
CITY QUAY
GEORGE'S QUAY
Tara Street Station
TOWNSEND ST
PEARSE ST
Pearse Station
Oscar Wilde House
WESTLAND ROW
MERRION SQ NORTH
Oscar Wilde Statue
Government Buildings
National Museum
Natural History Museum
Leinster House
National Gallery
National Library
KILDARE ST
CLARE ST
Dental School & Hospital
Trinity College-Book of Kells & The Dublin Experience
NASSAU ST
Heraldic Museum
Mansion House
DAWSON ST
Grafton Arcade
GRAFTON ST
Gaiety Theatre
St. Stephens Green Shopping Centre
AUNGIER ST
GEORGES ST
George's Arcade
Civic Mus.
Westbury Mall
SUFFOLK ST
COLLEGE GREEN
Bank of Ireland
The Screen
BURGH QY
EDEN QUAY
Abbey Theatre
Irish Life Centre
GARDINER ST LWR
AMIENS ST
LOMBARD ST E
James Joyce Centre
Gate Theatre
Ambassador Theatre
St. Mary's Cathedral
O'CONNELL ST
Dublin Spire
General Post Office
HENRY ST
Jervis Shopping Centre
BACHELORS WK QUAY
Ha'penny Bridge
ASTON QUAY
ILAC Shopping Centre
Central Library
Garden of Remembrance
PARNELL ST
Rotunda Hospital
Dublin Writers Museum
LIAS
ORMOND QUAY LOWER
Millennium Br.
WELLINGTON QY
Nat. Phot. Archive
Olympia Thea.
Andrews Lane Thea.
Temple Bar Info. Centre
DAME ST
City Hall
Dublin Castle
Chester Beatty Library
St. Patrick's Cathedral
Marsh's Library
PATRICK ST
Christ Church Cathedral
Civic Offices
ESSEX QY
WOOD QY
UPPER ORMOND QUAY
MARY ST
Vegetable Market
Cineworld
BOLTON ST
King's Inns
KING STREET NORTH
CHURCH STREET
CONSTITUTION HILL
Four Courts
INNS QUAY
MERCHANTS QUAY
Dublinia
HIGH ST
Tivoli Theatre
USHERS QUAY
National College of Art and Design
Vicar Street Theatre
ARRAN QUAY
Court
St Michan's
Old Jameson Distillery
Chimney Viewing Tower
National Wax Museum

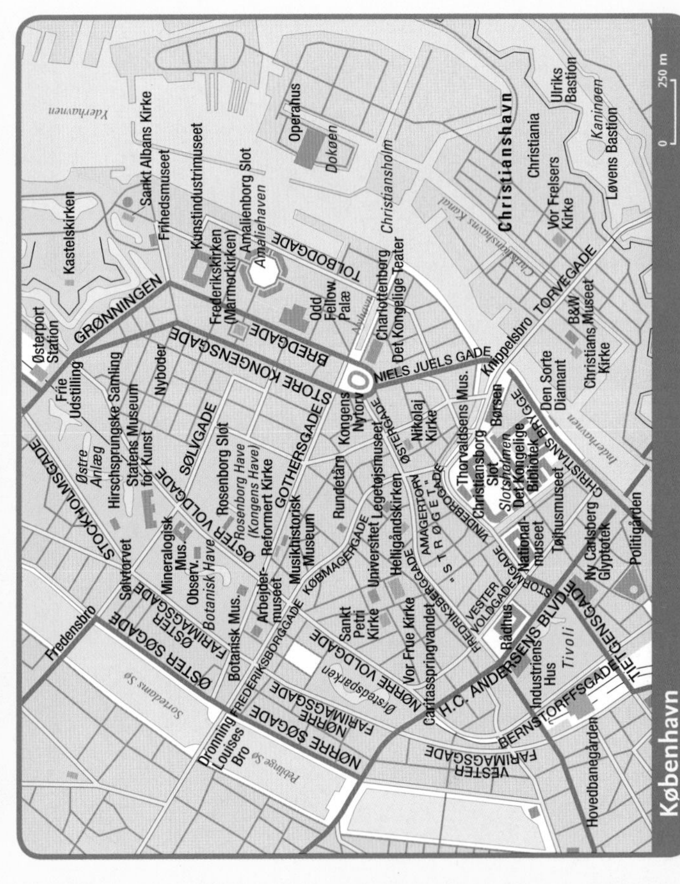
København
250 m
Yderhavnen
Operahus
Dokøen
Christianshavn
Christiania
Ulriks Bastion
Kaninøen
Løvens Bastion
Vor Frelsers Kirke
Sankt Albans Kirke
Frihedsmuseet
Kunstindustrimuseet
Amalienborg Slot
Amaliehaven
Frederikskirken (Marmorkirken)
Christiansholm
Kastelskirken
TOLBODGADE
Odd Fellow Palæ
Charlottenborg
Det Kongelige Teater
TORVEGADE
Knippelsbro
B&W
Christianskirke
Den Sorte Diamant
Christians Museet
Østerport Station
GRØNNINGEN
BREDGADE
STORE KONGENSGADE
NIELS JUELS GADE
Frie Udstilling
Nyboder
Hirschsprungske Samling
Statens Museum for Kunst
SØLVGADE
Østre Anlæg
STOCKHOLMSGADE
Rosenborg Slot
Rosenborg Have (Kongens Have)
Reformert Kirke
GOTHERSGADE
Kongens Nytorv
Nikolaj Kirke
Thorvaldsens Mus.
Børsen
Christiansborg Slot
Slotsholmen
Det Kongelige Bibliotek
Tøjhusmuseet
Nationalmuseet
Ny Carlsberg Glyptotek
Politigården
Mineralogisk Mus.
Observ.
Botanisk Have
Botanisk Mus.
Sølvtorvet
ØSTER VOLDGADE
Musikhistorisk Museum
Rundetårn
Universitet
Helligåndskirken
Sankt Petri Kirke
Vor Frue Kirke
Rådhus
Tivoli
Industriens Hus
Arbejder-museet
Fredensbro
ØSTER SØGADE
Sortedams Sø
FREDERIKSBORGGADE
NØRRE VOLDGADE
Ørstedsparken
H.C. ANDERSENS BLVD
BERNSTORFFSGADE
VESTER FARIMAGSGADE
NØRRE SØGADE
NØRRE FARIMAGSGADE
Dronning Louises Bro
Peblinge Sø
Hovedbanegården

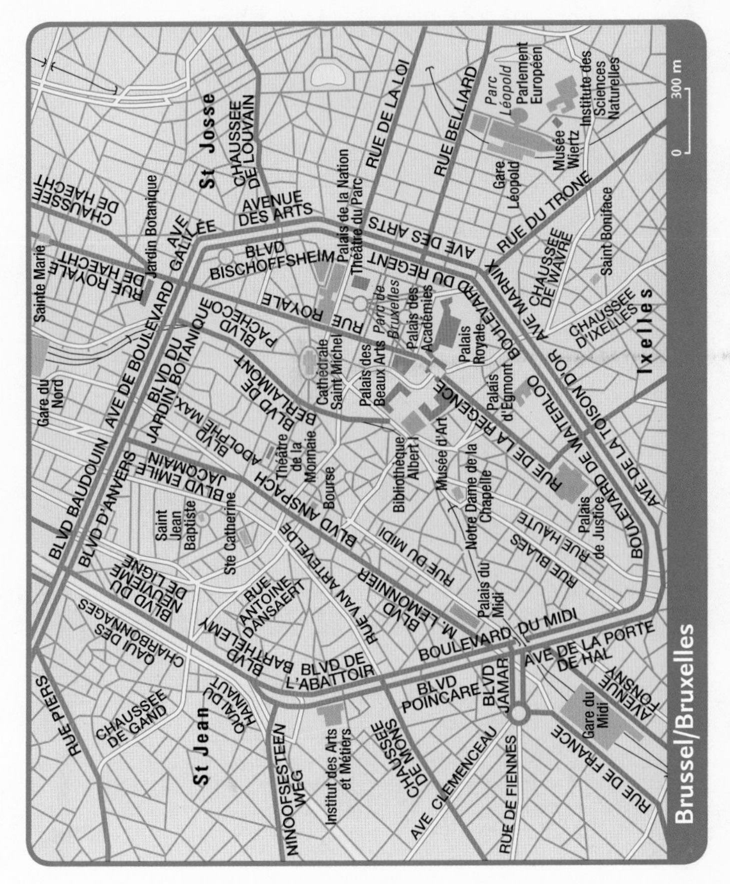
Brussel/Bruxelles
300 m
St Josse
CHAUSSEE DE LOUVAIN
RUE DE LA LOI
RUE BELLIARD
Parc Léopold
Parlement Européen
Institute des Sciences Naturelles
Musée Wiertz
Gare Léopold
CHAUSSEE DE HAECHT
Jardin Botanique
Palais de la Nation
Théâtre du Parc
AVENUE DES ARTS
BLVD BISCHOFFSHEIM
AVE DES ARTS
RUE DU TRONE
RUE ROYALE
RUE DU REGENT
Parc de Bruxelles
Palais des Académies
Palais Royale
AVE MARNIX
CHAUSSEE DE WAVRE
Saint Boniface
Ixelles
CHAUSSEE D'IXELLES
Sainte Marie
BLVD PACHECO
Cathédrale Saint Michel
Palais des Beaux Arts
Palais d'Egmont
BOULEVARD DE WATERLOO
Gare du Nord
AVE DE BOULEVARD
BLVD DU JARDIN BOTANIQUE
BLVD DE BERLAIMONT
BLVD ADOLPHE MAX
BLVD EMILE JACQMAIN
Théâtre de la Monnaie
Bourse
Bibliothèque Albert I
Musée d'Art
Notre Dame de la Chapelle
RUE DE LA REGENCE
Palais de Justice
BOULEVARD DE LA TOISON D'OR
BLVD BAUDOUIN
BLVD D'ANVERS
Saint Jean Baptiste
Ste Catherine
BLVD ANSPACH
RUE DU MIDI
RUE HAUTE
RUE BLAES
BLVD DE NIEUWE LIGNE
RUE ANTOINE DANSAERT
RUE VAN ARTEVELDE
BLVD M. LEMONNIER
Palais du Midi
BOULEVARD DU MIDI
AVE DE LA PORTE DE HAL
QUAI DES CHARBONNAGES
BLVD BARTHELEMY
BLVD DE L'ABATTOIR
BLVD POINCARE
BLVD JAMAR
Gare du Midi
AVENUE FONSNY
RUE PIERS
CHAUSSEE DE GAND
St Jean
QUAI DU HAINAUT
NINOOFSESTEENWEG
Institut des Arts et Métiers
CHAUSSEE DE MONS
AVE CLEMENCEAU
RUE DE FIENNES
RUE DE FRANCE

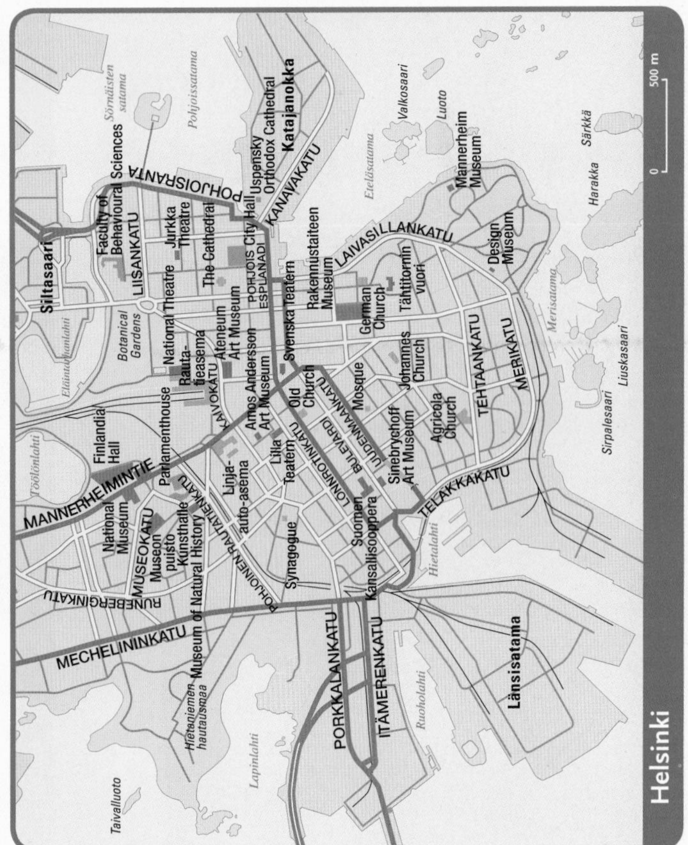
Helsinki
500 m
Katajanokka
Sörnäisten satama
Pohjoissatama
Uspensky Orthodox Cathedral
KANAVAKATU
POHJOISRANTA
Faculty of Behavioural Sciences
Siltasaari
Jurkka Theatre
The Cathedral
LIISANKATU
City Hall
POHJOIS ESPLANADI
Svenska Teatern
Rakennustaiteen Museum
LAIVASILLANKATU
German Church
Tähtitornin vuori
Design Museum
Mannerheim Museum
Valkosaari
Luoto
Eteläsatama
Herakka
Särkkä
Merisatama
Liuskasaari
Sirpalesaari
National Theatre
Botanical Gardens
Eläintarhanlahti
Rautatieasema
Ateneum Art Museum
Amos Anderson Art Museum
Old Church
Mosque
Johannes Church
Agricola Church
TEHTAANKATU
MERIKATU
Finlandia Hall
Parliament House
Lilla Teatern
Sinebrychoff Art Museum
Töölönlahti
MANNERHEIMINTIE
National Museum
Kunsthalle
Linja-auto-asema
Synagogue
Suomen Kansallisooppera
TELAKKAKATU
Hietalahti
RUNEBERGINKATU
MUSEOKATU
Museum of Natural History
MECHELININKATU
Hietaniemen hautausmaa
Lapinlahti
PORKKALANKATU
ITÄMERENKATU
Ruoholahti
Länsisatama
Taivalluoto

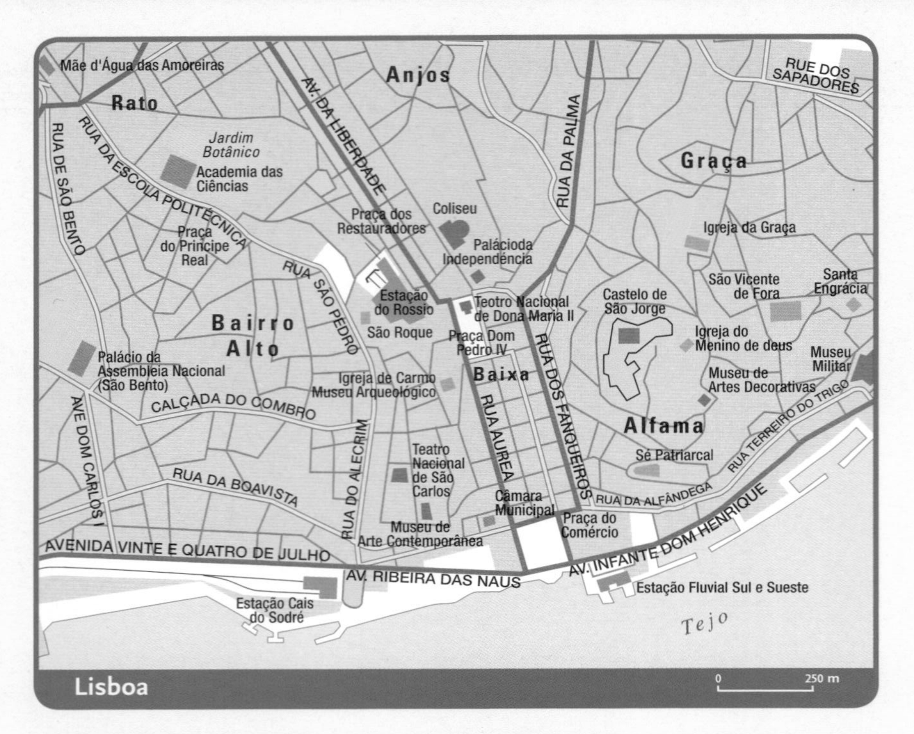
Lisboa
250 m
Mãe d'Água das Amoreiras
Rato
Anjos
AV. DA LIBERDADE
RUA DA PALMA
RUE DOS SAPADORES
Graça
Jardim Botânico
Academia das Ciências
RUA DA ESCOLA POLITÉCNICA
RUA DE SÃO BENTO
Praça do Príncipe Real
Praça dos Restauradores
Coliseu
Palácioda Independência
Igreja da Graça
São Vicente de Fora
Santa Engrácia
RUA SÃO PEDRO
Estação do Rossio
São Roque
Teatro Nacional de Dona Maria II
Praça Dom Pedro IV
Castelo de São Jorge
Igreja do Menino de deus
Museu Militar
Museu de Artes Decorativas
Bairro Alto
Palácio da Assembleia Nacional (São Bento)
Igreja de Carmo Museu Arqueológico
Baixa
RUA DOS FANQUEIROS
CALÇADA DO COMBRO
Alfama
RUA TERREIRO DO TRIGO
AVE DOM CARLOS I
RUA DA BOAVISTA
RUA DO ALECRIM
Teatro Nacional de São Carlos
RUA AUREA
Sé Patriarcal
Câmara Municipal
RUA DA ALFÂNDEGA
Museu de Arte Contemporânea
Praça do Comércio
AV. INFANTE DOM HENRIQUE
AVENIDA VINTE E QUATRO DE JULHO
AV. RIBEIRA DAS NAUS
Estação Fluvial Sul e Sueste
Estação Cais do Sodré
Tejo

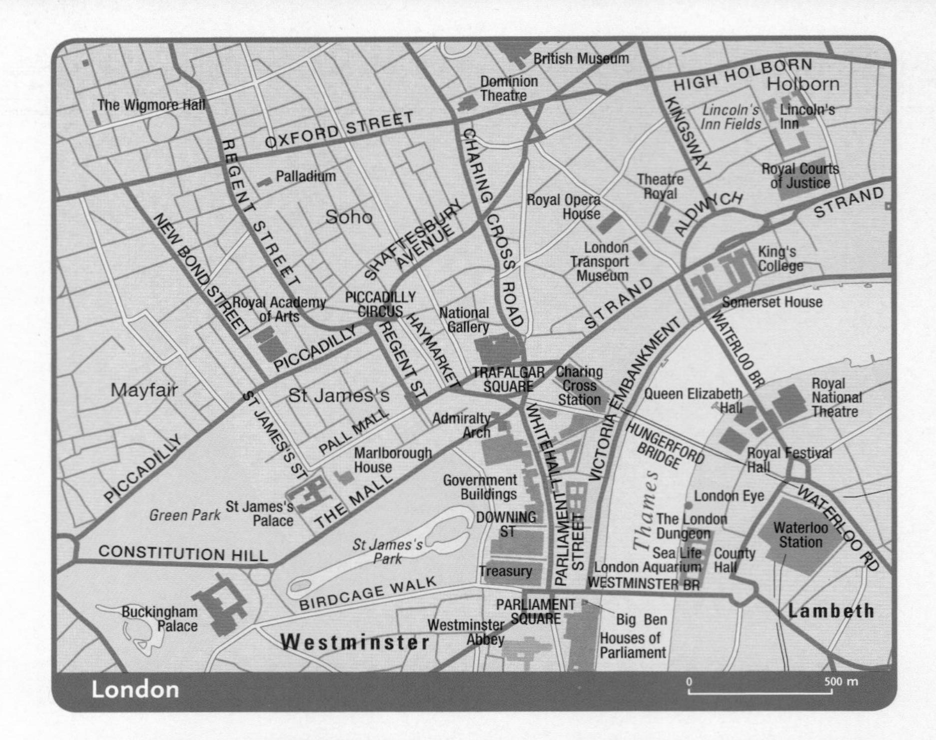
London
500 m
British Museum
Dominion Theatre
HIGH HOLBORN
Holborn
The Wigmore Hall
OXFORD STREET
CHARING CROSS ROAD
KINGSWAY
Lincoln's Inn Fields
Lincoln's Inn
Royal Courts of Justice
Palladium
Theatre Royal
REGENT STREET
Royal Opera House
ALDWYCH
STRAND
Soho
SHAFTESBURY AVENUE
London Transport Museum
King's College
NEW BOND STREET
Royal Academy of Arts
PICCADILLY CIRCUS
National Gallery
STRAND
Somerset House
PICCADILLY
REGENT ST
HAYMARKET
TRAFALGAR SQUARE
Charing Cross Station
VICTORIA EMBANKMENT
WATERLOO BR
Mayfair
St James's
Admiralty Arch
Queen Elizabeth Hall
Royal National Theatre
ST JAMES'S ST
PALL MALL
WHITEHALL
HUNGERFORD BRIDGE
Royal Festival Hall
PICCADILLY
Marlborough House
Government Buildings
London Eye
WATERLOO RD
Green Park
St James's Palace
THE MALL
DOWNING ST
PARLIAMENT STREET
Thames
The London Dungeon
Waterloo Station
CONSTITUTION HILL
St James's Park
Sea Life London Aquarium
County Hall
Treasury
WESTMINSTER BR
BIRDCAGE WALK
Buckingham Palace
PARLIAMENT SQUARE
Big Ben
Lambeth
Westminster
Westminster Abbey
Houses of Parliament

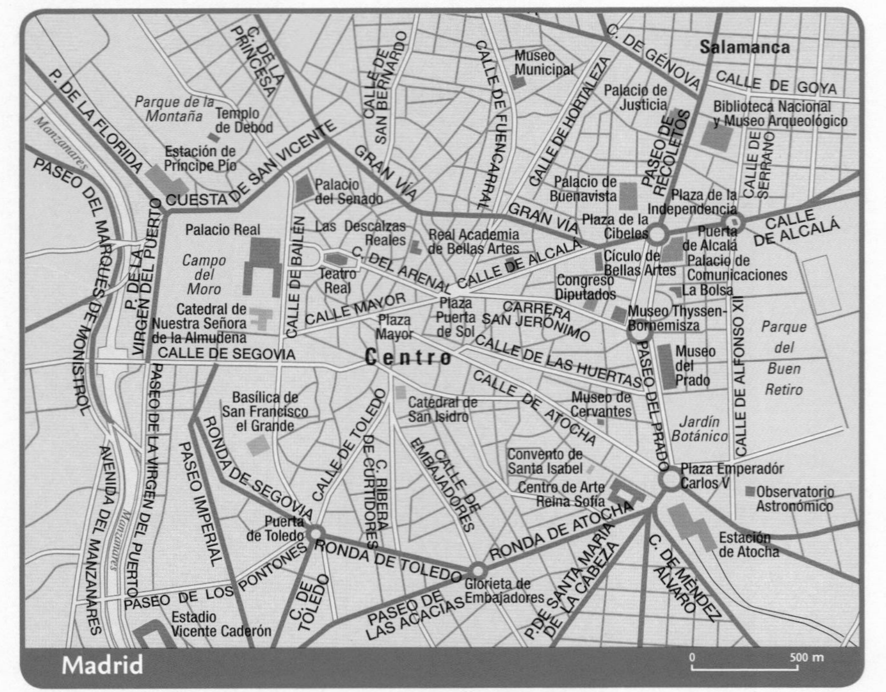
Madrid
500 m
C. DE LA PRINCESA
CALLE DE SAN BERNARDO
Museo Municipal
C. DE GÉNOVA
Salamanca
P. DE LA FLORIDA
CALLE DE FUENCARRAL
CALLE DE HORTALEZA
Palacio de Justicia
CALLE DE GOYA
Parque de la Montaña
Templo de Debod
Manzanares
PASEO DE RECOLETOS
Biblioteca Nacional y Museo Arqueológico
Estación de Príncipe Pío
CUESTA DE SAN VICENTE
GRAN VÍA
CALLE DE SERRANO
Palacio del Senado
Palacio de Buenavista
Plaza de la Independencia
PASEO DEL MARQUÉS DE MONISTROL
CUESTA DEL PUERTO
GRAN VÍA
Plaza de la Cibeles
Puerta de Alcalá
CALLE DE ALCALÁ
Palacio Real
Las Descalzas Reales
Real Academia de Bellas Artes
Campo del Moro
C. DEL ARENAL
CALLE DE ALCALÁ
Círculo de Bellas Artes
Palacio de Comunicaciones
Teatro Real
Congreso Diputados
La Bolsa
P. DE LA VIRGEN DEL PUERTO
CALLE DE BAILÉN
CALLE MAYOR
Plaza Mayor
Plaza Puerta de Sol
CARRERA SAN JERÓNIMO
Museo Thyssen-Bornemisza
CALLE DE ALFONSO XII
Parque del Buen Retiro
Catedral de Nuestra Señora de la Almudena
CALLE DE SEGOVIA
Centro
CALLE DE LAS HUERTAS
Museo del Prado
PASEO DEL PRADO
Basílica de San Francisco el Grande
CALLE DE TOLEDO
Catedral de San Isidro
Museo de Cervantes
CALLE DE ATOCHA
Jardín Botánico
AVENIDA DEL MANZANARES
PASEO DE LA VIRGEN DEL PUERTO
PASEO IMPERIAL
RONDA DE SEGOVIA
C. RIBERA DE CURTIDORES
CALLE DE EMBAJADORES
Convento de Santa Isabel
Plaza Emperador Carlos V
Centro de Arte Reina Sofía
Observatorio Astronómico
Puerta de Toledo
RONDA DE ATOCHA
PONTONES
RONDA DE TOLEDO
Estación de Atocha
PASEO DE LOS
Estadio Vicente Calderón
C. DE TOLEDO
PASEO DE LAS ACACIAS
Glorieta de Embajadores
P. DE SANTA MARÍA DE LA CABEZA
C. DE MÉNDEZ ÁLVARO

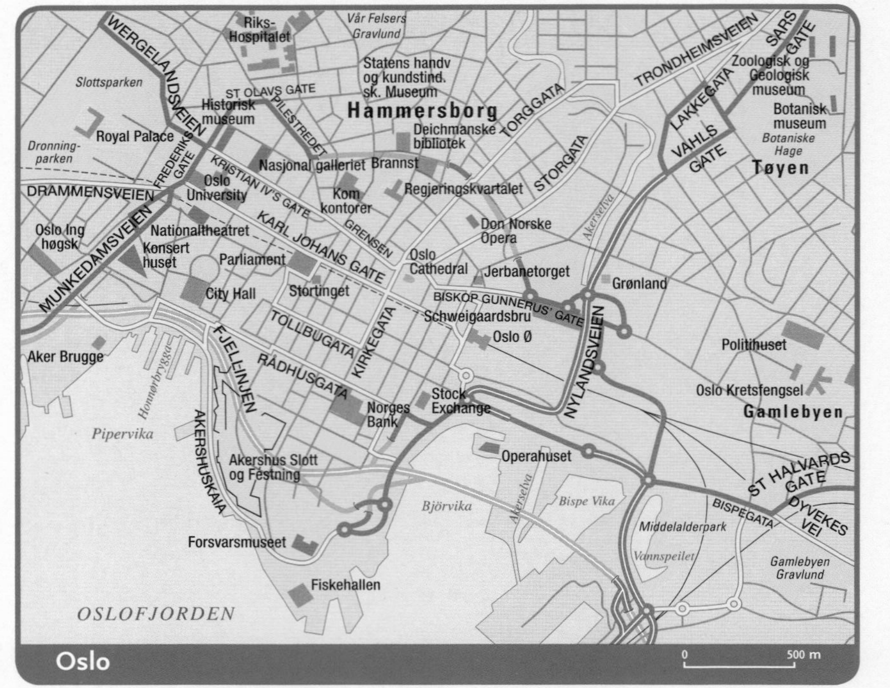
Oslo
500 m
WERGELANDSVEIEN
Riks-Hospitalet
Vår Felsers Gravlund
Statens handv og kundstind. sk. Museum
TRONDHEIMSVEIEN
SARS GATE
Slottsparken
ST OLAVS GATE
Historisk museum
PILESTREDET
Hammersborg
TORGGATA
Zoologisk og Geologisk museum
LAKKEGATA
Royal Palace
Deichmanske bibliotek
Botanisk museum
Botaniske Hage
Dronning-parken
FREDERIKS GATE
Nasjonalgalleriet
Brannst
STORGATA
VAHLS GATE
Tøyen
KRISTIAN IV'S GATE
Oslo University
Kom kontorer
Regjeringskvartalet
DRAMMENSVEIEN
GRENSEN
KARL JOHANS GATE
Don Norske Opera
Akerselva
Oslo ing høgsk
MUNKEDAMSVEIEN
Nationaltheatret
Konserthuset
Parliament
Oslo Cathedral
Jerbanetorget
Grønland
City Hall
Stortinget
BISKOP GUNNERUS' GATE
Schweigaardsbru
TOLLBUGATA
KIRKEGATA
Oslo Ø
NYLANDSVEIEN
Politihuset
Aker Brugge
FJELLINJEN
RÅDHUSGATA
Oslo Kretsfengsel
Gamlebyen
Stock Exchange
Norges Bank
Pipervika
AKERSHUSKAIA
Akershus Slott og Festning
Operahuset
ST HALVARDS GATE
Björvika
Bispe Vika
BISPEGATA
DYVEKES VEI
Forsvarsmuseet
Middelalderpark
Gamlebyen Gravlund
Fiskehallen
OSLOFJORDEN

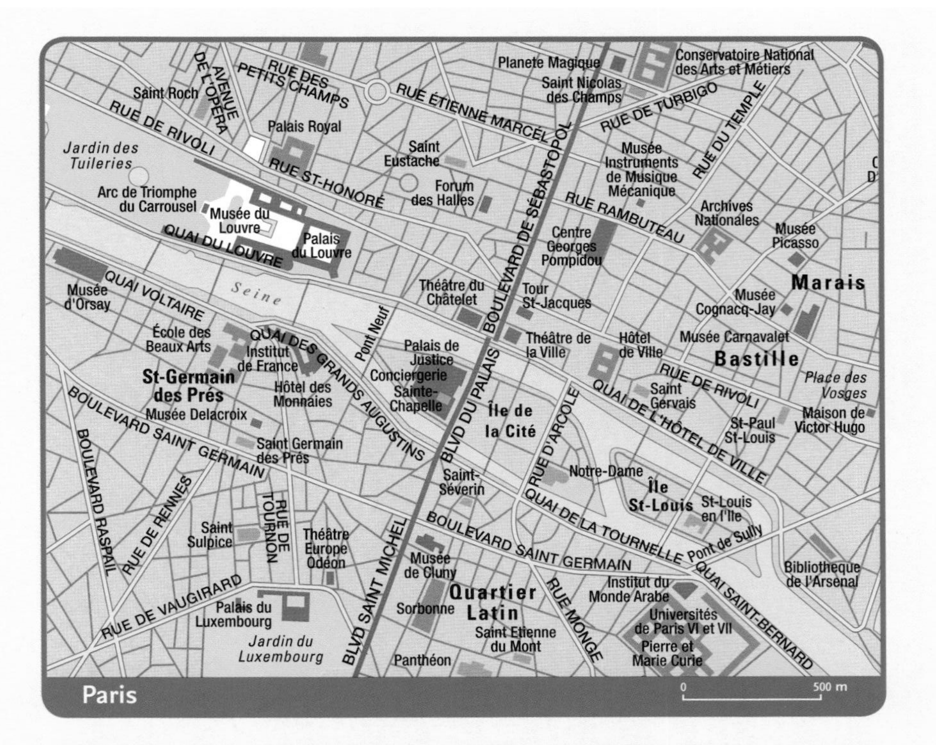
Paris
0
500 m
Marais
Bastille
Île de la Cité
Île St-Louis
Quartier Latin
St-Germain des Prés
Seine
RUE DE RIVOLI
RUE ST-HONORÉ
RUE ÉTIENNE MARCEL
RUE RAMBUTEAU
RUE DU TEMPLE
BOULEVARD DE SÉBASTOPOL
BLVD DU PALAIS
BOULEVARD SAINT GERMAIN
BLVD SAINT MICHEL
BOULEVARD RASPAIL
RUE DE RENNES
RUE DE VAUGIRARD
QUAI VOLTAIRE
QUAI DU LOUVRE
QUAI DES GRANDS AUGUSTINS
QUAI DE L'HÔTEL DE VILLE
QUAI DE LA TOURNELLE
QUAI SAINT-BERNARD
Jardin des Tuileries
Jardin du Luxembourg
Arc de Triomphe du Carrousel
Musée du Louvre
Palais du Louvre
Musée d'Orsay
Palais Royal
Saint Roch
Saint Eustache
Forum des Halles
Centre Georges Pompidou
Tour St-Jacques
Théâtre du Châtelet
Théâtre de la Ville
Hôtel de Ville
Palais de Justice
Conciergerie
Sainte-Chapelle
Notre-Dame
Pont Neuf
Saint-Séverin
Musée de Cluny
Sorbonne
Panthéon
Institut du Monde Arabe
Musée Picasso
Musée Carnavalet
Place des Vosges
Maison de Victor Hugo
Bibliothèque de l'Arsenal
Saint Sulpice
Palais du Luxembourg
Conservatoire National des Arts et Métiers

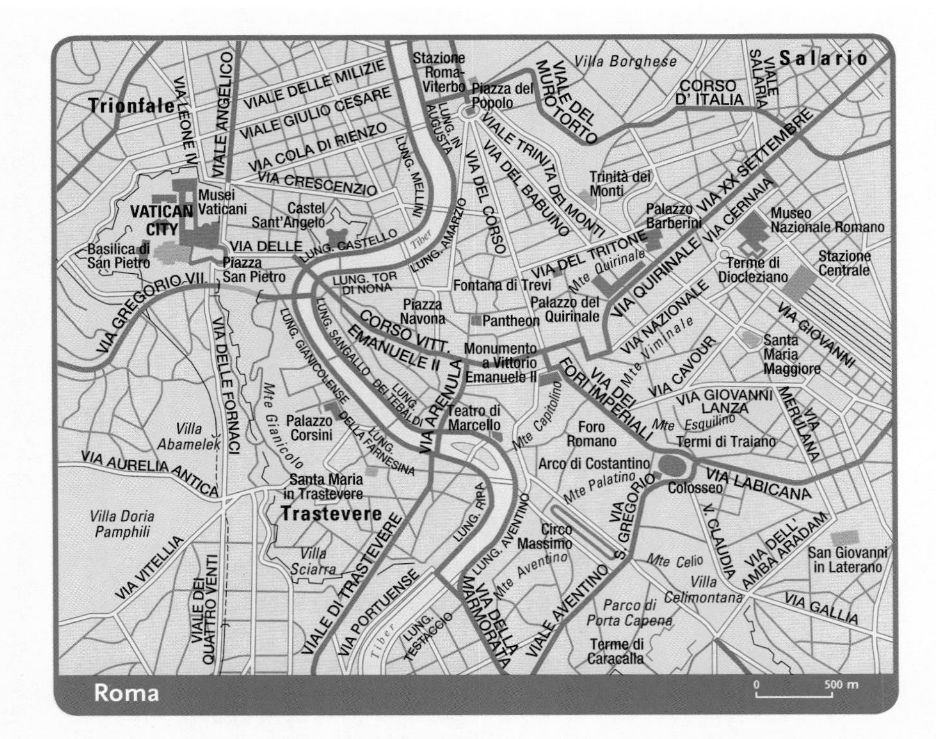
Roma
0
500 m
Salario
Trionfale
VATICAN CITY
Trastevere
VIA DEL CORSO
VIA NAZIONALE
VIA CAVOUR
VIA LABICANA
VIALE AVENTINO
VIALE DI TRASTEVERE
VIA AURELIA ANTICA
VIA GREGORIO VII
VIA DELLE FORNACI
VIA XX SETTEMBRE
VIA DEI FORI IMPERIALI
Villa Borghese
Villa Doria Pamphili
Mte Gianicolo
Tiber
Basilica di San Pietro
Piazza San Pietro
Musei Vaticani
Castel Sant'Angelo
Piazza del Popolo
Trinità dei Monti
Piazza Navona
Pantheon
Fontana di Trevi
Monumento a Vittorio Emanuele II
Colosseo
Foro Romano
Arco di Costantino
Circo Massimo
Terme di Caracalla
Terme di Diocleziano
Stazione Centrale
Santa Maria Maggiore
San Giovanni in Laterano
Santa Maria in Trastevere
Palazzo Corsini
Museo Nazionale Romano

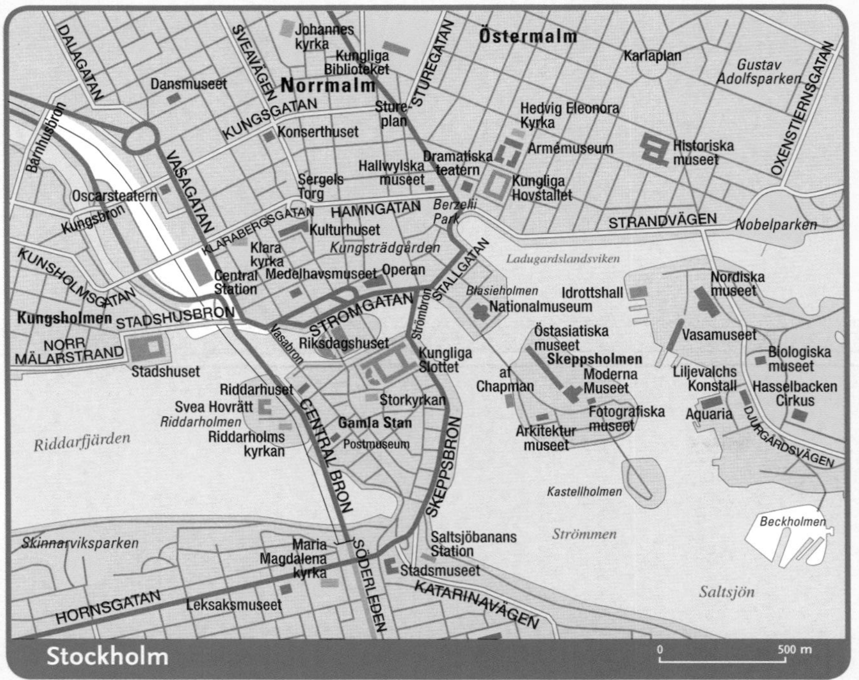
Stockholm
0
500 m
Östermalm
Norrmalm
Kungsholmen
Gamla Stan
Skeppsholmen
Riddarfjärden
Saltsjön
Strömmen
STRANDVÄGEN
VASAGATAN
KUNGSGATAN
HORNSGATAN
SÖDERLEDEN
CENTRAL BRON
SKEPPSBRON
STUREGATAN
Centralstation
Stadshuset
Kungliga Slottet
Storkyrkan
Riddarholms kyrkan
Riksdagshuset
Nationalmuseum
Moderna Museet
Vasamuseet
Nordiska museet
Historiska museet
Kungsträdgården
Sergels Torg
Operan
Dramatiska teatern
Beckholmen
Kastellholmen

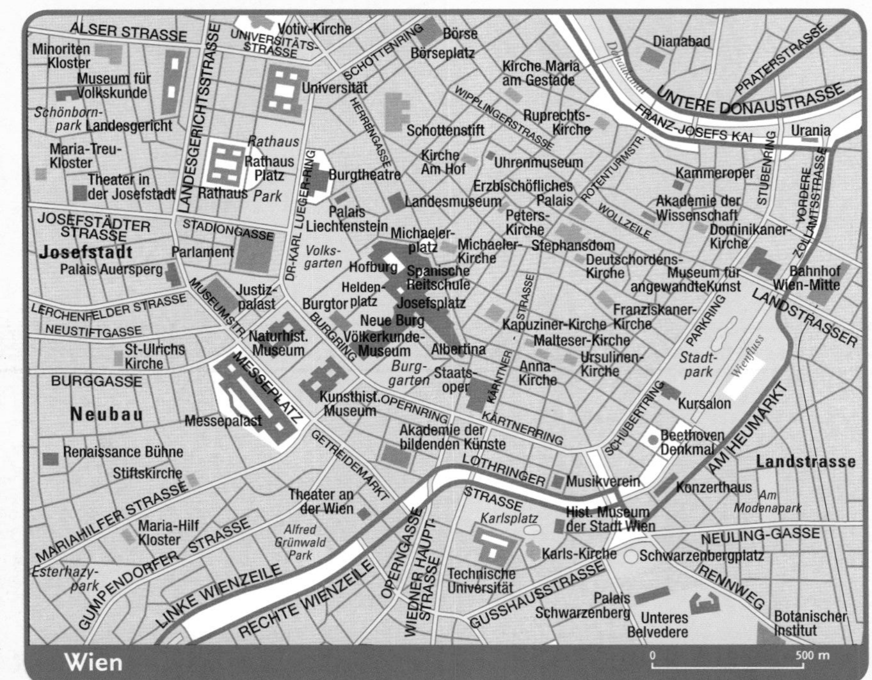
Wien
0
500 m
Landstrasse
Josefstadt
Neubau
UNTERE DONAUSTRASSE
FRANZ-JOSEFS KAI
LANDSTRASSER
AM HEUMARKT
LOTHRINGER STRASSE
KÄRNTNERRING
MESSEPLATZ
Stadtpark
Kursalon
Konzerthaus
Musikverein
Karlsplatz
Karls-Kirche
Staatsoper
Albertina
Hofburg
Neue Burg
Burggarten
Volksgarten
Burgtheatre
Rathaus
Parlament
Universität
Votiv-Kirche
Stephansdom
Schottenstift
Börse
Urania
Dianabad
Bahnhof Wien-Mitte
Kunsthist. Museum
Naturhist. Museum
Messepalast
Unteres Belvedere
Botanischer Institut

A

Å N 104 F7
Å N 110 E4
Å N 111 B12
Å N 111 C13
Aabenraa DK 86 E4
Aabybro DK 86 A5
Aachen D 20 C6
Aadorf CH 27 F10
Aakirkeby DK 89 E7
Aalborg DK 86 A5
Aalen D 75 E7
Aalestrup DK 86 B4
Aalsmeer NL 16 D3
Aalst B 19 C9
Aalst NL 183 B6
Aalten NL 17 E7
Aalter B 19 B7
Äänekoski FIN 123 E15
Aapajärvi FIN 115 D2
Aapajärvi FIN 119 B12
Aapajoki FIN 119 B12
Aapua S 117 E11
Aarau CH 27 F9
Aarberg CH 31 A11
Aardenburg NL 19 B7
Aareavaara S 117 D10
Aarhus DK 86 C6
Aarle NL 16 F5
A Armada E 38 B3
Aars DK 86 B5
Aarschot B 19 C10
Aartrijke B 182 C2
Aartselaar B 19 B9
Aarup DK 86 E6
Aarwangen CH 27 F8
Aasleagh IRL 6 E3
Ääsmäe EST 131 C9
Aaspere EST 131 C12
Aatsinki FIN 115 E5
Aavajärvi S 119 C11
Aavasaksa FIN 119 B11
Aba H 149 B11
Abaclia MD 154 E3
Abades E 46 C4
Abadín E 38 B5
Abadiño-Zelaieta E 41 B6
Abádszalók H 150 C6
A Baiuca E 38 B3
Abak TR 181 A7
Abalar TR 172 A6
Abánades E 47 C8
Abanilla E 56 E2
Abano Terme I 66 B4
Abarán E 55 C10
A Barrela E 38 C4
Abasár H 150 B5
Abaújszántó H 145 G3
Abbadia San Salvatore I 62 B1
Abbasanta I 64 C2
Abbekås S 87 E13
Abbeville F 18 D4
Abbey IRL 6 F6
Abbeydorney IRL 8 D3
Abbeyfeale IRL 8 D4
Abbeyleix IRL 9 C8
Abbey Town GB 5 F10
Abbiategrasso I 69 C6
Abborrberg S 109 F12
Abborrberget S 98 D8
Abborrträsk S 109 F17
Abbotsbury GB 13 D9
Abbots Langley GB 15 D8
Abcoude NL 16 D3
Abejar E 40 E6
Abejuela E 48 E3
Abela P 50 C2
Abelvær N 105 B10
Abenberg D 75 D8
Abenójar E 54 B4
Abensberg D 75 E10
Aberaeron GB 12 A6
Aberaman GB 13 B8
Aberchirder GB 3 K11
Aberdare GB 13 B8
Aberdaron GB 10 F2
Aberdeen GB 3 L12
Aberdovey GB 10 F3
Aberfeldy GB 5 B9
Aberffraw GB 10 E3
Aberford GB 11 D9
Aberfoyle GB 5 C8
Abergavenny GB 13 B8
Abergele GB 10 E4
Åberget S 109 E18
Abergwaun GB 12 B5
Abergynolwyn GB 10 F4
Aberlady GB 5 C11
Aberlour GB 3 L10
Abernethy GB 5 C10
Aberporth GB 12 A5
Abersoch GB 10 F2
Abertamy CZ 75 B12
Abertawe GB 13 B7
Abertillery GB 13 B8
Abertura E 45 F9
Aberuthven GB 5 C9
Aberystwyth GB 12 A6
Abetone I 66 D2
Abfaltersbach A 72 C6
Abhainnsuidhe GB 2 K2
Abia de la Obispalía E 47 D8
Abiego E 42 C3
Abild DK 86 F3
Abilly F 29 B7
Abingdon GB 13 B12
Abington GB 5 E9
Abisko Östra S 111 D16
Abja-Paluoja EST 131 E10
Abla E 55 E7
Ablis F 24 C6
Ablitas E 41 E8
Abmelaseter N 112 E6
Abo FIN 126 E7
Åbo S 103 C10
Åbodarna S 107 E14
Åbogen N 96 B7
Abondance F 31 C10
Abony H 150 C5
Åbosjö S 107 D13
Aboyne GB 5 A11
Abragão P 44 B4
Abram RO 151 C9
Abrămuț RO 151 C9
Abrantes P 44 F4
Abraur S 109 D16
Abreiro P 38 F5
Abreschviller F 27 C7
Abrest F 30 C3
Abriès F 31 F10
Abrigada P 44 F2
Abriola I 60 B5
Abrucena E 55 E7
Abrud RO 151 E11
Abrupe LV 135 B11
Absam A 72 B4
Absberg D 75 D8
Absdorf A 77 F9
Abtenau A 73 A7
Abtsgmünd D 74 E6
Abukhava BY 140 C10
Åby S 89 A7
Åby S 93 B8
Åbyen DK 90 D7
Åbyggeby S 103 E13
Åbyn S 118 D6
Åbytorp S 92 A6
Acaill IRL 6 E3
A Cañiza E 38 D3
A Carballa E 38 B2
Acarlar TR 177 D10
A Carreira E 38 B3
Acâș RO 151 B10
Acate I 58 E5
Accadia I 60 A4
Acceglio I 36 C5
Accettura I 60 C6
Acciano I 62 C5
Acciaroli I 60 C4
Accous F 32 E4
Accrington GB 11 D7
Accumoli I 62 B4
Acebo E 45 D7
Acedera E 45 F9
Acedo E 32 E1
Acehuche E 45 E7
Aceituna E 45 D8
Acered E 47 B9
Acerenza I 60 B5
Acerno I 60 B4
Acerra I 60 B2
Aceuchal E 51 B7
Ach A 76 F3
Achadh Mòr GB 2 J3
A Chan E 38 D3
Acharacle GB 4 B5
Acharnes GR 175 C8
Achavanich GB 3 J10
Achel B 183 C6
Achenkirch A 72 A4
Achern D 27 C9
Acheux-en-Amiénois F 18 D6
Achicourt F 18 D6
Achill IRL 6 E3
Achilleio GR 175 A6
Achim D 17 B12
Achintee GB 2 L6
Achladochori GR 169 B10
Achladokampos GR 175 D6
Achnacroish GB 4 B6
Achnasheen GB 2 K6
Achosnich GB 4 B4
Achstetten D 71 A9
Achtrup D 82 A6
Aci Castello I 59 D7
Aci Catena I 59 D7
Acireale I 59 D7
Aci Sant'Antonio I 59 D7
Aci Trezza I 59 D7
Acktjära S 103 D11
Acle GB 15 B12
A Coruña E 38 B3
Acquacadda I 64 E2
Acqualagna I 67 E6
Acquanegra sul Chiese I 66 B1
Acquapendente I 62 B1
Acquappesa I 60 E5
Acquaro I 59 B9
Acquarossa CH 71 E7
Acquasanta Terme I 62 B4
Acquasparta I 62 B3
Acquaviva Picena I 62 B5
Acquedolci I 59 C6
Acquigny F 24 B5
Acqui Terme I 37 B8
Acri I 61 E6
A Cruz do Incio E 38 C5
Ács H 149 A10
Acsa H 150 B3
Acuto I 62 D4
Ada SRB 150 F5
Adács H 150 B4
Adahuesca E 42 C3
Adak S 109 F16
Ådalsliden S 107 E11
Adamas GR 179 B7
Adamclisi RO 155 E1
Adamov CZ 77 D11
Adamova BY 133 E4
Adamów PL 141 G6
Adamówka PL 144 C6
Adamstown IRL 9 D9
Adămuș RO 152 E4
Adamuz E 53 A7
Adâncata RO 153 B8
Adâncata RO 161 D8
Ádánd H 149 C10
Adanero E 46 C3
Adão P 45 D6
Adare IRL 8 C5
Adatepe TR 173 D6
Adaúfe P 38 E3
Adavere EST 131 D11
Ādaži LV 135 B8
Adderbury GB 13 A12
Addlestone GB 15 E8
Adegem B 182 C2
Adelboden CH 31 C12
Adelebsen D 78 C6
Adelfia I 61 A7
Adelina PL 144 B8
Adelmannsfelden D 187 D8
Adelschlag D 75 E9
Adelsheim D 27 B11
Adelsried D 75 F8
Adelsö S 99 D9
Adenau D 21 D7
Adendorf D 83 D8
Adendro GR 169 C8
Adenstedt D 78 C6
Adjud RO 153 E10
Adlešiči SLO 148 E4
Adliswil CH 27 F10
Adlkofen D 75 E11
Admont A 73 A9
Adolfsström S 109 D12
Adony H 149 B11
Adorf D 75 B11
Adorf (Diemelsee) D 17 F11
Adoufe P 38 F4
Adra E 55 F6
Adradas E 41 F7
Adrados E 40 F3
Adrano I 59 D6
Adria I 66 B5
Adriani GR 171 B6
Adriers F 29 C7
Aduard NL 17 B6
Adulsbruk N 101 E14
Ådum DK 86 D3
Adunați RO 161 C7
Adunații-Copăceni RO 161 E8
Adutiškis LT 135 F13
Adzaneta de Albaida E 56 D4
Adžūni LV 135 D8
Aegviidu EST 131 C11
Aerino GR 169 F8
Ærøskøbing DK 86 F6
Aerzen D 17 D12
A Escusa E 38 C2
A Esfarrapada E 38 D2
A Estrada E 38 C3
Aetos GR 169 C6
Aetos GR 174 B3
Aetos GR 174 E4
Äetsä FIN 126 C8
Afantou GR 181 D8
Åfarnes N 100 A7
A Feira do Monte E 38 B4
Affing D 75 F8
Afife P 38 E2
Afissos GR 169 F9
Åfjord N 104 D8
Aflenz Kurort A 73 A11
A Fonsagrada E 38 B5
A Forxa E 38 D4
A Forxa E 38 D4
Åfoss N 90 A6
Afragola I 60 B2
Afritz A 73 C8
Afumați RO 160 E2
Afumați RO 161 D8
Afytos GR 169 D9
Aga D 79 E11
Ağaçli TR 173 B10
Ağaköy TR 173 D7
Agalas GR 174 D2
Agallas E 45 D8
A Gándara E 38 B3
A Gándara de Altea E 38 A3
Agapia RO 153 C8
Agăș RO 153 D8
Ágasegyháza H 150 D3
Agde F 34 D5
Agen F 33 B7
Àger E 42 C5
Agerbæk DK 86 D3
Agerskov DK 86 E4
Agersted DK 86 A6
Ågerup DK 87 D10
Ágfalva H 149 A7
Aggersund DK 86 A4
Aggius I 64 B3
Aggsbach Markt A 77 F8
Aghaboe IRL 9 C7
Aghagallon GB 7 C10
Aghalee GB 7 C10
Aghanloo GB 4 E3
Aghaville IRL 8 E4
Aghern IRL 8 D6
Aghione F 37 G10
Aghireșu RO 151 D11
Aghleam IRL 6 D2
Aghnagar Bridge IRL 8 E2
Agia GR 169 E8
Agia Anna GR 175 B7
Agia Anna GR 175 C6
Agia Effimia GR 174 C2
Agia Efthymia GR 174 C5
Agia Galini GR 178 E8
Agia Kyriaki GR 174 E4
Agia Marina GR 175 B6
Agia Marina GR 175 D8
Agia Marina GR 177 E8
Agia Paraskevi GR 168 D4
Agia Paraskevi GR 174 A3
Agia Paraskevi GR 177 E6
Agia Pelagia GR 178 C4
Agia Pelagia GR 178 E9
Agiasma GR 171 C7
Agiasos GR 177 A7
Agia Triada GR 174 D4
Agia Triada GR 175 D6
Agia Varvara GR 169 D7
Agia Varvara GR 178 E9
Agigea RO 155 E3
Agighiol RO 155 C3
Agino Selo BIH 157 C7
Agiofyllo GR 169 E6
Agioi Anargyroi GR 169 E7
Agioi Apostoloi GR 175 C8
Agioi Deka GR 178 E8
Agioi Theodoroi GR 169 E5
Agioi Theodoroi GR 175 A6
Agioi Theodoroi GR 175 D7
Agiokampos GR 169 E8
Agiokampos GR 175 B7
Agionori GR 175 D6
Agios Andreas GR 175 E6
Agios Athanasios GR 169 C8
Agios Athanasios GR 171 B6
Agios Charalampos GR 171 C9
Agios Christoforos GR 175 F5
Agios Dimitrios GR 169 D7
Agios Dimitrios GR 175 D8
Agios Dimitrios GR 175 F6
Agios Efstratios GR 171 E7
Agios Georgios GR 169 C7
Agios Georgios GR 174 B4
Agios Georgios GR 175 C6
Agios Georgios GR 177 F6
Agios Georgios GR 178 E9
Agios Germanos GR 168 C5
Agios Ioannis GR 174 E5
Agios Ioannis GR 175 C7
Agios Ioannis GR 178 B4
Agios Kirykos GR 177 D7
Agios Konstantinos GR 174 B3
Agios Konstantinos GR 174 D5
Agios Konstantinos GR 175 B6
Agios Konstantinos GR 175 D9
Agios Kyprianos GR 178 C3
Agios Leon GR 174 D2
Agios Loukas GR 169 C7
Agios Loukas GR 175 C9
Agios Mamas GR 169 D9
Agios Matthaios GR 168 F2
Agios Myronas GR 178 E9
Agios Nikolaos GR 168 E3
Agios Nikolaos GR 168 E5
Agios Nikolaos GR 169 D10
Agios Nikolaos GR 174 B2
Agios Nikolaos GR 174 B4
Agios Nikolaos GR 174 B4
Agios Nikolaos GR 178 B3
Agios Nikolaos GR 179 E10
Agios Panteleimonas GR 169 C6
Agios Paraskevi GR 171 F10
Agios Petros GR 169 C8
Agios Petros GR 174 B2
Agios Petros GR 175 E6
Agios Spyridonas GR 169 D7
Agios Spyridonas GR 174 A2
Agios Stefanos GR 175 C8
Agios Stefanos GR 176 E5
Agios Thomas GR 175 C8
Agios Vasileios GR 169 C9
Agios Vasileios GR 175 D6
Agira I 59 D6
Agivey GB 4 E3
Agkathia GR 169 C7
Agkistro GR 169 B9
Aglapsvik N 111 B15
Aglasterhausen D 187 C6
Agle N 105 C13
Aglen N 105 B10
Agliana I 66 E3
Aglientu I 64 A3
Aglish IRL 9 D7
Agluonėnai LT 134 E2
Agnadello I 69 C8
Agnagar Bridge IRL 8 E2
Agnanta GR 168 F5
Agnantero GR 169 F6
Agneaux F 23 B9
Agnita RO 152 F5
Agno CH 69 A6
Agnone I 63 D6
Agolada E 38 C3
Agoncillo E 32 F1
Agon-Coutainville F 23 B8
Agordo I 72 D5
Agost E 56 E3
Agos-Vidalos F 32 D5
Ågotnes N 94 B2
Agra GR 177 A7
Agramón E 55 C9
Agramunt E 42 D6
Agrate Brianza I 69 B7
Agreda E 41 E8
Agrés E 56 D4
Agria GR 169 F9
Agridi GR 174 D4
Agrigento I 58 E4
Agrili GR 174 E4
Agrinio GR 174 B3
Agriovotano GR 175 A7
Agrochão P 39 E5
Agropoli I 60 C3
Ågskaret N 108 C5
Aguadulce E 53 B7
Aguadulce E 55 F7
A Guarda E 38 E2
Aguarón E 41 F9
Aguas E 42 C3
Águas Belas P 44 E4
Aguas de Busot E 56 D4
Águas de Moura P 50 B2
Águas Frias P 38 E5
Aguaviva E 42 F3
A Gudiña E 38 D5
Agudo E 54 B3
Águeda P 44 C4
Aguessac F 34 B5
Agugliano I 67 E7
Aguiar P 50 C4
Aguiar da Beira P 44 C5
Aguilafuente E 46 B4
Aguilar de Alfambra E 42 F2
Aguilar de Campóo E 40 C3
Aguilar de la Frontera E 53 A7
Aguilar del Río Alhama E 41 E8
Águilas E 55 E9
Agullana E 34 F4
Agullent E 56 D3
Aha S 109 F14
Ahafona IRL 8 C3
Aham D 75 E11
Ahascragh IRL 6 F6
Ahaus D 17 D8
Åheim N 100 B3
Ahelva FIN 121 E11
Ahigal E 45 D8
Ahigal de Villarino E 45 B8
Ahillones E 51 C8
Ahja EST 131 E14
Ahjola FIN 121 D12
Ahlainen FIN 126 B6
Ahlatli TR 167 E8
Ahlbeck D 84 C6
Ahlbeck D 84 C6
Ahlden (Aller) D 82 E7
Ahlen D 17 E9
Ahlerstedt D 17 B12
Ahlhorn D 17 C10
Ahmas FIN 119 E17
Ahmavaara FIN 115 E4
Ahmetbey TR 173 B8
Ahmetbeyli TR 177 C9
Ahmetçeli TR 172 E6
Ahmetli TR 177 C9
Ahmovaara FIN 125 D13
Ahnsbeck D 79 A7
Ahoghill GB 4 F4
Ahoinen FIN 127 D11
Ahokylä FIN 123 C17
Ahola FIN 121 B11
Ahola FIN 121 C13
Ahola FIN 121 D13
Ahola FIN 124 D9
Aholanvaara FIN 115 E5
Ahonperä FIN 119 F13
Ahorn D 75 B8
Aho-Vastinki FIN 123 E14
Ahrbrück D 21 D7
Ahrensbök D 83 B9
Ahrensburg D 83 C8
Ahrenshagen D 83 B13
Ahrenshoop D 83 B12
Ähtäri FIN 123 E12
Ähtärinranta FIN 123 E12
Ahtme EST 132 C1
Ahula EST 131 C11
Ahun F 29 C10
Åhus S 88 D6
Ahveninen FIN 123 E16
Ahvenisto FIN 127 C16
Ahvensalmi FIN 125 F10
Ahvenselkä FIN 115 E4
Ahvenvittikko FIN 115 D4
Ahviosaari FIN 129 B10
Aiani GR 169 D6
Aianteio GR 175 D7
Aibar E 32 E3
Aibl A 73 C11
Aichach D 75 F9
Aichhalden D 27 D9
Aichstetten D 71 B10
Ai'dejav'ri N 117 A10
Aidenbach D 76 E4
Aidipsos GR 175 B7
Aidone I 58 E5
Aidonochori GR 169 C10
Aidt DK 86 C5
Aidu EST 131 D12
Aiello Calabro I 59 A9
Aielo de Malferit E 56 D3
Aieta I 60 D5
Aiffres F 28 C5
Aigeira GR 174 C5
Aigen im Ennstal A 73 A9
Aigen im Mühlkreis A 76 E5
Aigiali GR 177 F6
Aigina GR 175 D7
Aiginio GR 169 D8
Aigio GR 174 C5
Aigle CH 31 C10
Aiglemont F 184 E2
Aignan F 33 C6
Aignay-le-Duc F 25 E12
Aigre F 28 D6
Aigrefeuille-d'Aunis F 28 C4
Aigrefeuille-sur-Maine F 28 A3
A Igrexa E 38 D3
Aiguafreda E 43 D8
Aiguebelle F 31 D9
Aigueblanche F 31 D10
Aigueperse F 30 C3
Aigues-Mortes F 35 C7
Aigues-Vives F 33 E9
Aigues-Vives F 34 D4
Aigues-Vives F 35 C7
Aiguilhe F 30 E4
Aiguilles F 31 F10
Aiguillon F 33 B6
Aigurande F 29 C9
Äijäjoki FIN 116 B10
Äijälä FIN 123 E16
Aijala FIN 127 E9
Aijänneva FIN 123 F11
Aillant-sur-Tholon F 25 E9
Aillas F 32 B5
Aillevillers-et-Lyaumont F 26 E5
Ailly-le-Haut-Clocher F 18 D4
Ailly-sur-Noye F 18 E5
Ailly-sur-Somme F 18 E5
Ailt an Chorráin IRL 6 C6
Aimargues F 35 C7
Aime F 31 D10
Ainali FIN 119 F14
Ainali FIN 123 B11
Ainay-le-Château F 29 B11
Ainaži LV 131 F8
Aindling D 75 E8
Ainet A 73 C6
Ainsa E 33 F6
Ainzón E 41 E9
Airaines F 18 E4
Airaksela FIN 124 E8
Airasca I 31 F11
Aird Asaig GB 2 K3
Airdrie GB 5 D9
Aire-sur-l'Adour F 32 C5
Aire-sur-la-Lys F 18 C5
Airidh a'Bhruaich GB 2 J3
Airola I 60 A3
Airole I 37 D7
Airolo CH 71 D7
Airvault F 28 B5
Aisey-sur-Seine F 25 E12
Aïssey F 26 F5
Aisymi GR 171 B9
Aisy-sur-Armançon F 25 E11
Aitamännikkö FIN 117 D12
Aita Mare RO 153 F7
Aiterhofen D 75 E12
Aith GB 3 E14
Aith GB 3 G11
Aitolahti FIN 127 B10
Aitoliko GR 174 C3
Aiton RO 152 D3
Aitona E 42 E4
Aitoo FIN 127 C11
Aitrach D 71 B10
Aitrang D 71 B11
Aittaniemi FIN 121 B10
Aittijoki FIN 113 D17
Aittojärvi FIN 119 D17
Aittojärvi FIN 123 C16
Aittokoski FIN 124 C8
Aittokylä FIN 121 E10
Aittoperä FIN 123 C13
Aittovaara FIN 121 D13
Aiud RO 152 E3
Aiviekste LV 135 C11
Aix-en-Othe F 25 D10
Aix-en-Provence F 35 C9
Aixe-sur-Vienne F 29 D8
Aix-les-Bains F 31 D8
Aizenay F 28 B2
Aizkraukle LV 135 C10
Aizpún E 32 E2
Aizpurve LV 135 C12
Aizpute LV 134 C3
Aizviki LV 134 D3
Ajaccio F 37 H9
Ajanki FIN 117 E12
Ajankijärvi FIN 117 E12
Ajat F 29 E8
Ajaureforsen S 109 E10
Ajdovščina SLO 73 E8
Ajka H 149 B9
Ajo E 40 B4
Ajofrín E 46 E5
Ajos FIN 119 C13
Akācijas LV 134 C6
Åkarp S 87 D12
Äkäsjokisuu FIN 117 D11
Äkäslompolo FIN 117 C12
Akasztó H 150 D3
Akçaova TR 181 B7
Akçasusurluk TR 173 D9
Akeld GB 5 D12
Aken D 79 C11
Åkerbränna S 107 D11
Åkerby S 99 B9
Åkerholmen S 118 C6
Åkersberga S 99 D10
Akersjön S 105 D16
Åkers styckebruk S 98 D8
Åkerstrømmen N 101 C14
Akheloy BG 167 D9
Akhremawtsy BY 133 E2
Akhtopol BG 167 E9
Akkan S 109 F12
Akkarfjord N 113 B12
Akkarvik N 112 C5
Akkasæter N 111 B16
Akkavare S 109 E17
Akkerhaugen N 95 D10
Akköy TR 171 E10
Akköy TR 177 E9
Akkrum NL 16 B5
Akmeņdziras LV 134 B3
Akmenė LT 134 D5
Åknes N 110 C9
Aknīste LV 135 D11
Akonkoski FIN 121 F13
Akonpohja FIN 125 D10
Akpinar TR 173 B10
Akraifnio GR 175 C7
Åkran N 105 D12
Akrata GR 174 C5
Åkrehamn N 94 D2
Akrini GR 169 D6
Akrolimni GR 169 C7
Akropotamos GR 170 C6
Akrotiri GR 179 C9
Aksakal TR 173 D9
Aksaz TR 173 D7
Aksdal N 94 D2
Aksnes N 104 F4
Akujärvi FIN 114 F3
Åkullsjön S 118 F5
Åkvisslan S 107 E13
Ål N 101 E9
Ala I 69 B11
Ala S 93 E13
Alacaat TR 173 E10
Alacaoğlu TR 173 B7
Alaçatı TR 177 C7
Alà dei Sardi I 64 B3
Ala di Stura I 31 E11
Alaejos E 39 F9
Alagna Valsesia I 68 B4
A Lagoa E 38 C2
Alagoa P 44 F5
Alagón E 41 E9
Alahärmä FIN 122 D9
Ala-Honkajoki FIN 126 B7
Alaigne F 33 D10
Alaior E 57 B13
Alájar E 51 D6
Alajärvi FIN 117 E15
Alajärvi FIN 121 E12
Alajärvi FIN 123 D11
Alajõe EST 132 C1
Ala-Jokikylä FIN 119 C14
Ala-Kääntä FIN 119 F12
Ala-Keyritty FIN 125 D10
Alakurtti RUS 115 E8
Alakylä FIN 117 D13
Alakylä FIN 119 D15
Alakylä FIN 126 B6
Ala-Livo FIN 119 D17
Alameda E 53 B7
Alameda de Cervera E 47 F6
Alameda de la Sagra E 46 D5
Alamedilla E 55 D6
Alamillo E 54 B3
Alan HR 67 B10
Ala-Nampa FIN 117 E16
Alanäs S 106 C9
Alande LV 134 C2
Alandroal P 50 B5
Ålandsbro S 103 A14
Alange E 51 B7
Alaniemi FIN 119 C14
Alanís E 51 C8
Alanta LT 135 F10
Alap H 149 C11
Alapitkä FIN 124 D9
Alaquàs E 48 F4
Alaranta FIN 119 D14
Alaraz E 45 C10
Alarcón E 47 E8
Alar del Rey E 40 C3
Alaró E 49 E10
Alarup AL 168 C4
Ålåsen S 106 D7
Alaskylä FIN 127 B8
Alassio I 37 C8
Alastaipale FIN 123 F11
Alastaro FIN 126 D8
Ala-Sydänmaa FIN 123 B14
Alata F 37 H9
Ala-Temmes FIN 119 E15
Alatoz E 47 F10
Alatri I 62 D4
Alatskivi EST 131 D14
Alattyán H 150 C5
Ala-Valli FIN 123 F9
Alavattnet S 106 C9
Alavere EST 131 C10
Ala-Vieksi FIN 121 F12
Alavieska FIN 119 F12
Ala-Viirre FIN 123 B11
Ala-Vuokki FIN 121 E13
Ala-Vuotto FIN 119 D16
Alavus FIN 123 E11
Alba I 37 B8
Alba Adriatica I 62 B5
Albac RO 151 E10
Albacete E 55 A9
Albacken S 103 A11
Alba de Tormes E 45 C9
Albæk DK 90 D7
Albagiara I 64 D2
Albaida E 56 D4
Alba Iulia RO 152 E3
Albaladejo E 55 B7
Alba-la-Romaine F 35 A8
Albalate de Arzobispo E 42 E3
Albalate de Cinca E 42 D4
Albalate de las Nogueras E 47 D8
Albalate de Zorita E 47 D7
Albalatillo E 42 D3
Alban F 33 C10
Albánchez E 55 E8
Albanella I 60 C4
Albanitsa BG 165 C10
Albano di Lucania I 60 B6
Albano Laziale I 62 D3
Albano Vercellese I 68 C5
Albanyà E 43 C9
Albaredo per San Marco I 69 A8
Albaret-le-Comtal F 30 F3
Albareto I 69 E8
Albaret-Ste-Marie F 30 F3
Albaron F 35 C7
Albarracín E 47 D10
Albatana E 55 B9
Albatàrrec E 42 D5
Albatera E 56 E3
Albbruck D 27 E9
Albelda E 42 D4
Albelda de Iregua E 41 D7
Albella E 32 F5
Albendea E 47 C8
Albendín E 53 A8
Albenga I 37 C8
Albeni RO 160 C3
Albens F 31 D8
Albentosa E 48 D3
Ålberga S 93 B9
Alberga S 98 D6
Albergaria-a-Velha P 44 C4
Albergaria dos Doze P 44 E3
Albergen NL 183 A9
Alberic E 48 F4
Alberndorf in der Riedmark A 77 F6
Albernoa P 50 D4
Albero Alto E 41 D11
Alberobello I 61 B8
Alberona I 60 A4
Alberoni I 66 B5
Alberschwende A 71 C9
Albersdorf D 82 B6
Albert F 18 E6
Albertacce F 37 G9
Alberta Ligure I 37 B10
Albertirsa H 150 C4
Albertshofen D 187 B9
Albertville F 31 D9
Alberuela de Tubo E 42 D3
Albesa E 42 D5
Albești RO 152 E5
Albești RO 153 B10
Albești RO 153 D11
Albești RO 155 F2
Albești RO 161 D10
Albeștii de Argeș RO 160 C5
Albeștii de Muscel RO 160 C6
Albești-Paleologu RO 161 D8
Albestroff F 27 C6
Albi F 33 C10
Albias F 33 B8
Albidona I 61 D6
Albignasego I 66 B4
Albina RO 155 C1
Albino I 69 B8
Albires E 39 D9
Albisheim (Pfrimm) D 21 E10
Albisola Marina I 37 C9
Albisola Superiore I 37 C9
Alblasserdam NL 16 E3
Albo S 98 B7
Albocàsser E 48 D5
Alboloduy E 55 E7
Albolote E 53 B9
Albon F 30 E6
Albondón E 55 F6
Alboraya E 48 E4
Alborea E 47 F10
Albota RO 160 D5
Albox E 55 E8
Albrechtice nad Orlicí CZ 77 B10
Al'brekhtava BY 133 E5
Albstadt D 27 D11
Albu EST 131 C11
Albudeite E 55 C10
Albufeira P 50 E3
Albujón E 56 F2
Albuñol E 55 F6
Albuñuelas E 53 C9
Alburquerque E 45 F7
Alby S 89 C11
Alby S 103 A9
Alby-sur-Chéran F 31 D9
Alcácer E 48 F4
Alcácer do Sal P 50 C2
Alcáçovas P 50 C3
Alcadozo E 55 B9
Alcafozes P 45 E6
Alcaine E 42 F2
Alcains P 44 E6
Alcalá de Guadaira E 51 E8
Alcalá de Gurrea E 41 D10
Alcalá de Henares E 46 D6
Alcalá del Júcar E 47 F10
Alcalá de los Gazules E 52 D5
Alcalá del Río E 51 D8
Alcalá del Valle E 51 F9
Alcalà de Xivert E 48 D5
Alcalá la Real E 53 B9
Alcalalí E 56 D4
Alcamo I 58 D2
Alcampell E 42 D4
Alcanadre E 32 F1
Alcanede P 44 F3
Alcanena P 44 F3
Alcanhões P 44 F3
Alcañices E 39 E7
Alcañiz E 42 E3
Alcántara E 45 E7
Alcantarilla E 56 F2
Alcantud E 47 C8
Alcaracejos E 54 C3
Alcara li Fusi I 59 C6
Alcaraz E 55 B8
Alcaria Ruiva P 50 D4
Alcarràs E 42 D5
Alcaucín E 53 C8
Alcaudete E 53 A8
Alcaudete de la Jara E 46 E3
Alçay-Alçabéhéty-Sunharette F 32 D4
Alcázar del Rey E 47 D7
Alcázar de San Juan E 47 F6
Alcedar MD 154 B3
Alcester GB 13 A11
Alçitepe TR 171 D10
Alcoba E 46 F4
Alcobaça P 44 E3
Alcobendas E 46 C5
Alcocer E 47 D7
Alcocero de Mola E 40 D5
Alcochete P 50 B2
Alcoentre P 44 F3
Alcolea E 53 A7
Alcolea E 55 F7
Alcolea de Calatrava E 54 B4
Alcolea de Cinca E 42 D4
Alcolea del Pinar E 47 B8
Alcolea del Río E 51 D8
Alcollarín E 45 F9
Alconchel E 51 B5
Alcóntar E 55 E7
Alcorcón E 46 D5
Alcorisa E 42 F3
Alcoroches E 47 C9
Alcossebre E 48 D5
Alcoutim P 50 E5
Alcover E 42 E6
Alcoy-Alcoi E 56 D4
Alcsútdoboz H 149 B11
Alcubierre E 41 E11
Alcubilla de Avellaneda E 40 E5
Alcubillas E 55 B6
Alcublas E 48 E3
Alcúdia E 57 B11
Alcudia de Guadix E 55 E6
Alcudia de Monteagud E 55 E8
Alcuéscar E 45 F8
Aldbrough GB 11 D11
Aldeacentenera E 45 E9
Aldeadávila de la Ribera E 45 B7

Aucamville F 33 C8
Auce LV 134 D5
Auch F 33 C7
Auchallater GB 5 B10
Auchenbreck GB 4 D6
Auchencairn GB 5 F9
Auchencrow GB 5 D12
Auchnagatt GB 3 L12
Auchterarder GB 5 C9
Auchtermuchty GB 5 C10
Auchy-au-Bois F 18 C5
Aucun F 32 E5
Audenge F 32 A3
Auderville F 23 A8
Audeux F 26 F4
Audevälja EST 131 C8
Audierne F 22 D2
Audincourt F 27 F6
Audlem GB 10 F6
Audley GB 11 E7
Audnedal N 90 C1
Audon F 32 C4
Audresselles F 15 F12
Audriņi LV 133 C2
Audru EST 131 E8
Audruicq F 18 C5
Audun-le-Roman F 20 F5
Aue D 79 E12
Auerbach D 75 A11
Auerbach in der Oberpfalz D 75 C10
Auersthal A 77 F11
Auffay F 18 E3
Aufhausen D 75 E11
Augbrim IRL 6 F5
Auggen D 27 E8
Augher GB 7 D8
Aughnacloy GB 7 D9
Aughrim IRL 6 F5
Aughrim IRL 9 C10
Aughton GB 11 E9
Augignac F 29 D7
Augsburg D 75 F8
Augšlīgatne LV 135 B10
Augstkalne LV 133 E2
Augstkalne LV 134 D6
Augusta I 59 E7
Auguste LV 134 D3
Augustenborg DK 86 F5
Augustów PL 136 F6
Augustowo PL 141 E8
Augustusburg D 80 E4
Auho FIN 121 E10
Aukan N 104 E4
Aukra N 100 A5
Aukrug D 82 B7
Aukštadvaris LT 137 D10
Aukštelkai LT 134 E7
Aukštelkė LT 134 E6
Auktsjaur S 109 E17
Auleja LV 133 D2
Aulendorf D 71 B9
Auletta I 60 B4
Aulla I 69 E8
Aullène F 37 H10
Aulnat F 30 D3
Aulnay F 28 C5
Aulnay-sous-Bois F 25 C8
Aulnois sur-Seille F 26 C5
Aulnoye-Aymeries F 19 D8
Aulon F 33 D7
Aulosen D 83 E11
Ault F 18 D3
Aultbea GB 2 K5
Aultguish Inn GB 2 K7
Aulus-les-Bains F 33 E8
Auma D 79 E10
Aumale F 18 E4
Aumetz F 20 F5
Aumont F 31 B8
Aumont-Aubrac F 30 F3
Aumühle D 83 C8
Aunay-en-Bazois F 25 F10
Aunay-sur-Odon F 23 B10
Auneau F 24 D6
Aunegrenda N 105 F10
Aunfoss N 105 B13
Auning DK 86 C6
Auñón E 47 C7
Aups F 36 D4
Aura FIN 126 D8
Aurach D 75 D7
Aurach bei Kitzbühel A 72 B5
Aura im Sinngrund D 74 B6
Auran N 105 E9
Auray F 22 E6
Aurdal N 101 E10
Aure N 104 E5
Aurec-sur-Loire F 30 E5
Aureilhan F 33 D6
Aureille F 35 C8
Aurejärvi FIN 123 G10
Aurel F 35 A9
Aurel F 35 B9
Aurensan F 32 C5
Aureosen N 100 A6
Auri LV 134 C6
Aurich D 17 B8
Aurignac F 33 D7
Aurillac F 29 F10
Auriol F 35 D10
Aurisina I 73 E8
Auritz E 32 E3
Aurland N 100 E6
Aurolzmünster A 76 F4
Auron F 36 C5
Auronzo di Cadore I 72 C5
Auros F 32 A5
Auroux F 30 F4
Aurskog N 95 C14
Ausa-Corno I 73 E7
Ausejo E 32 F1
Auşeu RO 151 C10
Ausleben D 79 B9
Ausmas LV 135 B9
Ausonia I 62 E5
Außervillgraten A 72 C5
Aussillon F 33 C10
Aussonne F 33 C8
Austafjord N 105 B9
Austbø N 95 C8
Austborg N 105 C15
Austertana N 114 C5
Austis I 64 C3
Austmannli N 94 C5
Austnes N 100 A4
Austnes N 105 B15
Austnes N 111 C12
Austrått N 104 D7
Austsmøla N 104 E4
Auterive F 33 D8
Authon F 24 E4
Authon F 36 C4
Authon-du-Perche F 24 D4
Autio FIN 119 E17
Autio FIN 123 E13
Autol E 41 D7
Autrans F 31 E8
Autreville F 26 D4
Autrey-lès-Gray F 26 F3
Autry F 19 F10
Autti FIN 119 B18
Auttoinen FIN 127 C13
Autun F 30 B5
Auve F 25 B12
Auvelais B 19 D10
Auvers-le-Hamon F 23 E11
Auvillar F 33 B7
Auvillers-les-Forges F 184 E1
Auxerre F 25 E10
Auxi-le-Château F 18 D5
Auxonne F 26 F3
Auxy F 30 B5
Auzances F 29 C10
Auzat F 33 E8
Auzat-la-Combelle F 30 E3
Aužguļāni LV 135 E12
Auzon F 30 E3
Åva FIN 126 E5
Ava S 107 D16
Avafors S 118 B8
Availles-Limouzine F 29 C7
Avaldsnes N 94 D2
Avallon F 25 E10
Avan S 118 C7
Avanäs S 107 C17
Avanca P 44 C3
Avançon F 36 B4
Avantas GR 171 C9
Avant-lès-Ramerupt F 25 D11
Avasjö S 107 C11
Avato GR 171 C7
Avaträsk S 107 C10
Avaviken S 109 E16
Avdira GR 171 C7
Avdou GR 178 E9
A Veiga E 39 D6
Aveiras de Cima P 44 F3
Aveiro P 44 C3
Avelar P 44 E4
Avelãs de Caminho P 44 D4
Aveleda P 38 E3
Aveleda P 39 E6
Avelgem B 19 C7
Avella I 60 B3
Avellino I 60 B3
Avenay-Val-d'Or F 25 B11
Avenches CH 31 B11
Avenhorn NL 16 C3
Avenida do Marquês de Figueroa E 38 A3
Avermes F 30 B3
Avers CH 71 E9
Aversa I 60 B2
Avesnes-le-Comte F 18 D6
Avesnes-sur-Helpe F 19 D8
Avesta S 98 B6
Åvestbo S 97 C14
Avetrano I 61 C9
Avezzano I 62 C4
Avgerinos GR 168 D5
Avià E 43 C7
Aviano I 73 D6
Aviemore GB 3 L9
Avigliana I 31 E11
Avigliano I 60 B5
Avigliano Umbro I 62 B2
Avignon F 35 C8
Ávila E 46 C3
A Vila da Igrexa E 38 A4
Avilés E 39 A8
Avilley F 26 F5
Avintes P 44 B3
Avinurme EST 131 D13
Avinyó E 43 D7
Avio I 69 B10
Avion F 18 D6
Avioth F 19 E11
Avis P 44 F5
Avispea EST 131 C12
Åvist FIN 122 D9
Avize F 25 C11
Avižieniai LT 137 D11
Avlakia GR 177 D8
Avlemonas GR 178 C5
Avliotes GR 168 E2
Avlonari GR 175 B9
Avlonas GR 175 C8
Avlum DK 86 C3
Avoca IRL 9 C10
Avoine F 23 F12
Avola I 59 F7
Avon F 25 D8
Avonmouth GB 13 B9
Avord F 29 A11
Avoriaz F 31 C10
Avoudrey F 26 F5
Avrămeni RO 153 A9
Avrămești RO 152 E6
Avram Iancu RO 151 D8
Avram Iancu RO 151 E10
Avranches F 23 C9
Avren BG 171 B9
Avricourt F 186 D2
Avrig RO 152 F4
Avril F 20 F5
Avrillé F 23 E10
Avrillé F 28 C3
Avtovac BIH 157 F10
Av'že N 112 E10
Awans B 183 D6
Axams A 72 B3
Axat F 33 E10
Axel NL 16 F1
Axente Sever RO 152 E4
Axintele RO 161 D9
Axioupoli GR 169 C8
Ax-les-Thermes F 33 E9
Axmar S 103 D13
Axmarsbruk S 103 D13
Axminster GB 13 D9
Axos GR 169 C7
Axvall S 91 C14
Ayamonte E 50 E5
Aycliffe GB 5 F13
Aydat F 30 D2
Aydemir BG 161 E10
Ayen F 29 E8
Ayerbe E 32 F4
Aying D 72 A4
Aylesbury GB 15 D7
Ayllón E 40 F5
Aylsham GB 15 B11
Aymavilles I 31 D11
Ayna E 55 B8
Aynac F 29 F9
Ayoo de Vidriales E 39 D7
Ayora E 47 F10
Ayr GB 4 E7
Ayrancılar TR 177 C9
Ayron F 28 B6
Ayşebaci TR 173 E8
Aysgarth GB 11 C8
Äyskoski FIN 123 D17
Äystö FIN 122 F7
Aytos BG 167 D8
Aytré F 28 C3
Ayvacık TR 171 E10
Ayvalık TR 172 F6
Aywaille B 19 D12
Azagra E 32 F2
Azaila E 41 F11
Azambuja P 44 F3
Azanja SRB 159 E6
Azanúy E 42 D4
Azaruja P 50 B4
Azatli TR 172 B6
Azay-le-Ferron F 29 B8
Azay-le-Rideau F 24 F3
Azé F 23 E10
Azerables F 29 C8
Azina BY 133 E5
Azinhaga P 44 F3
Azinhal P 50 E5
Azinheira dos Barros P 50 C3
Azinhoso P 39 F6
Azkoitia E 32 D1
Aznalcázar E 51 E7
Aznalcóllar E 51 D7
Azóia P 50 C1
Azpeitia E 32 D1
Azuaga E 51 C8
Azuara E 41 F10
Azuel E 54 C4
Azuelo E 32 E1
Azuga RO 161 C7
Azuqueca de Henares E 47 C6
Azur F 32 C3
Azután E 45 E10
Azy-le-Vif F 30 B3
Azyory BY 140 C10
Azzano Decimo I 73 E6
Azzone I 69 B9

B

Baalberge D 79 C10
Baâlon F 19 F11
Baar CH 27 F10
Baarle-Hertog B 16 F3
Baarle-Nassau NL 16 F3
Baarn NL 16 D4
Baba Ana RO 161 D8
Babadag RO 155 D3
Babaeski TR 173 B7
Babaköy TR 173 E9
Baban AL 168 C4
Băbana RO 160 D5
Babberich NL 183 B8
Babchyntsi UA 154 A2
Babenhausen D 21 E11
Băbeni RO 151 C11
Băbeni RO 160 D4
Babiak PL 136 E1
Babiak PL 138 F6
Babice CZ 146 C4
Babice PL 143 F7
Babice nad Svitavou CZ 77 D11
Babići BIH 157 D7
Băbiciu RO 160 E5
Babilafuente E 45 C10
Babimost PL 81 B9
Babín SK 147 C8
Babina SRB 164 D5
Babina Greda HR 157 B10
Babino Polje HR 162 D4
Babīte LV 135 C7
Babno Polje SLO 73 E10
Babócsa H 149 D8
Bábolna H 149 A9
Baborów PL 142 F4
Baboszewo PL 139 E9
Babót H 149 A8
Babrrujë AL 168 B2
Babtai LT 137 C8
Babuk BG 161 E10
Babušnica SRB 164 C5
Babyak BG 165 F8
Babynichy BY 133 F4
Bać MNE 163 D9
Bač SRB 158 C3
Băcani RO 153 E11
Bacares E 55 E8
Bacău RO 153 D9
Baccarat F 27 D6
Baceno I 68 A5
Băceşti RO 153 D10
Bach A 71 C10
Bacharach D 21 D9
Bachkovo BG 165 F10
Bachórz PL 144 D5
Băcia RO 151 F11
Baciki Bliższe PL 141 F7
Băcioi MD 154 D3
Baciu RO 152 D3
Bäck S 105 E16
Backa S 91 E10
Backa S 97 A9
Backa S 97 B9
Backaland GB 3 G11
Bačka Palanka SRB 158 C3
Backaryd S 89 C8
Bačka Topola SRB 150 F4
Backberg S 103 E12
Backe S 107 D10
Bäckebo S 89 B10
Bäckefors S 91 B11
Bäckhammar S 91 A15
Bački Breg SRB 150 F2
Bački Brestovac SRB 158 B3
Bački Jarak SRB 158 C4
Bački Monoštor SRB 150 F2
Bäckininkai LT 137 D8
Bački Petrovac SRB 158 C4
Bäcklund S 109 E17
Bäckmark S 107 A11
Backnang D 27 C11
Bäcknäs S 109 F17
Bačko Dobro Polje SRB 158 B4
Bačko Gradište SRB 158 B5
Bačko Novo Selo SRB 157 B11
Bačko Petrovo Selo SRB 158 B5
Bačkowice PL 143 E11
Backträsk S 118 C6
Bäckvallen S 102 B8
Băcleş RO 159 E11
Bacoli I 60 B2
Bacqueville-en-Caux F 18 E2
Bácsalmás H 150 E3
Bácsbokod H 150 E3
Bácsborsód H 150 E3
Bacúch SK 147 D9
Baczyna PL 85 E8
Bada S 97 B9
Bad Abbach D 75 E11
Bad Aibling D 72 A5
Badajoz E 51 B6
Badalona E 43 E8
Badalucco I 37 D7
Bádames E 40 B5
Badarán E 40 D6
Bad Aussee A 73 A8
Bad Bayersoien D 71 B12
Bad Bederkesa D 17 A11
Bad Belzig D 79 B12
Bad Bentheim D 17 D8
Bad Bergzabern D 27 B8
Bad Berka D 79 E9
Bad Berleburg D 21 B10
Bad Berneck im Fichtelgebirge D 75 B10
Bad Bertrich D 21 D8
Bad Bevensen D 83 D9
Bad Bibra D 79 D10
Bad Birnbach D 76 F4
Bad Blankenburg D 79 E9
Bad Blumau A 148 B6
Bad Bocklet D 75 B7
Bad Boll D 74 E6
Bad Brambach D 75 B11
Bad Bramstedt D 83 C7
Bad Breisig D 185 D7
Bad Brückenau D 74 B6
Bad Buchau D 71 A9
Bad Camberg D 21 D10
Badcaul GB 2 K6
Badderen N 112 D9
Bad Doberan D 83 B11
Bad Driburg D 17 E12
Bad Düben D 79 C12
Bad Dürkheim D 21 F10
Bad Dürrenberg D 79 D11
Bad Dürrheim D 27 D10
Badeborn D 79 C9
Badefols-d'Ans F 29 E8
Bad Elster D 75 B11
Bademler TR 177 C8
Bademli TR 171 F10
Bademli TR 173 D10
Bademli TR 177 B8
Bad Ems D 21 D9
Baden A 77 F10
Baden CH 27 F9
Baden F 22 E6
Bádenas E 47 B10
Baden-Baden D 27 C9
Bad Endorf D 72 A5
Badenscoth GB 3 L12
Badenweiler D 27 E8
Baderna HR 67 B8
Badersleben D 79 C8
Badesi I 64 B2
Bad Essen D 17 D10
Bădeuți RO 153 B7
Bad Fallingbostel D 82 E7
Bad Feilnbach D 72 A5
Bad Frankenhausen (Kyffhäuser) D 79 D9
Bad Freienwalde D 84 E6
Bad Friedrichshall D 21 F12
Bad Füssing D 76 F4
Bad Gams A 73 C11
Bad Gandersheim D 79 C7
Badgastein A 73 B7
Bad Gleichenberg A 148 C5
Bad Goisern A 73 A8
Bad Griesbach im Rottal D 76 F4
Bad Grönenbach D 71 B10
Bad Großpertholz A 77 E7
Bad Grund (Harz) D 79 C7
Bad Hall A 76 F6
Bad Harzburg D 79 C8
Bad Herrenalb D 27 C9
Bad Hersfeld D 78 E6
Bad Hindelang D 71 B10
Badhoevedorp NL 182 A5
Bad Hofgastein A 73 B7
Bad Homburg vor der Höhe D 21 D11
Bad Honnef D 21 C8
Bad Hönningen D 185 C7
Badia I 72 C4
Badia Calavena I 69 B11
Badia Gran E 49 F10
Badia Polesine I 66 B3
Badia Tedalda I 66 E5
Bad Iburg D 17 D10
Bădiceni MD 153 A12
Badín SK 147 D8
Bad Ischl A 73 A8
Bad Karlshafen D 78 C5
Bad Kissingen D 75 B7
Bad Kleinen D 83 C10
Bad Kleinkirchheim A 73 C8
Bad König D 21 E12
Bad Königshofen im Grabfeld D 75 B7
Bad Kösen D 79 D10
Bad Köstritz D 79 E11
Bad Kötzting D 76 D3
Bądkowo PL 138 E6
Bad Kreuzen A 77 F7
Bad Kreuznach D 21 E9
Bad Krozingen D 27 E8
Bad Laasphe D 21 C10
Bad Laer D 17 D10
Bad Langensalza D 79 D8
Bad Lauchstädt D 79 D10
Bad Lausick D 79 D12
Bad Lauterberg im Harz D 79 C7
Bad Leonfelden A 76 E6
Bad Liebenstein D 79 E7
Bad Liebenwerda D 80 C4
Bad Liebenzell D 27 C10
Bad Lippspringe D 17 E11
Badljevina HR 149 E8
Bad Lobenstein D 75 B10
Bad Marienberg (Westerwald) D 21 C9
Bad Mergentheim D 74 D6
Bad Mitterndorf A 73 A8
Bad Münder am Deister D 78 B5
Bad Münstereifel D 21 C7
Bad Muskau D 81 C7
Bad Nauheim D 21 D11
Bad Nenndorf D 17 D12
Bad Neuenahr-Ahrweiler D 21 C8
Bad Neustadt an der Saale D 75 B7
Badolato I 59 B10
Badolatosa E 53 B7
Bad Oldesloe D 83 C8
Badonviller F 27 C6
Bad Orb D 21 D12
Badovinci SRB 158 D3
Bad Peterstal D 27 D9
Bad Pirawarth A 77 F11
Bad Pyrmont D 17 E12
Bad Radkersburg A 148 C5
Bad Ragaz CH 71 C9
Bad Rappenau D 187 C7
Bad Reichenhall D 73 A6
Bad Rodach D 75 B8
Bad Saarow-Pieskow D 80 B6
Bad Sachsa D 79 C8
Bad Säckingen D 27 E8
Bad Salzdetfurth D 79 B7
Bad Salzuflen D 17 D11
Bad Salzungen D 79 E7
Bad Sankt Leonhard im Lavanttal A 73 C10
Bad Sassendorf D 17 E10
Bad Schandau D 80 E6
Bad Schmiedeberg D 79 C12
Bad Schönborn D 187 C6
Bad Schussenried D 71 A9
Bad Schwalbach D 21 D10
Bad Schwartau D 83 C9
Bad Segeberg D 83 C8
Bad Sobernheim D 185 E8
Bad Soden-Salmünster D 74 B5
Bad Sooden-Allendorf D 79 D6
Bad Staffelstein D 75 B8
Bad Steben D 75 B10
Bad Sulza D 79 D10
Bad Sülze D 83 B13
Bad Tennstedt D 79 D8
Bad Tölz D 72 A4
Bad Überkingen D 187 D8
Badules E 47 B10
Bad Urach D 27 D11
Bad Vilbel D 21 D11
Bad Vöslau A 77 G10
Bad Waldsee D 71 B9
Bad Waltersdorf A 148 B6
Bad Wildbad im Schwarzwald D 187 D6
Bad Wildungen D 21 B12
Bad Wilsnack D 83 E11
Bad Wimpfen D 21 F12
Bad Windsheim D 75 C7
Bad Wörishofen D 71 B11
Bad Wurzach D 71 B9
Bad Zell A 77 F7
Bad Zurzach CH 27 E9
Bad Zwesten D 21 B12
Bad Zwischenahn D 17 B10
Bække DK 86 D4
Bækmarksbro DK 86 C2
Baelen B 183 D7
Bælum DK 86 B6
Baena E 53 A8
Bærums Verk N 95 C12
Baesweiler D 20 C6
Baeza E 53 A10
Baflo NL 17 B7
Bagà E 43 C7
Băgaciu RO 152 E4
Bagaladi I 59 C8
Bagamér H 151 C8
Bağarasi TR 177 B8
Bağarasi TR 177 D10
Bagard F 35 B7
Bağcılar TR 181 B8
Bâgé-le-Châtel F 30 C6
Bagenalstown IRL 9 C9
Bagenkop DK 83 A9
Bages F 34 E4
Baggå S 97 C14
Bagheria I 58 C4
Bagn N 101 E11
Bagnacavallo I 66 D4
Bagnac-sur-Célé F 33 A10
Bagnara Calabra I 59 C8
Bagnaria I 37 B10
Bagnaria Arsa I 73 E7
Bagnasco I 37 C8
Bagneaux-sur-Loing F 25 D8
Bagnères-de-Bigorre F 33 D6
Bagnères-de-Luchon F 33 E7
Bagni di Lucca I 66 D2
Bagni di Masino I 69 A8
Bagni di Rabbi I 71 E11
Bagno a Ripoli I 66 E3
Bagno di Romagna I 66 E4
Bagnoli del Trigno I 63 D6
Bagnoli di Sopra I 66 B4
Bagnoli Irpino I 60 B4
Bagnolo in Piano I 66 C2
Bagnolo Mella I 66 B1
Bagnolo Piemonte I 31 F11
Bagnolo San Vito I 66 B2
Bagnols-les-Bains F 35 A6
Bagnols-sur-Cèze F 35 B8
Bagnoregio I 62 B2
Bagod H 149 C7
Bagolino I 69 B9
Bagrationovsk RUS 136 E2
Bagrdan SRB 159 E7
Bagshot GB 15 E7
Bágueña E 47 B10
Bágyogszovát H 149 A8
Bağyurdu TR 177 C10
Bağyüzü TR 173 F6
Bahabón de Esgueva E 40 E4
Bahate UA 155 C3
Bahçeburun TR 181 B7
Bahçeköy TR 173 B10
Bahçeli TR 171 E10
Bahillo E 39 D10
Bahmut MD 153 C12
Bahna RO 153 D9
Bahnea RO 152 E4
Bahoň SK 146 E4
Bahrenborstel D 17 C11
Bahrendorf D 79 C10
Baia RO 153 C8
Baia RO 155 D3
Baia de Aramă RO 159 D10
Baia de Arieş RO 151 E11
Baia de Criş RO 151 E10
Baia de Fier RO 160 C3
Baia della Zagare I 63 D10
Baia Mare RO 152 B3
Baiano I 60 B3
Baiardo I 37 D7
Baia Sprie RO 152 B3
Băicoi RO 161 C7
Băiculeşti RO 160 C5
Baiersbronn D 27 C9
Baiersdorf D 75 C9
Baignes-Ste-Radegonde F 28 E5
Baigneux-les-Juifs F 25 E12
Baile an Bhiataigh IRL 7 E10
Baile an Bhuinneánaigh IRL 8 C3
Baile an Chinnéidigh IRL 7 F10
Baile an Dúlaigh IRL 6 F4
Baile an Fheirtéaraigh IRL 8 D2
Baile an Mhóta IRL 6 D5
Baile an Mhuilinn IRL 8 D2
Baile an Róba IRL 6 E4
Baile an Sceilg IRL 8 E2
Baile Átha an Rí IRL 6 F5
Baile Átha Buí IRL 7 E9
Baile Átha Cliath IRL 7 F10
Baile Átha Fhirdhia IRL 7 E9
Baile Átha Í IRL 7 G9
Baile Átha Luain IRL 7 F7
Baile Átha Troim IRL 7 E9
Baile Brigín IRL 7 E10
Baile Coimín IRL 7 F9
Băile Govora RO 160 C4
Băile Herculane RO 159 D9
Baile Loch Riach IRL 6 F5
Baile Mhartainn GB 2 K2
Baile Mhic Andáin IRL 9 C8
Baile Mhic Íre IRL 8 E4
Baile Mhistéala IRL 8 D6
Bailén E 54 C5
Baile na Finne IRL 6 C6
Baile na Lorgan IRL 7 D9
Băile Olăneşti RO 160 C4
Baile Órthaí IRL 7 E9
Băileşti RO 160 E2
Băile Tuşnad RO 153 E7
Baile Uilcín IRL 7 E9
Bailieborough IRL 7 E9
Baillargues F 35 C7
Bailleau-le-Pin F 24 D5
Bailleul F 18 C6
Baillonville B 19 D11
Bailo E 32 E4
Baimaclia MD 154 E2
Bainbridge GB 11 C7
Bain-de-Bretagne F 23 E8
Baindt D 71 B9
Bains F 30 E4
Bains-les-Bains F 26 D5
Bainton GB 11 D10
Baio E 38 B2
Baiona E 38 D2
Bais F 23 D9
Bais F 23 D11
Baiso I 66 D2
Băişoara RO 151 D11
Baisogala LT 134 E7
Băița RO 151 E10
Băița de sub Codru RO 151 B11
Baix F 35 A8
Baixa da Banheira P 50 B1
Baixas F 34 E4
Baj H 149 A10
Baja H 150 E2
Bajč SK 146 F6
Bajgorë RKS 164 D3
Bajina Bašta SRB 158 F4
Bajmok SRB 150 F3
Bajna H 149 A11
Bajót H 149 A11
Bajovo Polje MNE 157 F10
Bajram Curri AL 163 E9
Bajša SRB 150 F4
Bak H 149 C7
Baka SK 146 F5
Bakacak TR 173 D7
Bakałarzewo PL 136 E6
Bakar HR 67 B10
Bakel NL 16 F5
Bakır TR 177 A10
Bakırköy TR 173 C10
Bakkasund N 94 B2
Bakke N 111 A16
Bakkeby N 112 D6
Bakkejord N 111 A15
Bakken N 101 E15
Bakko N 95 C9
Bakonszeg H 151 C7
Bakonybél H 149 B9
Bakonycsernye H 149 B10
Bakonysárkány H 149 B10
Bakonyszentkirály H 149 B9
Bakonyszentlászló H 149 B9
Bakonyszombathely H 149 B9
Bakov nad Jizerou CZ 77 B7
Baks H 150 D5
Baksa H 149 E10
Baksha UA 154 A5
Baktalórántháza H 145 H5
Baktsjaur S 109 F17
Bakum D 17 C10
Bakvattnet S 105 D16
Bål S 93 D13
Bala GB 10 F4
Bala RO 159 D10
Balabancık TR 173 C6
Bălăbăneşti MD 154 C4
Bălăbăneşti RO 153 E11
Balabanu MD 154 F3
Bălăceanu RO 161 C10
Balaci RO 160 E5
Bălăciţa RO 159 E11
Balaciu RO 161 D9
Balaguer E 42 D5
Balallan GB 2 J3
Balan F 19 E10
Balan F 31 D7
Bălan RO 151 C11
Bălan RO 153 D7
Bălăneşti MD 153 C12
Bălăneşti RO 160 C2
Balanivka UA 154 A4
Balaruc-les-Bains F 35 D6
Bălăşeşti RO 153 E11
Bălăsineşti MD 153 A9
Balassagyarmat H 147 E8
Balástya H 150 E5
Balat TR 177 D9
Balaton H 145 G1
Balatonalmádi H 149 B10
Balatonberény H 149 C8
Balatonboglár H 149 C9
Balatonfőkajár H 149 B10
Balatonföldvár H 149 C9
Balatonfüred H 149 C9
Balatonfőzfő H 149 B10
Balatonkenese H 149 B10
Balatonlelle H 149 C9
Balatonszabadi H 149 C10
Balatonszárszó H 149 C9
Balatonvilágos H 149 C10
Bălăuşeri RO 152 E5
Balazote E 55 B8
Balbeggie GB 5 C10
Balbieriškis LT 137 D8
Balbigny F 30 D5
Balbriggan IRL 7 E10
Balcani RO 153 D9
Bălceşti RO 160 D3
Balchik BG 167 C10
Balcılar TR 173 D6
Balçova TR 177 C9
Balderton GB 11 E10
Baldock GB 15 D8
Baldone LV 135 C8
Baldones Muiža LV 135 C8
Baldovineşti RO 160 E4
Bale HR 67 B8
Baleizão P 50 C4
Balemartine GB 4 C3
Balen B 19 B11
Băleni RO 153 F11
Băleni RO 161 D7
Balephuil GB 4 C3
Balerma E 55 F7
Băleşti RO 159 C11
Balestrand N 100 D5
Balestrate I 58 C3
Balfour GB 3 G11
Balfron GB 5 C8
Balgale LV 134 B5
Balgown GB 2 K4
Bälgviken S 98 D6
Bali GR 178 E8
Baligród PL 145 E5
Balıkesir TR 173 E8
Balıkliçeşme TR 173 D7
Balikliova TR 177 C8
Bălileşti RO 160 C5
Bälinge S 99 C9
Bälinge S 118 C7
Balingen D 27 D10
Balinka H 149 B10
Balinț RO 151 F8
Balintore GB 3 K9
Balje D 17 A12
Baljevac BIH 156 C4
Baljevac SRB 163 C10
Baljvine BIH 157 D7
Balk NL 16 C5
Balkány H 151 B8
Balkbrug NL 16 C6
Balla IRL 6 E4
Ballaban AL 168 D3
Ballabio I 69 B7
Ballachulish GB 4 B6
Ballaghaderreen IRL 6 E5
Ballaghkeen IRL 9 D10
Ballangen N 111 D12
Ballantrae GB 4 E6
Ballao I 64 D3
Ballasalla GBM 10 C2
Ballater GB 5 A10
Ballaugh GBM 10 C2
Balle DK 87 C7
Ballée F 23 E11
Ballee GB 7 D11
Ballen DK 86 D7
Ballenstedt D 79 C9
Balleroy F 23 B10
Ballerup DK 87 D10
Ballesteros de Calatrava E 54 B5
Balli TR 173 C7
Ballina IRL 6 D4
Ballina IRL 8 C6
Ballinaboy IRL 6 F2
Ballinafad IRL 6 D6
Ballinagar IRL 7 F8
Ballinagh IRL 7 E8
Ballinakill IRL 9 C8
Ballinalack IRL 7 E8
Ballinalee IRL 7 E7
Ballinamallard GB 7 D7
Ballinamore IRL 7 D7
Ballinamult IRL 9 D7
Ballinasloe IRL 6 F6
Ballincollig IRL 8 E5
Ballindine IRL 6 E5
Ballindooly IRL 6 F4
Ballineen IRL 8 E5
Ballingarry IRL 8 D5
Ballingarry IRL 9 C7
Ballingeary IRL 8 E4
Ballingry GB 5 C10
Ballingslöv S 87 C13
Ballingurteen IRL 8 E4
Ballinhassig IRL 8 E5
Ballinlough IRL 6 E5
Ballinluig GB 5 B9
Ballinrobe IRL 6 E4
Ballinskelligs IRL 8 E2
Ballinspittle IRL 8 E5
Ballintober IRL 6 E4
Ballintoy GB 4 E4
Ballintra IRL 6 C6
Ballintubber IRL 6 E4
Ballinure IRL 9 C7
Ballivor IRL 7 E9
Ballobar E 42 D4
Ballon F 23 D12
Ballon IRL 9 C9
Ballószög H 150 D4
Ballots F 23 E9
Ballsh AL 168 C2
Ballsnes N 111 A16
Ballstad N 110 D6
Ballstädt D 79 D8
Ballum DK 86 E3
Ballum NL 16 B5
Ballure IRL 6 C6
Ballybay IRL 7 D9
Ballybofey IRL 7 C7
Ballybrack IRL 7 F10
Ballybrack IRL 8 E2
Ballybrittas IRL 7 F8
Ballybunion IRL 8 C3
Ballybunnion IRL 8 C3
Ballycahill IRL 9 C7
Ballycanew IRL 9 C10
Ballycarry GB 4 F5
Ballycastle GB 4 E4
Ballycastle IRL 6 D4
Ballyclare GB 4 F5
Ballycolla IRL 9 C8
Ballyconneely IRL 6 F2
Ballyconnell IRL 7 D7
Ballycotton IRL 8 E6
Ballycroy IRL 6 D3
Ballydavid IRL 6 F6
Ballydehob IRL 8 E4
Ballydesmond IRL 8 D4
Ballydonegan IRL 8 E2
Ballyduff IRL 8 D3
Ballyduff IRL 8 D6
Ballyfarnan IRL 6 D6
Ballyfarnon IRL 6 D6
Ballyfeard IRL 8 E6

Bellante I 62 B5
Bellaria I 66 D5
Bellavary IRL 6 E4
Bellavista E 51 E8
Bellclaire d'Urgell E 42 D5
Belleek GB 7 D10
Bellegarde F 25 E7
Bellegarde F 35 C8
Bellegarde-en-Marche F 29 D10
Bellegarde-sur-Valserine F 31 C8
Belle-Isle-en-Terre F 22 C5
Bellême F 24 D4
Bellenaves F 30 C3
Bellenberg D 71 A10
Bellencombre F 18 E3
Bellerive-sur-Allier F 30 C3
Belles-Forêts F 27 C6
Belleu F 19 F7
Bellevaux F 31 C10
Belleville F 30 C6
Belleville-sur-Meuse F 26 B3
Belleville-sur-Vie F 28 B3
Bellevue-la-Montagne F 30 E4
Belley F 31 D8
Bellheim D 21 F10
Bellherbe F 26 F6
Bellignat F 31 C8
Bellinge DK 86 E6
Bellingham GB 5 E12
Bellingwolde NL 17 B8
Bellinzago Novarese I 68 B6
Bellinzona CH 69 A7
Bellizzi I 60 B3
Bell-Lloc d'Urgell E 42 D5
Bello E 47 C10
Bellobradë RKS 163 C10
Bellopojë RKS 163 D10
Bellou-en-Houlme F 23 C11
Bellpuig E 42 D6
Bellreguard E 56 D4
Bellshill GB 5 D8
Belluno I 72 D5
Bellver de Cerdanya E 33 F9
Bellvik S 107 C10
Belm D 17 D10
Bélmegyer H 151 D7
Bélmez E 51 C9
Bélmez de la Moraleda E 53 A10
Belmont GB 3 D15
Belmont-de-la-Loire F 30 C5
Belmonte E 39 B7
Belmonte E 47 E7
Belmonte P 45 D6
Belmonte Calabro I 60 E6
Belmonte del Sannio I 63 D6
Belmonte in Sabina I 62 C3
Belmontejo E 47 E8
Belmont-sur-Rance F 34 C4
Belmullet IRL 6 D3
Belo Brdo RKS 163 C10
Beloci MD 154 B4
Belœil B 19 C8
Belogradchik BG 159 F10
Beloiannisz H 149 B11
Belojin SRB 164 C3
Belorado E 40 D5
Beloslav BG 167 C9
Bělotín CZ 146 B5
Belotintsi BG 165 B6
Belovo BG 165 E9
Belozem BG 166 E4
Belp CH 31 B11
Belpasso I 59 D6
Belpech F 33 D9
Belper GB 11 E9
Belsay GB 5 E13
Belsh AL 168 C2
Belsk Duży PL 141 G3
Beltheim D 21 D8
Beltinci SLO 148 C6
Beltiug RO 151 B10
Beltra IRL 6 D5
Beltra IRL 6 E4
Beltrum NL 183 A9
Belturbet IRL 7 D8
Beluša SK 146 C6
Belušić SRB 159 F7
Belvédère-Campomoro F 37 H9
Belvedere Marittimo I 60 D5
Belvedere Ostrense I 67 E7
Belver de Cinca E 42 D4
Belver de los Montes E 39 E9
Belvès F 29 F8
Belvèze-du-Razès F 33 D10
Belvì I 64 D3
Belville IRL 6 D4
Belvís de la Jara E 46 E3
Belz F 22 E5
Belz UA 144 C9
Bełżec PL 144 C7
Bełżyce PL 141 H6
Bembibre E 38 B2
Bembibre E 39 C7
Bemmel NL 16 E5
Bemposta P 39 F7
Bemposta P 44 F4
Bempton GB 11 C11
Benabarre E 42 C4
Benacazón E 51 E7
Benahadux E 55 F8
Benahavís E 53 C6
Benalmádena E 53 C7
Benalúa de Guadix E 55 E6
Benalúa de las Villas E 53 B9
Benalup de Sidonia E 52 D5
Benamargosa E 53 C8
Benamaurel E 55 D7
Benamejí E 53 B7
Benamocarra E 53 C8
Benaocaz E 53 C6
Benaoján E 53 C6
Benasal E 48 D4
Benasau E 56 D4
Benasque E 33 E7
Benassay F 28 B6
Benatae E 55 C7
Benátky nad Jizerou CZ 77 B7
Benavente E 39 D8
Benavente P 50 B2
Benavides de Orbigo E 39 D8
Benavila P 44 F5
Benburb GB 7 D9
Bencatel P 50 B5
Bendorf D 21 D9
Bēne LV 134 D6
Benecko CZ 81 E9
Beneden-Leeuwen NL 16 E4
Benediktbeuren D 72 A3
Benedita P 44 F3
Benegiles E 39 E8
Bénéjacq F 32 D5
Benejama E 56 D3
Benejúzar E 56 E3
Benesat RO 151 C11
Benešov CZ 77 C7
Benešov nad Černou CZ 77 E7
Benešov nad Ploučnicí CZ 80 E6
Bénesse-Maremne F 32 C3
Benestare I 59 C9
Bénestroff F 27 C6
Benet F 28 C4
Benetutti I 64 C3
Bene Vagienna I 37 B7
Bénévent-l'Abbaye F 29 C9
Benevento I 60 A3
Benfeld F 27 D8
Benfica do Ribatejo P 44 F3
Bengești-Ciocadia RO 160 C3
Bengtsfors S 91 A11
Bengtsheden S 103 E10
Benia de Onís E 39 B10
Beniarbeig E 56 D5
Beniarrés E 56 D4
Beničanci HR 149 E10
Benicarló E 48 D5
Benicasim E 48 D5
Benidorm E 56 D4
Beniel E 56 E3
Benifaió E 48 F4
Benifallet E 42 F5
Benifallim E 56 D4
Benigánim E 56 D4
Benilloba E 56 D4
Benissa E 56 D5
Benissanet E 42 E5
Benitachell E 56 D5
Benitses GR 168 E2
Benizalón E 55 E8
Benizar y la Tercia E 55 C9
Benken CH 27 F11
Benkovac HR 156 D4
Benkovski BG 161 F10
Benkovski BG 171 B8
Benllech GB 10 E3
Bennebroek NL 182 A5
Bennekom NL 183 A7
Bennewitz D 79 D12
Bennungen D 79 D9
Bénodet F 22 E3
Benquerença P 45 D6
Benquerenças P 44 E5
Benquerencia de la Serena E 51 B9
Benquet F 32 C4
Bensafrim P 50 E2
Bensbyn S 118 C8
Bensdorf D 79 B11
Benshausen D 79 E8
Bensheim D 21 E11
Bensjö S 103 A9
Benson GB 13 B12
Bentelo NL 17 D7
Bentivoglio I 66 C3
Bentley GB 11 D9
Bentwisch D 83 B12
Bentzin D 84 C4
Beňuš SK 147 D9
Benzingerode D 79 C8
Beočin SRB 158 C4
Beograd SRB 158 D5
Bera de Bidasoa E 32 D2
Beragh GB 7 C8
Berane MNE 163 D8
Beranga E 40 B4
Berango E 40 B6
Berantevilla E 40 C6
Berat AL 168 C2
Bérat F 33 D8
Beratzhausen D 75 D10
Berbegal E 42 D3
Berbești RO 160 C3
Berca RO 161 C9
Bercedo E 40 B5
Bercel H 147 F8
Berceni RO 161 D8
Berceni RO 161 E8
Bercero E 39 E9
Berceto I 69 D8
Berchem B 19 C8
Berchidda I 64 B3
Berching D 75 D9
Berchtesgaden D 73 A7
Bérchules E 55 F6
Bercianos del Páramo E 39 D8
Berck F 15 G12
Bercu RO 145 H6
Berdal N 104 E6
Berdalen N 94 D6
Berducedo E 39 B6
Berdún E 32 E4
Bere Alston GB 12 E6
Beregdaróc H 145 G6
Bereguardo I 69 C7
Berehomet UA 152 A6
Berehove UA 145 G6
Berek HR 149 E7
Berekböszörmény H 151 C8
Berekfürdő H 150 C6
Beremend H 149 E10
Berești RO 153 E11
Berești-Meria RO 153 E11
Berești-Tazlău RO 153 E9
Berettyóújfalu H 151 C8
Berevoești RO 160 C5
Berezeni RO 154 E2
Berezyne UA 154 E4
Berg D 71 B9
Berg D 75 B10
Berg D 183 D9
Berg L 20 E6
Berg N 96 B7
Berg N 108 F3
Berg N 111 B13
Berg NL 19 C12
Berg NL 183 D7
Berg S 92 C8
Berg S 102 A7
Berg S 107 E10
Berg (Pfalz) D 27 C9
Berga D 79 D9
Berga D 79 E11
Berga E 43 C7
Berga S 89 A10
Bergagård S 87 B11
Bergaland N 94 D4
Bergama TR 177 A9
Bergamo I 69 B8
Bergantino I 66 B3
Bergara E 32 D1
Bergasa E 32 F1
Bergatreute D 71 B9
Berg bei Neumarkt in der Oberpfalz D 75 D9
Bergby S 103 E13
Berge D 17 C9
Berge D 83 D11
Berge E 42 F3
Berge S 102 A8
Berge S 105 D14
Bergeforsen S 103 A13
Bergeggi I 37 C8
Bergen D 73 A6
Bergen D 83 E7
Bergen D 84 B4
Bergen N 94 B2
Bergen NL 16 C3
Bergen (Dumme) D 83 E9
Bergen op Zoom NL 16 F2
Berger N 95 C12
Bergerac F 29 F6
Bergères-lès-Vertus F 25 C11
Bergesserin F 30 C6
Berget N 108 D6
Bergeyk NL 16 F4
Bergfors S 111 D18
Berghamn S 103 A15
Bergharen NL 183 B7
Berghaupten D 186 E4
Bergheim A 73 A7
Bergheim D 75 E9
Bergheim (Edertal) D 21 B12
Bergheim (Erft) D 21 C7
Berghem NL 16 E5
Berghem S 91 E12
Berghin RO 152 E3
Berghülen D 74 F6
Berg im Drautal A 73 C7
Bergisch Gladbach D 21 C8
Bergkamen D 17 E9
Bergkarlås S 102 D8
Bergkvara S 89 C10
Bergland S 107 A10
Berglia N 105 C15
Bergmo N 112 D7
Bergnäs S 109 E13
Bergnäset S 118 C8
Bergnäsudden S 109 E15
Bergnäsviken S 109 D15
Bergneustadt D 185 B8
Bergö FIN 99 B13
Bergö FIN 122 E6
Bergom S 107 E15
Bergsåker S 103 B13
Bergsäng S 97 B10
Bergsäter S 107 B12
Bergsbyn S 118 E6
Bergschenhoek NL 182 B5
Bergsgården S 103 E10
Bergshamra S 99 C11
Bergsjö S 103 C13
Bergsnov N 105 B9
Bergs slussar S 92 C7
Bergstod N 95 D9
Bergstrøm N 96 D6
Bergsviken S 118 D6
Bergtheim D 75 C7
Bergues F 18 C5
Bergün CH 71 D9
Bergvik S 103 D12
Bergviken S 109 D16
Bergwitz D 79 C12
Berhida H 149 B10
Beringe NL 183 C7
Beringel P 50 C4
Beringen B 19 B11
Berislăvești RO 160 C4
Beriu RO 151 F11
Berja E 55 F7
Berka D 79 E7
Berkåk N 101 A12
Berkel NL 16 E2
Berkel-Enschot NL 16 E4
Berkeley GB 13 B10
Berkenthin D 83 C9
Berkheim D 71 A10
Berkhout NL 16 C4
Berkoviči BIH 157 F9
Berkovitsa BG 165 C7
Berlanga E 51 C8
Berlanga de Duero E 40 F6
Berlești RO 160 D3
Berlevåg N 114 B6
Berlicum NL 183 B6
Berlin D 80 A4
Berlingerode D 79 D7
Berliște RO 159 D7
Berlstedt D 79 D9
Bermatingen D 27 E11
Bermeo E 40 B6
Bermillo de Sayago E 39 F7
Bern CH 31 B11
Bernac-Dessus F 33 D6
Bernalda I 61 C7
Bernardos E 46 B4
Bernartice CZ 76 D6
Bernartice CZ 81 E9
Bernāti LV 134 D1
Bernau D 27 E9
Bernau D 84 E5
Bernau am Chiemsee D 72 A5
Bernaville F 18 D5
Bernay F 24 B4
Bernbeuren D 71 B11
Bernburg (Saale) D 79 C10
Berndorf A 77 G10
Berne D 17 B10
Bernecebaráti H 147 E7
Bernedo E 41 C7
Bernhardsthal A 77 E11
Bernhardswald D 75 D11
Bernin F 31 E8
Bernis F 35 C7
Bernisdale GB 2 L4
Bernissart B 19 D8
Bernitt D 83 C11
Bernkastel-Kues D 21 E8
Bernolákovo SK 146 E4
Bernsdorf D 80 D6
Bernshammar S 97 C14
Bernstadt D 74 E7
Bernstadt D 81 D7
Bernstein A 148 B6
Beromünster CH 27 F9
Beronovo BG 167 D7
Beroun CZ 76 C6
Berovo MK 165 F6
Berra I 66 C4
Berre-l'Étang F 35 D9
Berriedale GB 3 J9
Berrien F 22 D4
Berriozar E 32 E2
Berru F 19 F9
Berry-au-Bac F 19 F8
Bersenbrück D 17 C9
Bershad' UA 154 A5
Beršići SRB 158 E5
Bersone I 69 B10
Bērstele LV 135 D7
Bertamirans E 38 C2
Bertea RO 161 C7
Berteștii de Jos RO 155 D1
Bertinoro I 66 D5
Bertnes N 108 B8
Bertogne B 19 D12
Bertrange L 186 B1
Bertrichamps F 27 D6
Bertrix B 19 E11
Běrunice CZ 77 B8
Berveni RO 151 B9
Bērvircava LV 134 D7
Berwick-upon-Tweed GB 5 D12
Bērzaine LV 131 F10
Berzasca RO 159 D8
Bērzaune LV 135 C12
Bērzciems LV 134 B6
Berzence H 149 D8
Bērzgale LV 133 C3
Bērzieši LV 135 D11
Bērzkalne LV 133 B2
Berźniki PL 137 E7
Berzovia RO 159 C8
Bērzpils LV 133 C2
Berzunți RO 153 E9
Beșalma MD 154 E3
Besalú E 43 C9
Besançon F 26 F5
Besande E 39 C10
Bescanó E 43 D9
Beselich-Obertiefenbach D 21 D10
Bešeňov SK 146 E6
Besenyőtelek H 150 B5
Besenyszög H 150 C5
Besigheim D 27 C11
Beşiktaş TR 173 B11
Beška SRB 158 C5
Besko PL 145 D4
Besni Fok SRB 158 D5
Besnyő H 149 B11
Besozzo I 68 B6
Bessacarr GB 11 D9
Bessaker N 104 C8
Bessan F 34 D5
Bessay-sur-Allier F 30 C3
Bessbrook GB 7 D10
Besse F 31 E9
Besse-et-St-Anastaise F 30 D2
Bessèges F 35 B7
Bessenbach D 187 B7
Bessé-sur-Braye F 24 E4
Besse-sur-Issole F 36 E4
Bessières F 33 C9
Bessines-sur-Gartempe F 29 C8
Bessude I 64 B2
Best NL 16 E4
Bestensee D 80 B5
Bestorp S 92 C7
Bestwig D 17 F10
Bestwina PL 147 B8
Beszterec H 145 G4
Betanzos E 38 B3
Betelu E 32 D2
Bétera E 48 E4
Beteta E 47 C8
Bethausen RO 151 F8
Betheln D 78 B6
Bethesda GB 10 E3
Bethmale F 33 E8
Bethon F 25 C10
Béthune F 18 C6
Betna N 104 E4
Beton-Bazoches F 25 C9
Betschdorf F 186 D4
Betsele S 107 B15
Bettelainville F 186 C1
Bettembourg L 20 E6
Bettendorf L 20 E6
Bettingen D 20 E6
Bettna S 93 B9
Bettola I 37 B11
Betton F 23 D8
Bettyhill GB 3 H8
Bettystown IRL 7 E10
Betws-y-coed GB 10 E4
Betxi E 48 E4
Betygala LT 134 F6
Betz F 25 B8
Betzdorf D 21 C9
Betzdorf L 186 B1
Betzenstein D 75 C9
Betzigau D 71 B10
Beucha D 79 D12
Beuil F 36 C5
Beuningen NL 16 E5
Beuren D 79 D7
Beuron D 27 D10
Beurville F 25 D12
Beuvrages F 182 E2
Beuvry F 18 C6
Beuzeville F 18 F1
Bevagna I 62 B3
Bevaix CH 31 B10
Beveren B 19 B9
Beverley GB 11 D11
Beverlo B 183 C6
Bevern D 78 C5
Beverstedt D 17 B11
Beverungen D 21 A12
Beverwijk NL 16 D3
Béville-le-Comte F 24 D6
Bewdley GB 13 A10
Bex CH 31 C11
Bexbach D 21 F8
Bexhill GB 15 F9
Beyağaç TR 181 B9
Beyazköy TR 173 B8
Beyçayiri TR 173 D6
Beyel TR 173 E10
Beyendorf D 79 B10
Beykoz TR 173 B11
Beynac-et-Cazenac F 29 F8
Beynat F 29 E9
Beynost F 31 D7
Beyoba TR 177 B10
Beyobasi TR 181 C9
Bezas E 47 D10
Bezau A 71 C9
Bezdan SRB 150 F2
Bezdead RO 161 C6
Bezdonys LT 137 D12
Bèze F 26 F3
Bezenye H 146 F4
Bezhanitsy RUS 133 C7
Bezhanovo BG 155 F2
Bezhanovo BG 165 C9
Béziers F 34 D5
Bezledy PL 136 E2
Bezmer BG 161 F10
Bezmer BG 166 E6
Bezouce F 35 C8
Bežovce SK 145 F5
Biadki PL 142 C4
Biała PL 142 F4
Biała-Parcela Pierwsza PL 142 D5
Biała Piska PL 139 C13
Biała Podlaska PL 141 F8
Biała Rawska PL 141 G2
Białe Błota PL 138 D4
Białebłoto-Kobyla PL 139 E12
Białka PL 145 E1
Białobrzegi PL 141 G3
Białogard PL 85 C9
Białośliwie PL 85 D12
Białowieża PL 141 E9
Biały Bór PL 85 C11
Biały Dunajec PL 147 C10
Białystok PL 140 D8
Biancavilla I 59 D6
Bianco I 59 C9
Biandrate I 68 C5
Bians-les-Usiers F 31 B9
Bianzè I 68 C5
Biar E 56 D3
Biarritz F 32 D2
Biarrotte F 32 C3
Biars-sur-Cère F 29 F9
Bias F 32 B3
Bias F 33 B7
Biasca CH 71 E7
Biatorbágy H 149 B11
Bibbiena I 66 E4
Bibbona I 66 F2
Biberach D 27 D9
Biberach an der Riß D 71 A9
Biberbach D 75 E8
Biberist CH 27 F8
Bibinje HR 156 D3
Bibione I 73 E7
Biblis D 21 E10
Bibury GB 13 B11
Bicaz RO 151 C11
Bicaz RO 153 D8
Bicaz-Chei RO 153 D7
Bicazu Ardelean RO 153 D7
Biccari I 60 A4
Bicester GB 13 B12
Bichiș RO 152 E4
Bichl D 72 A3
Bichlbach A 71 C11
Bickleigh GB 13 D7
Bicorp E 48 F3
Bicos P 50 D3
Bicske H 149 A11
Bicton GB 10 F6
Bidache F 32 D3
Bidart F 32 D2
Biddenden GB 15 E10
Biddinghuizen NL 16 D5
Biddulph GB 11 E7
Bideford GB 12 C6
Bidjovagge N 112 E10
Bidos F 32 D4
Bidovce SK 145 F3
Bie S 93 A8
Bieber D 21 D12
Biebesheim am Rhein D 21 E10
Biecz PL 144 D3
Biedenkopf D 21 C11
Biel CH 27 F7
Biel E 32 F4
Bielany-Żytaki PL 141 F6
Bielawa PL 81 E11
Bielawy PL 143 B8
Bielefeld D 17 D11
Bielice PL 85 D7
Bieliny Kapitulne PL 143 E10
Biella I 68 B5
Bielle F 32 D5
Bielsa E 33 E6
Bielsk PL 139 E8
Bielsko-Biała PL 147 B8
Bielsk Podlaski PL 141 E8
Bienenbüttel D 83 D8
Bieniów PL 81 C8
Bienno I 69 B9
Bienservida E 55 B7
Bienvenida E 51 C7
Bierawa PL 142 F5
Bierdzany PL 142 E5
Bière CH 31 B9
Bierge E 42 C3
Bierné F 23 E10
Biersted DK 86 A5
Biert F 33 E8
Biertan RO 152 E5
Bieruń PL 143 F7
Bierutów PL 142 D4
Bierzwienna-Długa PL 142 B6
Bierzwnik PL 85 D9
Biesaidgohppi N 113 C16
Biescas E 32 E5
Biesenthal D 84 E5
Biesiekierz PL 85 B10
Biesles F 26 D3
Biesowice PL 85 B11
Biessenhofen D 71 B11
Bietigheim D 27 C9
Bietigheim-Bissingen D 27 C11
Bietikow D 84 D5
Bièvre B 19 E11
Bieżuń PL 139 E8
Biga TR 173 D7
Bigadiç TR 173 F9
Biganos F 32 A4
Bigastro E 56 E3
Bigauncierns LV 134 C7
Bigbury-on-Sea GB 13 E7
Biggar GB 5 D9
Biggleswade GB 15 C8
Bignan F 22 E6
Bignasco CH 71 E7
Bigor MNE 163 E7
Bigüézal E 32 E3
Biguglia F 37 F10
Bihać BIH 156 C4
Biharia RO 151 C8
Biharkeresztes H 151 C8
Biharnagybajom H 151 C7
Bihartorda H 151 C7
Biharugra H 151 D8
Bihosava BY 133 E3
Bijela MNE 163 E6
Bijele Poljane MNE 163 D6
Bijeljani BIH 157 F9
Bijeljina BIH 158 D3
Bijelo Brdo HR 149 E11
Bijelo Bucčje BIH 157 D8
Bijelo Polje MNE 163 C8
Biķernieki LV 135 E13
Bikovo SRB 150 F4
Biksēre LV 135 C12
Bílá Lhota CZ 77 C11
Bilalovac BIH 157 D9
Bilbao E 40 B6
Bilbo E 40 B6
Bilbor RO 153 C7
Bilca RO 153 B7
Bilciurești RO 161 D7
Bil'dzyuhi BY 133 F2
Bileća BIH 162 D5
Biled RO 151 F6
Biłgoraj PL 144 B6
Bilicenii Vechi MD 153 B12
Bílina CZ 80 E5
Bilisht AL 168 C4
Biljača SRB 164 E4
Bilje HR 149 E11
Bilky UA 145 G7
Billdal S 91 D10
Billerbeck D 17 E8
Billère F 32 D5
Billericay GB 15 D9
Billesholm S 87 C11
Billiat F 31 C8
Billigheim D 21 F12
Billingham GB 11 B9
Billinghay GB 11 E11
Billingsfors S 91 B11
Billingshurst GB 15 E8
Billom F 30 D3
Billsåsen S 105 F16
Billsbro S 92 A7
Billsta S 107 E15
Billum DK 86 D2
Billund DK 86 D4
Billy F 30 C3
Bilohirs'ya UA 154 F5
Bílovec CZ 146 B6
Bílovice CZ 146 C5
Bilska LV 135 B11
Bilston GB 5 D10
Bilthoven NL 16 D4
Bilto N 112 E7
Bilton GB 11 D11
Bilyayivka UA 154 E6
Bilychi UA 145 E6
Bilyn UA 152 A4
Bilyne UA 154 B5
Bilzen B 19 C12
Bimbister GB 3 G10
Bíňa SK 147 F7
Binaced E 42 D4
Binas F 24 E5
Binasco I 69 C7
Binbrook GB 11 E11
Binche B 19 D9
Bindalseit N 105 A12
Bindlach D 75 C10
Bindslev DK 90 D7
Binefar E 42 D4
Bingen D 27 D11
Bingen am Rhein D 21 E9
Bingerden NL 183 B8
Bingham GB 11 F10
Binghamstown IRL 6 D2
Bingley GB 11 D8
Bingsjö S 103 D10
Binic F 22 C6
Biniés E 32 E4
Binissalem E 49 E10
Binnen D 17 C12
Binz D 84 B5
Binzen D 27 E8
Biograd na Moru HR 156 E3
Biokovina BIH 157 D7
Biol F 31 E7
Bionaz I 31 D11
Biorra IRL 7 F7
Biosca E 43 D6
Biot F 36 D6
Biota E 41 D9
Birchington GB 15 E11
Birchiș RO 151 F9
Bircza PL 144 D5
Birdhill IRL 8 C6
Birgittelyst DK 86 C4
Biri H 151 B8
Biri N 101 E13
Bīriņi LV 135 B9
Biristrand N 101 D12
Birkeland N 90 C3
Birkelse DK 86 A5
Birkenau D 187 B6
Birkenfeld D 21 E8
Birkenfeld D 27 C10
Birkenfeld D 74 C6
Birkenhead GB 10 E5
Birken-Honigsessen D 185 C8
Birkenwerder Berlin D 84 E4
Birkerød DK 87 D10
Birket DK 87 F8
Birketveit N 90 C2
Birkfeld A 148 B5
Birkungen D 79 D7
Birmingham GB 13 A11
Birnbaum A 73 C6
Biron F 33 A7
Birori I 64 C2
Birr IRL 7 F7
Birresborn D 21 D7
Birsay GB 3 G10
Birstall GB 11 F9
Birstein D 21 D12
Birštonas LT 137 D9
Birtavarre N 112 E6
Birtley GB 5 F13
Biruința MD 153 B12
Biržai LT 135 D9
Birzes LV 135 D8
Birzgale LV 135 C9
Birži LV 135 D11
Birzuli LV 131 F12
Biš SLO 148 C5
Bisaccia I 60 A4
Bisacquino I 58 D3
Biscarrosse F 32 B3
Biscarrosse-Plage F 32 B3
Bisceglie I 61 A7
Bischberg D 75 C8
Bischbrunn D 187 B7
Bischhausen (Waldkappel) D 78 D6
Bischheim F 27 C8
Bischoffen D 21 C10
Bischofferode D 79 D7
Bischoffsheim F 186 E3
Bischofsheim D 21 E10
Bischofsheim an der Rhön D 74 B7
Bischofshofen A 73 B7
Bischofsmais D 76 E4
Bischofswerda D 80 D6
Bischofswiesen D 73 A6
Bischofszell CH 27 E11
Bischwiller F 27 C8
Bisenti I 62 B5
Biser BG 166 F5
Bisertsi BG 161 F9
Bishop Auckland GB 5 F13
Bishop's Castle GB 10 G6
Bishop's Cleeve GB 13 B10
Bishop's Lydeard GB 13 C8
Bishop's Stortford GB 15 D9
Bishop's Waltham GB 13 D12
Bishqem AL 168 B2
Bishtazhin RKS 163 E10
Bisignano I 60 D6
Bisingen D 27 D10
Biskupice PL 141 H7
Biskupice PL 142 D5
Biskupice SK 147 E9
Biskupiec PL 136 F2
Biskupiec PL 139 C7
Bislev DK 86 B5
Bismark (Altmark) D 83 E11
Bismervik N 113 B11
Bismo N 101 C8
Bisoca RO 161 B9
Bispgården S 107 E11
Bispingen D 83 D8
Bissen L 20 E6
Bissendorf D 17 D10
Bissendorf (Wedemark) D 78 A6
Bissingen D 75 E8
Bistagno I 37 B8
Bistarac BIH 157 C10
Bistra RO 151 E11
Bistra RO 152 B4
Bistreț RO 160 F3
Bistrets BG 167 E8
Bistrica BIH 157 B7
Bistrica BIH 157 C7
Bistrica BIH 157 E8
Bistrica BIH 157 F10
Bistrica SLO 73 D9
Bistrica SLO 148 D5
Bistričak BIH 157 D8
Bistrița RO 152 C5
Bistrița Bârgăului RO 152 C5
Bistritsa BG 165 D7
Bistritsa BG 165 E7
Bisztynek PL 136 E2
Bitburg D 21 E7
Bitche F 27 B7
Bitetto I 61 A7
Bitinckë AL 168 C4
Bitola MK 168 B5
Bitonto I 61 A7
Bitritto I 61 A7
Bitschwiller-lès-Thann F 27 E7
Bitterfeld D 79 C11
Bitterstad N 110 C9
Bitti I 64 C3
Bittkau D 79 B10
Bitton GB 13 C10
Bitz D 27 D11
Biurrun E 32 E2
Bivio CH 71 E9
Bivolari RO 153 B10
Bivona I 58 D3
Bixad RO 145 H7
Bixad RO 153 E7
Bixter GB 3 E14
Biyikali TR 173 B7
Biyikli TR 177 D10
Bizanet F 34 D4
Bizanos F 32 D5
Bizovac HR 149 E10
Bjåen N 94 C6
Bjærangen N 108 C6
Bjæverskov DK 87 E10
Bjännberg S 122 C3
Bjarkøy N 111 C12
Bjärnum S 87 C13
Bjärred S 87 D12
Bjärsjölagård S 87 D13
Bjärtrå S 107 F13
Bjästa S 107 E15
Bjela BIH 157 F10
Bjelajci BIH 157 B6
Bjelopolje HR 156 C4
Bjelovar HR 149 E7
Bjergby DK 90 D7
Bjerge DK 87 D8
Bjerka N 108 D6
Bjerkvik N 111 C14
Bjerreby DK 86 F7
Bjerregrav DK 86 B5
Bjerringbro DK 86 C5
Bjøllånes N 108 C8
Bjoneroa N 95 A12
Bjønnes N 108 D7
Björbo S 97 B12
Björboholm S 91 D11
Bjordal N 94 E4
Bjørgen N 105 F9
Bjørgo N 101 E10
Björkå S 107 E13
Bjørkåsen N 111 C17
Bjørkåsen N 111 D12
Björkberg S 103 C9
Björkberg S 107 B13
Björkberg S 118 C5
Björkboda FIN 126 E8
Björke S 93 D12
Björke S 103 E13
Bjørkefláta N 95 B9
Bjørkelangen N 95 C15
Bjørkeset N 95 C10
Bjørkestrand N 114 C4
Björketorp S 91 E12
Björkfors S 119 C10
Björkheden S 109 E12
Björkhöjden S 107 E10
Björkholmen S 109 C17
Björkland S 109 F16
Björklia N 105 E9
Björkliden S 111 D16
Björklinge S 99 B9
Björknäset S 107 F12
Björknes N 96 B6
Bjørknes N 114 D6
Björkö FIN 126 E4
Björköby FIN 122 D6
Björkösby S 92 D5
Björkön S 103 B14
Björksele S 107 B15
Björksele S 107 D12
Björksjön S 107 E13
Björkstugan S 111 D15
Björkvik S 93 B9
Bjorli N 100 B6
Bjørn N 108 D4
Björna S 107 D15
Björnänge S 105 E14
Björndalen S 91 C11
Björneborg S 97 D11
Bjørnengen N 113 D11

Bjørnera N 111 C12
Bjørnes N 113 B18
Bjørnevatn N 114 D7
Bjørnfjell N 111 D15
Björnhult S 89 A10
Björnliden S 102 B3
Björnlunda S 93 A10
Björnön S 103 A9
Bjørnrå N 111 C10
Björnrike S 102 B6
Björnsjö S 107 D14
Bjørnskinn N 111 B10
Bjørnstad N 105 B14
Bjørnstad N 114 D9
Björsarv S 103 B11
Björsäter S 92 C8
Björsbo S 103 C12
Björsjö S 97 B13
Bjugn N 104 D7
Bjurå S 118 B8
Bjuråker S 103 C12
Bjurberget S 97 A8
Bjurfors S 107 C17
Bjurfors S 118 E5
Bjurholm S 107 D16
Bjursås S 103 E9
Bjurselet S 118 E6
Bjurträsk S 107 B17
Bjuv S 87 C11
Blace MK 164 E3
Blace SRB 164 C3
Blachownia PL 143 E6
Black Bourton GB 13 B11
Black Bull IRL 7 F10
Blackburn GB 3 L12
Blackburn GB 5 D9
Blackburn GB 10 D7
Blackmoor Gate GB 13 C7
Blackpool GB 10 D5
Blackrock IRL 7 E10
Blackstad S 93 D8
Blacktown GB 7 C7
Blackwater IRL 9 D10
Blackwaterfoot GB 4 D6
Blackwood GB 13 B8
Bladel NL 16 F4
Blaenau Ffestiniog GB 10 F4
Blaenavon GB 13 B8
Blagaj BIH 157 F8
Blagaj Japra BIH 156 B5
Blagdon GB 13 C9
Blăgești RO 153 D9
Blăgești RO 153 E12
Blagnac F 33 C8
Blagoevgrad BG 165 E7
Blagoevo BG 166 C6
Blåhøj DK 86 D4
Blaibach D 75 D12
Blain F 23 F8
Blainville-sur-l'Eau F 186 D1
Blainville-sur-Mer F 23 B8
Blair Atholl GB 5 B9
Blairgowrie GB 5 B10
Blaj RO 152 E3
Blajan F 33 D7
Blăjani RO 161 C9
Blăjel RO 152 E4
Blăjeni RO 151 E10
Blakeney GB 13 B10
Blakeney GB 15 B11
Blakstad N 90 C4
Blâmont F 27 C6
Blan F 33 C10
Blanca E 55 C10
Blancafort F 25 E8
Blancas E 47 C10
Blandford Forum GB 13 D10
Blandiana RO 151 F11
Blanes E 43 D9
Blaney GB 7 D7
Blangy-sur-Bresle F 18 E4
Blankaholm S 93 D9
Blankenberg D 83 C11
Blankenberge B 19 B7
Blankenburg (Harz) D 79 C8
Blankenfelde D 80 B4
Blankenhain D 79 E9
Blankenhain D 79 E11
Blankenheim D 21 D7
Blankenrath D 21 D8
Blankensee D 84 D4
Blankenstein D 75 B10
Blanquefort F 28 F4
Blans DK 86 F5
Blansko CZ 77 D11
Blanzac-Porcheresse F 28 E6
Blanzay F 29 C6
Blanzy F 30 B5
Blaricum NL 183 A6
Blarney IRL 8 E5
Blasimon F 28 F5
Blåsjöfallet S 105 B16
Blåsmark S 118 D6
Błaszki PL 142 C5
Blatec MK 164 F6
Blatets BG 167 D7
Blatna BIH 156 C5
Blatná CZ 76 D5
Blatné SK 146 E4
Blatnica BIH 157 D8
Blato HR 162 D2
Blaton B 182 D3
Blattniksele S 109 F14
Blaubeuren D 74 F6
Blaufelden D 74 D6
Blausasc F 37 D6
Blaustein D 187 E8
Blåvik S 92 C6
Blåviksjön S 107 B14
Blavozy F 30 E4
Blaye F 28 E4
Blaževo SRB 163 C10
Błaziny Górne PL 141 H4
Blāzma LV 134 B4
Blažovice CZ 77 D11
Błażowa PL 144 D5
Blázquez E 51 C9
Blažuj BIH 157 E9
Bleckåsen S 105 E15
Bleckede D 83 D9
Blecua E 42 C3
Bled SLO 73 D9
Błędowo PL 138 D6
Bledzew PL 81 A8
Blegny B 19 C12
Bléharies B 19 C7
Bleialf D 20 D6
Bleiburg A 73 C10
Bleicherode D 79 D8
Bleidenstadt D 185 D9
Bleik N 111 B10
Bleikvassli N 108 E6
Bleiswijk NL 182 A5
Blejești RO 161 E6
Blejoi RO 161 D8
Blekendorf D 83 B9
Bleket S 91 D10
Blender D 17 C12
Bléneau F 25 E8
Blénod-lès-Toul F 26 C4
Blenstrup DK 86 B6
Blentarp S 87 D13
Blera I 62 C2
Blérancourt F 19 E7
Bléré F 24 F4
Blerick NL 16 F6
Blesa E 42 E2
Bleskensgraaf NL 182 B5
Blesle F 30 E3
Blessington IRL 7 F9
Blet F 29 B11
Bletchley GB 15 D7
Blīdene LV 134 C5
Blidsberg S 91 D14
Blieskastel D 21 F8
Bligny F 25 D12
Bligny-sur-Ouche F 25 F12
Blikstorp S 91 C15
Bliksund N 90 C3
Blimea E 39 B8
Blindow D 84 D5
Blinja HR 149 F6
Blistrup DK 87 C10
Blixterboda S 97 D13
Blizanów PL 142 C5
Blížejov CZ 76 D3
Blížkovice CZ 77 E9
Bliznatsi BG 167 C9
Bliżyn PL 141 H3
Bllacë RKS 163 E10
Blois F 24 E5
Blokhus DK 86 A5
Blokzijl NL 16 C5
Blombacka S 97 C10
Blomberg D 17 E12
Blome LV 135 B11
Blome LV 135 B13
Blomsøy N 108 E3
Blomstermåla S 89 B10
Błonie PL 141 F3
Błonie PL 143 B7
Blönsdorf D 79 C12
Blötberget S 97 B13
Blousson-Sérian F 33 D6
Blovice CZ 76 C5
Blowatz D 83 C11
Bloxham GB 13 A12
Bludenz A 71 C9
Bludov CZ 77 C11
Blue Ball IRL 7 F7
Blumberg D 27 E10
Blumberg D 80 A5
Blumenhagen D 84 C5
Blumenholz D 84 D4
Blŭskovo BG 167 C8
Blyberg S 102 D7
Blyth GB 5 E13
Blyth GB 11 E9
Blyth Bridge GB 5 D10
Blyton GB 11 E10
Bø N 95 D10
Bø N 110 C8
Bo N 111 B10
Bø N 111 D12
Boada E 45 C8
Boadilla del Monte E 46 D5
Boadilla de Rioseco E 39 D10
Boal E 39 B6
Boalhosa P 38 E3
Boan MNE 163 D7
Boara Pisani I 66 B4
Boat of Garten GB 3 L9
Boa Vista P 44 E3
Boavista P 44 F2
Bobadilla E 53 B7
Bobâlna RO 152 C3
Bobbio I 37 B10
Bobbio Pellice I 31 F11
Bobenheim-Roxheim D 187 B5
Boberg S 107 E9
Boberka UA 145 E6
Bobicești RO 160 E4
Böbing D 71 B12
Bobingen D 71 A11
Bobitz D 83 C10
Bobivtsi UA 153 A7
Böblingen D 27 C11
Bobolice PL 85 C11
Boborás E 38 D3
Boboshevo BG 165 E7
Bobota HR 149 F11
Bobota RO 151 C10
Bobovdol BG 165 E7
Bobove UA 145 G6
Bobowa PL 144 D2
Bobowo PL 138 C6
Bobrov SK 147 C9
Bobrovec SK 147 C9
Bobrowice PL 81 C8
Bobrówko PL 85 E8
Bobrowniki PL 138 E6
Bobrowniki PL 140 D9
Bobryk-Druhyy UA 154 B6
Bocacara E 45 C8
Bocairent E 56 D3
Bočar SRB 150 F5
Bocchigliero I 61 E7
Boceguillas E 40 F4
Bocfölde H 149 C7
Bochnia PL 144 D1
Bocholt B 19 B12
Bocholt D 17 E7
Bochov CZ 76 B4
Bochum D 17 F8
Bockara S 89 A10
Bockenem D 79 B7
Bockenheim an der Weinstraße D 187 B5
Bockhammar S 97 C14
Bockhorn D 17 B10
Bockhorn D 75 F10
Bockhorst D 17 B9
Boćki PL 141 E8
Bocksjö S 92 B5
Bockträsk S 109 F15
Bocognano F 37 G10
Boconád H 150 B5
Bőcs H 145 G2
Bócsa H 150 D3
Bocșa RO 151 C10
Bocșa RO 159 C8
Bocsig RO 151 E8
Boczów PL 81 B7
Bod RO 153 F7
Böda S 89 A12
Boda S 103 A12
Boda S 103 D9
Boda bruk S 103 C12
Bodaczów PL 144 B7
Bodafors S 92 D5
Boda glasbruk S 89 B9
Bodajk H 149 B10
Bodåsgruvan S 98 B6
Bodbacka FIN 122 E6
Bodbyn S 122 B4
Boddam GB 3 F14
Boddam GB 3 L13
Boddin D 83 C10
Bodegraven NL 182 A5
Bodelshausen D 187 E6
Boden S 118 C7
Bodenfelde D 78 C6
Bodenham GB 13 A9
Bodenheim D 21 E10
Bodenkirchen D 75 F11
Bodenmais D 76 D4
Bodenteich D 83 E9
Bodenwerder D 78 C6
Bodenwöhr D 75 D11
Bodești RO 153 C8
Bodman D 27 E11
Bodmin GB 12 E5
Bodnegg D 71 B9
Bodø N 108 B7
Bodom N 105 D11
Bodonal de la Sierra E 51 C6
Bodoney GB 7 C8
Bodony H 147 F10
Bodroghalom H 145 G4
Bodrogkisfalud H 145 G3
Bodrum TR 177 E9
Bodsjö S 102 A8
Bodsjöbyn S 102 A8
Bodträskfors S 118 B5
Bódvaszilas H 145 F2
Bodyke IRL 8 C5
Bodzanów PL 139 E9
Bodzanów PL 142 F3
Bodzentyn PL 143 E10
Boé F 33 B7
Boechout B 19 B9
Boecillo E 39 E10
Boekel NL 16 E5
Boekhoute B 182 C3
Boën-sur-Lignon F 30 D5
Boeslunde DK 87 E8
Boeza E 39 C7
Boffres F 30 F6
Boffzen D 21 A12
Boftsa N 113 C21
Bogács H 145 H2
Bogajo E 45 C7
Bogarra E 55 B8
Bogați RO 160 D6
Bogatić SRB 158 D4
Bogatići BIH 157 E9
Bogatynia PL 81 E7
Boğaziçi TR 177 C10
Bogda RO 151 F8
Bogdan BG 165 D10
Bogdana RO 153 D11
Bogdana RO 160 F6
Bogdanci MK 169 B8
Bogdand RO 151 C10
Bogdănești RO 153 E9
Bogdănești RO 154 E2
Bogdaniec PL 85 E8
Bogdănița RO 153 E11
Bogdan Vodă RO 152 B4
Boge S 93 D13
Bogen D 75 E12
Bogen N 105 A11
Bogen N 111 C12
Bogense DK 86 D6
Boggsjö S 106 E8
Boghești RO 153 E10
Bogilice BIH 158 F3
Bogliasco I 37 C10
Bognanco I 68 A5
Bognelv N 112 C9
Bognes N 111 D11
Bogniebrae GB 3 L11
Bognor Regis GB 15 F7
Bogny-sur-Meuse F 184 E2
Bogø DK 87 F10
Bogodol BIH 157 F8
Bogojevo SRB 157 A11
Bogomilovo BG 166 E5
Bogoria PL 143 E11
Bogorojca MK 169 B8
Bogovina SRB 159 F8
Bogovinje MK 163 F10
Bogøy N 110 E9
Bograngen S 102 E4
Boguchwała PL 144 D4
Bogumiłowice PL 143 D7
Boguszów-Gorce PL 81 E10
Boguty-Pianki PL 141 E6
Bogyiszló H 149 D11
Bohain-en-Vermandois F 19 E7
Bohars F 22 D3
Bohdalov CZ 77 D9
Bohdan UA 152 A4
Bohdíkov CZ 77 B11
Boherboy IRL 8 D4
Boherbue IRL 8 D4
Bohinjska Bistrica SLO 73 D8
Böhl D 187 C5
Böhlen D 79 D11
Böhme D 82 E6
Bohmte D 17 D10
Böhne D 79 A11
Bohola IRL 6 E4
Bohonal de Ibor E 45 E10
Böhönye H 149 D8
Bohoyo E 45 D10
Bohumín CZ 146 B6
Bohuňovice CZ 146 B4
Bohuslavice CZ 146 B6
Bohutín CZ 76 C5
Boianu Mare RO 151 C10
Boiro de Arriba E 38 C2
Boiscommun F 25 D7
Bois-d'Amont F 31 B9
Boisgervilly F 23 D7
Bois-Guillaume F 18 F3
Boișoara RO 160 C4
Boisset-et-Gaujac F 35 B7
Boissezon F 33 C10
Boitzenburg D 84 D5
Boiu Mare RO 152 C3
Boizenburg D 83 D9
Bojadła PL 81 C9
Bojano I 63 E6
Bojanów PL 144 C4
Bojanowo PL 81 C11
Bøjden DK 86 E6
Bojkovice CZ 146 C5
Bojná SK 146 D6
Bojnice SK 147 D7
Bojnický SK 146 E5
Bojnik SRB 164 C4
Bojszów PL 142 F5
Bojszowy PL 143 F7
Boka SRB 159 C6
Bokel D 17 B11
Böklund D 82 A7
Bokod H 149 A10
Bököny H 151 B8
Bokšić HR 149 E10
Boksjön S 109 E10
Bol HR 156 F6
Bolån S 103 D12
Bolanden D 186 B5
Bolandoz F 31 A9
Bolaños de Calatrava E 54 B5
Bolătău RO 153 D8
Bolayir TR 173 C6
Bolbaite E 56 C3
Bolbec F 18 E1
Bolboși RO 159 D11
Bölcske H 150 D2
Boldekow D 84 C5
Bolderslev DK 86 F4
Boldești-Grădiștea RO 161 D9
Boldești-Scăeni RO 161 C8
Boldog H 150 B4
Boldogkőváralja H 145 G3
Boldre GB 13 D11
Boldu RO 161 C10
Boldur RO 159 B8
Boldva H 145 G2
Böle S 99 B9
Böle S 102 B7
Böle S 105 D14
Böle S 105 E15
Böle S 118 C8
Böle S 118 D6
Bolea E 41 D10
Bolekhiv UA 145 E8
Boleráz SK 146 E5
Bolesław PL 143 F7
Bolesław PL 143 F10
Bolesławiec PL 81 D9
Bolesławiec PL 142 D5
Boleszkowice PL 84 E7
Bolga N 108 C5
Bolgatovo RUS 133 C5
Bolhan UA 154 A3
Bolhrad UA 155 B3
Boliden S 118 E4
Bolimów PL 141 F2
Bolintin-Deal RO 161 E7
Bolintin-Vale RO 161 E7
Boliqueime P 50 E3
Boljanić BIH 157 C9
Boljanići MNE 163 C7
Boljevac SRB 159 F8
Boljevci SRB 158 D5
Bölkow D 83 B11
Bolków PL 81 E10
Bollebygd S 91 D12
Bollène F 35 B8
Bollengo I 68 C4
Bollermoen N 108 D6
Bolligen CH 31 B11
Bolling DK 86 D3
Bollingstedt D 82 A6
Bollnäs S 103 D11
Bollsbyn S 91 A12
Bollstabruk S 107 E13
Bollullos Par del Condado E 51 E6
Bolnes NL 182 B5
Bolnhurst GB 15 C8
Bologna I 66 D3
Bologne F 26 D3
Bolognetta I 58 D3
Bolognola I 62 B4
Bolotana I 64 C2
Bolotești RO 153 F10
Bolsena I 62 B1
Bol'shakovo RUS 136 D4
Bolsover GB 11 E9
Bolsward NL 16 B5
Bolszewo PL 138 A5
Boltaña E 33 F6
Boltåsen N 111 C12
Boltenhagen D 83 C10
Boltigen CH 31 B11
Bolton GB 5 D11
Bolton GB 11 D7
Bölüntü TR 181 A7
Bolvașnița RO 159 C9
Bolventor GB 12 D5
Bóly H 149 E11
Bolyarovo BG 167 E7
Bolzano I 72 D3
Bomal B 19 D12
Bomba I 63 C6
Bombarral P 44 F2
Bomlitz D 82 E7
Bompas F 34 E4
Bompensiere I 58 E4
Bompietro I 58 D5
Bomporto I 66 C3
Bomsund S 107 E9
Bona F 30 A3
Bonaduz CH 71 D8
Bonakas N 113 C21
Bönan S 103 E13
Bonanza E 52 C4
Boñar E 39 C9
Bonar Bridge GB 3 K8
Bonarcado I 64 C2
Bonares E 51 E6
Bonäs S 102 D7
Bonäset S 106 D8
Bonäset S 107 E15
Bonassola I 37 C11
Bonawe GB 4 C6
Bonboillon F 26 F4
Bonchamp-lès-Laval F 23 D10
Bonchester Bridge GB 5 E11
Boncourt CH 27 F7
Bondeno I 66 C3
Bondersbyn S 119 C9
Bonderup DK 86 A4
Bondorf D 187 D6
Bondsjö S 103 A14
Bondues F 182 D2
Bönebüttel D 83 B8
Bonefro I 63 D7
Bönen D 17 E9
Bo'ness GB 5 C9
Bonete E 55 B10
Bönhamn S 103 A15
Bonheiden B 19 B10
Boniches E 47 E9
Boniewo PL 138 F6
Bonifacio F 37 J10
Bonifati I 60 D5
Bönigen CH 70 D5
Bonin PL 85 B10
Bonn D 21 C8
Bonnåsjøen N 109 A10
Bonnat F 29 C9
Bonndorf im Schwarzwald D 27 E9
Bønnerup Strand DK 87 B7
Bonnes N 111 C15
Bonnet DK 86 B2
Bonnétable F 24 D3
Bonneuil-Matours F 29 B7
Bonneval F 24 D5
Bonneval F 31 D10
Bonneval-sur-Arc F 31 E11
Bonnevaux F 31 B9
Bonneville F 31 C9
Bonnieux F 35 C9
Bönnigheim D 27 B11
Bonnyrigg GB 5 D10
Bonny-sur-Loire F 25 E8
Bono F 22 E6
Bono I 64 C3
Bonorva I 64 C2
Bons-en-Chablais F 31 C9
Bonson F 30 D5
Bonțida RO 152 D3
Bőny H 149 A9
Bonyhád H 149 D11
Boo S 99 D10
Boock D 84 D6
Boom B 19 B9
Boortmeerbeek B 19 C10
Boos F 18 F3
Boostedt D 83 B8
Bootle GB 10 C5
Bopfingen D 75 E7
Boppard D 21 D9
Bor CZ 75 C12
Bor S 88 A6
Bor SRB 159 E9
Borač SRB 158 F6
Borås S 91 D12
Borăscu RO 160 D2
Borba P 50 B5
Borbjerg DK 86 C3
Borca RO 153 C7
Borča SRB 158 D5
Borcea RO 155 E1
Borchen D 17 E11
Borci BIH 157 C7
Borci BIH 157 E9
Börcs H 149 A9
Borculo NL 17 D7
Bordalba E 41 F7
Bordány H 150 E4
Bordeaux F 28 F4
Bordeira P 50 E2
Bordei Verde RO 161 C11
Bordelum D 82 A5
Bordères-Louron F 33 E6
Bordères-sur-l'Échez F 33 D6
Bordes F 32 D5
Bordes F 33 D6
Bordesholm D 83 B8
Bordești RO 161 B10
Bordighera I 37 D7
Bordils E 43 C9
Bording DK 86 C4
Bordón E 42 F3
Bordușani RO 155 E1
Bore I 69 D8
Boreham GB 15 D10
Borehamwood GB 15 D8
Borek PL 143 F10
Borek Strzeliński PL 81 E12
Borek Wielkopolski PL 81 C12
Boreland GB 5 E10
Børelva N 108 B8
Borensberg S 92 B6
Borg D 20 E6
Borgå FIN 127 E14
Borgafjäll S 106 B8
Borgentreich D 17 E12
Börger D 17 C9
Borger NL 17 C7
Borggård S 92 B7
Borghamn S 92 C5
Borgheim N 90 A7
Borghetto d'Arroscia I 37 C7
Borghetto di Borbera I 37 B9
Borghetto di Vara I 69 E8
Borghetto Santo Spirito I 37 C8
Borgholm S 89 B11
Borgholzhausen D 17 D10
Borgia I 59 B10
Borgloon B 19 C11
Børglum DK 90 E6
Borgo F 37 F10
Borgo a Mozzano I 66 E2
Borgo d'Ale I 68 C5
Borgoforte I 66 B2
Borgofranco d'Ivrea I 68 B4
Borgo Grappa I 61 C10
Borgolavezzaro I 68 C6
Borgomanero I 68 B5
Borgomaro I 37 D7
Borgone Susa I 31 E11
Borgonovo Val Tidone I 69 C7
Borgo Pace I 66 E5
Borgorose I 62 C4
Borgo San Dalmazzo I 37 C6
Borgo San Lorenzo I 66 E3
Borgo San Martino I 68 C6
Borgosesia I 68 B5
Borgo Tossignano I 66 D4
Borgo Val di Taro I 69 E8
Borgo Valsugana I 72 D3
Borgo Velino I 62 C4
Borgo Vercelli I 68 C5
Borgsjö S 103 A10
Borgsjö S 107 C13
Borgstedt D 82 B7
Borgstena S 91 D13
Borgue GB 5 F8
Borgvattnet S 107 E9
Borhaug N 94 F5
Boriaeva BG 171 B7
Borike BIH 157 E11
Borino BG 165 F9
Bořitov CZ 77 D11
Borja E 41 E8
Borjabad E 41 E7
Borjana SLO 73 D7
Borjelslandet S 118 C8
Borkan S 106 A8
Borkavichy BY 133 E4
Borken D 17 E7
Borken (Hessen) D 21 B12
Borkenes N 111 C11
Borki PL 141 G7
Borki PL 143 D9
Børkop DK 86 D5
Borkowice PL 141 H3
Borkowo PL 139 D12
Borkum D 17 A7
Borlänge S 97 B13
Borlești RO 153 D9
Bormaņi LV 135 C10
Børmarka N 104 C8
Bormio I 71 E10
Born D 79 B9
Born NL 183 C7
Borna D 79 D12
Borna D 80 D4
Born am Darß D 83 B13
Borne NL 17 D7
Bornem B 19 B9
Bornerbroek NL 17 D7
Bornes P 39 F6
Bornes de Aguiar P 38 E4
Borne Sulinowo PL 85 C11
Bornheim D 21 C7
Bornhofen D 21 D9
Bornhöved D 83 B8
Bornich D 185 D8
Bornos E 51 F8
Bornova TR 177 C9
Börnsen D 83 D8
Boroaia RO 153 C8
Borobia E 41 E8
Borod RO 151 D10
Borodino UA 154 E4
Borodinskoye RUS 129 C11
Borohrádek CZ 77 B10
Borojevići BIH 157 F8
Boronów PL 143 E6
Borore I 64 C2
Boroșneu Mare RO 153 F8
Boroszów PL 142 E5
Borota H 150 E3
Boroughbridge GB 11 C9
Borovan BG 165 C8
Borovany CZ 77 E7
Borov Dol BG 166 D6
Borovets BG 165 E8
Borovik HR 149 F10
Borovitsa BG 165 B6
Borovka LV 133 E1
Borovnica BIH 157 D9
Borovnica SLO 73 E9
Borovo BG 166 C5
Borovo Selo HR 157 B10
Borovtsi BG 165 C7
Borów PL 81 E11
Borów PL 144 B4
Borowa PL 143 F11
Borowie PL 141 G5
Borox E 46 D5
Borrby S 88 E6
Borre DK 87 F10
Borre N 95 D12
Borrentin D 84 C3
Borrèze F 29 F8
Borriol E 48 D4
Borris DK 86 D3
Borris IRL 9 C9
Borris-in-Ossory IRL 9 C7
Borrisokane IRL 6 G6
Borrisoleigh IRL 9 C7
Borrowdale GB 10 B5
Børrud N 96 C7
Börrum S 93 C9
Borș RO 151 C8
Børsa N 104 E8
Borșa RO 152 B5
Borșa RO 152 D3
Borša SK 145 G4
Borsbeek B 19 B10
Borsec RO 153 D7
Børselv N 113 C16
Borsh AL 168 D2
Borshchi UA 154 B5
Borshchovychi UA 144 D9
Boršice u Buchlovic CZ 146 C4
Borsio GR 174 D3
Borský Svätý Jur SK 77 E12
Borsodbóta H 145 G1
Borsodnádasd H 145 G1
Borsodszentgyörgy H 145 G1
Borsodszirák H 145 G2
Borsosberény H 147 F8
Borssele NL 182 C3
Borstel D 17 C11
Borth GB 10 G3
Bortigali I 64 C2
Bortigiadas I 64 B3
Bort-les-Orgues F 29 E10
Börtnan S 102 A6
Bortnen N 100 C2
Borum DK 86 C6
Borup DK 87 E9
Borve GB 2 L4
Borynya UA 145 E6
Boryslav UA 145 E7
Borzęciczki PL 81 C12
Borzonasca I 37 C10
Borzytuchom PL 85 B12
Bosa I 64 C2
Bošáca SK 146 D5
Bosa Marina I 64 C1
Bosanci RO 153 B8
Bosanka Rača BIH 158 D3
Bosanska Dubica BIH 157 B6
Bosanska Gradiška BIH 157 B7
Bosanska Kostajnica BIH 156 B6
Bosanska Krupa BIH 156 C5
Bosanski Brod BIH 157 B9
Bosanski Kobas BIH 157 B8
Bosanski Novi BIH 156 B5
Bosanski Petrovac BIH 156 C5
Bosanski Šamac BIH 157 B9
Bosansko Grahovo BIH 156 D5
Bošany SK 146 D6
Bősárkány H 149 A8
Bosau D 83 B8
Boscastle GB 12 D5
Bosco I 66 F5
Bosco Chiesanuova I 69 B11
Bosco Marengo I 37 B9
Boscotrecase I 60 B2
Bösdorf D 83 B8
Bösebo S 89 A9
Bösel D 17 B9
Boshulya BG 165 E9
Bosia RO 153 C11
Bosilegrad SRB 164 E5
Bosiljevo HR 148 F4
Boskoop NL 16 D3
Boskovice CZ 77 D11
Bošnjace SRB 164 D4
Bošnjaci HR 157 B10
Bošnjane SRB 159 F7
Bošnjane SRB 159 F7
Boșorod RO 159 B11
Bössbod S 102 D7
Bosset F 29 F6
Bossolasco I 37 B8
Bössost E 33 E7
Bostad N 110 D6
Bostan BIH 157 F7
Bøstølen N 100 B6
Boston GB 11 F11
Boston Spa GB 11 D9
Bostrak N 90 A4
Bosundet S 107 C10
Botão P 44 D4
Boteå S 107 E13
Boteni RO 160 C6
Botesdale GB 15 C11
Botești RO 153 C9
Botești RO 160 C6
Botevgrad BG 165 D8
Botevo BG 167 C9
Bothel GB 5 F10
Boticas P 38 E4
Botiz RO 151 B10
Botiza RO 152 B4
Botn N 110 E9
Botn N 111 A18
Botn N 112 D4
Botngård N 104 D7
Botnhamn N 111 A14
Botoroaga RO 161 E7
Botorrita E 41 E9
Botoš SRB 158 C6
Botoșana RO 153 B7
Botoșani RO 153 B9
Botoșești-Paia RO 159 E11
Botricello I 61 F7
Bötsle S 103 A14
Botsmark S 118 F4
Bottendorf (Burgwald) D 21 B11
Bottesford GB 11 D10
Bottidda I 64 C3
Bottnaryd S 91 D14
Bottrop D 17 E7
Botun MK 168 B4
Bötzingen D 27 D8
Bouafles F 24 B5
Boucau F 32 C3
Bouc-Bel-Air F 35 D9
Boucé F 23 C11
Bouchain F 19 D7
Bouchemaine F 23 F10
Bouchoir F 18 E6
Boudry CH 31 B10
Boué F 19 D8
Bouglon F 33 B6
Bouguenais F 23 F8
Bouillargues F 35 C7
Bouillon B 19 E11
Bouilly F 25 D10
Bouin F 28 B1
Boujailles F 31 B9
Boujan-sur-Libron F 34 D5
Boulay-Moselle F 26 B5
Boulazac F 29 E7
Boulbon F 35 C8
Bouligny F 19 F12
Bouloc F 33 C8
Boulogne-Billancourt F 25 C7
Boulogne-sur-Gesse F 33 D7
Boulogne-sur-Mer F 15 F12
Bouloire F 24 E4
Boulouris F 36 E5
Boult-aux-Bois F 19 F10
Boulzicourt F 19 E10
Bouniagues F 29 F7
Bøur FO 2 A2
Bourbon-Lancy F 30 B4
Bourbon-l'Archambault F 30 B3
Bourbonne-les-Bains F 26 E4
Bourbourg F 18 C5
Bourbriac F 22 D5
Bourcefranc-le-Chapus F 28 D3
Bourdeaux F 35 A9
Bourdeilles F 29 E7
Bourdonnay F 27 C6
Bouresse F 29 C7
Bourg F 28 E4
Bourg-Achard F 18 F2
Bourganeuf F 29 D9
Bourg-Argental F 30 E6
Bourg-de-Péage F 31 E7
Bourg-de-Thizy F 30 C5
Bourg-de-Visa F 33 B7
Bourg-Dun F 18 E2
Bourg-en-Bresse F 31 C7
Bourges F 29 A10
Bourg-et-Comin F 19 F8
Bourg-Lastic F 29 D11
Bourg-lès-Valence F 30 F6
Bourgneuf-en-Mauges F 23 F10
Bourgneuf-en-Retz F 28 A2
Bourgogne F 19 F9
Bourgoin-Jallieu F 31 D7
Bourg-St-Andéol F 35 B8
Bourg-St-Bernard F 33 C9
Bourg-St-Maurice F 31 D10
Bourgtheroulde-Infreville F 18 F2
Bourguébus F 23 B11
Bourgueil F 23 F12
Bourmont F 26 D4
Bourne GB 11 F11
Bournemouth GB 13 D11
Bournezeau F 28 B3
Bourran F 33 B6
Bourriot-Bergonce F 32 B5
Bourron-Marlotte F 25 D8
Bourscheid L 184 E5
Bourtange NL 17 B8
Bourton GB 13 C10
Boussac F 29 C10
Bousse F 186 C1
Boussens F 33 D7
Boussières F 26 F4
Boussois F 19 D9
Boussu B 19 D8
Boutersem B 19 C10
Bouveret CH 31 C10
Bouvières F 35 A9
Bouvron F 23 F8
Bouxières-aux-Dames F 26 C5
Bouxwiller F 27 C7
Bouy F 25 B11
Bouzonville F 21 F7
Bouzov CZ 77 C11
Bova I 59 C8
Bøvær N 111 B13
Bovalino I 59 C9
Bovallstrand S 91 C9
Bova Marina I 59 D8
Bovan SRB 159 F8
Bovec SLO 73 D8
Bóveda E 38 C5

C

Cerbère F 34 F5
Cercal P 44 F3
Cercal P 50 D2
Čerčany CZ 77 C7
Cercedilla E 46 C4
Cercemaggiore I 63 E7
Cerchezu RO 155 F2
Cerchiara di Calabria I 61 D6
Cerchio I 62 C5
Cercy-la-Tour F 30 B4
Cerda I 58 D4
Cerdanyola del Vallès E 43 E8
Cerdedo E 38 C3
Cerdeira P 44 D5
Cerdon F 25 E7
Cēre LV 134 B5
Cerea I 66 B3
Cered H 147 E9
Ceregnano I 66 B4
Cerekwica PL 85 E13
Cérences F 23 C9
Ceres GB 5 C11
Ceres I 31 E11
Ceresole Reale I 31 E11
Céreste F 35 C10
Céret F 34 F4
Čerević SRB 158 C4
Cerezo de Abajo E 46 B5
Cerezo de Arriba E 40 F4
Cerezo de Riotirón E 40 C5
Cerfontaine B 184 D1
Cergău RO 152 E3
Cergy F 24 B7
Cerhenice CZ 77 B8
Ceriale I 37 C8
Ceriana I 37 D7
Cerignola I 60 A5
Cérilly F 30 B2
Čerin BIH 157 F8
Cerisano I 60 E6
Cerisiers F 25 D9
Cerisy-la-Forêt F 23 B10
Cerisy-la-Salle F 23 B9
Cerizay F 28 B4
Çerkezköy TR 173 B9
Çerkezmüsellim TR 173 B7
Cerklje SLO 73 D9
Cerklje SLO 148 E5
Cerknica SLO 73 E9
Cerkno SLO 73 D8
Cerkwica PL 85 B8
Cermei RO 151 D8
Çermë-Proshkë AL 168 B2
Cermignano I 62 B5
Cërmjan RKS 163 E9
Cerna HR 157 B10
Cerna RO 155 C2
Cernache do Bonjardim P 44 E4
Černá Hora CZ 77 D11
Cernat RO 153 F8
Cernătești RO 160 E2
Cernătești RO 161 C9
Cernavodă RO 155 E2
Cernay F 27 E7
Cernay-en-Dormois F 19 F10
Černčice CZ 76 B5
Cernégula E 40 C4
Cernele RO 160 E3
Cernești RO 152 C3
Cernica RO 161 E8
Cernier CH 31 A10
Černik HR 157 B7
Černík SK 146 E6
Černilov CZ 77 B9
Cernișoara RO 160 C4
Cernobbio I 69 B7
Cernoleuca MD 153 A11
Černošice CZ 76 C6
Černošín CZ 76 C3
Černilov LV 133 D2
Černovice CZ 77 D7
Černožice CZ 77 B9
Cerová SK 146 D4
Cerovac SRB 159 E6
Cerovak Tušilovički HR 148 F5
Ceroviljani BIH 157 B7
Cerovlje HR 67 B9
Cerovo SK 147 E8
Cerralbo E 45 C7
Cerreto d'Esi I 67 F6
Cerreto di Spoleto I 62 B3
Cerreto Sannita I 60 A3
Cerrigydrudion GB 10 E4
Cërrik AL 168 B2
Cerro al Volturno I 62 D6
Cersay F 28 A5
Cersosimo I 61 C6
Certaldo I 66 E3
Certeju de Sus RO 151 F10
Certești RO 153 E11
Certeze RO 145 H7
Certosa di Pavia I 69 C7
Certosa di Pesio I 37 C7
Ceru-Băcăinți RO 151 F11
Cërujë AL 168 C3
Cerva P 38 F4
Cervaro I 62 E5
Cervatos de la Cueza E 39 D10
Červená Voda CZ 77 B11
Cervenia RO 161 F6
Červená Voda CZ 77 C12
Červený Kostelec CZ 77 B10
Cervera E 42 D6
Cervera de la Cañada E 41 F8
Cervera del Llano E 47 E8
Cervera del Maestre E 48 D5
Cervera de los Montes E 46 D3
Cervera del Río Alhama E 41 D8
Cervera de Pisuerga E 40 C3
Cerveteri I 62 D2
Cervia I 66 D5
Cervignano del Friuli I 73 E7
Cervinara I 60 A3
Červiná Řečice CZ 77 C8
Cervione F 37 G10
Cervo E 38 A5
Cervo I 37 D8
Cervon F 25 F10
Cerzeto I 60 E6
Cesano Boscone I 69 C7
Cesano Maderno I 69 B7
Cesarò I 59 D6
Cesena I 66 D5
Cesenatico I 66 D5
Cesio I 37 C7
Cēsis LV 135 B10
Česká Kamenice CZ 80 E6
Česká Lípa CZ 81 E7
Česká Skalice CZ 77 B10
Česká Ves CZ 77 B12
Česke Brezovo SK 147 E9
České Budějovice CZ 77 E6
České Meziříčí CZ 77 B10
Český Brod CZ 77 B7
Český Dub CZ 81 E7
Český Krumlov CZ 76 E6
Český Těšín CZ 147 B7
Česljeva Bara SRB 159 D7
Çeşme TR 177 C7
Cespedosa E 45 C9
Cessalto I 73 E6
Cessenon-sur-Orb F 34 D5
Cessole I 37 B8
Cesson F 25 C8
Cesson-Sévigné F 23 D8
Cestas F 28 F4
Čestobrodica SRB 158 F5
Cesuras E 38 B3
Cesvaine LV 135 C12
Cetariu RO 151 C9
Cetate RO 152 C5
Cetate RO 159 E11
Cetatea de Baltă RO 152 E4
Cetățeni RO 160 C6
Cetina E 41 F8
Cetingrad HR 156 B4
Cetinje MNE 163 E6
Ceto I 69 A9
Ceton F 24 D4
Cetona I 62 B1
Cetraro I 60 D5
Ceuta WHAT 53 E6
Ceutí E 56 E2
Ceva I 37 C8
Cevico de la Torre E 40 E3
Cevico Navero E 40 E3
Cevins F 31 D9
Cevio CH 68 A6
Çevizköy TR 173 A8
Čevo MNE 163 D6
Cewice PL 85 B13
Ceyreste F 35 D10
Ceyzériat F 31 C7
Cezieni RO 160 E4
Chã P 38 E4
Chaam NL 16 F3
Chabanais F 29 D7
Chabeuil F 31 F7
Chabielice PL 143 D7
Chablis F 25 E10
Chabówka PL 147 B9
Chabreloche F 30 D4
Chabris F 24 F6
Chacim P 39 F6
Chagford GB 13 D7
Chagny F 30 B6
Chaïkali GR 174 C4
Chaillac F 29 C8
Chailland F 23 D10
Chaillé-les-Marais F 28 C3
Chailley F 25 D10
Chaintrix-Bierges F 25 C11
Chaironeia GR 175 C6
Chalabre F 33 E10
Chalais CH 31 C12
Chalais F 28 E6
Chalamera E 42 D4
Chalamont F 31 C7
Chalampé F 27 E8
Chalandri GR 175 C8
Chalandritsa GR 174 C4
Chalastra GR 169 C8
Chale GB 13 D12
Chaleix F 29 D7
Châlette-sur-Loing F 25 D8
Chalford GB 13 B10
Chalgrove GB 13 B12
Chaligny F 26 C5
Chalin PL 139 E7
Chalindrey F 26 E3
Chalivoy-Milon F 29 B11
Chalki GR 169 E8
Chalki GR 181 D7
Chalkiades GR 169 F7
Chalkiades GR 174 A2
Chalkida GR 175 C8
Chalkidona GR 169 C8
Chalkio GR 175 D6
Challans F 28 B2
Challerange F 19 F10
Challes-les-Eaux F 31 D8
Chalmoux F 30 B4
Chalonnes-sur-Loire F 23 F10
Châlons-en-Champagne F 25 C11
Chalon-sur-Saône F 30 B6
Châlus F 29 D7
Cham CH 27 F9
Cham D 75 D12
Chamalières F 30 D3
Chamaloc F 31 F7
Chamberet F 29 D9
Chambéria F 31 C8
Chambéry F 31 D8
Chambley-Bussières F 26 B4
Chambois F 23 C12
Chambon-sur-Voueize F 29 C10
Chambord F 24 E6
Chamboulive F 29 E9
Chambray-lès-Tours F 24 F4
Chambry F 19 E8
Chamesson F 25 E12
Chamonix-Mont-Blanc F 31 D10
Chamoux-sur-Gelon F 31 D9
Champagnac F 29 E10
Champagnac-de-Belair F 29 E7
Champagnac-le-Vieux F 30 E4
Champagne-Mouton F 29 D6
Champagne-sur-Seine F 25 D8
Champagney F 26 E6
Champagnole F 31 B8
Champaubert F 25 C10
Champdeniers-St-Denis F 28 C5
Champ-d'Oiseau F 25 E11
Champeix F 30 D3
Champéry CH 31 C10
Champex CH 31 C11
Champforgeuil F 30 B6
Champgenéteux F 23 D11
Champier F 31 E7
Champigné F 23 E10
Champignelles F 25 E9
Champigneulles F 186 D1
Champigny F 25 D9
Champlemy F 25 F9
Champlitte F 26 E4
Champniers F 29 D6
Champoléon F 31 F9
Champoluc I 68 B4
Champsecret F 23 C10
Champs-sur-Tarentaine-Marchal F 29 E11
Champs-sur-Yonne F 25 E10
Champ-sur-Drac F 31 E8
Champtoceaux F 23 F9
Chamrousse F 31 E8
Chamusca P 44 F4
Chanac F 34 B5
Chanas F 30 E6
Chança P 44 F5
Chanceaux F 25 E12
Chanceaux-sur-Choisille F 24 F4
Chancelade F 29 E7
Chancelaria P 44 E3
Chandras GR 179 E11
Chandrinos GR 174 F4
Chañe E 40 F3
Changé F 23 D10
Changé F 23 E12
Changy F 30 C5
Chania GR 178 D7
Chaniotis GR 169 D10
Chantada E 38 C4
Chantelle F 30 C3
Chantilly F 25 B7
Chantonnay F 28 B3
Chanu F 23 C10
Chaource F 25 D11
Chapaevo BG 166 C5
Chapayevka UA 154 A5
Chapel-en-le-Frith GB 11 E8
Chapelle-lez-Herlaimont B 182 E4
Chapeltown GB 11 E9
Chapinería E 46 D4
Charakas GR 178 E9
Charavgi GR 169 D6
Charbonnat F 30 B5
Charcenne F 26 F4
Charchilla F 31 C8
Chard GB 13 D9
Chardstock GB 13 D9
Charenton-du-Cher F 29 B11
Charfield GB 13 B10
Chargey-lès-Gray F 26 F4
Charlbury GB 13 B12
Charlemont GB 7 D9
Charleroi B 19 D9
Charlestown IRL 6 E5
Charleville IRL 8 D5
Charleville-Mézières F 19 E10
Charlieu F 30 C5
Charlottenberg S 96 C7
Charlton GB 13 C12
Charlton Kings GB 13 B10
Charly F 25 C9
Charmé F 29 D6
Charmes F 26 D5
Charmes-sur-Rhône F 30 F6
Charmey CH 31 B11
Charmouth GB 13 D9
Charmoy F 25 E9
Charnay-lès-Mâcon F 30 C6
Charny F 25 E9
Charokopeio GR 178 B2
Charolles F 30 C5
Charomkhava BY 133 F3
Charopo GR 169 B9
Chârost F 29 B10
Charquemont F 27 F6
Charrat CH 31 C11
Charrey-sur-Seine F 25 E12
Charrin F 30 B4
Charroux F 29 C6
Charsznica PL 143 F8
Chartres F 24 D5
Charvensod I 31 D11
Charvieu-Chavagneux F 31 D7
Charzyno PL 85 B9
Chassagne-Montrachet F 30 B6
Chasseneuil-sur-Bonnieure F 29 D6
Chasseradès F 35 A6
Chasse-sur-Rhône F 30 D6
Chassigny-Aisey F 26 E3
Chassillé F 23 D11
Chastre B 19 C10
Château-Arnoux F 35 B10
Châteaubernard F 28 D5
Châteaubourg F 23 D9
Châteaubriant F 23 E9
Château-Chinon F 30 A4
Château-d'Oex CH 31 C11
Château-d'Olonne F 28 B2
Château-du-Loir F 24 E3
Châteaudun F 24 D5
Châteaugiron F 23 D8
Château-Gontier F 23 E10
Château-Landon F 25 D8
Château-la-Vallière F 24 E3
Châteaulin F 22 D3
Châteaumeillant F 29 B10
Châteauneuf-de-Galaure F 31 E6
Châteauneuf-de-Randon F 35 A6
Châteauneuf-d'Ille-et-Vilaine F 23 C8
Châteauneuf-du-Faou F 22 D4
Châteauneuf-en-Thymerais F 24 C5
Châteauneuf-la-Forêt F 29 D9
Châteauneuf-les-Martigues F 35 D9
Châteauneuf-sur-Charente F 28 D5
Châteauneuf-sur-Cher F 29 B10
Châteauneuf-sur-Loire F 25 E7
Châteauneuf-sur-Sarthe F 23 E11
Châteauneuf-Val-de-Bargis F 25 F9
Châteauponsac F 29 C8
Châteaurenard F 35 C8
Châteauredon F 36 C4
Châteaurenard F 25 E8
Châteaurenard F 35 C8
Châteaurenaud F 31 B7
Château-Renault F 24 E4
Châteauroux F 29 B9
Châteauroux F 36 B5
Château-Salins F 26 C6
Château-Thierry F 25 B9
Châteauvillain F 25 D12
Châtel F 31 C10
Châtelaillon-Plage F 28 C3
Châtelaudren F 22 C6
Châtel-Censoir F 25 E10
Châteldon F 30 D4
Châtelet B 19 D10
Châtel-Gérard F 25 E11
Châtelguyon F 30 D3
Châtellerault F 29 B7
Châtel-Montagne F 30 C4
Châtel-St-Denis CH 31 B10
Châtel-sur-Moselle F 26 D5
Châtelus-Malvaleix F 29 C10
Châtenois F 26 D4
Châtenois F 27 D7
Châtenois-les-Forges F 27 E6
Châtenoy-le-Royal F 30 B6
Chatham GB 15 E10
Châtillon B 19 E12
Châtillon I 68 B4
Châtillon-Coligny F 25 E8
Châtillon-en-Bazois F 30 A4
Châtillon-en-Diois F 35 A9
Châtillon-en-Michaille F 31 C8
Châtillon-la-Palud F 31 D7
Châtillon-sur-Chalaronne F 31 C6
Châtillon-sur-Colmont F 23 D10
Châtillon-sur-Indre F 29 B8
Châtillon-sur-Loire F 25 E8
Châtillon-sur-Marne F 25 B10
Châtillon-sur-Seine F 25 E12
Châtillon-sur-Thouet F 28 B5
Chatte F 31 E7
Chatteris GB 15 C9
Chatton GB 5 D13
Chatuzange-le-Goubet F 31 F7
Chatzis GR 174 E4
Chauchina E 53 B9
Chaudenay F 26 E4
Chaudes-Aigues F 30 F3
Chaudeyrac F 35 A6
Chaudfontaine B 19 C12
Chauffailles F 30 C5
Chauffayer F 31 F9
Chaulnes F 18 E6
Chaumergy F 31 B7
Chaumont F 26 D3
Chaumont-en-Vexin F 18 F4
Chaumont-Porcien F 19 E9
Chaumont-sur-Aire F 26 C3
Chaumont-sur-Loire F 24 F5
Chaunay F 29 C6
Chauny F 19 E7
Chaussin F 31 B7
Chauvigny F 29 B7
Chavanay F 30 E6
Chavanges F 25 C12
Chavanoz F 31 D7
Chavari GR 174 D3
Chavelot F 26 D5
Chaves P 38 E5
Chazelles-sur-Lyon F 30 D5
Cheadle GB 11 F8
Cheb CZ 75 B11
Checa E 47 C9
Chechel'nyk UA 154 A4
Chęciny PL 143 E9
Chécy F 24 E7
Chedburgh GB 15 C10
Cheddar GB 13 C9
Chef-Boutonne F 28 C5
Chekhpare BG 166 E4
Cheles E 51 B5
Chella E 56 C3
Chełm PL 141 H8
Chełmek PL 143 F7
Chełmiec PL 145 D2
Chełmno PL 138 D5
Chełmno PL 142 B6
Chelmsford GB 15 D9
Chełmża PL 138 D6
Cheltenham GB 13 B10
Chelva E 47 E11
Chemazé F 23 E10
Chémery F 24 F5
Chémery-sur-Bar F 19 E10
Chemillé F 23 F10
Chemin F 31 B7
Cheminon F 25 C12
Chemiré-le-Gaudin F 23 E11
Chemnitz D 80 E3
Chenecey-Buillon F 26 F4
Chénérailles F 29 C10
Cheniménil F 26 D6
Chenôve F 26 F3
Cheny F 25 E10
Chepelare BG 165 F10
Chepintsi BG 165 D7
Chepstow GB 13 B9
Chepy F 25 C11
Chera E 48 E3
Chérac F 28 D5
Cherasco I 37 B7
Chéraute F 32 D4
Cherbourg-Octeville F 23 A8
Cheremule I 64 B2
Cherepkivtsi UA 153 A7
Chereshovo BG 161 F8
Cherlenivka UA 153 A8
Cherna BG 155 F1
Cherna Gora BG 166 E4
Chernevo BG 167 C9
Chernevo RUS 132 D3
Cherni Osŭm BG 165 D10
Cherni Vrŭkh BG 167 E8
Chernivtsi UA 153 A7
Chernogorovo BG 165 E9
Cherno More BG 167 D8
Chernoochene BG 166 F4
Chernyakhovsk RUS 136 D4
Chernyshevskoye RUS 136 D6
Chéroy F 25 D9
Cherskaya RUS 132 F3
Cherso GR 169 B8
Chert E 42 F4
Cherveix-Cubas F 29 E8
Cherven BG 161 F8
Chervena voda BG 161 F8
Cherven Bryag BG 165 C9
Cherventsi BG 167 B8
Cherves-Richemont F 28 D5
Chervona Hreblya UA 154 A4
Chervonoarmiys'ke UA 154 F3
Chervonohrad UA 144 C9
Chesham GB 15 D7
Cheshunt GB 15 D8
Chesley F 25 E11
Chessy-les-Prés F 25 D10
Cheste E 48 F3
Chester GB 10 E6
Chesterfield GB 11 E9
Chester-le-Street GB 5 F13
Chețani RO 152 E4
Chetrosu MD 153 A11
Chevagnes F 30 B4
Chevanceaux F 28 E5
Chevereșu Mare RO 159 B7
Chevillon F 26 C3
Chevilly F 24 D6
Chevreuse F 24 C7
Chew Magna GB 13 C9
Cheylade F 30 E2
Chezal-Benoît F 29 B10
Chèze F 32 E5
Chiajna RO 161 E8
Chiampo I 66 A3
Chianciano Terme I 62 A1
Chianni I 66 E2
Chiaramonte Gulfi I 59 E6
Chiaramonti I 64 B2
Chiaravalle I 67 E7
Chiaravalle Centrale I 59 B9
Chiari I 69 B8
Chiaromonte I 60 C6
Chiasso CH 69 B7
Chiavari I 37 C10
Chiavenno I 69 A7
Chiché F 28 B5
Chichester GB 15 F7
Chichiș RO 153 F7
Chiclana de la Frontera E 52 D4
Chiclana de Segura E 55 C6
Chieming D 72 A6
Chienes I 72 C4
Chieri I 37 A7
Chiesa in Valmalenco I 69 A8
Chieșd RO 151 C10
Chiesina Uzzanese I 66 E2
Chieti I 63 C6
Chieuti I 63 D8
Chieveley GB 13 C12
Chièvres B 19 C8
Chigwell GB 15 D9
Chiheru de Jos RO 152 D5
Chikhachevo RUS 133 B7
Chilches E 48 E4
Chilcompton GB 13 C9
Chilham GB 15 E10
Chiliile RO 161 C9
Chiliomodi GR 175 D6
Chilleurs-aux-Bois F 24 D7
Chillón E 54 B3
Chilluévar E 55 C6
Chiloeches E 47 C6
Chimay B 19 D9
Chimeneas E 53 B9
Chinanale I 36 B6
Chinchilla de Monte Aragón E 55 B9
Chinchón E 46 D6
Chindrieux F 31 D8
Chinon F 23 F12
Chinteni RO 152 D3
Chiochiș RO 152 D4
Chioggia I 66 B5
Chiojdeni RO 161 B9
Chiojdu RO 161 C8
Chiomonte I 31 E10
Chiona GR 174 C4
Chionata GR 174 C2
Chios GR 177 C7
Chiperceni MD 154 B3
Chipiona E 52 C4
Chippenham GB 13 C10
Chipping Campden GB 13 A11
Chipping Norton GB 13 B11
Chipping Ongar GB 15 D9
Chipping Sodbury GB 13 B10
Chippis CH 31 C12
Chiprana E 42 E3
Chiprovtsi BG 165 C6
Chirbury GB 10 F5
Chiren BG 165 C8
Chiriet-Lunga MD 154 E3
Chirivel E 55 D8
Chirk GB 10 F5
Chirnogeni RO 155 F2
Chirnogi RO 161 E9
Chirnside GB 5 D12
Chiroubles F 30 C6
Chirpan BG 166 E4
Chirpăr RO 152 F5
Chirsova MD 154 E3
Chiscani RO 155 C1
Chișcăreni MD 153 B12
Chișcăreni MD 154 C3
Chiselet RO 161 E9
Chișinău MD 154 C3
Chisindia RO 151 E9
Chișineu-Criș RO 151 D8
Chistye-Prudy RUS 136 E5
Chițcani MD 154 D5
Chitignano I 66 E4
Chitila RO 161 D7
Chiuiești RO 152 C3
Chiuro I 69 A8
Chiusa I 72 C4
Chiusa di Pesio I 37 C7
Chiusaforte I 73 D7
Chiusa Sclafani I 58 D3
Chiusavecchia I 37 D7
Chiusdino I 66 F3
Chiusi I 62 A1
Chiusi della Verna I 66 E4
Chiuza RO 152 C4
Chiva E 48 F3
Chivasso I 68 C4
Chizé F 28 C5
Chlebičov CZ 146 B5
Chlebnice SK 147 C8
Chlebowo PL 81 B7
Chlewiska PL 141 H3
Chłopice PL 144 D6
Chludowo PL 81 A11
Chlumčany CZ 76 C4
Chlumec CZ 80 E5
Chlumec nad Cidlinou CZ 77 B8
Chlum u Třeboně CZ 77 E7
Chmielnik PL 143 E10
Chmielno PL 85 C10
Chmiel Pierwszy PL 144 A6
Chminianske Jakubovany SK 145 F3
Chobienia PL 81 C10
Chobienice PL 81 B9
Choceň CZ 77 B10
Choceń PL 138 F7
Chocholná-Velčice SK 146 D5
Chocianów PL 81 D9
Chocicza PL 81 B12
Chociwel PL 85 D8
Chocz PL 142 C4
Choczewo PL 138 A4
Chodecz PL 138 F7
Chodel PL 141 H6
Chodov CZ 75 B12
Chodová Planá CZ 75 C12
Chodów PL 141 F6
Chodów PL 143 B7
Chodzież PL 85 E11
Chojna PL 84 E6
Chojnice PL 85 C13
Chojno PL 81 C12
Chojnów PL 81 D9
Cholet F 28 A4
Chomakovtsi BG 165 C9
Chomelix F 30 E4
Chomérac F 35 A8
Chomutov CZ 76 B4
Chonikas GR 175 D6
Chooz F 19 D10
Chop UA 145 G5
Chora GR 174 E4
Chora GR 175 A8
Chora GR 177 D8
Chora GR 179 B9
Chora GR 179 B9
Chorafakia GR 178 D7
Chora Sfakion GR 178 E7
Chorefto GR 169 F9
Chorges F 36 B4
Chorio GR 177 F8
Choristi GR 171 B6
Chorkówka PL 145 D4
Chorley GB 10 D6
Chorna UA 154 B4
Chorna Tysa UA 152 A4
Chornoholova UA 145 F6
Chornomyn UA 154 A4
Chorzele PL 139 D10
Chorzów PL 143 F6
Chorzyna PL 142 D6
Choszczno PL 85 D8
Chotča SK 145 E4
Chotěboř CZ 77 C9
Chotěšov CZ 76 C4
Chotín SK 149 A10
Chouilly F 25 B11
Chouni GR 174 B4
Chouto P 44 F4
Chouzy-sur-Cisse F 24 E5
Chovar E 48 E4
Choye F 26 F4
Chozas de Abajo E 39 C8
Chrást CZ 76 C4
Chrast CZ 77 C9
Chrastava CZ 81 E7
Chříbská CZ 81 E6
Christchurch GB 13 D11
Christiansfeld DK 86 E4
Christon Bank GB 5 E13
Chropyně CZ 146 C4
Chróścina PL 142 E3
Chrostkowo PL 139 E7
Chroustovice CZ 77 C9
Chrudim CZ 77 C9
Chruślin PL 143 B8
Chruszczobród PL 143 F7
Chrysa GR 171 B7
Chrysafa GR 175 E6
Chryso GR 169 B10
Chrysochorafa GR 169 B9
Chrysochori GR 171 C7
Chrysokellaria GR 178 B2
Chrysoupoli GR 171 C7
Chrzanów PL 143 F7
Chrząstowa Wielka PL 81 D12
Chrząstowice PL 142 E5
Chrzypsko Wielkie PL 81 A10
Chtelnica SK 146 D5
Chuchelná CZ 142 G5
Chudleigh GB 13 D7
Chudoba PL 142 E5
Chulilla E 48 E3
Chulmleigh GB 13 D7
Chuprene BG 165 B6
Chur CH 71 D9
Churchdown GB 13 B10
Church Hill IRL 7 C7
Church Stretton GB 10 F6
Churek BG 165 D8
Churwalden CH 71 D9
Chuzelles F 30 D6
Chvalčov CZ 146 C5
Chvaletice CZ 77 B8
Chvalšiny CZ 76 E6
Chwaszczyno PL 138 B5
Chynadiyeve UA 145 F6
Chyňava CZ 76 B6
Chýnov CZ 77 D7
Chynów PL 141 G4
Chyšky CZ 77 C6
Ciacova RO 159 B7
Ciadîr MD 154 D2
Ciadîr-Lunga MD 154 E3
Ciadoux F 33 D7
Ciampino I 62 D3
Cianciana I 58 D3
Ciasna PL 142 E6
Ciążeń PL 142 B4
Cibakháza H 150 D5
Ciborro P 50 B3
Ciboure F 32 D2
Cicagna I 37 C10
Cicărlău RO 151 B11
Cicciano I 60 B3
Cicerale I 60 C4
Ćićevac SRB 159 F7
Cicibór Duży PL 141 F8
Ciclova Română RO 159 C8
Čičov SK 149 A9
Çidhën AL 163 F9
Cidones E 41 E6
Ciechanów PL 139 E10
Ciechanowiec PL 141 E7
Ciechocinek PL 138 E6
Cielądz PL 141 G2
Ciempozuelos E 46 D5
Ciepielów PL 141 H5
Cieplowody PL 81 E11
Čierna nad Tisou SK 145 G5
Čierne Kľačany SK 146 E6
Čierny Balog SK 147 D9
Cierp-Gaud F 33 E7
Cierznie PL 85 C12
Cieszanów PL 144 C7
Cieszków PL 81 C12
Cieszyn PL 142 D4
Cieszyn PL 147 B7
Cieutat F 33 D6
Cieux F 29 D8
Cieza E 55 C10
Cijżkowice PL 144 D2
Cifer SK 146 E5
Çifliq AL 168 E3
Çiftlikköy TR 173 B7
Çiftlikköy TR 173 B9
Cifuentes E 47 C7
Cigales E 39 E10
Cigánd H 145 G4
Cigliano I 68 C5
Cikó H 149 D11
Cilibia RO 161 C10
Cilieni RO 160 F5
Çilipi HR 162 D5
Čilizská Radvaň SK 146 F5
Cill Airne IRL 8 D4
Cillas E 47 C9
Cill Chainnigh IRL 9 C8
Cill Chaoi IRL 8 C3
Cill Charthaigh IRL 6 C5
Cill Chiaráin IRL 6 F3
Cill Choca IRL 7 F9
Cill Chomhghaill IRL 7 F10
Cill Chormaic IRL 7 F7
Cill Chuillin IRL 7 F9
Cill Dalua IRL 8 C6
Cill Dara IRL 7 F9
Cill Dhéagláin IRL 7 E10
Cill Droichid IRL 7 F9
Cille Bhrighde GB 2 L2
Cilleros E 45 D7
Cill Mhantáin IRL 7 G10
Cill Mocheallóg IRL 8 D5
Cill na Mallach IRL 8 D5
Cill Orglan IRL 8 D3
Cill Rois IRL 8 C4
Cill Rónáin IRL 6 F3
Cilybebyll GB 13 B7
Cimanes del Tejar E 39 C8
Cimballa E 47 B9
Cimdenieki LV 134 C2
Čimelice CZ 76 D6
Ciminna I 58 D4
Cimișlia MD 154 D3
Cimolais I 72 D5
Çinarcik TR 173 C11
Cinco Casas E 47 F6
Cinctorres E 42 F3
Cincu RO 152 F5
Cinderford GB 13 B10
Çine TR 181 A8
Ciñera E 39 C8
Ciney B 19 D11
Cinfães P 44 B4
Cinge TR 177 A9
Cingoli I 67 F7
Cinigiano I 65 B4
Cinisello Balsamo I 69 B7
Cinn Mhara IRL 6 F3
Cinobaňa SK 147 E9
Cinq-Mars-la-Pile F 24 F3
Cinquefrondi I 59 C9
Cintegabelle F 33 D9
Cintrey F 26 E4
Cintruénigo E 41 D8
Ciobănița RO 155 E2
Ciobanu RO 155 D1
Čiobiškis LT 137 D10
Ciocănești RO 161 D7
Ciocănești RO 161 E10
Ciocârlia RO 155 E2
Ciocârlia RO 161 D9
Ciochina RO 161 D10
Ciocile RO 161 D10
Cioc-Maidan MD 154 E3
Ciofrângeni RO 160 C5
Cióirtheach IRL 7 F7
Ciolănești RO 160 E6
Ciolpani RO 161 D8
Cionn tSáile IRL 8 E5
Ciorani RO 161 D8
Ciorăști RO 161 C10
Ciorogârla RO 161 E7
Cioroiași RO 160 E2
Cioropcani MD 153 C11
Ciortești RO 153 D11
Ciprian Porumbescu RO 153 B8
Cirat E 48 D4
Ciraqui E 32 E2
Cīrava LV 134 C2
Circello I 60 A3
Cirencester GB 13 B11
Cireșu RO 159 D10
Cireșu RO 161 D10
Cirey-sur-Blaise F 26 D2
Cirey-sur-Vezouze F 27 C6
Ciria E 41 E8
Ciriè I 68 C4
Cirigliano I 60 C6
Ciripcău MD 154 A2
Cirkale LV 134 B4
Cirma LV 133 C3
Cirò I 61 E8
Cirò Marina I 61 E8
Çirpi TR 177 C10
Ciruelos E 46 E5
Ciruelos del Pinar E 47 B8
Cīruļi LV 134 B4
Ciry-le-Noble F 30 B5
Cisano sul Neva I 37 C8
Cisek PL 142 F5
Cislău RO 161 C8
Cișmichioi MD 155 B2
Cisna PL 145 E5
Cisnădie RO 160 B4
Cisneros E 39 D10
Cisòn di Valmarino I 72 E5
Cissé F 29 B6
Cista Provo HR 157 E6
Cisterna di Latina I 62 D3
Cisternino I 61 B8
Cistierna E 39 C9
Citerna I 66 F5
Čitluk BIH 157 B6
Čitluk BIH 157 F8
Cittadella I 72 E4
Città della Pieve I 62 B2
Città di Castello I 66 F5
Cittanova I 59 C9
Cittareale I 62 B4
Città Sant'Angelo I 62 B6
Cittiglio I 68 B6
Ciucea RO 151 D10
Ciuchici RO 159 D8
Ciuciulea MD 153 B10
Ciucsângeorgiu RO 153 E7
Ciucur-Mingir MD 154 E3
Ciucurova RO 155 D2
Ciudad Real E 54 B5
Ciudad Rodrigo E 45 C7
Ciudanovița RO 159 C8
Ciugud RO 152 E3
Ciuhoi RO 151 C9
Ciulnița RO 161 D10
Ciumani RO 153 D7
Ciumeghiu RO 151 D8
Ciuperceni RO 159 D11
Ciuperceni RO 160 F5
Ciupercenii Noi RO 159 F10
Ciurila RO 152 D3
Ciuruleasa RO 151 E11
Ciutadella E 57 A12
Civaux F 29 C7
Cividale del Friuli I 73 D7
Civita I 61 D6
Civita Castellana I 62 C2
Civita d'Antino I 62 D4
Civitanova del Sannio I 63 D6
Civitanova Marche I 67 F8
Civitaquana I 62 C5
Civitavecchia I 62 C1
Civitella Casanova I 62 C5
Civitella del Tronto I 62 B5
Civitella di Romagna I 66 D4
Civitella in Val di Chiana I 66 F4

Crosby GB 10 E5
Crosia I 61 D7
Cross IRL 6 E4
Crossaig GB 4 D6
Crossakeel IRL 7 E8
Cross Barry IRL 8 E5
Crosscanonby GB 5 F10
Crossdoney IRL 7 E8
Crossgar GB 7 D11
Crossgare GB 4 E3
Crossgates GB 13 A8
Crosshands GB 5 D8
Crosshaven IRL 8 E6
Crosshill GB 4 E7
Cross Inn GB 12 A6
Cross Keys IRL 7 E9
Crossmaglen GB 7 D9
Crotone I 61 E8
Crots F 36 B4
Crottendorf D 76 B3
Croughton GB 13 B12
Croutelle F 29 B6
Crouy F 19 F7
Crouy-sur-Ourcq F 25 B9
Crowborough GB 15 E9
Crowland GB 11 F11
Crowle GB 11 D10
Crowthorne GB 15 E7
Croy GB 3 K8
Croyde GB 12 C6
Crozant F 29 C9
Crozes-Hermitage F 30 E6
Crozon F 22 D3
Cruas F 35 A8
Crucea RO 153 C7
Crucea RO 155 D2
Crucișor RO 151 B11
Crucoli I 61 E7
Cruden Bay GB 3 L13
Cruglic MD 154 C4
Crumlin GB 4 F4
Cruseilles F 31 C9
Crușeț RO 160 D3
Crusheen IRL 8 C5
Crusnes F 20 F5
Cruzy F 34 D4
Cruzy-le-Châtel F 25 E11
Crvenka SRB 158 B3
Crymych GB 12 B5
Csabacsőd H 150 D6
Csabrendek H 149 B8
Csákánydoroszló H 149 C7
Csákberény H 149 B10
Császár H 149 B10
Csanádapáca H 151 D6
Csanádpalota H 150 E6
Csány H 150 B4
Csanytelek H 150 D5
Császár H 149 A10
Császártöltés H 150 E3
Csátalja H 150 E2
Csávoly H 150 E3
Csécse H 147 F9
Csemő H 150 C4
Csengele H 150 D4
Csenger H 151 B10
Csengőd H 150 D3
Csépa H 150 D5
Csepreg H 149 B7
Cserépfalu H 145 H2
Cserháthsurány H 147 F8
Cserkeszőlő H 150 D5
Csernely H 145 G1
Csesztreg H 149 C7
Csetény H 149 B9
Csévharaszt H 150 C3
Csikéria H 150 E3
Csókakő H 149 B10
Csökmő H 151 C7
Csököly H 149 D9
Csokonyavisonta H 149 D8
Csokvaomány H 145 G1
Csolnok H 149 A11
Csólyospálos H 150 E4
Csongrád H 150 D5
Csopak H 149 C9
Csór H 149 B10
Csorna H 149 A8
Csörnyeföld H 149 D7
Csorvás H 150 D6
Csősz H 149 B10
Csót H 149 B9
Csurgó H 149 D8
Cuacos de Yuste E 45 D9
Cuadros E 39 C8
Cualedro E 38 E4
Cuarte de Huerva E 41 E10
Cuba P 50 C4
Cubalhão P 38 D3
Cubells E 42 D5
Cubjac F 29 E7
Cubla E 47 D10
Cubo de Bureba E 40 C5
Cubo de la Solana E 41 E7
Cubolta MD 153 B12
Cubzac-les-Ponts F 28 F5
Cuca RO 153 F11
Cuca RO 160 D5
Cucalón E 47 B10
Cucerdea RO 152 E4
Cuci RO 152 E4
Cuckfield GB 15 E8
Cucuron F 35 C9
Cucuteni RO 153 C9
Cudalbi RO 153 F11
Cudillero E 39 A7
Čudnići BIH 157 D8
Cudos F 32 B5
Cuéllar E 40 F3
Cuenca E 47 D8
Cuenca de Campos E 39 D9
Cuers F 36 E4
Cuerva E 46 E4
Cueva de Agreda E 41 E8
Cuevas Bajas E 53 B8
Cuevas de Almanzora E 55 E9
Cuevas del Becerro E 53 C6
Cuevas del Campo E 55 D7
Cuevas de San Clemente
E 40 D4
Cuevas de San Marcos E 53 B8
Cuevas Labradas E 42 G1
Cuffley GB 15 D8
Cugand F 28 A3
Cuges-les-Pins F 35 D10
Cugir RO 151 F11
Euglieri I 64 C2
Cugnaux F 33 C8
Cuguen F 23 D8
Cuhureștii de Sus MD 154 B3
Cuijk NL 16 E5
Cúil an tSúdaire IRL 7 F8
Cuiseaux F 31 C7
Cuise-la-Motte F 18 F7
Cuisery F 31 B6
Cujmir RO 159 E10
Çukë AL 168 E3
Çukuryurt TR 173 B8
Culan F 29 B10
Culciu RO 151 B11
Culdaff IRL 4 E2
Culdrain GB 3 L11
Culemborg NL 16 E4
Culjković SRB 158 D4
Culla E 48 D4
Cullahill IRL 9 C8
Cúllar-Baza E 55 D7
Cullen GB 3 K11
Cullera E 48 F4
Cullivoe GB 3 D14
Cullompton GB 13 D8
Cully CH 31 C10
Cullybackey GB 4 F4
Cullyhanna GB 7 D9
Culmstock GB 13 D8
Culnaknock GB 2 K4
Culoz F 31 D8
Culswick GB 3 E13
Cumbernauld GB 5 D9
Cumbres de San Bartolomé
E 51 C6
Cumbres Mayores E 51 C6
Cumeada P 50 E3
Cumiana I 31 F11
Cumieira P 38 F4
Cuminestown GB 3 K12
Cumlosen D 83 D11
Cumnock GB 5 E8
Cumpăna RO 155 E3
Cunault F 23 F11
Cunegès F 29 F6
Cuneo I 37 C7
Cunewalde D 81 D7
Cunfin F 25 D12
Cungrea RO 160 D4
Cunha P 44 C6
Cunicea MD 154 B3
Čunište BIH 157 D10
Cunit E 43 E7
Cunningsburgh GB 3 E14
Cuntis E 38 C2
Cuorgnè I 68 C4
Cupar GB 5 C10
Cupcina MD 153 A10
Cupello I 63 C7
Cupra Marittima I 62 A5
Cupramontana I 67 F7
Ćuprija SRB 159 F7
Cupșeni RO 152 B3
Cuq-Toulza F 33 C9
Curățele RO 151 D9
Curcani RO 161 E9
Curcuris I 64 D2
Cureggio I 68 B5
Curesnița MD 153 A12
Curgy F 30 B5
Curinga I 59 B9
Curon Venosta I 71 D11
Curracloe IRL 9 D10
Curraghroe IRL 6 E6
Curragh West IRL 6 E5
Currás E 38 C2
Curry IRL 6 E5
Curry Rivel GB 13 C9
Cursi I 61 C10
Curtea RO 151 F9
Curtea de Argeș RO 160 C5
Curtici RO 151 E7
Curtișoara RO 160 E4
Curtuișeni RO 151 B9
Čurug SRB 158 C5
Cusano Mutri I 60 A3
Cushendall GB 4 E4
Cushendun GB 4 E4
Cushina IRL 7 F8
Cussac F 29 D7
Cusset F 30 C3
Cussy-les-Forges F 25 F11
Custines F 26 C5
Custonaci I 58 C2
Cutigliano I 66 D2
Cutro I 61 E7
Cutrofiano I 61 C10
Cuxac-Cabardès F 33 D10
Cuxac-d'Aude F 34 D4
Cuxhaven D 17 A11
Cuzăplac RO 151 D11
Cuza Vodă RO 161 E10
Cuzmin MD 154 A3
Cuzorn F 33 A7
Cvikov CZ 81 E7
Cwmafan GB 13 B7
Cwmbrân GB 13 B8
Cybinka PL 81 B7
Cybowo PL 85 D9
Cychry PL 85 E7
Cyców PL 141 H8
Cydweli GB 12 B6
Cynghordy GB 13 A7
Cynwyl Elfed GB 12 B6
Cyprianka PL 138 E7
Cysoing F 182 D2
Czacz PL 81 B11
Czajków PL 142 D5
Czaplinek PL 85 C10
Czarna PL 143 F11
Czarna PL 144 C5
Czarna Białostocka PL 140 D8
Czarna Dąbrówka PL 85 B13
Czarna Górna PL 145 E6
Czarna Woda PL 138 C5
Czarnca PL 143 E8
Czarne PL 85 C11
Czarnia PL 139 D11
Czarnków PL 85 E11
Czarnocin PL 143 F10
Czarnów PL 81 A7
Czarnowąsy PL 142 E4
Czarnożyły PL 142 D6
Czarny Bór PL 81 E10
Czarny Dunajec PL 147 C9
Czastary PL 142 D5
Czaszyn PL 145 E5
Czchów PL 144 D2
Czechowice-Dziedzice PL 147 B8
Czechy PL 85 C11
Czechy PL 143 C6
Czekarzewice PL 143 D12
Czeladź PL 143 F7
Czemierniki PL 141 G7
Czempiń PL 81 B11
Czeremcha PL 141 E8
Czermin PL 142 C4
Czermno PL 141 H2
Czernica PL 81 D12
Czernice Borowe PL 139 D10
Czernichów PL 143 G8
Czernichów PL 147 B8
Czerniejewo PL 85 F12
Czerniewice PL 141 G2
Czernikowo PL 138 E6
Czernina PL 81 C11
Czersk PL 138 C4
Czerwieńsk PL 81 B8
Czerwin PL 139 E12
Czerwińsk nad Wisłą PL 139 F9
Czerwionka-Leszczyny PL 142 F6
Czerwonak PL 81 B11
Czerwone PL 139 D12
Czestków PL 143 C7
Częstochowa PL 143 E7
Czeszów PL 81 D12
Człopa PL 85 D10
Człuchów PL 85 C12
Czmoń PL 81 B12
Czorsztyn PL 145 E1
Czosnów PL 139 F10
Czudec PL 144 D4
Czyże PL 141 E8
Czyżew-Osada PL 141 E6

D

Daaden D 185 C8
Dăbâca RO 152 D3
Dabar HR 156 C3
Dabar HR 156 E6
Dabas H 150 C3
Dabel D 83 C11
Dąbie PL 81 B8
Dąbie PL 141 G6
Dąbie PL 142 B6
Dąbki PL 85 B10
Dabo F 27 C7
Daborgrad BIH 157 C9
Dabrac BIH 157 D7
Dabravolya BY 140 E10
Dabrica BIH 157 F9
Dąbroszyn PL 81 A7
Dąbroszyn PL 142 B5
Dąbrowa PL 138 E4
Dąbrowa PL 142 E4
Dąbrowa PL 142 E4
Dąbrowa Białostocka PL 140 C8
Dąbrowa Biskupia PL 138 E6
Dąbrowa Chełmińska PL 138 D5
Dąbrowa Górnicza PL 143 F7
Dąbrowa Tarnowska PL 143 F10
Dąbrowa Zielona PL 143 E8
Dąbrowice PL 141 G2
Dąbrowice PL 143 B7
Dąbrówka Wielka PL 143 C7
Dąbrówka Wielkopolska
PL 81 B9
Dąbrówno PL 139 D9
Dăbuleni RO 160 F4
Dabyeya BY 133 F7
Dachau D 75 F9
Dachnów PL 144 C7
Dachrieden D 79 D7
Dachwig D 79 D8
Dačice CZ 77 D8
Dacre GB 5 F11
Dad H 149 A10
Dadia GR 171 B10
Dădran S 103 E10
Dăeni RO 155 D2
Dăești RO 160 C4
Dåfjord N 112 D3
Dafnes GR 174 C4
Dafni GR 171 D6
Dafni GR 174 D5
Dafni GR 175 C8
Dafni GR 175 F6
Dåg H 149 A11
Daganzo de Arriba E 46 C6
Dağardi TR 173 F11
Dagâța RO 153 D10
Dagda LV 133 D3
Dagebüll D 82 A5
Dağkizilca TR 177 C9
Daglan F 29 F8
Daglösen S 97 C11
Dagmersellen CH 27 F8
Dağpinar TR 181 B8
Dagsmark FIN 122 F7
Dahlem D 21 D7
Dahlen D 80 D4
Dahlenburg D 83 D9
Dahlhausen D 183 C10
Dahme D 80 C4
Dahme D 83 B10
Dahn D 27 B8
Dähre D 83 E9
Daia RO 161 F7
Daia Română RO 152 E3
Daikanberg S 107 A10
Daikanvik S 107 A10
Dailly GB 4 E7
Daimiel E 46 F5
Daimonia GR 178 B4
Daingean IRL 7 F8
Daingean Uí Chúis IRL 8 D2
Dainville F 18 D6
Dainville-Bertheléville F 26 D4
Dairsie GB 5 C11
Daknam B 182 C3
Đakovo HR 149 F10
Dal N 95 B14
Dal S 107 E13
Đala SRB 150 E5
Dalaas A 71 C10
Dalabrog GB 2 L2
Dalaman TR 181 C9
Dalarö S 93 A12
Dala Rostock S 91 B11
Dalåsen S 102 A7
Dalasjö S 107 B11
Dalbe LV 135 C7
Dalbeattie GB 5 F9
Dalberg-Wendelstorf D 83 C10
Dalboșeț RO 159 D8
Dalby DK 86 D7
Dalby DK 87 E10
Dalby GBM 10 C2
Dalby S 87 D12
Dalbyn S 103 D9
Dalbyover DK 86 B6
Daldenäs S 92 A4
Dale GB 9 E12
Dale N 90 B3
Dale N 100 D2
Dale N 100 E3
Dale N 111 C11
Daleiden D 20 D6
Dalen N 90 A5
Dalen N 94 D7
Dalen NL 17 C7
Daleszyce PL 143 E10
Dalfors S 103 D9
Dalfsen NL 16 C6
Dalgety Bay GB 5 C10
Dalham GB 15 C10
Dalhem B 19 C12
Dalhem S 93 D13
Dalholen N 101 B11
Dalias E 55 F7
Dalików PL 143 C7
Dalj HR 157 B10
Dalkarlsberg S 97 D12
Dalkeith GB 5 D10
Dalkey IRL 7 F10
Dallas GB 3 K10
Dallgow D 80 A4
Dall Villaby DK 86 B5
Dalmally GB 4 C7
Dalmand H 149 D10
Dalmellington GB 5 E8
Dalmine I 69 B8
Dalmose DK 87 E8
Dalovice CZ 76 B3
Dalry GB 4 D7
Dalrymple GB 4 E7
Dalsbruk FIN 126 E8
Dalsbygda N 101 A14
Dalselv N 108 D6
Dalsjöfors S 91 D13
Dals Långed S 91 B11
Dalstein F 20 F6
Dalston GB 5 F11
Dalstorp S 91 D14
Dalstuga S 103 D10
Dalton-in-Furness GB 10 C5
Daluis F 36 C5
Dalum S 91 D13
Dalur FO 2 B3
Dalvadas FIN 113 D17
Dalwhinnie GB 5 B8
Dalyan TR 181 C9
Dalyokiya BY 135 F13
Dalystown IRL 6 F6
Damachava BY 141 G9
Damas-aux-Bois F 26 D5
Damasi GR 169 E7
Damaskinia GR 168 D5
Damasławek PL 85 E13
Damazan F 33 B6
Dambach-la-Ville F 186 E3
Dambaslar TR 173 B7
Dambeck D 83 D11
Dâmbovicioara RO 160 C6
Damelevières F 26 C5
Damerstown IRL 9 C8
Damery F 25 B10
Damës AL 168 C2
Damgan F 22 E6
Damhead GB 4 E3
Damhliag IRL 7 E10
Dămienești RO 153 D9
Damigny F 23 D12
Damjan RKS 163 E10
Dammarie F 24 D6
Dammartin-en-Goële F 25 B8
Damme B 19 B7
Damme D 17 C10
Damnica PL 85 B12
Damno PL 85 A12
Damp D 83 A7
Dampierre F 26 F4
Dampierre-sur-Linotte F 26 E5
Dampierre-sur-Salon F 26 E4
Dampricharð F 27 F6
Damshagen D 83 C10
Damsholte DK 87 F10
Dämsta S 107 E13
Dămuc RO 153 D7
Damüls A 71 C9
Damvant CH 27 F6
Damville F 24 C5
Damvillers F 19 F11
Damwoude NL 16 B6
Damyanovo BG 165 D10
Danaçali TR 173 E10
Danakos GR 177 E6
Danamandira TR 173 B9
Danasjö S 109 E12
Dănciulești RO 160 D3
Dăneasa RO 160 E5
Daneș RO 152 E5
Danesfort IRL 7 E7
Dănești RO 153 D7
Dănești RO 153 D11
Dănești RO 160 D2
Danețí RO 160 F4
Dângebo S 89 B8
Dângeni RO 153 B9
Dangé-St-Romain F 29 B7
Danholn S 103 E10
Dănicei RO 160 D4
Daniec PL 142 E5
Danilovgrad MNE 163 D7
Dänischenhagen D 83 B8
Danişment TR 173 E8
Danjoutin F 27 E6
Dankerode D 79 C9
Danndorf D 79 B8
Dannemare DK 83 A10
Dannemarie F 27 E7
Dannemora S 99 B9
Dannenberg (Elbe) D 83 D10
Dannenwalde D 84 D4
Dány H 150 B4
Daon F 23 E10
Daoulas F 22 D3
Darabani RO 153 A9
Dărăști Ilfov RO 161 E8
Darbėnai LT 134 D2
Dar Ben Karricha el Behri
MA 53 E6
Darby's Bridge IRL 8 D2
Dar Chaoui MA 52 E5
Darda HR 149 E11
Dardesheim D 79 C8
Dardhas AL 168 C4
Darè I 69 A10
Darfo Boario Terme I 69 B9
Dargun D 83 C13
Darica TR 173 D8
Darici TR 173 F10
Dârjiu RO 152 E6
Darkley GB 7 D9
Darlington GB 11 B8
Dârlos RO 152 E4
Darłówko PL 85 B10
Darłowo PL 85 B10
Dărmănești RO 153 B8
Dărmănești RO 153 E8
Dărmănești RO 160 C5
Dărmănești RO 161 D7
Darmstadt D 21 E11
Darney F 26 D5
Darnieulles F 26 D5
Darnózseli H 146 F4
Daroca E 47 B10
Darova RO 159 B8
Darque P 38 E2
Darra GB 3 K12
Darragh IRL 8 C4
Darro E 55 E6
Dartford GB 15 E9
Dartmeet GB 13 D7
Dartmouth GB 13 E7
Darton GB 11 D8
Dartsel S 118 C4
Daruvar HR 149 E8
Dârvari RO 159 E11
Darwen GB 10 D7
Dascălu RO 161 D8
Dashava UA 145 E9
Dašice CZ 77 B9
Dasing D 75 F9
Dasochori GR 169 B9
Dasochori GR 171 C7
Dassel D 78 C6
Dassendorf D 83 D8
Dassow D 83 C9
Daszyna PL 143 B7
Datça TR 181 C7
Datteln D 17 E8
Datterode (Ringgau) D 79 D7
Daudzese LV 135 D10
Daudzeva LV 135 C10
Daugai LT 137 E9
Daugailiai LT 135 E11
Daugård DK 86 D5
Daugavpils LV 135 E13
Daugėlaičiai LT 134 E7
Dauguļi LV 135 A10
Daujėnai LT 135 E9
Daumazan-sur-Arize F 33 D8
Daumeray F 23 E11
Daun D 21 D7
Dauphin F 35 C10
Dava GB 3 L9
Daventry GB 13 A12
Davézieux F 30 E6
Davidești RO 160 C6
Davidkovo BG 165 F10
Daviot GB 3 L8
Davle CZ 76 C6
Davleia GR 175 B6
Dávod H 150 E2
Davoli I 59 B9
Davor HR 157 B8
Davos CH 71 D9
Davutlar TR 177 D9
Davydiv UA 144 D9
Dawhinava BY 133 E3
Dawlish GB 13 D8
Dax F 32 C3
Deal GB 15 E11
Dealu RO 152 E6
Dealu Morii RO 153 E10
Dearham GB 5 F10
Deauville F 23 B12
Deba E 32 D1
Debar MK 168 A4
Debeli Lug SRB 159 E8
Debeljača SRB 158 C6
Debenham GB 15 C11
Dębe Wielkie PL 141 F4
Dębica PL 143 F11
De Bilt NL 16 D4
Dęblin PL 141 G5
Debnevo BG 165 D10
Dębnica Kaszubska PL 85 B12
Dębno PL 85 E7
Dębno PL 143 G10
Dęborzeczka PL 141 H2
Debovo BG 165 B10
Dębowa Kłoda PL 141 G8
Dębowa Łąka PL 138 D7
Dębowiec PL 147 B7
Debrc SRB 158 D4
Debrecen H 151 B8
Debrešte MK 168 B5
Debrzno PL 85 C12
Dębsko PL 85 D9
Debür BG 166 E4
Deçan RKS 163 D9
Decazeville F 33 A10
Dechtice SK 146 D5
Decimomannu I 64 E2
Decimoputzu I 64 E2
Děčín CZ 80 E6
Decize F 30 B3
De Cocksdorp NL 16 B3
Decollatura I 59 A9
Decs H 149 D11
Deda RO 152 D5
Deddington GB 13 B12
Dedeleben D 79 B8
Dedeler TR 173 F9
Dedelow D 84 D5
Dedelstorf D 83 E9
Dedemsvaart NL 17 C6
Dédestapolcsány H 145 G2
Dedham GB 15 D10
Dedovichi RUS 132 F6
Deensen D 78 C6
Deerlijk B 19 C7
Dég H 149 C10
Degaña E 39 C6
Degeberga S 88 D6
Degerbäcken S 118 C6
Degerby FIN 99 B14
Degerby FIN 127 E11
Degerfors S 92 A4
Degerhamn S 89 C10
Degersjö S 107 D12
Degerträsk S 118 D4
Deggendorf D 76 E3
Deggingen D 74 E6
Değirmen TR 173 B9
Değirmendere TR 177 C9
Değirmendüzü TR 171 D10
Değirmenyeni TR 167 F7
Dego I 37 C8
Degučiai LT 135 E12
Degumnieki LV 135 C13
De Haan B 19 B7
Dehesa de Campoamor E 56 F3
Dehesas de Guadix E 55 D6
Deià E 49 E10
Deidesheim D 21 F10
Deifontes E 53 B9
Deilão P 39 E6
Deining D 75 D10
Deiningen D 75 E8
Deinste D 17 A12
Deinze B 19 C8
Deiva Marina I 37 C11
Dej RO 152 C3
Deje S 97 C9
Dejtár H 147 E8
Dekani SLO 67 A8
Dekeleia GR 175 C8
De Koog NL 16 B3
De Kooy NL 16 C3
Dekov BG 165 B11
Delabole GB 12 D5
Delary S 87 B13
Delbrück D 17 E11
Delčevo MK 165 F6
Delden NL 17 D7
Délegyháza H 150 C3
Deleitosa E 45 E9
Đelekovec HR 149 D7
Delémont CH 27 F7
Delen' UA 154 F4
Deleni RO 153 C9
Deleni RO 155 E2
Deleria GR 169 E7
Delești RO 153 D11
Delfoi GR 175 C6
Delft NL 16 D2
Delfzijl NL 17 B7
Delia I 58 E4
Delianuova I 59 C8
Deliblato SRB 159 D7
Deliceto I 60 A4
Deligrad SRB 159 F8
Deliktaş TR 177 B8
Delingsdorf D 83 C8
Delitzsch D 79 C11
Delle F 27 E7
Delligsen D 78 C6
Dello I 66 B1
Delme F 26 C5
Delmenhorst D 17 B11
Delnice HR 67 B10
Delsbo S 103 C12
Deltebre E 42 F5
Delvin IRL 7 E8
Delvinaki GR 168 E3
Delvinë AL 168 E3
Demandice SK 147 E7
Demange-aux-Eaux F 26 C3
Dembava LT 135 E8
Demecser H 145 G4
De Meern NL 183 A6
Demen D 83 C11
Demene LV 135 E13
Demigny F 30 B6
Demiraj AL 163 E7
Demirciḥalil TR 167 F8
Demirdere TR 173 D9
Demirhanli TR 167 F7
Demir Hisar MK 168 B5
Demir Kapija MK 169 B7
Demirköy TR 167 F9
Demirli TR 181 C9
Demirtaş TR 173 D11
Demmin D 84 C4
Demonte I 37 C6
Dému F 33 C6
Denain F 19 D7
Denbigh GB 10 E5
Den Bommel NL 182 B4
Den Burg NL 16 B3
Denderleeuw B 182 D4
Dendermonde B 19 B9
Den Dungen NL 16 E4
Denekamp NL 17 D8
Denguin F 32 D5
Den Haag NL 16 D2
Den Haag NL 182 A4
Denham GB 15 D8
Den Ham NL 17 D7
Den Helder NL 16 C3
Denholm GB 5 E11
Denia E 56 D5
Denkendorf D 27 C11
Denkendorf D 75 E9
Denkingen D 27 D10
Denkingen D 27 E11
Denklingen D 71 B11
Dennewitz D 80 C4
Dennhausen (Fuldabrück)
D 78 D5
Denny GB 5 C9
Den Oever NL 16 C4
Densow D 84 D4
Densuș RO 159 B10
Denta RO 159 C7
Dentergem B 19 C7
Dentlein am Forst D 75 D7
Denver GB 11 F12
Denzlingen D 27 D8
Déols F 29 B9
De Panne B 18 B6
Deppis S 109 E18
Deråsbrenna N 105 C10
Derby GB 11 F9
Derecske H 151 C8
Dereham GB 15 B10
Derekegyház H 150 D5
Dereköy TR 167 F8
Dereköy TR 173 F7
Derenburg D 79 C8
Derenti TR 173 E7
De Rijp NL 16 C3
Dermantsi BG 165 C9
Dermbach D 79 E7
Dermenas AL 168 C2
Derna RO 151 C9
Dernau D 21 C8
Derreen IRL 6 D4
Derreendaragh IRL 8 E3
Derreeny Bridge IRL 8 E4
Derry GB 4 F2
Derrygonnelly GB 7 D7
Derrylin GB 7 D7
Derrymore IRL 8 D3
Derrynawilt GB 7 D8
Derryrush IRL 6 F3
Derrywode IRL 6 E5
Dersca RO 153 B8
Dersingham GB 11 F13
Dersum D 17 C8
Deruta I 62 B2
Dervaig GB 4 B4
Derval F 23 E8
Dervenakia GR 175 D6
Derveni GR 174 C5
Derventa BIH 157 C8
Derviçan AL 168 D3
Dervio I 69 A7
Derviziana GR 168 F4
Dervock GB 4 E4
Desa RO 159 F11
Desana I 68 C5
Desantne UA 155 B5
Descargamaría E 45 D8
Descartes F 29 B7
Desenzano del Garda I 66 B2
Désertines F 29 C11
Desești RO 152 B3
Desfina GR 175 C6
Deskati GR 169 E6
Deskle SLO 73 D8
Despotovac SRB 159 E7
Despotovo SRB 158 C4
Dessau D 79 C11
Dessel B 16 F4
De Steeg NL 16 D6
Destelbergen B 19 B8
Deštná CZ 77 D7
Destriana E 39 D7
Desulo I 64 C3
Desvres F 15 F12
Deszczno PL 85 E8
Deszk H 150 E5
Deta RO 159 C7
Detern D 17 B9
Detk H 150 B5
Detkovac HR 149 E9
Dětmarovice CZ 146 B6
Detmold D 17 E11
Dettelbach D 75 C7
Dettenhausen D 187 D7
Dettingen an der Erms D
187 D7
Dettmannsdorf D 83 B13
Dettum D 79 B8
Dettwiller F 186 D3
Detva SK 147 D8
Deurne NL 16 F5
Deutsch Evern D 83 D8
Deutschfeistritz A 148 B4
Deutschhof D 84 E3
Deutschkreutz A 149 A7
Deutschlandsberg A 73 C11
Deutschneudorf D 80 E4
Deutsch-Wagram A 77 F11
Deutzen D 79 D11
Deva RO 151 F10
Dévaványa H 151 C6
Devecikonağı TR 173 E10
Devecser H 149 B8
Devene BG 165 C8
Deventer NL 16 D6
Devesel RO 159 E10
Deveselu RO 160 E4
Devetaki BG 165 C10
Deville F 184 E2
Devil's Bridge GB 13 A7
Devin BG 165 F9
Devizes GB 13 C11
Devletliağaç TR 167 F8
Devnya BG 167 C9
Devrske HR 156 E4
De Wijk NL 16 C6
Dewsbury GB 11 D8
Deza E 41 F7
Dežanovac HR 149 E8
Dezghingea MD 154 E3
Dezna RO 151 E9
Dhërmi AL 168 D2
Dhron D 185 E6
Diafani GR 181 E6
Diakofto GR 174 C5
Dialampi GR 171 B8
Diamante I 60 D5
Dianalund DK 87 D8
Diano d'Alba I 37 B8
Diano Marina I 37 D8
Diavata GR 169 C8
Diavolitsi GR 174 E4
Dichiseni RO 161 E11
Dicomano I 66 E4
Didam NL 16 E6
Didcot GB 13 B12
Didderse D 79 B7
Didești RO 160 E5
Didyma GR 175 E7
Didymoteicho GR 171 B10
Didžiasalis LT 135 F13
Die F 31 F7
Dieblich D 21 D8
Dieburg D 21 E11
Dieci RO 151 E9
Diedorf D 75 F8
Diego Álvaro E 45 C10
Diekhof D 83 C12
Diekholzen D 78 B6
Diekirch L 20 E6
Dielheim D 21 F11
Dielmissen D 78 C6
Dielsdorf CH 27 F9
Diemen NL 16 D3
Diémoz F 31 D7
Dienheim D 185 E9
Dienne F 30 E2
Dienville F 25 D12
Diepenau D 17 D11
Diepenbeek B 19 C11
Diepenheim NL 183 A9
Diepenveen NL 183 A8
Diepholz D 17 C10
Dieppe F 18 E3
Dierdorf D 21 C9
Dieren NL 16 D6
Dierhagen D 83 B12
Diesdorf D 83 E9
Dieskau D 79 D11
Diespeck D 75 C8
Diessen NL 183 C6
Dießen am Ammersee D 72 A3
Diessenhofen CH 27 E10
Diest B 19 C11
Dietachdorf A 77 F6
Dietenheim D 71 A10
Dietersburg D 76 E3
Dietfurt an der Altmühl D
75 D10
Dietikon CH 27 F9
Dietingen D 27 D10
Dietmanns A 77 E7
Dietmanns A 77 E8
Dietmannsried D 71 B10
Dietzenbach D 21 D11
Dietzhölztal-Ewersbach D
185 C9
Dieue-sur-Meuse F 26 B3
Dieulefit F 35 A9
Dieulouard F 26 C5
Dieuze F 26 C6
Dieveniškės LT 137 E12
Diever NL 16 C6
Diex A 73 C10
Diezma E 55 E6
Differdange L 20 E5
Digerberget S 97 B9
Digerberget S 102 A8
Digermulen N 110 D8
Digernes N 100 B5
Dignac F 29 D6
Dignāja LV 135 D12
Dignano I 73 D6
Digne-les-Bains F 36 C4

Digny F 24 C5
Digoin F 30 C4
Dihtiv UA 144 B9
Dijon F 26 F3
Dikaia GR 166 F6
Dikanäs S 107 A10
Dikancë RKS 163 E10
Dikili TR 177 A8
Dikkebus B 18 C6
Dikļi LV 131 F10
Diksmuide B 18 B6
Dilar E 53 B9
Dilbeek B 182 D4
Dilesi GR 175 C8
Dilinata GR 174 C2
Dillenburg D 21 C10
Dilling N 95 D13
Dillingen (Saar) D 21 F7
Dillingen an der Donau D 75 E7
Dilove UA 145 H9
Dilsen B 19 B12
Dimaro I 71 E11
Diminio GR 169 F8
Dimitrie Cantemir RO 153 D12
Dimitritsi GR 169 C9
Dimitrovgrad BG 166 E5
Dimitrovgrad SRB 165 C6
Dimitsana GR 174 D5
Dimovo BG 159 F10
Dimzukalns LV 135 C8
Dinami I 59 B9
Dinan F 23 D7
Dinant B 19 D10
Dinard F 23 C7
Dingé F 23 D8
Dingelstädt D 79 D7
Dingelstedt am Huy D 79 C8
Dingle IRL 8 D2
Dingle S 91 B10
Dingolfing D 75 E12
Dingtuna S 98 C6
Dingwall GB 2 K8
Dinjiška HR 67 D11
Dinkelsbühl D 75 D7
Dinkelscherben D 75 F8
Dinklage D 17 C10
Dinnet GB 5 A11
Dinslaken D 17 E7
Dinteloord NL 16 E2
Dinther NL 183 B6
Dinxperlo NL 17 E6
Diö S 88 B6
Dion GR 169 D7
Diósd H 149 B11
Diosig RO 151 C9
Diósjenő H 147 F8
Dioști RO 160 E4
Diou F 30 B4
Dipignano I 60 E6
Dipotama GR 171 B7
Dipotamia GR 168 D4
Dippach L 20 E6
Dippoldiswalde D 80 E5
Dirdal N 94 E4
Dirhami EST 130 C7
Dirivaara S 116 E8
Dirkshorn NL 16 C3
Dirksland NL 16 E2
Dirlewang D 71 A11
Dirmstein D 187 B5
Dirvonėnai LT 134 E5
Dischingen D 75 E7
Disentis Muster CH 71 D7
Diseröd S 91 D11
Dison B 19 C12
Diss GB 15 C11
Dissay F 29 B6
Dissay-sous-Courcillon F 24 E3
Dissen am Teutoburger Wald D 17 D10
Distington GB 10 B4
Distomo GR 175 C6
Distrato GR 168 D5
Ditfurt D 79 C9
Ditrău RO 153 D7
Ditton GB 15 E9
Ditzingen D 27 C11
Divača SLO 73 E8
Divarata GR 174 C2
Diva Slatina BG 165 C6
Divci SRB 158 E5
Divčibare SRB 158 E5
Dives-sur-Mer F 23 B11
Dividalen N 111 C18
Divieto I 59 C7
Divín SK 147 E9
Divina SK 147 C7
Divion F 18 D6
Divišov CZ 77 C7
Divjakë AL 168 C2
Divonne-les-Bains F 31 C9
Divuša HR 156 B5
Dixmont F 25 D9
Dizy F 25 B10
Dizy-le-Gros F 19 E9
Djäkneboda S 122 B5
Djäkneböle S 122 C4
Djupen N 111 B18
Djupfjord N 110 C9
Djupfors S 109 E11
Djupsjö S 107 E14
Djuptjärn S 107 D15
Djupvik N 109 B10
Djupvik N 112 D5
Djupvik S 89 A11
Djura S 103 E8
Djurås S 97 A13
Djurmo S 97 A13
Djurö S 99 D11
Dlhá nad Oravou SK 147 C8
Dlouhá Loučka CZ 77 C12
Dlouhá Třebová CZ 77 C10
Długołęka PL 81 D12
Długołęka PL 140 D7
Długosiodło PL 139 E12
Dłutów PL 143 C7
Dlŭzhka Polyana BG 166 C6
Dmytrivka UA 154 F3
Dmytrivka UA 154 F4
Dmytrivka UA 155 B4
Dnestrovsc MD 154 D5
Dno RUS 132 F6
Doagh GB 4 F4
Doba RO 151 B10
Dobanovci SRB 158 D5
Dobârceni RO 153 B10
Dobârlău RO 153 F7
Dobbertin D 83 C12
Dobbiaco I 72 C5
Dobczyce PL 144 D1
Dobele LV 134 C6
Döbeln D 80 D4
Doberçan RKS 164 E4
Doberlug-Kirchhain D 80 C5
Döbern D 81 C7
Dobersberg A 77 E8
Doberschütz D 79 D12
Dobiegniew PL 85 E9
Dobieszewo PL 85 B12
Dobieszyn PL 141 G4
Doboj BIH 157 C9
Dobova SLO 148 E5
Doboz H 151 D7
Dobrá CZ 146 B6
Dobra PL 85 C8
Dobra PL 142 C6
Dobra PL 144 D1
Dobra RO 151 F10
Dobra RO 161 D7
Dobra SRB 159 D8
Dobrá Niva SK 147 E8
Dobřany CZ 76 C4
Dobre PL 138 E6
Dobre PL 139 F12
Dobre Miasto PL 136 F1
Dobreni RO 153 D8
Dobreşinci MK 169 A8
Dobreşti RO 151 D9
Dobreşti RO 160 D6
Dobreşti RO 160 F3
Dobrevo MK 164 E5
Dobrica SRB 159 C6
Dobričevo SRB 159 D7
Dobrich BG 155 F1
Dobrich BG 166 E5
Dobri Do SRB 164 D3
Dobri Dol BG 159 F11
Dobrin RO 151 C11
Dobrinishte BG 165 F8
Dobříš CZ 76 C6
Dobritz D 79 B11
Dobřív CZ 76 C5
Dobrljin BIH 156 B5
Dobrna SLO 73 D11
Dobrnič SLO 73 E10
Dobrnja BIH 157 C7
Dobrnja BIH 157 C10
Dobrnje SRB 159 E7
Dobro E 40 C4
Dobrodzień PL 142 E5
Döbrököz H 149 D10
Dobromierz PL 81 E10
Dobromir RO 155 E1
Dobromirka BG 166 C4
Dobromirtsi BG 171 B8
Dobromyl' UA 145 D6
Dobroń PL 143 C7
Dobron' UA 145 G5
Dobronín CZ 77 D9
Dobro Polje BIH 157 E10
Dobro Polje SRB 159 F9
Dobrošane MK 164 E4
Dobrosloveni RO 160 E4
Dobrosyn UA 144 C8
Dobroszyce PL 81 D12
Doboteasa RO 160 D4
Dobroteşti RO 160 E5
Dobrotić SRB 164 C4
Dobrotich BG 167 C8
Dobrotino MK 169 B6
Dobrotitsa BG 161 F9
Dobrovăţ RO 153 D11
Dobrovci BIH 157 C9
Dobrovice CZ 77 B7
Dobrovnik SLO 149 C6
Dobrovol'sk RUS 136 D5
Dobrowoda PL 143 F10
Dobruchi RUS 132 D2
Dobrun BIH 158 F3
Dobrun RO 160 E4
Dobruşa MD 154 B3
Dobruševo MK 169 B5
Dobruška CZ 77 B10
Dobrzankowo PL 139 E10
Dobrzany PL 85 D8
Dobrzeń Wielki PL 142 E4
Dobrzyca PL 142 C4
Dobrzyków PL 139 F8
Dobrzyń nad Wisłą PL 139 E7
Dobšiná SK 145 F1
Dóc H 150 E5
Docking GB 15 B10
Dockmyr S 103 A10
Docksta S 107 E14
Dockweiler D 21 D7
Doclin RO 159 C8
Doddington GB 5 D12
Dodewaard NL 183 B7
Dodonoupoli GR 168 E4
Dödre S 102 A8
Doesburg NL 16 D6
Doetinchem NL 16 E6
Dofteana RO 153 E9
Doğanbey TR 177 C8
Doğanbey TR 177 D9
Doğanci TR 173 D10
Doğanköy TR 173 D10
Döge H 145 G5
Dogliani I 37 B7
Dognecea RO 159 C8
Döğüşbelen TR 181 C9
Dohna D 80 E5
Dohňany SK 146 C6
Dohren D 17 C9
Doiceşti RO 160 D6
Doïrani GR 169 B8
Doire Iorrais IRL 6 F3
Doische B 19 D10
Dojč SK 146 D4
Dojkinci SRB 165 C6
Dokka N 101 E12
Dokkas S 116 D6
Dokkedal DK 86 B6
Dokkum NL 16 B5
Doksy CZ 76 B6
Doksy CZ 81 E7
Doktor Yosifovo BG 165 C7
Dokupe LV 134 B3
Dolanog GB 10 F5
Dolbenmaen GB 10 F3
Dolceacqua I 37 D7
Dol-de-Bretagne F 23 C8
Dole BIH 157 D10
Dole F 26 F3
Dølemo N 90 B3
Dolenci MK 168 B5
Dolenja Vas SLO 73 E10
Dolenjske Toplice SLO 73 E11
Dolgarrog GB 10 E4
Dolgellau GB 10 F4
Dolgen D 84 D4
Dolgorukovo RUS 136 E2
Dolhan TR 167 F8
Dolhasca RO 153 C9
Dolheşti RO 153 C9
Dolheşti RO 153 D11
Dołhobyczów PL 144 B9
Dolianova I 64 E3
Dolice PL 85 D8
Dolichi GR 169 D7
Doljani BIH 157 E8
Doljani HR 156 D5
Doljevac SRB 164 C4
Dolla IRL 8 C6
Dolle D 79 B10
Dollern D 82 C7
Döllnitz D 79 D11
Dollnstein D 75 E9
Dollon F 24 D4
Dolna MD 154 C2
Dolna Banya BG 165 E8
Dolna Dikanya BG 165 E7
Dolna Gradeshnitsa BG 165 F7
Dolnaja LV 135 D12
Dolná Krupá SK 146 E5
Dolna Lipnitska BG 166 C4
Dolna Makhala BG 165 E10
Dolna Melna BG 164 D6
Dolna Mitropoliya BG 165 C10
Dolna Oryakhovitsa BG 166 C5
Dolná Strehová SK 147 E8
Dolná Súča SK 146 D6
Dolná Tižina SK 147 C7
Dolna Vasilitsa BG 165 E8
Dolné Orešany SK 146 E4
Dolné Vestenice SK 146 D6
Dolní Bousov CZ 77 B8
Dolní Bukovsko CZ 77 D7
Dolní Čermná CZ 77 C11
Dolni Chiflik BG 167 D9
Dolní Dobrouč CZ 77 C11
Dolni Dŭbnik BG 165 C9
Dolní Dvořiště CZ 77 E7
Dolni Glavanak BG 166 F5
Dolní Kounice CZ 77 D10
Dolni Lom BG 165 C6
Dolní Loučky CZ 77 D10
Dolní Němčí CZ 146 D5
Dolní Podluží CZ 81 E7
Dolní Újezd CZ 77 C10
Dolní Újezd CZ 146 B5
Dolni Voden BG 165 E10
Dolní Šandov CZ 75 B12
Dolno Dupeni MK 168 C5
Dolno Ezerovo BG 167 D8
Dolno Kamartsi BG 165 D8
Dolno Konjare MK 164 F4
Dolno Levski BG 165 E9
Dolno Osenovo BG 165 F7
Dolno Selo BG 164 E5
Dolno Tserovene BG 159 F11
Dolno Uyno BG 164 E6
Dolný Hričov SK 147 C7
Dolný Kubín SK 147 C8
Dolný Pial SK 146 E6
Dolný Štál SK 146 F5
Dolo I 66 B5
Dolomieu F 31 D8
Dolores E 56 E3
Dolovo SRB 159 D6
Dölsach A 73 C6
Dolsk PL 81 C12
Dołubowo PL 141 E7
Dolus-d'Oléron F 28 D3
Dolyna UA 145 F8
Dolynivka UA 154 A5
Dolyns'ke UA 154 B5
Dolzhitsy RUS 132 D5
Domaháza H 147 E10
Domaniewice PL 141 G2
Domaniewice PL 143 B8
Domanín CZ 146 C4
Domaradz PL 144 D4
Domart-en-Ponthieu F 18 D5
Domaševo BIH 162 D5
Domašinec HR 149 D7
Domaşnea RO 159 C9
Domaszek H 150 E5
Domaszków PL 77 B11
Domaszowice PL 142 D4
Domat Ems CH 71 D8
Domats F 25 D9
Domažlice CZ 76 D3
Dombås N 101 B10
Dombasle-en-Xaintois F 26 D4
Dombasle-sur-Meurthe F 186 D1
Dombegyház H 151 E7
Dombóvár H 149 D10
Dombrád H 145 G4
Dombresson CH 31 A10
Domburg NL 16 E1
Domegge di Cadore I 72 D5
Domeikava LT 137 D8
Domène F 31 E8
Domeniko GR 169 E7
Domérat F 29 C11
Domèvre-en-Haye F 26 C4
Domèvre-sur-Vezouze F 27 C6
Domfront F 23 C10
Domgermain F 26 C4
Dominée HR 162 D3
Domingo Pérez E 46 E4
Dömitz D 83 D10
Domlyan BG 165 D10
Dommartin-le-Franc F 26 D2
Dommartin-Varimont F 25 C12
Domme F 29 F8
Dommershausen D 21 D8
Dommitzsch D 80 C3
Domneşti RO 160 C5
Domneşti RO 161 E7
Domnitsa GR 174 B4
Domnovo RUS 136 E2
Domodossola I 68 A5
Domokos GR 174 A5
Domont F 25 B7
Domoroc RKS 164 D4
Dömös H 149 A11
Domoszló H 147 F10
Dompcevrin F 26 C3
Dompierre-les-Ormes F 30 C5
Dompierre-sur-Besbre F 30 B4
Dompierre-sur-Mer F 28 C3
Dompierre-sur-Yon F 28 B3
Domrémy-la-Pucelle F 26 D4
Dömsöd H 150 C3
Domsühl D 83 D11
Domus de Maria I 64 F2
Domusnovas I 64 E2
Domvaina GR 175 C6
Domžale SLO 73 D10
Donagh GB 7 D8
Donaghadee GB 4 F5
Donaghmore GB 7 C9
Donaghmore IRL 7 F10
Don Álvaro E 51 B7
Doña Mencía E 53 A8
Donard IRL 7 F9
Donaueschingen D 27 E9
Donauwörth D 75 E8
Don Benito E 51 B8
Doncaster GB 11 D9
Donchery F 19 E10
Donduşeni MD 153 A11
Donegal IRL 6 C6
Doneraile IRL 8 D5
Doneztebe E 32 D2
Dønfoss N 100 C8
Dongen NL 16 E3
Donges F 23 F7
Dongo I 69 A7
Donici MD 154 C3
Doñinos de Salamanca E 45 C9
Donja Bela Reka SRB 159 E9
Donja Brela HR 157 F6
Donja Bukovica MNE 163 C7
Donja Dubrava HR 149 D7
Donja Kupčina HR 148 E5
Donja Lepenica BIH 157 B8
Donja Mahala BIH 157 B10
Donja Motičina HR 149 F10
Donja Šatornja SRB 158 E6
Donja Stubica HR 148 E5
Donja Višnjica HR 148 D6
Donja Vrijeska HR 149 E8
Donja Zelina HR 148 E6
Donje Pazarište HR 67 C11
Donjeux F 26 D3
Donji Andrijevci HR 157 B9
Donji Čaglić HR 149 F8
Donji Dubovnik BIH 156 C5
Donji Dušnik SRB 164 C5
Donji Kosinj HR 156 C3
Donji Krčin SRB 159 F7
Donji Krivodol SRB 165 C6
Donji Lapac HR 156 C4
Donji Miholjac HR 149 E10
Donji Milanovac SRB 159 E9
Donji Proložac HR 157 F7
Donji Rujani BIH 157 E6
Donji Seget HR 156 E5
Donji Srb HR 156 D5
Donji Striževac SRB 164 C5
Donji Svilaj BIH 157 B9
Donji Vakuf BIH 157 D7
Donji Vijačani BIH 157 C8
Donji Zemunik HR 156 D3
Donji Širovac HR 156 B5
Donk NL 183 B7
Donkerbroek NL 16 B6
Donnalucata I 59 F6
Donnas I 68 B4
Donnemarie-Dontilly F 25 D9
Donnersbach A 73 B9
Donnersdorf D 75 C7
Donohill IRL 8 C6
Donori I 64 E3
Donostia E 32 D2
Donskoye RUS 139 A8
Donville-les-Bains F 23 C8
Donzdorf D 74 E6
Donzenac F 29 E9
Donzère F 35 B8
Donzy F 25 F9
Dooagh IRL 6 E2
Doochary IRL 6 C6
Dooish GB 4 F2
Doolin IRL 6 F4
Doon IRL 8 C6
Doonbeg IRL 8 C3
Doorn NL 16 D4
Doornspijk NL 183 A7
Dopiewo PL 81 B11
Ɖorče Petrov MK 164 E3
Dorchester GB 13 D10
Dørdal N 90 B5
Dordives F 25 D8
Dordrecht NL 16 E3
Dore-l'Église F 30 E4
Dörentrup D 17 D12
Dores GB 3 L8
Dorfen D 75 F11
Dorfgastein A 73 B7
Dorfmark D 82 E7
Dorf Mecklenburg D 83 C10
Dorf Zechlin D 83 D13
Dorgali I 64 C4
Dorgoş RO 151 E8
Dorio GR 174 E4
Dorking GB 15 E8
Dorkovo BG 165 E9
Dorlisheim F 186 D3
Dormagen D 21 B7
Dormánd H 150 B5
Dormans F 25 B10
Dor Mărunt RO 161 E9
Dorna-Arini RO 152 C6
Dorna Candrenilor RO 152 C6
Dornava SLO 148 D5
Dörnberg (Habichtswald) D 17 F12
Dornbirn A 71 C9
Dornburg (Saale) D 79 D10
Dornburg-Frickhofen D 185 C9
Dornbusch D 17 A12
Dorndorf D 79 E7
Dorndorf-Steudnitz D 79 D10
Dornelas P 38 E4
Dornes F 30 B3
Dorneşti RO 153 B8
Dornhan D 187 E6
Dornie GB 2 L5
Dornişoara RO 152 C6
Dörnitz D 79 B11
Dorno I 69 C6
Dornoch GB 3 K8
Dornstadt D 74 F6
Dornstetten D 27 D9
Dornum D 17 A8
Dornumersiel D 17 A8
Dorobanţu RO 155 D2
Dorobanţu RO 161 E9
Dorog H 149 A11
Dorogháza H 147 F9
Dorohoi RO 153 B8
Dorohusk PL 141 H9
Dorolţ RO 151 B10
Doroţcaia MD 154 C4
Dorotea S 107 C10
Dörpen D 17 C8
Dorras N 112 D8
Dorris S 107 B9
Dorstadt D 79 B8
Dorsten D 17 E7
Dorstfeld D 185 A7
Dortan F 31 C8
Dortmund D 17 E8
Dörttepe TR 177 E10
Doruchów PL 142 D5
Dorum D 17 A11
Dorupe LV 134 C7
Dörverden D 17 C12
Dörzbach D 74 D6
Dos Aguas E 48 F3
Dosbarrios E 46 E6
Dos Hermanas E 51 E8
Dospat BG 165 F9
Dossenheim D 21 F11
Doştat RO 152 F3
Dos Torres E 54 C3
Døstrup DK 86 E3
Dotnuva LT 134 F7
Dotternhausen D 27 D10
Döttingen CH 27 E9
Douai F 19 D7
Douarnenez F 22 D3
Doubrava CZ 147 B7
Doubravice nad Svitavou CZ 77 D11
Doubs F 31 B9
Douchy F 25 E9
Douchy-les-Mines F 19 D7
Doucier F 31 B8
Doudeville F 18 E2
Doudleby nad Orlicí CZ 77 B10
Doué-la-Fontaine F 23 F11
Doullens F 18 D5
Dounaiika GR 174 D3
Doune GB 5 C8
Dounreay GB 3 H9
Dour B 19 D8
Dourdan F 24 C7
Dourgne F 33 D10
Douriez F 18 D4
Doussard F 31 D9
Douvaine F 31 C9
Douvres-la-Délivrande F 23 B11
Douzy F 19 E11
Dovadola I 66 D4
Dover GB 15 E11
Dovhe UA 145 G7
Döviken S 103 A9
Dovilai LT 134 E2
Dovre N 101 C10
Dowally GB 5 B9
Downham Market GB 11 F12
Downpatrick GB 7 D11
Downton GB 13 D11
Dowra IRL 6 D6
Dowsby GB 11 F11
Doxato GR 171 B6
Doyet F 30 C2
Doyrentsi BG 165 C10
Dozulé F 23 B11
Drabeši LV 135 B10
Drâby DK 86 C7
Dračevo BIH 162 D5
Dračevo MK 164 F4
Drachhausen D 80 C6
Drachselsried D 76 D4
Drachten NL 16 B6
Drag N 105 B10
Drag N 111 D11
Dragacz PL 138 C6
Dragalijevac BIH 157 C11
Dragalina RO 161 E10
Dragalovci BIH 157 C8
Drăgăneşti RO 151 D9
Drăgăneşti RO 153 F10
Drăgăneşti RO 161 D8
Drăgăneşti de Vede RO 160 E6
Drăgăneşti-Olt RO 160 E5
Drăgăneşti-Vlaşca RO 161 E7
Draganići HR 148 E5
Draganovo BG 166 C5
Drăganu RO 160 D5
Drăgăşani RO 160 D4
Dragash RKS 163 E10
Dragatuš SLO 67 A11
Drage D 83 D8
Drage HR 156 E4
Drăgeşti RO 151 D9
Draghiceni RO 160 E4
Draginac SRB 158 D3
Draginje SRB 158 D4
Draginovo BG 165 E8
Dragland N 111 C11
Dragnes N 111 C10
Dragnić BIH 157 D7
Dragobi AL 163 E8
Dragočaj BIH 157 C7
Dragocvet SRB 159 F7
Dragodana RO 160 D6
Dragoeşti RO 160 D4
Drăgoeşti RO 161 D9
Dragoevo BG 167 C7
Dragoevo MK 164 F5
Drăgoieşti RO 153 B8
Dragoman BG 165 D6
Dragomance MK 164 E4
Dragomir BG 165 E9
Dragomireşti RO 152 B4
Dragomireşti RO 153 C9
Dragomireşti RO 153 D10
Dragomireşti RO 160 D6
Dragomirovo BG 166 B4
Dragoni I 60 A2
Dragør DK 87 D11
Dragoš MK 168 C5
Dragoslavele RO 160 C6
Dragoş Vodă RO 161 E10
Drăgoteşti RO 159 D11
Drăgoteşti RO 160 E4
Dragotina HR 156 B5
Dragović HR 149 F8
Dragovishtitsa BG 165 E6
Dragoychintsi BG 164 D5
Dragoynovo BG 166 F4
Dragsfjärd FIN 126 E7
Draguignan F 36 D4
Drăguşeni RO 153 A9
Drăguşeni RO 153 C8
Drăguşeni RO 153 F11
Drăguţeşti RO 159 D11
Drahnsdorf D 80 C5
Drahovce SK 146 D5
Drahove UA 145 G8
Drahovica Donja BIH 157 C9
Drajna RO 161 C8
Draka BG 167 E8
Drakenburg D 17 C12
Draksenić BIH 157 B6
Dralfa BG 167 C6
Drama GR 170 B6
Drammen N 95 C12
Drânceni RO 153 D12
Drange N 94 F5
Drangedal N 90 A5
Drangstedt D 17 A11
Drănic RO 160 E3
Dranse D 83 D13
Dransfeld D 78 D6
Dranske D 84 A4
Draperstown GB 4 F3
Drasenhofen A 77 E11
Draßmarkt A 149 A6
Drávafok H 149 E9
Dravagen S 102 B6
Draviskos GR 170 C5
Dravograd SLO 73 C11
Drawno PL 85 D9
Drawsko PL 85 E10
Drawsko Pomorskie PL 85 C9
Drayton GB 15 B11
Drążdżewo PL 139 D11
Dražen Vrh SLO 148 C5
Draževac SRB 158 D5
Dražgoše SLO 73 D9
Drebber D 17 C10
Drebkau D 80 C6
Drégelypalánk H 147 E8
Dreieich D 21 D11
Dreileben D 79 B9
Dreis D 21 E7
Drelów PL 141 G7
Drelsdorf D 82 A6
Drem GB 5 C11
Drenchia I 73 D8
Drenovac SRB 159 F7
Drenovci HR 157 C10
Drenovë AL 168 C4
Drenovets BG 159 F10
Drenovicë AL 168 C2
Drenovo MK 164 F4
Drenovo MK 169 B6
Drense D 84 D5
Drensteinfurt D 17 E9
Drenta BG 166 D5
Drentwede D 17 C11
Drepano GR 169 D6
Drepano GR 175 D6
Dresden D 80 D5
Dretun' BY 133 E6
Dretyń PL 85 B11
Dreumel NL 183 B6
Dreux F 24 C5
Dreverna LT 134 E2
Drevja N 108 E5
Drevjesætra N 102 D4
Dřevohostice CZ 146 C5
Drevsjø N 102 C3
Drevvatn N 108 D5
Drewitz D 79 B11
Drewnica PL 138 B6
Drezdenko PL 85 E9
Drežnica BIH 157 E8
Drežnik SRB 158 F4
Driceni LV 133 C2
Dridu RO 161 D8
Driebergen NL 16 D4
Driebes E 47 D6
Driedorf D 185 C9
Drienov SK 145 F3
Drietoma SK 146 D5
Driffield GB 11 C11
Drimmo IRL 7 F7
Drimnin GB 4 B5
Drimoleague IRL 8 E4
Drinić BIH 156 C5
Drinjača BIH 157 D11
Drinovci BIH 157 F7
Dripsey IRL 8 E5
Drisht AL 163 E8
Dříteň CZ 76 D6
Drithas AL 168 C4
Driva N 101 A11
Drivstua N 101 B11
Drmno SRB 159 D7
Drnholec CZ 77 E11
Drniš HR 156 E5
Drnje HR 149 D7
Drnovice CZ 77 D11
Drnovice CZ 77 D11
Dro I 69 B10
Drøbak N 95 C13
Drobeta-Turnu Severin RO 159 D10
Drobin PL 139 E8
Drochia MD 153 A11
Drochtersen D 17 A12
Drogheda IRL 7 E10
Drohiczyn PL 141 F7
Drohobych UA 145 E8
Droichead Abhann IRL 8 C5
Droichead Átha IRL 7 E10
Droichead na Bandan IRL 8 E5
Droichead Nua IRL 7 F9
Droitwich Spa GB 13 A10
Drolshagen D 185 B8
Drolsum N 95 B12
Dromara GB 7 D10
Dromina IRL 8 D5
Drommahane IRL 8 D5
Drömme S 107 E14
Dromod IRL 7 E7
Dromore GB 7 C8
Dromore GB 7 D10
Dromore West IRL 6 D5
Dronero I 37 C6
Dronfield GB 11 E9
Drongan GB 5 E8
Drongen B 182 C3
Dronninglund DK 86 A6
Dronrijp NL 16 B5
Dronten NL 16 C5
Dropla BG 155 F2
Drosato GR 169 B8
Drosbacken S 102 C3
Drosendorf A 77 E9
Drosia GR 175 C8
Drösing A 77 E11
Drosopigi GR 168 C5
Droué F 24 D5
Droyßig D 79 D11
Drugan BG 165 E7
Drugovo MK 168 B4
Druid GB 10 F5
Druimdrishaig GB 4 D5
Drulingen F 27 C7
Drumandoora IRL 6 G5
Drumanespick IRL 7 E8
Drumatober IRL 6 F6
Drumbeg GB 2 J6
Drumbilla IRL 7 D10
Drumcard GB 7 D7
Drumcollogher IRL 8 D5
Drumcondra IRL 7 E9
Drumconrath IRL 7 E9
Drumcree IRL 7 E8
Drumettaz-Clarafond F 31 D8
Drumevo BG 167 C8
Drumfree IRL 4 E2
Drumkeeran IRL 6 D6
Drumlea IRL 7 D7
Drumlish IRL 7 E7
Drumlithie GB 5 B12
Drummin IRL 9 D9
Drummore GB 4 F7
Drumnadrochit GB 2 L8
Drumquin GB 4 F2
Drumshanbo IRL 6 D6
Drung IRL 7 D8
Drusenheim F 27 C8
Druskininkai LT 137 F9
Drusti LV 135 B11
Druten NL 183 B7
Druviena LV 135 B12
Druya BY 133 E2
Druyes-les-Belles-Fontaines F 25 E9
Druysk BY 133 E2
Drużbice PL 143 D7
Druzhba RUS 136 E3
Druzhnaya Gorka RUS 132 C7
Družstevná pri Hornáde SK 145 F3
Drvenik HR 157 F7
Drwalew PL 141 G4
Drwinia PL 143 F9
Dryanovets BG 161 F8
Dryanovo BG 166 D4
Dryazhno RUS 132 E4
Drygały PL 139 C13
Drymen GB 5 C8
Drymos GR 169 C8
Dryna N 100 A5
Dryopida GR 175 E9
Dryos GR 176 E5
Drysvyaty BY 135 E13
Dryszczów PL 144 A8
Drzewce PL 142 B6
Drzewiany PL 85 C11
Drzewica PL 141 H2
Drzonowo PL 85 C11
Drzycim PL 138 C5
Duagh IRL 8 D3
Dualchi I 64 C2
Dually IRL 9 C7
Duas Igrejas P 39 F7
Dub SRB 158 F4
Dubá CZ 77 A7
Dubăsari MD 154 C4
Dubăsarii Vechi MD 154 C4
Duba Stonska HR 162 D4
Dubău MD 154 C4
Dubeczno PL 141 H8
Düben D 79 C11
Duben D 80 C5
Dübendorf CH 27 F10
Dubeņi LV 134 D2
Dubeninki PL 136 E6
Dubí CZ 80 E5
Dubičiai LT 137 E10
Dubicko CZ 77 C11
Dubicze Cerkiewne PL 141 E8
Dubidze PL 143 D7
Dubiecko PL 144 D5
Dubienka PL 144 A8
Dubingiai LT 137 C11
Dubino I 69 A7
Dubivka UA 153 A8
Dublin IRL 7 F10
Dublje SRB 158 D4
Dublovice CZ 76 C6
Dublyany UA 144 D9
Dublyany UA 145 E7
Dubna LV 135 D13
Dub nad Moravou CZ 146 C4
Dubňany CZ 77 E12
Dubnica nad Váhom SK 146 D6
Dubník SK 146 F6
Dubošbica BIH 157 D9
Dubova RO 159 D9
Dubovac SRB 159 D7
Dubove UA 145 G8
Dŭbovets BG 166 F5
Dubovica SK 145 E2
Dŭbovo BG 166 D5
Dubovo SRB 164 C4
Dubovsko BIH 156 C5
Dubrava BIH 157 C8
Dubrava HR 149 E7
Dubrave BIH 157 C10
Dubrave BIH 157 D6
Dubrave BIH 157 D10
Dubravica BIH 157 D8
Dubravica HR 148 E5
Dubravica SRB 159 D7
Dŭbravy SK 147 D8
Dubrawka BY 133 F6
Dubrovka RUS 129 F14
Dubrovka RUS 132 F6
Dubrovka RUS 133 D5
Dubrovnik HR 162 D5
Dubrovytsya UA 144 D8
Dubuļi LV 133 D3
Dubynove UA 154 A6
Ducey F 23 C9
Ducherow D 84 C5
Duchov CZ 80 E5
Duck End GB 15 D9
Duclair F 18 F2
Duda-Epureni RO 153 D12
Dudar H 149 B9
Duddo GB 5 D12
Dudelange L 20 F6
Dudeldorf D 21 E7
Duderstadt D 79 C7
Dudeşti RO 161 D10
Dudeştii Vechi RO 150 E5
Dudince SK 147 E7
Düdingen CH 31 B11
Dudley GB 11 F7
Dudovica SRB 158 E5
Dueñas E 40 E2
Duesund N 100 E2
Dueville I 72 E4
Duffel B 19 B10
Dufftown GB 3 L10
Duga Poljana SRB 163 C9
Duga Resa HR 148 F5
Dugi Rat HR 156 F6
Dugny-sur-Meuse F 26 B3
Dugopolje HR 156 E6
Dugo Selo HR 148 E6
Düğüncübaşı TR 173 B7
Duhort-Bachen F 32 C5
Duino I 73 E8
Duirinish GB 2 L5
Duisburg D 17 F7
Dukas AL 168 C2
Dukat AL 168 D2
Dukat i Ri AL 168 D1

F

Hämeenkyrö FIN 127 B9
Hämeenlinna FIN 127 D11
Hämelhausen D 17 C12
Hameln D 17 D12
Hämerten D 79 A10
Hamica HR 148 E5
Hamidiye TR 167 F9
Hamidiye TR 172 B6
Hamilton GB 5 D8
Hamilton's Bawn GB 7 D9
Hamina FIN 128 D7
Haminalahti FIN 124 E9
Hamit TR 181 C9
Hamitabat TR 173 A7
Hamlagrø N 94 A4
Hamlot N 111 D10
Hamm D 17 E9
Hamm (Sieg) D 185 C8
Hammar S 92 B5
Hammarland FIN 99 B13
Hammarn S 97 C12
Hammarnäs S 105 E16
Hammarsbyn S 102 E5
Hammarstrand S 107 E10
Hammarvika N 104 D5
Hamme B 19 B9
Hammel DK 86 C5
Hammelburg D 74 B6
Hammelev DK 86 E4
Hammelspring D 84 D4
Hamme-Mille B 19 C10
Hammenhög S 88 D6
Hammer N 105 C12
Hammerbrücke D 75 B11
Hammerdal S 106 D8
Hammerfest N 113 B12
Hammershøj DK 86 C5
Hammerum DK 86 C4
Hamminkeln D 17 E7
Hamn N 108 E3
Hamn N 111 B13
Hamna N 114 B8
Hamnavoe GB 3 D14
Hamnavoe GB 3 E14
Hamnbukt N 112 C8
Hamnbukta N 111 B18
Hamneidet N 112 D6
Hamnes N 105 B10
Hamnes N 108 E4
Hamnes N 112 D6
Hamningberg N 114 B9
Hamnøy N 110 E5
Hamnvågnes N 111 B16
Hamoir B 19 D12
Hamois B 19 D11
Hamont B 16 F5
Hampen DK 86 C4
Hampetorp S 92 A7
Hämpjäkk S 116 D4
Hampont F 26 C6
Hampreston GB 13 D11
Hamra S 93 F12
Hamra S 103 C9
Hamrångefjärden S 103 E13
Hamre N 112 C4
Hamry nad Sázavou CZ 77 C9
Ham-sous-Varsberg F 186 C2
Hamstreet GB 15 E10
Hamsund N 111 D10
Ham-sur-Heure B 19 D9
Hamula FIN 123 D16
Hamula FIN 124 D9
Hamzabeyli TR 167 F7
Hanaskog S 88 C6
Hanau D 187 A6
Handbjerg DK 86 C3
Handeloh D 83 D7
Handen S 93 A12
Handest DK 86 B5
Handewitt D 82 A6
Handlová SK 147 D7
Handog S 106 E7
Handöl S 105 E12
Handrabury UA 154 B5
Handrup D 17 C9
Handsjö S 102 B8
Handstein N 108 D4
Handzame B 182 C2
Hanebo S 103 D12
Hanerau-Hademarschen D 82 B6
Hanestad N 101 C13
Hănești RO 153 B9
Hangastenmaa FIN 128 B7
Hangelsberg D 80 B5
Hånger S 87 A13
Hangö FIN 127 F8
Hangony H 145 G1
Hangu RO 153 C8
Hangvar S 93 D13
Hanhikoski FIN 115 E2
Hanhimaa FIN 117 C14
Han i Elezit RKS 164 E3
Hanikase EST 132 F1
Haniska SK 145 F3
Hankamäki FIN 125 D10
Hankasalem asema FIN 123 F16
Hankasalmi FIN 123 F16
Hankensbüttel D 83 E9
Han Knežica BIH 157 B6
Hanko FIN 127 F8
Hanna PL 141 G9
Hannäs S 93 C8
Hannover D 78 B6
Hannoversch Münden D 78 D6
Hannukainen FIN 117 C11
Hannusperä FIN 119 D15
Hannusranta FIN 121 F10
Hannut B 19 C11
Hanøy N 110 D9
Han-Pijesak BIH 157 D10
Hanshagen D 83 C10
Hańsk Pierwszy PL 141 H8
Hansnes N 112 D4
Hanstedt D 83 D8
Hanstholm DK 86 A3
Han-sur-Nied F 26 C5
Hanušovce nad Topľou SK 145 E4
Hanušovice CZ 77 B11
Hanvec F 22 D3
Haparanda S 119 C12
Hapert NL 183 C6
Häppälä FIN 123 F16
Happburg D 75 D9
Happisburgh GB 15 B12
Haps NL 183 B7
Hapträsk S 118 B4
Hara S 106 E6
Hårad S 98 D7
Haradok BY 133 F7
Harads S 118 B5
Häradsbäck S 88 B6
Häradsbygden S 103 E9
Häradshammar S 93 B9
Haradzilavichy Pyershaya BY 133 D4
Haraldseng N 112 B9
Haram N 100 A4
Harang N 104 E6
Harany BY 133 F6
Harasiuki PL 144 C5
Hărău RO 151 F10
Haraudden S 116 E3
Harbacheva BY 133 E6
Harbak N 104 C8
Harbke D 79 B9
Harbo S 98 B8
Harboør DK 86 B2
Harbost GB 2 J4
Harburg (Schwaben) D 75 E8
Harbury GB 13 A12
Hard A 71 C9
Hardbakke N 100 D1
Hardegg A 77 E9
Hardegsen D 78 C6
Hardelot-Plage F 15 F12
Hardenberg NL 17 C7
Harderwijk NL 16 D5
Hardheim D 27 A11
Hardinxveld-Giessendam NL 182 B5
Hardt D 27 D9
Hareid N 100 B4
Harelbeke B 19 C7
Haren NL 17 B7
Haren (Ems) D 17 C8
Hare Street GB 15 D9
Harestua N 95 B13
Harfleur F 23 A12
Harg S 99 B10
Hargesheim D 21 E9
Hargimont B 19 D11
Hargla EST 131 F12
Hargnies F 19 D10
Hargshamn S 99 B10
Harichovce SK 145 F2
Harinkaa FIN 123 E16
Harjakangas FIN 126 B6
Härjåro S 99 D8
Härjåsjön S 102 C7
Harjavalta FIN 126 C7
Harjula FIN 119 C15
Harjumaa FIN 128 B7
Harjunkylä FIN 122 E7
Harjunpää FIN 126 C6
Harju-Risti EST 131 C7
Harka H 149 A7
Härkäjoki FIN 115 D2
Harkakötöny H 150 E4
Harkány H 149 E10
Härkmeri FIN 122 F6
Härkönen FIN 119 C13
Harku EST 131 C9
Hârlău RO 153 C9
Harlech GB 10 F3
Harleston GB 15 C11
Hårlev DK 87 E10
Harlingen NL 16 B4
Harlow GB 15 D9
Harly F 19 E7
Hărman RO 153 F7
Harmånger S 103 C13
Härmänkylä FIN 121 F13
Harmanli TR 173 D9
Härmänmäki FIN 121 F11
Harmannsdorf A 77 F10
Harmelen NL 182 A5
Harmoinen FIN 127 C13
Harmsdorf D 83 C9
Harmston GB 11 E10
Harnes F 18 D6
Härnösand S 103 A14
Haro E 40 C6
Harodz'ki BY 137 E13
Haroldswick GB 3 D15
Haroué F 26 D5
Härpe FIN 127 E14
Harpefoss N 101 C11
Harpenden GB 15 D8
Harplinge S 87 B11
Harpstedt D 17 C11
Harra D 75 B10
Harrachov CZ 81 E8
Harran N 105 B13
Harre DK 86 B3
Harridslev DK 86 C6
Harrietfield GB 5 C9
Harrioja S 119 C11
Harrislee D 82 A6
Harrogate GB 11 D8
Harrsjö S 106 B9
Harrström FIN 122 E6
Harrvik S 107 A10
Harsa S 103 C10
Hårsbäck S 98 C7
Harsefeld D 82 D7
Hărseni RO 152 F6
Harsești RO 160 D5
Harsleben D 79 C9
Harslev DK 86 D6
Hârșova RO 155 D1
Harsprånget S 116 E3
Harstad N 111 C12
Harsum D 78 B6
Harsvik N 104 C8
Harta H 150 D3
Hartberg A 148 B5
Hårte S 103 C13
Hartenholm D 83 C8
Hartha D 80 D3
Harthausen D 21 F10
Hartheim D 27 E8
Hărtiești RO 160 C6
Hart im Zillertal A 72 B4
Hartkirchen A 76 F5
Hartland GB 12 D6
Hartlepool GB 11 B9
Hartmanice CZ 76 D4
Hartola FIN 127 B15
Harwich GB 15 D11
Harzgerode D 79 C9
Hasanağa TR 173 D10
Hasbuğa TR 173 A8
Haselünne D 17 C8
Hasirciarnavutköy TR 171 B10
Håsjö S 107 F10
Hasköy TR 173 A6
Hasköy TR 177 C9
Haslach an der Mühl A 76 E6
Haslach im Kinzigtal D 27 D9
Hasle CH 70 C5
Hasle DK 88 E7
Haslemere GB 15 E7
Haslev DK 87 E9
Hasloh D 83 C7
Hasløya N 104 E2
Haslund DK 86 C6
Hășmaș RO 151 D9
Hasparren F 32 D3
Haßbergen D 17 C12
Hassel (Weser) D 17 C12
Hassela S 103 B12
Hassela kyrkby S 103 B12
Hasselfelde D 79 C8
Hasselfors S 92 A5
Hasselt B 19 C11
Hasselt NL 16 C6
Haßfurt D 75 B8
Hassi FIN 127 B13
Hässjö S 103 A14
Haßleben D 79 D9
Haßleben D 84 D5
Hässleholm S 87 C13
Hasslö S 89 C8
Haßloch D 21 F10
Hasslöv S 87 C12
Haßmersheim D 187 C7
Hästbo S 103 E13
Hästholmen S 92 C5
Hastière-Lavaux B 19 D10
Hastings GB 15 F10
Hästnäs S 97 D14
Håstrup DK 86 E6
Hästveda S 87 C13
Hasvåg N 105 C9
Hasvik N 112 C9
Hať CZ 146 B6
Hat' UA 145 G6
Hateg RO 159 B10
Hatfield GB 11 D10
Hatherleigh GB 12 D6
Hätilä FIN 127 C11
Hatipkişlasi TR 181 B7
Hatsola FIN 128 B8
Hattarvík FO 2 A4
Hattem NL 16 D6
Hattersheim am Main D 21 D10
Hattert D 21 C9
Hattfjelldal N 108 E6
Hédé F 23 D8
Hatting DK 86 D5
Hattingen D 17 F8
Hatton GB 3 L13
Hattstedt D 82 A6
Hattula FIN 127 C11
Hattuvaara FIN 125 E16
Hatulanmäki FIN 124 C8
Hatunkylä FIN 125 D15
Hatvan H 150 B4
Hatzenbühl D 27 B9
Hatzendorf A 148 C6
Hatzfeld (Eder) D 21 C11
Haubourdin F 18 C6
Hauenstein D 186 C4
Haugan N 105 D9
Haugastøl N 94 A7
Hauge N 94 F4
Hauge N 114 E6
Haugen N 110 D7
Haugesund N 94 D2
Haugh of Urr GB 5 F9
Haugland N 108 D5
Haugli N 111 C15
Haugnes N 111 B11
Haugnes N 112 C6
Haugset N 112 D7
Hauho FIN 127 C12
Haukå N 100 C2
Haukela FIN 125 B14
Haukeligrend N 94 C7
Haukijärvi FIN 127 B9
Haukilahti FIN 121 F13
Haukiniemi FIN 121 C13
Haukipudas FIN 119 D14
Haukivaara FIN 125 E15
Haukivuori FIN 124 F8
Haukøy N 111 D11
Haulerwijk NL 16 B6
Haurukylä FIN 119 E15
Haus A 73 B8
Haus N 94 B2
Hausach D 187 E5
Hausen D 75 E11
Hausen bei Würzburg D 187 B9
Häusern D 27 E9
Hausham D 72 A4
Hausjärvi FIN 127 D12
Hauske N 94 D3
Hausleiten A 77 F10
Hausmannstätten A 148 C5
Hautajärvi FIN 115 E6
Hautakylä FIN 121 D10
Hautakylä FIN 123 E12
Haute-Amance F 26 E4
Hautefort F 29 E8
Hauterives F 31 E7
Hauteville-Lompnes F 31 D8
Haut-Fays B 184 D3
Hautmont F 19 D8
Hautomäki FIN 123 E17
Haux F 32 D4
Hauzenberg D 76 E5
Havant GB 14 F7
Havârna RO 153 A9
Havbro DK 86 B4
Havdhem S 93 E12
Hávdna N 113 C15
Havelange B 19 D11
Havelberg D 83 E12
Havelte NL 16 C6
Håven S 103 C9
Haverdal S 87 B11
Haverfordwest GB 12 B5
Haverhill GB 15 C9
Haverlah D 79 B7
Haverö S 103 B9
Haversin B 19 D11
Haverslev DK 86 B5
Håverud S 91 B11
Havířov CZ 146 B6
Havixbeck D 17 E8
Håvla S 92 B7
Havlíčkův Brod CZ 77 C9
Havndal DK 86 B6
Havneby DK 86 E3
Havnebyen DK 87 D8
Havnsø DK 87 D8
Havøysund N 113 A14
Håvra S 103 C10
Havran TR 173 E7
Havrebjerg DK 87 E8
Havsa TR 173 A6
Havsskogen S 99 B11
Havtun N 94 B2
Hawarden GB 10 E5
Hawes GB 11 C7
Hawick GB 5 E11
Hawkhurst GB 15 E10
Hawkinge GB 15 E11
Haxby GB 11 C9
Hayange F 20 F6
Haybes F 184 D2
Haydarli TR 177 D10
Haydere TR 181 A8
Haydon Bridge GB 5 F12
Haydon Wick GB 13 B11
Hayingen D 71 A8
Hayle GB 12 E4
Hay-on-Wye GB 13 A8
Hayrabolu TR 173 B7
Hayton GB 11 D10
Hayvoron UA 154 A5
Haywards Heath GB 15 F8
Hazebrouck F 18 C6
Hazerswoude-Rijndijk NL 182 A5
Haźlach PL 147 B7
Hažlín SK 145 E3
Hazlov CZ 75 B11
Heacham GB 11 F12
Headcorn GB 15 E10
Headford IRL 6 F4
Healeyfield GB 5 F13
Heanor GB 11 E9
Heathfield GB 15 F9
Hebdów PL 143 F9
Hebenhausen (Neu-Eichenberg) D 78 D6
Heberg S 87 B11
Hebertsfelden D 76 F3
Hebnes N 94 D3
Heby S 98 C7
Hèches F 33 D6
Hechingen D 27 D10
Hecho E 32 E4
Hechtel B 19 B11
Hechthausen D 17 A12
Heckelberg D 84 E5
Heckington GB 11 F11
Hedared S 91 D12
Hedberg S 109 F16
Heddesheim D 21 F11
Hédé F 23 D8
Hede S 98 B6
Hede S 102 B6
Hedekas S 91 B10
Hedel NL 16 E4
Hedemora S 97 B14
Heden DK 86 E6
Heden S 102 C4
Heden S 118 C7
Hedenäset S 119 B11
Hedensbyn S 118 B9
Hedensted DK 86 D5
Hedersleben D 79 C9
Hédervár H 146 F4
Hedesunda S 98 B8
Hedeviken S 102 B6
Hedge End GB 13 D12
Hedlunda S 107 B15
Hedmark S 107 B13
Hedsjön S 103 E12
Hee DK 86 C2
Heeg NL 16 C5
Heek D 17 D8
Heel NL 183 C7
Heemsen D 17 C12
Heemskerk NL 16 C3
Heemstede NL 16 D3
Heenvliet NL 182 B4
Heer B 19 D10
Heerde NL 16 D6
Heerenveen NL 16 C5
Heerewaarden NL 183 B6
Heerhugowaard NL 16 C3
Heerlen NL 20 C5
Heers B 19 C11
Heesch NL 16 E5
Heeslingen D 17 B12
Heeßen D 17 D12
Heeswijk NL 16 E4
Heeten NL 183 A8
Heeze NL 16 F5
Heggeli N 111 B13
Heggem N 104 E4
Heggenes N 101 D10
Heggjabygda N 100 C4
Heggland N 90 A5
Heggmoen N 108 B8
Hegra N 105 E10
Hegyeshalom H 146 F4
Hehlen D 78 C5
Heia N 105 C12
Heia N 111 B17
Heide D 82 B6
Heideck D 75 D9
Heidelberg D 21 F11
Heiden D 17 E7
Heidenau D 80 E5
Heidenheim D 75 D8
Heidenheim an der Brenz D 75 E7
Heidenreichstein A 77 E8
Heigenbrücken D 187 A7
Heikendorf D 83 B8
Heikkilä FIN 121 C14
Heikkilä FIN 122 F7
Heiland N 90 B4
Heilbronn D 27 B11
Heilbrunn A 148 B5
Heiligenberg D 27 E11
Heiligenfelde D 83 E10
Heiligenhafen D 83 B9
Heiligenhaus D 17 F7
Heiligenkreuz am Waasen A 148 C5
Heiligenkreuz im Lafnitztal A 148 C6
Heiligenstadt Heilbad D 79 D7
Heiligenstedten D 82 C6
Heiloo NL 16 C3
Heilsbronn D 75 D8
Heiltz-le-Maurupt F 25 C12
Heim N 104 E6
Heimbach D 21 E8
Heimbuchenthal D 187 B7
Heimdal N 100 E3
Heimdal N 104 E8
Heimertingen D 71 A10
Heimseta N 100 C3
Heimsheim D 187 D6
Heinade D 78 C6
Heinämaa FIN 127 D14
Heinämäki FIN 121 F12
Heinämäki FIN 123 D17
Heinävaara FIN 125 E14
Heinävesi FIN 125 F11
Heinebach (Alheim) D 78 D6
Heinersbrück D 81 C7
Heinersdorf D 80 B6
Heinersreuth D 75 C10
Heinijärvi FIN 119 E14
Heinijoki FIN 126 D7
Heiningen D 79 B8
Heinisuo FIN 119 C16
Heinkenszand NL 16 F1
Heinlahti FIN 128 E6
Heino NL 183 A8
Heinola FIN 127 C15
Heinolan kirkonkylä FIN 127 C15
Heinolanperä FIN 119 E14
Heinoniemi FIN 125 F13
Heinsberg D 20 B6
Heinsen D 78 C5
Heinsnes N 105 B12
Heisingen D 183 C10
Heistadmoen N 95 C11
Heist-op-den-Berg B 19 B10
Heitersheim D 27 E8
Heituinlahti FIN 128 C8
Hejls DK 86 E5
Hejnice CZ 81 E8
Hejnsvig DK 86 D4
Hejőpapi H 145 H2
Hejsager DK 86 E5
Hekelgem B 19 C9
Hel PL 138 A6
Helbra D 79 C9
Helchteren B 183 C6
Heldburg D 75 B8
Heldenbergen D 21 D11
Heldrungen D 79 D9
Helechal E 51 B9
Helegiu RO 153 E9
Helensburgh GB 4 C7
Helfenberg A 76 E6
Helgenes N 110 C9
Helgeroa N 90 B6
Helgum S 107 E11
Hell N 105 E9
Hella N 100 D5
Helland N 104 E5
Helland N 111 D11
Hellanmaa FIN 122 D9
Hellarmo N 109 B10
Helle N 90 B5
Hellebæk DK 87 C11
Hellefjord N 113 B11
Hellendoorn NL 183 A8
Hellenthal D 20 D6
Hellenurme EST 131 E12
Hellesøy N 100 E1
Hellested DK 87 E10
Hellesvik N 104 D5
Hellesylt N 100 B5
Hellevad DK 86 E4
Hellevoetsluis NL 16 E2
Helligskogen N 112 E6
Hellín E 55 B9
Hellingly GB 15 F9
Hellnes N 112 C6
Hellsö FIN 126 F4
Hellvi S 93 D13
Hellvik N 94 F3
Helmbrechts D 75 B10
Helme EST 131 E11
Helmond NL 16 F5
Helmsdale GB 3 J9
Helmsley GB 11 C9
Helmstadt D 74 C6
Helmstedt D 79 B9
Heľpa SK 147 D9
Helppi FIN 117 D13
Helpringham GB 11 F11
Helse D 82 C6
Helsingborg S 87 C11
Helsinge DK 87 C10
Helsingfors FIN 127 E12
Helsingør DK 87 C11
Helsinki FIN 127 E12
Helstad N 105 A12
Helston GB 12 E4
Heltermaa EST 130 D6
Heltersberg D 21 F9
Helvaci TR 177 B9
Helvécia H 150 D4
Helvoirt NL 183 B6
Hem DK 86 B3
Hem F 182 D2
Hemau D 75 D10
Hemavan S 108 E9
Hemeiuș RO 153 D9
Hemel Hempstead GB 15 D8
Hemer D 185 B8
Hemfjäll S 109 E12
Hemfjällstangen S 102 D5
Hemhofen D 75 C8
Hemling S 107 D15
Hemme D 82 B6
Hemmet DK 86 D2
Hemmingen D 78 B6
Hemmingen S 107 B17
Hemmingsmark S 118 D6
Hemmoor D 17 A12
Hemnesberget N 108 D6
Hemnestad N 111 C11
Hempnall GB 15 C11
Hempstead GB 15 C9
Hemsbach D 21 E11
Hemsbünde D 82 D6
Hemsby GB 15 B12
Hemse S 93 E12
Hemsedal N 101 E9
Hemsjö S 107 D14
Hemslingen D 82 D7
Hemsloh D 17 C11
Hemsö S 103 A15
Hemyock GB 13 D8
Henån S 91 C10
Hénanbihen F 23 C7
Henarejos E 47 E10
Hencida H 151 C8
Hendaye F 32 D2
Hendon GB 15 D8
Hengelo NL 16 D6
Hengelo NL 17 D7
Hengersberg D 76 E4
Hengevelde NL 183 A9
Henggart CH 27 E10
Hengoed GB 13 B8
Hénin-Beaumont F 18 D6
Henley-on-Thames GB 15 D7
Hennan S 103 B10
Henndorf am Wallersee A 73 A7
Hennebont F 22 E5
Hennef (Sieg) D 21 C8
Hennes N 110 C9
Henne Stationsby DK 86 D2
Hennezel F 26 D5
Hennickendorf D 80 B4
Hennigsdorf Berlin D 80 A4
Henningskälen S 106 D8
Henningsvær N 110 D7
Hennseid N 90 A5
Hennset N 104 E4
Hennstedt D 82 B6
Hennweiler D 21 E8
Henrichemont F 25 F8
Henryków PL 81 E12
Henrykowo PL 139 B9
Henstridge GB 13 D10
Hepola FIN 119 C13
Heppen B 183 C6
Heppenheim (Bergstraße) D 21 E11
Herálec CZ 77 C8
Herálec CZ 77 C9
Herbault F 24 E5
Herbertingen D 27 D11
Herbertstown IRL 8 C6
Herbés E 42 F3
Herbeumont B 184 E3
Herbignac F 23 F7
Herbolzheim D 27 D8
Herborn D 21 C10
Herbrechtingen D 75 E7
Herbstein D 21 C12
Herby PL 142 E6
Herceghalom H 149 A11
Herceg-Novi MNE 162 E6
Hercegovac HR 149 E8
Hercegszántó H 150 F2
Herdecke D 17 F8
Herdorf D 21 C9
Hereclean RO 151 C11
Heréd H 150 B4
Hereford GB 13 A9
Héreg H 149 A11
Herencia E 46 F6
Herend H 149 B9
Herent B 19 C10
Herentals B 19 B10
Herenthout B 182 C5
Hérépian F 34 C5
Herford D 17 D11
Hergatz D 71 B9
Hergiswil CH 70 D6
Herguijuela E 45 F9
Héric F 23 F8
Héricourt F 27 E6
Hérimoncourt F 27 F6
Heringen (Helme) D 79 D8
Heringen (Werra) D 79 E7
Heringsdorf D 83 B10
Heringsdorf D 84 C6
Heriot GB 5 D11
Herisau CH 27 F11
Hérisson F 29 B11
Herk-de-Stad B 19 C11
Herkenbosch NL 183 C8
Herkingen NL 182 B4
Herleshausen D 79 D7
Herlev DK 87 D10
Herlufmagle DK 87 E9
Herm F 32 C3
Hermagor A 73 C7
Hermannsburg D 83 E8
Hermanovce SK 145 E3
Hermanowice PL 144 D6
Hermansverk N 100 D5
Heřmanův Městec CZ 77 C9
Herment F 29 D11
Hermersberg D 186 C4
Hermeskeil D 21 E7
Hermisende E 39 E6
Hermsdorf D 79 E10
Hernád H 150 C3
Hernádnémeti H 145 G2
Hernani E 32 D2
Hernansancho E 46 C3
Herne B 19 C9
Herne D 17 E8
Herne Bay GB 15 E11
Herning DK 86 C3
Heroldsbach D 75 C8
Héron B 19 C11
Hérouville-St-Clair F 23 B11
Herøy N 100 B3
Herpf D 79 E7
Herrala FIN 127 D13
Herramélluri E 40 C5
Herräng S 99 B11
Herré F 32 C5
Herre N 90 A6
Herrenberg D 27 C10
Herrera E 53 B7
Herrera del Duque E 45 F10
Herrera de los Navarros E 42 E1
Herrera de Pisuerga E 40 C3
Herrería E 47 C9
Herreruela E 45 F7
Herrestad S 91 C10
Herrieden D 75 D8
Herringbotn N 108 E6
Herrlisheim F 186 D4
Herrljunga S 91 C13
Herrnhut D 81 D7
Herrö S 102 B7
Herrsching am Ammersee D 75 G9
Herrskog S 103 A15
Herrvik S 93 E13
Herry F 25 F8
Hersbruck D 75 C9
Herschbach D 21 C9
Herscheid D 21 B9
Herschweiler-Pettersheim D 186 C3
Herselt B 19 B10
Herslev DK 86 D5
Herstal B 19 C12
Herstmonceux GB 15 F9
Herston GB 3 H11
Herten D 17 E8
Hertford GB 15 D8
Hertník SK 145 E3
Hertsa UA 153 A8
Hertsånger S 118 F6
Hertsjö S 103 D11
Herve B 19 C12
Hervik N 94 D3
Herwijnen NL 183 B6
Herzberg D 80 C4
Herzberg D 83 C11
Herzberg D 84 E3
Herzberg am Harz D 79 C7
Herzebrock-Clarholz D 17 E10
Herzele B 19 C8
Herzfelde D 80 B5
Herzhorn D 17 A12
Herzlake D 17 C9
Herzogenaurach D 75 C8
Herzogenbuchsee CH 27 F8
Herzogenburg A 77 F9
Herzogenrath D 183 D8
Herzsprung D 83 D12
Hesdin F 18 D5
Hesel D 17 B9
Hesjeberg N 111 C13
Hesjestranda N 100 A6
Heskestad N 94 F4
Hespérange L 20 E6
Heßdorf D 75 C8
Hesselager DK 87 E7
Hessen D 79 B8
Hessfjorden N 112 D3
Heßheim D 21 E10
Hessisch Lichtenau D 78 D6
Hessisch Oldendorf D 17 D12
Hest N 100 D3
Hestenesøyri N 100 C4
Hestnes N 104 D5
Hestøy N 108 E3
Hestra S 91 E14
Hestra S 92 D6
Hestvik N 105 B10
Hestvika N 104 D6
Heswall GB 10 E5
Hetekylä FIN 119 D17
Hetés H 149 D9
Hethersett GB 15 B11
Hetlingen D 82 C7
Hettange-Grande F 186 C1
Hettenleidelheim D 186 B5
Hettenshausen D 75 E10
Hettingen D 27 D11
Hetton GB 11 C7
Hettstedt D 79 C10
Hetzerath D 21 E7
Heubach D 187 D8
Heuchelheim D 21 C11
Heuchin F 18 D5
Heudicourt-sous-les-Côtes F 26 C4
Heukelum NL 16 E4
Heusden B 19 B11
Heusden NL 183 B6
Heusenstamm D 21 D11
Heustreu D 75 B7
Heusweiler D 186 C2
Heves H 150 B5
Hévíz H 149 C8
Hevlín CZ 77 E10
Hexham GB 5 F12
Heyrieux F 31 D7
Heysham GB 10 C6
Heythuysen NL 19 B12
Heywood GB 11 D7
Hida RO 151 C11
Hidas H 149 D10
Hidasnémeti H 145 G3
Hiddenhausen D 17 D11
Hiddensee D 84 A4
Hidirköylü TR 177 D10
Hidişelu de Sus RO 151 D9
Hieflau A 73 A10
Hiendelaencina E 47 B7
Hiersac F 28 D5
Hietakangas FIN 115 D3
Hietama FIN 123 E15
Hietanen FIN 117 D11
Hietanen FIN 128 B7
Hietaniemi FIN 115 D6
Hietaniemi FIN 121 B11
Hietaperä FIN 121 F13
Higham Ferrers GB 15 C7
Highampton GB 12 D6
High Bentham GB 10 C6
Highbridge GB 13 C9
Highclere GB 13 C12
High Halden GB 15 E10
High Hawsker GB 11 C10
High Hesket GB 5 F11
High Lorton GB 5 F10
Highnam GB 13 B10
Highworth GB 13 B11
High Wycombe GB 15 D7
Higuera de Arjona E 53 A9
Higuera de la Serena E 51 B8
Higuera de la Sierra E 51 D7
Higuera de Llerena E 51 C8
Higuera de Vargas E 51 C6
Higuera la Real E 51 C6
Higueruela E 55 B10
Higueruelas E 48 E3
Hihnavaara FIN 115 D4
Hiidenkylä FIN 123 C15
Hiidenlahti FIN 125 E10
Hiilikumpu FIN 119 C15
Hiirikylä FIN 125 C10
Hiirola FIN 128 B7
Hiisijärvi FIN 121 F12
Híjar E 42 E3
Hikiä FIN 127 D12
Hilbersdorf D 80 E4
Hilchenbach D 21 C10
Hildburghausen D 75 B8
Hilden D 21 B7
Hilders D 79 E7
Hilderthorpe GB 11 C11
Hildesheim D 78 B6
Hilgertshausen D 75 F9
Hilișeu-Horia RO 153 A8
Hiliuți MD 153 B10
Hillared S 91 D13
Hille D 17 D11
Hille S 103 E13
Hillebola S 99 B9
Hillegom NL 16 D3
Hillerød DK 87 D10
Hillerse D 79 B7
Hillerslev DK 86 A3
Hillerslev DK 86 E6
Hillerstorp S 88 A5
Hilleshamn N 111 C13
Hillesheim D 21 D7
Hillesøy N 111 A15
Hillevik S 103 E13
Hilli FIN 123 C11
Hillilä FIN 123 B11
Hill of Fearn GB 3 K9
Hillosensalmi FIN 128 C6
Hillsand S 106 C8
Hillsborough GB 7 D10
Hillside GB 5 B12
Hillswick GB 3 E14
Hilltown GB 7 D10
Hilpoltstein D 75 D9
Hilsenheim F 186 E4
Hilton GB 11 F8
Hiltpoltstein D 75 C9
Hiltula FIN 129 B9
Hilvarenbeek NL 183 C6
Hilversum NL 16 D4
Himalansaari FIN 128 C8
Himanka FIN 123 B11
Himarë AL 168 D2
Himberg A 77 F10
Himbergen D 83 D9
Himesháza H 149 D11
Himma EST 131 F14

Karaköy TR 181 B9
Karakurt TR 177 A10
Karala EST 130 E3
Karaman TR 173 E9
Karamanovo BG 166 B5
Karamehmet TR 173 B8
Karamyshevo RUS 132 F4
Karamyshevo RUS 136 E5
Karancsberény H 147 E9
Karancskeszi H 147 E9
Karancslapujtő H 147 E9
Karancsság H 147 E9
Karankamäki FIN 124 C8
Karaoğlanli TR 177 B10
Karaorman TR 173 E9
Karaova TR 177 E10
Karapchiv UA 152 A6
Karapelit BG 161 F11
Karasjok N 113 E15
Karatoulas GR 174 D4
Karats S 109 C16
Karavas GR 178 C4
Karavelovo BG 165 D10
Karavelovo BG 167 E7
Käravete EST 131 C11
Karavomylos GR 175 B6
Karavukovo SRB 157 B11
Karben D 21 D11
Kårberg S 92 B5
Karbinci MK 164 F5
Kårböle S 103 C9
Kårböleskog S 103 C9
Karbow-Vietlübbe D 83 D12
Karbunarë e Vogël AL 168 C2
Karby D 83 A7
Karby DK 86 B3
Karby S 99 C10
Karcag H 151 C6
Karcsa H 145 G4
Karczew PL 141 F4
Karczmiska Pierwsze PL 141 H6
Kärda S 87 A13
Kardakata GR 174 C1
Kardam BG 155 F2
Kardam BG 166 C6
Kardamaina GR 177 F9
Kardamyli GR 174 F5
Kardašova Řečice CZ 77 D7
Karden D 21 D8
Kardiani GR 176 D5
Kardis S 117 E11
Karditsa GR 169 F6
Karditsomagoula GR 169 F6
Kärdla EST 130 D5
Kardon BY 133 F6
Kardos H 150 D6
Kardoskút H 150 E6
Karegasnjarga FIN 113 E16
Kareļi LV 134 D4
Karesuando S 116 B8
Kargowa PL 81 B9
Karhi FIN 123 C10
Karhila FIN 123 F13
Karhujärvi FIN 115 F4
Karhukangas FIN 119 F14
Karhula FIN 128 D6
Kariani GR 170 C5
Karigasniemi FIN 113 E16
Karihaugen N 111 D12
Karijoki FIN 122 F7
Karinainen FIN 126 D8
Käringberg S 107 A12
Käringen N 111 D10
Käringsjön S 102 B3
Käringsjövallen S 102 B4
Karinkanta FIN 119 E13
Karis FIN 127 E10
Karise DK 87 E10
Karisjärvi FIN 127 D11
Karitaina GR 174 E5
Karitsa GR 169 D7
Karjalaisenniemi FIN 121 B11
Karjalan kirkonkylä FIN 126 D7
Karjalankylä FIN 119 D15
Karjalankylä FIN 126 D7
Karjalanvaara FIN 120 B9
Karjalanvaara FIN 121 F10
Karjalohja FIN 127 E10
Kärjenkoski FIN 122 F7
Karjulanmäki FIN 123 C13
Karkalou GR 174 D5
Kärķi LV 131 F11
Kärkinen FIN 119 F12
Kärkkäälä FIN 123 E16
Kärkkäälä FIN 124 E8
Karkkila FIN 127 D11
Karkku FIN 127 C9
Kārklinieki LV 133 B2
Kärkölä FIN 127 D10
Kärkölä FIN 127 D13
Karksi EST 131 E11
Karksi-Nuia EST 131 E11
Kärkul S 118 B5
Kärla EST 130 E4
Karlå FIN 122 F7
Karlby FIN 126 F4
Karlebotn N 114 C5
Karleby FIN 123 C10
Karlholmsbruk S 99 A9
Karlino PL 85 B9
Kārlmuiža LV 134 B4
Karlobag HR 67 C11
Karlovac HR 148 F5
Karlovasi GR 177 D8
Karlovice CZ 142 F3
Karlovo BG 165 D10
Karlovy Vary CZ 76 B3
Karłowice PL 142 E4
Karlsbäck S 107 D15
Karlsbad D 27 C10
Karlsberg S 103 C9
Karlsborg S 92 B5
Karlsburg D 84 C5
Karlsdal S 97 D12
Karlsdorf-Neuthard D 27 B10
Karlsfeld D 75 F9
Karlsfors S 103 C9
Karlshagen D 84 B5
Karlshamn S 89 C7
Karlshöfen D 17 B12
Karlskoga S 97 D12
Karlskrona S 89 C9
Karlsøy N 112 C4
Karlsruhe D 27 B9
Karlstad S 97 D10
Karlstadt D 74 C6
Karlstein an der Thaya A 77 E8
Karlstetten A 77 F9
Karlukovo BG 165 C9
Karmansbo S 97 C14
Karmas S 109 B17
Karmėlava LT 137 D9
Kärnä FIN 123 D11
Kärnä FIN 123 D15
Kärna S 91 D10
Karnaliyivka UA 154 E6
Karnice PL 85 B8
Karniewo PL 139 E10
Karnjarga FIN 113 D19
Karnobat BG 167 D7
Karojba HR 67 B8
Karolinka CZ 146 C6
Karonsbo S 107 B15
Karoti GR 171 B10
Karousades GR 168 E2
Karow D 79 B11
Karow D 83 C12
Karpacz PL 81 E9
Kärpänkylä FIN 121 C14
Karpathos GR 181 E6
Karpenisi GR 174 B4
Karperi GR 169 B9
Karpero GR 169 E6
Kärppälä FIN 127 C9
Karpuzlu TR 171 C10
Karpuzlu TR 181 A7
Kärrbackstrand S 102 E4
Karrebæksminde DK 87 E9
Karrenzin D 83 D11
Kärrsjö S 107 D15
Karsakiškis LT 135 E9
Kärsämä FIN 119 E15
Kärsämäki FIN 123 C15
Kārsava LV 133 C3
Karsikas FIN 123 C14
Karsikkoniemi FIN 117 C11
Karsikkovaara FIN 124 B9
Karsimus FIN 115 E2
Karsin PL 138 C4
Karşiyaka TR 173 D9
Karşiyaka TR 177 C9
Karsko PL 85 E8
Kårsta S 99 C10
Karstädt D 83 D10
Karstädt D 83 D11
Kärstna EST 131 E11
Karstula FIN 123 E13
Karszew PL 142 B6
Kartal H 150 B4
Kartavoll N 94 E3
Kartena LT 134 E2
Kartitsch A 72 C6
Kartuzy PL 138 B5
Käru EST 131 D10
Käru EST 131 D12
Karuna FIN 126 E8
Karungi S 119 B11
Karunki FIN 119 B12
Karup DK 86 C4
Kårvåg N 104 E3
Karvala FIN 123 D11
Kärväskylä FIN 123 D15
Karvia FIN 122 F9
Kårvikhamn N 111 B15
Karviná CZ 147 B7
Karvoskylä FIN 123 C14
Karvounari GR 168 F3
Karwica PL 139 C11
Karya GR 169 E7
Karya GR 174 B2
Karya GR 175 D6
Karyes GR 171 D6
Karyes GR 175 E5
Karyotissa GR 169 C7
Karyoupoli GR 178 B3
Karystos GR 175 C9
Kås DK 86 A5
Kašalj SRB 163 C10
Kasejovice CZ 76 D5
Kasendorf D 75 B9
Kasepää EST 131 D14
Kasfjord N 111 C11
Kashirskoye RUS 136 D2
Kaşikçi TR 173 B7
Kašina HR 148 E6
Kaskantyú H 150 D3
Kåskats S 116 F4
Kaskii FIN 129 B9
Kaskinen FIN 122 F6
Kaskö FIN 122 F6
Käsmä FIN 121 C12
Kåsmo N 108 B9
Kåsmolia N 108 B9
Käsmu EST 131 B11
Kaspakas GR 171 E8
Kašperské Hory CZ 76 D5
Kaspichan BG 167 C8
Kassa S 117 D11
Kassandreia GR 169 D9
Kasseedorf D 83 B9
Kassel D 78 D6
Kassiopi GR 168 E2
Kastania GR 168 D4
Kastania GR 168 E5
Kastania GR 169 D7
Kastania GR 169 F6
Kastanies GR 171 A10
Kastanochori GR 169 C10
Kastari FIN 127 C13
Kastellaun D 21 D8
Kastelli GR 178 E9
Kastellia GR 174 B5
Kaštel Stari HR 156 E5
Kaštel Sućurac HR 156 E5
Kaštel Šegarski HR 156 D4
Kasterlee B 16 F3
Kastīre LV 135 D13
Kastl D 75 D10
Kastlösa S 89 C10
Kastneshamn N 111 C13
Kastorf D 83 C9
Kastoria GR 168 C5
Kastorio GR 174 E5
Kastraki GR 174 B3
Kastraki GR 176 E5
Kastrāne LV 135 C10
Kastre EST 131 E14
Kastri GR 169 E8
Kastri GR 175 E6
Kastro GR 175 C7
Kastrosykia GR 174 A2
Kastrova BY 133 D4
Kaszaper H 150 E6
Kaszczor PL 81 C10
Katafyto GR 169 B10
Katajamäki FIN 125 D10
Katakolo GR 174 D3
Kåtaliden S 109 F15
Kataloinen FIN 127 C12
Katapola GR 177 F6
Katarraktis GR 177 C7
Kåtaselet S 118 D3
Katastari GR 174 D2
Katerini GR 169 D8
Katerma FIN 125 B12
Kathenoi GR 175 B8
Kathlow D 81 C6
Kätkänjoki FIN 123 E11
Kätkäsuvanto FIN 117 B10
Kätkävaara FIN 119 B13
Kätkesuando S 117 B10
Katlenburg-Lindau D 79 C7
Kátlovce SK 146 D5
Kato Achaïa GR 174 C4
Kato Alepochori GR 175 C7
Kato Asites GR 178 E9
Katochi GR 174 C3
Kato Chorio GR 179 E10
Kato Doliana GR 175 E6
Kato Glykovrysi GR 178 B4
Kato Kamila GR 169 B9
Kato Makrinou GR 174 C4
Kato Nevrokopi GR 169 B10
Kato Sounio GR 175 D9
Kato Tithorea GR 175 B6
Katouna GR 174 B3
Kato Vermio GR 169 C7
Katovice CZ 76 D5
Kato Vlasia GR 174 C4
Kato Vrontou GR 169 B10
Katowice PL 143 F7
Katranca TR 173 B7
Katrineberg S 103 D11
Katrineholm S 93 B8
Katrineholm S 103 E13
Katsdorf A 77 F6
Katsikas GR 168 E4
Kattavia GR 181 E7
Kattbo S 102 E7
Kattelus FIN 123 F11
Kattilasaari S 119 C11
Kattilaitojа FIN 123 D15
Kättilstad S 92 C7
Kättilstorp S 91 C14
Kattisavan S 107 B14
Kattisträsk S 118 E3
Katundishtë AL 168 D3
Katunets BG 165 C10
Katunitsa BG 165 E10
Katuntsi BG 169 B9
Katwijk aan Zee NL 16 D2
Katyčiai LT 134 F3
Katymár H 150 E3
Kąty Wrocławskie PL 81 D11
Katzenelnbogen D 21 D9
Katzweiler D 21 E9
Kaub D 21 D9
Kaufbeuren D 71 B11
Kaufungen D 78 D6
Kaugurieši LV 135 B11
Kauhajärvi FIN 122 F8
Kauhajärvi FIN 123 D10
Kauhajoki FIN 122 F8
Kauhava FIN 123 D10
Kaukalampi FIN 127 D13
Kaukolikai LT 134 D3
Kaukonen FIN 117 D13
Kauksi EST 131 C14
Kaulille B 183 C7
Kaulinranta FIN 119 B11
Kaulsdorf D 79 E9
Kaunas LT 137 D8
Kaunata LV 133 D3
Kauniainen FIN 127 E12
Kaunisjoensuu S 117 D11
Kaunisvaara S 117 D10
Kaupanger N 100 D6
Kaupiškiai LT 136 D6
Kauppila FIN 123 F17
Kauppilanmäki FIN 124 C8
Kaurajärvi FIN 122 D9
Kaurissalo FIN 126 D5
Kaustinen FIN 123 C11
Kautenbach L 184 E5
Kautokeino N 112 E11
Kautzen A 77 E8
Kauvatsa FIN 126 C8
Kauvosaarenpää FIN 119 B11
Kavacik TR 172 B6
Kavacik TR 173 E9
Kavadarci MK 169 B7
Kavajë AL 168 B2
Kavak TR 173 C6
Kavakdere TR 173 A7
Kavakli TR 173 A7
Kavaklidere TR 181 B8
Kavala GR 171 C6
Kavarna BG 167 C10
Kavarskas LT 135 F9
Kavasilas GR 174 D3
Kavastu EST 131 E14
Kavelstorf D 83 C12
Kävlinge S 87 D12
Kavos GR 168 F3
Kavousi GR 179 E10
Kavs'ke UA 145 E8
Kavyli GR 171 A11
Kaxås S 105 D15
Kåxed S 107 E14
Kaxholmen S 92 D4
Kayabaşi TR 181 B9
Kayalar TR 173 E8
Kayali TR 167 F8
Kayalioğlu TR 177 B10
Kayapa TR 173 F7
Kayatepe TR 173 E7
Käylä FIN 121 B13
Käymäjärvi S 116 D9
Kayna D 79 E11
Kaynaklar TR 177 C9
Kaynarca TR 173 A7
Kaynardzha BG 161 F10
Käyrämö FIN 117 E16
Kaysersberg F 27 D7
Kazanka BG 166 E4
Kazanlŭk BG 166 D4
Kazanów PL 141 H4
Kazár H 147 E9
Kazdanga LV 134 C3
Kazichane BG 165 D7
Kazikli TR 177 E9
Kazimierza Wielka PL 143 F9
Kazimierz Biskupi PL 142 B5
Kazimierz Dolne PL 141 H5
Kazincbarcika H 145 G2
Kazlowshchyna BY 133 E4
Kazlų Rūda LT 137 D7
Kaźmierz PL 81 A11
Kaznějov CZ 76 C4
Kazyany BY 133 E7
Kaz'yany BY 135 F13
Kçirë AL 163 E8
Kcynia PL 85 E12
Kdyně CZ 76 D4
Keadue IRL 6 D6
Keady GB 7 D9
Kealkill IRL 8 E4
Kebal S 91 B9
Kecel H 150 D3
Kecerovce SK 145 F3
Kechrokampos GR 171 B7
Kechros GR 171 B9
Kecskéd H 149 A10
Kecskemét H 150 D4
Kėdainiai LT 135 F7
Kedros GR 174 A5
Kędzierzyn-Koźle PL 142 F5
Keele GB 11 E7
Keenagh IRL 7 E7
Keeni EST 131 F12
Kefalos GR 181 C5
Kefalovryso GR 169 E7
Kefenrod D 21 D12
Kefermarkt A 77 F7
Ķegums LV 135 C9
Kegworth GB 11 F9
Kehidakustány H 149 C8
Kehl D 27 C8
Kehlen L 20 E6
Kehra EST 131 C10
Kehrig D 21 D8
Kehtna EST 131 D9
Kehvo FIN 124 D9
Keighley GB 11 D8
Keihärinkoski FIN 123 D15
Keikyä FIN 126 C8
Keila EST 131 C8
Keila-Joa EST 131 C8
Keillmore GB 4 D5
Keinäsperä FIN 119 D17
Ķeipene LV 135 C10
Keiprod N 111 C14
Keiss GB 3 H10
Keitele FIN 123 D16
Keitelepohja FIN 123 D15
Keith GB 3 K11
Kék H 145 G4
Ķekava LV 135 C8
Kékcse H 145 G5
Kelankylä FIN 119 C18
Kelberg D 21 D7
Kelbra (Kyffhäuser) D 79 D9
Kelč CZ 146 C5
Këlcyrë AL 168 D3
Kelebia H 150 E4
Kelechyn UA 145 F7
Kelheim D 75 E10
Kelkheim (Taunus) D 187 A5
Kell D 21 E7
Kellas GB 3 K10
Kellas GB 5 B11
Kellenhusen D 83 B10
Kelli GR 169 C6
Kellinghusen D 82 C7
Kellmünz an der Iller D 71 A10
Kello FIN 119 D14
Kellokoski FIN 127 D13
Kelloniemi FIN 115 E3
Kelloniemi FIN 117 D11
Kelloselkä FIN 115 E5
Kells GB 4 F4
Kells IRL 7 E9
Kells IRL 8 E2
Kells IRL 9 C8
Kelmė LT 134 E5
Kelmis B 20 C6
Kelontekemä FIN 117 C15
Kelottijärvi FIN 116 A8
Kelso GB 5 D12
Kelujärvi FIN 115 D2
Kelvä FIN 125 D14
Kelvedon GB 15 D10
Kemalpaşa TR 177 C9
Kemberg D 79 C12
Kemecse H 145 G4
Kemence H 147 E7
Kemenesmagasi H 149 B8
Kemenessömjén H 149 B8
Kemerburgaz TR 173 B10
Kémes H 149 E10
Kemeten A 148 B6
Kemi FIN 119 C13
Kemihaara FIN 115 C5
Kemijärvi FIN 115 E2
Kemilä FIN 121 C14
Keminmaa FIN 119 C13
Keminperä FIN 121 D12
Këmishtaj AL 168 C2
Kemmel B 18 C6
Kemnath D 75 C10
Kemnay GB 3 L12
Kemnitz D 81 D7
Kemnitz D 84 B5
Kempele FIN 119 E15
Kempen D 16 F6
Kempenich D 21 D8
Kempsey GB 13 A10
Kempston GB 15 C8
Kempten (Allgäu) D 71 B10
Kendal GB 10 C6
Kenderes H 150 C6
Kendice SK 145 F3
Kenézlő H 145 G4
Kenfig GB 13 B7
Kengis S 117 D10
Kengyel H 150 C5
Kenilworth GB 13 A11
Kenmare IRL 8 E3
Kenmore GB 5 B9
Kenn D 21 E7
Kennacraig GB 4 D6
Kensaleyre GB 2 L4
Kensworth GB 15 D7
Kentavros GR 171 B7
Kentriko GR 169 B8
Kentro GR 174 D3
Kenyeri H 149 B8
Kenzingen D 27 D8
Kepez TR 171 D10
Kępice PL 85 B11
Kępno PL 142 D4
Kepsut TR 173 E9
Keqekollë RKS 164 D3
Keramitsa GR 168 E3
Keramoti GR 171 C7
Keräntöjärvi S 116 C9
Kerasia GR 169 D6
Kerasona GR 168 F4
Keräs-Sieppi FIN 117 B11
Keratea GR 175 D8
Kerava FIN 127 E13
Kerecsend H 147 F10
Kerekegyháza H 150 D3
Kerepestarcsa H 150 B3
Kerets'ky UA 145 G7
Kergu EST 131 D9
Keri GR 174 D2
Kerimäki FIN 129 B11
Kerisalo FIN 125 F9
Kerkdriel NL 16 E4
Kerkejaure S 118 B3
Kerken D 16 F6
Kerkini GR 169 B9
Kerkkoo FIN 127 E14
Kerkonkoski FIN 123 E17
Kerkrade NL 20 C6
Kerkwijk NL 183 B6
Kerkyra GR 168 E2
Kerlouan F 22 C3
Kerma FIN 125 F11
Kermen BG 166 D6
Kernascléden F 22 D5
Kernavė LT 137 D10
Kernhof A 148 A5
Kerns CH 70 D6
Kerpen D 21 C7
Kerrykeel IRL 7 B7
Kershopefoot GB 5 E11
Kersilö FIN 117 C17
Kerspleben D 79 D9
Kerstinbo S 98 B7
Kerteminde DK 86 E7
Kertészsziget H 151 C7
Kertezi GR 174 D4
Kerttuankylä FIN 123 D10
Kerzers CH 31 B11
Kesälahti FIN 129 B12
Keşan TR 172 C6
Kesäniemenkylä FIN 121 B12
Kesarevo BG 166 C5
Kesasjärv S 118 B8
Kesh GB 7 C7
Kesh IRL 6 D6
Kesik TR 177 B8
Keskijärvi FIN 125 E14
Keskikylä FIN 119 E13
Keskikylä FIN 119 E15
Keskikylä FIN 119 F13
Keskikylä FIN 122 F9
Keskikylä FIN 123 E11
Keskinen FIN 121 E13
Keskipiiri FIN 119 E14
Keski-Posio FIN 121 B11
Keskusvankila FIN 124 C8
Kęsowo PL 138 C4
Kessel B 182 C5
Kessel NL 183 C8
Kesselinkylä FIN 125 C14
Kessingland GB 15 C12
Ķesterciems LV 134 B6
Kesteren NL 183 B7
Kestilä FIN 119 D14
Kestilä FIN 119 F16
Kestrini GR 168 E3
Keswick GB 10 B5
Keszthely H 149 C8
Kesztölc H 149 A11
Kétegyháza H 151 D7
Kéthely H 149 C8
Ketola FIN 115 E2
Ketomella FIN 117 B12
Keträvaara FIN 121 D13
Kętrzyn PL 136 E3
Ketsch D 21 F11
Kétsoprony H 151 D6
Kettering GB 15 C7
Kettershausen D 71 A10
Kettinge DK 83 A11
Kettletoft GB 3 G11
Kettlewell GB 11 C7
Kettwig D 183 C9
Kęty PL 147 B8
Ketzin D 79 B12
Keula D 79 D8
Keuruu FIN 123 F13
Keutschach am See A 73 C9
Keväjärvi FIN 114 F3
Kevelaer D 16 E6
Ķevele LV 134 D5
Kevermes H 151 E7
Kevo FIN 113 D19
Keynsham GB 13 C9
Keyritty FIN 125 D10
Kežmarok SK 145 E1
Khadzhidimovo BG 169 A10
Khalamyer"ye BY 133 E7
Kharlu RUS 129 B14
Kharmanli BG 166 F5
Khaskovo BG 166 F5
Khayredin BG 160 F3
Khelyulya RUS 129 B14
Khisarya BG 165 D10
Khiytola RUS 129 C12
Khlivchany UA 144 C8
Kholmets' UA 145 F5
Kholms'ke UA 155 B4
Khorio GR 179 B8
Khrabrovo RUS 136 D2
Khrishteni BG 166 E5
Khust UA 145 G7
Khvoyna BG 165 F10
Khyriv UA 145 D6
Kiannanniemi FIN 121 D13
Kiato GR 175 C6
Kiaunoriai LT 134 E6
Kibæk DK 86 C3
Kibworth Harcourt GB 11 F10
Kiby N 114 C7
Kičevo MK 168 A4
Kichenitsa BG 161 F8
Kichevo BG 167 C9
Kidderminster GB 13 A10
Kidlington GB 13 B12
Kidričevo SLO 148 D5
Kidsgrove GB 11 E7
Kidwelly GB 12 B6
Kiefersfelden D 72 A5
Ķieģeļceplis LV 135 C10
Kiekinkoski FIN 125 B14
Kiekrz PL 81 B11
Kiel D 83 B8
Kielajoki FIN 113 E18
Kielce PL 143 E10
Kiełczygłów PL 143 D6
Kielder GB 5 E11
Kieldrecht B 182 C4
Kiełpino PL 138 B5
Kiemėnai LT 135 D8
Kiemozia PL 141 F1
Kienberg D 75 F11
Kierinki FIN 117 D15
Kierspe D 21 B9
Kieselbach D 79 E7
Kiesilä FIN 128 C7
Kiesimä FIN 123 E17
Kietrz PL 142 F5
Kietz D 81 A7
Kifisia GR 175 C8
Kifjord N 113 B19
Kihelkonna EST 130 E4
Kihlanki FIN 117 C11
Kihlanki S 117 C10
Kihlepa EST 131 E8
Kihlevere EST 131 C12
Kihniö FIN 123 F10
Kiihtelysvaara FIN 125 F14
Kiikala FIN 127 E10
Kiikka FIN 126 C8
Kiikla EST 131 C14
Kiikoinen FIN 126 C8
Kiili EST 131 C9
Kiiminki FIN 119 D15
Kiisa EST 131 C9
Kiiskilä FIN 123 C13
Kiistala FIN 117 C14
Kiiu EST 131 C10
Kiiu-Aabla EST 131 B11
Kije PL 143 E10
Kijevë RKS 163 D10
Kijevo HR 156 E5
Kijewo Królewskie PL 138 D5
Kikerino RUS 132 C6
Kikinda SRB 150 F5
Kikół PL 138 E7
Kikorze PL 85 C8
Ķikuri LV 134 C3
Kil N 90 B5
Kil S 97 C9
Kilafors S 103 D12
Kilargue IRL 6 D6
Kilb A 77 F8
Kilbaha IRL 8 C3
Kilbeggan IRL 7 F8
Kilbeheny IRL 8 D6
Kilberry GB 4 D5
Kilberry IRL 7 F8
Kilbirnie GB 4 D7
Kilboghamn N 108 D5
Kilbotn N 111 C12
Kilbrittain IRL 8 E5
Kilby S 99 B10
Kilcar IRL 6 C5
Kilchoan GB 4 B4
Kilchrenan GB 4 C6
Kilcock IRL 7 F9
Kilcolgan IRL 6 F5
Kilcommon IRL 9 D7
Kilconnell IRL 6 F6
Kilconney IRL 7 D8
Kilcoole IRL 7 F10
Kilcormac IRL 7 F7
Kilcreggan GB 4 D7
Kilcullen IRL 7 F9
Kildare IRL 7 F9
Kildavin IRL 9 C9
Kilden DK 90 E7
Kildimo New IRL 8 C5
Kildonan Lodge GB 3 J9
Kile N 90 A2
Kilen N 95 D9
Kilfenora IRL 6 G4
Kilfinan GB 4 D6
Kilfinnane IRL 8 D6
Kilforsen S 107 D11
Kilgarvan IRL 8 E4
Kilgetty GB 12 B5
Kilglass IRL 6 E6
Kilglass IRL 6 F6
Kilham GB 5 D12
Kilidülbahir TR 171 D10
Kilifarevo BG 166 C5
Kilingi-Nõmme EST 131 E9
Kiliya UA 155 C4
Kilkea IRL 9 C9
Kilkee IRL 8 C3
Kilkeel GB 7 D11
Kilkelly IRL 6 E5
Kilkenny IRL 9 C8
Kilkerrin IRL 6 E5
Kilkhampton GB 12 D6
Kilkieran IRL 6 F3
Kilkinlea IRL 8 D4
Kilkis GR 169 C8
Kilkishen IRL 8 C5
Kill IRL 7 F9
Kill IRL 9 D8
Killabunane IRL 8 E3
Killadysert IRL 8 C4
Killagan Bridge GB 4 E4
Killala IRL 6 D4
Killaloe IRL 8 C6
Killamerry IRL 9 D8
Killann IRL 9 C9
Killarga IRL 6 D6
Killarney IRL 8 D4
Killavullen IRL 8 D5
Killeagh IRL 8 E7
Killean GB 4 D5
Killearn GB 5 C8
Killeberg S 88 C6
Killeenleagh IRL 8 E4
Killeigh IRL 7 F8
Killen GB 7 C7
Killenaule IRL 9 C7
Killerrig IRL 9 C9
Killeshandra IRL 7 D7
Killichonan GB 5 B8
Killiecrankie GB 5 B9
Killimor IRL 6 F6
Killin GB 5 C8
Killinaboy IRL 6 G4
Killinchy GB 7 D11
Killinge S 116 C4
Killingworth GB 5 E13
Killinick IRL 9 D10
Killinkoski FIN 123 F11
Killorglin IRL 8 D3
Killough GB 7 D11
Killough IRL 7 F10
Killucan IRL 7 E8
Killukin IRL 6 E6
Killundine GB 4 B5
Killurin IRL 9 D9
Killybegs IRL 6 C6
Killyclogher GB 4 F2
Killylea GB 7 D9
Kilmacanogue IRL 7 F10
Kilmacrenan IRL 7 B7
Kilmacthomas IRL 9 D8
Kilmaganny IRL 9 D8
Kilmaine IRL 6 E4
Kilmaley IRL 8 C4
Kilmallock IRL 8 D5
Kilmaluag GB 2 K4
Kilmarnock GB 4 D8
Kilmartin GB 4 C6
Kilmeague IRL 7 F9
Kilmeedy IRL 8 D5
Kilmelford GB 4 C6
Kilmichael IRL 8 E4
Kilmihill IRL 8 C4
Kilmona IRL 8 E5
Kilmoon IRL 7 E10
Kilmore IRL 8 C5
Kilmore IRL 9 D9
Kilmore Quay IRL 9 D9
Kilmuckridge IRL 9 C10
Kilmurry IRL 8 C5
Kilmurry McMahon IRL 8 C4
Kilnaboy IRL 6 G4
Kilnaleck IRL 7 E8
Kilnamanagh IRL 9 C10
Kilninian GB 4 B4
Kilninver GB 4 C5
Kilnock IRL 6 E5
Kiloran GB 4 C4
Kilpelä FIN 115 D4
Kilpilahti FIN 127 E14
Kilpisjärvi FIN 112 E6
Kilpua FIN 119 F13
Kilquiggin IRL 9 C9
Kilrane IRL 9 D10
Kilrea GB 4 F3
Kilrean IRL 6 C6
Kilreekill IRL 6 F6
Kilrenny GB 5 C11
Kilronan IRL 6 F3
Kilrush IRL 8 C4
Kilsallagh IRL 6 E5
Kilsaran IRL 7 E10
Kilshanchoe IRL 7 F9
Kilshanny IRL 6 G4
Kilskeer IRL 7 E9
Kilsmo S 92 A7
Kilsund N 90 B4
Kilsyth GB 5 D8
Kiltartan IRL 6 F5
Kiltealy IRL 9 C9
Kiltegan IRL 9 C9
Kiltimagh IRL 6 E5
Kiltogan IRL 9 C9
Kiltoom IRL 6 F6
Kiltsi EST 131 C12
Kiltullagh IRL 6 F5
Kilvakkala FIN 127 B9
Kilvenaapa FIN 119 B16
Kilvo S 116 E6
Kilwaughter GB 4 F5
Kilwinning GB 4 D7
Kilworth IRL 8 D6
Kimasozero RUS 121 F17
Kimberley GB 15 B11
Kimbolton GB 15 C8
Kiminki FIN 123 E13
Kimito FIN 126 E8
Kimle H 146 F4
Kimmeria GR 171 B7
Kimo FIN 122 D8
Kimola FIN 127 C15
Kimonkylä FIN 127 D15
Kimovaara RUS 125 C16
Kimpton GB 15 D8
Kimstad S 92 B7
Kinahmo FIN 125 E13
Kinbrace GB 3 J9
Kincardine GB 5 C9
Kincraig GB 3 L9
Kincses H 149 B10
Kindberg A 148 A4
Kindelbrück D 79 D9
Kinderbeuern D 21 D8
Kinding D 75 E9
Kindsbach D 186 C4
Kindsjön S 102 E4
Kineta GR 175 D7
Kingarrow IRL 6 C6
Kingarth GB 4 D6
Kingisepp RUS 132 C4
Kingsbridge GB 13 E7
Kingsclere GB 13 C12
Kingscourt IRL 7 E9
Kingskerswell GB 13 E7
Kingsland IRL 6 E6
King's Lynn GB 11 F12
Kingsnorth GB 15 E10
Kingsteignton GB 13 D7
Kingsthorne GB 13 B9
Kingston GB 3 K10
Kingston Bagpuize GB 13 B12
Kingston Seymour GB 13 C9
Kingston upon Hull GB 11 D11
Kingswear GB 13 E7
Kingswood GB 13 C9
Kings Worthy GB 13 C12
Kington GB 13 A8
Kingussie GB 5 A8
Kingwilliamstown IRL 8 D4
Kinik TR 173 E10
Kinik TR 177 A9
Kinisjärvi FIN 117 D14
Kinloch GB 4 A4
Kinlochard GB 4 C7
Kinlochewe GB 2 K6
Kinlochleven GB 4 B7
Kinloch Rannoch GB 5 B8
Kinloss GB 3 K9
Kinlough IRL 6 D6
Kinn N 111 C10
Kinna S 91 D12
Kinnared S 87 A12
Kinnarp S 91 C14
Kinnarumma S 91 D12
Kinnegad IRL 7 F8
Kinnitty IRL 7 F7
Kinnula FIN 123 D13
Kinnulanlahti FIN 124 D8
Kinrooi B 19 B12
Kinross GB 5 C10
Kinsale IRL 8 E5
Kinsalebeg IRL 9 E7
Kinsarvik N 94 B5
Kintai LT 134 F2
Kintaus FIN 123 F14
Kintbury GB 13 C12
Kintore GB 3 L12
Kinvara IRL 6 F5
Kinvarra IRL 6 F3
Kioni GR 174 C2
Kipen' RUS 132 B6
Kipfenberg D 75 E9
Kipilovo BG 166 D6
Kipinä FIN 119 D17
Kipoi GR 168 E4
Kipoureio GR 168 E5
Kippel CH 70 E5
Kippen GB 5 C8
Kippenheim D 27 D8
Kir AL 163 E8
Kirakkajärvi FIN 114 D5
Kirakkaköngäs FIN 113 F19
Királd H 145 G1
Királyegyháza H 149 D9
Királyhegyes H 150 E6
Kiran N 104 C8
Kiran TR 181 B8
Kirazli TR 172 D6
Kirbla EST 131 D7
Kirby Muxloe GB 11 F9
Kircasalih TR 173 B6
Kirchanschöring D 73 A6
Kirchardt D 21 F11

La Portera E 47 F10
Lapoş RO 161 C8
La Pouëze F 23 E10
Lapoutroie F 27 D7
Lapovo SRB 159 E7
Lappajärvi FIN 123 D11
Lappe S 92 A7
Lappea FIN 117 D11
Lappeenranta FIN 129 C9
Lappersdorf D 75 D11
Lappetelä FIN 124 D8
Lappfjärd FIN 122 F7
Lappfors FIN 123 C10
Lappi FIN 119 E14
Lappi FIN 121 D13
Lappi FIN 126 C6
Lappila FIN 127 D13
Lappo FIN 126 E5
Lappohja FIN 127 F9
Lappträsk S 119 B11
Lappuluobbal N 113 E13
La Preste F 33 F10
La Proveda de Soria E 41 D7
Lâpseki TR 172 D6
Laptevo RUS 133 C5
Lapua FIN 123 E10
La Puebla de Almoradiel E 47 E6
La Puebla de Arganzón E 40 C6
La Puebla de Cazalla E 51 E9
La Puebla de los Infantes E 51 D9
La Puebla del Río E 51 E7
La Puebla de Montalbán E 46 E4
La Puebla de Valdavia E 39 C10
La Puebla de Valverde E 48 D3
La Puerta de Segura E 55 C7
Lăpugiu de Jos RO 151 F10
La Punt CH 71 D9
Lăpuş RO 152 C4
Lăpuşata RO 160 D4
Lapuşna MD 154 D2
Lăpuşnicel RO 159 D9
Lăpuşnicu Mare RO 159 D8
Łapy PL 140 E7
L'Aquila I 62 C4
Laracha E 38 B2
Laracor IRL 7 E9
Laragh IRL 7 F10
Laragne-Montéglin F 35 B10
La Rambla E 53 A7
Laranueva E 47 C7
La Rasa E 40 E5
La Ravoire F 31 D8
Larbert GB 5 C9
L'Arboç E 43 E7
L'Arbresle F 30 D6
Lärbro S 93 D13
Larceveau-Arros-Cibits F 32 D3
Larchamp F 23 D9
Larchant F 25 D8
Larche F 29 E8
Larche F 36 C5
Lardaro I 69 B10
Larderello I 66 F2
Lardero E 41 D7
Lardos GR 181 D8
Laredo E 40 B5
La Redorte F 34 D4
Laren NL 16 D4
Laren NL 183 A8
La Réole F 32 A5
Larga MD 153 A9
Largan IRL 6 D5
L'Argentière-la-Bessée F 31 F10
Largoward GB 5 C11
Largs GB 4 D7
Largu RO 161 D10
Lari I 66 E2
Lariano I 62 D3
La Riba E 42 E6
La Riba de Escalote E 40 F6
La Ricamarie F 30 E5
La Riche F 24 F4
La Rinconada E 51 E8
Larino I 63 D7
Larionovo RUS 129 D13
Larisa GR 169 E7
Larkhall GB 5 D9
Larkollen N 95 D13
Larling GB 15 C10
L'Armentera E 43 C10
Larmor-Plage F 22 E5
Larne GB 4 F5
La Robla E 39 C8
La Roca de la Sierra E 45 F7
La Roche CH 31 B11
La Roche-Bernard F 23 E7
La Roche-Canillac F 29 E9
La Roche-Chalais F 28 E6
La Roche-de-Rame F 31 F10
La Roche-Derrien F 22 C5
La Roche-des-Arnauds F 35 A10
La Roche-en-Ardenne B 19 D12
La Rochefoucauld F 29 D6
La Rochelle F 28 C3
Larochemillay F 30 B5
La Roche-Posay F 29 B7
La Rochepot F 30 B6
La Roche-sur-Foron F 31 C9
La Roche-sur-Yon F 28 B3
La Rochette F 31 E9
Larochette L 20 E6
La Roda E 47 F8
La Roda de Andalucía E 53 B7
La Roë F 23 E9
Laroles E 55 E7
La Romana E 56 E3
La Romieu F 33 C6
Laroquebrou F 29 F10
Laroque-d'Olmes F 33 E9
La Roque-Ste-Marguerite F 34 B5
Laroque-Timbaut F 33 B7
La Rouquette F 33 B9
Larraga E 32 E2
Larrasoaina E 32 E2
Larrau F 32 D4
Larrazet F 33 C8
Larressore F 32 D3
Larrión E 32 E1
Larsbo S 97 B14
Larseng N 111 A16
Larsmo FIN 122 C9
Larsnes N 100 B3
Laruns F 32 E5
Laruscade F 28 E5
Larv S 91 C13
Larva E 55 D6
Larvik N 90 A7
Larymna GR 175 B7
Lasà I 71 D11
Lasalle F 35 B6
La Salle I 31 D11
La Salle les Alpes F 31 F10
La Salvetat-Peyralès F 33 B10
La Salvetat-sur-Agout F 34 C4
La Salzadella E 48 D5
Läsänkoski FIN 128 B6
Las Arenas E 39 B10
La Sauvetat-du-Dropt F 33 A6
La Savina E 57 D7
Lasberg A 77 F7
Las Berlanas E 46 C3
Låsby DK 86 C5
Las Cabezas de San Juan E 51 F8
Lascari I 58 D4
Las Casas E 48 E4
Lascuarre E 42 C5
La Seca E 39 F10
La Secuita E 43 E6
La Séguinière F 28 A4
La Selva del Camp E 42 E6
La Selve F 33 B11
La Sènia E 42 F4
La Seyne-sur-Mer F 35 D10
Las Herencias E 46 E3
Łasin PL 138 C7
Lasinja HR 148 E5
Łask PL 143 C7
Łaskarzew PL 141 G5
Laško SLO 148 D4
Laskowa PL 144 D1
Laskowice PL 138 D5
Laskowiec PL 139 D12
Las Labores E 46 F5
Laslea RO 152 E5
Las Majadas E 47 D8
Las Menas E 55 E8
Las Mesas E 47 F7
Las Navas de la Concepción E 51 D9
Las Navas del Marqués E 46 C4
Lasne B 182 D4
Las Negras E 55 F9
La Solana E 55 B6
La Souterraine F 29 C8
Lasovo SRB 159 F9
Lasowice Małe PL 142 E5
Las Palas E 56 F2
Las Pedroñeras E 47 F7
Las Pedrosas E 41 D10
La Spezia I 69 E8
Las Plassas I 64 D2
Las Rotas E 56 D5
Las Rozas de Madrid E 46 C5
Lassahn D 83 C9
Lassan D 84 C5
Lassay-les-Châteaux F 23 D11
Lassemoen N 105 B13
Lässerud S 96 C7
Lasseube F 32 D5
Lassigny F 18 E6
Lassila FIN 126 B7
Lassing A 73 A9
Lassing A 73 A10
Laßnitzhöhe A 148 B5
Lastebasse I 69 B11
Las Terreras E 55 D9
Las Torres de Cotillas E 56 E2
Lastours F 33 D10
Lastovo HR 162 D2
Lastra a Signa I 66 E3
Lastras de Cuéllar E 40 F3
Lastrup D 17 C9
Lastukoski FIN 125 D10
Lastva BIH 162 D5
La Suze-sur-Sarthe F 23 E12
Lašva BIH 157 D8
Lasva EST 131 F14
Las Veguillas E 45 C9
Las Ventas con Peña Aguilera E 46 E4
Las Ventas de San Julián E 45 D10
Łaszczów PL 144 B8
Laszki PL 144 C6
Laterza I 61 B7
La Teste-de-Buch F 32 A3
Lathen D 17 C8
Latheron GB 3 J10
Latheronwheel GB 3 J10
La Thuile I 31 D10
Lathus F 29 C7
Latiano I 61 B9
Latikberg S 107 B12
Latillé F 28 B6
Latina I 62 E3
Latisana I 73 E7
Latorpsbruk S 97 D12
La Torre de Cabdella E 33 F7
La Torre de Esteban Hambrán E 46 D4
La Torre de l'Espanyol E 42 E5
La Tour-Blanche F 29 E6
La Tour-d'Auvergne F 29 D11
Latour-de-France F 34 E4
La Tour-du-Crieu F 33 D9
La Tour-du-Pin F 31 D7
La Tour-sur-Orb F 34 C5
Latowicz PL 141 F5
La Tranche-sur-Mer F 28 C3
La Tremblade F 28 D3
La Trimouille F 29 C8
La Trinité F 37 D6
La Trinité-Porhoët F 22 D6
La Trinité-sur-Mer F 22 E5
Latronico I 60 C6
Latronquière F 29 F10
Lattarico I 60 E6
Lattes F 35 C6
Lattomeri FIN 126 C6
Lattrop NL 183 A9
La Turballe F 22 F7
Latva FIN 119 F15
Latva FIN 120 C9
Latvajärvenperä FIN 121 D11
Laubach D 21 C11
Laubach D 21 D8
Lauben D 71 A10
Laubere LV 135 C10
Laubusch D 80 D6
Lauchhammer D 80 D5
Lauchringen D 27 E9
Lauciene LV 134 B5
Lauda-Königshofen D 74 C6
Lauder GB 5 D11
Lauderi LV 133 D4
Laudona LV 135 C12
Laudun F 35 B8
Lauenau D 17 D12
Lauenbrück D 82 D7
Lauenburg (Elbe) D 83 D9
Lauenförde D 21 A12
Lauf D 186 D5
Laufach D 187 A7
Lauf an der Pegnitz D 75 C9
Laufen CH 27 F8
Laufenberg CH 27 E9
Lauffen am Neckar D 187 C7
Laugnac F 33 B7
Lauingen (Donau) D 75 E7
Laujar de Andarax E 55 F7
Laukaa FIN 123 F15
Laukeng N 112 D9
Lauker S 118 C3
Laukka FIN 119 E15
Laukkala FIN 123 D17
Laukkoski FIN 127 E13
Laukkuluspa S 111 E18
Laukna EST 131 D8
Lauksargiai LT 134 F4
Laukslett N 111 A17
Lauksletta N 112 C6
Lauksodis LT 135 D8
Laukuva LT 134 E4
Laukvik N 105 C9
Laukvik N 110 D7
Laukvik N 110 E8
Laukvik N 111 A14
Laukvik N 113 C11
Laukvik N 114 B6
Laukžemė LT 134 D2
Laulasmaa EST 131 C8
Launac F 33 C8
Launceston GB 12 D6
La Unión E 56 F3
Launkalne LV 135 B11
Launonen FIN 127 D12
Laupen CH 31 B11
Laupheim D 71 A9
Laupstad N 110 D8
Lauragh IRL 8 E3
Lauraguel F 33 D10
Laurbjerg DK 86 C5
Laureana di Borrello I 59 C9
Laurencekirk GB 5 B12
Laurencetown IRL 6 F6
Laurens F 34 C5
Laurenzana I 60 C5
Lauria I 60 C5
Laurière F 29 C8
Laurieston GB 5 F8
Laurila FIN 119 C13
Laurino I 60 C4
Lauris F 35 C9
Laurito I 60 C4
Lausanne CH 31 B10
Lauscha D 75 B9
Laußig D 79 C12
Laußnitz D 80 D5
Laussonne F 30 F5
Laussou F 33 A7
Lauta D 80 D6
Lautamaa FIN 119 C12
Lautenbach D 27 C9
Lauter D 79 E12
Lauterbourg F 27 C9
Lauterbrunnen CH 70 D5
Lautere LV 135 C12
Lauterecken D 186 B4
Lauterhofen D 75 D10
Lautersbach (Hessen) D 78 E5
Lauterstein D 187 D8
Lautertal D 75 B8
Lautiosaari FIN 119 C13
Lautrec F 33 C10
Lauttavaara FIN 121 E9
Lauttijärvi FIN 126 B6
Lauve N 90 A7
Lauvsnes N 105 C9
Lauvstad N 100 B3
Lauvuskylä FIN 125 C13
Lauvvik N 94 E4
Lauzerte F 33 B8
Lauzès F 33 A9
Lauzun F 33 A6
Lavagna I 37 C10
Laval F 23 D10
Lavala FIN 121 D14
Lavalette F 33 D10
La Valette-du-Var F 35 D10
La Vall d'Uixó E 48 E4
La Valle I 72 C4
Lavamünd A 73 C10
Lavangen N 111 C14
Lavangsnes N 111 C13
Lavara GR 171 B10
Lavardac F 33 B6
Lavassaare EST 131 D8
Lavaur F 33 C9
Lavaveix-les-Mines F 29 C10
Lavda GR 168 D5
Lavdar i Korçës AL 168 C4
La Vecilla E 39 C9
La Vega E 39 B8
La Vega E 39 B8
La Vega E 39 B10
Lavelanet F 33 E9
La Vellés E 45 B9
Lavello I 60 A5
Laven DK 86 C5
Lavena Ponte Tresa I 69 B6
Lavenham GB 15 C10
Laveno I 68 B6
La Ventosa E 47 D8
La Verdière F 35 C10
La Vernarède F 35 B6
La Verpillière F 31 D7
La Verrie F 28 B4
La Veuve F 25 B11
Lavia FIN 126 B8
Laviano I 60 B4
La Victoria E 53 A7
La Vid E 40 E5
Lavik N 111 B14
La Villa de Don Fadrique E 47 E6
La Ville-aux-Clercs F 24 E5
La Villedieu F 30 F4
La Villedieu-du-Clain F 29 C6
La Villedieu-en-Fontenette F 26 E5
Lavinio-Lido di Enea I 62 E3
Laviron F 26 F6
Lavis I 69 A11
Lavit F 33 C7
Lavoriškės LT 137 D12
La Voulte-sur-Rhône F 30 F6
Lavoûte-Chilhac F 30 E4
Lavoûte-sur-Loire F 30 E4
Lavradio P 50 B1
Lavre P 50 B3
Lavrio GR 175 D9
Lavsjö S 107 C11
La Wantzenau F 186 D4
Lawers GB 5 B8
Lawford GB 15 D11
Lawrencetown GB 7 D10
Ławsk PL 140 D6
Ławszowa PL 81 D8
Ławy PL 85 E7
Laxå S 92 B5
Laxbäcken S 107 B10
Laxe E 38 B2
Laxey GBM 10 C3
Laxford Bridge GB 2 J6
Laxnäs S 108 E9
Laxne S 93 A10
Laxo GB 3 E14
Laxou F 26 C5
Laxsjö S 106 D7
Laxvik S 87 B11
Laxviken S 106 D7
Layana E 32 F3
La Yesa E 48 E3
Läyliäinen FIN 127 D11
Layos E 46 E4
Layrac F 33 B7
Laz HR 148 E6
Laza E 38 D5
Laza RO 153 D11
Lazagurría E 32 F1
Lazarata GR 174 B2
Lăzarea RO 153 D7
Lăzăreni RO 151 D9
Lazarevac SRB 158 E5
Lazarev Krst MNE 163 D7
Lazarevo SRB 158 C6
Lazdijai LT 137 E8
Lazdininkai LT 134 E2
Lazdona LV 135 C12
Lazdukalns LV 133 C2
Lazeshchyna UA 152 A4
Lazise I 66 B2
Łaziska PL 141 H5
Łaziska Górne PL 142 F6
Lazkao E 32 D1
Lázně Bělohrad CZ 77 B9
Lázně Bohdaneč CZ 77 B9
Lázně Kynžvart CZ 75 B12
Laznica SRB 159 E8
Lazonby GB 5 F11
Lazuri RO 151 B10
Lazuri de Beiuş RO 151 D9
Leabgarrow IRL 6 C5
Leacht Seoirse IRL 6 F5
Leadburn GB 5 D10
Leadenham GB 11 E10
Leadhills GB 5 E9
Leamhcán IRL 7 F10
Leamington Spa, Royal GB 13 A11
Leányfalu H 150 B3
Leap IRL 8 E4
Leasingham GB 11 E11
Leatherhead GB 15 E8
Leavvajohka N 113 D17
Łeba PL 85 A13
Lebach D 21 F7
Lebane SRB 164 D4
Le Ban-St-Martin F 186 C1
Le Barp F 32 A4
Le Bar-sur-Loup F 36 D5
Lebbeke B 19 B9
Le Béage F 30 F5
Le Beausset F 35 D10
Lebedivka UA 154 F6
Lébényimiklós H 149 A8
Lebesby N 113 B18
Le Bez F 33 C10
Lebiez F 18 D4
Le Biot F 31 C10
Le Blanc F 29 B8
Le Bleymard F 35 B6
Łebno PL 138 B5
Le Bois-d'Oingt F 30 D6
Le Bois-Plage-en-Ré F 28 C3
Le Boréon F 37 C6
Ljbork PL 85 A13
Le Boulou F 34 E4
Le Boupère F 28 B4
Le Bourg F 29 F9
Le Bourg-d'Oisans F 31 E9
Le Bourget-du-Lac F 31 D8
Le Bousquet-d'Orb F 34 C5
Le Breuil F 25 C10
Le Breuil F 30 B5
Lebrija E 51 F7
Lebring-Sankt Margarethen A 148 C5
Le Brouilh-Monbert F 33 C6
Le Brusquet F 36 C4
Lebução P 38 E5
Le Bugue F 29 F7
Le Buisson F 34 A5
Le Buisson-de-Cadouin F 29 F7
Lebunia PL 138 B4
Lebus D 81 B7
Lebusa D 80 C4
Lebyazh'ye RUS 129 F11
Leça da Palmeira P 44 B3
Leça do Bailio P 44 B3
Le Cannet F 36 D6
Le Cannet-des-Maures F 36 E4
Le Castellet F 35 D10
Le Cateau-Cambrésis F 19 D8
Le Catelet F 19 D7
Le Caylar F 34 C5
Le Cayrol F 34 A4
Lecce I 61 C10
Lecco I 69 B7
Lece SRB 164 D4
Lécera E 42 E2
Lech A 71 C10
Lechaina GR 174 D3
Lechaio GR 175 D6
Le Chambon-Feugerolles F 30 E5
Le Chambon-sur-Lignon F 30 E5
Lechaschau A 71 C11
Le Château-d'Oléron F 28 D3
Le Châtelard F 31 D9
Le Châtelet F 29 B10
Lechbruck D 71 B11
Le Chêne F 25 C11
Le Chesne F 19 E10
Le Cheylard F 30 F5
Le Cheylas F 31 E8
Lechinţa RO 152 C4
Lechlade GB 13 B11
Lechovo GR 169 C5
Lechtingen (Wallenhorst) D 17 D10
Leciñena E 41 E10
Leck D 82 A5
Leckaun IRL 6 D6
Leckmelm GB 2 K6
Le Clapier F 34 C5
Le Collet-de-Dèze F 35 B6
Le Conquet F 22 D2
Le Coteau F 30 C5
Le Coudray-St-Germer F 18 F4
Lécousse F 23 D9
Le Crès F 35 C6
Le Creusot F 30 B5
Lecrín E 53 C9
Le Croisic F 22 F6
Le Crotoy F 18 D4
Lectoure F 33 C7
Łęczna PL 141 H7
Łęczyca PL 143 B7
Łęczyce PL 138 A4
Ledaig GB 4 C6
Ledaña E 47 F9
Ledanca E 47 C7
Lēdas LV 134 B5
Ledbury GB 13 A10
Lede B 19 C8
Ledeč nad Sázavou CZ 77 C8
Ledegem B 182 D2
Ledenice BIH 157 C9
Ledenice CZ 77 E7
Lédergues F 33 B10
Ledesma E 45 B9
Lédignan F 35 C7
Ledigos E 39 D10
Ledmore GB 2 J7
Lednica SK 146 C6
Lednice CZ 77 E11
Lednické Rovne SK 146 C6
Le Donjon F 30 C4
Le Dorat F 29 C8
Ledrada E 45 D9
Lēdurga LV 135 B9
Ledusjö S 107 D16
Ledvattsfors S 109 F16
Lidyczek PL 85 C11
Lidzin PL 85 B8
Lidziny PL 143 F7
Leeds GB 11 D8
Leedstown GB 12 E4
Leek GB 11 E7
Leek NL 16 B6
Leeming GB 11 C8
Lee Moor GB 12 E6
Leende NL 16 F5
Leer (Ostfriesland) D 17 B8
Leerdam NL 16 E4
Leersum NL 183 A6
Leese D 17 C12
Leeuwarden NL 16 B5
Leevaku EST 131 E14
Leevi EST 131 F14
Leezen D 83 C8
Leezen D 83 C10
Le Faou F 22 D3
Le Faouët F 22 D5
Le Fenouiller F 28 B2
Leffinge B 182 C1
Lefkada GR 174 B2
Lefkes GR 176 E5
Lefkimmi GR 168 F3
Lefkimmi GR 171 B10
Lefkonas GR 169 B10
Lefkopigi GR 169 D6
Lefkothea GR 168 D5
Lefktra GR 175 C7
Le Fleix F 29 F6
Le Folgoët F 22 C3
Leforest F 182 E2
Le Fossat F 33 D8
Le Fousseret F 33 D8
Le Fugeret F 36 C5
Le Fuilet F 23 F9
Leganés E 46 D5
Leganiel E 47 D7
Legau D 71 B10
Le Gault-Soigny F 25 C10
Le Gault-St-Denis F 24 D5
Legazpi E 32 D1
Legde D 83 E11
Legden D 17 D8
Legé F 28 B2
Lège-Cap-Ferret F 28 F3
Le Genest-St-Isle F 23 D10
Leggs GB 7 C7
Legionowo PL 139 F10
Léglise B 19 E12
Legnago I 66 B3
Legnano I 69 B6
Legnica PL 81 D10
Legnickie Pole PL 81 D10
Le Gond-Pontouvre F 29 D6
Łęgowo PL 138 B6
Legrad HR 149 D7
Le Grand-Bornand F 31 D9
Le Grand-Bourg F 29 C9
Le Grand-Lemps F 31 E7
Le Grand-Lucé F 24 E3
Le Grand-Pressigny F 29 B7
Le Grand-Quevilly F 18 F3
Le Grand-Serre F 31 E7
Le Grau-du-Roi F 35 C7
Le Gros Theil F 18 F2
Le Gua F 31 E8
Legutiano E 41 C6
Legyesbénye H 145 G3
Le Havre F 23 A12
Lehe D 82 B6
Lehliu RO 161 E9
Lehliu-Gară RO 161 E9
Lehmäjoki FIN 122 D8
Lehmen D 21 D8
Lehmikumpu FIN 119 B14
Lehmivaara FIN 117 E11
Lehmo FIN 125 E13
Lehndorf D 79 E11
Lehnice SK 146 E4
Lehnin D 79 B12
Le Hohwald F 27 D7
Léhon F 23 D7
Le Horps F 23 D11
Lehota SK 146 E5
Le Houga F 32 C5
Lehrberg D 75 D8
Lehre D 79 B8
Lehrte D 79 B6
Lehsen D 83 D10
Lehtimäki FIN 123 E11
Lehtiniemi FIN 121 B10
Lehto FIN 121 B14
Lehtopää FIN 119 F13
Lehtovaara FIN 117 D17
Lehtovaara FIN 121 C10
Lehtovaara FIN 121 D14
Lehtovaara FIN 121 F14
Lehtovaara FIN 124 B9
Lehtovaara FIN 125 D11
Lehtse EST 131 C11
Leianokladi GR 174 B5
Leibertingen D 27 D11
Leiblfing D 75 E11
Leibnitz A 148 C5
Leicester GB 11 F9
Leichlingen (Rheinland) D 183 C10
Leiden NL 16 D3
Leiderdorp NL 16 D3
Leidschendam NL 16 D2
Leie EST 131 E12
Leifear IRL 4 F2
Leiferde D 79 B7
Leigh GB 10 E6
Leighlinbridge IRL 9 C9
Leighton Buzzard GB 15 D7
Leikanger N 100 B2
Leikanger N 100 D5
Léim an Bhradáin IRL 7 F10
Leimaņi LV 135 D11
Leimen D 21 F11
Leimuiden NL 182 A5
Leinburg D 75 D9
Leine N 101 D9
Leinefelde D 79 D7
Leinfelden-Echterdingen D 187 D7
Leini I 68 C4
Leino FIN 121 D12
Leinzell D 74 E6
Leioa E 40 B6
Leipalingis LT 137 E8
Leipheim D 75 F7
Leipivaara FIN 121 E10
Leipojärvi S 116 D6
Leipzig D 79 D11
Leira N 101 E10
Leira N 104 E4
Leira N 108 D5
Leirado E 38 D3
Leirāmoen N 108 C8
Leiranger N 110 E8
Leirbotn N 113 C11
Leiria P 44 E3
Leirlia N 105 B15
Leiro E 38 D3
Leirvåg N 100 E2
Leirvík FO 2 A3
Leirvik N 94 C2
Leirvik N 100 D2
Leirvik N 105 B11
Leirvika N 108 D6
Leisach A 73 C6
Leisi EST 130 D5
Leisnig D 80 D3
Leißling D 79 D10
Leiston GB 15 C12
Leitir Ceanainn IRL 7 C7
Leitir Mhic an Bhaird IRL 6 C6
Leitrim IRL 6 D6
Leitza E 32 D2
Leitzkau D 79 B10
Leive FIN 119 B14
Leivonmäki FIN 127 B15
Leivset N 108 B9
Leiwen D 21 E7
Leixlip IRL 7 F10
Lejasciems LV 135 B13
Lejasstrazdi LV 134 C6
Leka GR 177 D8
Lekaj AL 168 B2
Lekangen N 111 B13
Lekani GR 171 B7
Łęka Opatowska PL 142 D5
Lekárovce SK 145 F5
Łękawica PL 147 B8
Lekbibaj AL 163 E8
Lekėčiai LT 137 D7
Lekenik HR 148 E6
Lekeryd S 92 D4
Lekhchevo BG 165 B8
Łęki Szlacheckie PL 143 D8
Leknes N 100 B5
Łęknica PL 81 C7
Lekoes N 110 D6
Lekowo PL 85 C9
Leksand S 103 E9
Leksvik N 105 D9
Lekunberri E 32 D2
Leland N 108 D4
Le Langon F 28 C4
Le Lardin-St-Lazare F 29 E8
Le Lauzet-Ubaye F 36 C4
Le Lavandou F 36 E4
Leleasca RO 160 D4
Leles SK 145 G5
Leleşti RO 159 C11
Le Leuy F 32 C4
Lelice PL 139 E8
Le Lion-d'Angers F 23 E10
Lelīunai LT 135 F10
Lelkowo PL 139 B9
Lelle EST 131 D9
Le Locle CH 31 A10
Le Louroux-Béconnais F 23 E10
Lelów PL 143 E8
Le Luc F 36 E4
Le Lude F 23 E12
Lelystad NL 16 C4
Lem DK 86 C2
Le Malzieu-Ville F 30 F3
Le Mans F 23 D12
Le Markstein F 27 E7
Le Martinet F 35 B7
Le Mas-d'Agenais F 33 B6
Le Mas-d'Azil F 33 D8
Le Masnau-Massuguiès F 34 C4
Le Massegros F 34 B5
Le Mayet-de-Montagne F 30 C4
Le May-sur-Èvre F 23 F10
Lembach im Mühlkreis A 76 E5
Lembeke B 182 C3
Lemberg D 27 B8
Lemberg F 27 B7
Lembeye F 32 D5
Lembras F 29 F7
Lembruch D 17 C10
Lemele NL 16 D6
Lemelerveld NL 16 D6
Le Mêle-sur-Sarthe F 24 C3
Le Merlerault F 23 C12
Le Mesnil-sur-Oger F 25 C11
Lemetinvaara FIN 121 F12
Lemgo D 17 D11
Lemi FIN 128 C8
Lemierzyce PL 81 A7
Lemland FIN 99 B14
Lemmenjoki FIN 117 A16
Lemmer NL 16 C5
Lemnia RO 153 E8
Le Molay-Littry F 23 B10
Le Monastier F 34 A5
Le Monastier-sur-Gazeille F 30 F4
Le Monêtier-les-Bains F 31 F10
Le Montet F 30 C3
Lempäälä FIN 127 C10
Lempdes F 30 D3
Lempdes F 30 E3
Lempyy FIN 124 E8
Lemu FIN 126 D6
Le Muy F 36 E5
Lemvig DK 86 B2
Lemwerder D 17 B11
Lemybrien IRL 9 D7
Lena N 101 E13
Lenart SLO 148 C5
Lēnas LV 134 C3
Lenauheim RO 150 F6
Lencloître F 29 B6
Lencouacq F 32 B5
Lend A 73 B7
Lendak SK 145 E1
Lendava SLO 149 C6
Lendelede B 182 D2
Lendery RUS 125 D16
Lendinara I 66 B4
Lendum DK 90 E7
Lenë AL 168 B3
Lenešice CZ 76 B5
Le Neubourg F 24 B4
Lengau A 72 B6
Lengau A 76 F4
Lengdorf D 75 F11
Lengefeld D 80 E4
Lengenes N 111 D13
Lengenfeld D 79 E11
Lengenwang D 71 B11
Lengerich D 17 C9
Lengerich D 17 D9
Lenggries D 72 A4
Lengnau CH 27 F7
Lengyeltóti H 149 C9
Lenham GB 15 E10
Lenhovda S 89 B8
Lenine UA 154 C5
Léning F 27 C6
Le Nizan F 32 B5
Lenk CH 31 C11
Lenkimai LT 134 D2
Lenna I 69 B8
Lennartsfors S 96 D6
Lennartsnäs S 99 D9
Lenne D 78 C6
Lennestadt D 21 B10
Lenningen D 27 C11
Lennsjö S 103 B12
Leno I 66 B1
Le Noirmont CH 27 F6
Lenola I 62 E4
Le Nouvion-en-Thiérache F 19 D8
Lens B 19 C8
Lens F 18 D6
Lensahn D 83 B9
Lensvik N 104 D7
Lent F 31 C7
Lent NL 183 B7
Lentas GR 178 F8
Lenti H 149 C7
Lentiai I 72 D5
Lentiira FIN 121 F14
Lenting D 75 E9
Lentini I 59 E7
Lentvaris LT 137 D11
Lenvik N 111 C13
Lenzburg CH 27 F9
Lenzen D 83 D10
Lenzing A 76 G5
Lenzkirch D 27 E9
Leoben A 73 B11
Leoben A 73 C8
Leobendorf A 77 F10
Leobersdorf A 77 G10
Leogang A 73 B6
Léognan F 28 F4
Leominster GB 13 A9
León E 39 C8
Léon F 32 C3
Leonberg D 27 C11
Léoncel F 31 F7
Leonding A 76 F6
Leonessa I 62 B3
Leonforte I 58 D5
Leonidio GR 175 E6
Leontari GR 174 A5
Leontari GR 174 E5
Leopoldov SK 146 E5
Leopoldsburg B 19 B11
Leopoldsdorf im Marchfelde A 77 F11
Leopoldshagen D 84 C5
Leopoldshöhe D 17 D11
Leorda RO 153 B8
Leordeni RO 160 D6
Leordina RO 152 B4
Leova MD 154 E2
Leovo Brdo MNE 157 F11
Lepaa FIN 127 C11
Le Palais F 22 F5
Le Palais-sur-Vienne F 29 D8
Le Pallet F 23 F9
Le Parcq F 18 D5
Lepassaare EST 132 F1
Le Passage F 33 B7
Le Pavillon-Ste-Julie F 25 D10
Lepe E 51 E5
Le Péage-de-Roussillon F 30 E6
Le Pellerin F 23 F8
Le Périer F 31 F8
Le Perthus F 34 F4
Le Pertre F 23 D9
Le Petit-Quevilly F 18 F3
Le Pian-Médoc F 28 F4
Le Pin-au-Haras F 23 C12
L'Épine F 35 B10
Le Pin-la-Garenne F 24 D4
Lepistönmäki FIN 123 D10
Lepitsa BG 165 C9
Le Pizou F 28 E6
Le Plan F 33 D8
Le Plessis-Belleville F 25 B8
Le Poët F 35 B10
Lepoglava HR 148 D6
Le Poinçonnet F 29 B9
Le Poiré-sur-Vie F 28 B2
Le Pont-de-Beauvoisin F 31 D8
Le Pont-de-Claix F 31 E8
Le Pont-de-Monvert F 35 B6
Le Pontet F 35 C8
Leporano I 61 C8
Le Porge F 28 F3
Le Porge-Océan F 28 F3
Le Portel F 15 F12
Leposavić RKS 163 C10
Leposaviq RKS 163 C10
Le Pouldu F 22 E4
Le Pouliguen F 22 F7
Lepoura GR 175 C9

Le Pouzin F 30 F6
Leppäjärvi FIN 117 B10
Leppäkoski FIN 127 D12
Leppälä FIN 113 D19
Leppälä FIN 121 D11
Leppälähkylä FIN 123 E11
Leppälahti FIN 124 D8
Leppälahti FIN 125 F12
Leppäselkä FIN 123 D16
Leppävesi FIN 123 F15
Leppävirta FIN 124 F9
Leppiaho FIN 119 C15
Leppikoski FIN 119 D17
Leppiniemi FIN 119 E16
Leppneeme EST 131 B9
Lepsala FIN 127 C15
Lepsäma FIN 127 E12
Lepsény H 149 B10
Leptokarya GR 169 D8
Le Puy-en-Velay F 30 E4
Le Puy-Notre-Dame F 23 F11
Le Quesnoy F 19 D8
Lequile I 61 C10
Ler N 104 E8
Le Raincy F 25 C8
Léran F 33 E9
Lerberget S 87 C11
Lercara Friddi I 58 D4
Lerdala S 91 C14
Léré F 25 F8
Le Relecq-Kerhuon F 22 D3
Lerești RO 160 C6
Lerici I 69 E8
Lérida E 42 D5
Lerín E 32 F2
Lerkaka S 89 B11
Lerma E 40 D4
Lerm-et Musset F 32 B5
Lermoos A 71 C11
Lerot S 96 C7
Le Rouget F 29 F10
Lérouville F 26 C4
Le Rozier F 34 B5
Lerum S 91 D11
Le Russey F 26 F6
Lervik N 95 D13
Lerwick GB 3 E14
Lesa I 68 B6
Les Abrets F 31 D8
Les Aix-d'Angillon F 25 F8
Lešak RKS 163 C10
Lesaka E 32 D2
Les Andelys F 18 F3
Les Angles F 33 E10
Les Angles F 35 C8
Lešani MK 168 B4
Les Arcs F 31 D10
Les Arcs F 36 E4
Les Aubiers F 28 B4
Les Avellanes E 42 D5
Les Avenières F 31 D8
Les Bondons F 35 B6
Les Bordes F 25 E7
Les Borges Blanques E 42 D5
Les Borges del Camp E 42 E6
Les Bouchoux F 31 C8
Les Brenets CH 31 A10
Lesbury GB 5 E13
Les Cabannes F 33 E9
L'Escala E 43 C10
L'Escale F 35 B11
Les Cammazes F 33 D10
Lescar F 32 D5
L'Escarène F 37 D6
Les Cases d'Alcanar E 42 F5
Lesce SLO 73 D9
Lesconil F 22 E3
Les Contamines-Montjoie F 31 D10
Les Coves de Vinromà E 48 D5
Lescun F 32 E4
Lescure-d'Albigeois F 33 C10
Les Deux-Alpes F 31 E9
Les Diablerets CH 31 C11
Les Échelles F 31 E8
Les Églisottes-et-Chalaures F 28 E5
Le Sel-de-Bretagne F 23 E8
Le Sen F 32 B4
Le Sentier CH 31 B9
Les Éparges F 26 B4
Les Epesses F 28 B4
Les Escaldes AND 33 E9
Les Essards-Taignevaux F 31 B7
Les Essarts F 28 B3
Le Seu d'Urgell E 33 F8
Les Eyzies-de-Tayac-Sireuil F 29 F8
Les Fins F 31 A10
Les Forges F 26 D5
Les Fourgs F 31 B9
Les Gets F 31 C10
Leshak RKS 163 C10
Leshan RKS 163 D9
Les Hautes-Rivières F 184 E2
Les Herbiers F 28 B3
Les Houches F 31 D10
Lesichevo BG 165 E9
Lesično SLO 148 D5
Lesidren BG 165 D9
Lesina I 63 D8
Les Issambres F 36 E5
Lesja N 101 B9
Lesjöfors S 97 C11
Leskava LT 137 D8
Leskelä FIN 119 F15
Lesko PL 145 E5
Leskoec MK 168 B4
Leskova SRB 163 C9
Leskovac SRB 164 D4
Leskovik AL 168 D4
Leskovo BG 161 F11
Les Landes-Genusson F 28 B3
Leslie GB 5 C10
Les Lucs-sur-Boulogne F 28 B3
Lesmahagow GB 5 D9
Les Maillys F 26 F3
Les Marches F 31 E9
Les Martres-de-Veyre F 30 D3
Les Matelles F 35 C6
Les Mazures F 184 E2
Les Mées F 35 B10
Les Menuires F 31 E10
Lesmont F 25 D11
Les Mureaux F 24 C6
Lešná CZ 146 B5
Leśna PL 81 D8
Lesneven F 22 C3
Leśnica PL 142 F5
Lešnica SRB 158 D3
Leśniów Wielki PL 81 C8
Lesogorskiy RUS 129 C10
Les Ollières-sur-Eyrieux F 30 F6
Lesovaara FIN 121 D13
Lesovo BG 167 F7
Lesparre-Médoc F 28 E4
Les Peintures F 28 E5
Les Pennes-Mirabeau F 35 D9
Lesperon F 32 C3
Lespezi RO 153 C9
Les Pieux F 23 A8
Lespignan F 34 D5
Lespinassière F 34 D4
Les Planches-en-Montagne F 31 B9
Les Planes d'Hostoles E 43 C9
L'Espluga Calba E 42 E6
L'Espluga de Francolí E 42 E6
Les Ponts-de-Cé F 23 F10
Les Ponts-de-Martel CH 31 A10
Les Preses E 43 C8
Lespugue F 33 D7
Les Rosiers-sur-Loire F 23 F11
Les Rousses F 31 C9
Les Sables-d'Olonne F 28 C2
Lessach A 73 B8
Les Salles-du-Gardon F 35 B7
Lessay F 23 B8
Lessebo S 89 B8
Les Sièges F 25 D10
Lessines B 19 C8
Les Sorinières F 23 F8
Lestene LV 134 C6
Les Ternes F 30 E3
Les Thuiles F 36 C5
Lestijärvi FIN 123 C13
Leština CZ 77 C11
Lestrade F 34 B4
Les Trois-Moutiers F 24 F3
Leșu RO 152 C5
Lesura BG 165 C8
Les Vans F 35 B7
Les Vignes F 34 B5
Leszczyn PL 85 C9
Leszno PL 81 C11
Leszno PL 141 F3
Leszno Górne PL 81 D9
Létavértes H 151 C8
Letca RO 151 C11
Lețcani RO 153 C10
Letca Nouă RO 161 E7
Letchworth Garden City GB 15 D8
Letea Veche RO 153 D9
Le Teich F 32 A3
Le Teil F 35 A8
Le Teilleul F 23 C10
Le Temple F 28 F4
Letenye H 149 D7
Le Theil F 24 D4
Le-Theil-de-Bretagne F 23 E9
Le Thillot F 27 E6
Le Tholy F 27 D6
Le Thor F 35 C8
Letino I 63 E6
Letkés H 147 F7
Letnitsa BG 165 C11
Letoianni I 59 D7
Letonice CZ 77 D11
Le Touquet-Paris-Plage F 15 F12
Le Touvet F 31 E8
Letovice CZ 77 C11
L'Étrat F 30 E5
Le Trayas F 36 E5
Le Tréport F 18 D3
Letsbo S 103 C10
Letschin D 80 A6
Letterfinish IRL 8 E3
Letterkenny IRL 7 C7
Lettermacaward IRL 6 C6
Letterston GB 12 B5
Letur E 55 C8
Le Tuzan F 32 B4
Letzlingen D 79 B9
Leu RO 160 E4
Leuc F 33 D10
Leucate F 34 E5
Leuchars GB 5 C11
Leuchtenberg D 75 C11
Leud RO 152 B4
Leuenberg D 84 E5
Leuglay F 25 E12
Leuk CH 68 A4
Leukerbad CH 70 E5
Leumrabhagh GB 2 J4
Leun D 185 C9
Leuna D 79 D11
Leusden NL 16 D4
Leușeni MD 154 D2
Leutasch A 72 B3
Leutenberg D 79 E9
Leutershausen D 75 D7
Leutesdorf D 185 D7
Leutkirch im Allgäu D 71 B10
Leuvanjoki FIN 119 D15
Leuven B 19 C10
Leuze-en-Hainaut B 19 C8
Le Val F 36 E4
Levan AL 168 C1
Levänen FIN 128 C8
Levang N 108 D5
Levanger N 105 D10
Levanjska Varoš HR 149 F10
Levanto FIN 127 D13
Levanto I 37 C11
Leva Reka BG 165 D6
Leväsjoki FIN 126 B6
Levél H 146 F4
Levelek H 145 H4
Leven GB 5 C11
Leven GB 11 D11
Levens F 37 D6
Levens GB 10 C6
Levenwick GB 3 F14
Leverano I 61 C10
Leverburgh GB 2 K2
Le-Verdon-sur-Mer F 28 D3
Leverkusen D 21 B7
Le Vernet F 33 D9
Lèves F 24 D5
Levet F 29 B10
Levice SK 147 E7
Levico Terme I 69 A11
Levidi GR 174 D5
Levie F 37 H10
Levier F 31 B9
Le Vigan F 35 C6
Lévignac F 33 C8
Lévignacq F 32 B3
Levijoki FIN 123 E11
Le Ville I 66 F5
Levinovac HR 149 E8
Le-Vivier-sur-Mer F 23 C8
Levka BG 166 F6
Levkogeia GR 170 B5
Levoča SK 145 E2
Levonperä FIN 123 C14
Levo-oja FIN 119 D16
Levroux F 29 B9
Levski BG 166 C4
Levunovo BG 169 B9
Lewes GB 15 F9
Lewin Brzeski PL 142 E4
Lewin Kłodzki PL 77 B10
Leyburn GB 11 C8
Leyland GB 10 D6
Leyme F 29 F9
Leysin CH 31 C11
Leytron CH 31 C11
Leżajsk PL 144 C5
Lézan F 35 B7
Lézat-sur-Lèze F 33 D8
Lezay F 28 C5
Lezhë AL 163 F8
Lézignan-Corbières F 34 D4
Lezoux F 30 D3
Lezuza E 55 B8
Lgota Górna PL 143 E7
Lgota Wielka PL 143 D7
Lhenice CZ 76 D6
Lherm F 33 D8
L'Hermenault F 28 B4
L'Honor-de-Cos F 33 B8
L'Hôpital F 186 C2
L'Horme F 30 E6
Lhospitalet F 33 B8
L'Hospitalet de l'Infant E 42 F5
L'Hospitalet de Llobregat E 43 E8
L'Hospitalet-du-Larzac F 34 C5
L'Hospitalet-près-l'Andorre F 33 E9
L'Hostal del Alls E 42 F5
L'Huisserie F 23 D10
Lhuître F 25 C11
Lia N 111 C14
Liabøen N 104 E4
Liancourt F 18 F5
Liapades GR 168 E2
Liart F 19 E9
Liarvåg N 94 D3
Liatorp S 88 B6
Liatroim IRL 6 D6
Libáň CZ 77 B8
Libatse EST 131 D8
Libberton GB 5 D9
Libčany CZ 77 B9
Libčeves CZ 76 B5
Liberadz PL 139 D9
Liberec CZ 81 E8
Liběšice CZ 80 E6
Libiąż PL 143 F7
Libice nad Cidlinou CZ 77 B8
Libin B 19 E11
Libina CZ 77 C12
Libochovice CZ 76 B6
Libofshë AL 168 C2
Libohovë AL 168 D3
Libouchec CZ 80 E6
Libourne F 28 F5
Libramont B 19 E11
Librazhd AL 168 B3
Librilla E 55 D10
Libros E 47 D10
Licata I 58 E4
Licciana Nardi I 69 E9
Licenza I 62 C3
Liceras E 40 F5
Lich D 21 C11
Lichfield GB 11 F8
Lichnov CZ 142 F4
Lichnowy PL 138 B6
Lichtaart B 182 C5
Lichte D 75 A9
Lichtenau D 17 E11
Lichtenau D 27 C9
Lichtenau im Waldviertel A 77 E8
Lichtenfels D 75 B9
Lichtenstein D 79 E12
Lichtentanne D 79 E11
Lichtenvoorde NL 17 E7
Lichtenwörth A 77 G10
Lichterfelde D 84 E5
Lichtervelde B 19 B7
Līči LV 135 B10
Līči LV 135 D13
Lička Jesenica HR 156 C3
Lički Osik HR 156 C3
Licko Lešće HR 156 C3
Licodia Eubea I 59 E6
Licques F 15 F12
Līčupe LV 135 C10
Licurici RO 160 D3
Lida BY 137 F11
Lidečko CZ 146 C6
Liden S 103 A12
Lidhult S 87 B12
Lidingö S 99 D10
Lidköping S 91 B13
Lido I 66 B5
Lido Adriano I 66 D5
Lido di Classe I 66 D5
Lido di Foce Verde I 62 E3
Lido di Jesolo I 66 A6
Lido di Metaponto I 61 C7
Lido di Ostia I 62 D2
Lido di Siponto I 63 D9
Lido di Spina I 66 C5
Lidoriki GR 174 B5
Lidsälen S 102 E5
Lidsjöberg S 106 C8
Līdumnieki LV 133 C3
Lidzbark PL 139 D8
Lidzbark Warmiński PL 136 E2
Liebenau D 17 C12
Liebenau D 17 F12
Liebenburg D 79 B7
Liebenfels A 73 C9
Liebenwalde D 84 E4
Lieberose D 80 C6
Liebertwolkwitz D 79 D11
Liebling RO 159 B7
Lieboch A 148 C4
Liebstadt D 80 E5
Liedakkala FIN 119 C13
Liédena E 32 E3
Liedenpohja FIN 123 F11
Liège B 19 C12
Lieģi LV 134 C2
Liehittäjä S 119 B10
Liekokylä FIN 119 C16
Lieksa FIN 125 D14
Lielauce LV 134 C5
Lielbērze LV 134 C6
Lielirbe LV 130 F4
Lielklapari LV 135 D13
Lielmēmele LV 135 D10
Lielvārde LV 135 C9
Lielvircava LV 134 C7
Liempde NL 183 B6
Lien S 105 D15
Lien S 107 E10
Lienden NL 183 B7
Lienen D 17 D9
Lienz A 73 C6
Liepa LV 135 B10
Liepāja LV 134 C2
Liepāre LV 134 C7
Liepas LV 135 D12
Liepe D 84 E5
Liepen D 84 C4
Liepene LV 134 B3
Liepgarten D 84 C6
Liepimäjärvi FIN 117 B11
Lieplaukalė LT 134 E3
Lieplaukė LT 134 E4
Liepna LV 133 B2
Lieponys LT 137 E10
Liepupe LV 135 B8
Lier B 19 B10
Lier N 96 B7
Lierbyen N 95 C12
Liernais F 25 F11
Lierneux B 19 D12
Liesek SK 147 C9
Lieser D 21 E8
Lieshout NL 183 B7
Lieso FIN 127 C12
Liessel NL 16 F5
Liestal CH 27 F8
Lieštany SK 146 D6
Liești RO 161 B11
Lietavská Lúčka SK 147 C7
Lietekylä FIN 121 E11
Lieto FIN 126 D7
Liétor E 55 B9
Lievestuore FIN 123 F16
Lievoperä FIN 119 F16
Liezen A 73 A9
Liezēre LV 135 B12
Liffol-le-Grand F 26 D4
Lifford IRL 4 F2
Liffré F 23 D8
Lifton GB 12 D6
Ligardes F 33 B6
Līgatne LV 135 B10
Ligist A 73 C11
Lignano Pineta I 73 E7
Lignano Sabbiadoro I 73 E7
Lignan-sur-Orb F 34 D5
Ligné F 23 F9
Ligneuville B 20 D6
Lignières F 29 B10
Ligny-en-Barrois F 26 C3
Ligny-le-Châtel F 25 E10
Ligonchio I 66 D1
Ligota PL 142 C4
Ligowo PL 139 E7
Ligueil F 29 A7
Ligugé F 29 B6
Lihme DK 86 B3
Lihula EST 130 D7
Liigvalla EST 131 C12
Liikasenvaara FIN 121 B14
Liikavaara S 116 D6
Liimattala FIN 123 E15
Liimattala FIN 123 E17
Liipantönkkä FIN 122 E9
Liittoperä FIN 123 C16
Liiva EST 130 D6
Lijar E 55 E8
Liješće BIH 157 B9
Lijeska BIH 158 F3
Lijeva Rijeka MNE 163 D7
Lijevi Dubravčak HR 149 E6
Likavka SK 147 C8
Likenäs S 102 E5
Līksna LV 135 E12
Lilaia GR 175 B5
Liland N 110 D6
Liland N 111 D12
Lilaste LV 135 B8
L'Île-Bouchard F 24 F3
L'Île-Rousse F 37 F9
Lilienfeld A 77 F9
Lilienthal D 17 B11
Liljendal FIN 127 D15
Liljendal S 97 B11
Lilkovo BG 165 F10
Lillå S 118 B5
Lilla Edet S 91 C11
Lillåfors S 118 B6
Lilla Tjärby S 87 B12
Lillby FIN 123 D10
Lille B 16 F3
Lille F 19 C7
Lillebo N 102 C3
Lillebonne F 18 E2
Lillehammer N 101 D12
Lillers F 18 C5
Lillesand N 90 C3
Lilleshall GB 11 F7
Lille Skensved DK 87 D10
Lillestrøm N 95 C14
Lille Værløse DK 87 D10
Lillfjäten S 102 C4
Lillhamra S 102 C8
Lillhärdal S 102 C7
Lillholmsjö S 105 D16
Lillholmträsk S 107 B16
Lilliesleaf GB 5 D11
Lillkågeträsk S 118 E5
Lillkyrka S 98 C8
Lillmörtsjö S 103 B11
Lillo E 47 E6
Lillögda S 107 C13
Lillpite S 118 D6
Lillroten S 103 A14
Lillsaivis S 118 B7
Lillsele S 107 C16
Lillselet S 116 E9
Lillsjöhögen S 106 E8
Lillskog S 103 C9
Lillström S 103 B12
Lillsved S 102 A7
Lillviken S 109 C11
Lilyache BG 165 C8
Lilyak BG 167 C6
Lilyanovo BG 169 A9
Lima S 102 E5
Limana I 72 D5
Limanköy TR 167 F10
Limanowa PL 144 D1
Limanu RO 155 F3
Limatola I 60 A2
Limavady GB 4 E3
Limay F 24 B6
Limbach D 21 F12
Limbach D 186 C2
Limbach-Oberfrohna D 79 E12
Limbadi I 59 B8
Limbaži LV 135 A9
Limbourg B 20 C5
Limburg an der Lahn D 21 D10
Limburgerhof D 187 C5
Lime DK 86 C6
Limedsforsen S 102 E5
Limenaria GR 171 C7
Limenas GR 177 C6
Limenas Chersonisou GR 178 E9
Limerick IRL 8 C5
Limingen N 105 B15
Limingoån S 116 E9
Liminka FIN 119 E14
Liminpuro FIN 120 E9
Limmared S 91 D13
Limmen NL 16 C3
Limnes GR 175 D6
Limni GR 175 B7
Limnochori GR 169 C6
Limoges F 29 D8
Limogne-en-Quercy F 33 B9
Limone Piemonte I 37 C7
Limonest F 30 D6
Limone sul Garda I 69 B10
Limosano I 63 D7
Limoux F 33 D10
Limpias E 40 B5
Lin AL 168 B4
Linå DK 86 C5
Lina älv S 116 D4
Linakhamari RUS 114 D10
Linards F 29 D9
Linares E 54 C5
Linares de Mora E 48 D3
Linares de Riofrío E 45 C9
Linaria GR 175 B10
Lincent B 19 C11
Lincoln GB 11 E10
Lind DK 86 C3
Lindas N 100 E2
Lindau D 79 B11
Lindau D 82 A7
Lindau (Bodensee) D 71 B9
Lindberg D 76 D4
Linde DK 86 C2
Lindelse DK 87 F7
Linden D 21 C11
Linden D 82 B6
Lindenberg D 80 B6
Lindenberg D 83 D12
Lindenberg im Allgäu D 71 B9
Lindenfels D 21 E11
Lindern (Oldenburg) D 17 C9
Lindesberg S 97 C13
Lindesnäs S 97 B12
Lindewitt D 82 A6
Lindfield GB 15 E8
Lindholmen S 99 C10
Lindi EST 131 E8
Lindknud DK 86 D4
Lindkoski FIN 127 D15
Lindlar D 21 B8
Lindome S 91 D11
Lindores GB 5 C10
Lindos GR 181 D8
Lindoso P 38 E3
Lindow D 84 E3
Lindsdal S 89 B10
Lindsjö S 103 B12
Lindstedt D 79 A10
Lindved DK 86 D5
Lindwedel D 78 A6
Linge N 100 B6
Lingen (Ems) D 17 C8
Lingenfeld D 21 F10
Lingfield GB 15 E8
Linghed S 103 E10
Linghem S 92 C7
Lingolsheim F 27 C8
Lingrasmo N 111 B18
Linguaglossa I 59 D7
Linguizzetta F 37 G10
Linhares P 44 C6
Linia PL 138 B4
Liniewo PL 138 B5
Linkmenys LT 135 F11
Linköping S 92 C7
Linksness GB 3 H10
Linkuva LT 135 D7
Linlithgow GB 5 D9
Linna EST 131 E11
Linnamäe EST 130 D7
Linnamäe EST 131 F13
Linnankylä FIN 123 F10
Linneryd S 89 B8
Linnich D 20 C6
Linow D 83 D13
Linsell S 102 B6
Linsidemore GB 2 K8
Linthal CH 71 D8
Linthe D 79 B12
Lintig D 17 A11
Lintrup DK 86 E3
Lintula FIN 117 C14
Lintzoain E 32 E3
Linum D 84 E3
Linxe F 32 C3
Linyola E 42 D5
Linz A 76 F6
Linz am Rhein D 21 C8
Lioboml' UA 141 H10
Lioliai LT 134 E5
Lioni I 60 B4
Lion-sur-Mer F 23 B11
Liorac-sur-Louyre F 29 F7
Lios Mór IRL 9 D7
Lios Póil IRL 8 D2
Lios Tuathail IRL 8 D4
Lipa BIH 157 E7
Lipa PL 139 D10
Lipănești RO 161 C8
Lipany SK 145 E2
Lipar SRB 158 B4
Lipari I 59 C6
Lipawki BY 133 E3
Lipcani MD 153 A9
Lipce Reymontowskie PL 141 G1
Liperi FIN 125 E12
Liphook GB 15 E7
Lipiany PL 85 D7
Lipik HR 149 F8
Lipinki PL 144 D3
Lipinki Łużyckie PL 81 C8
Lipiny PL 81 C9
Lipjan RKS 164 D3
Lipka PL 85 D12
Lipki Wielkie PL 85 E9
Lipkovo MK 164 E4
Lipnica BIH 157 D9
Lipnica PL 85 C12
Lipnica PL 138 D7
Lipnica PL 143 E9
Lipnik PL 143 E11
Lipník nad Bečvou CZ 146 B5
Lipnița RO 161 E11
Lipnitsa BG 165 C8
Lipno PL 81 C11
Lipno PL 139 E7
Lipolist SRB 158 D4
Liposthey F 32 B4
Lipova RO 151 E8
Lipova RO 153 D10
Lipová SK 146 E6
Lipovac HR 157 B11
Lipovac SRB 164 B4
Lipová-Lázně CZ 77 B12
Lipovăț RO 153 D11
Lipovec CZ 77 D11
Lipoveni MD 154 D3
Lipovljani HR 149 F7
Lipovo RUS 136 D5
Lipovu RO 160 E3
Lipowiec PL 139 D11
Lipowiec Kościelny PL 139 D9
Lipowina PL 139 B8
Lippoldsberg (Wahlsburg) D 78 C6
Lippstadt D 17 E10
Lipsk PL 140 C8
Lipsko PL 141 H5
Liptál CZ 146 C5
Liptovská Kokava SK 147 C9
Liptovská Lúžna SK 147 D8
Liptovská Osada SK 147 D8
Liptovská Teplička SK 147 D10
Liptovské Revúce SK 147 D8
Liptovský Hrádok SK 147 C9
Liptovský Mikuláš SK 147 C9
Lipusz PL 138 B4
Lipůvka CZ 77 D11
Liqenas AL 168 C4
Liré F 23 F9
Lis AL 168 A3
Lisa RO 152 F5
Lisa RO 160 F6
Lisac BIH 157 D8
Lisac HR 162 D4
Iisaku EST 131 C14
Lisacul IRL 6 E5
Lisbane GB 7 C11
Lisbellaw GB 7 D7
Lisboa P 50 B1
Lisburn GB 7 C10
Liscannor IRL 8 C4
Liscarney IRL 6 E3
Liscarroll IRL 8 D5
Lisciano Niccone I 66 F5
Lișcoteanca RO 161 C11
Lisdoonvarna IRL 6 F4
Liseleje DK 87 C9
Lisets BG 165 C10
Lisewo PL 138 D6
Lisgarode IRL 8 C6
Lisgoold IRL 8 E6
Lisia Góra PL 143 F11
Lisijcice PL 142 F4
Lisieux F 23 B12
Lisiy Nos RUS 129 E13
Lisjö S 97 C15
Liskeard GB 12 E6
Lisková SK 147 C8
Lisków PL 142 C5
Lisky UA 155 C4
Lisle F 29 E7
Lislea GB 4 F3
L'Isle-Adam F 25 B7
L'Isle-de-Noé F 33 C6
L'Isle-d'Espagnac F 29 D6
L'Isle-en-Dodon F 33 D7
L'Isle-Jourdain F 29 C7
L'Isle-Jourdain F 33 C8
L'Isle-sur-la-Sorgue F 35 C9
L'Isle-sur-le-Doubs F 26 F6
L'Isle-sur-Serein F 25 E11
Lisle-sur-Tarn F 33 C9
Lisma FIN 117 B14
Lismakin IRL 9 C7
Lismanaapa FIN 117 D17
Lismarka N 101 D13
Lismore IRL 9 D7
Lisna BY 133 D4
Lisnagry IRL 8 C5
Lisnakill IRL 9 D8
Lisnarrick GB 7 D7
Lisnaskea GB 7 D8
Lisne UA 154 E4
Lišov CZ 77 D7
Lisów PL 142 E6
Lispole IRL 8 D2
Lisronagh IRL 9 D7
Lisryan IRL 7 E8
Liss GB 15 E7
Lissan GB 4 F3
Lisse NL 16 D3
Lissendorf D 185 D6
Lisskogsbrändan S 97 A10
Lissone I 69 B7
Lissycasey IRL 8 C4
List D 86 E2
Listed DK 89 E8
Listerby S 89 C8
Listerlin IRL 9 D8
Listowel IRL 8 D4
Listrac-Médoc F 28 E4
Listry IRL 8 D3
Liszki PL 143 F8
Liszkowo PL 85 D12
Lit S 106 E7
Lița RO 160 F5
Litakovo BG 165 D8
Litava SK 147 E8
Litene LV 133 B2
Liteni RO 153 B9
Litér H 149 B9
Lit-et-Mixe F 32 B3
Lith NL 183 B6
Lithakia GR 174 D2
Lithi GR 177 C7
Lithines GR 179 E11
Litija SLO 73 D10
Litke H 147 E9
Litlefjord N 113 B14
Litmalahti FIN 125 E9
Litmaniemi FIN 125 E10
Litochoro GR 169 D8
Litoměřice CZ 76 A6
Litomyšl CZ 77 C10
Litovel CZ 77 C12
Litschau A 77 E8
Littau CH 70 C6
Littleborough GB 11 D7
Littlehampton GB 15 F7
Littlemill GB 3 K9
Littlemore GB 13 B12
Little Oakley GB 15 D11
Littleport GB 15 C9
Littlestone-on-Sea GB 15 F10
Littleton IRL 9 C7
Littoinen FIN 126 E7
Litva BIH 157 D10
Litvínov CZ 80 E5
Litzendorf D 75 C9
Liudvinavas LT 136 E7
Liukkunen FIN 125 D14
Liuža LV 133 C2
Livada RO 145 H7
Livada RO 151 E7
Livadaki GR 174 D4
Livadeia GR 175 C6
Livădeni MD 153 A11
Livadero GR 169 D6
Livadero GR 171 B6
Livadi GR 169 D7
Livadi GR 175 E10
Livadia GR 169 B9
Livanates GR 175 B7
Līvāni LV 135 D12
Livari MNE 163 E7
Livarot F 23 B12
Līvbērze LV 134 C6
Livernon F 33 A9
Liverpool GB 10 E6
Livezeni RO 152 D5
Livezi RO 153 E9
Livezi RO 160 D3
Livezile RO 152 C5
Livezile RO 152 E3
Livezile RO 159 D10
Līvi LV 135 B10
Livigno I 71 D10
Livingston GB 5 D9
Livno BIH 157 E7
Livo FIN 119 C17
Livold SLO 73 E10
Livonniska FIN 121 C10
Livorno I 66 E1
Livorno Ferraris I 68 C5
Livron-sur-Drôme F 30 F6
Liw PL 139 F12
Lixing-lès-St-Avold F 186 C2
Lixnaw IRL 8 D3
Lixouri GR 174 C1
Lizard GB 12 F4
Lizarraga E 32 E1
Lizdēni LV 131 F10
Lizums LV 135 B12
Lizy-sur-Ourcq F 25 B9
Lizzanello I 61 C10
Lizzano I 61 C8
Ljaljenča BIH 157 C11
Ljeskode Vode BIH 157 C8
Ljig SRB 158 E5
Ljønes N 108 B8
Ljørdal N 102 D4
Ljosland N 90 B1
Ljøsne N 100 D7
Ljuberađa SRB 164 C5
Ljubija BIH 156 C6
Ljubinje BIH 162 D5
Ljubiš SRB 158 F4
Ljubljana SLO 73 D10
Ljubogošta BIH 157 E10
Ljubovija SRB 158 E3
Ljubuški BIH 157 F8
Ljugarn S 93 E13
Ljung S 91 D13
Ljungå S 103 A11
Ljungaverk S 103 B11
Ljungby S 87 B13
Ljungby S 109 F15
Ljungbyhed S 87 C12
Ljungbyholm S 89 B10
Ljungdalen S 102 A4
Ljungsarp S 91 D14
Ljungsbro S 92 B7
Ljungskile S 91 C10
Ljupina HR 157 B7
Ljuša BIH 157 D7
Ljuså S 118 C7
Ljušči Palanka BIH 156 C5
Ljusdal S 103 C11
Ljusfallshammar S 92 B7
Ljusne S 103 D13
Ljusnedal S 102 A4
Ljustorp S 103 A13
Ljusträsk S 118 C3
Ljusvattnet S 118 E6
Ljuti Dolac BIH 157 F8
Ljutomer SLO 148 C6
Llabjan RKS 164 D3
Llagostera E 43 D9
Llamas de la Ribera E 39 C8
Llanaelhaearn GB 10 F3
Llanarth GB 12 A6
Llanarthney GB 12 B6
Llanbadarn Fawr GB 12 A6
Llanbadrig GB 10 E3
Llanbedr GB 10 F3
Llanbedrog GB 10 F3
Llanberis GB 10 E3
Llanbister GB 13 A8
Llanblethian GB 13 C8
Llançà E 34 F5
Llandanwg GB 10 F3
Llandderfel GB 10 F4
Llandeilo GB 12 B7
Llandissilio GB 12 B5
Llandovery GB 13 B7
Llandrillo GB 10 F5
Llandrindod Wells GB 13 A8
Llandudno GB 10 E4
Llandwrog GB 10 E3
Llandysul GB 12 A6
Llanegwad GB 12 B6
Llaneilian GB 10 E3
Llanelli GB 12 B6
Llanelltyd GB 10 F4
Llanelwy GB 10 E5
Llanes E 39 B10
Llanfaelog GB 10 E3
Llanfair Caereinion GB 10 F5
Llanfairfechan GB 10 E4
Llanfairpwllgwyngyll GB 10 E3
Llanfair Talhaiarn GB 10 E4
Llanfihangel-ar-arth GB 12 A6
Llanfyllin GB 10 F5
Llangadfan GB 10 F5
Llangadog GB 13 B7
Llangefni GB 10 E3
Llangeler GB 12 A6
Llangelynin GB 10 F3
Llangoed GB 10 E3
Llangollen GB 10 F5
Llangurig GB 13 A7
Llangynidr GB 13 B8
Llanidloes GB 13 A7
Llanilar GB 12 A6
Llanishen GB 13 B8

Lutnes N 102 D4
Lutocin PL 139 E8
Lutomiersk PL 143 C7
Luton GB 15 D8
Lutowiska PL 145 E6
Lutriņi LV 134 C4
Lutry PL 136 E2
Luttenberg NL 183 A8
Lutter am Barenberge D 79 C7
Lutterbach F 27 E7
Lutterworth GB 13 A12
Lututów PL 142 D5
Lützelbach D 21 E12
Lützen D 79 D11
Lutzerath D 21 D8
Lutzingen D 75 E8
Lutzmannsburg A 149 B7
Lützow D 83 C10
Luua EST 131 D13
Luujoki FIN 119 C14
Luukkola FIN 129 C9
Luukkonen FIN 129 B9
Luumäen kk FIN 128 D8
Luumäki FIN 128 D8
Luunja EST 131 E13
Luupujoki FIN 123 C17
Luupuvesi FIN 123 C17
Luusniemi FIN 124 G7
Luusua FIN 115 F2
Luvia FIN 126 C6
Luvos S 109 C16
Lux F 26 F3
Luxembourg L 20 E6
Luxe-Sumberraute F 32 D3
Luxeuil-les-Bains F 26 E5
Luxey F 32 B4
Luyego de Somoza E 39 D7
Luyksgestel NL 183 C6
Luz P 50 E2
Luz P 50 E4
Luz P 51 C5
Luzaga E 47 C8
Lužani HR 157 B8
Luzarches F 25 B7
Luz-Ardiden F 32 E5
Luže CZ 77 C10
Luzech F 33 B8
Lužec nad Vltavou CZ 76 B6
Luzenac F 33 E9
Luzern CH 70 C6
Luzhany UA 153 A7
Luzhki BY 133 F3
Luzianes P 50 D3
Luz i Madh AL 168 B2
Luzino PL 138 A5
Luzmela E 40 B3
Łużna PL 144 D3
Lūžņa LV 130 F3
Lūznava LV 133 D2
Luzón E 47 B8
Luz-St-Sauveur F 32 E6
Luzy F 30 B4
Luzzara I 66 C2
Luzzi I 60 E6
L'viv UA 144 D9
Lwówek PL 81 B10
Lwówek Śląski PL 81 D9
Lyady RUS 132 D4
Lyaskelya RUS 129 B15
Lyaskovets BG 166 C5
Lyavoshki BY 133 E2
Lybokhora UA 145 F6
Lybster GB 3 J10
Lychen D 84 D4
Lycksaberg S 107 A14
Lycksele S 107 B15
Lydd GB 15 F10
Lyderslev DK 87 E10
Lydford GB 12 D6
Lydney GB 13 B9
Lyeninski BY 141 F10
Lyfjord N 111 A16
Lygna N 95 B13
Lygumai LT 134 D7
Lykofi GR 171 B10
Lykoporia GR 175 C6
Lyly FIN 127 B11
Lylykylä FIN 121 E11
Lyman UA 155 B5
Lymans'ke UA 154 D5
Lymans'ke UA 155 C2
Lyme Regis GB 13 D9
Lymington GB 13 D11
Lymm GB 10 E7
Lynäs S 103 D12
Lyndhurst GB 13 D11
Lyne DK 86 D3
Lyneham GB 13 B11
Lynemore GB 3 L9
Lyness GB 3 H10
Lyngby DK 87 C7
Lyngdal N 94 F6
Lyngmoen N 112 D5
Lyngså DK 86 A7
Lyngseidet N 111 A19
Lyngsnes N 105 B10
Lynmouth GB 13 C7
Lynton GB 13 C7
Lyntupy BY 137 C13
Lyökki FIN 126 D5
Lyon F 30 D6
Lyons-la-Forêt F 18 F3
Lyrestad S 91 B15
Lyrkeia GR 175 D6
Lysabild DK 86 F6
Lysá pod Makytou SK 146 C6
Łyse PL 139 D12
Lysebotn N 94 D5
Lysekil S 91 C9
Lyshchytsy BY 141 F9
Lysice CZ 77 D11
Lysnes N 111 B14
Łysomice PL 138 D6
Lysøysund N 104 D7
Lysroll N 111 D11
Lyss CH 31 A11
Lysvik S 97 B9
Łyszkowice PL 141 G1
Lytchett Minster GB 13 D10
Lytham St Anne's GB 10 D5
Lytovezh UA 144 B9
Lyubashivka UA 154 B6
Lyuben BG 165 E10
Lyubimets BG 166 F6
Lyublino RUS 136 D1
Lyubomyrka UA 154 B4
Lyubyntsi UA 145 E8
Lyulyakovo BG 167 D8

M

Maakeski FIN 127 C13
Maalahti FIN 122 E7
Maalismaa FIN 119 D15
Maam IRL 6 E3
Maaninka FIN 124 D8
Maaninkavaara FIN 115 F4
Maanselkä FIN 125 C10
Maaralanpera FIN 123 C16
Maardu EST 131 B10
Maarheeze NL 183 C7
Maaria FIN 126 D7
Maarianvaara FIN 125 E11
Maarn NL 183 A6
Maarssen NL 16 D4
Maarssenbroek NL 183 A6
Maas IRL 6 C6
Maasbracht NL 19 B12
Maasbree NL 16 F6
Maasdam NL 182 B5
Maaseik B 19 B12
Maaselkä FIN 121 F14
Maasen D 17 C11
Maasland NL 16 E2
Maasmechelen B 19 C12
Maassluis NL 16 E2
Maastricht NL 19 C12
Määttälä FIN 123 C12
Määttälänvaara FIN 121 B14
Maavesi FIN 124 F9
Mablethorpe GB 11 E12
Macael E 55 E8
Maçanet de Cabrenys E 34 F4
Maçanet de la Selva E 43 D9
Mação P 44 E5
Măcărești MD 153 C11
Macastre E 48 F3
Maccagno I 68 A6
Macchiagodena I 63 D6
Macclesfield GB 11 E7
Macduff GB 3 K12
Macea RO 151 E7
Maceda E 38 D4
Maceda P 44 C3
Macedo de Cavaleiros P 39 E6
Maceira P 44 C6
Maceira P 44 E3
Macelj HR 148 D5
Macerata I 67 F7
Macerata Feltria I 66 E5
Măceșu de Jos RO 160 F3
Măceșu de Sus RO 160 F3
Machados P 50 C5
Machairas GR 174 B3
Machault F 19 F10
Machecoul F 28 B2
Machelen B 182 D4
Machen GB 13 B8
Machern D 79 D12
Machliny PL 85 D10
Machov CZ 77 A10
Machowa PL 143 F11
Machrihanish GB 4 E5
Machynlleth GB 10 F4
Maciejowice PL 141 G5
Măcin RO 155 C2
Macinaggio F 37 F10
Măciuca RO 160 D4
Mačkatica SRB 164 D5
Mackenbach D 21 F9
Mackenrode D 79 C8
Mačkovci SLO 148 C6
Macomer I 64 C2
Mâcon F 30 C6
Macosquin GB 4 E3
Macotera E 45 C10
Macroom IRL 8 E5
Macugnaga I 68 B4
Mačvanska Mitrovica SRB 158 D4
Mačvanski Pričinović SRB 158 D4
Mád H 145 G3
Madan BG 165 B7
Madan BG 171 A7
Mådan S 103 A15
Madängsholm S 91 C14
Madara BG 167 C8
Madaras H 150 E3
Mădăraș RO 151 D8
Mădârjac RO 153 C10
Maddalena Spiaggia I 64 E3
Maddaloni I 60 A2
Made NL 16 E3
Madekoski FIN 119 E15
Madeley GB 10 F7
Mäder A 71 C9
Madetkoski FIN 115 C1
Madiran F 32 C5
Madley GB 13 A9
Madliena LV 135 C10
Madocsa H 150 D2
Madona LV 135 C12
Madonna di Campiglio I 69 A10
Madrid E 46 D5
Madridejos E 46 F5
Madrigal de las Altas Torres E 45 B11
Madrigal de la Vera E 45 D10
Madrigal del Monte E 40 D4
Madrigalejo E 45 F9
Madrigueras E 47 F9
Madroñera E 45 F9
Mădulari RO 160 D4
Madzharovo BG 171 A9
Mæl N 95 C9
Maël-Carhaix F 22 D5
Maella E 42 E4
Maello E 46 C3
Maenclochog GB 12 B5
Maenza I 62 D4
Mære N 105 D10
Măeriște RO 151 C10
Mäetaguse EST 131 C14
Maeztu E 41 C7
Mafra P 50 B1
Magacela E 51 B8
Magallón E 41 E9
Magalluf E 49 E10
Magaña E 41 E7
Magašići BIH 158 E3
Magaz E 40 E3
Magdala D 79 E9
Magdeburg D 79 B10
Magdeburgerforth D 79 B11
Magenta I 69 C6
Magescq F 32 C3
Măgești RO 151 C9
Maggia CH 68 A6
Maghera GB 4 F3
Magherafelt GB 4 F3
Magheralin GB 7 D10
Măgherani RO 152 D5
Maghery GB 7 C9
Maghull GB 10 D6
Magione I 66 F5
Măgiotsa EST 132 E1
Măgirești RO 153 D9
Magisano I 59 A10
Maglaj BIH 157 C9
Magland F 31 C10
Maglavit RO 159 E11
Magliano de'Marsi I 62 C4
Magliano in Toscana I 65 B4
Magliano Sabina I 62 C2
Magliĉ SRB 158 F6
Maglie I 61 C10
Maglód H 150 C3
Magnac-Laval F 29 C8
Magné F 28 C4
Magnières F 26 D6
Magnor N 96 C7
Magnuszew PL 141 G4
Magny-Cours F 30 B3
Magny-en-Vexin F 24 B6
Mágocs H 149 D10
Magoula GR 174 E5
Magstrup DK 86 E4
Magueija P 44 B5
Maguilla E 51 C8
Maguiresbridge GB 7 D8
Măgura RO 153 D9
Măgura RO 160 E6
Măgura Ilvei RO 152 C5
Magurë RKS 164 D3
Măgurele RO 161 C8
Măgurele RO 161 E8
Măgureni RO 161 C7
Măguri-Răcătău RO 151 D11
Magy H 145 H4
Magyaralmás H 149 B10
Magyaratád H 149 D9
Magyarbánhegyes H 151 E6
Magyarbóly H 149 E10
Magyaregregy H 149 D10
Magyarhomorog H 151 C8
Magyarkeszi H 149 C10
Magyarnándor H 147 F8
Magyarpolány H 149 B9
Magyarszék H 149 D10
Mahala UA 153 A8
Maheriv UA 144 C8
Mahíde E 39 E7
Mahlberg D 186 E4
Mahlsdorf D 83 E10
Mahlu FIN 123 E14
Mahlwinkel D 79 B10
Mahmudia RO 155 C4
Mahmudiye TR 171 E10
Mahmutköy TR 173 C6
Mahón E 57 B13
Mahora E 47 F9
Mahovo HR 149 E6
Mähring D 75 C12
Mahtra EST 131 C10
Maia P 44 B3
Maials E 42 E5
Măicănești RO 161 C10
Maîche F 27 F6
Maida I 59 B9
Maiden Bradley GB 13 C10
Maidenhead GB 15 D7
Maiden Newton GB 13 D9
Maidens GB 4 E7
Maidstone GB 15 E10
Maienfeld CH 71 C9
Maierato I 59 B9
Maierhöfen D 71 B10
Maieru RO 152 C5
Măieruș RO 153 F7
Maigh Chromtha IRL 8 E5
Maigh Cuilinn IRL 6 F4
Maiglean Rátha IRL 7 F8
Maignelay-Montigny F 18 E6
Maijanen FIN 117 D14
Maikammer D 186 C5
Maillas F 32 B5
Maillebois F 24 C5
Maillezais F 28 C4
Mailly-le-Camp F 25 C11
Mailly-le-Château F 25 E10
Mailly-Maillet F 18 D6
Mailovac SRB 159 D7
Mainaschaff D 187 B7
Mainbernheim D 75 C7
Mainburg D 75 E10
Mainham IRL 7 F9
Mainhardt D 74 D6
Mainiemi FIN 127 B16
Mainistir Eimhín IRL 7 F8
Mainistir Fhear Maí IRL 8 D6
Mainistir Laoise IRL 9 C8
Mainistir na Búille IRL 6 E6
Mainistir na Corann IRL 8 E6
Mainistir na Feile IRL 8 D4
Mäinnikkö S 116 D8
Mainsat F 29 C10
Maintenon F 24 C6
Mainua FIN 121 F9
Mainvilliers F 24 D5
Mainz D 21 D10
Maiolati Spontini I 67 F7
Maiorca P 44 D3
Maiorga P 44 E3
Mairena del Alcor E 51 E8
Maisach D 75 F9
Maishofen A 73 B6
Maišiagala LT 137 D11
Maissau A 77 E9
Maisse F 25 D7
Maissin B 184 E3
Maivala FIN 121 B14
Maizières-lès-Metz F 186 C1
Majadahonda E 46 D5
Majadas de Tiétar E 45 E9
Majava FIN 121 C12
Majavatn N 105 A14
Majdan BIH 157 D7
Majdan Królewski PL 144 C4
Majdan Niepryski PL 144 C7
Majdanpek SRB 159 E8
Majovakylä FIN 119 C17
Majs H 149 E11
Majšperk SLO 148 D5
Majtum S 109 D18
Makád H 149 B11
Makarove UA 145 G6
Makarove UA 154 C6
Makarska HR 157 F7
Mäkelänranta FIN 121 E13
Makhnovka RUS 133 B6
Mäkikylä FIN 123 E12
Makkola FIN 125 G11
Makkoshotyka H 145 G4
Makkum NL 16 B4
Maklár H 147 F10
Makljenovac BIH 157 C9
Makó H 150 E5
Makoc RKS 164 D3
Mākoņkalns LV 133 D2
Mąkoszyce PL 142 E4
Makov SK 147 C7
Maków PL 141 G2
Maków PL 141 H4
Mąkowarsko PL 138 D4
Maków Mazowiecki PL 139 E11
Maków Podhalański PL 147 B9
Makrakomi GR 174 B5
Makresh BG 159 F10
Makri GR 171 C9
Makrisia GR 174 D4
Makrochori GR 169 C7
Makrychori GR 169 E7
Makrygialos GR 169 D8
Makrygialos GR 179 E10
Makrynitsa GR 169 F8
Makryrrachi GR 174 A5
Maksamaa FIN 122 D8
Maksniemi FIN 119 C13
Maksymilianowo PL 138 D5
Malá E 53 B9
Mala IRL 8 D5
Mala S 87 C13
Malå S 107 A15
Mala Bosna SRB 150 E4
Mala Čista HR 156 E4
Malacky SK 77 F12
Málaga E 53 C8
Malagón E 46 F5
Malahide IRL 7 F10
Malahvianvaara FIN 121 E14
Malaia RO 160 C4
Mălăiești MD 154 D5
Málainn Bhig IRL 6 C5
Málainn Mhóir IRL 6 C5
Mala Kladuša BIH 156 B4
Malalbergo I 66 C4
Malá Lehota SK 147 D7
Malamocco I 66 B5
Malancourt F 19 F11
Malandrino GR 174 C5
Malangen N 111 B16
Malangseidet N 111 B16
Malanów PL 142 C5
Malansac F 23 E7
Malaryta BY 141 G10
Mäläskä FIN 119 F16
Mala Subotica HR 149 D7
Malaucène F 35 B9
Malaunay F 18 E3
Malaussanne F 32 C5
Malåvaara FIN 115 E4
Malåvännäs S 107 A14
Mała Wieś PL 139 F9
Malax FIN 122 E7
Malaya Byerastavitsa BY 140 D9
Malbekkvatn N 114 E7
Malbork PL 138 B7
Malborn D 21 E7
Malbouzon F 30 F3
Malbuisson F 31 B9
Malcesine I 69 B10
Malchin D 83 C13
Malchow D 83 D12
Malcocinado E 51 C8
Malcov SK 145 E3
Malczyce PL 81 D10
Măldăeni RO 160 E5
Măldărești RO 160 C4
Maldegem B 19 B7
Malden NL 16 E5
Maldon GB 15 D10
Małdyty PL 139 C8
Malè I 71 E11
Malechowo PL 85 B11
Malején E 41 E8
Maleme GR 178 D6
Malemort-du-Comtat F 35 B9
Malemort-sur-Corrèze F 29 E9
Malente D 83 B9
Målerås S 89 B9
Males GR 179 E10
Malesco I 68 A6
Malesherbes F 25 D7
Malesina GR 175 B7
Malestroit F 23 E7
Maletto I 59 D6
Malevo BG 166 F5
Malexander S 92 C6
Malfa I 59 B6
Malgersdorf D 75 E12
Malgovik S 107 B10
Malgrat de Mar E 43 D9
Malhadas P 39 E7
Malia GR 178 E9
Malicorne-sur-Sarthe F 23 E11
Maliena LV 133 B2
Mali Iđoš SRB 158 B4
Malijai F 36 C4
Målilla S 92 E7
Mali Lošinj HR 67 C9
Mali Mokryany UA 144 D7
Malin IRL 4 E2
Malin Beg IRL 6 C5
Málinec SK 147 D9
Malines B 19 B9
Malines B 182 C4
Mălini RO 153 C8
Malin More IRL 6 C5
Malinovka LV 135 E13
Malinska HR 67 B10
Maliq AL 168 C4
Malishevë RKS 163 E10
Maliskylä FIN 123 C14
Malissard F 30 F6
Maliuc RO 155 C4
Mali Zvornik SRB 157 D11
Maljasalmi FIN 125 E11
Malkara TR 173 C6
Małkinia Górna PL 139 E13
Malko Gradishte BG 166 F5
Malko Tŭrnovo BG 167 F9
Mallaig GB 4 A5
Mällångsbo S 103 D10
Mallén E 41 E9
Mallentin D 83 C10
Mallersdorf D 75 E11
Malles Venosta I 71 D11
Mallica TR 173 F7
Malling DK 86 C6
Mallíß D 83 D10
Mallnitz A 73 C7
Mallow IRL 8 D5
Mallusjoki FIN 127 D14
Mallwyd GB 10 F4
Malm N 105 C10
Malmån S 107 E12
Malmbäck S 92 D4
Malmberget S 116 D5
Malmby S 98 D8
Malmédy B 20 D6
Malmein N 94 E4
Malmesbury GB 13 B10
Malmköping S 93 A9
Malmö S 87 D12
Malmslätt S 92 C7
Malnaș RO 153 E7
Malnate I 69 B6
Malnava LV 133 C3
Malnes N 110 C8
Malo I 69 B11
Malo Crniće SRB 159 D7
Małogoszcz PL 143 E9
Malo Konare BG 165 E9
Małomice PL 81 C8
Malomir BG 167 E7
Malomozhayskoye RUS 136 D5
Malón E 41 E8
Malona GR 181 D8
Malonno I 69 A9
Malonty CZ 77 E7
Malorad BG 165 C8
Malošište SRB 164 C4
Malo Titavo BIH 156 D5
Malovăț RO 159 D10
Måløy N 100 C2
Maloye-Lugovoye RUS 136 D2
Maloye Sitna BY 133 E6
Malpartida P 45 C7
Malpartida de Cáceres E 45 F8
Malpartida de la Serena E 51 B8
Malpartida de Plasencia E 45 E8
Malpas GB 10 E6
Malpica E 38 B2
Malpica de Tajo E 46 E3
Malpica do Tejo P 44 E6
Mālpils LV 135 B9
Malsch D 27 C9
Målselv N 111 B16
Malsfeld D 78 D6
Malšice CZ 77 D7
Målsnes N 111 B16
Målsryd S 91 D13
Målsta S 106 E7
Malta A 73 C8
Malta LV 133 D2
Malta P 45 C6
Maltas Trūpi LV 135 D13
Maltby GB 11 E9
Maltby le Marsh GB 11 E12
Maltepe TR 173 D7
Malterdingen D 27 D8
Malters CH 70 C6
Malton GB 11 C10
Malu cu Flori RO 160 C6
Maluenda E 41 F8
Malŭk Izvor BG 166 F5
Malu Mare RO 160 E3
Malung S 102 E6
Malungsfors S 102 E6
Mālupe LV 133 B2
Malureni RO 160 C5
Malușteni RO 153 E11
Małuszów PL 81 B8
Małuszyn PL 143 E8
Malva E 39 E9
Malvaglia CH 71 E7
Malveira P 50 B1
Malvik N 105 E9
Malý Horeš SK 145 G4
Mályi H 145 G2
Mały Płock PL 139 D13
Malý Šariš SK 145 E3
Malyy Bereznyy UA 145 F5
Mamaia RO 155 E3
Mamarchevo BG 167 E7
Mamarrosa P 44 D3
Mambrilla de Castejón E 40 E4
Mamer L 20 E6
Mamers F 24 D3
Mamiči BIH 157 F8
Mamirolle F 26 F5
Mammaste EST 131 E14
Mammendorf D 75 F9
Mammola I 59 C9
Mamoiada I 64 C3
Mamone I 64 B3
Mamonovo RUS 139 B8
Mamuras AL 168 B2
Mamushë RKS 163 E10
Mana MD 154 C3
Maña SK 146 E6
Manacor E 57 B11
Manage B 19 D9
Manamansalo FIN 120 F9
Mañaria E 41 B6
Månäs S 97 A9
Manasia RO 161 D9
Manasterz PL 144 D5
Manastir BG 165 F10
Mânăstirea RO 161 E9
Mânăstirea Cașin RO 153 E9
Mânăstirea Humorului RO 153 B7
Manastirica SRB 159 D7
Manastirsko BG 167 C7
Mânăștiur RO 151 F9
Mancera de Abajo E 45 C10
Mancha Real E 53 A9
Manchester GB 11 E7
Manching D 75 E9
Manchita E 51 B7
Manciano I 65 B5
Manciet F 33 C6
Mandal N 90 C1
Måndalen N 100 A6
Mandalo GR 169 C7
Mandas I 64 D3
Mandatoriccio I 61 E7
Mandayona E 47 C7
Mandelbachtal-Ormesheim D 186 C3
Mandelieu-la-Napoule F 36 D5
Mandello del Lario I 69 B7
Manderscheid D 21 D7
Mandeure F 27 F6
Mandino Selo BIH 157 E7
Mândok H 145 G5
Mandra GR 175 C7
Mândra RO 152 F6
Mandraki GR 181 C6
Mandres-en-Barrois F 26 D3
Mandriko GR 181 D7
Manditsa BG 171 B10
Manduria I 61 C9
Mane F 33 D7
Mane F 35 C10
Manea GB 11 G12
Măneciu RO 161 C7
Manerbio I 66 B1
Mañeru E 32 E2
Mănești RO 160 D6
Mănești RO 161 D7
Manětín CZ 76 C4
Manfredonia I 63 D9
Mangalia RO 155 F3
Manganeses de la Lampreana E 39 E8
Manganeses de la Polvorosa E 39 D8
Mångberg S 102 E8
Mångbyn S 118 F6
Manger N 100 E2
Mangiennes F 19 F12
Mangotsfield GB 13 C9
Mångsbodarna S 102 D6
Mangualde P 44 C5
Manhay B 19 D12
Manhuelles F 26 B4
Mani GR 171 B10
Maniace I 59 D6
Maniago I 73 D6
Maniakoi GR 168 D5
Maniecki PL 81 B11
Manilva E 53 D6
Manisa TR 177 B9
Manises E 48 E4
Manjärvträsk S 118 C4
Manjaur S 107 B16
Mank A 77 F8
Månkarbo S 99 B8
Mankila FIN 119 E15
Manlay F 25 F11
Manlleu E 43 D8
Manna GR 175 D6
Männamaa EST 130 D5
Mannersdorf an der Rabnitz A 149 B7
Mannheim D 21 F10
Männikuste EST 131 E8
Manningtree GB 15 D11
Manolada GR 174 C3
Manole BG 165 E10
Manoleasa RO 153 B10
Manoppello I 62 C6
Manorbier GB 12 B5
Manorhamilton IRL 6 D6
Manosque F 35 C10
Manowo PL 85 B10
Manresa E 43 D7
Månsåsen S 105 E16
Manschnow D 81 A7
Mansfeld D 79 C9
Mansfield GB 11 E9
Mansfield Woodhouse GB 11 E9
Mansilla E 40 D6
Mansilla de las Mulas E 39 D9
Mansle F 29 D6
Manso F 37 G9
Mansonville F 33 B7
Mansores P 44 C4
Manston GB 13 D10
Månsträsk S 109 E16
Mantamados GR 171 F10
Mantasia GR 174 A5
Manteigas P 44 D5
Mantel D 75 C11
Manternach L 186 B1
Mantes-la-Jolie F 24 C6
Mantes-la-Ville F 24 C6
Manthelan F 24 F4
Mantila FIN 122 F9
Mantoche F 26 F4
Mantorp S 92 C6
Mantoudi GR 175 B7
Mantova I 66 B2
Mäntsälä FIN 127 D13
Mänttä FIN 123 F13
Mäntyharju FIN 128 C6
Mäntyjärvi FIN 117 E14
Mäntyjärvi FIN 121 B10
Mäntylahti FIN 124 D8
Mäntyluoto FIN 126 B5
Mäntyvaara S 116 E7
Manuel E 56 C4
Manulla IRL 6 E4
Mány H 149 A11
Manyas TR 173 D8
Manzac-sur-Vern F 29 E7
Mânzălești RO 161 C9
Manzanal de Arriba E 39 E7
Manzanal del Puerto E 39 C7
Manzanares E 55 A6
Manzanares el Real E 46 C5
Manzaneda E 38 D5
Manzanedo E 40 C4
Manzaneque E 46 E5
Manzanera E 48 D3
Manzanilla E 51 E7
Manzano I 73 E7
Manzat F 30 D2
Manziana I 62 C2
Manziat F 30 C6
Mäo EST 131 D11
Maoča BIH 157 C10
Maqellarë AL 168 A3
Maqueda E 46 D4
Mar P 38 E2
Mara I 64 C2
Marac F 26 E3
Maracalagonis I 64 E3
Marachkova BY 133 E4
Mărăcineni RO 160 D5
Mărăcineni RO 161 C9
Maradik SRB 158 C5
Maråker S 103 D13
Maranchón E 47 B8
Maranello I 66 C2
Marange-Silvange F 186 C1
Maranhão P 50 A4
Marano I 60 B2
Marano di Napoli I 60 B2
Marano sul Panaro I 66 D2
Marans F 28 C4
Maranville F 25 D12
Mărășești RO 153 F10
Mărașu RO 155 D1
Maratea I 60 D5
Marateca P 50 B2
Marathea GR 169 E6
Marathias GR 174 C5
Marathokampos GR 177 D8
Marathonas GR 175 C8
Marathopoli GR 174 E4
Maraussan F 34 D5
Maraye-en-Othe F 25 D10
Marazion GB 12 E4
Marazliyivka UA 154 E6
Marbach CH 70 D5
Marbach am Neckar D 27 C11
Marbäck S 91 D13
Marbella E 53 C7
Marboz F 31 C7
Marburg an der Lahn D 21 C11
Marby S 105 E16
Marça E 42 E5
Marcali H 149 C8
Marcaltő H 149 B8
Marčana HR 67 C8
Marcaria I 66 B2
Marcăuți MD 153 A10
Marcellina I 62 C3
Marcelová SK 149 A10
Marcenais F 28 E5
Marcenat F 30 E2
March GB 11 F12
Marchamalo E 47 C6
Marchaux F 26 F5
Marche-en-Famenne B 19 D11
Marchegg A 77 F11
Marchena E 51 E9
Marchenoir F 24 E5
Marcheprime F 28 F4
Marchiennes F 19 D7
Marchin B 19 D11
Marchtrenk A 76 F6
Marciac F 33 C6
Marciana I 65 B2
Marciana Marina I 65 B2
Marcianise I 60 A2
Marciano della Chiana I 66 F4
Mārciena LV 135 C12
Marcigny F 30 C5
Marcilhac-sur-Célé F 33 A9
Marcilla E 32 F2
Marcillac F 28 E4
Marcillac-la-Croisille F 29 E10
Marcillac-Vallon F 33 B10
Marcillat-en-Combraille F 29 C11
Marcilly-en-Gault F 24 F6
Marcilly-en-Villette F 24 E7
Marcilly-le-Hayer F 25 D10
Marcilly-sur-Eure F 24 C5
Marcinkonys LT 137 E9
Marcinkowice PL 85 D10
Marcinkowice PL 144 D2
Marcinowice PL 81 E11
Marciszów PL 81 E10
Marck F 18 C4
Marckolsheim F 27 D8
Marco de Canaveses P 44 B4
Marcoing F 19 D7
Marcòn I 66 A5
Marcoux F 36 C4
Marcq-en-Barœul F 19 C7
Mărculești MD 153 B12
Mårdaklev S 87 A11
Mardarivka UA 154 B5
Mardeuil F 25 B10
Mårdsele S 107 B16
Mårdsjö S 106 E9
Mårdsjö S 107 C11
Mårdudden S 118 B6
Marebbe I 72 C4
Marennes F 28 D3
Maresfield GB 15 F9
Mareuil F 29 E6
Mareuil-sur-Arnon F 29 B10
Mareuil-sur-Ay F 25 B11
Mareuil-sur-Lay-Dissais F 28 B3
Marey-sur-Tille F 26 E3
Marga RO 159 B9
Margarites GR 178 E8
Mărgăritești RO 161 C9
Margariti GR 168 F3
Margate GB 15 E11
Mărgău RO 151 D10
Margecany SK 145 F3
Margerie-Hancourt F 25 C12
Margherita di Savoia I 60 A6
Marghita RO 151 C9
Margina RO 151 F9
Marginea RO 153 B7
Mărgineni RO 153 D9
Mărgineni RO 153 D9
Margionys LT 137 F9
Margone I 31 E11
Margonin PL 85 E12
Margraten NL 19 C12
Marguerittes F 35 C7
Margut F 19 E11
Marhaň SK 145 E3
María E 55 D8
Mariac F 30 F5
Mariager DK 86 B5
Maria Lankowitz A 73 B11
Maria Luggau A 73 C6
Marialva P 45 C6
Mariampole UA 133 D2
Mariana E 47 D8
Mariannelund S 92 D7
Mariano Comense I 69 B7
Marianopoli I 58 D4
Marianowo PL 85 D8
Mariánské Lázně CZ 75 C12
Mariapfarr A 73 B8
Maria Saal A 73 C9
Mariazell A 148 A4
Maribo DK 83 A10
Maribor SLO 148 C5
Marieberg S 92 A6
Marieby S 106 E7
Mariefred S 98 D8
Mariehamn FIN 99 B13
Marieholm S 87 D12
Marieholm S 91 E14
Mariembourg B 19 D10
Marienberg D 80 E4
Marienhafe D 17 A8
Marienhagen D 78 B6
Marienheide D 21 B9
Mariental D 79 B8
Mariestad S 91 B14
Marifjøra N 100 D6
Marigliano I 60 B3
Marignana F 37 G9
Marignane F 35 D9
Marigné-Laillé F 24 E3
Marigny F 23 B9
Marigny-le-Châtel F 25 D10
Marijampolė LT 136 D7
Marikaj AL 168 B2
Marikostinovo BG 169 B9
Marín E 38 D2
Marina di Alberese I 65 B4
Marina di Amendolara I 61 D7
Marina di Arbus I 64 D1
Marina di Camerota I 60 C4
Marina di Campo I 65 B2
Marina di Carrara I 69 E9
Marina di Castagneto Donoratico I 66 F2
Marina di Cecina I 66 F1
Marina di Chieuti I 63 D8
Marina di Gioiosa Ionica I 59 C9
Marina di Grosseto I 65 B3
Marina di Leuca I 61 D10
Marina di Massa I 69 E9
Marina di Novaglie I 61 D10
Marina di Palma I 58 E4

Mesopotamia GR 168 C5
Mesopotamos GR 168 F4
Mesoraca I 59 A10
Mesotopos GR 177 A7
Mespelbrunn D 187 B7
Mesquer F 22 F7
Messac F 23 E8
Messanges F 32 C3
Meßdorf D 83 E11
Messei F 23 C10
Messeix F 29 D11
Messejana P 50 D3
Messina I 59 C8
Messincourt F 19 E11
Messingen D 17 D8
Messini GR 174 E5
Meßkirch D 27 E11
Messlingen S 102 A4
Meßstetten D 27 D10
Mesta BG 165 F8
Mesta GR 177 C6
Mestanza E 54 B4
Městec Králové CZ 77 B8
Mestervik N 111 B16
Mesti GR 171 C9
Mestlin D 83 C11
Město Albrechtice CZ 142 F4
Město Touškov CZ 76 C4
Mestre I 66 B5
Mesves-sur-Loire F 25 F8
Mesztegnyő H 149 C8
Meta I 60 B2
Métabief F 31 B9
Metagkitsi GR 169 D10
Metajna HR 67 C11
Metalliko GR 169 B8
Metallostroy RUS 129 F14
Metaxades GR 171 B10
Metelen D 17 D8
Meteş RO 151 E11
Metfield GB 15 C11
Methana GR 175 D7
Metheringham GB 11 E11
Methlick GB 3 L12
Methoni GR 178 B2
Methven GB 5 C9
Methwold GB 11 F13
Metković HR 157 F8
Metlika SLO 148 E4
Metnitz A 73 C9
Metochi GR 174 C3
Metochi GR 175 B8
Metovnica SRB 159 F9
Mētriena LV 135 C12
Metsäkansa FIN 127 C10
Metsäkylä FIN 121 D11
Metsäkylä FIN 128 D7
Metsälä FIN 120 C9
Metsämaa FIN 127 D9
Metschow D 84 C3
Metsküla EST 130 D5
Metslawier NL 16 B6
Metsovo GR 168 E5
Mettäjärvi S 117 E11
Mettendorf D 20 E6
Mettenheim D 75 F11
Mettet B 19 D10
Mettevoll N 112 D7
Mettingen D 17 D9
Mettlach D 21 F7
Mettmann D 17 F7
Mettray F 24 F4
Metz F 26 B5
Metzervisse F 20 F6
Metzingen D 27 C11
Meudt D 185 D8
Meulan F 24 B6
Meulebeke B 19 C7
Meung-sur-Loire F 24 E6
Meursault F 30 B6
Meuselwitz D 79 D11
Meuzac F 29 D8
Mevagissey GB 12 E5
Mexborough GB 11 E9
Meximieux F 31 D7
Mey GB 3 H10
Meyenburg D 83 D12
Meylan F 31 E8
Meymac F 29 D10
Meyrargues F 35 C10
Meyreuil F 35 D10
Meyronnes F 36 C5
Meyrueis F 34 B5
Meyssac F 29 E9
Meysse F 35 A8
Meythet F 31 D9
Mezapos GR 178 B3
Mežāre LV 135 C12
Mežciems LV 134 C7
Mezdra BG 165 C8
Mèze F 35 D6
Mézel F 36 D4
Mežgale LV 135 D11
Mezhdurech'ye RUS 136 D4
Meziboří CZ 80 E5
Mežica SLO 73 C10
Mézidon-Canon F 23 B11
Mézières-en-Brenne F 29 B8
Mézières-sur-Issoire F 29 C7
Mézilhac F 30 F5
Mézilles F 25 E9
Meziměstí CZ 81 E10
Mézin F 33 B6
Mezio P 44 C5
Mezőberény H 151 D7
Mezőcsát H 147 F11
Mezőcsokonya H 149 D9
Mezőfalva H 149 C11
Mezőgyán H 151 D8
Mezőhegyes H 150 E6
Mezőkeresztes H 145 H2
Mezőkovácsháza H 151 E6
Mezőkövesd H 147 F11
Mezőlak H 149 B8
Mezőnyárád H 145 H2
Mezőörs H 149 A9
Mézos F 32 B3
Mezőszemere H 150 B6
Mezőszentgyörgy H 149 B10
Mezőszilas H 149 C10
Mezőtárkány H 150 B5
Mežotne LV 135 D8
Mezőtúr H 150 D6
Mezőzombor H 145 G3
Mezquita de Jarque E 42 F2
Mežvalde LV 134 C4
Mežvidi LV 133 C3
Mežvidi LV 134 C4
Mezzana I 69 A10
Mezzanego I 37 C10
Mezzano I 72 D4
Mezzocorona I 69 A11
Mezzojuso I 58 D3
Mezzoldo I 69 A8
Mezzolombardo I 69 A11
Mga RUS 129 F15
Miączyn PL 144 B8
Miajadas E 45 F9
Mialet F 29 D7
Miały PL 85 E10
Miasteckzo Krajeńskie PL 85 D12
Miastko PL 85 B11
Miastków Kościelny PL 141 G5
Miastkowo PL 139 D12
Miavaig GB 2 J3
Mica RO 152 C3
Mica RO 152 E4
Micăsasa RO 152 E4
Miceşti RO 160 D5
Miceştii de Câmpie RO 152 D4
Michaľany SK 145 F4
Michalová SK 147 D9
Michalovce SK 145 F4
Michałów PL 143 F9
Michałów Górny PL 141 G4
Michałowice PL 142 E3
Michałowice PL 143 F8
Michałowo PL 140 D9
Michelau in Oberfranken D 75 B9
Michelbach an der Bilz D 74 D6
Micheldorf A 73 C9
Micheldorf in Oberösterreich A 73 A9
Michelfeld D 74 D6
Michelstadt D 21 E12
Michendorf D 80 B4
Michorzewo PL 81 B10
Michów PL 141 G6
Mickelspiltom FIN 127 D15
Mickelsträsk S 118 F4
Mickleton GB 5 F12
Mickleton GB 13 A11
Micleşti MD 154 C3
Midbea GB 3 G11
Middagsbukt N 111 B17
Middelbeers NL 183 C6
Middelburg NL 16 E1
Middelfart DK 86 D5
Middelharnis NL 16 E2
Middelkerke B 18 B6
Middelstum NL 17 B7
Middenbeemster NL 16 C3
Middenmeer NL 16 C4
Middleham GB 11 C8
Middlemarsh GB 13 D10
Middlesbrough GB 11 B9
Middleton GB 11 D7
Middleton Cheney GB 13 A12
Middleton in Teesdale GB 5 F12
Middletown GB 7 D9
Middlewich GB 10 E7
Midhurst GB 15 F7
Midleton IRL 8 E6
Midlum D 17 A11
Midsund N 100 A5
Midtgård N 114 D8
Midtskogberget N 102 D3
Miðvágur FO 2 A2
Midwolda NL 17 B8
Mid Yell GB 3 D14
Miechów PL 143 F9
Miechów Charsznica PL 143 F8
Miedes E 41 F9
Miedziana Góra PL 143 E10
Miedzichowo PL 81 B9
Miedzna PL 139 F13
Miedźna PL 143 G7
Miedźno PL 143 E6
Międzybórz PL 142 D4
Międzychód PL 81 A9
Międzylesie PL 77 B11
Międzyrzec Podlaski PL 141 G7
Międzyrzecz PL 81 B9
Międzyzdroje PL 84 C6
Miehikkälä FIN 128 D8
Miehlen D 185 D8
Miejsce Piastowe PL 145 D4
Miejska Górka PL 81 C11
Miękinia PL 81 D11
Miekojärvi S 119 B10
Miélan F 33 D6
Mielec PL 143 F11
Mielęcin PL 85 D10
Mieleszyn PL 85 E12
Mielno PL 85 B10
Mieluskylä FIN 119 F14
Mielżyn PL 138 F4
Mieming A 71 C12
Mierasjärvi FIN 113 D19
Mieraslompolo FIN 113 D19
Miercurea-Ciuc RO 153 E7
Miercurea Nirajului RO 152 D5
Miercurea Sibiului RO 152 F3
Mieres E 39 B8
Mieres E 43 C9
Mierlo NL 16 F5
Mierojärvi N 113 E11
Mieroszów PL 81 E10
Miers F 29 F9
Mierzęcice PL 143 F7
Mierzyn PL 84 D6
Miesau D 186 C3
Miesbach D 72 A4
Mieścisko PL 85 E12
Miesenbach D 186 C4
Mieslahti FIN 121 F10
Miessaure S 116 E4
Mieste D 79 B9
Mieszków PL 142 B3
Mieszkowice PL 84 E6
Mietingen D 71 A9
Mietków PL 81 E11
Mietoinen FIN 126 D6
Miettilä FIN 129 C11
Mieussy F 31 C10
Mieza E 45 B7
Migennes F 25 E10
Miglianico I 63 C6
Migliarino I 66 C4
Migliaro I 66 C4
Miglionica I 61 B6
Mignaloux-Beauvoir F 29 B6
Mignano Monte Lungo I 60 A1
Migné-Auxances F 29 B6
Mignovillard F 31 B9
Miguel Esteban E 47 E6
Migueltura E 54 B5
Migushino RUS 133 E7
Mihăeşti RO 160 C4
Mihăeşti RO 160 C6
Mihăeşti RO 160 E5
Mihai Bravu RO 155 D3
Mihai Bravu RO 161 E8
Mihăileni RO 152 F4
Mihăileni RO 153 B8
Mihăileni RO 153 E7
Mihăileşti RO 161 D9
Mihăileşti RO 161 E7
Mihail Kogălniceanu RO 155 C3
Mihail Kogălniceanu RO 155 D1
Mihail Kogălniceanu RO 155 E2
Mihailovca MD 154 D3
Mihai Viteazu RO 152 D3
Mihai Viteazu RO 155 D3
Mihajlovac SRB 159 D6
Mihajlovac SRB 159 E9
Mihajlovo SRB 158 C5
Mihălăşeni RO 153 B10
Mihálď H 149 D8
Mihalţ RO 152 E3
Mihályi H 149 A8
Miheşu de Câmpie RO 152 D4
Mihla D 79 D7
Miiluranta FIN 123 C16
Mijares E 46 D3
Mijas E 53 C7
Mijdrecht NL 16 D3
Mijoska MNE 163 D7
Mikalayeva BY 133 F6
Mikepércs H 151 C8
Mikhalishki BY 137 D13
Mikhalkovo BG 165 F9
Mikhaltsi BG 166 C4
Mikhaylovo BG 165 B8
Mikhaylovo BG 166 E5
Mikitamäe EST 132 E2
Mikitsikha BY 133 F6
Mikkeli FIN 128 B7
Mikkelin mlk FIN 128 B7
Mikkelvik N 112 C3
Mikkola FIN 117 D16
Mikladalur FO 2 A3
Miklavž SLO 148 C5
Miklebostad N 111 C13
Mikleuš HR 149 E9
Mikołajki PL 136 F4
Mikołajki Pomorskie PL 139 C7
Mikołów PL 143 F6
Mikoszewo PL 138 B6
Mikre BG 165 C10
Mikri Volvi GR 169 C10
Mikro Dereio GR 171 B10
Mikrokambos GR 169 C8
Mikromilia GR 170 B6
Mikropoli GR 169 B10
Mikrothives GR 169 F8
Mikrovalto GR 169 D6
Mikstat PL 142 C4
Mikuláš CZ 77 C8
Mikulasovice CZ 80 E6
Mikulčice CZ 77 E12
Mikulov CZ 77 E11
Mikulovice CZ 142 F3
Mikušovce SK 146 C6
Miladinovci MK 164 F4
Milagro E 41 D8
Milagros E 40 E4
Miłakowo PL 139 B9
Milano I 69 C7
Milano Marittima I 66 D5
Milanówek PL 141 F3
Milaş RO 152 D4
Milas TR 181 B7
Milatkoviće SRB 163 C10
Milatos GR 179 E10
Milazzo I 59 C7
Milborne Port GB 13 D10
Milcoiu RO 160 C4
Milcov RO 160 E4
Milcovul RO 161 B10
Mildenhall GB 15 C10
Mildstedt D 82 B6
Mileanca RO 153 A9
Milejczyce PL 141 E8
Milejewo PL 139 B8
Milejów PL 141 H7
Milena I 58 E4
Mileşti MD 153 C12
Milestone IRL 8 C6
Mileto I 59 B9
Milevsko CZ 76 D6
Milfield GB 5 D12
Milfontes P 50 D2
Milford IRL 7 B7
Milford IRL 8 D5
Milford Haven GB 12 B4
Milhão P 39 E6
Milhaud F 35 C7
Milići BIH 157 D11
Milicz PL 81 C12
Milies GR 169 F9
Milíkov CZ 147 B7
Milín CZ 76 C6
Milina GR 175 A7
Milis I 64 C2
Militello in Val di Catania I 59 E6
Miliyeve UA 152 A6
Milizac F 22 D2
Miljana HR 148 D5
Miljeno BIH 157 E11
Miljevina BIH 157 E10
Milkel D 81 D6
Miłki PL 136 F4
Milkovitsa BG 160 F5
Milk'ovtsi BG 165 D6
Mill NL 16 E5
Millares E 48 F3
Millas F 34 E4
Millau F 34 B5
Millay F 30 B5
Millbrook GB 12 E6
Millbrook IRL 7 E8
Millesimo I 37 C8
Millevaches F 29 D10
Millford GB 7 D9
Millhouse GB 4 D6
Millières F 26 D3
Millingen aan de Rijn NL 183 B8
Millisle GB 7 C11
Millom GB 10 C5
Millosheve RKS 164 D3
Millport GB 4 D7
Millstatt A 73 C8
Millstreet IRL 8 D4
Millstreet IRL 9 D7
Milltown IRL 6 E5
Milltown IRL 7 F9
Milltown IRL 8 D2
Milltown IRL 8 D3
Milltown Malbay IRL 8 C4
Milly-la-Forêt F 25 D7
Milmarcos E 47 B9
Milmersdorf D 84 D5
Milmort B 183 D7
Milna HR 156 F5
Milnathort GB 5 C10
Milngavie GB 5 D8
Milnthorpe GB 10 C6
Milo I 59 D7
Miłocice PL 85 C11
Milohnić HR 67 B9
Miłomłyn PL 139 C8
Miłoradz PL 138 B6
Miloşeşti RO 161 D10
Miłosław PL 142 B3
Milot AL 163 F8
Milotice CZ 77 E12
Milovaig GB 2 L3
Milovice CZ 77 B7
Milow D 79 A11
Milow D 83 D11
Miłówka PL 147 B8
Miltach D 75 D12
Miltenberg D 21 E12
Miltiņi LV 134 C6
Milton GB 2 L8
Milton GB 5 B9
Milton Keynes GB 15 C7
Miltzow D 84 B4
Milutinovac SRB 159 F7
Milverton GB 13 C8
Milz D 75 B8
Mimetiz E 40 B5
Mimizan F 32 B3
Mimizan-Plage F 32 B3
Mimoň CZ 81 E7
Mina de São Domingos P 50 D5
Mín an Chladaigh IRL 6 B6
Minas de Riotinto E 51 D6
Minateda E 55 C9
Minaya E 47 F8
Minde P 44 E3
Mindelheim D 71 A10
Mindelstetten D 75 E10
Minden D 17 D11
Minderhout B 182 C5
Mindnes N 108 E3
Mîndreşti MD 154 B2
Mindszent H 150 D5
Mindszentgodisa H 149 D10
Mindtangen N 108 E3
Mindūnai LT 135 F11
Mindya BG 166 C5
Minehead GB 13 C8
Mineo I 59 E6
Mineralni Bani BG 166 F4
Minerbio I 66 C3
Minervino Murge I 60 A6
Minfeld D 27 B9
Minger MD 154 D2
Minglanilla E 47 E9
Mingorría E 46 C3
Miniac-Morvan F 23 C8
Minićevo SRB 159 F9
Mín na bhFiann IRL 6 C5
Minne S 103 B9
Minnertsga NL 16 B5
Minnesund N 95 B14
Minnigaff GB 4 F8
Minot F 25 E12
Mińsk Mazowiecki PL 141 F5
Minsterley GB 10 F6
Mintiloglio GR 174 C4
Mintiu Gherlii RO 152 C3
Mintlaw GB 3 K13
Mintraching D 75 E11
Minturno I 62 E5
Minucciano I 66 D1
Minusio CH 68 A6
Mioarele RO 160 C6
Mionica SRB 158 E5
Mionnay F 30 D6
Mios F 32 A4
Mira E 47 E10
Mira I 66 B5
Mira P 44 D3
Mirabeau F 35 C10
Mirabel E 45 E8
Mirabel F 33 B8
Mirabel-aux-Baronnies F 35 B9
Mirabella Eclano I 60 A4
Mirabella Imbaccari I 58 E5
Miradoux F 33 C7
Miraflores de la Sierra E 46 C5
Miralcamp E 42 D5
Miramare I 66 D6
Miramas F 35 C9
Mirambeau F 28 E4
Mirambel E 42 F3
Miramont-de-Guyenne F 33 A6
Miranda de Arga E 32 F2
Miranda de Ebro E 40 C6
Miranda do Corvo P 44 D4
Miranda do Douro P 39 E7
Mirande F 33 C6
Mirandela P 38 F5
Mirandilla E 51 A7
Mirandola I 66 C3
Mirandol-Bourgnounac F 33 B10
Miranje HR 156 E4
Mirano I 66 B5
Miras AL 168 C4
Mirash RKS 164 E3
Mirăslău RO 152 E3
Miratovac SRB 164 E4
Miravci MK 169 B7
Miravet E 42 E5
Miravete de la Sierra E 42 F2
Mircea Vodă RO 155 E2
Mircea Vodă RO 161 C10
Mirceşti RO 153 C9
Mircze PL 144 B8
Mirebeau F 26 F3
Mirebeau F 29 B6
Mirecourt F 26 D5
Miren SLO 73 E8
Mirepoix F 33 D9
Mireşu Mare RO 151 C11
Miřetice CZ 77 C9
Mireval F 35 C6
Miričina BIH 157 C9
Mirkovci HR 157 B10
Mirkovo BG 165 D9
Mirlović Zagora HR 156 E5
Mirna SLO 73 E11
Mirna Peč SLO 73 E11
Mirocin PL 144 C6
Mirocin Górny PL 81 C9
Mironeasa RO 153 D10
Miroševce SRB 164 D4
Miroşi RO 160 E5
Miroslava RO 153 C10
Miroslavas LT 137 E8
Mirosławiec PL 85 D10
Miroslovești RO 153 C9
Mirošov CZ 76 C5
Mirotice CZ 76 D6
Mirovice CZ 76 C6
Mirovtsi BG 167 C8
Mirow D 83 D13
Mirşid RO 151 C11
Mirsk PL 81 E8
Mirto Crosia I 61 D7
Mirueña de los Infanzones E 45 C10
Mirzec PL 141 H4
Misano Adriatico I 67 E6
Mişca RO 151 D8
Mischii RO 160 E3
Miserey-Salines F 26 F4
Mishnyevichy BY 133 F7
Misi FIN 117 E17
Misilmeri I 58 C3
Mišinci BIH 157 C8
Miske H 150 E3
Miskolc H 145 G2
Mislina HR 162 D4
Mislinja SLO 73 D11
Mišnjak HR 67 C10
Mison F 35 B10
Missanello I 60 C6
Missenträsk S 107 A17
Missillac F 23 F7
Misso EST 131 F14
Mistelbach A 77 E11
Mistelgau D 75 C9
Misten N 108 B8
Misterbianco I 59 D7
Misterhult S 93 E9
Misterton GB 11 E10
Mistretta I 58 D5
Mistros GR 175 B8
Misurina I 72 C5
Misvær N 108 B9
Mitandersfors S 96 B7
Mitchelstown IRL 8 D6
Mithymna GR 171 F10
Mitoc RO 153 A10
Mitrašinci MK 165 F6
Mitreni RO 161 E9
Mitropoli GR 169 F6
Mitrousi GR 169 B9
Mitrova Reka SRB 163 C9
Mitrovicë RKS 163 D10
Mitry-Mory F 25 C8
Mittådalen S 102 A4
Mittelberg A 71 C10
Mittelberg A 71 D11
Mittelbiberach D 71 A9
Mittelkalbach D 74 B6
Mittelsinn D 187 A8
Mittenwald D 72 B3
Mittenwalde D 80 B5
Mittenwalde D 84 D5
Mitterbach am Erlaufsee A 148 A4
Mitterding A 76 F4
Mitterdorf im Mürztal A 148 A5
Mittersheim F 27 C6
Mittersill A 72 B5
Mitterskirchen D 75 F12
Mitterteich D 75 C11
Mittet N 100 A7
Mittiliden S 105 B16
Mittweida D 80 E3
Mitwitz D 75 B9
Mizhhir"ya UA 145 F8
Mizil RO 161 C8
Miziya BG 160 F3
Mjällby S 88 C7
Mjällom S 107 F14
Mjedë AL 163 F8
Mjelde N 110 E9
Mjelde N 111 A15
Mjöbäck S 88 A3
Mjölby S 92 C6
Mjølfjell N 100 E5
Mjolnarodden N 110 D5
Mjönäs S 97 C10
Mjøndalen N 95 C12
Mjønes N 108 B8
Mjösjöby S 107 D15
Mjösund FIN 126 E7
Mjöträsk S 119 B9
Mjövattnet S 103 A14
Mjövattnet S 118 E5
Mladá Boleslav CZ 77 B7
Mladá Vožice CZ 77 C7
Mladé Buky CZ 81 E9
Mladenovac SRB 158 E6
Mladenovo SRB 158 C3
Mladikovine BIH 157 D8
Mladinovo BG 166 F6
Mlado Nagoričane MK 164 E4
Mława PL 139 D9
Mlekarevo BG 166 E6
Mlinice BIH 157 D7
Mlinište BIH 157 D6
Młodzieszyn PL 141 F2
Młynary PL 139 B8
Młynarze PL 139 E11
Mlynys'ka UA 145 E9
Mnichovice CZ 77 C7
Mnichovo Hradiště CZ 77 A7
Mnichów PL 143 E9
Mniów PL 143 D9
Mníšek nad Hnilcom SK 145 F2
Mníšek pod Brdy CZ 76 C6
Mniszew PL 141 G4
Mniszków PL 141 H2
Mo N 100 E3
Mo S 103 D12
Mo S 103 E12
Mo S 107 D11
Mo S 107 E11
Moacşa RO 153 F7
Moaña E 38 D2
Moara RO 153 B8
Moara Domnească MD 153 B10
Moara Vlăsiei RO 161 D8
Moate IRL 7 F7
Mobberley GB 11 E7
Moča SK 149 A10
Moçarria P 44 F3
Mocejón E 46 E5
Močenok SK 146 E5
Mochales E 47 B9
Mochos GR 178 E9
Mochowo PL 139 E8
Mochy PL 81 B10
Mociu RO 152 D4
Möckern D 79 B10
Mockfjärd S 97 A12
Möckmühl D 27 B11
Mockrehna D 79 C12
Mockträsk S 118 C7
Moclín E 53 B9
Moclinejo E 53 C8
Mocra MD 154 B4
Mocsa H 149 A10
Modane F 31 E10
Modave B 19 D11
Modbury GB 13 E7
Modelu RO 161 E10
Modena I 66 C2
Modi GR 175 B6
Modica I 59 F6
Modigliana I 66 D4
Modliborzyce PL 144 B5
Mödling A 77 F10
Modliszewice PL 141 H2
Modra SK 146 E4
Modran BIH 157 C8
Modrany SK 146 F6
Modreeny IRL 8 C6
Modriach A 73 C11
Modriča BIH 157 C9
Modrište MK 168 A5
Modruš HR 156 B3
Modrý Kameň SK 147 E8
Modugno I 61 A7
Moëlan-sur-Mer F 22 E4
Moelfre GB 10 E3
Moelv N 101 E13
Moen N 105 D12
Moen N 111 B16
Moena I 72 D4
Moerbeke B 182 C3
Moergestel NL 16 E4
Moerkerke B 182 C2
Moers D 17 F7
Moffat GB 5 E10
Mofreita P 39 E6
Moftin RO 151 B10
Mogadouro P 39 F6
Mogata S 93 C8
Mögelin D 79 A11
Møgeltønder DK 86 F3
Mogenstrup DK 87 E9
Moggio Udinese I 73 D7
Mögglingen D 187 D8
Mogielnica PL 141 G3
Mogila MK 168 B5
Mogilany PL 147 B9
Mogilishte BG 167 C10
Mogilno PL 138 E4
Moglia I 66 C2
Mogliano I 67 F7
Mogliano Veneto I 66 A5
Möglingen D 187 D7
Mogón E 55 C6
Mogorella I 64 D2
Mogoş RO 151 E11
Mogoşani RO 160 D6
Mogoşeşti RO 153 C10
Mogoşeşti-Siret RO 153 C9
Mogoşoaia RO 161 D7
Moguer E 51 E6
Mogyoród H 150 B3
Mohács H 149 E11
Moharque E 55 C9
Mohed S 103 D12
Moheda S 88 A7
Mohedas de Granadilla E 45 D8
Mohedas de la Jara E 45 E10
Mohelnice CZ 77 C11
Mohelno CZ 77 D10
Mohernando E 47 C6
Mohil IRL 9 C8
Mohill IRL 7 E7
Möhkö FIN 125 E16
Möhlau D 79 C11
Möhlin CH 27 E8
Moholm S 91 B15
Mohora H 147 F8
Mohorn D 80 E4
Mohyliv Podil's'kyy UA 154 A1
Moi N 94 F5
Moi N 94 F6
Moià E 43 D8
Moiano I 60 A3
Moieciu RO 160 C6
Moimenta da Beira P 44 C5
Moineşti RO 153 E8
Moingt F 30 D5
Móinteach Milie IRL 7 F8
Moira GB 7 D10
Mo i Rana N 108 D7
Moirans F 31 E8
Moirans-en-Montagne F 31 C8
Moirax F 33 B7
Moires GR 178 E8
Mõisaküla EST 131 E10
Moisburg D 82 D7
Moisdon-la-Rivière F 23 E9
Moisei RO 152 B5
Moisiovaara FIN 121 E13
Moislains F 18 E6
Moissac F 33 B8
Moissac-Bellevue F 36 D4
Moissey F 26 F4
Moïta F 37 G10
Moita P 44 D4
Moita P 44 E3
Moita P 50 B2
Moixent-Mogente E 56 D3
Mojácar E 55 E9
Mojados E 39 F10
Mojkovac MNE 163 D8
Mojmírovce SK 146 E6
Mojstrana SLO 73 D8
Mojzesovo SK 146 E6
Møkkevik N 110 D6
Möklinta S 98 B7
Mokobody PL 141 F6
Mokrá Hora CZ 77 D11
Mokrance SK 145 F3
Mokre PL 143 F10
Mokren BG 167 D7
Mokresh BG 160 F2
Mokrievo MK 169 B8
Mokrin SRB 150 F5
Mokro BIH 157 E10
Mokronog SLO 73 E11
Mokronoge BIH 156 D5
Mokronoge BIH 157 E7
Möksy FIN 123 D12
Mol B 19 B11
Mol SRB 150 F5
Mola di Bari I 61 A8
Molaoi GR 178 B4
Molare I 37 B9
Molares P 38 F4
Molbergen D 17 C9
Mölbling A 73 C9
Mølby DK 86 E4
Mold GB 10 E5
Moldava nad Bodvou SK 145 F2
Molde N 100 A6
Moldjord N 108 B8
Moldova Nouă RO 159 D8
Moldova-Suliţa RO 152 B6
Moldoveni RO 153 D9
Moldoviţa RO 153 B7
Møldrup DK 86 B5
Moldvik N 111 C11
Moledo P 38 E2
Moledo P 44 C5
Molelos P 44 C4
Molenbeek-St-Jean B 182 D4
Molenstede B 183 C6
Molescroft GB 11 D11
Molesmes F 25 E11
Moleşti MD 154 D3
Molētai LT 135 F10
Molfetta I 61 A7
Molfsee D 83 B8
Moliden S 107 E14
Molières F 29 F9
Molières F 33 B8
Molières-sur-Cèze F 35 B7
Moliets-et-Maa F 32 C3
Molina Aterno I 62 C5
Molina de Aragón E 47 C9
Molina de Segura E 56 E2
Molina di Ledro I 69 B10
Molinara I 60 A3
Molinaseca E 39 C7
Molinella I 66 C4
Molines-en-Queyras F 31 F10
Molinet F 30 C4
Molinges F 31 C8
Molinicos E 55 C8
Molini di Tures I 72 C4
Molino de Villobas E 32 F5
Molinos E 42 F3
Molins de Rei E 43 E8
Moliterno I 60 C5
Molitg-les-Bains F 33 E10
Molkojärvi FIN 117 D14
Molkom S 97 C10
Mollas AL 168 C3
Mölle S 87 C11
Molledo E 40 B3
Möllenbeck D 84 D4
Möllenhagen D 84 C3
Mollerussa E 42 D5
Molles F 30 C4
Mollet del Vallès E 43 D8
Molliens-Dreuil F 18 E5
Mollis CH 27 F11
Molln A 73 A9
Mölln D 83 C9
Mölln D 84 C4
Molló E 33 F10
Mollösund S 91 C9
Mölltorp S 92 C4
Mölnbo S 93 A10
Mölnlycke S 91 D11
Molnytsya UA 153 A8
Moloha UA 154 E6
Molompize F 30 E3
Molos GR 175 B6
Moloy F 26 E2
Molpe FIN 122 E6
Molschleben D 79 D8
Molsheim F 186 D3
Molunat HR 162 E5
Molve HR 149 D8
Molveno I 69 A10
Molvízar E 53 C9
Mombaldone I 37 B8
Mombeltrán E 45 D10
Mombercelli I 37 B8
Mömbris D 21 D12
Mombuey E 39 D7
Momchilgrad BG 171 A8
Momignies B 19 D9
Momo I 68 B6
Monå FIN 122 D8
Monachil E 53 B9
Monacia-d'Aullène F 37 H10
Monaghan IRL 7 D9
Monamolin IRL 9 C10
Monäs FIN 122 D8
Monashi UA 154 E6
Monasterace I 59 C10
Monasterevin IRL 7 F8
Monastir I 64 E3
Monastiraki GR 174 B2
Monbahus F 33 A7
Monbazillac F 29 F6
Moncada E 48 E4
Moncalieri I 37 A7
Moncalvo I 68 C5
Monção P 38 D3
Moncarapacho P 50 E4
Moncaut F 33 B6
Moncel-sur-Seille F 26 C5
Mönchengladbach D 20 B6
Mönchhof A 77 G11
Monchio delle Corti I 66 D1
Monchique P 50 E2
Mönchsdeggingen D 75 E8
Monclar F 33 B7
Moncofa E 48 E4
Moncontour F 22 D6
Moncontour F 28 B5
Moncoutant F 28 B4
Moncrabeau F 33 B6
Monda E 53 C7
Mondariz E 38 D3
Mondariz-Balneario E 38 D3
Mondavezan F 33 D8
Mondavio I 67 E6
Mondéjar E 47 D6
Mondello I 58 C3
Mondeville F 23 B11
Mondolfo I 67 E7
Mondoñedo E 38 B5
Mondorf-les-Bains L 20 E6
Mondoubleau F 24 E4
Mondovì I 37 C7
Mondragon F 35 B8
Mondragone I 62 E5
Mondsee A 73 A7
Monea GB 7 D7
Moneasa RO 151 E9
Moneen IRL 6 F5
Moneglia I 37 C10
Monegrillo E 41 E11
Monein F 32 D4
Monemvasia GR 178 B5
Monesiglio I 37 C8
Monesterio E 51 C7
Monestier-de-Clermont F 31 F8
Monestiés F 33 B10
Monéteau F 25 E10
Moneygall IRL 9 C7
Moneymore GB 4 F3
Moneyneany GB 4 F3
Moneyreagh GB 7 C11
Monfalcone I 73 E8
Monfecorvino Rovella I 60 B3
Monflanquin F 33 A7
Monfort F 33 C7
Monforte P 44 F6
Monforte da Beira P 45 E6

Mungret IRL 8 C5
Muñico E 45 C10
Muniesa E 42 E2
Munilla E 41 D7
Munka-Ljungby S 87 C11
Munkbyn S 103 B11
Munkebakken N 114 D6
Munkebo DK 86 E7
Munkedal S 91 C10
Munken N 104 D6
Munkflohögen S 106 D7
Munkfors S 97 C10
Munklia N 111 D14
Munksund S 118 D7
Munktorp S 98 C6
Munkzwalm B 19 C8
Munne FIN 128 C7
Münnerstadt D 75 B7
Munningen D 75 E8
Muñogalindo E 46 C3
Munsala FIN 122 D8
Münsingen CH 31 B12
Münsingen D 74 F5
Münster A 72 B4
Münster CH 70 E6
Münster D 17 E9
Münster D 21 E11
Münster D 83 E8
Munster F 27 D7
Münsterdorf D 82 C7
Munstergeleen NL 183 D7
Münsterhausen D 75 F7
Münstermaifeld D 185 D7
Muntendam NL 17 B7
Munteni RO 153 F10
Munteni-Buzău RO 161 D9
Muntenii de Jos RO 153 D11
Münzenberg D 21 D11
Münzkirchen A 76 F5
Muodoslompolo S 117 C10
Muonio FIN 117 C11
Muonionalusta S 117 C11
Muotathal CH 71 D7
Muotkajärvi FIN 117 B10
Muotkavaara FIN 117 C12
Mur SRB 163 C9
Muradiye TR 173 D9
Muradiye TR 177 B9
Murakeresztúr H 149 D7
Muráň SK 147 D10
Muras E 38 B4
Murasson F 34 C4
Muraste EST 131 C8
Muraszemenye H 149 D7
Murat F 30 E2
Muratlar TR 181 B9
Muratli TR 173 B7
Murato F 37 F10
Murat-sur-Vèbre F 34 C4
Murau A 73 B9
Muravera I 64 E4
Murazzano I 37 C8
Murça P 38 F5
Murchante E 41 D8
Mŭrchevo BG 165 B7
Murchin D 84 C5
Murcia E 56 F2
Murczyn PL 138 E4
Mur-de-Barrez F 29 F11
Mûr-de-Bretagne F 22 D6
Mur-de-Sologne F 24 F6
Mureck A 148 C5
Mürefte TR 173 C7
Muret F 33 D8
Murgeni RO 153 E12
Murgenthal CH 27 F8
Murgeşti RO 161 C9
Murgia E 40 C6
Muri CH 27 F9
Muri CH 31 B11
Murias de Paredes E 39 C7
Muriedas E 40 B4
Murighiol RO 155 C4
Murillo de Río Leza E 32 F1
Murillo el Fruto E 32 F3
Murino MNE 163 D8
Murisengo I 68 C5
Murjāni LV 135 B9
Murjek S 116 F5
Murley GB 7 D8
Murlo I 66 F3
Murmastiene LV 135 C13
Murnau am Staffelsee D 72 A3
Muro E 57 B11
Muro F 37 F9
Muro P 38 F2
Muro de Alcoy E 56 D4
Murol F 30 D2
Murole FIN 127 B10
Muro Lucano I 60 B4
Muron F 28 C4
Murony H 151 D7
Muros E 38 C1
Muros E 39 A7
Muros I 64 B2
Murovane UA 144 C9
Murów PL 142 E4
Murowana Goślina PL 81 A12
Murrë AL 168 A3
Murrhardt D 74 E6
Murronkylä FIN 119 E16
Murrough IRL 6 F4
Mursalli TR 177 D10
Mûrs-Erigné F 23 F10
Murska Sobota SLO 148 C6
Murski Središće HR 149 C6
Murtas E 55 F6
Murtede P 44 D4
Murten CH 31 B11
Murter HR 156 E4
Murtino MK 169 B8
Murto FIN 119 E15
Murtolahti FIN 125 D9
Murtomäki FIN 124 B9
Murtovaara FIN 121 C13
Murumoen N 105 C16
Murvica HR 156 D3
Murviel-lès-Béziers F 34 D5
Mürzsteg A 148 A5
Murzynowo PL 81 A8
Mürzzuschlag A 148 A5
Mūsa LV 135 D8
Musbury GB 13 D8
Müschenbach D 185 C8
Musei I 64 E2
Muselievo BG 160 F5
Mushtisht RKS 163 E10
Musile di Piave I 72 E6
Muskö S 93 B12
Mussalo FIN 128 E6
Musselburgh GB 5 D10
Musselkanaal NL 17 C8
Mussidan F 29 E6
Mussomeli I 58 D4
Musson B 19 E12
Mussy-sur-Seine F 25 E12
Mustafakemalpaşa TR 173 D9
Müstair CH 71 D10
Mustamaa FIN 119 F17
Mustamaa FIN 123 D10
Mustasaari FIN 122 D7
Mustavaara FIN 121 D12
Mustavaara FIN 121 F12
Mustinlahti FIN 125 E10
Mustjala EST 130 E4
Mustla EST 131 E11
Mustola FIN 114 F4
Mustolanmäki FIN 125 C10
Mustolanmutka FIN 125 B10
Mustvee EST 131 D13
Muszaki PL 139 D10
Muszyna PL 145 E2
Muta SLO 73 C11
Mutala FIN 127 B10
Mutalahti FIN 125 F16
Mütevelli TR 177 B10
Muthill GB 5 C9
Mutilva Baja E 32 E2
Mutné SK 147 C8
Mutriku E 32 D1
Mutterstadt D 21 F10
Mutxamel E 56 E4
Mutzig F 27 C7
Mutzschen D 80 D3
Muuga EST 131 C13
Muukajärvi S 116 E10
Muuksi EST 131 B11
Muurame FIN 123 F15
Muurasjärvi FIN 123 C14
Muurikkala FIN 128 D8
Muurla FIN 127 E9
Muurola FIN 119 B14
Muurola FIN 128 D8
Muuruvesi FIN 125 D10
Muxía E 38 B1
Muzillac F 22 E7
Mužla SK 149 A11
Myahuny BY 137 C14
Myakishevo RUS 133 C5
Myaretskiya BY 133 F3
Myazhany BY 135 E13
Mybster GB 3 J10
Myckelgensjö S 107 D13
Myckle S 118 E5
Myedna BY 141 G9
Myggenäs S 91 C10
Myggsjö S 102 C8
Myhinpää FIN 124 F7
Myjava SK 146 D5
Mykanów PL 143 E7
Mykhal'cha UA 153 A7
Mykhaylivka UA 154 F5
Myki GR 171 B7
Myklebostad N 110 E9
Mykolayiv UA 145 D8
Mykolayivka UA 154 E4
Mykolayivka-Novorosiys'ka
UA 154 E5
Mykonos GR 176 E5
Mykulychyn UA 152 A5
Mykytychi UA 144 B9
Myllykoski FIN 128 D6
Myllykylä FIN 122 E8
Myllykylä FIN 127 E10
Myllykylä FIN 128 D7
Myllylahti FIN 121 D13
Myllymäki FIN 123 E12
Myloi GR 175 D6
Mylopotamos GR 178 C4
Mynämäki FIN 126 D7
Mynttilä FIN 128 C6
Myon F 31 A8
Myory BY 133 E3
Myra GR 169 F8
Myrås S 109 E14
Myre N 110 C9
Myre N 111 B10
Myresjö S 92 E5
Myrhaug N 101 A14
Myrheden S 118 D4
Myrhult S 92 B4
Myrina GR 171 E8
Myriokefala GR 178 E7
Myrkky FIN 122 F7
Myrland N 110 D5
Myrland N 110 D9
Myrland N 111 C10
Myrlandshaugen N 111 C13
Myrmoen N 101 A15
Myrne UA 155 B4
Myrnes N 112 C9
Myrnopillya UA 154 E4
Myrsini GR 174 D3
Myrsini GR 178 B3
Myrskylä FIN 127 D14
Myrties GR 177 F8
Myrtos GR 179 E10
Myrviken S 105 E16
Mysen N 95 C14
Myshall IRL 9 C9
Myślachowice PL 143 F7
Mysłakowice PL 81 E9
Myślenice PL 147 B9
Myślibórz PL 85 E7
Myślice PL 139 C8
Mysłowice PL 143 F7
Mysovka RUS 134 F2
Myssjö S 102 A7
Mystegna GR 177 A7
Mystras GR 174 E5
Myszków PL 143 E7
Myszyniec PL 139 D11
Mytikas GR 174 B2
Mytilini GR 177 A8
Mytilinioi GR 177 D8
Mýtna SK 147 E9
Mýto CZ 76 C5

N

Nå N 94 B5
Naaldwijk NL 16 E2
Naamankylä FIN 119 E17
Naamijoki FIN 117 E11
Naantali FIN 126 E7
Naapurinvaara FIN 121 F11
Naarden NL 183 A6
Näärinki FIN 128 B8
Naarn im Machlande A 77 F7
Naartijärvi S 119 C11
Naarva FIN 125 D16
Naas IRL 7 F9
Näätämö FIN 114 D6
Näätänmaa FIN 125 F10
Näätävaara FIN 121 E13
Nabburg D 75 D11
Nábrád H 145 G5
Na Cealla Beaga IRL 6 C6
Načeradec CZ 77 C7
Nacha BY 137 E10
Náchod CZ 77 B10
Nacina Ves SK 145 F4
Näckådalen S 102 D7
Nackel D 83 E13
Nackenheim D 185 E9
Näcksjö S 103 C12
Na Clocha Liathe IRL 7 F10
Nacpolsk PL 139 E9
Nad IRL 8 D5
Nadalj SRB 158 C4
Nadarzyce PL 85 D11
Nadarzyn PL 141 F3
Naddvik N 100 D7
Nadeş RO 152 E5
Nădlac RO 150 E6
Nădrag RO 159 B9
Nadrichne UA 154 E4
Nádudvar H 151 C7
Năeni RO 161 C8
Nærbø N 94 E3
Næroset N 101 E13
Nærsnes N 95 C13
Næsbjerg DK 86 D3
Næstved DK 87 E9
Näfels CH 27 F11
Nafferton GB 11 C11
Nafpaktos GR 174 C4
Nafplio GR 175 D6
Nagele NL 16 C5
Naggen S 103 B11
Naglarby S 97 B14
Na Gleannta IRL 6 C6
Nagli LV 133 C1
Nagłowice PL 143 E9
Nagold D 27 C10
Nagore E 32 E3
Nago-Torbole I 69 B10
Nagu FIN 126 E6
Nagyatád H 149 D8
Nagybajom H 149 D9
Nagybánhegyes H 151 E6
Nagybaracska H 150 E2
Nagybarca H 145 G2
Nagyberény H 149 C10
Nagyberki H 149 D10
Nagycenk H 149 A7
Nagycsécs H 145 H2
Nagycserkesz H 145 H4
Nagydobos H 145 G5
Nagydorog H 149 C11
Nagyecsed H 145 H5
Nagyfüged H 150 B5
Nagyhalász H 145 G4
Nagyharsány H 149 E10
Nagyhegyes H 151 B7
Nagyigmánd H 149 A10
Nagyiván H 151 C6
Nagykálló H 145 H4
Nagykanizsa H 149 D7
Nagykapornak H 149 C7
Nagykáta H 150 C4
Nagykereki H 151 C8
Nagykónyi H 149 C10
Nagykőrös H 150 C4
Nagykovácsi H 149 A11
Nagylak H 150 E6
Nagylóc H 147 E9
Nagylók H 149 C11
Nagylózs H 149 A7
Nagymágocs H 150 D5
Nagymaros H 149 A11
Nagynyárád H 149 E11
Nagyoroszi H 147 F8
Nagyrécse H 149 C8
Nagyréde H 150 B4
Nagyszénás H 150 D6
Nagyszokoly H 149 C10
Nagytarcsa H 150 B3
Nagytőke H 150 D5
Nagyvarsány H 145 G5
Nagyvázsony H 149 C9
Nagyvisnyó H 145 G1
Naha EST 132 E1
Naharros E 47 D8
Nahe D 83 C8
Nahirne UA 155 C2
Nahrendorf D 83 D9
Naidăş RO 159 D8
Naila D 75 B10
Nailloux F 33 D9
Nailsworth GB 13 B10
Naimakka S 116 A7
Naintré F 29 B6
Naipköy TR 173 C7
Nairn GB 3 K9
Naives-Rosières F 26 C3
Naizin F 22 E6
Najac F 33 B9
Nájera E 40 D6
Näkkälä FIN 117 A11
Nakkerud N 95 B12
Nakkila FIN 126 C7
Náklo CZ 77 C12
Nakło PL 143 E8
Naklo SLO 73 D9
Nakło nad Notecią PL 85 D13
Nakomiady PL 136 E3
Näkotne LV 134 C6
Nakovo SRB 150 F6
Nakskov DK 83 A10
Nalbach D 186 C2
Nalbant RO 155 C3
Nalda E 41 D7
Nälden S 105 E16
Nałęczów PL 141 H6
Nálepkovo SK 145 F2
Näljänkä FIN 121 D11
Nalkki FIN 121 E10
Nalliers F 28 C3
Nalžovské Hory CZ 76 D5
Namborn D 21 E8
Nambroca E 46 E5
Namdalseid N 105 C10
Náměšť nad Oslavou CZ 77 D10
Náměšť na Hané CZ 77 C12
Námestovo SK 147 C8
Nämpnäs FIN 122 E6
Namsos N 105 C11
Namsskogan N 105 B14
Namsvatn N 105 B15
Namur B 19 D10
Namysłów PL 142 D4
Nana RO 161 E9
Nána SK 147 F7
Nançay F 24 F7
Nanclares de la Oca E 40 C6
Nancy F 26 C5
Nandrin B 183 D6
Năneşti RO 161 B10
Nangis F 25 C9
Nannestad N 95 B13
Nanov RO 160 F6
Nans-les-Pins F 35 D10
Nant F 34 B5
Nanterre F 25 C7
Nantes F 23 F8
Nanteuil-le-Haudouin F 25 B8
Nantiat F 29 C8
Nantua F 31 C8
Nantwich GB 10 E6
Naousa GR 169 C7
Naousa GR 176 E5
Napajedla CZ 146 C5
Napiwoda PL 139 D9
Napkor H 145 H4
Napola I 58 D2
Napoli I 60 B2
Napp N 110 D5
Năpradea RO 151 C11
Náquera E 48 E4
När S 93 E13
Nåra N 100 D1
Nárai H 149 B7
Narberth GB 12 B5
Narbolia I 64 C2
Narbonne F 34 D5
Narbonne-Plage F 34 D5
Narborough GB 15 B10
Narbuvoll N 101 B14
Narcao I 64 E2
Narcy F 25 F9
Nardò I 61 C10
Narechenski Bani BG 165 F10
Narew PL 140 E9
Narewka PL 141 E9
Närhilä FIN 123 E16
Narin IRL 6 C6
Nāriņciems LV 134 B5
Narkaus FIN 119 B16
Narken S 116 E9
Narlidere TR 177 C9
Narni I 62 B3
Naro I 58 E4
Narol PL 144 C7
Närpes FIN 122 F6
Narrosse F 32 C3
Narta HR 149 E7
Nartë AL 168 D1
Năruja RO 153 F9
Naruska FIN 115 D6
Naruszewo PL 139 E9
Narva EST 132 C3
Narva FIN 127 C10
Narva-Jõesuu EST 132 C3
Närvijoki FIN 122 E7
Narvik N 111 D13
Narzole I 37 B7
Narzym PL 139 D9
Näs FIN 99 B14
Nås N 90 A5
Näs S 93 E12
Näs S 97 B12
Näs S 102 A8
Näsåker S 107 E11
Năsăud RO 152 C4
Nasavrky CZ 77 C9
Näsberg S 103 C10
Nasbinals F 34 A5
Näs bruk S 98 B6
Näsby S 89 C10
Na Sceirí IRL 7 E10
Näset S 103 D9
Nashec RKS 163 E10
Našice HR 149 F10
Nasielsk PL 139 E10
Näske S 107 E15
Näsliden S 107 A16
Naso I 59 C6
Nassau D 21 D9
Nassereith A 71 C11
Nässja S 92 C5
Nässjö S 92 D5
Nässjö S 107 D10
Nassogne B 19 D11
Nästansjö S 107 B11
Nastätten D 185 D8
Nästeln S 102 A7
Nastola FIN 127 D14
Năsturelu RO 161 F6
Näsum S 88 C7
Nasutów PL 141 H6
Näsviken S 103 C12
Näsviken S 106 D9
Naszály H 149 A10
Natalinci SRB 159 E6
Nateby GB 11 C7
Naters CH 68 A4
Nattavaara S 116 E5
Nattavaara by S 116 E6
Nattheim D 75 E7
Nättraby S 89 C9
Naturno I 71 D11
Naucelle F 33 B10
Naucelles F 29 F10
Naudaskalns LV 133 B2
Nauders A 71 D11
Naudīte LV 134 C6
Nauen D 79 A12
Nauendorf D 79 C10
Nauheim D 21 E10
Naujac-sur-Mer F 28 E3
Naujamiestis LT 135 E8
Naujasis Daugėliškis LT 135 F12
Naujoji Akmenė LT 134 D5
Naujoji Vilnia LT 137 D11
Naukšēni LV 131 F10
Naul IRL 7 E10
Naulaperä FIN 121 E10
Naulavaara FIN 125 C10
Naumburg (Hessen) D 17 F12
Naumburg (Saale) D 79 D10
Naundorf D 80 D4
Naundorf D 80 E4
Naunhof D 79 D12
Nauroth D 21 C9
Naurstad N 108 B8
Naustbukta N 105 B11
Naustdal N 100 C3
Nauste N 101 A8
Nautijaur S 109 C17
Nautsi RUS 114 E6
Nautsund N 100 D2
Nava E 39 B9
Navacepeda de Tormes
E 45 D10
Navaconcejo E 45 D9
Nava de Arévalo E 46 C3
Nava de la Asunción E 46 B4
Nava del Rey E 39 F9
Nava de Sotrobal E 45 C10
Navadrutsk BY 133 F2
Navafría E 46 B5
Navahermosa E 46 E4
Navajas E 48 E4
Naval E 42 C4
Navalagamella E 46 D4
Navalcaballo E 41 E6
Navalcán E 45 D10
Navalcarnero E 46 D4
Navalero E 40 E6
Navalmanzano E 46 B4
Navalmoral E 46 D3
Navalmoral de la Mata E 45 E9
Navalonguilla E 45 D10
Navalosa E 46 D3
Navalperal de Pinares E 46 C4
Navalpino E 46 F3
Navaluenga E 46 D3
Navalvillar de Ibor E 45 E10
Navalvillar de Pela E 45 F10
Navamorcuende E 46 D3
Navan IRL 7 E9
Navapolatsk BY 133 E5
Navarcles E 43 D7
Navardún E 32 E3
Navarredonda de la Rinconada
E 45 C8
Navarrenx F 32 D4
Navarrés E 48 F3
Navarrete E 41 D6
Navarrevisca E 46 D3
Navàs E 43 D7
Navascués E 32 E3
Navas de Estrena E 46 E3
Navas de Jorquera E 47 F9
Navas del Madroño E 45 E7
Navas del Rey E 46 D4
Navas de Oro E 46 B4
Navas de San Juan E 55 C6
Navasfrías E 45 D7
Navata E 43 C9
Navatalgordo E 46 D3
Nave I 69 B9
Nave P 50 E2
Nave de Haver P 45 C7
Nävekvarn S 93 B9
Navelli I 62 C5
Näverdal N 101 A12
Näverede S 106 E8
Nave Redonda P 50 E3
Näverkärret S 97 C14
Näverrys FIN 119 C15
Naverstad S 91 B10
Navès E 43 D7
Naves F 29 E9
Navezuelas E 45 E10
Navia E 39 A6
Navilly F 31 B7
Navit N 112 D8
Năvodari RO 155 E3
Nävragöl S 89 C9
Nawojowa PL 145 D2
Naxos GR 176 E5
Nay-Bourdettes F 32 D5
Nazaré P 44 E2
Nazelles-Négron F 24 F4
Nazza D 79 D7
Ndroq AL 168 B2
Nea Agathoupoli GR 169 D8
Nea Alikarnassos GR 178 E9
Nea Anchialos GR 169 F8
Nea Apollonia GR 169 C9
Nea Artaki GR 175 B8
Nea Efesos GR 169 D7
Nea Epidavros GR 175 D7
Nea Figaleia GR 174 E4
Nea Filadelfeia GR 175 C8
Nea Fokaia GR 169 D9
Nea Ionia GR 169 F8
Nea Iraklitsa GR 171 C6
Nea Kallikrateia GR 169 D9
Nea Karvali GR 171 C6
Nea Karya GR 171 C7
Nea Kerdylia GR 169 C10
Nea Kios GR 175 D6
Nea Koroni GR 174 F4
Nea Lampsakos GR 175 C8
Neale IRL 6 E4
Nea Liosia GR 175 C8
Nea Madytos GR 169 C10
Nea Makri GR 175 C8
Nea Malgara GR 169 C8
Nea Mesimvria GR 169 C8
Nea Michaniona GR 169 D8
Nea Moudania GR 169 D9
Nea Olynthos GR 169 D9
Nea Pella GR 169 C8
Nea Peramos GR 171 C6
Nea Peramos GR 175 C7
Nea Plagia GR 169 D9
Neapoli GR 168 D5
Neapoli GR 178 B5
Neapoli GR 179 E10
Nea Poteidaia GR 169 D9
Nea Roda GR 170 D5
Nea Santa GR 169 C8
Nea Santa GR 171 B9
Nea Silata GR 169 D9
Nea Styra GR 175 C9
Neath GB 13 B7
Nea Tiryntha GR 175 D6
Nea Triglia GR 169 D9
Neaua RO 152 E5
Nea Vravrona GR 175 D9
Nea Vyssa GR 171 A11
Nea Zichni GR 169 B10
Nebel D 82 A4
Nébias F 33 E10
Nebljusi HR 156 C4
Nebra (Unstrut) D 79 D10
Nebreda E 40 E4
Nechanice CZ 77 B9
Neckarbischofsheim D 187 C6
Neckargemünd D 21 F11
Neckarsteinach D 21 F11
Neckarsulm D 21 F12
Neckartenzlingen D 27 C11
Necşeşti RO 160 E6
Necton GB 15 B10
Nečujam HR 156 F5
Neda E 38 B3
Nedansjö S 103 B12
Nedašov CZ 146 C6
Neddemin D 84 C4
Neded SK 146 E5
Nedelino BG 171 B8
Nedelišće HR 149 D6
Nederby DK 86 B4
Nederhögen S 102 B7
Nederhorst den Berg NL 183 A6
Neder Hvam DK 86 C4
Nederlangbroek NL 183 A6
Nedervetil FIN 123 C10
Neder Vindinge DK 87 E9
Nederweert NL 16 F5
Nedlitz D 79 B11
Nedožery-Brezany SK 147 D7
Nedrebø N 94 E4
Nedre Saxnäs S 109 F14
Nedre Soppero S 116 B7
Nedstrand N 94 D3
Nedvědice CZ 77 D10
Nedyalsko BG 167 E7
Nędza PL 142 F5
Neede NL 17 D7
Needham Market GB 15 C11
Neer NL 183 C8
Neerijnen NL 183 B6
Neermoor D 17 B8
Neeroeteren B 183 C7
Neerpelt B 19 B11
Neetze D 83 D9
Nefyn GB 10 F2
Negenborn D 78 C6
Negoi RO 160 F2
Negomir RO 159 D11
Negorci MK 169 B7
Negoslavci HR 157 B11
Negotin SRB 159 E10
Negotino MK 163 F10
Negotino MK 169 B7
Negrar I 66 A2
Negraşi RO 160 D6
Negredo E 47 B7
Negreira E 38 C2
Nègrepelisse F 33 B9
Negreşti RO 153 D10
Negreşti-Oaş RO 145 H7
Negri RO 153 D9
Negru Vodă RO 155 F2
Nehoiu RO 161 C8
Neiden N 114 D6
Neidin IRL 8 E3
Neitaskaite S 116 E8
Neitsuanto S 116 D5
Neittävä FIN 119 E17
Neive I 37 B8
Nejdek CZ 75 B12
Nekézseny H 145 G1
Nekla PL 81 B12
Neksø DK 89 E8
Nelas P 44 C5
Nellim FIN 114 F4
Nellingen D 74 E6
Nelson GB 11 D7
Nemaitonys LT 137 D9
Neman RUS 136 C5
Nemanjica MK 164 F4
Nemanskoye RUS 136 C5
Nembro I 69 B8
Nemea GR 175 D6
Nemenčinė LT 137 D11
Nemesgulács H 149 C8
Nemesnádudvar H 150 E3
Nemesvámos H 149 B9
Nemesvid H 149 C8
Nemetker H 149 C11
Nemėžis LT 137 D11
Nemours F 25 D8
Nemsdorf-Göhrendorf D 79 D10
Nemšová SK 146 D6
Nemunaitis LT 137 E9
Nemunėlio Radviliškis LT
135 D9
Nemyriv UA 144 C7
Nenagh IRL 8 C6
Nendaz CH 31 C11
Nenince SK 147 E8
Nenita GR 177 C7
Nennhausen D 79 A12
Nennslingen D 75 D9
Nenonpelto FIN 124 F8
Nentershausen D 21 D9
Nentershausen D 78 D6
Nenthead GB 5 F12
Nenzing A 71 C9
Neo Agioneri GR 169 C8
Neochoraki GR 175 C7
Neochori GR 169 B9
Neochori GR 169 F6
Neochori GR 171 B10
Neochori GR 174 A3
Neochori GR 174 C3
Neo Erasmio GR 171 C7
Neoi Epivates GR 169 C8
Neo Monastiri GR 169 F7
Neoneli I 64 C2
Neo Petritsi GR 169 B9
Neorić HR 156 E6
Neos Kafkasos GR 168 C5
Neos Marmaras GR 169 D10
Neos Mylotopos GR 169 C7
Neo Souli GR 169 B10
Neos Pagontas GR 175 B8
Neos Pyrgos GR 175 B7
Neos Skopos GR 169 B10
Néoules F 36 E4
Nepi I 62 C2
Nepomuk CZ 76 D5
Nérac F 33 B6
Neratovice CZ 77 B7
Nerău RO 150 F6
Neravai LT 137 E9
Nerchau D 79 D12
Nercillac F 28 D5
Nerdal N 101 A9
Nerde Gärdsjö S 103 E9
Néré F 28 D5
Nereju RO 153 F9
Neresheim D 75 E7
Neresnica SRB 159 E8
Neresnytsya UA 145 G8
Nereta LV 135 D10
Nereto I 62 B5
Nerezine HR 67 C9
Nerežišće HR 156 F6
Néris-les-Bains F 29 C11
Nerja E 53 C9
Nerkoo FIN 124 D8
Nerlia N 108 E7
Nerokouros GR 178 E7
Néronde F 30 D5
Nérondes F 30 B2
Neroth D 21 D7
Nerpio E 55 C8
Nersac F 28 D6
Nersingen D 75 F7
Nerskogen N 101 A11
Nerushay UA 155 B5
Nerva E 51 D6
Nervesa della Battaglia I 72 E5
Nervieux F 30 D5
Nes FO 2 A3
Nes N 95 D9
Nes N 96 A2
Nes N 110 D9
Nes N 111 D10
Nes NL 16 B5
Nesbyen N 101 E10
Neschwitz D 80 D6
Nesebŭr BG 167 D9
Neset N 112 C7
Nes Flaten N 94 C5
Nesgrenda N 90 B4
Nesheim N 94 B3
Nesje N 110 D6
Nesjegjerde N 100 A6
Nesland N 110 D5
Neslandsvatn N 90 B5
Nesle F 18 E6
Nesna N 108 D5
Nesovice CZ 77 D12
Nessa F 37 F9
Nesse D 17 A8
Nesseby N 114 C6
Nesselwang D 71 B11
Nesslau CH 27 F11
Nessodtangen N 95 C13
Nestani GR 175 D5
Nestby N 108 B9
Nesterov RUS 136 D6
Neston GB 10 E5
Nestorio GR 168 D5
Nestoyita UA 154 B4
Nesttun N 94 B2
Nesvady SK 146 F6
Nesvatnstemmen N 90 B3
Nesvik N 94 D4
Nethy Bridge GB 3 L9
Netolice CZ 76 D6
Netphen D 21 C10
Netra (Ringgau) D 79 D7
Netretić HR 148 E4
Netstal CH 71 C8
Nettancourt F 25 C12
Nettersheim D 21 D7
Nettetal D 16 F6
Nettuno I 62 E3
Netvořice CZ 77 C7
Neu-Anspach D 21 D11
Neuberend D 82 A7
Neuberg an der Mürz A 148 A5
Neubeuern D 72 A5
Neubiberg D 75 F10
Neubrandenburg D 84 C4
Neubruchhausen D 17 C11
Neubrunn D 187 B8
Neubukow D 83 B11
Neubulach D 27 C10
Neuburg am Rhein D 187 D5
Neuburg an der Donau D 75 E9
Neuburg-Steinhausen D 83 C11
Neuburxdorf D 80 D4
Neuchâtel CH 31 B10
Neu Darchau D 83 D9
Neudietendorf D 79 E8
Neudorf A 146 F2
Neudrossenfeld D 75 B10
Neuenbürg D 27 C10
Neuendettelsau D 75 D8
Neuenhagen Berlin D 80 A5
Neuenhaus D 17 D7
Neuenhof CH 27 F9
Neuenkirch CH 27 F9
Neuenkirchen D 17 A11
Neuenkirchen D 17 C11
Neuenkirchen D 17 D8
Neuenkirchen D 17 D9
Neuenkirchen D 82 B6
Neuenkirchen D 82 D7
Neuenkirchen D 84 A4
Neuenkirchen D 84 B4
Neuenkirchen (Oldenburg)
D 17 C10
Neuenkirchen-Seelscheid
D 21 C8
Neuenrade D 185 B8
Neuenstadt am Kocher D
27 B11
Neuenstein D 187 C8
Neuenwalde D 17 A11
Neuerburg D 20 D6
Neufahrn bei Freising D 75 F10
Neufahrn in Niederbayern
D 75 E11
Neufchâteau B 19 E11
Neufchâteau F 26 D4
Neufchâtel-en-Bray F 18 E3
Neufchâtel-Hardelot F 15 F12
Neufchâtel-sur-Aisne F 19 F9
Neufeld D 17 A12
Neufeld an der Leitha A 77 G10
Neuffen D 27 C11
Neufmanil F 184 E2
Neufra D 27 D11
Neugersdorf D 81 E7
Neuharlingersiel D 17 A9
Neuhaus A 73 A11
Neuhaus A 73 C10
Neuhaus (Oste) D 17 A12
Neuhaus am Inn D 76 F4
Neuhaus am Klausenbach
A 148 C6
Neuhaus am Rennweg D 75 A9
Neuhaus an der Pegnitz
D 75 C10
Neuhausen CH 27 E10
Neuhausen D 80 E4
Neuhausen D 187 D6
Neuhausen ob Eck D 27 E10
Neuhof D 74 B6
Neuhof an der Zenn D 75 D8
Neuhofen D 187 C5
Neuhofen an der Krems A 76 F6
Neuillé-Pont-Pierre F 24 E4
Neuilly F 25 F10
Neuilly-en-Thelle F 18 F5
Neuilly-le-Réal F 30 C3
Neuilly-l'Évêque F 26 E3
Neuilly-St-Front F 25 B9
Neu-Isenburg D 187 A6
Neukalen D 83 C13
Neu Kaliß D 83 D10
Neukirch D 80 D6
Neukirchen D 21 C12
Neukirchen D 80 E3
Neukirchen D 83 B10
Neukirchen D 86 F3
Neukirchen am Großvenediger
A 72 B5
Neukirchen an der Enknach
A 76 F4
Neukirchen an der Vöckla
A 76 F5
Neukirchen-Balbini D 75 D11
Neukirchen beim Heiligen Blut
D 76 D3
Neukirchen vorm Wald D 76 E4
Neukloster D 83 C11
Neulengbach A 77 F9

Neuler D 75 E7
Neulewin D 84 E6
Neulikko FIN 121 E10
Neulise F 30 D5
Neu Lübbenau D 80 B5
Neum BIH 162 D4
Neumagen D 185 E6
Neumark D 79 E11
Neumarkt am Wallersee A 73 A7
Neumarkt im Mühlkreis A 77 F6
Neumarkt in der Oberpfalz D 75 D9
Neumarkt in Steiermark A 73 B9
Neumarkt-Sankt Veit D 75 F12
Neu Mukran D 84 B5
Neumünster D 83 B7
Neunburg vorm Wald D 75 D11
Neundorf D 75 A11
Neung-sur-Beuvron F 24 E6
Neunkirch CH 27 E10
Neunkirchen A 148 A6
Neunkirchen D 21 C10
Neunkirchen D 21 F8
Neunkirchen am Brand D 75 C9
Neunkirchen am Sand D 75 C9
Neuötting D 75 F12
Neupetershain D 80 C6
Neupölla A 77 E8
Neureichenau D 76 E5
Neuruppin D 83 E13
Neuschönau D 76 E4
Neusiedl am See A 77 G11
Neusorg D 75 C10
Neuss D 21 B7
Neussargues-Moissac F 30 E2
Neustadt D 27 E9
Neustadt D 79 E10
Neustadt D 83 E12
Neustadt (Harz) D 79 C8
Neustadt (Hessen) D 21 C12
Neustadt (Wied) D 21 C8
Neustadt am Kulm D 75 C10
Neustadt am Rübenberge D 78 A5
Neustadt an der Aisch D 75 C8
Neustadt an der Donau D 75 E10
Neustadt an der Waldnaab D 75 C11
Neustadt an der Weinstraße D 21 F10
Neustadt bei Coburg D 75 B9
Neustadt-Glewe D 83 D11
Neustadt in Holstein D 83 B9
Neustadt in Sachsen D 80 D6
Neustift im Stubaital A 72 B3
Neustrelitz D 84 D4
Neutraubling D 75 E11
Neutrebbin D 80 A6
Neu-Ulm D 74 F7
Neuvéglise F 30 F2
Neuves-Maisons F 186 D1
Neuvic F 29 E6
Neuvic F 29 E10
Neuville-aux-Bois F 24 D7
Neuville-de-Poitou F 29 B6
Neuville-les-Dames F 31 C7
Neuville-lès-Dieppe F 18 E3
Neuville-sur-Saône F 30 D6
Neuvilly-en-Argonne F 26 B3
Neuvy-Grandchamp F 30 B4
Neuvy-le-Roi F 24 E4
Neuvy-Pailloux F 29 B9
Neuvy-St-Sépulchre F 29 B9
Neuvy-sur-Barangeon F 25 F7
Neuweiler D 27 C10
Neuwied D 21 D8
Neuwittenbek D 83 B8
Neu Wulmstorf D 83 D7
Neu Zauche D 80 C6
Neuzelle D 81 B7
Neu Zittau D 80 B5
Névache F 31 E10
Nevarėnai LT 134 D4
Neveja LV 130 F4
Neveklov CZ 77 C7
Nevel' RUS 133 D7
Nevele B 19 B8
Neverfjord N 113 C12
Nevernes N 108 F4
Neverness N 110 C9
Neveronys LT 137 D9
Nevers F 30 A3
Nevesinje BIH 157 F9
Nevestino BG 165 E6
Névez F 22 E4
Neviano I 61 C10
Néville F 18 E2
Nevlunghavn N 90 B6
Nevsha BG 167 C8
New Abbey GB 5 F9
New Aberdour GB 3 K12
New Alresford GB 13 C12
Newark-on-Trent GB 11 E10
Newbawn IRL 9 D9
Newbiggin-by-the-Sea GB 5 E13
Newbliss IRL 7 D8
Newborough GB 11 F11
Newbridge GB 13 B8
Newbridge IRL 7 F9
New Buildings GB 4 F2
Newburgh GB 3 L12
Newburgh GB 5 C10
Newbury GB 13 C12
Newby Bridge GB 10 C6
Newcastle GB 7 D11
Newcastle GB 13 A8
Newcastle IRL 7 F10
Newcastle IRL 7 F10
Newcastle Emlyn GB 12 A6
Newcastleton GB 5 E11
Newcastle-under-Lyme GB 11 E7
Newcastle upon Tyne GB 5 F13
Newcastle West IRL 8 D4
New Cumnock GB 5 E8
New Deer GB 3 K12
Newel D 21 E7
Newent GB 13 B10
New Galloway GB 5 E8
New Inn IRL 6 F6
New Inn IRL 7 E8
Newinn IRL 9 D7
New Kildimo IRL 8 C5
Newmarket GB 2 J4
Newmarket GB 15 C9
Newmarket IRL 8 D4
Newmarket IRL 9 D8
Newmarket-on-Fergus IRL 8 C5
Newmill GB 3 K11
New Milton GB 13 D11
Newnham GB 13 B10
New Pitsligo GB 3 K12
Newport GB 3 J10
Newport GB 11 F7
Newport GB 12 A5
Newport GB 13 B9
Newport GB 13 D12
Newport GB 15 D9
Newport IRL 6 E3
Newport IRL 8 C6
Newport-on-Tay GB 5 C11
Newport Pagnell GB 15 C7
Newport Trench GB 4 F3
New Quay GB 12 A6
Newquay GB 12 E4
New Radnor GB 13 A8
New Romney GB 15 F10
New Ross IRL 9 D9
Newry GB 7 D10
Newton GB 4 C6
Newton GB 10 D7
Newton Abbot GB 13 D7
Newton Aycliffe GB 5 F13
Newton Ferrers GB 12 E6
Newtonhill GB 3 L12
Newton-le-Willows GB 10 E6
Newton Mearns GB 5 D8
Newtonmore GB 5 A8
Newton Stewart GB 4 F8
Newtown GB 10 F5
Newtown GB 13 A9
Newtown IRL 6 F6
Newtown IRL 8 D5
Newtown IRL 8 D6
Newtown IRL 9 C8
Newtownabbey GB 4 F5
Newtownards GB 7 C11
Newtownbarry IRL 9 C9
Newtownbutler GB 7 D8
Newtown Crommelin GB 4 F4
Newtown Forbes IRL 7 E7
Newtown Mount Kennedy IRL 7 F10
Newtown St Boswells GB 5 D11
Newtownstewart GB 4 F2
Nexon F 29 D8
Neyland GB 12 B5
Nezamyslice CZ 77 D12
Nezavertailovca MD 154 D5
Nézsa H 147 F8
Nezvěstice CZ 76 C5
Nianfors S 103 C12
Niata GR 175 F6
Nibbiano I 37 B10
Nibe DK 86 B5
Nīca LV 134 D2
Nicastro I 59 B9
Nice F 37 D6
Nīcgale LV 135 D12
Nichelino I 37 A7
Nickelsdorf A 77 G12
Nicolae Bălcescu RO 153 B9
Nicolae Bălcescu RO 153 E9
Nicolae Bălcescu RO 155 D3
Nicolae Bălcescu RO 155 E2
Nicolae Bălcescu RO 160 D4
Nicolae Bălcescu RO 161 E9
Nicolae Titulescu RO 160 E5
Nicolaevca MD 154 B2
Nicolosi I 59 D7
Nicoreni MD 153 B11
Nicorești RO 153 F10
Nicosia I 58 D5
Nicotera I 59 B8
Nicșeni RO 153 B9
Niculești RO 161 D7
Niculițel RO 155 C2
Nida LT 134 F1
Nidau CH 27 F7
Nidda D 21 D12
Nidzica PL 139 D9
Niebla E 51 E6
Nieborów PL 141 F2
Niebüll D 82 A5
Niebylec PL 144 D4
Niechanowo PL 138 F4
Niechcice PL 143 D8
Niechłonin PL 139 D9
Niechlów PL 81 C10
Niechorze PL 85 B8
Niederaichbach D 75 E11
Niederanven L 20 E6
Niederau D 80 D5
Niederaula D 78 E6
Niederbipp CH 27 F8
Niederbrechen D 21 D10
Niederbreitbach D 185 C7
Niederbronn-les-Bains F 27 C8
Niederfinow D 84 E5
Niederfischbach D 185 C8
Niedergörsdorf D 80 C3
Niederkassel D 21 C8
Niederkirchen D 21 E9
Niederkrüchten D 20 B6
Niederndorf A 72 A5
Niederneisen D 21 D10
Niedernhall D 74 D6
Niedernhausen D 21 D10
Niederoderwitz D 81 E7
Nieder-Olm D 185 E9
Nieder-Rodenbach D 21 D12
Niederrößla D 79 D9
Niedersachswerfen D 79 C8
Niederselters D 21 D10
Niederstetten D 74 D6
Niederurnen CH 27 F11
Niederviehbach D 75 E11
Niederwerrn D 75 B7
Niederwörresbach D 186 B3
Niederzissen D 21 D8
Niedrzwica Duża PL 141 H6
Niedźwiada PL 141 G7
Niedźwiadna PL 139 C13
Niefern-Öschelbronn D 27 C10
Niegosław PL 85 E9
Niegosławice PL 81 C9
Niegowa PL 143 E7
Niegripp D 79 B10
Nieheim D 17 E12
Niekerk NL 16 B6
Niekłań Wielki PL 141 H3
Niekursko PL 85 D10
Niel B 182 C4
Nielisz PL 144 B7
Niemberg D 79 C11
Niemce PL 141 H7
Niemcza PL 81 E11
Niemegk D 79 B12
Niemelä FIN 113 C20
Niemelä FIN 115 E5
Niemelänkylä FIN 119 F12
Niemenkylä FIN 122 E7
Niemenkylä FIN 126 C6
Niemenpää FIN 119 B11
Niemis S 119 B11
Niemisel S 118 B7
Niemisjärvi FIN 123 F16
Niemisjärvi FIN 124 E8
Niemiskylä FIN 123 C17
Niemodlin PL 142 E4
Niemysłów PL 142 C6
Nienadówka PL 144 C5
Nienburg (Saale) D 79 C10
Nienburg (Weser) D 17 C12
Niepars D 84 B3
Niepołomice PL 143 F9
Nieporjt PL 139 F11
Nierstein D 21 E10
Niesa FIN 117 D11
Niesi FIN 117 D15
Niesky D 81 D7
Nieświń PL 141 H2
Nieszawa PL 138 E6
Nietsak S 116 D4
Nietulisko Duże PL 143 E11
Nieul F 29 D8
Nieuw-Amsterdam NL 17 C7
Nieuw-Bergen NL 16 E6
Nieuwegein NL 16 D4
Nieuwe-Niedorp NL 16 C3
Nieuwe Pekela NL 17 B7
Nieuwerkerk NL 16 E2
Nieuwerkerk aan de IJssel NL 16 E3
Nieuwerkerken B 19 C11
Nieuwe-Tonge NL 16 E2
Nieuw-Heeten NL 16 D6
Nieuwkoop NL 16 D3
Nieuw-Loosdrecht NL 183 A6
Nieuw-Milligen NL 183 A7
Nieuw-Namen NL 182 C4
Nieuwolda NL 17 B7
Nieuwpoort B 18 B6
Nieuwveen NL 182 A5
Nieuw-Vennep NL 16 D3
Nieuw-Vossemeer NL 182 B4
Nieuw-Weerdinge NL 17 C7
Nievern D 185 D8
Niewjgłosz PL 141 G7
Niezabyszewo PL 85 B12
Nigrán E 38 D2
Nīgrande LV 134 D4
Nigrita GR 169 C10
Nigüelas E 53 C9
Niherne F 29 B9
Niinilahti FIN 123 E15
Niinimaa FIN 123 E10
Niinimäki FIN 125 F10
Niinisalo FIN 126 B8
Niinivaara FIN 125 D11
Niinivesi FIN 123 E16
Niirokumpu FIN 121 B11
Níjar E 55 F8
Nijemci HR 157 B11
Nijkerk NL 16 D4
Nijlen B 19 B10
Nijmegen NL 16 E5
Nijverdal NL 17 D6
Nikaia GR 169 E7
Nikaranperä FIN 123 E14
Nikel' RUS 114 E8
Niki GR 168 C5
Nikisiani GR 170 C6
Nikiti GR 169 D10
Nikkala S 119 C11
Nikkaluokta S 111 E17
Nikkaroinen FIN 127 C14
Nikkeby N 112 C6
Nikodin MK 169 B6
Nikokleia GR 169 C9
Nikolaevo BG 165 C10
Nikolaevo BG 166 D5
Nikola-Kozlevo BG 161 F10
Nikolovo BG 161 F8
Nikolsdorf A 73 C6
Nikopol BG 160 F5
Nikopoli GR 174 A2
Nīkrāce LV 134 C3
Nikšić MNE 163 D6
Nikyup BG 166 C5
Nilivaara FIN 117 C14
Nilivaara S 116 D7
Nilsiä FIN 125 D10
Nilvange F 20 F6
Nim DK 86 D5
Nîmes F 35 C7
Nimigea RO 152 C4
Nimis I 73 D7
Nimisenkangas FIN 125 C11
Nimisjärvi FIN 119 E17
Nimtofte DK 86 C7
Nin HR 67 D11
Nina EST 131 D14
Nindorf D 82 B6
Ninemile Bar GB 5 E9
Ninemilehouse IRL 9 D8
Ninove B 19 C9
Niort F 28 C5
Nirza LV 133 D3
Niš SRB 164 C4
Nisa P 44 E5
Nisbet GB 5 D11
Niscemi I 58 E5
Niška Banja SRB 164 C5
Niskankorpi FIN 123 C13
Niskanpera FIN 119 B15
Nisko PL 144 B5
Niskos FIN 123 F10
Nismes B 19 D10
Nispen NL 16 F2
Nisporeni MD 154 C2
Nissafors S 91 E14
Nissan-lez-Enserune F 34 D5
Nissilä FIN 123 C17
Nissinvaara FIN 121 B13
Nissoria I 58 D5
Nissumby DK 86 B2
Nissum Seminarieby DK 86 B2
Nistelrode NL 16 E5
Nistorești RO 153 F9
Nītaure LV 135 B10
Nitra SK 146 E6
Nitrianske Hrnčiarovce SK 146 E6
Nitrianske Pravno SK 147 D7
Nitrianske Rudno SK 146 D6
Nitrianske Sučany SK 146 D6
Nitry F 25 E10
Nitta S 91 D13
Nittedal N 95 B13
Nittel D 20 E6
Nittenau D 75 D11
Nittendorf D 75 D10
Nittorp S 91 D14
Niukkala FIN 129 B12
Nivå DK 87 D11
Niva FIN 121 F14
Nivala FIN 123 C13
Nivankylä FIN 117 E15
Nivanpää FIN 117 E11
Nivelles B 19 C9
Nivenskoye RUS 136 D2
Nivillac F 23 E7
Nivillers F 18 F5
Nivnice CZ 146 D5
Nivolas-Vermelle F 31 D7
Nivyanin BG 165 C8
Niwiska PL 143 F12
Nižbor CZ 76 C6
Nižná SK 147 C9
Nižná Slaná SK 145 F1
Nižný Hrabovec SK 145 F4
Nižný Hrušov SK 145 F4
Nižný Šipov SK 145 F4
Nizza di Sicilia I 59 D7
Nizza Monferrato I 37 B8
Njavve S 109 C15
Njegovuđa MNE 163 C7
Një Maj AL 168 C3
Njetjavare S 116 E4
Njivice HR 67 B10
Njurundabommen S 103 B13
Njutånger S 103 C13
No DK 86 C2
Noaillan F 32 B5
Noailles F 18 F5
Noain E 32 E2
Noale I 66 A5
Noalejo E 53 A9
Noasca I 31 E11
Nöbbele S 89 B8
Nobber IRL 7 E9
Nobitz D 79 E11
Noblejas E 46 E6
Noćaj SRB 158 D4
Nocé F 24 D4
Nocera Inferiore I 60 B3
Nocera Terinese I 59 A9
Nocera Umbra I 62 A3
Noceto I 66 C1
Noci I 61 B8
Nociglia I 61 C10
Nociūnai LT 135 F8
Nocrich RO 152 F4
Nødebo DK 87 D10
Nodeland N 90 C2
Nödinge S 91 D11
Nodland N 94 F4
Nods F 26 F5
Noé F 33 D8
Noepoli I 61 C6
Noer D 83 B8
Nœux-les-Mines F 18 D6
Noez E 46 E4
Nofuentes E 40 C5
Nogales E 51 B6
Nogara I 66 B3
Nogaro F 32 C5
Nogent F 26 D3
Nogent-le-Bernard F 24 D3
Nogent-le-Roi F 24 C6
Nogent-le-Rotrou F 24 D4
Nogent-sur-Aube F 25 D11
Nogent-sur-Oise F 18 F5
Nogent-sur-Seine F 25 D10
Nogent-sur-Vernisson F 25 E8
Nogersund S 89 C7
Nógrád H 147 F8
Nógrádmegyer H 147 E9
Nógrádsáp H 147 F8
Nograles E 40 F6
Noguera de Albarracín E 47 D9
Noguères F 32 D4
Nogueruelas E 48 D3
Nohant-Vic F 29 B9
Nohfelden D 21 E8
Nohic F 33 C8
Noia E 38 C2
Noicattaro I 61 A7
Noidans-lès-Vesoul F 26 E5
Noilhan F 33 C7
Noirétable F 30 D4
Noirmoutier-en-l'Île F 28 A1
Noisseville F 26 B5
Noja E 40 B4
Nojorid RO 151 C8
Nokia FIN 127 C10
Nol S 91 D11
Nolay F 30 B6
Noli I 37 C8
Nolimo FIN 121 B11
Nolmyra S 99 B8
Nólsoy FO 2 A3
Nombela E 46 D4
Nomeland N 90 A2
Nomenj SLO 73 D9
Nomeny F 26 C5
Nomexy F 26 D5
Nomia GR 178 B5
Nonancourt F 24 C5
Nonantola I 66 C3
Nonaspe E 42 E4
None I 37 B7
Nonnenweier D 186 E4
Nonnweiler D 21 E7
Nontron F 29 D7
Nonza F 37 F10
Nõo EST 131 E13
Noordwijk aan Zee NL 182 A4
Noordwijk-Binnen NL 16 D2
Noordwijkerhout NL 16 D3
Noordwolde NL 16 C6
Noormarkku FIN 126 B6
Nootdorp NL 182 A4
Nopankylä FIN 122 E8
Noppikoski S 102 D8
Nor S 103 C11
Nora S 97 C13
Nora S 103 A12
Nørager DK 86 B5
Noragugume I 64 C2
Norberg S 97 B14
Norcia I 62 B4
Nordagutu N 95 D10
Nordanå S 103 A13
Nordanås S 107 C14
Nordanås S 109 E16
Nordanås S 109 F11
Nordanede S 103 A11
Nordankäl S 107 D10
Nordannälden S 105 E16
Nordano S 98 B6
Nordborg DK 86 E5
Nordbotn N 112 D9
Nordby DK 86 D7
Nordby DK 86 E2
Norddeich D 17 A8
Norðdepil FO 2 A3
Norddorf D 82 A4
Norddyrøy N 104 D5
Nordeide N 100 D3
Nordeidet N 112 D4
Norden D 17 A8
Nordendorf D 75 E8
Nordenham D 17 B10
Nordenskov DK 86 D3
Norderåsen S 106 E7
Norderney D 17 A8
Norderö S 105 E16
Norderstedt D 83 C8
Nordfjord N 114 B8
Nordfjordbotn N 111 B17
Nordfjordeid N 100 C3
Nordfold N 110 E9
Nordhalben D 75 B10
Nordhallen S 105 E13
Nordhastedt D 82 B6
Nordhausen D 79 D8
Nordheim D 27 B11
Nordholz D 17 A11
Nordhorn D 17 D8
Nordhuglo N 94 C3
Nordingrå S 103 A15
Nordkil N 111 D10
Nordkirchen D 17 E9
Nordkisa N 95 B14
Nordkjosbotn N 111 B18
Nordland N 110 E4
Nord-Leirvåg N 114 D7
Nordlenangen N 111 A19
Nordli N 105 C15
Nördlingen D 75 E7
Nordmaling S 107 D17
Nordmannvik N 112 D5
Nordmela N 111 B10
Nordnesøy N 108 C4
Nordøyvågen N 108 D4
Norðragøta FO 2 A3
Nordråk N 101 E12
Nordsand N 111 C12
Nordsinni N 101 E11
Nordsjö S 103 C12
Nordsjö S 107 D10
Nordsjona N 108 D5
Norðskáli FO 2 A2
Nordskjør N 104 C8
Nordskot N 110 E8
Nordstemmen D 78 B6
Nord-Værnes N 108 C5
Nordvågen N 113 B17
Nordvik N 108 B9
Nordvik S 103 A14
Nordvika N 104 E4
Nordwalde D 17 D8
Nore S 103 C11
Noreikiškės LT 137 D8
Norem N 105 D10
Noreña E 39 B8
Noresund N 95 B11
Norg NL 17 B6
Norheimsund N 94 B4
Norinkylä FIN 122 E8
Norje S 88 C7
Norma I 62 D3
Norn S 97 B14
Nornäs S 102 D5
Noroy-le-Bourg F 26 E5
Norppa FIN 123 C11
Norra Åsum S 88 D6
Norra Blommaberg S 103 C9
Norra Bredåker S 118 C6
Norra bro S 92 A6
Norra Fjällnäs S 109 E10
Norra Holmnäs S 118 C3
Norråker S 106 C9
Norra Klagshamn S 87 D11
Norra Malånäs S 107 A15
Norra Prästholm S 118 C8
Norra Rödupp S 118 B9
Norra Skärvången S 105 D16
Norra Vallgrund FIN 122 D6
Norra Vi S 92 D6
Norrbäck S 103 B12
Norrbäck S 107 B13
Norrbo S 103 C12
Norrboda S 99 B10
Norrboda S 103 D9
Norrby FIN 122 C9
Norrby S 99 B11
Norrbyberg S 107 B14
Norrbyn S 122 C3
Norrbyskär S 122 C3
Nørre Aaby DK 86 E5
Nørre Alslev DK 84 A1
Nørreballe DK 83 A10
Nørre Bork DK 86 D2
Nørre Broby DK 86 E6
Nørre Felding DK 86 C3
Nørre Halne DK 86 A5
Nørre Kongerslev DK 86 B6
Nørre Nebel DK 86 D2
Norrent-Fontes F 18 C5
Nørre Snede DK 86 D4
Nørresundby DK 86 A5
Nørre Vejrup DK 86 D3
Nørre Vorupør DK 86 B2
Norrfällsviken S 107 F15
Norrfjärden S 103 B13
Norrfjärden S 118 D7
Norrfjärden S 122 C5
Norrfläke S 107 D14
Norrfors S 107 C14
Norrfors S 107 D15
Norrgårdssälen S 102 E6
Norr-Greningen S 106 E8
Norrhult-Klavreström S 89 A8
Norrköping S 93 B8
Norrlångträsk S 118 D5
Norr-Moflo S 107 E11
Norrnäs FIN 122 E6
Norrsjön S 106 B8
Norrskedika S 99 B10
Norrstig S 103 A14
Norrstrand S 109 E16
Norrsundet S 103 E13
Norrtälje S 99 C11
Norrtjärn S 103 E12
Norrvåge S 107 E15
Norrvik S 107 B13
Nors DK 86 A3
Norsholm S 92 B7
Norsjö S 107 B17
Nörten-Hardenberg D 78 C6
Northallerton GB 11 C9
Northam GB 12 C6
Northampton GB 15 C7
North Berwick GB 5 C11
Northborough GB 11 F11
North Cave GB 11 D10
North Dell GB 2 J4
North Duffield GB 11 D10
Northeim D 79 C6
North Ferriby GB 11 D10
North Grimston GB 11 C10
North Hykeham GB 11 E10
North Leigh GB 13 B12
North Shields GB 5 E14
North Somercotes GB 11 E12
North Sunderland GB 5 D13
North Tidworth GB 13 C11
Northton GB 2 K2
North Walsham GB 15 B11
Northwich GB 10 E6
Nortmoor D 17 B9
Norton GB 11 C10
Norton GB 15 C10
Norton Fitzwarren GB 13 C8
Nortorf D 83 B7
Nortrup D 17 C9
Nort-sur-Erdre F 23 F8
Norup DK 86 B6
Norvasalmi FIN 117 E15
Norwich GB 15 B11
Norwick GB 3 D15
Noșlac RO 152 E3
Nøss N 111 B10
Nossa Senhora da Boa Fé P 50 B3
Nossa Senhora da Graça de Póvoa e Meadas P 44 E5
Nossa Senhora da Graça do Divor P 50 B4
Nossa Senhora da Graça dos Degolados P 45 F6
Nossa Senhora das Neves P 50 C4
Nossa Senhora de Machede P 50 B4
Nossebro S 91 C12
Nossen D 80 D4
Nossendorf D 84 C3
Nossentiner Hütte D 83 C12
Noszlop H 149 B8
Nosztaj H 145 H1
Notaresco I 62 B5
Notia GR 169 B7
Nőtincs H 147 F8
Nötö FIN 126 F6
Noto I 59 F7
Notodden N 95 C10
Notre-Dame-de-Bellecombe F 31 D10
Notre-Dame-de-Gravenchon F 18 F2
Notre-Dame-de-Monts F 28 B1
Notre-Dame-d'Oé F 24 F4
Nötsch im Gailtal A 73 C8
Nottensdorf D 82 D7
Nottingham GB 11 F9
Nottuln D 17 E8
Notviken S 118 C8
Nouan-le-Fuzelier F 24 E7
Nouans-les-Fontaines F 24 F5
Nouart F 19 F11
Nõuni EST 131 E13
Nousiainen FIN 126 D7
Nousionmäki FIN 125 D10
Nousu FIN 115 D5
Nouvion F 18 D4
Nouzilly F 24 E4
Nouzonville F 19 E10
Nõva EST 130 C7
Nova H 149 C7
Nová Baňa SK 147 E7
Nova Breznica MK 164 F3
Nova Bukovica HR 149 E9
Nová Bystřice CZ 77 D8
Nová Cerekev CZ 77 D8
Novachene BG 165 B10
Novachene BG 165 D8
Novaci MK 168 B5
Novaci RO 160 C3
Nova Crnja SRB 158 B6
Nová Dedina SK 147 E7
Novadnieki LV 134 C4
Nová Dubnica SK 146 D6
Novafeltria I 66 E5
Nova Gorica SLO 73 E8
Nova Gradiška HR 157 B7
Nova Ivanivka UA 154 F4
Novaj H 145 H1
Novajidrány H 145 G3
Nova Kamena BG 161 F10
Nova Kasaba BIH 157 D11
Novaki HR 148 E5
Novakovo BG 166 F4
Nováky SK 147 D7
Novales E 40 B3
Novales E 41 E11
Nova Levante I 72 D4
Novalja HR 67 C10
Novallas E 41 E8
Nová Ľubovňa SK 145 E2
Nova Makhala BG 165 F9
Nova Nadezhda BG 166 F5
Nova Nekrasivka UA 155 C3
Nová Paka CZ 77 B9
Nova Pazova SRB 158 D5
Nova Pokrovka UA 155 B4
Novara I 68 C6
Novara di Sicilia I 59 C7
Nová Role CZ 75 B12
Nova Sela HR 157 F8
Nova Siri I 61 C7
Nova Siri Scalo I 61 C7
Novate Mezzola I 69 A7
Nova Topola BIH 157 B7
Nova Varoš SRB 163 C8
Nova Vas SLO 73 E9
Nová Včelnice CZ 77 D8
Nová Ves CZ 77 B8
Nová Ves nad Žitavou SK 146 E6
Nova Zagora BG 166 E6
Nové Hrady CZ 77 E7
Novelda E 56 E3
Novellara I 66 C2
Nové Město nad Metují CZ 77 B10
Nové Mesto nad Váhom SK 146 D5
Nové Město na Moravě CZ 77 C10
Nové Město pod Smrkem CZ 81 E8
Nove Misto UA 145 D6
Noventa di Piave I 72 E6
Noventa Vicentina I 66 B4
Novés E 46 D4
Noves F 35 C8
Nové Veselí CZ 77 C9
Nové Zámky SK 146 F6
Novgorodka RUS 133 B5
Novgrad BG 161 F7
Novi Banovci SRB 158 D5
Novi Bečej SRB 158 B5
Novi di Modena I 66 C2
Novi Dojran MK 169 B8
Noviergas E 41 E7
Novi Grad BIH 157 B9
Novigrad HR 67 B8
Novigrad HR 156 D4
Novigrad Podravski HR 149 D7
Novi Iskŭr BG 165 D7
Novi Karlovci SRB 158 C5
Novi Khan BG 165 D8
Novi Kneževac SRB 150 E5
Novi Kozarci SRB 150 F6
Novi Ligure I 37 B9
Novillars F 26 F5
Noville B 182 D5
Novi Marof HR 149 D6
Novion-Porcien F 19 E9
Novi Pazar BG 167 C8
Novi Pazar SRB 163 C10
Novi Sad SRB 158 C4
Novi Šeher BIH 157 C9
Novi Slankamen SRB 158 C5
Novi Travnik BIH 157 D8
Novi Vinodolski HR 67 B10
Novo Beograd SRB 158 D5
Novoborysivka UA 154 C5
Novoćići BIH 157 F9
Novo Delchevo BG 169 B9
Novokhovansk RUS 133 E7
Novo Korito SRB 159 F9
Novo Mesto SLO 73 E11
Novo Miloševo SRB 158 B5
Novomoskovskiy RUS 139 A9
Novomykolayivka UA 155 B5
Novo Orahovo SRB 150 F4
Novo Oryakhovo BG 167 D9
Novopetrivka UA 154 C5
Novorzhev RUS 133 B6
Novosamarka UA 154 B5
Novosedly CZ 77 E11
Novoselë AL 163 F10
Novoselë AL 168 C1
Novoselec HR 149 E7
Novoselets BG 166 E6
Novoselija BIH 157 C7
Novoselivka UA 154 B5
Novoselivka UA 154 D5
Novo Selo BG 159 E10
Novo Selo BG 161 F8
Novo Selo BG 165 E6
Novo Selo BG 166 E6
Novo Selo BIH 157 B8
Novo Selo BIH 157 B9
Novo Selo MK 169 B8
Novo Selo SRB 159 F6
Novoselovo RUS 139 B9
Novoseltsi BG 167 E8
Novosel'ye RUS 132 E4
Novoselytsya UA 153 A8
Novoselytsya UA 154 A6
Novosil's'ke UA 155 C3
Novostroyevo RUS 136 E4
Novot SK 147 C8
Novo Virje HR 149 D8
Novovolyns'k UA 144 B9
Novoyavorivs'ke UA 144 D8
Novska HR 149 F7
Nový Bor CZ 81 E7
Nový Bydžov CZ 77 B9
Novy-Chevrières F 19 E9
Novy Dvor BY 137 F10
Nový Hrozenkov CZ 146 C6
Nový Jičín CZ 146 B5
Nový Knín CZ 76 C6
Nový Malín CZ 77 C12
Nový Pahost BY 133 F2
Nový Rychnov CZ 77 D8
Novyya Kruki BY 133 E3
Novyy Izborsk RUS 132 F2
Novyy Rozdil UA 145 E9
Nový Šivot SK 146 E4
Nowa Brzeźnica PL 143 D7
Nowa Cerekwia PL 142 F4
Nowa Chodorówka PL 140 C8
Nowa Dęba PL 143 F12
Nowa Karczma PL 138 B5
Nowa Ruda PL 81 E11
Nowa Sarzyna PL 144 C5
Nowa Słupia PL 143 E11
Nowa Sól PL 81 C9
Nowa Sucha PL 141 F2
Nowa Wieś Ełcka PL 140 C6
Nowa Wieś Lęborskie PL 85 A13
Nowa Wieś Wielka PL 138 E5
Nowa Wola PL 140 D9
Nowa Wola Gołębiowska PL 141 H4
Nowe PL 138 C6
Nowe Brusno PL 144 C7
Nowe Brzesko PL 143 F9
Nowe Czarnowo PL 84 D6
Nowe Miasteczko PL 81 C9
Nowe Miasto PL 139 E10
Nowe Miasto Lubawskie PL 139 D8
Nowe Miasto nad Pilicą PL 141 G3
Nowe Miasto nad Wartą PL 81 B12
Nowe Ostrowy PL 143 B7
Nowe Piekuty PL 141 E7
Nowe Skalmierzyce PL 142 C4
Nowe Warpno PL 84 C6
Nowinka PL 136 F6
Nowogard PL 85 C8
Nowogród PL 139 D12
Nowogród Bobrzański PL 81 C8
Nowogródek Pomorski PL 85 E8
Nowogrodziec PL 81 D8
Nowosady PL 141 E9
Nowosielce PL 145 D5
Nowosolna PL 143 C8
Nowotaniec PL 145 D5
Nowowola PL 140 D8
Nowy Bartków PL 141 F7
Nowy Duninów PL 139 E7
Nowy Dwór PL 138 D4
Nowy Dwór PL 140 C9
Nowy Dwór Gdański PL 138 B7
Nowy Dwór Mazowiecki PL 139 F10
Nowy Kawęczyn PL 141 G2
Nowy Korczyn PL 143 F10
Nowy Lubliniec PL 144 C7
Nowy Sącz PL 145 D2
Nowy Staw PL 138 B7
Nowy Targ PL 147 C10
Nowy Tomyśl PL 81 B10
Nowy Wiśnicz PL 144 D1
Nowy Żmigród PL 145 D4
Noyal-Muzillac F 22 E7
Noyalo F 22 E6
Noyal-Pontivy F 22 D6
Noyant F 23 E12
Noyarey F 31 E8

Psača MK 164 E5
Psachna GR 175 B8
Psara GR 177 B6
Psarades GR 168 C5
Psari GR 174 E4
Psari GR 175 D6
Psathopyrgos GR 174 C4
Psinthos GR 181 D8
Pskov RUS 132 F3
Psychiko GR 169 B10
Psychro GR 178 E9
Pszczew PL 81 B9
Pszczółki PL 138 B6
Pszczonów PL 141 G1
Pszczyna PL 147 B7
Pteleos GR 175 A6
Pteri GR 174 C5
Ptolemaïda GR 169 C6
Ptuj SLO 148 D5
Publier F 31 C10
Puchberg am Schneeberg A 146 F1
Pucheni RO 160 C6
Puchenii Mari RO 161 D8
Puchheim D 75 F9
Púchov SK 146 C6
Pucioasa RO 161 C6
Pučišće HR 157 F6
Puck PL 138 A5
Puckaun IRL 8 C6
Puçol E 48 E4
Pudasjärven kirkko FIN 119 D17
Pudasjärvi FIN 119 D17
Puddletown GB 13 D10
Puderbach D 185 C8
Pudinava LV 133 C3
Pudsey GB 11 D8
Puebla de Albortón E 41 F10
Puebla de Alcocer E 51 B9
Puebla de Alfindén E 41 E10
Puebla de Almenara E 47 E7
Puebla de Beleña E 47 C6
Puebla de Don Fadrique E 55 D8
Puebla de Don Rodrigo E 46 F3
Puebla de Guzmán E 51 D5
Puebla de la Calzada E 51 B6
Puebla de la Reina E 51 B7
Puebla de Lillo E 39 B9
Puebla del Maestre E 51 C7
Puebla del Príncipe E 55 B7
Puebla del Prior E 51 B7
Puebla del Salvador E 47 E9
Puebla de Obando E 45 F7
Puebla de Sanabria E 39 D6
Puebla de Sancho Pérez E 51 C7
Puebla de San Miguel E 47 D10
Puebla de Yeltes E 45 C8
Puente de Domingo Flórez E 39 D6
Puente de Génave E 55 C7
Puente del Congosto E 45 D9
Puente de Montañana E 42 C5
Puente de San Miguel E 40 B3
Puente-Genil E 53 B7
Puente la Reina E 32 E2
Puentenansa E 40 B3
Puente Viesgo E 40 B4
Puerto de Béjar E 45 D9
Puerto de Mazarrón E 56 F2
Puerto de San Vicente E 45 E10
Puerto Lápice E 46 F6
Puertollano E 54 B4
Puerto Lumbreras E 55 D9
Puertomingalvo E 48 D4
Puerto Real E 52 C4
Puerto Seguro E 45 C7
Puerto Serrano E 51 F8
Pueyo E 32 E2
Pueyo de Santa Cruz E 42 D4
Pufești RO 153 E10
Puget-Théniers F 36 D5
Puget-Ville F 36 E4
Pugnochiuso I 63 D10
Puhja EST 131 E12
Puhoi MD 154 D4
Puhos FIN 121 D10
Puhos FIN 125 F13
Puhovac BIH 157 D9
Pui RO 159 B11
Puiatu EST 131 E10
Puiești RO 153 E11
Puiești RO 161 C10
Puig E 48 E4
Puigcerdà E 33 F9
Puigpunyent E 49 E10
Puig-reig E 43 D7
Puikkola FIN 115 E3
Puikule LV 131 F9
Puimoisson F 36 D4
Puiseaux F 25 D7
Puisieux F 18 D6
Puisseguin F 28 F5
Puisserguier F 34 D5
Puivert F 33 E10
Pujaut F 35 B8
Pujols F 28 F5
Pujols F 33 B7
Puka EST 131 E12
Pukanec SK 147 E7
Pukaro FIN 127 D15
Pukavik S 88 C7
Pukë AL 163 E8
Pukiš BIH 157 C10
Pukkila FIN 127 D14
Pula HR 67 C8
Pula I 64 E3
Puławy PL 141 H5
Pulborough GB 15 F7
Pulfero I 73 D7
Pulgar E 46 E4
Pulheim D 21 B7
Pulju FIN 117 B13
Pulkau A 77 E9
Pulkkaviita FIN 115 D5
Pulkkila FIN 119 F15
Pulkkinen FIN 123 D11
Pulkonkoski FIN 124 D8
Pulpí E 55 E9
Pulsa FIN 128 D8
Pulsano I 61 C8
Pulsen D 80 D4
Pulskala FIN 115 D4
Pulsnitz D 80 D6
Pulsujärvi S 116 B6
Pułtusk PL 139 E11
Pulversheim F 27 E7
Pumpėnai LT 135 E8
Pumpuri LV 134 C4
Pumsaint GB 13 A7
Pūņas LV 134 B4
Punat HR 67 B10
Pundsvik N 111 D12
Punduri LV 133 D3
Pungești RO 153 D10
Punghina RO 159 E10
Punia LT 137 D9
Punkaharju FIN 129 B11
Punkalaidun FIN 127 C9
Punkka FIN 128 C7
Punta Ala I 65 B3
Punta Križa HR 67 C9
Punta Sabbioni I 66 B5
Punta Umbría E 51 E6
Puokio FIN 120 E9
Puolakkovaara FIN 115 D1
Puolanka FIN 121 E10
Puolivali FIN 124 D9
Puoltikasvaara S 116 D6
Puottaure S 118 B4
Pūpoli LV 133 D2
Purаći BIH 157 C8
Puračić BIH 157 C10
Purani RO 161 F6
Puras FIN 121 E14
Purbach am Neusiedler See A 77 G11
Purcari MD 154 D5
Purchena E 55 E8
Pūre LV 134 B5
Purgstall an der Erlauf A 77 F8
Purila EST 131 C9
Purkersdorf A 77 F10
Purkijaur S 109 C18
Pürksi EST 130 C7
Purley GB 15 E8
Purmerend NL 16 C3
Purmo FIN 123 C9
Purmojärvi FIN 123 D10
Purmsāti LV 134 D3
Purnu S 116 E6
Purnumukka FIN 115 B2
Purnuvaara FIN 121 C12
Purnuvaara S 116 D6
Purola FIN 128 E6
Purontaka FIN 123 C12
Purujärvi FIN 129 B12
Purujosa E 41 E8
Purullena E 55 E6
Pŭrvenets BG 165 E10
Purviniškė LT 137 D7
Pŭrvomay BG 166 E4
Pŭrvomay BG 169 B9
Puša LV 133 D2
Pušalotas LT 135 E8
Puschendorf D 75 C8
Pushkinskiye Gory RUS 133 B5
Pušmucova LV 133 C3
Püspökladány H 151 C7
Püssi EST 131 C14
Pusterwald A 73 B9
Pusté Úľany SK 146 E5
Pustków PL 143 F11
Pustomyty UA 144 D8
Pustoshka RUS 133 D6
Püstrovo BG 166 E4
Pusula FIN 127 E10
Puszcza Mariańska PL 141 G2
Puszczykowo PL 81 B11
Pusztaföldvár H 150 D6
Pusztakovácsi H 149 C9
Pusztamérges H 150 E4
Pusztamonostor H 150 B4
Pusztaszabolcs H 149 B11
Pusztaszer H 150 D4
Pusztavacs H 150 C4
Pusztavám H 149 B10
Putaja FIN 126 C8
Putanges-Pont-Écrepin F 23 C11
Putbus D 84 B4
Putifigari I 64 B1
Putignano I 61 B8
Putikko FIN 129 B11
Putinci SRB 158 C4
Putineiu RO 160 F5
Putineiu RO 161 F7
Putkivaara FIN 119 B17
Putlitz D 83 D12
Putna RO 153 B7
Putnok H 145 G1
Putte B 19 B10
Putte NL 16 F2
Puttelange-aux-Lacs F 27 B6
Putten NL 16 D5
Puttgarden D 83 A10
Püttlingen D 21 F7
Putula FIN 127 C13
Putyla UA 152 B6
Putzar D 84 C5
Putzkau D 80 D6
Puukari FIN 125 C11
Puukkokumpu FIN 119 C14
Puumala FIN 129 B9
Puurmani EST 131 D12
Puurs B 19 B9
Puurtila FIN 125 F9
Puutossalmi FIN 124 E9
Puutturinjärvi FIN 119 E17
Puybrun F 29 F9
Puycasquier F 33 C7
Puygouzon F 33 C10
Puylaroque F 33 B9
Puylaurens F 33 C10
Puy-l'Évêque F 33 A8
Puymirol F 33 B7
Puymoyen F 29 D6
Puyôo F 32 C4
Pwllheli GB 10 F3
Pyaozerskiy RUS 121 C17
Pyatidorozhnoye RUS 139 B9
Pyatirech'ye RUS 129 D14
Pyelishcha BY 141 F9
Pyershamayski BY 137 F11
Pyhäjärvi FIN 113 F16
Pyhäjärvi FIN 115 D2
Pyhäjoki FIN 119 F12
Pyhäjoki FIN 126 C7
Pyhäkylä FIN 121 D12
Pyhältö FIN 128 D7
Pyhämaa FIN 126 D5
Pyhänkoski FIN 119 F12
Pyhäntä FIN 119 F16
Pyhäntä FIN 121 F11
Pyhäntaka FIN 127 C14
Pyhäranta FIN 126 D5
Pyhäsalmi FIN 123 C15
Pyhäselkä FIN 125 F13
Pyhe FIN 126 D6
Pyhra A 77 F9
Pyhtää FIN 128 E6
Pyle GB 13 B7
Pyles GR 181 E6
Pyli GR 169 F6
Pyli GR 175 C8
Pyli GR 177 F9
Pylkönmäki FIN 123 E13
Pylos GR 174 F4
Pylypets' UA 145 F7
Pyntäinen FIN 126 B6
Pyrbaum D 75 D9
Pyrgetos GR 169 E8
Pyrgi GR 177 C6
Pyrgiotika GR 175 D6
Pyrgoi GR 169 C6
Pyrgoi GR 170 B6
Pyrgos GR 174 D3
Pyrgos GR 176 D5
Pyrgos GR 177 D8
Pyrgos GR 178 E9
Pyrgos Dirou GR 178 B3
Pyrrönperä FIN 123 B15
Pyrsogianni GR 168 D4
Pyrzyce PL 85 D7
Pyšely CZ 77 C7
Pyskowice PL 142 F6
Pyssyperä FIN 121 D10
Pystan' UA 152 A6
Pysznica PL 144 B5
Pytalovo RUS 133 B3
Pythagoreio GR 177 D8
Pythio GR 169 D7
Pythio GR 172 B6
Pyykkölänvaara FIN 121 E12
Pyykköskylä FIN 121 D13
Pyyli FIN 125 F11

Q

Qafzez AL 168 D4
Qelëz AL 163 E8
Qeparo AL 168 D2
Qerret AL 168 B2
Quadrazais P 45 D7
Quadri I 63 D6
Quakenbrück D 17 C9
Qualiano I 60 B2
Quaregnon B 182 E3
Quargnento I 37 B9
Quarona I 68 B5
Quarrata I 66 E2
Quarré-les-Tombes F 25 F10
Quarteira P 50 E3
Quartell E 48 E4
Quarten CH 27 F11
Quartu Sant'Elena I 64 E3
Quatre-Champs F 19 F10
Quatretonda E 56 D4
Quattro Castella I 66 C1
Quedlinburg D 79 C9
Queenborough GB 15 E10
Queensbury GB 11 D8
Queenstown IRL 8 E6
Queidersbach D 21 F9
Queige F 31 D9
Queiriga P 44 C5
Quel E 41 D7
Quelaines-St-Gault F 23 E10
Quellendorf D 79 C11
Queluz P 50 B1
Quemada E 40 E4
Quend F 18 D4
Quendorf D 17 D8
Queralbs E 33 F10
Quercianella I 66 F1
Querenhorst D 79 B8
Querfurt D 79 D10
Quérigut F 33 E10
Quern D 82 A7
Quernheim D 17 D10
Quero E 47 E6
Quero I 72 E4
Querrieu F 18 E5
Quesa E 48 F3
Quesada E 55 D6
Quesnoy-sur-Deûle F 18 C7
Quessoy F 22 D6
Questembert F 22 E7
Quettehou F 23 A9
Quettreville-sur-Sienne F 23 C9
Quevauvillers F 18 E5
Queyrac F 28 E4
Quézac F 29 F10
Quiaios P 44 D3
Quiberon F 22 F5
Quickborn D 83 C7
Quierschied D 21 F8
Quiévrain B 19 D8
Quiévrechain F 182 E3
Quiliano I 37 C8
Quillan F 33 E10
Quillebeuf-sur-Seine F 18 F2
Quimper F 22 E3
Quimperlé F 22 E4
Quin IRL 8 C5
Quincinetto I 68 B4
Quincy-Voisins F 25 C8
Quingey F 26 F4
Quinson F 36 D4
Quinssaines F 29 C11
Quintana de la Serena E 51 B8
Quintana del Castillo E 39 C7
Quintana del Pino E 40 C4
Quintana del Puente E 40 D3
Quintana de Rueda E 39 C9
Quintana-Martín Galíndez E 40 C5
Quintanapalla E 40 D4
Quintanar de la Orden E 47 E6
Quintanar de la Sierra E 40 E5
Quintanar del Rey E 47 F9
Quintana Redonda E 41 E6
Quintanilla de Onésimo E 40 E3
Quintenas F 30 E6
Quintin F 22 D6
Quinto CH 71 D7
Quinto E 41 F11
Quintos P 50 D4
Quinzano d'Oglio I 69 C9
Quiroga E 38 D5
Quiruelas de Vidriales E 39 D8
Quismondo E 46 D4
Quissac F 35 C7
Quittebeuf F 24 B4
Qukës AL 168 B3

R

Raab A 76 F5
Raabs an der Thaya A 77 E8
Raahe FIN 119 E12
Raajärvi FIN 115 E1
Rääkkylä FIN 125 F13
Raalte NL 16 D6
Raamsdonksveer NL 16 E3
Raanujärvi FIN 117 E13
Raappananmäki FIN 121 E10
Raasiku EST 131 C10
Raate FIN 121 E14
Raattama FIN 117 B12
Rab HR 67 C10
Rabac HR 67 B9
Rabaçal P 44 D4
Rabaçal P 45 C6
Rābade E 38 B4
Răbăgani RO 151 D9
Rábahidvég H 149 B7
Rábakecöl H 149 B8
Rabanales E 39 E7
Rábapaty H 149 B7
Rabastens F 33 C9
Rabastens-de-Bigorre F 33 D6
Rábatamási H 149 A8
Raba Wyżna PL 147 B9
Rabbalshede S 91 B9
Rabča SK 147 C8
Rabčice SK 147 B9
Rabe SRB 150 E5
Rabenstein an der Pielach A 77 F8
Raben Steinfeld D 83 C11
Råberg S 107 B13
Rąbino PL 85 C9
Rabisha BG 159 F10
Rabivere EST 131 C9
Rabka PL 147 B9
Räbke D 79 B8
Rabrovo BG 159 E10
Rabrovo SRB 159 D8
Rača SRB 159 E6
Rača SRB 164 D3
Răcăciuni RO 153 E9
Racale I 61 D10
Rácalmás H 149 B11
Racalmuto I 58 E4
Răcari RO 161 D7
Răcășdia RO 159 D8
Racconigi I 37 B7
Rače SLO 148 D5
Rachanie PL 144 B8
Rachecourt-sur-Marne F 26 C3
Raches GR 175 B6
Raches GR 177 D7
Răchiți RO 153 B9
Răchitoasa RO 153 E10
Răchitova RO 159 B10
Rachoni GR 171 C7
Raciąż PL 138 C4
Raciąż PL 139 E9
Racibórz PL 142 F5
Raciechowice PL 144 D1
Racimierz PL 85 C7
Račinovci HR 157 C10
Račišće HR 162 D3
Răciu RO 152 D4
Răciula MD 154 C2
Ráckeve H 149 B11
Racksätter S 97 D14
Racksund S 109 D14
Racławice PL 143 F9
Răcoasa RO 153 F9
Racoș RO 152 E6
Racova RO 153 D9
Racovița RO 159 B8
Racovița RO 160 B4
Racovița RO 161 C10
Racovițeni RO 161 C9
Raczki PL 136 F6
Rączki PL 139 D9
Råd H 150 B3
Råda S 91 C13
Råda S 97 B9
Råda S 97 B10
Rada de Haro E 47 E7
Radalj SRB 158 E3
Radanovo BG 166 C5
Rădășeni RO 153 C8
Rădăuți RO 153 B7
Rădăuți-Prut RO 153 A9
Raddestorf D 17 D11
Raddi in Chianti I 66 F3
Raddusa I 59 E6
Radë AL 168 B2
Rade N 95 D13
Radeberg D 80 D5
Radebeul D 80 D5
Radeburg D 80 D5
Radeče SLO 73 D11
Radejčin PL 85 D9
Radefeld D 79 D11
Radegast D 79 C11
Rådelsbråten S 102 E3
Radenci SLO 148 C6
Rădeni MD 153 C12
Radensleben D 84 E3
Radenthein A 73 C8
Rădești RO 152 E3
Radevormwald D 21 B8
Radibor D 80 D6
Radići BIH 157 C7
Radicofani I 62 B1
Radicondoli I 66 F3
Radilovo BG 165 E9
Radimĕř CZ 77 C10
Radiovce MK 163 F10
Radis D 79 C12
Radizelj SLO 148 D5
Radko Dimitrievo BG 167 C8
Radków PL 77 A10
Radlje ob Dravi SLO 73 C11
Radłów PL 142 E6
Radłów PL 143 F10
Radnejaur S 109 E15
Radnevo BG 166 E5
Radnice CZ 76 C5
Radoaia MD 153 B12
Radoč BIH 157 F8
Radohova BIH 157 D8
Rădoiești RO 160 E6
Radojevo SRB 150 F6
Radolfzell am Bodensee D 27 E10
Radom PL 141 H4
Rådom S 107 E11
Radomin PL 139 D7
Radomir BG 165 D6
Radomirești RO 160 E5
Radomirtsi BG 165 C9
Radomsko PL 143 D7
Radomyšl CZ 76 D5
Radomyśl nad Sanem PL 144 B4
Radomyśl Wielki PL 143 F11
Radonice CZ 76 B4
Radopole LV 133 C1
Radošina SK 146 D5
Radošovce SK 146 D4
Radoszyce PL 143 D9
Radoszyn PL 81 B8
Radovan RO 160 E3
Radovanu RO 161 E9
Radovets BG 167 F6
Radovići MNE 163 E6
Radoviš MK 169 A7
Radovljica SLO 73 D9
Radovnica SRB 164 E5
Radowo Małe PL 85 C8
Radožda MK 168 B4
Radslavice CZ 146 C5
Radstadt A 73 B7
Radstock GB 13 C10
Răducăneni RO 153 D11
Raduč HR 156 D5
Raduil BG 165 E8
Radujevac SRB 159 E10
Radun' BY 137 E10
Radvanice CZ 81 E10
Radvaň nad Laborcom SK 145 E4
Radviliškis LT 134 E7
Radwanice PL 81 C9
Radymno PL 144 D6
Radzanów PL 139 E9
Radzanów PL 141 G3
Radzanowo PL 139 E8
Radzice Duże PL 141 H2
Radzicz PL 85 D12
Radzieje PL 136 E4
Radziejów PL 138 E6
Radziejowice PL 141 F3
Radziemice PL 143 F9
Radzików PL 81 B7
Radziłów PL 140 D6
Radzymin PL 139 F11
Radzyń Chełmiński PL 138 D6
Radzyń Podlaski PL 141 G7
Ræhr DK 86 A3
Rækker Mølle DK 86 C3
Raeren B 20 C6
Raesfeld D 17 E7
Rafelbunyol E 48 E4
Raffadali I 58 E4
Rafford GB 3 K9
Rafina GR 175 C9
Råforsen S 97 B10
Răfov RO 161 D8
Rafsbotn N 113 C12
Raften N 110 D9
Raftsjöhöjden S 106 D8
Ragaciems LV 134 B6
Rågama E 45 C10
Ragana LV 135 B9
Rageliai LT 135 E11
Rägelin D 83 D13
Raglan GB 13 B9
Råglanda S 91 A13
Ragösen D 79 B12
Raguhn D 79 C11
Ragunda S 107 E10
Ragunda S 107 E10
Ragusa I 59 F6
Raguva LT 135 E9
Rahden D 17 D11
Rahkio FIN 127 D8
Rahkonen FIN 123 C12
Rahman RO 155 D2
Råholt N 95 B14
Rahovec RKS 163 E10
Rahumäe EST 132 E1
Raiano I 62 C5
Raikuu FIN 125 F12
Räimä FIN 124 D9
Rain D 75 E8
Rain D 75 E11
Rainbach im Mühlkreis A 77 E6
Raippo FIN 129 D9
Räisälä FIN 115 E3
Raisdorf D 83 B8
Raisio FIN 126 E7
Raiskio FIN 119 C16
Raiskio FIN 125 B12
Raismes F 19 D7
Raistakka FIN 121 B11
Rait GB 5 C10
Raitajärvi S 119 B10
Raja EST 131 D13
Raja-Jooseppi FIN 115 B4
Rajala FIN 117 C16
Rajamäki FIN 127 D12
Rajastrand S 106 B8
Rajcza PL 147 B8
Rájec CZ 77 D11
Rajec SK 147 C7
Rajecká Lesná SK 147 C7
Rajgród PL 140 C7
Rajhrad CZ 77 D11
Rajince SRB 164 E4
Rajka H 146 E4
Raka EST 131 C9
Raka SLO 148 E4
Rakamaz H 145 G3
Rakek SLO 73 E9
Rakevo BG 165 C7
Rakhiv UA 152 A4
Rakh'ya RUS 129 E14
Rakita BG 165 C9
Rakita BG 165 D6
Rakitna SLO 73 E9
Rakitovec SLO 67 B8
Rakitovo BG 165 F9
Rakke EST 131 D12
Rakkeby DK 90 E6
Rakkestad N 95 D14
Raklitsa BG 167 D7
Rákóczifalva H 150 C5
Rákócziújfalu H 150 C5
Rakoniewice PL 81 B10
Rakoshyn UA 145 G6
Rakova Bara SRB 159 D8
Rakovica HR 156 C4
Rakovinë RKS 163 E10
Rakovitsa BG 159 F9
Rakovník CZ 76 B5
Rakovo BG 165 E6
Rakovski BG 165 E10
Rakow D 84 B4
Raków PL 143 E11
Rakvere EST 131 C12
Ralingen D 21 E7
Ralja SRB 158 D6
Rälla S 89 B11
Ram SRB 159 D7
Ramacca I 59 E6
Rämälä FIN 123 E12
Ramales de la Victoria E 40 B5
Ramalhal P 44 F2
Ramatuelle F 36 E5
Ramberg N 110 D5
Rambervillers F 26 D6
Rambin D 84 B4
Rambouillet F 24 C6
Rambrouch L 19 E12
Rambucourt F 26 C4
Ramelton IRL 7 B7
Râmeț RO 152 E3
Ramillies B 182 D5
Ramingstein A 73 B8
Ramirás E 38 D4
Ramløse DK 87 C10
Rämma S 102 D6
Ramme DK 86 C2
Rammelsbach D 186 B3
Rammingen D 75 E7
Râmna RO 159 C8
Ramnäs S 98 C6
Ramnes N 95 D12
Râmnicelu RO 161 C10
Râmnicelu RO 161 C11
Râmnicu Sărat RO 161 C10
Râmnicu Vâlcea RO 160 C4
Ramonville-St-Agne F 33 C8
Ramosch CH 71 D10
Rämpsänkylä FIN 121 F13
Rampside GB 10 C5
Ramsä N 111 B11
Ramsau im Zillertal A 72 B4
Ramsberg S 97 C13
Ramsbottom GB 11 D7
Ramsele S 107 C17
Ramsele S 107 D10
Ramsen CH 27 E10
Ramsey GB 15 C8
Ramsey GBM 10 C3
Ramsey St Mary's GB 15 C8
Ramsgate GB 15 E11
Ramsi EST 131 E11
Ramsing DK 86 B3
Ramsjö S 103 B10
Ramsloh (Saterland) D 17 B9
Ramstadlandet N 105 B10
Ramstein D 21 F9
Ramsund N 111 D12
Ramučiai LT 134 F3
Ramundberget S 102 A3
Ramvik S 103 A14
Ramygala LT 135 E8
Råna N 111 D13
Rånäs S 99 C10
Rånäs S 102 C5
Rånåsfoss N 95 B14
Rance B 19 D9
Randaberg N 94 E3
Randalstown GB 4 F4
Randan F 30 C3
Randaträsk S 118 B6
Randazzo I 59 D6
Randdalen S 102 B5
Randegg A 77 F7
Randen N 101 C9
Randen N 101 D8
Randers DK 86 C6
Randersacker D 187 B8
Randijaur S 109 C17
Randonnai F 24 C4
Randsjö S 102 B6
Randsverk N 101 C10
Råne N 111 E11
Råneå S 118 C8
Rânes F 23 C11
Rångedala S 91 D13
Rangendingen D 187 E6
Rangersdorf A 73 C6
Rangsby FIN 122 E6
Rangsdorf D 80 B4
Ranhados P 44 C5
Ranilović SRB 158 E6
Ranis D 79 E10
Ranizów PL 144 C4
Ranka LV 135 B12
Rankì LV 134 C3
Rankinen FIN 119 F14
Rankweil A 71 C9
Ranna EST 131 D14
Rannankylä FIN 123 C15
Rannankylä FIN 123 C16
Rannapungerja EST 131 D14
Rännavåg S 91 D13
Ränneslöv S 87 C12
Rännö S 103 B12
Rannsundet S 102 B5
Rannu EST 131 E12
Ranovac SRB 159 E7
Ransbach-Baumbach D 21 D9
Ransberg S 92 C4
Ransby S 102 E4
Ranskill GB 11 E9
Ranst B 182 C5
Ransta S 98 C7
Ranta FIN 113 F19
Rantajärvi S 117 E11
Rantakangas FIN 123 E11
Rantasalmen asema FIN 125 F10
Rantasalmi FIN 125 F10
Ranta-Töysä FIN 123 E11
Ranten A 73 B9
Rantsila FIN 119 E15
Ranttila FIN 113 E16
Rantum D 82 A4
Rantzausminde DK 86 E7
Ranua FIN 119 C17
Ranum DK 86 B4
Rånvassbotn N 111 D13
Ranxë AL 163 F8
Raon-l'Étape F 27 D6
Raossi I 69 B11
Rapakkojoki FIN 123 C17
Rapallo I 37 C10
Raphoe IRL 4 F1
Rapice PL 81 B7
Rāpina EST 132 E1
Rapla EST 131 D9
Rapolano Terme I 66 F4
Rapolla I 60 B5
Rapoltu Mare RO 151 F11
Raposa P 44 F3
Raposeira P 50 E2
Rapotín CZ 77 B12
Rapoula do Côa P 45 D6
Rapperswil CH 27 F10
Rapplinge S 89 B11
Rapsani GR 169 E8
Raron CH 68 A4
Raša HR 67 B9
Räsälä FIN 125 E9
Rasanovci BIH 156 D5
Râșca RO 153 C8
Rascafría E 46 C5
Rascăieți MD 154 D5
Raschau D 75 A12
Rașcov MD 154 B3
Rasdorf D 78 E6
Raseiniai LT 134 F6
Råsele S 107 C11
Rasen N 96 A6
Rasharkin GB 4 F4
Rašica SLO 73 E10
Rasina EST 131 E14
Rășinari RO 160 B4
Rasines E 40 B5
Rasinja HR 149 D7
Rasinkylä FIN 121 E10
Rasinvaara FIN 121 D14
Rasivaara FIN 125 F13
Råsjö S 103 B10
Raška SRB 163 C10
Rask Mølle DK 86 D5
Raškovice CZ 146 B6
Raslavice SK 145 E3
Râșmirești RO 161 F7
Rasno SRB 163 C9
Râșnov RO 161 B6
Rasony BY 133 E5
Rasova RO 155 E1
Rasovo BG 159 F11
Raspenava CZ 81 E8
Rasquera E 42 E5
Rast RO 160 F2
Raštani BIH 157 F8
Rastatt D 27 C9
Rastdorf D 17 C9
Rasteby N 111 B19
Råsted DK 86 B5
Rastede D 17 B10
Rastenfeld A 77 E8
Raštević HR 156 D4
Rasti FIN 117 C14
Rasti FIN 125 G13
Rastinkylä FIN 125 C13
Rastolița RO 152 D5
Rastošnica BIH 157 C10
Rastovac MNE 163 D6
Rastow D 83 D10
Råstrand S 107 A14
Răsuceni RO 161 E7
Rasueros E 45 B10
Rasvåg N 94 F5
Raszków PL 142 C4
Raszyn PL 141 F3
Rataje SRB 164 C3
Rätan S 102 B8
Ratan S 122 C5
Rätansbyn S 102 B8
Ratasjärvi FIN 117 E11
Ratasvuoma FIN 119 B12
Rateče SLO 73 C8
Ratekau D 83 C9
Rătești RO 160 D6
Rathangan IRL 7 F9
Ráth Bhoth IRL 4 F1
Ráth Caola IRL 8 C5
Rathconrath IRL 7 E7
Rathcoole IRL 7 F10
Ráth Cúil IRL 7 F10
Ráth Domhnaigh IRL 9 C7
Rathdowney IRL 9 C7
Ráth Droma IRL 9 C10
Rathdrum IRL 9 C10
Rathenow D 79 A11
Rathfriland GB 7 D10
Rathgormuck IRL 9 D7
Ráth Iomgháin IRL 7 F9
Rathkeale IRL 8 C5
Rathkeevin IRL 9 D7
Rathlee IRL 6 D4
Rathluirc IRL 8 D5
Ráth Mealtain IRL 7 B7
Rathmolyon IRL 7 F9
Rathmore IRL 8 D4
Rathmullan IRL 4 E1
Ráth Naoi IRL 7 G10
Rathnew IRL 7 G10
Rathnure IRL 9 D9
Ratho GB 5 D10
Rathowen IRL 7 E7
Rathstock D 81 A7
Rathumney IRL 9 D9
Rathvilly IRL 9 C9
Ratiboř CZ 146 C5
Ratić BIH 158 D3
Ratingen D 17 F7
Ratiškovice CZ 77 E12
Rátka H 145 G3
Ratkoc RKS 163 E10
Ratkovo SRB 158 C3
Ratnieki LV 133 D2
Ratoath IRL 7 E10
Rattelsdorf D 75 B8
Ratten A 148 B5
Rattenberg A 72 B4
Rattosjärvi FIN 117 E13
Rattray GB 5 B10
Rättsel S 118 C3
Rättvik S 103 E9
Ratvika N 104 D8
Ratzeburg D 83 C9
Rätzlingen D 79 B9
Raubach D 185 C8
Rauda LV 135 E12
Raudåna N 90 B4
Raudanjoki FIN 117 D16
Raudaskylä FIN 123 B13
Raudasmäki FIN 123 B13
Raudeberg N 100 C2
Râu de Mori RO 159 C10
Raudėnai LT 134 D5
Raudondvaris LT 137 D8
Raudonė LT 136 C7
Rauen D 80 B6
Raufoss N 101 E13
Rauha FIN 129 C10
Rauhala FIN 117 C12
Raulhac F 29 F11
Rauma FIN 126 C6
Rauna LV 135 B11
Raunds GB 15 C7
Rauris A 73 B6
Râu Sadului RO 160 B4
Rauschenberg D 21 C11
Raussila FIN 128 D6
Rautajärvi FIN 127 C12
Rautalampi FIN 124 E7
Rautaperä FIN 114 E4
Rautas S 111 D18
Rautavaara FIN 125 C10
Rautenkranz D 75 B11
Rautila FIN 119 F11
Rautila FIN 126 D6
Rautio FIN 120 F3
Rautionmäki FIN 123 E16
Rautjärven kk FIN 129 C11
Rautjärvi FIN 129 C11
Rautuskylä FIN 117 C13
Rauvanniemi FIN 129 B11
Rauzan F 28 F5
Ravadinovo BG 167 E9
Ravanusa I 58 E4
Rava-Rus'ka UA 144 C8
Ravasd H 149 A9
Ravča HR 157 F7
Ravda BG 167 D9
Ravels B 16 F3
Ravelsbach A 77 E9

Rävemåla S 89 B8
Ravenglass GB 10 C5
Ravenna I 66 D5
Ravensburg D 71 B9
Ravenstein NL 16 E5
Ravières F 25 E11
Ravijoki FIN 128 D8
Ravik N 108 B7
Rävlanda S 91 D12
Ravna Dubrava SRB 164 C5
Ravna Gora HR 67 B10
Ravna Reka SRB 159 E8
Ravne SLO 73 D11
Ravne na Koroškem SLO 73 C10
Ravnets BG 167 D8
Ravni BIH 157 F8
Ravnište SRB 164 C3
Ravnje SRB 158 D3
Ravnkilde DK 86 B5
Ravno BIH 157 E7
Ravno BIH 162 D4
Ravnogor BG 165 F9
Ravno Selo SRB 158 C4
Ravnshøj DK 90 E7
Ravnstrup DK 86 C4
Råvsön S 103 A15
Ravsted DK 86 E4
Rawa Mazowiecka PL 141 G2
Rawicz PL 81 C11
Rawmarsh GB 11 E9
Rawtenstall GB 11 D7
Raykovo BG 171 A7
Rayleigh GB 15 D10
Rayol-Canadel-sur-Mer F 36 E4
Räyrinki FIN 123 D11
Ražana SRB 158 E4
Ražanac HR 156 D3
Ražanj SRB 159 F8
Războieni RO 153 C9
Razboj BIH 157 B7
Razbojna SRB 164 C3
Razdelna BG 167 C9
Razdol BG 169 A9
Razdrto SLO 73 E9
Razès F 29 C8
Razgrad BG 160 F2
Razgrad BG 167 B7
Ražljevo BIH 157 C10
Razlog BG 165 F7
Razlovci MK 165 F6
Ražňany SK 145 E3
Ráztočno SK 147 D7
Răzvad RO 161 D6
Reading GB 14 E7
Reaghstown IRL 7 E9
Real P 38 F3
Réalmont F 33 C10
Realmonte I 58 E3
Réalville F 33 B8
Rear Cross IRL 8 C6
Réaup F 33 B6
Reay GB 3 H9
Rebais F 25 C9
Rebbenesbotn N 112 C2
Rebecq B 19 C9
Rébénacq F 32 D5
Rebild DK 86 B5
Rebollosa de Jadraque E 47 B7
Reboly RUS 125 C15
Rebordelo E 38 B3
Rebordelo P 38 E5
Rebra RO 152 C4
Rebricea RO 153 D11
Rebrişoara RO 152 C4
Rebrovo BG 165 D7
Rebŭrkovo BG 165 C8
Reca SK 146 E4
Reçan RKS 163 E10
Recanati I 67 F8
Recaş RO 151 F8
Recco I 37 C10
Recea MD 153 B11
Recea MD 154 C3
Recea RO 151 B12
Recea RO 152 F5
Recea RO 160 D6
Recea-Cristur RO 152 C3
Recess IRL 6 F3
Recey-sur-Ource F 25 E12
Réchicourt-le-Château F 27 C6
Rechlin D 83 D13
Rechnitz A 149 B6
Recht B 20 D6
Rechtenbach D 74 C6
Reci RO 153 F7
Rečica SLO 73 D11
Rečice BIH 157 F8
Recke D 17 D9
Reckingen CH 70 E6
Recklinghausen D 17 E8
Recoaro Terme I 69 B11
Recoubeau-Jansac F 35 A9
Recsk H 147 F10
Recuerda E 40 F6
Recz PL 85 D9
Ręczno PL 141 H1
Reda PL 138 A5
Redalen N 101 E13
Redange L 20 E5
Redcar GB 11 B9
Redcastle IRL 4 E2
Redcross IRL 9 C10
Reddelich D 83 B11
Redditch GB 13 A11
Réde H 149 B9
Redea RO 160 E4
Redefin D 83 D10
Redhill GB 15 E8
Rédics H 149 C6
Réding F 27 C7
Redinha P 44 D3
Rediu RO 153 C11
Rediu RO 153 D9
Rediu RO 153 F11
Rediul Mare MD 153 A11
Rednitzhembach D 75 D9
Redon F 23 E7
Redondela E 38 D2
Redondelo P 38 E4
Redondo P 50 B4
Redován E 56 E3
Red Point GB 2 K5
Redruth GB 12 E4
Redsted DK 86 B3
Reduzum NL 16 B5
Rędzikowo PL 85 B12
Rędziny PL 143 E7
Reen IRL 8 E3
Reens IRL 8 C5
Reepham GB 15 B11
Rees D 16 E6
Reeßum D 17 B12
Reetz D 79 B11
Reetz D 83 D11
Reftele S 87 A13
Regalbuto I 59 D6
Regen D 76 E4
Regensburg D 75 D11
Regensdorf CH 27 F9
Regenstauf D 75 D11
Reggello I 66 E4
Reggio di Calabria I 59 C8
Reggiolo I 66 C2
Reggio nell'Emilia I 66 C2
Reghin RO 152 D5
Reghiu RO 153 F9
Regna S 92 B7
Regnitzlosau D 75 B11
Régny F 30 D5
Regöly H 149 C10
Regozero RUS 121 D17
Regstrup DK 87 D9
Reguengo E 38 D2
Reguengos de Monsaraz P 50 C4
Rehau D 75 B11
Rehburg (Rehburg-Loccum) D 17 D12
Rehden D 17 C10
Rehling D 75 F8
Rehlingen-Siersburg D 21 F7
Řehlovice CZ 80 E5
Rehmsdorf D 79 D11
Rehna D 83 C10
Rehula FIN 129 C9
Reibitz D 79 C11
Reichelsheim (Odenwald) D 187 B6
Reichenau an der Rax A 148 A5
Reichenbach CH 70 D5
Reichenbach D 79 E11
Reichenbach D 187 B6
Reichenberg D 74 C6
Reichenfels A 73 B10
Reichenthal A 76 E6
Reichertsheim D 75 F11
Reichia GR 178 B5
Reichling D 71 B11
Reichmannsdorf D 75 A9
Reicholzheim D 74 C6
Reichraming A 73 A9
Reichshoffen F 27 C8
Reichstett F 186 D4
Reiden CH 27 F8
Reigada P 45 C7
Reigate GB 15 E8
Reignac F 28 E4
Reignier F 31 C9
Reil D 21 D8
Reilingen D 187 C6
Reillanne F 35 C10
Reillo E 47 E9
Reims F 19 F9
Reina E 51 C8
Reinach CH 27 F8
Reinach CH 27 F9
Reinbek D 83 C8
Reinberg D 84 B4
Reine N 110 E5
Reinfeld (Holstein) D 83 C8
Reinheim D 21 E11
Reinosa E 40 C3
Reinøysund N 114 D8
Reinsfeld D 21 E7
Reinskard N 112 D4
Reinskloster N 104 D7
Reinstad N 111 C10
Reinsvik N 104 E3
Reinsvoll N 101 E13
Reipa N 108 C6
Reisbach D 75 E12
Reischach D 75 F12
Reisjärvi FIN 123 C13
Reiskirchen D 21 C11
Reiss GB 3 J10
Reitan N 100 B8
Reitan N 101 A14
Reitano I 58 D5
Reith bei Seefeld A 72 B3
Reit im Winkl D 72 A5
Reittiö FIN 125 D9
Reivyčiai LT 134 D4
Rejmyre S 92 B7
Rejowiec PL 141 H8
Rejsby DK 86 E3
Reka HR 149 D7
Rekava LV 133 B3
Rekavice BIH 157 C7
Reken D 17 E8
Rekijoki FIN 127 E9
Rekken NL 17 D7
Reklynets' UA 144 C9
Rekovac SRB 159 F7
Rekowo PL 85 B12
Rekvik N 111 A15
Rėkyva LT 134 E6
Relíquias P 50 D3
Relletti FIN 119 E13
Relleu E 56 D4
Rellingen D 83 C7
Rém H 150 E3
Remagen D 21 C8
Rémalard F 24 D4
Rembercourt-Sommaisne F 26 C3
Remda D 79 E9
Remels (Uplengen) D 17 B9
Remennikovo RUS 133 C5
Remeskylä FIN 123 C16
Remetea RO 151 D9
Remetea RO 152 D6
Remetea Chioarului RO 152 B3
Remetea Mare RO 151 F7
Remeţi RO 145 H8
Remetinec HR 149 D6
Remetské Hámre SK 145 F5
Remich L 20 E6
Remicourt B 183 D6
Remiremont F 26 D6
Remmam S 107 D14
Remmen S 102 B8
Remmet S 102 B7
Remnes N 108 E4
Remolinos E 41 E9
Remouchamps B 183 E7
Remoulins F 35 C8
Remplin D 83 C13
Remptendorf D 75 A10
Remscheid D 21 B8
Remte LV 134 C5
Remungol F 22 E6
Rémuzat F 35 B9
Rena E 45 F9
Rena N 101 D14
Renaison F 30 C4
Renålandet S 106 D8
Renazé F 23 E9
Rencēni LV 131 F10
Renchen D 27 C9
Renda LV 134 B4
Rende I 60 E6
Rendsburg D 82 B7
Renedo E 39 E10
Renedo E 40 B4
Renedo de la Vega E 39 D10
Renens CH 31 B10
Renesse NL 16 E1
Renfrew GB 5 D8
Renginio GR 175 B6
Rengsdorf D 21 C8
Rengsjö S 103 D12
Renholmen S 118 D6
Reni UA 155 C2
Renko FIN 127 D11
Renkomäki FIN 127 D14
Renkum NL 183 B7
Renndal N 104 E5
Rennerod D 21 C10
Rennertshofen D 75 E9
Rennes F 23 D8
Rennes-les-Bains F 33 E10
Renningen D 27 C10
Rennweg A 73 B8
Renòn I 72 C3
Rens DK 86 F4
Rensjön S 111 D18
Reńska Wieś PL 142 F5
Renström S 118 E4
Renswoude NL 183 A7
Rentina GR 174 A4
Rentjärn S 107 A15
Rentweinsdorf D 75 B8
Renwez F 19 E10
Renzow D 83 C10
Repbäcken S 97 A13
Répcelak H 149 B8
Repedea RO 152 B4
Repino RUS 129 E12
Repki PL 141 F6
Replot FIN 122 D6
Repojoki FIN 117 B15
Repolka RUS 132 C6
Reposaari FIN 126 B5
Repparfjord N 113 C13
Reppelin D 83 B12
Reppen N 108 C6
Reppenstedt D 83 D8
Reps AL 163 F9
Repton GB 11 F8
Repvåg N 113 B16
Requejo E 39 D6
Requena E 47 F10
Réquista F 33 B11
Rerik D 83 B11
Resana I 72 E4
Resarö S 99 D10
Resavica SRB 159 E8
Resele S 107 E12
Resen BG 166 C5
Resen MK 168 B5
Resenbro DK 86 C5
Resende P 44 B5
Rešetari HR 157 B7
Reşiţa RO 159 C8
Resko PL 85 C8
Resna MNE 163 E6
Resolven GB 13 B7
Respenda de la Peña E 39 C10
Resse (Wedemark) D 78 A6
Ressons-sur-Matz F 18 E6
Restelicë RKS 163 F10
Restinga MA 53 E6
Reston GB 5 D12
Resuttano I 58 D5
Retamal E 51 B8
Retford GB 11 E10
Rethel F 19 E9
Rethem (Aller) D 17 C12
Rethymno GR 178 E7
Retie B 16 F4
Retiers F 23 E9
Retje SLO 73 E10
Retortillo E 45 C8
Retortillo de Soria E 40 F6
Retournac F 30 E5
Rétság H 147 F8
Retuerta del Bullaque E 46 F4
Retunen FIN 125 E11
Retz A 77 E9
Reuden D 79 B11
Reuilly F 24 F7
Reurieth D 75 B8
Reusel NL 16 F4
Reut D 76 F3
Reute D 27 D8
Reuţel MD 153 B11
Reuterstadt Stavenhagen D 84 C3
Reutlingen D 27 D11
Reutte A 71 C11
Reutuaapa FIN 119 B15
Reuver NL 16 F6
Revel F 33 D10
Revello I 37 B6
Revest-du-Bion F 35 B10
Révfülöp H 149 C9
Revholmen N 91 A8
Reviga RO 161 D10
Revigny-sur-Ornain F 26 C2
Revilla de Collazos E 40 C3
Revilla del Campo E 40 D4
Revin F 19 E10
Revine-Lago I 72 E5
Řevnice CZ 76 C6
Řevničov CZ 76 B5
Revò I 72 D3
Revonlahti FIN 119 E13
Revsnes N 100 D6
Revsnes N 111 C11
Revsund S 103 A9
Revúca SK 147 D10
Rewal PL 85 B8
Rexbo S 103 E9
Reyrieux F 30 D6
Rezé F 23 F8
Rēzekne LV 133 C2
Rezi H 149 C8
Rezina MD 154 B3
Rēzna LV 133 D2
Rezovo BG 167 F10
Rezzato I 66 A1
Rezzo I 37 C7
Rezzoaglio I 37 B10
Rgotina SRB 159 E9
Rhade D 17 B12
Rhaunen D 21 E8
Rhayader GB 13 A7
Rheda-Wiedenbrück D 17 E10
Rhede D 17 E7
Rhede (Ems) D 17 B8
Rheden NL 183 A8
Rheinau D 27 C8
Rheinbach D 21 C7
Rheinberg D 17 E7
Rheinböllen D 185 E8
Rheinbreitbach D 21 C8
Rheinbrohl D 185 D7
Rheine D 17 D8
Rheinfelden (Baden) D 27 E8
Rheinsberg D 84 D3
Rheinstetten D 27 C9
Rheinzabern D 187 C5
Rhêmes-Notre-Dame I 31 D11
Rhêmes-St-Georges I 31 D11
Rhenen NL 16 E5
Rhens D 185 D8
Rhiconich GB 2 J7
Rhinau F 27 D8
Rhinow D 83 E12
Rhisnes B 182 D5
Rho I 69 B7
Rhode IRL 7 F8
Rhoden (Diemelstadt) D 17 F12
Rhoon NL 182 B4
Rhoose GB 13 C8
Rhosllanerchrugog GB 10 E5
Rhôs-on-Sea GB 10 E4
Rhossili GB 12 B6
Rhuddlan GB 10 E5
Rhydaman GB 12 B7
Rhyl GB 10 E5
Rhymney GB 13 B8
Riace I 59 C9
Riachos P 44 F3
Riaillé F 23 E9
Rialp E 33 F8
Riaño E 39 C10
Riano I 62 C3
Rians F 35 C10
Riantec F 22 E5
Rianxo E 38 C2
Riaz CH 31 B11
Riba E 40 B4
Ribadavia E 38 D3
Ribadelago E 39 D6
Riba de Mouro P 38 D3
Ribadeo E 38 A5
Riba de Saelices E 47 C8
Ribadesella E 39 B9
Ribaforada E 41 D8
Ribafrecha E 32 F1
Ribarci SRB 164 E6
Ribare SRB 164 C4
Ribari SRB 158 D3
Ribaritsa BG 165 D9
Riba-roja d'Ebre E 42 E4
Riba-roja de Turia E 48 E3
Ribbåsen S 102 D7
Ribchester GB 10 D6
Ribe DK 86 E3
Ribeauvillé F 27 D7
Ribécourt-Dreslincourt F 18 E6
Ribeira P 38 E3
Ribeira de Pena P 38 E4
Ribemont F 19 E7
Ribera I 58 E3
Ribérac F 29 E6
Ribera del Fresno E 51 B7
Ribesalbes E 48 D4
Ribes de Freser E 33 F10
Ribiţa RO 151 E10
Ribnica BIH 157 D9
Ribnica SLO 73 E10
Ribnica SLO 148 C4
Ribnica SRB 158 F4
Ribnik HR 148 E4
Rîbniţa MD 154 B4
Ribnitz-Damgarten D 83 B12
Ribnovo BG 165 F8
Ribota E 40 F5
Ricadi I 59 B8
Říčany CZ 77 C7
Říčany CZ 77 D10
Riccia I 63 E7
Riccio I 66 F5
Riccione I 66 D6
Riccò del Golfo di Spezia I 69 E8
Richardménil F 26 C5
Richelieu F 29 A6
Richhill GB 7 D9
Richka UA 152 A5
Richmond GB 11 C8
Richvald SK 145 E3
Rickebo S 103 D11
Rickenbach D 27 E8
Rickinghall GB 15 C10
Rickling D 83 B8
Rickmansworth GB 15 D8
Ricla E 41 E9
Ricse H 145 G4
Ridasjärvi FIN 127 D13
Riddarhyttan S 97 C14
Ridderkerk NL 16 E3
Riddes CH 31 C11
Riđica SRB 150 F3
Rīdzene LV 135 B10
Riebiņi LV 135 D13
Riebnesluspen S 109 D13
Riec-sur-Belon F 22 E4
Ried CH 68 A5
Riede D 17 C11
Riedenburg D 75 E10
Rieder D 79 C9
Ried im Innkreis A 76 F4
Ried im Oberinntal A 71 C11
Ried im Zillertal A 72 B4
Ried in der Riedmark A 77 F7
Riedlingen D 71 A8
Riegelsberg D 21 F7
Riegersburg A 148 B5
Riego de la Vega E 39 D8
Riehe (Suthfeld) D 78 B5
Riehen CH 27 E8
Rielasingen-Worblingen D 27 E10
Riello E 39 C8
Rielves E 46 E4
Riemst B 19 C12
Rieneck D 187 A8
Rieni RO 151 D9
Rieponlahti FIN 124 E7
Riepsdorf D 83 B9
Riesa D 80 D4
Rieseby D 83 A7
Riesi I 58 E5
Riestedt D 79 D9
Rietavas LT 134 E3
Rietberg D 17 E10
Rieth D 84 C6
Riethoven NL 183 C6
Rieti I 62 C3
Rietschen D 81 D7
Rieumes F 33 D8
Rieupeyroux F 33 B10
Rieutort-de-Randon F 34 A5
Rieux F 23 E7
Rieux F 33 D8
Riez F 36 D4
Rifiano I 72 C3
Rīga LV 135 C8
Rigaio GR 169 F8
Rigaud F 36 D5
Riggisberg CH 31 B11
Rignac F 33 B10
Rignano Flaminio I 62 C2
Rignano Garganico I 63 D9
Rignano sull'Arno I 66 E3
Rigny-le-Ferron F 25 D10
Rigny-sur-Arroux F 30 B5
Rigny-Ussé F 24 F3
Rigside GB 5 D9
Rihtniemi FIN 126 C5
Riihimäki FIN 127 D12
Riihivaara FIN 125 C14
Riikonkumpu FIN 117 C14
Riipi FIN 117 D16
Riippi FIN 122 F7
Riisipere EST 131 C8
Riistavesi FIN 125 E10
Riitiala FIN 127 B8
Riječa BIH 157 E10
Rijeka BIH 157 D9
Rijeka BIH 157 F11
Rijeka HR 67 B9
Rijeka Crnojevića MNE 163 E7
Rijen NL 16 E3
Rijkevorsel B 16 F3
Rijnsburg NL 16 D2
Rijsbergen NL 16 E3
Rijsel F 19 C7
Rijssen NL 17 D7
Rijswijk NL 16 D2
Rikava LV 133 C2
Riksgränsen S 111 D15
Rila BG 165 E7
Rilhac-Rancon F 29 D8
Rilland NL 182 C4
Rillé F 23 F12
Rillieux-la-Pape F 30 D6
Rillo E 42 F2
Rillo de Gallo E 47 C9
Rimavská Baňa SK 147 D9
Rimavská Seč SK 145 G1
Rimavská Sobota SK 147 E10
Rimavské Janovce SK 147 E10
Rimbach D 76 D3
Rimbach D 187 B6
Rimbo S 99 C10
Rimetea RO 152 E3
Rimforsa S 92 C7
Rimicāni LV 135 D12
Rimini I 66 D6
Rimjokk S 118 B5
Rimmilä FIN 127 D11
Rimóc H 147 E9
Rimogne F 184 E2
Rimont F 33 E8
Rimpar D 74 C6
Rimsbo S 103 D11
Rimšė LT 135 E12
Rimšėnai LT 135 F12
Rimske Toplice SLO 73 D11
Rimsting D 72 A5
Rinchnach D 76 E4
Rincón de la Victoria E 53 C8
Rincón de Soto E 41 D8
Rinda LV 134 A3
Rindal N 104 E6
Rindsholm DK 86 C4
Rineia GR 176 E5
Rinella I 59 B6
Ringarum S 93 C8
Ringaudai LT 137 D8
Ringe D 17 C7
Ringe DK 86 E6
Ringebu N 101 C12
Ringelia N 101 E12
Ringen N 95 B12
Ringford GB 5 F8
Ringhals S 87 A10
Ringkøbing DK 86 C2
Ringleben D 79 D9
Ringsend GB 4 E3
Ringsta S 106 E7
Ringsted DK 87 E9
Ringvattnet S 106 C8
Ringville IRL 9 D7
Ringwood GB 13 D11
Rinkaby S 88 D6
Rinkabyholm S 89 B10
Rinkenæs DK 86 F5
Rinkilä FIN 129 B10
Rinloan GB 5 A10
Rinn S 97 B9
Rinneen IRL 8 C4
Rinøyvåg N 111 D10
Rintala FIN 123 D10
Rinteln D 17 D12
Rio GR 174 C4
Rio Caldo P 38 E3
Rio de Mel P 44 C6
Rio de Moinhos P 50 B4
Rio de Moinhos P 50 C3
Rio de Moinhos P 50 D3
Rio de Onor P 39 E6
Rio di Pusteria I 72 C4
Riofrío E 46 C3
Riofrío de Aliste E 39 E7
Riogordo E 53 C8
Rioja E 55 F8
Riola Sardo I 64 D2
Riolobos E 45 E8
Riolo Terme I 66 D4
Riols F 34 C4
Riom F 30 D3
Riomaggiore I 69 E8
Rio Maior P 44 F3
Rio Marina I 65 B2
Riom-ès-Montagnes F 29 E11
Rion-des-Landes F 32 C4
Rionegro del Puente E 39 D7
Rio nell'Elba I 65 B2
Rionero in Vulture I 60 B5
Rionero Sannitico I 63 D6
Rions F 32 A5
Riorges F 30 C5
Ríos E 38 E5
Rioseco de Tapia E 39 C8
Rio Tinto P 44 B3
Rio Torto P 38 E5
Rioz F 26 F5
Ripač BIH 156 C4
Ripacandida I 60 B5
Ripalimosano I 63 D7
Ripanj SRB 158 D6
Riparbella I 66 F2
Ripatransone I 62 B5
Ripe I 67 E7
Ripi I 62 D4
Ripiceni RO 153 B10
Ripley GB 11 C8
Ripley GB 11 E9
Ripoll E 43 C8
Ripon GB 11 C8
Riposto I 59 D7
Rips NL 183 B7
Riquewihr F 27 D7
Risan MNE 163 D6
Risarven S 103 C10
Risbäck S 106 B9
Risberg S 102 D6
Risca GB 13 B8
Rişca RO 151 D11
Rîşcani MD 153 B11
Riscle F 32 C5
Risdal N 90 B3
Risede S 106 C8
Rish BG 167 D7
Risinge S 92 B7
Risliden S 107 B16
Risnabben S 118 D3
Risnes N 94 E5
Risør N 90 B5
Risøyhamn N 111 C10
Rissa N 104 D7
Rissna S 106 E8
Rissnaben S 118 D4
Riste FIN 126 C7
Risteli FIN 125 B12
Risti EST 131 D8
Ristiina FIN 128 B7
Ristijärvi FIN 121 F11
Ristilä FIN 121 B11
Ristilampi FIN 117 E17
Ristinen FIN 124 D7
Ristinkylä FIN 125 E12
Ristioja FIN 117 E13
Ristonmännikkö FIN 117 D16
Risträsk S 107 B12
Risudden S 119 B11
Risum-Lindholm D 82 A5
Rītausmas LV 135 D8
Rite LV 135 D10
Rīteri LV 135 C11
Ritini GR 169 D7
Ritola FIN 123 E11
Ritterhude D 17 B11
Rittersdorf D 185 D5
Rittersgrün D 75 B12
Riudarenes E 43 D9
Riudecols E 42 E5
Riudoms E 42 E6
Riutta FIN 123 C12
Riutula FIN 113 F18
Rīva LV 134 C2
Riva del Garda I 69 B10
Riva di Solto I 69 B9
Riva di Tures I 72 C5
Rivanazzano I 37 B10
Rivardo Ligure I 37 C9
Rivarolo Canavese I 68 C4
Rivarolo Mantovano I 66 B1
Rivas-Vaciamadrid E 46 D6
Rive-de-Gier F 30 D6
Rivedoux-Plage F 28 C3
Rivello I 60 C5
Riverchapel IRL 9 C10
Rivergaro I 37 B11
Rivero E 40 B3
Riverstown IRL 7 F7
Riverstown IRL 8 E6
Rivery F 18 E5
Rives F 31 E8
Rivesaltes F 34 E4
Rivière-sur-Tarn F 34 B5
Rivignano I 73 E7
Rivinperä FIN 119 F16
Rivodutri I 62 B3
Rivoli I 68 C4
Rivolta d'Adda I 69 C8
Rixensart B 19 C10
Rixheim F 27 E7
Rixö S 91 C9
Riza GR 175 C6
Rizes GR 174 E5
Rizia GR 171 A10
Rizomata GR 169 D7
Rizomylos GR 169 F8
Rizziconi I 59 C8
Rjånes N 100 B3
Rjukan N 95 C9
Rø DK 89 E7
Ro I 66 C4
Rö S 103 A14
Roa E 40 E4
Roa N 95 B13
Roade GB 15 C7
Roadside GB 3 H10
Roadside of Kinneff GB 5 B12
Roager DK 86 E3
Roaillan F 32 B5
Roald N 100 A4
Roan N 104 C8
Roanne F 30 C5
Roata de Jos RO 161 E7
Roath GB 13 C8
Röbäck S 122 C4
Robănești RO 160 E4
Robbio I 68 C6
Robeasca RO 161 C10
Robecco d'Oglio I 69 C9
Röbel D 83 D13
Robella I 68 C5
Robert-Espagne F 26 C3
Roberton GB 5 D9
Roberton GB 5 E11
Robertsfors S 118 F5
Robežnieki LV 135 E13
Robiac-Rochessadoule F 35 B7
Robilante I 37 C6
Robin Hood's Bay GB 11 C10
Robion F 35 C9
Robledo E 55 B8
Robledo de Chavela E 46 C4
Robledo del Mazo E 46 E3
Robledollano E 45 E9
Robles de la Valcueva E 39 C9
Robliza de Cojos E 45 C9
Robøle N 101 E11
Robregordo E 46 B5
Robres E 41 E11
Robres del Castillo E 32 F1
Roč HR 67 B9
Rocafort de Queralt E 43 E6
Rocamadour F 29 F9
Roca Vecchia I 61 C10
Roccabianca I 66 B1
Roccadaspide I 60 C4
Rocca d'Evandro I 60 A1
Rocca di Cambio I 62 C4
Rocca di Mezzo I 62 C5
Rocca di Neto I 61 E7
Rocca di Papa I 62 D3
Roccafranca I 69 C8
Roccagloriosa I 60 C4
Roccagorga I 62 D4
Rocca Grimalda I 37 B9
Rocca Imperiale I 61 C7
Roccalbegna I 65 B5
Roccalumera I 59 D7
Roccamandolfi I 63 D6
Rocca Massima I 62 D3
Roccamena I 58 D3
Roccamonfina I 60 A1
Roccamontepiano I 62 C6
Roccanova I 60 C6
Roccapalumba I 58 D4
Rocca Pia I 62 D5
Roccaraso I 62 D6
Rocca San Casciano I 66 D4
Rocca San Giovanni I 63 C6
Roccasecca I 62 D5
Roccasecca dei Volsci I 62 E4
Rocca Sinibalda I 62 C3
Roccastrada I 65 A4
Roccavione I 37 C6
Roccella Ionica I 59 C9
Rocchetta Sant'Antonio I 60 A4
Rochdale GB 11 D7
Roche GB 12 E5
Rochechouart F 29 D7
Rochefort B 19 D11
Rochefort F 28 D4
Rochefort-en-Terre F 23 E7
Rochefort-Montagne F 30 D2
Rochefort-sur-Nenon F 26 F4
Rochehaut B 184 E3
Roche-la-Molière F 30 E5
Rochemaure F 35 A8
Roches-Bettaincourt F 26 D3
Rocheservière F 28 B2
Rochester GB 5 E12
Rochester GB 15 E10
Rochetaillée F 26 E3
Rochford GB 15 D10
Rochfortbridge IRL 7 F8
Rochin F 19 C7
Rochlitz D 79 D12
Rociana del Condado E 51 E6
Ročinj SLO 73 D8
Rociu RO 160 D6
Rockanje NL 182 B4
Rockchapel IRL 8 D4
Rockcliffe GB 5 F9
Rockcorry IRL 7 D8
Rockenhausen D 21 E9
Rockesholm S 97 C12
Rockhammar S 97 C13
Rockhill IRL 8 D5
Rockingham GB 11 F10
Rockmills IRL 8 D6
Rockneby S 89 B10
Röcknitz D 79 D12
Rocourt-St-Martin F 25 B9
Rocroi F 19 E10
Roda de Bara E 43 E6
Roda de Ter E 43 D8
Rodalben D 21 F9
Rodaljice HR 156 D4
Rödåsel S 118 F3
Rodberg N 95 B9
Rødbergshamn N 111 B15
Rødby DK 83 A10
Rødbyhavn DK 83 A10
Rødding DK 86 B3
Rødding DK 86 C5
Rødding DK 86 E4
Rödeby S 89 C9
Rodeiro E 38 C4
Rødekro DK 86 E4
Rodel GB 2 K3
Rodellar E 32 F5
Rodelle F 34 A4
Roden NL 17 B6
Ródenas E 47 C10
Rodenkirchen (Stadland) D 17 B10
Rödental D 75 B9
Rodewald D 82 E6
Rodewisch D 75 A11
Rodez F 33 B11
Rodi Garganico I 63 D9
Roding D 75 D12
Rödingträsk S 107 C14
Rödjebro S 98 B8
Rødkærsbro DK 86 C4
Rodleben D 79 C11
Rødlia N 108 E7
Rödmyra S 103 C11
Rodna RO 152 C5
Rododafni GR 174 C5
Rodolivos GR 170 C5
Rödön S 105 E16
Rodopoli GR 169 B9
Rodopos GR 178 D6
Rodos GR 181 D8
Rødovre DK 87 D10
Rødsand N 111 B13
Rødsand N 114 D8
Rødseidet N 105 B11
Rödvattnet S 107 D13
Rødvig DK 87 E10
Roela EST 131 C13
Roermond NL 20 B5
Roeselare B 19 C7
Roeşti RO 160 D4
Roetgen D 20 C6
Röfors S 92 B5
Rofrano I 60 C4
Rogač HR 156 F5
Rogačica SRB 158 E4
Rogaška Slatina SLO 148 D5
Rogaszyce PL 142 D4
Rogate GB 15 E7
Rogatec SLO 148 D5
Rogatica BIH 157 E11
Rogätz D 79 B10
Roggel NL 16 F5
Roggenburg D 75 F7
Roggendorf D 83 C10
Roggentin D 84 D3
Roggiano Gravina I 60 D6
Roghudi I 59 C8
Rogienice Wielkie PL 139 D13
Rogil P 50 E2
Rogliano F 37 F10
Rogliano I 61 E6
Rognac F 35 D9
Rognan N 108 B9
Rognes F 35 C9

Sälen S 102 D5
Salernes F 36 D4
Salerno I 60 B3
Salers F 29 E10
Salettes F 30 F4
Saleux F 18 E5
Salford GB 11 E7
Şalgamli TR 173 B6
Salgótarján H 147 E9
Salgueiro P 44 E5
Salhus N 94 A2
Sali HR 156 E3
Salice Salentino I 61 C9
Saliceto I 37 C8
Saliena LV 135 C7
Saliena LV 135 E13
Salies-de-Béarn F 32 D4
Salies-du-Salat F 33 D7
Salignac-Eyvignes F 29 F8
Salillas de Jalón E 41 E9
Salinas E 39 A8
Salinas E 56 D3
Salinas del Manzano E 47 D9
Salinas de Pamplona E 32 E2
Salinas de Pisuerga E 40 C3
Salin-de-Giraud F 35 D8
Saline di Volterra I 66 F2
Sälinkää FIN 127 D13
Salins F 29 E10
Salins-les-Bains F 31 B8
Salir P 50 E3
Salisbury GB 13 C11
Săliște RO 152 F3
Săliștea RO 151 F11
Săliștea de Sus RO 152 B4
Salka SK 147 F7
Sal'kove UA 154 A5
Sall DK 86 C5
Salla EST 131 D12
Salla FIN 115 E5
Sallanches F 31 D10
Sallent E 43 D7
Sallent de Gállego E 32 E5
Salles F 32 A4
Salles-Curan F 34 B4
Salles-d'Angles F 28 D5
Salles-la-Source F 33 B11
Salles-sur-l'Hers F 33 D9
Sallgast D 80 C5
Sälliku EST 131 C14
Sallingberg A 77 F8
Sallins IRL 7 F9
Sällsjö S 105 E15
Sallypark IRL 8 C6
Salme EST 130 E4
Salmerón E 47 C8
Salmeroncillos de Abajo E 47 C7
Salmi FIN 123 E10
Salmi S 119 B10
Salmijärvi FIN 121 D10
Salminen FIN 121 B12
Salminen FIN 124 E8
Salmivaara FIN 115 E4
Salmiyarvi RUS 114 E8
Salmoral E 45 C10
Salmtal D 21 E7
Salnava LV 133 C3
Salnö S 99 C11
Salo FIN 127 E9
Salò I 69 B10
Salobre E 55 B7
Salobreña E 53 C9
Saločiai LT 135 D8
Saloinen FIN 119 E12
Salon F 25 C11
Salon-de-Provence F 35 C9
Salonkylä FIN 123 C11
Salonpää FIN 119 E14
Salonta RO 151 D8
Salorino E 45 F6
Salornay-sur-Guye F 30 B6
Salorno I 69 A11
Salou E 42 E6
Salouël F 18 E5
Šalovci SLO 148 C6
Salsåker S 107 F14
Salsbruket N 105 B11
Salsburgh GB 5 D9
Salses-le-Château F 34 E4
Sălsig RO 151 B11
Salsomaggiore Terme I 69 D8
Salt E 43 D9
Saltara I 67 E6
Saltash GB 12 E6
Saltburn-by-the-Sea GB 11 B10
Saltcoats GB 4 D7
Salteras E 51 E7
Salthill IRL 6 F4
Salto P 38 E4
Saltoniškės LT 137 D11
Saltrød N 90 C4
Saltsjöbaden S 99 D10
Saltum DK 90 E6
Saltvik FIN 99 B14
Saltvik S 103 C13
Saludecio I 67 E6
Saluggia I 68 C5
Salur TR 173 D8
Salussola I 68 C5
Salutaguse EST 131 C9
Saluzzo I 37 B6
Salva RO 152 C4
Salvacañete E 47 D10
Salvagnac F 33 C9
Salvaleón E 51 B6
Salvaterra de Magos P 50 A2
Salvaterra do Extremo P 45 E7
Salvatierra E 32 E1
Salvatierra de los Barros E 51 C6
Salvatierra de Santiago E 45 F8
Salve I 61 D10
Salviac F 33 A8
Sály H 145 H2
Salzburg A 73 A7
Salzgitter D 79 B7
Salzhausen D 83 D8
Salzhemmendorf D 78 B6
Salzkotten D 17 E11
Salzmünde D 79 C10
Salzwedel D 83 E10
Salzweg D 76 E4
Samadet F 32 C5
Samaila SRB 158 F6
Samarate I 68 B6
Samarica HR 149 E7
Samarina GR 168 D5
…rineşti RO 159 D11
… 64 E2
… D7
Samboal E 40 F3
Samborzec PL 143 E12
Sambuca di Sicilia I 58 D3
Sambuca Pistoiese I 66 D3
Sambuco I 36 C6
Sâmbureşti RO 160 D4
Samedan CH 71 D9
Sameiro P 44 D6
Samer F 15 F12
Sames E 39 B9
Sami GR 174 C2
Samil P 39 E6
Samir de los Caños E 39 E7
Şamli TR 173 E8
Sammakko S 116 E7
Sammakkola FIN 125 C10
Sammaljoki FIN 127 C9
Sammatti FIN 127 E10
Sammichele di Bari I 61 B7
Samnaun CH 71 D10
Samobor HR 148 E5
Samoëns F 31 C10
Samões P 38 F5
Samokov BG 165 E8
Samokov MK 164 F3
Samolaco I 69 A7
Samora Correia P 50 B2
Šamorín SK 146 E4
Samos E 38 C5
Samos GR 177 D8
Samoš SRB 159 C6
Samothraki GR 171 D9
Samovodene BG 166 C5
Samper de Calanda E 42 E3
Sampeyre I 37 B6
Sampierdarena I 37 C9
Sampieri I 59 F6
Sampigny F 26 C4
amşud RO 151 C10
Samswegen D 79 B10
Samtens D 84 B4
Samuelsberg N 112 D6
Samugheo I 64 D2
Samuil BG 167 B7
Samuilovo BG 166 E5
San Adrián E 32 F2
San Agustín de Guadalix E 46 C5
Sanaigmore GB 4 D4
San Amaro E 38 D3
Sânandrei RO 151 F7
San Andrés del Rabanedo E 39 C8
San Antolín E 39 B6
San Antonio E 47 E10
Sanary-sur-Mer F 35 D10
San Asensio E 40 C6
San Bartolomé de las Abiertas E 46 E3
San Bartolomé de la Torre E 51 E5
San Bartolomé de Pinares E 46 C3
San Bartolomeo al Mare I 37 D8
San Bartolomeo in Galdo I 60 A4
San Basilio I 64 D3
San Benedetto dei Marsi I 62 C5
San Benedetto del Tronto I 62 B5
San Benedetto Po I 66 B2
San Benito E 54 B3
San Benito de la Contienda E 51 B5
San Biagio di Callalta I 72 E5
San Biago Platani I 58 D4
San Bonifacio I 66 B3
San Buono I 63 D7
San Candido I 72 C5
San Carlos del Valle E 55 B6
San Casciano dei Bagni I 62 B1
San Casciano in Val di Pesa I 66 E3
San Cataldo I 58 E4
San Cataldo I 61 C10
San Cebrián de Castro E 39 E8
Sâncel RO 152 E3
Sancergues F 25 F8
Sancerre F 25 F8
San Cesario sul Panaro I 66 C3
Sancey-le-Grand F 26 F6
Sancheville F 24 D6
Sanchidrián E 46 C3
San Chirico Nuovo I 60 B6
San Chirico Raparo I 60 C6
San Cibrão das Viñas E 38 D4
San Cipirello I 58 D3
San Cipriano d'Aversa I 60 B2
San Clemente E 47 F8
San Clodio E 38 D5
Sancoins F 30 B2
San Colombano al Lambro I 69 C7
San Cosme E 38 A5
San Costantino Albanese I 61 C6
San Costanzo I 67 E7
Sâncrăieni RO 153 E7
Sâncraiu RO 151 D10
Sâncraiu de Mureş RO 152 D5
San Cristóbal de Entreviñas E 39 D8
San Cristóbal de la Vega E 46 B3
Sancti-Spíritus E 45 C8
Sancti-Spíritus E 51 B9
Sand N 94 D4
Sand N 95 B15
Sand N 110 D5
Sand (Bad Emstal) D 17 F12
Sanda S 93 E12
Sandager DK 86 E5
Sandamendi E 40 B5
San Damiano d'Asti I 37 B8
San Damiano Macra I 37 C6
Sandane N 100 C4
San Daniele del Friuli I 73 D7
San Daniele Po I 66 B1
Sandanski BG 169 A9
Sandared S 91 D12
Sandarne S 103 D13
Sandau D 83 E12
Sandbach GB 11 E7
Sandberg D 74 B7
Sandby DK 87 F8
Sande D 17 B10
Sande N 95 C12
Sande N 100 D3
Sande P 44 B4
Sandefjord N 90 A7
Sandeggen N 111 A17
Sandeid N 94 C3
Sandelva N 112 D7
San Demetrio Corone I 61 D6
San Demetrio ne Vestini I 62 C5
Sander N 96 B6
Sandersdorf D 79 C11
Sandershausen (Niestetal) D 78 D6
Sandersleben D 79 C10
Sandes N 110 C8
Sandes N 110 C9
Sandfjord N 114 B9
Sandfors S 118 E5
Sandgarth GB 3 G11
Sandhausen D 21 F11
Sandhead GB 4 F7
Sandhem S 91 D14
Sandhult S 91 D12
Sandhurst GB 15 E7
Sandiás E 38 D4
Sandillon F 24 E7
Sandkrug D 84 E5
Sandl A 77 E7
Sandland N 112 C8
Sandnäset S 102 A8
Sandnes N 90 A5
Sandnes N 94 E3
Sandnes N 105 C12
Sandneshamn N 111 A15
Sandness N 111 C11
Sandnessjøen N 108 D4
Sando E 45 C8
Sandomierz PL 143 E12
Sândominic RO 153 D7
San Donaci I 61 C9
San Donà di Piave I 72 E6
San Donato di Lecce I 61 C10
San Donato di Ninea I 60 D6
San Donato Milanese I 69 C7
San Donato Val di Comino I 62 D5
Sándorfalva H 150 E5
Sandown GB 13 D12
Sandøy N 100 A5
Sandplace GB 12 E6
Šandrovac HR 149 E8
Sandsele S 107 A13
Sandsend GB 11 B10
Sandsjö S 102 C8
Sandsjöfors S 92 E5
Sandsjönäs S 107 A13
Sandslån S 107 E13
Sandstad N 104 D6
Sandstedt D 17 B11
Sandstrak N 108 D3
Sandstrand N 111 C12
Sandtangen N 114 D7
Sandtorg N 111 C12
Sandträsk S 118 B6
Sânduleni RO 153 E9
Sânduleşti RO 152 D3
Sandur FO 2 B3
Sandvatn N 94 F5
Sandved DK 87 E9
Sandvik FO 2 B3
Sandvik N 101 D15
Sandvik N 108 B7
Sandvik N 111 A16
Sandvik N 111 B14
Sandvik N 113 B16
Sandvik S 103 C11
Sandvika N 95 C13
Sandvika N 105 D12
Sandviken S 103 E12
Sandviken S 107 E15
Sandviken S 107 F13
Sandviksjön S 106 D7
Sandvikvåg N 94 C2
Sandwich GB 15 E11
Sandwick GB 3 F14
Sandy GB 15 C8
Sanem L 20 E5
San Emiliano E 39 C8
San Esteban de Gormaz E 40 E5
San Esteban de la Sierra E 45 C9
San Esteban de Litera E 42 D4
San Esteban del Molar E 39 E8
San Esteban del Valle E 46 D3
San Fele I 60 B5
San Felice a Cancello I 60 A2
San Felice Circeo I 62 E4
San Felices de los Gallegos E 45 C7
San Felice sul Panaro I 66 C3
San Ferdinando I 59 C8
San Ferdinando di Puglia I 60 A6
San Fernando E 52 D4
San Fernando de Henares E 46 D5
San Fili I 60 E6
San Filippo del Mela I 59 C7
Sanfins do Douro P 38 F5
San Francisco Javier E 57 D7
San Fratello I 59 C6
Sanfront I 37 B6
Sånga S 107 E13
Sangarcía E 46 C4
Sangaste EST 131 F12
Sangatte F 15 F12
San Gavino Monreale I 64 D2
Sångbäcken S 102 B7
San Gemini I 62 B3
Sângeorgiu de Mureş RO 152 D5
Sângeorgiu de Pădure RO 152 E5
Sângeorz-Băi RO 152 C5
Sânger RO 152 D4
Sangerhausen D 79 D9
San Germano Chisone I 31 F11
Săngeru RO 161 C8
Sangijän S 119 C11
San Gimignano I 66 F3
San Ginesio I 62 A4
Sanginjoki FIN 119 E16
Sanginkylä FIN 119 E17
San Giorgio a Liri I 62 E5
San Giorgio della Richinvelda I 73 D6
San Giorgio del Sannio I 60 A3
San Giorgio di Lomellina I 68 C6
San Giorgio di Nogaro I 73 E7
San Giorgio di Piano I 66 C3
San Giorgio Ionico I 61 C8
San Giorgio la Molara I 60 A3
San Giorgio Lucano I 61 C6
San Giovanni a Piro I 60 C4
San Giovanni Bianco I 69 B8
San Giovanni d'Asso I 66 F4
San Giovanni Gemini I 58 D4
San Giovanni Incarico I 62 D4
San Giovanni in Croce I 66 B1
San Giovanni in Fiore I 61 E7
San Giovanni in Persiceto I 66 C3
San Giovanni Lupatoto I 66 B3
San Giovanni Rotondo I 63 D9
San Giovanni Suegiu I 64 E2
San Giovanni Teatino I 63 C6
San Giovanni Valdarno I 66 E4
Sangis S 119 C10
San Giuliano Terme I 66 E1
San Giuseppe Jato I 58 D3
San Giuseppe Vesuviano I 60 B3
San Giustino I 66 E5
San Godenzo I 66 E4
San Gregorio I 59 C8
San Gregorio Magno I 60 B4
San Gregorio Matese I 60 A2
Sangüesa E 32 E3
San Guiliano Milanese I 69 C7
San Guim de Freixenet E 43 D6
Sanguinet F 32 B3
Sanguinetto I 66 B3
Sani GR 169 D9
San Ildefonso E 46 C5
Sanislău RO 151 B9
Sanitz D 83 B12
San Javier E 56 F3
San Jordi E 42 F4
San Jorge de Alor E 51 B5
San José E 55 F8
San José del Valle E 52 C5
San José de Malcocinado E 52 D5
San Juan E 41 B6
San Juan de Alicante E 56 E4
San Juan de Aznalfarache E 51 E7
San Juan de la Nava E 46 D3
San Juan del Puerto E 51 E6
San Justo de la Vega E 39 D7
Sankt Aegyd am Neuwalde A 77 G9
Sankt Andrä A 73 C10
Sankt Andrä am Zicksee A 149 A7
Sankt Andreasberg D 79 C8
Sankt Anna S 93 C9
Sankt Anna am Aigen A 148 C5
Sankt Anton an der Jeßnitz A 77 G8
Sankt Augustin D 21 C8
Sankt Gallen A 73 A10
Sankt Gallen CH 27 F11
Sankt Gallenkirch A 71 C9
Sankt Gangloff D 79 E10
Sankt Georgen am Walde A 77 F7
Sankt Georgen im Schwarzwald D 27 D9
Sankt Gilgen A 73 A7
Sankt Goar D 21 D9
Sankt Goarshausen D 21 D9
Sankt Ingbert D 21 F8
Sankt Jakob im Rosental A 73 C9
Sankt Jakob im Walde A 148 B5
Sankt Jakob in Defereggen A 72 C5
Sankt Johann am Tauern A 73 B9
Sankt Johann im Pongau A 73 B7
Sankt Johann im Walde A 73 C6
Sankt Johann in Tirol A 72 A5
Sankt Julian D 21 E9
Sankt Katharinen D 185 C7
Sankt Lambrecht A 73 B9
Sankt Leonhard am Forst A 77 F8
Sankt Leonhard am Hornerwald A 77 E9
Sankt Leonhard im Pitztal A 71 C11
Sankt Lorenz A 73 A7
Sankt Lorenzen im Gitschtal A 73 C7
Sankt Lorenzen im Lesachtal A 73 C6
Sankt Lorenzen im Mürztal A 148 B4
Sankt Lorenzen ob Murau A 73 B9
Sankt Marein im Mürztal A 148 B4
Sankt Margarethen D 17 A12
Sankt Margarethen an der Raab A 148 B5
Sankt Margarethen bei Knittelfeld A 73 B10
Sankt Margarethen im Burgenland A 77 G11
Sankt Märgen D 27 D9
Sankt Martin A 73 B7
Sankt Martin A 77 E7
Sankt Martin im Mühlkreis A 76 F6
Sankt Michael im Burgenland A 148 B6
Sankt Michael im Lungau A 73 B8
Sankt Michael in Obersteiermark A 73 B11
Sankt Michaelisdonn D 82 C6
Sankt Moritz CH 71 D9
Sankt Nikolai im Saustal A 148 C4
Sankt Nikolai im Sölktal A 73 B9
Sankt Olof S 88 D6
Sankt Oswald bei Freistadt A 77 E7
Sankt Oswald ob Eibiswald A 73 C11
Sankt Pankraz A 73 A9
Sankt Paul im Lavanttal A 73 C10
Sankt Peter am Kammersberg A 73 B9
Sankt Peter am Ottersbach A 148 C5
Sankt-Peterburg RUS 129 F13
Sankt Peter-Freienstein A 73 B11
Sankt Peter in der Au A 77 F7
Sankt Peter-Ording D 82 B5
Sankt Pölten A 77 F9
Sankt Radegund A 76 F3
Sankt Ruprecht an der Raab A 148 B5
Sankt Stefan im Gailtal A 73 C8
Sankt Stefan ob Leoben A 73 B10
Sankt Stefan ob Stainz A 148 C4
Sankt Ulrich bei Steyr A 76 F6
Sankt Valentin A 77 F7
Sankt Veit am Vogau A 148 C5
Sankt Veit an der Glan A 73 C9
Sankt Veit an der Gölsen A 77 F9
Sankt Veit im Pongau A 73 B7
Sankt Veit in Defereggen A 72 C5
Sankt Wendel D 21 F8
Sankt Wolfgang D 75 F11
Sankt Wolfgang im Salzkammergut A 73 A7
San Lazzaro di Savena I 66 D3
San Leo I 66 E5
San Leonardo de Yagüe E 40 E5
San Leonardo in Passiria I 72 C3
San Lorenzo I 59 D8
San Lorenzo al Mare I 37 D7
San Lorenzo Bellizzi I 61 D6
San Lorenzo de Calatrava E 54 C5
San Lorenzo de El Escorial E 46 C4
San Lorenzo de la Parrilla E 47 E8
San Lorenzo di Sebato I 72 C4
San Lorenzo in Campo I 67 E6
San Lorenzo Nuovo I 62 B1
San Luca I 59 C9
Sanlúcar de Barrameda E 52 C4
Sanlúcar de Guadiana E 50 E5
Sanlúcar la Mayor E 51 E7
San Lucido I 60 E6
Sanluri I 64 D2
San Maddalena Vallalta I 72 C5
San Mamés de Campos E 40 D2
San Marcello I 67 E7
San Marcello Pistoiese I 66 D2
San Marco Argentano I 60 D6
San Marco dei Cavoti I 60 A3
San Marco in Lamis I 63 D9
San Marcos E 38 B3
San Marino RSM 66 E5
San Martín E 32 D1
San Martín E 40 B4
Sânmartin RO 151 C8
Sânmartin RO 152 C4
Sânmartin RO 153 E7
San Martín de la Vega E 46 D5
San Martín de la Vega del Alberche E 45 D10
San Martín del Pimpollar E 45 D10
San Martín de Montalbán E 46 E4
San Martín de Pusa E 46 E3
San Martín de Unx E 32 E2
San Martín de Valdeiglesias E 46 D4
San Martino Buon Albergo I 66 B3
San Martino di Castrozza I 72 D4
San Martino di Lupari I 72 E4
San Martino di Venezze I 66 B4
San Martino in Badia I 72 C4
San Martino in Passiria I 72 C3
San Martino in Pensilis I 63 D8
San Mateo de Gállego E 41 E10
San Mauro Castelverde I 58 D5
San Mauro Forte I 60 C6
San Mauro Marchesato I 61 E7
San Mauro Pascoli I 66 D5
San Mauro Torinese I 68 C4
San Menaio I 63 D9
San Michele al Tagliamento I 73 E6
San Michele Mondovì I 37 C7
San Michele Salentino I 61 B9
San Miguel de Arroyo E 40 F3
San Miguel de Bernuy E 40 F4
San Miguel de Salinas E 56 F3
Sânmihaiu Almaşului RO 151 C11
Sânmihaiu de Câmpie RO 152 D4
Sânmihaiu Român RO 159 B7
San Millán de la Cogolla E 40 D6
San Miniato I 66 E2
Sänna S 92 B5
Sannahed S 92 A6
Sannazzaro de'Burgondi I 69 C6
Sannicandro di Bari I 61 B7
Sannicandro Garganico I 63 D9
Sannicola I 61 C10
San Nicola dell'Alto I 61 E7
San-Nicolao F 37 G10
San Nicolás del Puerto E 51 C8
Sânnicolau Mare RO 150 E6
San Nicolò I 66 C4
San Nicolò d'Arcidano I 64 D2
San Nicolò Gerrei I 64 E3
Sanniki PL 139 F8
Sanok PL 145 D5
San Pablo de los Montes E 46 E4
San Pancrazio I 72 C3
San Pancrazio Salentino I 61 C9
San Paolo di Civitate I 63 D8
Sânpaul RO 151 D11
Sânpaul RO 152 E4
San Pedro E 55 B8
San Pedro de Alcántara E 53 D7
San Pedro de Ceque E 39 D7
San Pedro del Arroyo E 46 C3
San Pedro de Latarce E 39 E9
San Pedro del Pinatar E 56 F3
San Pedro del Romeral E 40 B4
San Pedro de Rozados E 45 C9
San Pedro Manrique E 41 D7
San Pedro Palmiches E 47 D8
San Pellegrino Terme I 69 B8
Sânpetru RO 153 F7
Sânpetru de Câmpie RO 152 D4
Sânpetru Mare RO 150 E6
San Piero a Sieve I 66 E3
San Piero Patti I 59 C6
San Pietro I 59 B7
San Pietro di Cadore I 73 C6
San Pietro in Cariano I 66 A2
San Pietro in Casale I 66 C3
San Pietro in Guarano I 61 E6
San Pietro Vernotico I 61 C10
San Polo d'Enza I 66 C1
San Prospero I 66 C3
Sanquhar GB 5 E9
San Quirico d'Orcia I 65 A5
San Rafael del Río E 42 F4
San Remo I 37 D7
San Román E 38 C5
San Román de Cameros E 41 D7
San Román de la Cuba E 39 D10
San Román de los Montes E 46 D3
San Roque E 38 B2
San Roque E 38 D3
San Roque E 53 D6
San Rufo I 60 C4
Sansac-de-Marmiesse F 29 F10
San Salvador de Cantamunda E 40 C3
San Salvatore I 64 D1
San Salvatore Monferrato I 37 B9
San Salvatore Telesino I 60 A2
San Salvo I 63 C7
San Sebastián E 32 D2
San Sebastián de los Ballesteros E 53 A7
San Sebastián de los Reyes E 46 C5
San Secondo Parmense I 66 C1
Sansepolcro I 66 E5
San Severa I 62 C1
San Severino Lucano I 60 C6
San Severino Marche I 67 F7
San Severo I 63 D8
San Silvestre de Guzmán E 51 E5
Sânsimion RO 153 E7
Sanski Most BIH 157 C6
Sansol E 32 E1
San Sosti I 60 D6
San Sperate I 64 E3
San Spirito I 61 A7
Şanţ RO 152 C5
Santa Amalia E 51 A7
Santa Ana E 55 B9
Santa Ana de Pusa E 46 E3
Santa Ana la Real E 51 D6
Santa Bàrbara E 42 F5
Santa Bárbara de Casa E 51 D5
Santacara E 32 F2
Santa Catalina de Armada E 38 B2
Santa Catarina P 50 C3
Santa Catarina da Fonte do Bispo P 50 E4
Santa Caterina dello Ionio I 59 B10
Santa Caterina di Pittinuri I 64 C2
Santa Caterina Villarmosa I 58 D5
Santa Cesarea Terme I 61 C10
Santa Cilia de Jaca E 32 E4
Santa Clara-a-Nova P 50 E3
Santa Clara-a-Velha P 50 D3
Santa Clara de Louredo P 50 D4
Santa Coloma de Farners E 43 D9
Santa Coloma de Queralt E 43 D6
Santa Colomba de Somoza E 39 D7
Santa Columba de Curueño E 39 C9
Santa Comba Dão P 44 D4
Santa Comba de Rossas P 39 E6
Santa Cristina d'Aro E 43 D9
Santa Cristina de la Polvorosa E 39 D8
Santa Croce Camerina I 59 F6
Santa Croce del Sannio I 60 A3
Santa Croce di Magliano I 63 D8
Santa Croce sull'Arno I 66 E2
Santa Cruz P 50 C2
Santa Cruz da Tapa P 44 C4
Santa Cruz de Bezana E 40 B4
Santa Cruz de Campézo E 32 E1
Santa Cruz de la Serós E 32 E4
Santa Cruz de la Sierra E 45 F9
Santa Cruz de la Zarza E 47 E6
Santa Cruz de los Cáñamos E 55 B7
Santa Cruz del Retamar E 46 D4
Santa Cruz de Moya E 47 E10
Santa Cruz de Mudela E 55 B6
Santadi I 64 E2
Santa Domenica Talao I 60 D5
Santa Domenica Vittoria I 59 D6
Santa Elena E 55 C5
Santa Elena de Jamuz E 39 D8
Santa Elisabetta I 58 E4
Santaella E 53 A7
Santa Engracia E 32 F1
Santa Eufemia E 54 B3
Santa Eugèni E 49 E10
Santa Eulalia E 39 B8
Santa Eulalia E 39 B9
Santa Eulalia E 47 C10
Santa Eulália P 51 A5
Santa Eulalia del Río E 57 D8
Santa Eulalia de Oscos E 38 B5
Santa Eulàlia de Riuprimer E 43 D8
Santa Fé E 53 B9
Santa Fiora I 65 B5
Sant'Agata de'Goti I 60 A3
Sant'Agata del Bianco I 59 C9
Sant'Agata di Esaro I 60 D5
Sant'Agata di Militello I 59 C6
Sant'Agata di Puglia I 60 A4
Sant'Agata Feltria I 66 E5
Santa Giusta I 64 D2
Santa Giustina I 72 D5
Sant'Agostino I 66 C3
Sant Agustí de Lluçanès E 43 C8
Santahamina FIN 127 E13
Santa Iria P 50 D4
Santa Justa P 50 A3
Sant'Alberto I 66 C5
Santalha P 38 E5
Santa Liestra y San Quílez E 33 F6
Santa Luce I 66 F2
Santa Lucia I 64 B4
Santa Lucia del Mela I 59 C7
Santa Lucía de Moraña E 38 C2
Santa Luzia P 50 D3
Santa Magdalena de Pulpís E 48 D5
Santa Mare RO 153 B10
Santa Margalida E 57 B11
Santa Margarida da Serra P 50 C2
Santa Margarida de Montbui E 43 D7
Santa Margarida do Sádão P 50 C3
Santa Margherita di Belice I 58 D3
Santa Margherita Ligure I 37 C10
Santa Maria CH 71 D10
Santa María E 32 F4
Santa Maria Capua Vetere I 60 A2
Santa Maria da Feira P 44 C3
Santa María de Cayón E 40 B4
Santa María de Corcó E 43 C8
Santa María de Huertas E 41 F7
Santa María del Berrocal E 45 C10
Santa María del Camí E 49 E10
Santa María del Campo E 40 D4
Santa María del Campo Rus E 47 E8
Santa Maria del Cedro I 60 D5
Santa Maria della Versa I 37 B10
Santa María de los Llanos E 47 F7
Santa María del Páramo E 39 D8
Santa María del Val E 47 C8
Santa María de Nieva E 55 E9
Santa María de Palautordera E 43 D8
Santa Maria di Castellabate I 60 C3
Santa Maria di Sala I 66 A5
Santa María la Real de Nieva E 46 B4
Santa Maria Maggiore I 68 A5
Santa Maria Navarrese I 64 D4
Santa Maria Nuova I 67 F7
Sântămăria-Orlea RO 159 B10
Santa Maria Rezzonico I 69 A7
Santa-Maria-Siché F 37 H9
Santa Marina I 60 C5
Santa Marina del Rey E 39 C8
Santa Marina Salina I 59 B6
Santa Marinella I 62 C1
Santa Marta E 47 F8
Santa Marta E 51 B6
Santa Marta de Penaguião P 44 B5
Santa Marta de Tormes E 45 C9
Sant'Ambroggio F 37 F9
Santana P 44 D3
Santana P 50 C1
Sântana RO 151 E8
Santana da Serra P 50 D3
Santana de Cambas P 50 D4
Santana do Mato P 50 B3
Sant'Anastasia I 60 B2
Sant'Anatolia di Narco I 62 B3
Santander E 40 B4
Sant'Andrea Apostolo dello Ionio I 59 B10
Sant'Andrea Frius I 64 E3
Sântandrei RO 151 C8
Sant'Angelo I 59 B9
Sant'Angelo a Fasanella I 60 C4
Sant'Angelo dei Lombardi I 60 B4
Sant'Angelo di Brolo I 59 C6
Sant'Angelo in Lizzola I 67 E6
Sant'Angelo in Vado I 66 E5
Sant'Angelo Lodigiano I 69 C7
Sant'Angelo Muxaro I 58 E4
Santa Ninfa I 58 D2
Sant'Anna Arresi I 64 E2
Sant'Antimo I 60 B2
Sant'Antioco I 64 E1
Sant Antoni de Portmany E 57 D7
Sant'Antonio Abate I 60 B3
Sant'Antonio di Gallura I 64 B3
Sant'Antonio di Santadi I 64 D1
Santanyí E 57 C11
Santa Olalla E 46 D4
Santa Oliva E 43 E7
Santa Ollala del Cala E 51 D7
Santa Pau E 43 C9
Santa Pola E 56 E3
Santar P 44 C5
Sant'Arcangelo I 60 C6
Santarcangelo di Romagna I 66 D5
Santarém P 44 F3
Sant'Arsenio I 60 C4
Santa Severina I 61 E7
Santas Martas E 39 D9
Santa Sofia I 66 E4
Santa Sofia P 50 B3
Santa Sofia d'Epiro I 61 D6
Santa Susana P 50 B4
Santa Susana P 50 C3
Santa Teresa di Gallura I 64 A3
Santa Teresa di Riva I 59 D7
Santău RO 151 C10
Santa Uxía de Ribeira E 38 C2
Santa Venerina I 59 D7
Santa Vitória P 50 D3
Santa Vitória do Ameixial P 50 B4
Sant Boi de Llobregat E 43 E8
Sant Carles de la Ràpita E 42 F5
Sant Celoni E 43 D8
Sant Cugat del Vallès E 43 E8
Sant'Egidio alla Vibrata I 62 B5
Sant'Elia a Pianisi I 63 D7
Sant'Elia Fiumerapido I 62 D5
Sant Elm E 49 E9
San Telmo E 51 D6
Sant'Elpidio a Mare I 67 F8
San Teodoro I 64 B4
Santeramo in Colle I 61 B7
Santervás de la Vega E 39 C10
Santes Creus E 43 E6
Sant Feliu de Guíxols E 43 D10
Sant Feliu de Pallerols E 43 C9
Sant Feliu Sasserra E 43 D8
Santhià I 68 C5
Sant Hilari Sacalm E 43 D9
Sant Hipòlit de Voltregà E 43 C8
Santiago de Alcántara E 45 E6
Santiago de Calatrava E 53 A8
Santiago de Compostela E 38 C2
Santiago de Covelo E 38 D3
Santiago de la Espada E 55 C7
Santiago de la Ribera E 56 F3
Santiago del Campo E 45 E8
Santiago do Cacém P 50 C2
Santiago do Escoural P 50 B3
Santiagomillas E 39 D7
Santibáñez de Béjar E 45 D9
Santibáñez de la Peña E 39 C10
Santibáñez de la Sierra E 45 C9
Santibáñez de Tera E 39 E8
Santibáñez de Vidriales E 39 D7
Santibáñez el Bajo E 45 D8
Santibáñez Zarzaguda E 40 D4
Sant'Ilario d'Enza I 66 C1
Santillana E 40 B3
Santimbru RO 152 E3
Santiponce E 51 E7

Them DK 86 C5
Themar D 75 A8
The Mumbles GB 12 B6
Thenay F 29 B8
Thénezay F 28 B5
Thenon F 29 E8
Theologos GR 171 C7
Théoule-sur-Mer F 36 D5
The Pike IRL 9 D7
Therma GR 171 D9
Thermi GR 169 C9
Thermisia GR 175 E7
Thermo GR 174 B4
Thermopyles GR 175 B6
Thérouanne F 18 C5
The Sheddings GB 4 F4
Thespies GR 175 C7
Thesprotiko GR 168 F4
Thessaloniki GR 169 C8
The Stocks GB 15 E10
Thetford GB 15 C10
Theth AL 163 E8
Theux B 19 C12
Thèze F 32 D5
Thèze F 35 B10
Thiaucourt-Regniéville F 26 C4
Thiberville F 24 B3
Thibie F 25 C11
Thiéblemont-Farémont F 25 C12
Thiendorf D 80 D5
Thiene I 72 E3
Thierhaupten D 75 E8
Thierrens CH 31 B10
Thiers F 30 D4
Thiersee A 72 A5
Thiersheim D 75 B11
Thiesi I 64 B2
Thießow D 84 B5
Thiézac F 29 E11
Thimert-Gâtelles F 24 C5
Thin-le-Moutier F 19 E10
Thionville F 20 F6
Thiron Gardais F 24 D4
Thirsk GB 11 C9
Thisted DK 86 B3
Thisvi GR 175 C6
Thiva GR 175 C7
Thivars F 24 D5
Thiviers F 29 E7
Thizy F 30 C5
Thoirette F 31 C8
Thoiry F 24 C6
Thoissey F 30 C6
Tholen NL 16 E2
Tholey D 21 F8
Thomastown IRL 9 C8
Thommen B 20 D6
Thônes F 31 D9
Thonnance-lès-Joinville F 26 D3
Thonon-les-Bains F 31 C9
Thorame-Haute F 36 C5
Thoras F 30 F4
Thoré-la-Rochette F 24 E4
Thorenc F 36 D5
Thorigny-sur-Oreuse F 25 D9
Thörl A 73 A11
Thorn NL 19 B12
Thornaby-on-Tees GB 11 B9
Thornbury GB 13 B9
Thorne GB 11 D10
Thorney GB 11 F11
Thornhill GB 5 E9
Thorning DK 86 C4
Thornton GB 10 D5
Thorpe-le-Soken GB 15 D11
Thorpe Market GB 15 B11
Thorpeness GB 15 C12
Thorsager DK 86 C6
Thorshøj DK 90 E7
Thorsø DK 86 C5
Thouarcé F 23 F11
Thouaré-sur-Loire F 23 F9
Thouars F 28 B5
Thouria GR 174 E5
Thourotte F 18 F6
Thrapston GB 15 C7
Threshfield GB 11 C7
Thropton GB 5 E13
Thrumster GB 3 J10
Thuès-entre-Valls F 33 E10
Thueyts F 35 A7
Thuin B 19 D9
Thuine D 17 D9
Thuir F 34 E4
Thum D 80 E3
Thun CH 70 D5
Thundersley GB 15 D10
Thüngen D 74 C6
Thüngersheim D 74 C6
Thuré F 29 B6
Thuret F 30 D3
Thurey F 31 B7
Thüringen A 71 C9
Thurins F 30 D6
Thürkow D 83 C13
Thurlby GB 11 F11
Thurles IRL 9 C7
Thurnau D 75 B9
Thursby GB 5 F10
Thurso GB 3 H9
Thury-Harcourt F 23 C11
Thusis CH 71 D8
Thwaite GB 11 C7
Thyborøn DK 86 B2
Thyez F 31 C10
Thymiana GR 177 C7
Thyregod DK 86 D4
Thyrnau D 76 E5
Tia Mare RO 160 F5
Tiana I 64 C3
Țibana RO 153 D10
Țibănești RO 153 D10
Tibble S 99 D9
Tiberget S 102 D6
Tibi E 56 D3
Tibolddaróc H 145 H2
Tibro S 92 C4
Țibucani RO 153 C9
Tice BIH 156 D6
Ticehurst GB 15 E9
Ticha BG 167 D6
Tichá CZ 146 B6
Tichilești RO 155 C1
Tičići BIH 157 D9
Ticknall GB 11 F9
Țicleni RO 160 D2
Țicușu RO 152 F6
Ticvaniu Mare RO 159 C8
Tidaholm S 91 C14
Tidan S 91 B15
Tiddische D 79 A8
Tidenham GB 13 B9
Tidersrum S 92 D7
Tiebas E 32 E2
Tiedra E 39 E9
Tiefenbach D 75 D12
Tiefenbach D 76 E4
Tiefenbronn D 27 C10
Tiefencastel CH 71 D9
Tiefensee D 84 E5
Tiel NL 16 E4
Tielen B 182 C5
Tielt B 19 C7
Tiemassaari FIN 125 F10
Tienen B 19 C10
Tiengen D 27 E9
Tiercé F 23 E11
Tierga E 41 E8
Tierp S 99 B9
Tierzo E 47 C9
Țifești RO 153 F10
Țigănași RO 153 C10
Țigănești RO 160 F6
Tigare BIH 158 E3
Tighina MD 154 D4
Țighira MD 153 C11
Tighnabruaich GB 4 D6
Tignale I 69 B10
Tignes F 31 E10
Tigveni RO 160 C5
Tigy F 25 E7
Tiha Bârgăului RO 152 C5
Tihany H 149 C9
Tihemetsa EST 131 E10
Tihilä FIN 123 C16
Tihusniemi FIN 124 F9
Tiistenjoki FIN 123 E10
Tiitilänkylä FIN 123 E17
Tijesno HR 156 E4
Tijnje NL 16 B5
Tíjola E 55 E8
Tikkakoski FIN 123 F15
Tikkala FIN 123 F14
Tikkala FIN 125 F14
Tikkurila FIN 127 E13
Tikob DK 87 C10
Tilburg NL 16 E4
Tilbury GB 15 E9
Til-Châtel F 26 E3
Tildarg GB 4 F4
Tileagd RO 151 C9
Tilehurst GB 13 C12
Tilh F 32 C4
Tilișca RO 152 F3
Tillac F 33 D6
Tillberga S 98 C7
Tillicoultry GB 5 C9
Tillières-sur-Avre F 24 C5
Tilloy-et-Bellay F 25 B12
Tillyfourie GB 3 L11
Tilly-sur-Seulles F 23 B10
Tilvikai LT 134 E3
Tilža LV 133 C2
Tim DK 86 C2
Timahoe IRL 7 G8
Timár H 145 G3
Timau I 73 C7
Timelkam A 76 F5
Timiryazevo RUS 136 C4
Timișești RO 153 C9
Timișoara RO 151 F7
Timmele S 91 D13
Timmendorfer Strand D 83 C9
Timmernabben S 89 B10
Timmersdala S 91 B14
Timola FIN 125 F9
Timoleague IRL 8 E5
Timolin IRL 7 G9
Timoniemi FIN 121 F13
Timovaara FIN 125 D12
Timrå S 103 A13
Timring DK 86 C3
Timsgearraidh GB 2 J2
Tinahely IRL 9 C10
Tinajas E 47 D7
Tinalhas P 44 E5
Tinca RO 151 D8
Tinchebray F 23 C10
Tineo E 39 B7
Tingere LV 134 B5
Tinglev DK 86 F4
Tingsryd S 89 B7
Tingstad S 93 B8
Tingstäde S 93 D13
Tingvatn N 94 F6
Tingvoll N 100 A8
Tingwall GB 3 G10
Tinja BIH 157 C10
Tinjan HR 67 B8
Tinn N 95 C9
Tinnoset N 95 C10
Tinos GR 176 D5
Tiñosillos E 46 C3
Tinosu RO 161 D8
Tinqueux F 19 F8
Tintagel GB 12 D5
Tinténiac F 23 D8
Tintern Parva GB 13 B9
Țintești RO 161 C9
Tintigny B 19 E12
Tīnūži LV 135 C9
Tiobraid Árann IRL 8 D6
Tione di Trento I 69 A10
Tipasoja FIN 125 B11
Tipperary IRL 8 D6
Tiptree GB 15 D10
Tipu EST 131 E10
Tira MD 154 B2
Tiranë AL 168 B2
Tiranges F 30 E4
Tirano I 69 A9
Tiraspol MD 154 D5
Tiraspolul Nou MD 154 D5
Tire TR 177 C10
Tiream RO 151 B9
Tīreļi LV 134 C7
Tirgo E 40 C6
Tiriez E 55 B8
Tirig E 48 D5
Tiriolo I 59 B10
Tirkšliai LT 134 D4
Tîrnova MD 153 A11
Tirrenia I 66 E1
Tirro FIN 113 F18
Tirschenreuth D 75 C11
Tirstrup DK 86 C7
Tirteafuera E 54 B4
Tirza LV 135 B12
Tisău RO 161 C9
Tišća BIH 157 D10
Tishevitsa BG 165 C8
Tishono RUS 136 E2
Tišice CZ 77 B7
Tismana RO 159 C10
Tišnov CZ 77 D10
Tisovec SK 147 D9
Tistrup Stationsby DK 86 D3
Tisvilde DK 87 C10
Tiszaalpár H 150 D4
Tiszabecs H 145 G6
Tiszabezdéd H 145 G5
Tiszabő H 150 C5
Tiszabura H 150 C5
Tiszacsege H 151 B7
Tiszadada H 145 G3
Tiszaderzs H 150 B6
Tiszadob H 145 G3
Tiszaeszlár H 145 G3
Tiszaföldvár H 150 D5
Tiszafüred H 150 B6
Tiszagyenda H 150 C6
Tiszaigar H 150 B6
Tiszajenő H 150 C5
Tiszakanyár H 145 G4
Tiszakarád H 145 G4
Tiszakécske H 150 D5
Tiszakerecseny H 145 G5
Tiszakeszi H 151 B6
Tiszakürt H 150 D5
Tiszalök H 145 G3
Tiszalúc H 145 G3
Tiszanagyfalu H 145 G3
Tiszanána H 150 B6
Tiszaörs H 150 B6
Tiszapalkonya H 145 H3
Tiszapüspöki H 150 C5
Tiszaroff H 150 C5
Tiszasas H 150 D5
Tiszasüly H 150 C5
Tiszaszalka H 145 G5
Tiszaszentimre H 150 C6
Tiszasziget H 150 E5
Tiszatarján H 147 F12
Tiszatelek H 145 G4
Tiszatenyő H 150 C5
Tiszaug H 150 D5
Tiszaújváros H 145 H3
Tiszavárkony H 150 C5
Tiszavasvári H 145 H3
Titaguas E 47 E10
Titel SRB 158 C5
Țițești RO 160 C6
Tithorea GR 175 B6
Tito I 60 B5
Titova Korenica HR 156 C4
Titov Drvar BIH 156 D5
Titran N 104 D4
Tittelsnes N 94 C3
Titting D 75 E9
Tittmoning D 76 F3
Titu RO 161 D7
Titulcia E 46 D5
Tiukuvaara FIN 117 C13
Tiurajärvi FIN 117 C12
Tivat MNE 163 E6
Tivenys E 42 F5
Tiverton GB 13 D8
Tivissa E 42 E5
Tivoli I 62 D3
Tizzano F 37 H9
Tjæreborg DK 86 E3
Tjäkkjokk S 109 E15
Tjällmo S 92 B6
Tjåmotis S 109 C16
Tjappsåive S 109 E17
Tjärmyrberget S 106 C9
Tjärn S 107 D13
Tjärnäs S 98 A6
Tjärnberg S 107 A15
Tjärstad S 92 C7
Tjärutträsk S 118 B8
Tjautas S 116 D5
Tjeldnes N 111 D11
Tjeldstø N 100 E1
Tjelle N 100 A7
Tjentište BIH 157 F10
Tjöck FIN 122 F6
Tjøme N 90 A7
Tjønnefoss N 90 B4
Tjorhom N 94 E5
Tjörnarp S 87 D13
Tjøtta N 108 E3
Tjuda FIN 126 E8
Tjuvskjær N 111 C13
Tkon HR 156 E3
Tleń PL 138 C5
Tlmače SK 147 E7
Tłuchowo PL 139 E7
Tlumačov CZ 146 C5
Tłuszcz PL 139 F11
Toab GB 3 F14
Toaca RO 152 D5
Toálmás H 150 C4
Toano I 66 D2
Tobar an Choire IRL 6 D5
Tobarra E 55 B9
Tobercurry IRL 6 D5
Tobermore GB 4 F3
Tobermory GB 4 B4
Tobo S 99 B9
Tobyn S 97 C8
Tocane-St-Apre F 29 E6
Tocco da Casauria I 62 C5
Tocha P 44 D3
Töcksfors S 96 C6
Tocón E 53 B9
Todal N 104 E5
Toddington GB 13 B11
Todi I 62 B2
Todireni RO 153 B10
Todirești RO 153 B8
Todirești RO 153 C9
Todirești RO 153 D10
Todmorden GB 11 D7
Todolella E 42 F3
Todorići BIH 157 D7
Todor-Ikonomovo BG 161 F10
Todorovo BG 161 F9
Todtmoos D 27 E8
Todtnau D 27 E8
Toén E 38 D4
Toft GB 3 E14
Toft N 108 F3
Tofta S 87 A10
Tofta S 93 D12
Tofte N 95 C13
Tøftedal S 91 B10
Tofterup DK 86 D3
Toftir FO 2 A3
Toftlund DK 86 E4
Tofyeli BY 133 E5
Togher IRL 7 E10
Togher IRL 7 F7
Togher IRL 8 E4
Togston GB 5 E13
Tohmajärvi FIN 125 F14
Tohmo FIN 115 E2
Toholampi FIN 123 C12
Toija FIN 127 E9
Toijala FIN 127 C10
Toila EST 132 C2
Toirano I 37 C8
Toivakka FIN 119 B17
Toivakka FIN 123 F16
Toivala FIN 124 E9
Toivola FIN 128 C6
Tojaci MK 169 B6
Töjby FIN 122 E6
Tök H 149 A11
Tokachka BG 171 B9
Tokaj H 145 G3
Tokarnia PL 143 E9
Tokarnia PL 147 B9
Tokod H 149 A11
Tököl H 149 B11
Tokrajärvi FIN 125 E15
Toksovo RUS 129 E14
Tolastadh Úr GB 2 J4
Tolbaños E 46 C3
Tolbert NL 16 B6
Tolcsva H 145 G3
Toledo E 46 E4
Tolentino I 67 F7
Tolfa I 62 C1
Tolga N 101 B14
Toliejai LT 135 F10
Tolja FIN 119 B17
Tolk D 82 A7
Tolkmicko PL 139 B8
Tollarp S 88 D5
Tollered S 91 D11
Tollesbury GB 15 D10
Tollo I 63 C6
Tølløse DK 87 D9
Töllsjö S 91 D12
Tolmachevo RUS 132 D6
Tolmezzo I 73 D7
Tolmin SLO 73 D8
Tolna H 149 D11
Tolnanémedi H 149 C10
Tolne DK 90 E7
Tolo GR 175 D6
Tolocănești MD 153 A11
Tolonen FIN 117 E14
Tolosa E 32 D1
Tolosa P 44 F5
Tolosenmäki FIN 125 F14
Tolox E 53 C7
Tolšići BIH 157 D10
Tolva E 42 C5
Tolva FIN 121 B12
Tolvayarvi RUS 125 F16
Tolve I 60 B6
Tomai MD 154 D2
Tomai MD 154 E3
Tomar P 44 E4
Tomares E 51 E7
Tomaševac SRB 158 C6
Tomaševo MNE 163 C8
Tomašica BIH 157 C6
Tomášikovo SK 146 E5
Tomášovce SK 147 E9
Tomaszów Lubelski PL 144 C7
Tomaszów Mazowiecki PL 141 G2
Tomatin GB 3 L9
Tombebœf F 33 A6
Tomelilla S 88 D5
Tomelloso E 47 F6
Tomești RO 151 E10
Tomești RO 151 F9
Tomești RO 153 C11
Tomice PL 147 B8
Tomintoul GB 3 L10
Tomislavgrad BIH 157 E7
Tømmerneset N 111 E10
Tommerup DK 86 E6
Tomnavoulin GB 3 L10
Tömörkény H 150 D5
Tompa H 150 E4
Tomra N 100 A5
Tomșani RO 161 D8
Tona E 43 D8
Tonara I 64 C3
Tonbridge GB 15 E9
Tondela P 44 C4
Tønder DK 86 F3
Tonezza del Cimone I 69 B11
Tongeren B 19 C11
Tongland GB 5 F8
Tongue GB 2 J8
Tönisvorst D 183 C8
Tonkopuro FIN 115 E4
Tonna GB 13 B7
Tonnay-Boutonne F 28 D4
Tonnay-Charente F 28 D4
Tonneins F 33 B6
Tonnerre F 25 E10
Tonnes N 108 C5
Tönning D 82 B5
Tønsberg N 95 D12
Tönsen S 103 D12
Tonstad N 94 E5
Tonsvik N 111 A17
Toombeola IRL 6 F3
Toomebridge GB 4 F4
Tootsi EST 131 D9
Topalu RO 155 D2
Topana RO 160 D5
Topares E 55 D8
Toparlar TR 181 C9
Topchii BG 161 F9
Töpchin D 80 B5
Topčic-Polje BIH 157 D8
Topcliffe GB 11 C9
Töpen D 75 B10
Topeno FIN 127 D11
Tophisar TR 173 D9
Topleț RO 159 D9
Topliceni RO 161 C10
Topli Do SRB 165 C6
Toplița RO 152 D6
Toplița RO 159 B10
Töplitz D 79 B12
Topojë AL 168 C1
Topola SRB 158 E6
Topolčani MK 168 B5
Topoľčany SK 146 D6
Topoľčianky SK 146 E6
Topolia GR 178 E6
Topólka PL 138 E6
Topolnica SRB 159 E9
Topoľníky SK 146 F5
Topolog RO 155 D2
Topolovac HR 149 F6
Topolovățu Mare RO 151 F8
Topoloveni RO 160 D6
Topolovgrad BG 166 E6
Topolovnik SRB 159 D7
Topolovo BG 166 F4
Topolšica SLO 73 D11
Toponica SRB 158 F6
Toporec SK 145 E1
Toporivtsi UA 153 A8
Topórów PL 81 B8
Toporu RO 161 E7
Topozyk PL 85 C10
Toppenstedt D 83 D8
Topraisar RO 155 E2
Topsham GB 13 D8
Topusko HR 156 B4
Torà E 43 D6
Toral de los Guzmanes E 39 D8
Toral de los Vados E 39 C6
Torano Castello I 60 E6
Torasalo FIN 125 F10
Toras-Sieppi FIN 117 C11
Torbali TR 177 C9
Torbjörntorp S 91 C14
Torbygget S 102 A4
Torchiara I 60 C4
Torchiarolo I 61 C10
Torcy F 30 B5
Torda SRB 158 B5
Tordas H 149 B11
Tordehumos E 39 E9
Tordera E 43 D9
Tordesillas E 39 E10
Tordesilos E 47 C9
Töre S 118 C9
Töreboda S 91 B15
Toreby DK 83 A11
Torekov S 87 C11
Torella del Sannio I 63 D7
Torellano E 56 E3
Torelló E 43 C8
Toreno E 39 C6
Torestorp S 91 E12
Torgau D 80 C3
Torgelow D 84 C6
Torgiano I 62 A2
Torhamn S 89 C9
Torhout B 19 B7
Tori EST 131 E9
Torigni-sur-Vire F 23 B10
Torija E 47 C6
Torino I 68 C4
Toritto I 61 B7
Torkanivka UA 154 A4
Torkovichi RUS 132 D7
Torla E 32 E5
Torma EST 131 D13
Tormac RO 159 B7
Törmänen FIN 113 E19
Törmänen FIN 115 A2
Törmänki FIN 117 E13
Törmänmäki FIN 121 E10
Törmäsenvaara FIN 121 C13
Törmäsjärvi FIN 119 B12
Tormestorp S 87 C13
Tormón E 47 D10
Tormore GB 4 D6
Tornadizos de Ávila E 46 C3
Tornaľa SK 145 G1
Tornavacas E 45 D9
Tornby DK 90 D6
Tornemark DK 87 E9
Tornes N 100 A6
Tørnes N 111 D11
Tornesch D 82 C7
Torneträsk S 111 D18
Tornimäe EST 130 D6
Tornio FIN 119 C12
Tornjoš SRB 150 F4
Torno I 69 B7
Tornos E 47 C10
Tornow D 84 D4
Toro E 39 E9
Torö S 93 B11
Törökbálint H 149 B11
Törökszentmiklós H 150 C5
Torony H 149 B7
Toros BG 165 C9
Toroshino RUS 132 F4
Torp FIN 99 B13
Torpa S 92 D6
Torphins GB 3 L11
Torpo N 101 E9
Torpoint GB 12 E6
Torpsbruk S 88 A7
Torpshammar S 103 B11
Torquay GB 13 E7
Torquemada E 40 D3
Torraiba de Calatrava E 54 A5
Torralba E 47 D8
Torralba I 64 B2
Torralba de Aragón E 41 E10
Torralba de El Burgo E 40 E6
Torralba de los Sisones E 47 C10
Torralba de Oropesa E 45 E10
Torrão P 50 C3
Torrböle S 107 D17
Torre-Alháquime E 51 F9
Torre Annunziata I 60 B2
Torrebaja E 47 D10
Torreblanca E 48 D5
Torreblascopedro E 53 A9
Torrebruna I 63 D7
Torrecaballeros E 46 C4
Torrecampo E 54 C3
Torre Canne I 61 B8
Torre-Cardela E 55 D6
Torrecilla de Alcañiz E 42 F3
Torrecilla de la Jara E 46 E3
Torrecilla de la Orden E 45 B10
Torrecilla del Rebollar E 42 F1
Torrecillas de la Tiesa E 45 E9
Torrecuso I 60 A3
Torre da Gadanha P 50 B3
Torre das Vargens P 44 F5
Torre de Coelheiros P 50 C4
Torre de Dona Chama P 38 E5
Torre de Embesora E 48 D4
Torredeita P 44 C4
Torre de Juan Abad E 55 B6
Torre del Bierzo E 39 C7
Torre del Burgo E 47 C6
Torre del Campo E 53 A9
Torre del Greco I 60 B2
Torre del Mar E 53 C8
Torredembarra E 43 E6
Torre de Miguel Sesmero E 51 B6
Torre de Moncorvo P 45 B6
Torre de'Passeri I 62 C5
Torre de Santa María E 45 F8
Torredonjimeno E 53 A9
Torre do Terrenho P 44 C6
Torrefarrera E 42 D5
Torregamones E 39 F7
Torregrossa E 42 D5
Torreiglesias E 46 B4
Torreira P 44 C3
Torrejoncillo E 45 E8
Torrejoncillo del Rey E 47 D7
Torrejón de Ardoz E 46 D6
Torrejón del Rey E 46 C6
Torrejón el Rubio E 45 E9
Torrelacarcel E 47 C10
Torrelaguna E 46 C5
Torrelapaja E 41 E8
Torrelavega E 40 B3
Torrellas E 41 E8
Torrelles de Foix E 43 E7
Torrelobatón E 39 E9
Torrelodones E 46 C5
Torremaggiore I 63 D8
Torremanzanas-La Torre de les Macanes E 56 D4
Torremayor E 51 B6
Torremegía E 51 B7
Torre Mileto I 63 D9
Torremocha E 45 F8
Torremocha de Jiloca E 47 C10
Torremolinos E 53 C7
Torrenostra E 48 D5
Torrent E 48 F4
Torrente del Cinca E 42 E4
Torrenueva E 55 B6
Torreorgaz E 45 F8
Torre Orsaia I 60 C4
Torre-Pacheco E 56 F3
Torre Pellice I 31 F11
Torreperogil E 55 C6
Torres E 53 A9
Torresandino E 40 E4
Torre San Giovanni I 61 D10
Torre Santa Susanna I 61 C9
Torres de Albánchez E 55 C7
Torres de Berrellén E 41 E9
Torres de la Alameda E 46 D6
Torres del Carrizal E 39 E8
Torresmenudas E 45 B9
Torres Novas P 44 F3
Torres Vedras P 44 F2
Torrevelilla E 42 F3
Torrevieja E 56 F3
Torrice I 62 D4
Torricella I 61 C9
Torricella in Sabina I 62 C3
Torricella Peligna I 63 C6
Torricella Sicura I 62 B5
Torricella Taverne CH 69 A6
Torrico E 45 E10
Torri del Benaco I 69 B10
Torridon GB 2 K5
Torriglia I 37 B10
Torrijas E 48 D3
Torrijo E 41 F8
Torrijo del Campo E 47 C10
Torrijos E 46 E4
Torrin GB 2 L4
Torring DK 86 D4
Torring N 105 C10
Torrita di Siena I 66 F4
Torroal P 50 C2
Torroella de Montgrí E 43 C10
Torrox E 53 C9
Torrubia del Campo E 47 E7
Torrubia de Soria E 41 E7
Torrvika N 104 C7
Torsåker S 98 A6
Torsång S 97 B14
Torsås S 89 C10
Torsbøl DK 86 F4
Torsbole S 107 E15
Torsborg S 102 A5
Torsby S 97 B9
Torsby S 97 C9
Torsebro S 88 C6
Torshälla S 98 D6
Tórshavn FO 2 A3
Torsholma FIN 126 E5
Torsken N 111 B13
Torslanda S 91 D10
Torsminde DK 86 C2
Torsö S 91 B14
Torsvåg N 112 C4
Törtel H 150 C4
Tortellà E 43 C9
Torteval GBG 22 B6
Torthorwald GB 5 E9
Tortinmäki FIN 126 D7
Tórtola de Henares E 47 C6
Tórtoles de Esgueva E 40 E3
Tortoli I 64 D4
Tortomanu RO 155 E2
Tortona I 37 B9
Tortora I 60 D5
Tortoreto I 62 B5
Tortorici I 59 C6
Tortosa E 42 F5
Tortozendo P 44 D5
Tortuera E 47 C9
Tortuna S 98 C7
Toruń PL 138 D6
Torun' UA 145 F8
Torup S 87 B12
Tõrva EST 131 E11
Tor Vaianica I 62 D2
Torvandi EST 131 E13
Torvenkylä FIN 119 F11
Torvik N 100 B3
Torvik N 104 F4
Torvikbukt N 104 F3
Tørvikbygd N 94 B4
Torvinen FIN 117 D17
Torvizcón E 55 F6
Torvsjö S 107 C12
Torysa SK 145 E2
Torzym PL 81 B8
Tosbotn N 108 F4
Toscolano-Maderno I 69 B10
Tossa E 43 D9
Tossåsen S 102 A5
Tossåsen S 102 A7
Tossavanlahti FIN 123 D16
Tosse F 32 C3
Tösse S 91 B12
Tossicia I 62 B5
Tosside GB 11 C7
Tõstamaa EST 131 E7
Tostedt D 82 D7
Tószeg H 150 C5
Toszek PL 142 F6
Totana E 55 D10
Totebo S 93 D8
Tôtes F 18 E3
Totești RO 159 B10
Tótkomlós H 150 E6
Totland GB 13 D11
Totnes GB 13 E7
Totra S 103 E13
Tótszerdahely H 149 D7
Tøttdal N 105 C10
Tottijärvi FIN 127 C9
Totton GB 13 D12
Tótvázsony H 149 B9
Touça P 45 B6
Toucy F 25 E9
Touffailles F 33 B8
Touget F 33 C7
Toul F 26 C4
Toulon F 35 D10
Toulon-sur-Allier F 30 B3
Toulon-sur-Arroux F 30 B5
Toulouges F 34 E4
Toulouse F 33 C8
Tounj HR 156 B3
Touques F 23 B12
Tourch F 22 D4
Tourcoing F 19 C7
Tourlaville F 23 A8
Tournai B 19 C7
Tournan-en-Brie F 25 C8
Tournay F 33 D6
Tournecoupe F 33 C7
Tournefeuille F 33 C8
Tournon-d'Agenais F 33 B7
Tournon-St-Martin F 29 B7
Tournon-sur-Rhône F 30 E6
Tournus F 30 B6
Tourny F 24 B6
Tourouvre F 24 C4
Tours F 24 F4
Tourteron F 19 E10
Tourtoirac F 29 E8
Toury F 24 D6
Tous E 48 F3
Tõusi EST 131 D7
Touvois F 28 B2
Toužim CZ 76 B3
Tovačov CZ 146 C4
Tovariševo SRB 158 C3
Tovarné SK 145 F4
Tovarnik HR 157 B11
Toven N 108 D5
Tovrljane SRB 164 C3
Towcester GB 14 C7
Tower IRL 8 E5
Toymskardlia N 106 A5
Töysä FIN 123 E11
Traar D 183 C9
Trabada E 38 B5
Trabanca E 45 B8
Trabazos E 39 E7
Traben D 21 E8
Trąbki PL 144 D1
Trąbki Wielkie PL 138 B6
Traboch A 73 B10
Trabotivište MK 165 F6
Traby BY 137 E12
Trachili GR 175 B9
Tradate I 69 B6
Trädet S 91 D14
Trædal N 111 D14
Trafrask IRL 8 E3
Tragacete E 47 D9
Tragana GR 175 B7
Tragano GR 174 D3
Tragjas AL 168 D2
Tragwein A 77 F7
Traian RO 153 D10
Traian RO 155 C1
Traian RO 155 C2
Traian RO 160 E4
Traian RO 160 F6
Traian Vuia RO 151 F9
Traid E 47 C9
Traiguera E 42 F4
Train D 75 E10
Traînel F 25 D9
Traînou F 24 E7
Traisen A 77 F9
Traiskirchen A 77 F10
Traismauer A 77 F9
Traitsching D 75 D12
Trakai LT 137 D10
Trakovice SK 146 E5
Trakšėdžiai LT 134 F2
Tralee IRL 8 D3
Trá Li IRL 8 D3
Tramacastilla E 47 D9
Tramagal P 44 F4
Tramariglio I 64 B1
Tramatza I 64 C2
Tramayes F 30 C6
Tramelan CH 27 F7
Trá Mhór IRL 9 D8
Tramonti di Sopra I 73 D6
Tramonti di Sotto I 73 D6
Tramore IRL 9 D8
Tramutola I 60 C5
Tranås S 92 C5
Tranbjerg DK 86 C6
Trancoso P 44 C6
Tranebjerg DK 86 D7
Tranemo S 91 E13
Trången S 105 D15
Trånghalla S 92 D4
Trängslet S 102 D6
Trångsviken S 105 E16
Trani I 61 A6
Trannes F 25 D12
Tranovalto GR 169 D6
Tranøy N 111 D10
Trans F 23 D8
Trans-en-Provence F 36 D4
Transtrand S 102 D5
Transtrand S 102 E5
Tranum DK 86 A4
Tranvik S 99 D11
Trapani I 58 C2
Trapene LV 135 B13
Traplice CZ 146 C4
Trappes F 24 C7
Trarbach D 185 E7
Traryd S 87 B13
Trasacco I 62 D5
Träskvik FIN 122 F7
Trasmiras E 38 D4
Trasobares E 41 E8
Tratalias I 64 E2
Traun A 76 F6
Traunreut D 73 A6
Traunstein A 77 F8
Traunstein D 73 A6
Traupis LT 135 E9
Trava SLO 73 E10
Trävad S 91 C13
Travagliato I 66 A1
Travanca do Mondego P 44 D4
Travassô P 44 C4
Travemünde D 83 C9
Travenbrück D 83 C8
Travers CH 31 B10
Traversetolo I 66 C1
Trávnica SK 146 E6
Travnik BIH 157 D8
Travo I 37 B11
Trawniki PL 141 H8

U

V

Viişoara RO 153 D8
Viisoara RO 153 E11
Viişoara RO 160 F6
Viitaila FIN 127 C13
Viitala FIN 123 E10
Viitamäki FIN 123 C16
Viitaniemi FIN 125 D10
Viitapohja FIN 127 B11
Viitaranta FIN 115 D3
Viitaranta FIN 121 B12
Viitasaari FIN 123 D15
Viitavaara FIN 121 E13
Viitavaara FIN 121 F12
Viitka EST 132 F1
Viitna EST 131 C12
Viivikonna EST 132 C2
Vijciems LV 131 F11
Vik N 90 C4
Vik N 94 B2
Vik N 108 B9
Vik N 108 F3
Vik N 110 D7
Vik S 88 D6
Vika FIN 117 E16
Vika N 101 A15
Vika S 97 A14
Vikajärvi FIN 117 E16
Vikan N 104 E5
Vikan N 105 B10
Vikarbyn S 97 B15
Vikarbyn S 103 E9
Vikartovce SK 145 F1
Vikbyn S 97 B15
Vike N 100 E3
Vike S 103 A12
Vikebukt N 100 A6
Vikedal N 94 D3
Viken S 87 C11
Viken S 103 B9
Viken S 103 B11
Vikersund N 95 C11
Vikeså N 94 E4
Vikevåg N 94 D3
Vikholmen N 108 D4
Vīķi LV 131 F9
Vikingstad S 92 C6
Vikmanshyttan S 97 B14
Vikna N 105 B9
Vikoč BIH 157 F10
Vikøyri N 100 D5
Vikran N 111 A16
Vikran N 111 C12
Vikran N 113 A12
Viksberg S 97 B14
Viksjö S 103 A13
Viksjöfors S 103 D10
Viksmon S 107 E12
Vīksna LV 133 B2
Viktarinas LT 137 E8
Vikten N 110 D5
Viktorivka UA 154 C6
Vikýřovice CZ 77 C11
Vila E 38 E3
Vila Boa P 45 D7
Vila Boa do Bispo P 44 B4
Vila Caiz P 38 F3
Vila Chã de Sá P 44 C5
Vila Cova da Lixa P 38 F3
Vilada E 43 C7
Viladamat E 43 C10
Vila da Ponte P 38 E4
Viladecans E 43 E8
Vila de Cruces E 38 C3
Vila de Frades P 50 C4
Vila de Rei P 44 E4
Vila do Bispo P 50 E2
Vila do Conde P 38 F2
Viladrau E 43 D8
Vilafamés E 48 D4
Vilafant E 43 C9
Vila Fernando P 51 B5
Vila Flor P 38 F5
Vila Franca das Naves P 45 C6
Vilafranca de Bonany E 57 B11
Vilafranca del Penedès E 43 E7
Vila Franca de Xira P 50 B2
Vilagarcía de Arousa E 38 C2
Vilajuïga E 34 F5
Viļaka LV 133 B3
Vilalba E 38 B4
Vilallonga E 33 F10
Vilamartín E 38 D5
Vilamarxant E 48 E3
Vilamoura P 50 E3
Viļāni LV 133 C1
Vila Nogueira de Azeitão P 50 B1
Vilanova E 38 B5
Vila Nova da Baronia P 50 C3
Vila Nova da Barquinha P 44 F4
Vilanova d'Alcolea E 48 D5
Vilanova de Arousa E 38 C2
Vila Nova de Cacela P 50 E4
Vila Nova de Famalicão P 38 F2
Vila Nova de Foz Coa P 45 B6
Vila Nova de Gaia P 44 B3
Vilanova de la Barca E 42 D5
Vilanova de L'Aguda E 42 D6
Vilanova de Meià E 42 D6
Vila Nova de Paiva P 44 C5
Vila Nova de Poiares P 44 D4
Vilanova de Prades E 42 E5
Vila Nova de São Bento P 50 D5
Vilanova de Sau E 43 D8
Vilanova i la Geltrú E 43 E7
Vila Pouca da Beira P 44 D5
Vila Pouca de Aguiar P 38 E4
Vila Praia de Âncora P 38 E2
Vilar P 38 E3
Vilar P 44 F2
Vilarandelo P 38 E5
Vilarchao E 38 D4
Vilar da Veiga P 38 E3
Vilar de Andorinho P 44 B3
Vilar de Barrio E 38 D4
Vilar de Santos E 38 D4
Vilardevós E 38 E5
Vila Real P 38 F4
Vila Real de Santo António P 50 E5
Vilarelho da Raia P 38 E5
Vilar Formoso P 45 C7
Vilarinho da Castanheira P 45 B6
Vilarinho do Bairro P 44 D3
Vilariño de Conso E 38 D5
Vila-rodona E 43 E6
Vila Ruiva P 50 C4
Vila Seca P 38 E2
Vilaseca de Solcina E 42 E6
Vilassar de Mar E 43 D8
Vilasund S 108 D8
Vila Velha de Ródão P 44 E5
Vila Verde P 38 E3
Vila Verde P 38 F4
Vila Verde P 44 D3
Vila Verde da Raia P 38 E5
Vila Verde de Ficalho P 51 D5
Vila Viçosa P 50 B5
Vilce LV 134 D7
Vilches E 55 C6
Vildbjerg DK 86 C3
Vilémov CZ 77 C9
Vilgāle LV 134 C3
Vilhelmina S 107 B11
Vilia GR 175 C7
Viljakkala FIN 127 B9
Viljandi EST 131 E11
Viljevo HR 149 E10
Viljolahti FIN 125 F10
Vilkaviškis LT 136 D7
Vilkene LV 131 F9
Vilkija LT 137 C8
Vilkjärvi FIN 128 D8
Vilkyškiai LT 134 F4
Villa Bartolomea I 66 B3
Villabate I 58 C3
Villablanca E 51 E5
Villablino E 39 C7
Villabona E 32 D1
Villabrágima E 39 E9
Villabuena del Puente E 39 F9
Villac F 29 E8
Villacañas E 46 E6
Villa Carcina I 69 B9
Villacarriedo E 40 B4
Villacarrillo E 55 C6
Villa Castelli I 61 B8
Villacastín E 46 C4
Villach A 73 C8
Villacidro I 64 E2
Villaciervos E 41 E6
Villaconejos E 46 D6
Villaconejos de Trabaque E 47 D8
Villada E 39 D10
Villa d'Almè I 69 B8
Villa del Prado E 46 D4
Villa del Río E 53 A8
Villadepera E 39 E7
Villa de Ves E 47 F10
Villadiego E 40 C3
Villadose I 66 B4
Villadossola I 68 A5
Villaeles de Valdavia E 39 C10
Villaescusa de Haro E 47 E7
Villaescusa la Sombría E 40 D5
Villafáfila E 39 E8
Villafeliche E 47 B10
Villaflores E 45 B10
Villafranca d'Asti I 37 B8
Villafranca de Córdoba E 53 A7
Villafranca de Ebro E 41 E10
Villafranca del Bierzo E 39 C6
Villafranca del Campo E 47 C10
Villafranca del Cid E 48 D4
Villafranca de los Barros E 51 B7
Villafranca de los Caballeros E 46 F6
Villafranca di Verona I 66 B2
Villafranca in Lunigiana I 69 E8
Villafranca-Montes de Oca E 40 D5
Villafranca Tirrena I 59 C7
Villafranco del Guadalquivir E 51 E7
Villafrati I 58 D3
Villafrechos E 39 E9
Villafruela E 40 E4
Villafuerte E 40 E3
Villagarcía de Campos E 39 E9
Villagarcía de la Torre E 51 C7
Villagarcía del Llano E 47 F9
Villaggio Mancuso I 59 A10
Villagonzalo E 51 B7
Villagrande Strisaili I 64 D4
Villaharta E 54 C3
Villähde FIN 127 D14
Villahermosa E 55 B7
Villahermosa del Campo E 47 B10
Villahermosa del Río E 48 D4
Villaherreros E 40 D3
Villahizán E 40 D4
Villahoz E 40 D4
Villaines-en-Duesmois F 25 E12
Villaines-la-Juhel F 23 D11
Villajoyosa-La Vila Joíosa E 56 D4
Villala FIN 125 F13
Villala FIN 129 D9
Villa Lagarina I 69 B11
Villalago I 62 D5
Villalar de los Comuneros E 39 E9
Villa Latina I 62 D5
Villalba I 58 D4
Villalba de Duero E 40 E4
Villalba de Guardo E 39 C10
Villalba del Alcor E 51 E7
Villalba de la Sierra E 47 D8
Villalba de los Alcores E 39 E10
Villalba de los Barros E 51 B6
Villalba del Rey E 47 D7
Villalba dels Arcs E 42 E4
Villalba de Rioja E 40 C6
Villalcampo E 39 E7
Villalcázar de Sirga E 40 D2
Villalengua E 41 F8
Villalgordo del Júcar E 47 F8
Villa Literno I 60 A2
Villalobos E 39 E9
Villalón de Campos E 39 D9
Villalonga E 56 D4
Villalpando E 39 E9
Villalpardo E 47 F9
Villaluenga de la Sagra E 46 D5
Villalumbroso E 39 D10
Villamalea E 47 F9
Villamañán E 39 D8
Villamandos E 39 D8
Villamanrique E 55 B7
Villamanrique de la Condesa E 51 E7
Villamanta E 46 D4
Villamar I 64 D2
Villamartín E 51 F8
Villamartín de Campos E 39 D10
Villamassargia I 64 E2
Villamayor E 45 C9
Villamayor de Calatrava E 54 B4
Villamayor de Campos E 39 E9
Villamayor de Santiago E 47 E7
Villamayor de Treviño E 40 D3
Villamblard F 29 E7
Villamediana E 40 D3
Villamediana de Iregua E 32 F1
Villamejil E 39 C7
Villamesías E 45 F9
Villamiel E 45 D7
Villa Minozzo I 66 D1
Villamo FIN 122 F7
Villamor de los Escuderos E 39 F8
Villamuelas E 46 E5
Villamuriel de Cerrato E 40 E3
Villandraut F 32 B5
Villanova I 61 B9
Villanova d'Albenga I 37 C8
Villanova d'Asti I 37 B7
Villanova del Battista I 60 A4
Villanovafranca I 64 D3
Villanova Monferrato I 68 C5
Villanova Monteleone I 64 B1
Villanova Truschedu I 64 D2
Villanova Tulo I 64 D3
Villanterio I 69 C7
Villanúa E 32 E4
Villanubla E 39 E10
Villanueva de Alcardete E 47 E6
Villanueva de Alcorón E 47 C8
Villanueva de Algaidas E 53 B8
Villanueva de Argaño E 40 D4
Villanueva de Bogas E 46 E5
Villanueva de Cameros E 41 D6
Villanueva de Castellón E 56 C4
Villanueva de Córdoba E 54 C3
Villanueva de Gállego E 41 E10
Villanueva de Gómez E 46 C3
Villanueva de la Cañada E 46 D5
Villanueva de la Concepción E 53 C7
Villanueva de la Fuente E 55 B7
Villanueva de la Jara E 47 F9
Villanueva de la Reina E 53 A9
Villanueva del Arzobispo E 55 C6
Villanueva de las Cruces E 51 D5
Villanueva de la Serena E 51 B8
Villanueva de la Sierra E 45 D8
Villanueva de las Torres E 55 D6
Villanueva de la Vera E 45 D10
Villanueva del Campo E 39 E9
Villanueva del Duque E 54 C3
Villanueva del Fresno E 51 C5
Villanueva de los Castillejos E 51 D5
Villanueva de los Infantes E 55 B7
Villanueva del Rey E 51 C9
Villanueva del Río Segura E 55 C10
Villanueva del Río y Minas E 51 D8
Villanueva del Rosario E 53 C8
Villanueva del Trabuco E 53 B8
Villanueva de Mesía E 53 B8
Villanueva de San Carlos E 54 B5
Villanueva de San Juan E 51 E9
Villanueva de Tapia E 53 B8
Villanueva de Valdegovia E 40 C5
Villanuño de Valdavia E 40 C2
Villány H 149 E10
Villa Opicina I 73 E8
Villapalacios E 55 B7
Villaperuccio I 64 E2
Villapiana I 61 D6
Villapiana Lido I 61 D6
Villa Poma I 66 C3
Villapourçon F 30 B4
Villaputzu I 64 E4
Villaquejida E 39 D8
Villaquilambre E 39 C8
Villaralbo E 39 F8
Villaralto E 54 C3
Villarcayo E 40 C4
Villard-Bonnot F 31 E8
Villard-de-Lans F 31 E8
Villar de Cañas E 47 E7
Villar de Chinchilla E 55 B9
Villar de Ciervo E 45 C7
Villardeciervos E 39 E7
Villardefrades E 39 E9
Villar del Arzobispo E 48 E3
Villar de la Yegua E 45 C7
Villar del Buey E 39 F7
Villar del Cobo E 47 D9
Villar del Humo E 47 E9
Villar de los Barrios E 39 C6
Villar de los Navarros E 42 E1
Villar del Pedroso E 45 E10
Villar del Rey E 45 F7
Villar del Salz E 47 C10
Villar de Olalla E 47 D8
Villar de Peralonso E 45 B8
Villar de Rena E 45 F9
Villar de Torre E 40 D6
Villardompardo E 53 A8
Villareal E 48 E4
Villarejo de Fuentes E 47 E7
Villarejo de Montalbán E 46 E3
Villarejo de Orbigo E 39 D8
Villarejo de Salvanés E 47 D6
Villa Rendena I 69 A10
Villarente E 39 C9
Villares de la Reina E 45 B9
Villargordo E 53 A9
Villargordo del Cabriel E 47 E10
Villarino de los Aires E 39 F7
Villarluengo E 42 F2
Villarosa I 58 D5
Villarquemado E 47 C10
Villarramiel E 39 D10
Villarrasa E 51 E6
Villarreal de Huerva E 47 B10
Villarrín de Campos E 39 E8
Villarrobledo E 47 F7
Villarrodrigo E 55 C7
Villarroya de la Sierra E 41 F8
Villarroya de los Pinares E 42 F2
Villarrubia de los Ojos E 46 F5
Villarrubia de Santiago E 46 E6
Villarrubio E 47 E7
Villars F 29 E7
Villars F 30 E5
Villars-Colmars F 36 C5
Villars del Saz E 47 E8
Villars-les-Dombes F 31 D7
Villars-sur-Var F 36 D6
Villar-St-Pancrace F 31 F10
Villarta E 47 F9
Villarta de los Montes E 46 F3
Villarta de San Juan E 46 F6
Villasalto I 64 E3
Villasana de Mena E 40 B5
Villasandino E 40 D3
Villa San Giovanni I 59 C8
Villa San Pietro I 64 E3
Villa Santa Maria I 63 D6
Villasante de Montija E 40 B5
Villa Santina I 73 D6
Villasarracino E 40 D3
Villasavary F 33 D10
Villasayas E 41 F6
Villasbuenas E 45 B7
Villasdardo E 45 B8
Villaseca de Laciana E 39 C7
Villaseca de la Sagra E 46 E5
Villaseco de los Gamitos E 45 B8
Villaseco de los Reyes E 45 B8
Villaseco del Pan E 39 F8
Villasequilla de Yepes E 46 E5
Villasimius I 64 E4
Villasmundo I 59 E7
Villasor I 64 E2
Villaspeciosa I 64 E2
Villasrubias E 45 D7
Villastar E 47 D10
Villasur de Herreros E 40 D5
Villatobas E 46 E6
Villatoro E 45 C10
Villatoya E 47 F10
Villatuerta E 32 E2
Villaturiel E 39 C9
Villaumbrales E 39 D10
Villaurbana I 64 D2
Villava E 32 E2
Villavallelonga I 62 D5
Villavelayo E 40 D6
Villaverde de Guadalimar E 55 C7
Villaverde del Río E 51 D8
Villaverde y Pasaconsol E 47 E8
Villavernia I 37 B9
Villaviciosa E 39 B9
Villaviciosa de Córdoba E 54 C2
Villaviciosa de Odón E 46 D5
Villavieja E 48 E4
Villavieja de Yeltes E 45 C8
Villaviudas E 40 E3
Villayón E 39 B6
Villazanzo de Valderaduey E 39 C10
Villé F 27 D7
Villebois-Lavalette F 29 E6
Villebrumier F 33 C8
Villecomtal-sur-Arros F 33 D6
Villecomte F 26 E3
Villecroze F 36 D4
Villedaigne F 34 D4
Villedieu-la-Blouère F 23 F9
Villedieu-les-Poêles F 23 C9
Villedieu-sur-Indre F 29 B9
Ville-en-Tardenois F 20 F1
Villefagnan F 28 C6
Villefontaine F 31 D7
Villefort F 35 B6
Villefranche-d'Albigeois F 33 C10
Villefranche-d'Allier F 30 C2
Villefranche-de-Lauragais F 33 D9
Villefranche-de-Lonchat F 28 F6
Villefranche-de-Panat F 34 B4
Villefranche-de-Rouergue F 33 B10
Villefranche-du-Périgord F 33 A8
Villefranche-sur-Cher F 24 F6
Villefranche-sur-Mer F 37 D6
Villefranche-sur-Saône F 30 D6
Villefranque F 32 D3
Villegas E 40 D3
Villel E 47 D10
Villelaure F 35 C9
Villemandeur F 25 E8
Villemorien F 25 D11
Villemoustaussou F 33 D10
Villemur-sur-Tarn F 33 C9
Villena E 56 D3
Villenauxe-la-Grande F 25 C10
Villeneuve CH 31 C10
Villeneuve F 33 B10
Villeneuve F 35 C10
Villeneuve-au-Chemin F 25 D10
Villeneuve-d'Allier F 30 E3
Villeneuve-d'Ascq F 19 C7
Villeneuve-de-Berg F 35 A8
Villeneuve-de-Marsan F 32 C5
Villeneuve-de-Rivière F 33 D7
Villeneuve-la-Guyard F 25 D9
Villeneuve-l'Archevêque F 25 D10
Villeneuve-lès-Avignon F 35 C8
Villeneuve-lès-Béziers F 34 D5
Villeneuve-Loubet F 36 D6
Villeneuve-sur-Allier F 30 B3
Villeneuve-sur-Lot F 33 B7
Villeneuve-sur-Yonne F 25 D9
Villeneuve-Tolosane F 33 C8
Villepinte F 33 D10
Villercomtal F 33 A11
Villeréal F 33 A7
Villerest F 30 D5
Villerías E 39 E10
Villerouge-Termenès F 34 D4
Villers-Bocage F 18 E5
Villers-Bocage F 23 B10
Villers-Bretonneux F 18 E6
Villers-Carbonnel F 18 E6
Villers-Cotterêts F 19 F7
Villers-Écalles F 18 E2
Villers-en-Argonne F 25 B12
Villersexel F 26 E5
Villers-Farlay F 31 A8
Villers-le-Bouillet B 183 D6
Villers-le-lac F 31 A10
Villers-lès-Nancy F 26 C5
Villers-Outréaux F 19 D7
Villers-Semeuse F 19 E10
Villers-sur-Glâne CH 31 B11
Villers-sur-Mer F 23 B11
Villerville F 23 B12
Villery F 25 D11
Villeseneux F 25 C11
Ville-sur-Tourbe F 20 F3
Villetta Barrea I 62 D5
Villeurbanne F 30 D6
Villeveyrac F 35 C6
Villevocance F 30 E6
Villié-Morgon F 30 C6
Villiers-Charlemagne F 23 E10
Villiers-en-Lieu F 25 C12
Villiers-en-Plaine F 28 C4
Villiers-le-Sec F 26 D3
Villiers-St-Benoît F 25 E9
Villiers-St-Georges F 25 C9
Villieu-Loyes-Mollon F 31 D7
Villikkala FIN 128 D6
Villingen D 27 D9
Villingsberg S 97 D12
Villmar D 185 D9
Villoldo E 39 D10
Villora E 47 E9
Villorba I 72 E5
Villoria E 45 C10
Villoruela E 45 B10
Villotte-sur-Aire F 26 C3
Villshärad S 87 B11
Villvattnet S 118 E4
Vilmány H 145 G3
Vilnius LT 137 D11
Vilovi d'Onyar E 43 D9
Vilppula FIN 123 F12
Vilpulka LV 131 F10
Vils A 71 B11
Vils DK 86 B3
Vilsbiburg D 75 F11
Vilseck D 75 C10
Vil'shanka UA 154 A3
Vilshofen D 76 E4
Vilshult S 88 C7
Vilslev DK 86 E3
Vilsted DK 86 B4
Vilsund Vest DK 86 B3
Vilusi BIH 157 C7
Vilusi MNE 162 D6
Viluste EST 132 F1
Vilvestre E 45 B7
Vilvoorde B 19 C9
Vilzēni LV 131 F10
Vima Mică RO 152 C3
Vimbodí E 42 E6
Vimeiro P 44 F2
Vimercate I 69 B7
Vimianzo E 38 B1
Vimieiro P 50 B4
Vimioso P 39 E6
Vimmarvattnet S 107 D9
Vimmerby S 92 D7
Vimory F 25 E8
Vimoutiers F 23 C12
Vimpeli FIN 123 D11
Vimperk CZ 76 D5
Vimy F 18 D6
Vinac BIH 157 D7
Vinadio I 37 C6
Vinaixa E 42 E5
Vinařice CZ 76 B6
Vinaròs E 42 G4
Vinarsko BG 167 D8
Vinäs S 102 E8
Vinassan F 34 D5
Vinay F 31 E7
Vinberg S 87 B11
Vinça F 34 E4
Vinča SRB 158 D6
Vincey F 26 D5
Vinchiaturo I 63 E7
Vinci I 66 E2
Vind DK 86 C3
Vindblæs DK 86 B4
Vindeballe DK 86 F6
Vindeby DK 86 E7
Vindel-Ånäset S 118 F3
Vindelgransele S 107 A14
Vindeln S 107 C16
Vinderei RO 153 E11
Vinderslev DK 86 C4
Vinderup DK 86 C3
Vindhella N 100 D7
Vindinge DK 87 D10
Vindinge DK 87 E7
Vindsvik N 94 D4
Vinebre E 42 E5
Vineuil F 24 E5
Vineuil F 29 B9
Vinga RO 151 E7
Vingåker S 92 A7
Vingång S 102 E4
Vingrau F 34 E4
Vingrom N 101 D12
Vingsand N 104 C8
Vinhais P 39 E6
Vinhas P 39 E6
Vinica HR 148 D6
Vinica MK 164 F5
Vinica SK 147 E8
Vinica SLO 67 B11
Viničné SK 146 E4
Viniegra de Arriba E 40 D6
Vinine BIH 157 G8
Viniště HR 156 F5
Vinje N 94 C7
Vinje N 100 E4
Vinjeøra N 104 E5
Vinkovci HR 149 F11
Vinkt B 182 C2
Vinliden S 107 B13
Vinné SK 145 F4
Vinnes N 94 B3
Vinnesvåg N 94 B2
Vinni EST 131 C12
Vinninga S 91 C13
Vinningen D 27 B8
Vinodol SK 146 E6
Vinograd BG 166 C5
Vinogradets BG 165 E9
Vinon-sur-Verdon F 35 C10
Vinsa S 116 E9
Vinslöv S 87 C13
Vinsobres F 35 B9
Vinsternes N 104 E4
Vinstra N 101 C11
Vintervollen N 114 D8
Vintilă Vodă RO 161 C9
Vintjärn S 103 E11
Vintrosa S 97 D12
Vintturi FIN 123 C11
Vinţu de Jos RO 152 E2
Viñuelas E 46 C6
Vinuesa E 40 E6
Vinzelberg D 79 A10
Viöl D 82 A6
Violay F 30 D5
Violès F 35 B8
Vipava SLO 73 E8
Vipe LV 135 D12
Viperești RO 161 C8
Vipiteno I 72 C3
Vipperød DK 87 D9
Vipperow D 83 D13
Vir BIH 157 E7
Vir HR 67 D11
Vir SLO 73 D10
Vira S 93 B8
Virawlya BY 133 E7
Virazeil F 33 A6
Virbalis LT 136 D6
Virbi LV 134 B5
Virče MK 165 F6
Vire F 23 C10
Virešl LV 135 B12
Vireux-Molhain F 184 D2
Vireux-Wallerand F 19 D10
Virey-sous-Bar F 25 D11
Virgen A 72 B5
Virginia IRL 7 E8
Viriat F 31 C7
Virieu-le-Grand F 31 D8
Virigneux F 30 D5
Virignin F 31 D8
Viriville F 31 E7
Virkēni LV 131 F10
Virkkala FIN 127 E11
Virkkula FIN 121 B13
Virkkunen FIN 121 C10
Virklund DK 86 C5
Virmaanpää FIN 124 E8
Virmaila FIN 127 C13
Virmutjoki FIN 129 C10
Virolahden kk FIN 128 D8
Virolahti FIN 128 D8
Virovitica HR 149 E8
Virpazar MNE 163 E7
Virpe LV 134 B4
Virrat FIN 123 F11
Virsbo S 97 C15
Virserum S 89 A9
Virtaniemi FIN 114 F4
Virtasalmi FIN 124 F8
Virton B 19 E12
Virtsu EST 130 D7
Viru-Jaagupi EST 131 C12
Viru-Nigula EST 131 C13
Viry F 31 C9
Vis HR 63 A10
Visaginas LT 135 E12
Višakio Rūda LT 137 D7
Visan F 35 B8
Vişani RO 161 C10
Visåsen S 103 A13
Visbek D 17 C10
Visborg DK 86 B6
Visby DK 86 E3
Visby S 93 D12
Visé B 19 C12
Višegrad BIH 158 F3
Visegrád H 149 A11
Viserba I 66 D6
Viseu P 44 C5
Vişeu de Jos RO 152 B4
Vişeu de Sus RO 152 B4
Vishnyeva BY 137 E13
Vishovgrad BG 166 C4
Visiedo E 42 F1
Visikums LV 133 B2
Vişina RO 160 D6
Vişina RO 160 F4
Vişineşti MD 154 E2
Vişineşti RO 161 C7
Visingsö S 92 C5
Visjövalen S 105 E12
Viskafors S 91 D12
Viskan S 103 B11
Viški LV 135 D13
Vislanda S 88 B6
Visnes N 94 D2
Višnja Gora SLO 73 E10
Višnjićevo SRB 158 D3
Višňová CZ 81 E8
Višňové CZ 77 E10
Višňové SK 147 C7
Visoca MD 153 A11
Viso del Marqués E 55 B5
Visokë AL 168 C2
Visoko BIH 157 E9
Visone I 37 B9
Visonta H 150 B5
Visp CH 68 A4
Vissac-Auteyrac F 30 E4
Vissani GR 168 E4
Visselfjärda S 89 B9
Visselhövede D 82 E7
Vissenbjerg DK 86 E6
Visso I 62 B4
Vissoie CH 68 A4
Vist N 105 D10
Vistabella del Maestrazgo E 48 D4
Vistbäcken S 118 C5
Viştea RO 152 F5
Vistheden S 118 C5
Visthus N 108 E4
Vištytis LT 136 E6
Visuvesi FIN 123 F11
Visvik S 150 B5
Vita I 58 D2
Vitå S 118 C8
Vitaby S 88 D6
Vitåfors S 118 C8
Vitanová SK 147 C9
Vitanovac SRB 159 F6
Vitanovac SRB 164 C5
Vitaz SK 145 F2
Vitberget S 118 C4
Viterbo I 62 C2
Viterne F 26 C5
Vitez BIH 157 D8
Vítězná CZ 77 B9
Viti RKS 164 E3
Vitigudino E 45 B8
Vitina BIH 157 F8
Vītiņi LV 134 D5
Vitis A 77 E8
Vítkov CZ 146 B5
Vitkovići BIH 157 E10
Vītoliņi LV 134 C7
Vitolište MK 169 B6
Vitomireşti RO 160 D4
Vitomiricë RKS 163 D9
Vitorchiano I 62 C2
Vitoria-Gasteiz E 41 C6
Vitoševac SRB 159 F8
Vitovlje BIH 157 D8
Vitré F 23 D9
Vitrey-sur-Mance F 26 E4
Vitrolles F 35 D9
Vitry-en-Artois F 18 D6
Vitry-en-Perthois F 25 C12
Vitry-le-François F 25 C12
Vitry-sur-Loire F 30 B4
Vittangi S 116 C7
Vittaryd S 87 B13
Vitteaux F 25 F12
Vittel F 26 D4
Vittikko FIN 115 E4
Vittikko FIN 119 B13
Vittikkovuoma FIN 117 E12
Vittinge S 98 C8
Vittjärv S 118 C7
Vittoria I 59 F6
Vittorio Veneto I 72 E5
Vittsjö S 87 C13
Vitulano I 60 A3
Vitulazio I 60 A2
Vitvattnet S 102 B8
Vitvattnet S 107 D16
Vitvattnet S 119 B10
Vitzenburg D 79 D10
Viuruniemi FIN 125 E11
Vivario F 37 G10
Vivastbo S 98 B7
Viveiro E 38 A4
Vivel del Río Martín E 42 F2
Viver E 48 E3
Viverols F 30 E4
Viveros E 55 B7
Vivier-au-Court F 19 E10
Viviers F 35 B8
Viviez F 33 A10
Vivild DK 86 C6
Viv-le-Fesq F 35 C7
Vivonne F 29 C6
Vix F 25 E12
Vix F 28 C4
Vizantea-Livezi RO 153 F9
Vize TR 173 A8
Vizille F 31 E8
Vižinada HR 67 B8
Viziru RO 155 C1
Vizitsa BG 167 E9
Vizovice CZ 146 C5
Vizslás H 147 E9
Vizsoly H 145 G3
Vizzini I 59 E6
Vlaardingen NL 16 E2
Vlachata GR 174 C2
Vlacherna GR 174 D5
Vlachia GR 175 B8
Vlachiotis GR 175 F6
Vlachokerasia GR 174 E5
Vlachovice CZ 146 C5
Vlădaia RO 159 E11
Vladaya BG 165 D7
Vlădeni RO 153 B9
Vlădeni RO 153 C10
Vlădeni RO 155 D1
Vlădeşti RO 154 F2
Vlădeşti RO 160 C4
Vlădeşti RO 160 C5
Vladičin Han SRB 164 D5
Vlădila RO 160 E4
Vladimir MNE 163 E7
Vladimir RO 160 D3
Vladimirci SRB 158 D4
Vladimirescu RO 151 E7
Vladimirovac SRB 159 C6
Vladimirovo BG 161 F11
Vladimirovo BG 165 B7
Vladinya BG 165 C10
Vladislav CZ 77 D9
Vlad Ţepeş RO 161 E10
Vladychen' UA 155 B3
Vlăhiţa RO 153 E7
Vlahovići BIH 157 F9
Vlanduk BIH 157 D8
Vlaole SRB 159 E8
Vlase SRB 164 D4
Vlasenica BIH 157 D10
Vlašići HR 156 D3
Vlašim CZ 77 C7
Vlasina Okruglica SRB 164 D5
Vlăsineşti RO 153 B9
Vlasotince SRB 164 D5
Vlatkovići BIH 157 D7
Vlčany SK 146 E5
Vlčnov CZ 146 D5
Vledder NL 16 C6
Vleuten NL 16 D4
Vlijmen NL 16 E4
Vlissingen NL 16 F1
Vlochos GR 169 E7
Vlorë AL 168 D1
Vlotho D 17 D11
Vlycho GR 174 B2
Vnanje Gorice SLO 73 D9
Vnorovy CZ 146 D4
Vočin HR 149 E9
Vöcklabruck A 76 F5
Vöcklamarkt A 76 F4
Voden BG 161 F9
Voden BG 167 E7
Voderady SK 146 E5
Vodica BIH 157 D7
Vodice HR 67 B9
Vodice HR 156 E4
Vodinci HR 157 B10
Voditsa BG 166 C6
Vodjenica BIH 156 C5
Vodňany CZ 76 D6
Vodnjan HR 67 C8
Vodskov DK 86 A6
Vodstrup DK 86 B3
Voe GB 3 E14
Voel DK 86 C5
Voerde (Niederrhein) D 17 E7
Voerendaal NL 183 D7
Voerladegård DK 86 C5
Voerså DK 86 A6
Vogatsiko GR 168 D5
Vogelenzang NL 182 A5
Vogelgrun F 27 D8
Vogelsang D 84 D4
Vogelsdorf D 80 B5
Vogelweh D 21 F9
Voghera I 37 B10
Voghiera I 66 C4
Vognill N 101 A11
Vognsild DK 86 B4
Vogošća BIH 157 E9
Vogt D 71 B9
Vogtareuth D 72 A5
Vogüé F 35 A7
Vohburg an der Donau D 75 E10
Vohenstrauß D 75 C11
Vöhl D 21 B11
Võhma EST 130 D4
Võhma EST 131 D11
Vohonjoki FIN 120 B9
Vöhringen D 27 D10
Vöhringen D 75 F7
Voiceşti RO 160 D4
Void-Vacon F 26 C4
Voikkaa FIN 128 D6
Voikoski FIN 128 C6
Voila RO 152 F5
Voillecomte F 25 C12
Voineasa RO 160 C3
Voineşti RO 153 C10
Voineşti RO 160 C6
Voiron F 31 E8
Võiste EST 131 E8
Voiteg RO 159 C7
Voiteur F 31 B8
Voitsberg A 73 B11
Voivodeni RO 152 D5

Vojakkala FIN 119 C12
Vojakkala FIN 127 D11
Vojčice SK 145 F4
Vojens DK 86 E4
Vojka SRB 158 D5
Vojkovic BIH 157 E9
Vojnić HR 148 F5
Vojnik MK 164 E4
Vojnik SLO 148 D4
Vojtjajaure S 108 E9
Voka EST 132 C2
Vokány H 149 E10
Vokil BG 161 F10
Voknavolok RUS 121 E16
Voksa N 100 B2
Volakas GR 170 B5
Volary CZ 76 E5
Volda N 100 B4
Voldby DK 86 C5
Voldby DK 87 C7
Voldum DK 86 C6
Volendam NL 16 D4
Volgsele S 107 B11
Volimes GR 174 D2
Volintiri MD 154 E5
Volissos GR 177 C6
Voljevac BIH 157 E8
Voljice BIH 157 E8
Volkach D 75 C7
Volkel NL 183 B7
Völkermarkt A 73 C10
Volketswil CH 27 F10
Völklingen D 21 F7
Volkmarsen D 17 F12
Volkovija MK 163 F10
Voll N 101 E13
Völlen D 17 B8
Vollenhove NL 16 C5
Vollersode D 17 B11
Vollsjö S 87 D13
Volmunster F 27 B7
Voloiac RO 159 D11
Voloka UA 153 A7
Volonne F 35 B11
Volos GR 169 F8
Voloshcha UA 145 D8
Volosovo RUS 132 C5
Volosyanka UA 145 F6
Volovăț RO 153 B7
Volovets' UA 145 F7
Volovo BG 166 B5
Volpago del Montello I 72 E5
Volpedo I 37 B9
Volpiano I 68 C4
Völs A 72 B3
Völschow D 84 C4
Voltaggio I 37 B9
Volta Mantovana I 66 B2
Volterra I 66 F2
Voltlage D 17 D9
Voltri I 37 C9
Voltti FIN 122 D9
Volturara Appula I 63 E8
Volturara Irpina I 60 B3
Volturino I 63 E8
Voluntari RO 161 E8
Volvic F 30 D3
Volx F 35 C10
Volya Arlamivs'ka UA 144 D7
Volyně CZ 76 D5
Vomp A 72 B4
Voneshta Voda BG 166 D5
Vonge DK 86 D4
Vonges F 26 F3
Voni GR 178 E9
Vonitsa GR 174 B2
Võnnu EST 131 E14
Vööpste EST 131 E14
Vöõpsu EST 132 E2
Voorburg NL 16 D2
Voore EST 131 D13
Voorhout NL 182 A4
Voorschoten NL 16 D2
Voorst NL 16 D6
Voorthuizen NL 183 A7
Voose EST 131 C10
Vörå FIN 122 D8
Voranava BY 137 E11
Vorbasse DK 86 D4
Vorchdorf A 76 F5
Vorden NL 16 D6
Vordernberg A 73 A10
Vordingborg DK 87 E9
Vordorf D 79 B8
Vorë AL 168 B2
Voreppe F 31 E8
Vorey F 30 E4
Vorgod DK 86 C3
Vormsele S 107 B15
Vormstad N 104 E7
Vormsund N 95 B14
Vormträsk S 107 B15
Vorna FIN 119 F15
Vorniceni RO 153 B9
Voroi GR 178 E8
Vorokhta UA 152 A5
Vorona RO 153 B9
Vorra D 75 C9
Vorsau A 148 B5
Vorst B 19 B11
Vorța RO 151 E10
Võru EST 131 F14
Vorwerk D 17 B12
Voskopojë AL 168 C4
Voșlăbeni RO 153 D7
Voss N 100 E4
Vosselaar B 16 F3
Voštane HR 157 E6
Võsu EST 131 B11
Votice CZ 77 C7
Votonosi GR 168 E5
Voudia GR 179 B8
Vougeot F 26 F2
Vouillé F 28 C5
Vouillé F 29 B6
Voukolies GR 178 E6
Voula GR 175 D8
Voulaines-les-Templiers F 25 E12
Vouliagmeni GR 175 D8
Voulpi GR 174 A4
Voulx F 25 D8
Vouneuil-sous-Biard F 29 B6
Vouneuil-sur-Vienne F 29 B7
Vourgareli GR 168 F5
Vourvourou GR 169 D10
Voutenay-sur-Cure F 25 E10
Voutezac F 29 E8
Voutianoi GR 174 E5
Vouvant F 28 B4
Vouvray F 24 F4
Vouvry CH 31 C10
Vouzela P 44 C4
Vouzi GR 174 A5
Vouziers F 19 F10
Vouzon F 24 E7
Voves F 24 D6
Vowchyn BY 141 F8
Vowkawshchyna BY 133 E2
Voxna S 103 D10
Voynika BG 167 E7
Voynitsa RUS 121 D15
Voynovo BG 161 F10
Voynyagovo BG 165 D10
Vozmediano E 41 E8
Voznesenka-Persha UA 154 E4
Vrå DK 90 E6
Vrabevo BG 165 D10
Vráble SK 146 E6
Vračev Gaj SRB 159 D7
Vraćevšnica SRB 158 E6
Vrachasi GR 179 E10
Vrachati GR 175 D6
Vrachesh BG 165 D8
Vrachnaiika GR 174 C4
Vrachos GR 168 D5
Vracov CZ 146 D4
Vrådal N 95 D8
Vrakúň SK 146 F5
Vrané nad Vltavou CZ 76 C6
Vrani RO 159 C8
Vranino BG 167 B10
Vranisht AL 163 E9
Vranisht AL 168 D2
Vranjak BIH 157 C9
Vranje SRB 164 D4
Vranjska Banja SRB 164 D5
Vranovice CZ 77 E11
Vranov nad Topľou SK 145 F4
Vransko SLO 73 D10
Vrapčište MK 163 F10
Vrapičići BIH 157 F8
Vrasene B 182 C4
Vrasna GR 169 C10
Vratarnica SRB 159 F9
Vratimov CZ 146 B6
Vratnica MK 164 E3
Vratsa BG 165 C8
Vrattsa BG 165 E6
Vražogrnac SRB 159 F9
Vrbanja BIH 157 C7
Vrbanja HR 157 C10
Vrbanjci BIH 157 C7
Vrbas SRB 158 B4
Vrbaška BIH 157 B7
Vrbica SRB 150 E5
Vrbice CZ 77 E11
Vrbnik HR 67 B10
Vrbnik HR 156 D5
Vrbno pod Pradědem CZ 142 F3
Vrbovac SRB 159 F9
Vrbovce SK 146 D4
Vrbové SK 146 D5
Vrbovec HR 149 E6
Vrbovsko HR 67 B11
Vrchlabí CZ 81 E9
Vrčin SRB 158 D6
Vrdy CZ 77 C8
Vrebac HR 156 C4
Vrécourt F 26 D4
Vreden D 17 D7
Vreeland NL 183 A6
Vrees D 17 C9
Vrellë RKS 163 D9
Vrelo SRB 164 C4
Vrena S 93 B9
Vrensted DK 90 E6
Vřesina CZ 146 B6
Vresse B 19 E10
Vresthena GR 175 E6
Vretstorp S 92 A5
Vrgorac HR 157 F7
Vrhnika SLO 73 E9
Vrhopolje BIH 157 C6
Vrhovine HR 156 C3
Vridsted DK 86 C4
Vries NL 17 B7
Vriezenveen NL 17 D7
Vrigstad S 92 E4
Vrinners DK 86 C6
Vrisa GR 177 A7
Vrizy F 19 F10
Vrlika HR 156 E5
Vrnjačka Banja SRB 163 B10
Vrnograč BIH 156 B4
Vron F 18 D4
Vrontados GR 177 C7
Vrontero GR 168 C5
Vrontou GR 169 D7
Vroomshoop NL 17 D7
Vrosina GR 168 E4
Vrouchas GR 179 E10
Vroutek CZ 76 B4
Vrouwenpolder NL 16 E1
Vrpolje HR 156 E5
Vrpolje HR 157 B9
Vrrin AL 168 B1
Vršac SRB 159 C7
Vršani BIH 157 C11
Vrsar HR 67 B8
Vrsi HR 156 D3
Vrtoče BIH 156 C5
Vrtojba SLO 73 E8
Vrulja MNE 163 C7
Vrútky SK 147 C7
Vrutok MK 163 F10
Vrův BG 159 E10
Vrysia GR 169 F7
Vrysoula GR 168 F4
Všemina CZ 146 C5
Všeruby CZ 76 C4
Všetaty CZ 77 B7
Vsetín CZ 146 C5
Vsevolozhsk RUS 129 E14
Vŭbel BG 160 F5
Vučijak BIH 157 C8
Vučja Lokva SRB 163 C10
Vučje SRB 164 D4
Vught NL 16 E4
Vŭglevtsi BG 166 D5
Vuka HR 149 F10
Vukova Gorica HR 148 F4
Vukovar HR 157 B11
Vuku N 105 D11
Vulcan RO 159 C11
Vulcan RO 160 B6
Vulcana-Băi RO 160 C6
Vulcănești MD 155 B2
Vŭlchedrŭm BG 160 F2
Vŭlchidol BG 167 C9
Vulpeni RO 160 E3
Vultureni RO 152 D3
Vultureni RO 153 E10
Vulturești RO 153 B8
Vulturești RO 153 D11
Vulturești RO 160 D4
Vulturu RO 155 D2
Vulturu RO 161 B10
Vuobmaved FIN 113 E16
Vuohijärvi FIN 128 C6
Vuohtomäki FIN 123 C16
Vuojärvi FIN 117 D17
Vuokatti FIN 121 F11
Vuokko FIN 125 D12
Vuolenkoski FIN 127 C15
Vuolijoki FIN 120 F8
Vuolle FIN 123 C11
Vuollerim S 118 B5
Vuonisjärvi FIN 125 D14
Vuonislahti FIN 125 D13
Vuonos FIN 125 E12
Vuontisjärvi FIN 117 B11
Vuorenmaa FIN 124 G9
Vuorenmaa FIN 126 C8
Vuoreslahti FIN 121 F9
Vuorimäki FIN 123 E11
Vuorimäki FIN 124 C9
Vuoriniemi FIN 129 B11
Vuosaari FIN 127 E13
Vuosanka FIN 121 F13
Vuostimo FIN 115 E2
Vuostimojärvi FIN 115 E2
Vuotner S 118 C3
Vuotso FIN 115 B2
Vuottas S 118 B7
Vuottolahti FIN 120 F9
Vuotunki FIN 121 B14
Vŭrbitsa BG 166 E4
Vŭrbitsa BG 167 D7
Vurpær RO 152 F4
Vŭrshets BG 165 C7
Vushtrri RKS 164 D2
Vustsye BY 133 E3
Vutcani RO 153 E11
Vuzenica SLO 73 C11
Vuzlove UA 145 G5
Vvedenka UA 154 E5
Vyalets BY 133 F3
Vyalikaya Byerastavitsa BY 140 D10
Vyalikaya Stayki BY 133 F7
Vyalikaye Syalo BY 133 F3
Vyarkhovichy BY 141 F8
Vyartsilya RUS 125 F15
Vyaz RUS 133 C7
Vyborg RUS 129 D10
Výčapy-Opatovce SK 146 E6
Východná SK 147 C9
Vydeniai LT 137 E10
Vydrany SK 146 E5
Vyerkhnyadzvinsk BY 133 E3
Vyetryna BY 133 F4
Vyhne SK 147 D7
Vyhoda UA 145 F8
Vy-lès-Lure F 26 E5
Vylkove UA 155 C5
Vylok UA 145 G6
Vynnyky UA 144 D9
Vynohradiv UA 145 G7
Vynohradivka UA 154 F4
Vyritsa RUS 132 C7
Vyronas GR 175 D8
Vyroneia GR 169 B9
Vyshgorodok RUS 133 B3
Vyshka UA 145 F6
Vyshkiv UA 145 F8
Vyshkove UA 145 G7
Vyshneve UA 154 F5
Vyshniv UA 141 H10
Vyskod' RUS 132 F7
Vyškov CZ 77 D12
Vyšné Ružbachy SK 145 E2
Vyšný Mirošov SK 145 E3
Vyšný Orlík SK 145 E4
Vyšný Šipov SK 145 F4
Vysoká nad Kysucou SK 147 C7
Vysokaye BY 141 F8
Vysoké Mýto CZ 77 C10
Vysokoye RUS 136 D4
Vysotsk RUS 129 D10
Vyšší Brod CZ 76 E6
Vyssinia GR 168 C5
Vytina GR 174 D5
Vyzhnytsya UA 152 A6
Vyžuonos LT 135 E11
Vzmor'ye RUS 139 A9

W

Waabs D 83 A7
Waal D 71 B11
Waalre NL 16 F4
Waalwijk NL 16 E4
Waarschoot B 19 B8
Wabern D 21 B12
Wąbrzeźno PL 138 D6
Wachenheim an der Weinstraße D 187 C5
Wąchock PL 143 D11
Wachow D 79 A12
Wachtebeke B 19 B8
Wächtersbach D 21 D12
Wacken D 82 B6
Wackersdorf D 75 D11
Waddeweitz D 83 D9
Waddington GB 11 E10
Waddinxveen NL 16 D3
Wadebridge GB 12 D5
Wädenswil CH 27 F10
Wadern D 21 E7
Wadersloh D 17 E10
Wadgassen D 21 F7
Wadhurst GB 15 E9
Wadlew PL 143 C7
Wadowice PL 147 B9
Wadowice Górne PL 143 F11
Wądroże Wielkie PL 81 D10
Waganiec PL 138 E6
Wagenfeld D 17 C11
Wagenhoff D 79 A8
Wageningen NL 16 E5
Waghäusel D 21 F11
Waging am See D 73 A6
Wagna A 148 C5
Wagrain A 73 B7
Wągrowiec PL 85 E12
Wahlhausen D 79 D6
Wahlsdorf D 80 C4
Wahlstedt D 83 C8
Wahrenholz D 79 A8
Waiblingen D 27 C11
Waibstadt D 187 C6
Waidhofen an der Thaya A 77 E8
Waidhofen an der Ybbs A 77 G7
Waigolshausen D 75 C7
Waimes B 20 D6
Wain D 71 A10
Wainfleet All Saints GB 11 E12
Wainhouse Corner GB 12 D5
Waischenfeld D 75 C9
Waizenkirchen A 76 F5
Wakefield GB 11 D8
Wakendorf II D 83 C8
Walberswick GB 15 C12
Wałbrzych PL 81 E10
Walburg D 78 D6
Walchum D 17 C8
Walcourt B 19 D9
Wałcz PL 85 D10
Wald CH 27 F10
Wald D 27 E11
Wald D 75 D11
Waldachtal D 27 D10
Waldböckelheim D 185 E8
Waldbreitbach D 185 C7
Waldbröl D 21 C9
Waldbrunn-Lahr D 21 C10
Waldburg D 71 B9
Waldbüttelbrunn D 74 C6
Walddrehna D 80 C5
Waldegg A 77 G10
Waldenbuch D 27 C11
Waldenburg CH 27 F8
Waldenburg D 74 D6
Walderbach D 75 D11
Waldershof D 75 C11
Waldesch D 185 D8
Waldfischbach-Burgalben D 21 F9
Waldhausen A 77 E8
Waldhausen im Strudengau A 77 F7
Waldheim D 80 D4
Walding A 76 F6
Waldkappel D 78 D6
Waldkirch D 27 D8
Waldkirchen D 76 E5
Waldkraiburg D 75 F11
Wald-Michelbach D 187 B6
Waldmohr D 21 F8
Waldmünchen D 75 D12
Wałdowo-Szlacheckie PL 138 D6
Waldrach D 21 E7
Waldsassen D 75 B11
Waldsee D 187 C5
Waldshut D 27 E9
Waldstatt CH 27 F11
Waldstetten D 75 F7
Waldstetten D 187 D8
Walenstadt CH 27 F11
Walferdange L 20 E6
Walim PL 81 E10
Walkendorf D 83 C13
Wallasey GB 10 E5
Walldorf D 21 D11
Walldorf D 21 F11
Walldorf D 79 E7
Walldürn D 27 A11
Wallenfels D 75 B9
Wallerfing D 76 E3
Wallern im Burgenland A 149 A7
Wallersdorf D 75 E12
Wallerstein D 75 E7
Wallgau D 72 A3
Wallhausen D 75 D7
Wallhausen D 185 E8
Wallisellen CH 27 F10
Walls GB 3 E13
Wallsbüll D 82 A6
Wallstawe D 83 E10
Walmer GB 15 E11
Wałowice PL 81 C7
Wals A 73 A6
Walsall GB 11 F8
Walschleben D 79 D8
Walsleben D 83 E13
Walsoken GB 11 F12
Walsrode D 82 E7
Waltenhofen D 71 B10
Waltershausen D 79 E8
Waltham on the Wolds GB 11 F10
Walton-on-Thames GB 15 E8
Walton on the Naze GB 15 D11
Wamba E 39 E10
Wamel NL 183 B6
Wanderup D 82 A6
Wandlitz D 84 E4
Wandre B 183 D7
Wang A 77 F8
Wangen CH 27 F8
Wangen im Allgäu D 71 B9
Wängi CH 27 E10
Wankendorf D 83 B8
Wanna D 17 A11
Wanne-Eikel D 183 B10
Wanroij NL 183 B7
Wanssum NL 183 B8
Wantage GB 13 B12
Wanze B 19 C11
Wanzleben D 79 B9
Wapenveld NL 16 D6
Wąpielsk PL 139 D8
Waplewo PL 139 C9
Wapnica PL 85 D8
Wapno PL 85 E12
Warberg D 79 B8
Warboys GB 15 C8
Warburg D 17 F12
Warcop GB 11 B7
Warcq F 20 F5
Wardenburg D 17 B10
Wardington GB 13 A12
Ware GB 15 D8
Waregem B 19 C7
Wareham GB 13 D10
Waremme B 19 C11
Waren D 83 C13
Warendorf D 17 E9
Warffum NL 17 B7
Warin D 83 C11
Waringstown GB 7 D10
Wark GB 5 E12
Warka PL 141 G4
Warkworth GB 5 E13
Warlingham GB 15 E8
Warloy-Baillon F 18 D6
Warlubie PL 138 C6
Warmeriville F 19 F9
Warmington GB 13 A12
Warminster GB 13 C10
Warmond NL 182 A5
Warmsen D 17 D11
Warnemünde D 83 B12
Warngau D 72 A4
Warnice PL 85 D7
Warnice PL 85 E7
Warnino PL 85 C10
Warnow D 83 C11
Warnsveld NL 16 D6
Warrenpoint GB 7 D10
Warrington GB 10 E6
Warsingsfehn D 17 B8
Warslow GB 11 E8
Warstein D 17 F10
Warszawa PL 141 F4
Warszkowo PL 85 B11
Warta PL 142 C6
Warta Bolesławiecka PL 81 D9
Wartberg an der Krems A 76 G6
Wartenberg D 75 F10
Wartenberg-Angersbach D 78 E5
Warth A 71 C10
Wartin D 84 D6
Wartkowice PL 143 C7
Wartmannsroth D 74 B6
Warwick GB 13 A11
Warwick Bridge GB 5 F11
Warzyce PL 144 D4
Wasbek D 83 B7
Wasbister GB 3 G10
Wäschenbeuren D 74 E6
Wąsewo PL 139 E12
Washington GB 5 F13
Wasigny F 19 E9
Wasilków PL 140 D8
Waśniów PL 143 E11
Wąsosz PL 81 C11
Wąsosz PL 140 C6
Wąsowo PL 81 B10
Waspik NL 16 E3
Wasseiges B 183 D6
Wasselonne F 27 C7
Wassen CH 71 D7
Wassenaar NL 16 D2
Wassenberg D 20 B6
Wasseralfingen D 75 E7
Wasserbillig D 186 B2
Wasserburg am Inn D 75 F11
Wasserliesch D 186 B2
Wasserlosen D 74 B7
Wassertrüdingen D 75 D8
Wassigny F 19 D8
Wassy F 26 C2
Wasungen D 79 E7
Watchet GB 13 C8
Watchgate GB 10 C6
Waterbeck GB 5 E10
Waterford IRL 9 D8
Watergrasshill IRL 8 D6
Wateringen NL 182 A4
Waterland-Oudeman B 182 C3
Waterloo B 19 C9
Waterlooville GB 14 F6
Waterville IRL 8 E2
Watford GB 15 D8
Wathlingen D 79 A7
Watlington GB 14 D6
Watten F 18 C5
Watten GB 3 J10
Wattenbek D 83 B8
Wattens A 72 B4
Watten-Scheid D 183 C10
Wattenwil CH 31 B12
Wattlebridge GB 7 D8
Watton GB 15 B10
Wattwil CH 27 F11
Wavre B 19 C10
Wavrin F 18 C6
Wąwelno PL 85 D13
Wąwelno PL 142 E4
Wąwolnica PL 141 H6
Wawrów PL 85 E8
Wawrzeńczyce PL 143 F9
Waxweiler D 20 D6
Waziers F 182 E2
Weaverham GB 10 E6
Wechmar D 79 E8
Wechselburg D 79 D12
Wedde NL 17 B8
Weddingstedt D 82 B6
Wedel (Holstein) D 82 C7
Wedmore GB 13 C9
Wednesbury GB 11 F7
Weede D 83 C8
Weedon Bec GB 13 A12
Weelde B 182 C5
Weem GB 5 B9
Weener D 17 B8
Weerberg A 72 B4
Weerselo NL 17 D7
Weert NL 16 F5
Weesen CH 27 F11
Weesp NL 16 D4
Weeze D 16 E6
Weferlingen D 79 B9
Wegberg D 20 B6
Wegenstedt D 79 B9
Weggis CH 71 C6
Wegscheid A 148 A4
Wegscheid D 76 E5
Wehdel D 17 A11
Wehl NL 16 E6
Wehr D 27 E8
Wehrbleck D 17 C11
Wehringen D 71 A11
Weibern D 183 E10
Weibersbrunn D 74 C5
Weichering D 75 E9
Weichs D 75 F9
Weida D 79 E11
Weidenberg D 75 C10
Weiden in der Oberpfalz D 75 C11
Weidenstetten D 187 D8
Weidenthal D 21 F9
Weiding D 75 D12
Weiersbach D 186 B3
Weigersdorf D 81 D7
Weihmichl D 75 E11
Weikersheim D 74 D6
Weil D 71 A11
Weil am Rhein D 27 E8
Weilbach D 21 E12
Weilburg D 21 D10
Weil der Stadt D 27 C10
Weilerbach D 186 C4
Weilerswist D 21 C7
Weilheim an der Teck D 74 E6
Weilheim in Oberbayern D 72 A3
Weilmünster D 21 D10
Weimar D 79 E9
Weinbach D 185 D9
Weinböhla D 80 D5
Weinfelden CH 27 E11
Weingarten D 71 B9
Weingarten (Baden) D 187 C6
Weinheim D 21 E11
Weinsberg D 21 F12
Weinsheim D 20 D6
Weinsheim D 21 E9
Weinstadt D 27 C11
Weischlitz D 75 B11
Weisen D 83 D11
Weiskirchen D 21 E7
Weismain D 75 B9
Weissach D 27 C10
Weißbriach A 73 C7
Weißenbach am Lech A 71 C11
Weißenberg D 81 D7
Weißenbrunn D 75 B9
Weißenburg in Bayern D 75 D8
Weißenfels D 79 D10
Weißenhorn D 75 F7
Weißensee D 79 D9
Weißenstadt D 75 B10
Weißenstein A 73 C8
Weißenthurm D 185 D7
Weißig D 80 D5
Weißkeißel D 81 D7
Weißkirchen in Steiermark A 73 B10
Weißkollm D 80 D6
Weißwasser D 81 C7
Weistrach A 77 F7
Weiswampach L 20 D6
Weisweil D 27 D8
Weitbruch F 186 D4
Weitefeld D 185 C8
Weiten A 77 F8
Weitensfeld A 73 C9
Weitersfeld A 77 E9
Weiterstadt D 187 B6
Weitra A 77 E7
Weixdorf D 80 D5
Weiz A 148 B5
Wejherowo PL 138 A5
Wekerom NL 16 D5
Welkenraedt B 20 C5
Well NL 16 E6
Wellaune D 79 C12
Welle D 82 D7
Wellen B 183 D6
Wellesbourne GB 13 A11
Wellheim D 75 E9
Wellin B 19 D11
Welling D 21 D8
Wellingborough GB 15 C7
Wellington GB 10 F6
Wellington GB 13 D8
Wellingtonbridge IRL 9 D9
Wellington Bridge IRL 9 D9
Wells GB 13 C9
Wells-next-the-Sea GB 15 B10
Welney GB 11 F12
Wels A 76 F6
Welschbillig D 21 E7
Welshpool GB 10 F5
Welsickendorf D 80 C4
Welsleben D 79 C10
Welver D 17 E9
Welwyn GB 15 D8
Welwyn Garden City GB 15 D8
Welzheim D 74 E6
Welzow D 80 C6
Wem GB 10 F6
Wembdon GB 13 C8
Wemding D 75 E8
Wemeldinge NL 182 B4
Wemyss Bay GB 4 D7
Wendeburg D 79 B7
Wendelsheim D 21 E10
Wendelstein D 75 D9
Wenden D 21 C9
Wendens Ambo GB 15 C9
Wendisch Priborn D 83 D12
Wendisch Rietz D 80 B6
Wendlingen am Neckar D 27 C11
Wendover GB 15 D7
Wenduine B 182 C2
Wengen CH 70 D5
Wengsel (Isterberg) D 17 D8
Wennigsen (Deister) D 78 B6
Wenningstedt D 86 F2
Wenns A 71 C11
Wentorf D 83 C8
Wentorf bei Hamburg D 83 D8
Wenzenbach D 75 D11
Wenzlow D 79 B11
Wépion B 182 E5
Werbach D 74 C6
Werbellin D 84 E5
Werben D 80 C6
Werben (Elbe) D 83 E11
Werbig D 80 C4
Werbkowice PL 144 B8
Werbomont B 19 D12
Werdau D 79 E11
Werder D 79 B12
Werder D 84 C4
Werdohl D 17 F9
Werfen A 73 B7
Werkendam NL 182 B5
Werl D 17 E9
Werlte D 17 C9
Wermelskirchen D 185 B7
Wermsdorf D 80 D3
Wernau D 27 C11
Wernberg-Köblitz D 75 C11
Werndorf A 148 C5
Werne D 17 E9
Werneck D 75 C7
Werneuchen D 80 A5
Wernigerode D 79 C8
Wernshausen D 79 E7
Werpeloh D 17 C9
Wertach D 71 B10
Wertheim D 74 C6
Werthenstein CH 70 C6
Werther D 79 D8
Werther (Westfalen) D 17 D10
Wertingen D 75 E8
Wervershoof NL 16 C4
Wervik B 19 C7
Wesel D 17 E7
Wesenberg D 84 D3
Wesendorf D 79 A8
Wesepe NL 183 A8
Wesoła PL 141 F4
Wesselburen D 82 B5
Wesseling D 21 C7
Wesseln D 82 B6
Wessem NL 183 C7
Weßling D 75 F9
Wessobrunn D 71 B12
West Auckland GB 5 F13
West Bridgford GB 11 F9
West Bromwich GB 11 F8
Westbury GB 13 C10
Westendorf A 72 B5
Westensee D 83 B7
Westerbeck (Sassenburg) D 79 A8
Westerbork NL 17 C7
Westerburg D 21 C9
Westerdale GB 3 J10
Westeregeln D 79 C9
Westerende-Kirchloog (Ihlow) D 17 B8
Westergate GB 15 F7
Westergellersen D 83 D8
Westerhaar NL 17 D7
Westerheim D 187 D8
Westerholt D 17 A8
Westerhorn D 82 C7
Westerhoven NL 183 C6
Westerland D 86 F2
Westerlo B 19 B10
Westerrönfeld D 82 B7
Westerstede D 17 B9
Westerstetten D 74 E6
Westervoort NL 16 E5
Westgate GB 5 F12
West Grinstead GB 15 F8
West Haddon GB 13 A12
Westhausen D 75 E7
Westhill GB 3 L12
Westhofen D 187 B5
Westhoffen F 186 D3
Westkapelle NL 19 A7
West Kilbride GB 4 D7
West Kirby GB 10 E5
West Knapton GB 11 C10
West Lavington GB 13 C11
Westleton GB 15 C12
West Linton GB 5 D10
West Looe GB 12 E6
West Lulworth GB 13 D10
Westmalle B 16 F3
West Malling GB 15 E9
West Meon Hut GB 13 C12
West Mersea GB 15 D10
West Moors GB 13 D11
Westness GB 3 G10
Westnewton GB 5 F10
Weston GB 11 F7
Weston GB 13 D10
Weston-super-Mare GB 13 C9
Westonzoyland GB 13 C9
Westport IRL 6 E3
Westport Quay IRL 6 E3
West Somerton GB 15 B12
West Tarbert GB 4 D6
West-Terschelling NL 16 B4
Westward Ho! GB 12 C6
West Wellow GB 13 D11
West Winch GB 11 F12
Wethau D 79 D10
Wetheral GB 5 F11
Wetherby GB 11 D9
Wetlina PL 145 E5
Wetter (Hessen) D 21 C11
Wetter (Ruhr) D 185 B7
Wetteren B 19 B8
Wetterzeube D 79 D11
Wettin D 79 C10
Wettingen CH 27 F9
Wettrup D 17 C9
Wetzikon CH 27 F10
Wetzlar D 21 C11
Wevelgem B 19 C7
Wewelsfleth D 17 A12
Wexford IRL 9 D10
Weyarn D 72 A4
Weybridge GB 15 E8
Weyerbusch D 21 C9
Weyer Markt A 73 A10
Weyersheim F 27 C8
Weyhausen D 79 B8
Weyhe D 17 C11
Weymouth GB 13 D10
Whalton GB 5 E13
Whauphill GB 4 F8
Wheddon Cross GB 13 C7
Wherwell GB 13 C12
Whiddon Down GB 13 D7
Whitburn GB 5 D9
Whitby GB 11 C10
Whitchurch GB 10 F6
Whitchurch GB 13 B8
Whitchurch GB 15 D7
Whitecross GB 7 D10
Whitegate IRL 8 C6
Whitegate IRL 8 E6
Whitehall GB 3 G11
Whitehall IRL 9 C8
Whitehaven GB 10 B4
Whitehead GB 4 F5
Whitehill GB 15 E7
Whitehills GB 3 K11
Whitfield GB 15 E11
Whithorn GB 5 F8
Whiting Bay GB 4 E6
Whitland GB 12 B5
Whitley Bay GB 5 E14
Whitstable GB 15 E11
Whittington GB 10 F5
Whittlesey GB 11 F11
Wiartel PL 139 C12
Wiatrowo PL 85 E12
Wiązów PL 81 E12
Wiązowna PL 141 F4
Wiązownica PL 144 C6
Wichelen B 19 B8
Wick GB 3 J10
Wick GB 13 C7
Wick GB 15 F7
Wickede (Ruhr) D 185 B8
Wickenrode (Helsa) D 78 D6
Wickford GB 15 D10
Wickham GB 13 D12
Wickham Market GB 15 C11
Wicklow IRL 7 G10
Wicko PL 85 A13
Widawa PL 143 D6
Widecombe in the Moor GB 13 D7
Widnau CH 71 C9
Widnes GB 10 E6
Widuchowa PL 84 D6
Więcbork PL 85 D12
Wieck am Darß D 83 B13
Wieczfnia Kościelna PL 139 D9
Wieda D 79 C8
Wiedensahl D 17 D12
Wiederau D 80 E3
Wiednitz D 80 D6
Wiefelstede D 17 B10
Wiehe D 79 D9
Wiehl D 21 C9
Wiek D 84 A4
Większyce PL 142 F5
Wielbark PL 139 D10
Wieleń PL 85 E10
Wielenbach D 72 A3
Wielgie PL 139 E7
Wielgomłyny PL 143 D8

Wielichowo PL 81 B10
Wieliczka PL 143 G9
Wieliczki PL 136 F6
Wielka Wieś PL 143 F8
Wielkie Oczy PL 144 C7
Wielki Klincz PL 138 B5
Wielopole Skrzyńskie PL 143 G12
Wielowieś PL 142 E6
Wielsbeke B 182 D2
Wieluń PL 142 D6
Wiemersdorf D 83 C7
Wien A 77 F10
Wienerbruck A 77 G8
Wiener Neustadt A 77 G10
Wieniawa PL 141 H3
Wieniec PL 138 E6
Wienrode D 79 C8
Wiepke D 79 A9
Wieprz PL 147 B8
Wieprz PL 147 B8
Wiercień Duży PL 141 F7
Wierden NL 17 D7
Wieren D 83 E9
Wieringerwerf NL 16 C4
Wiernsheim D 187 D6
Wieruszów PL 142 D5
Wierzawice PL 144 C5
Wierzbica PL 141 H4
Wierzbica PL 141 H8
Wierzbica Górna PL 142 D4
Wierzbięcin PL 85 C8
Wierzbinek PL 138 F6
Wierzbnik PL 142 E3
Wierzbno PL 139 F12
Wierzbowa PL 81 D9
Wierzchlas PL 142 D6
Wierzchosławice PL 138 E5
Wierzchosławice PL 143 F10
Wierzchowo PL 85 C11
Wierzchowo PL 85 D10
Wierzchucino PL 138 A5
Wies A 148 C4
Wiesa D 80 E3
Wiesau D 75 C11
Wiesbaden D 21 D10
Wieselburg A 77 F8
Wiesen A 149 A6
Wiesen CH 71 D9
Wiesen D 74 B5
Wiesenau D 81 B7
Wiesenburg D 79 B11
Wiesenfelden D 75 D12
Wiesensteig D 187 D8
Wiesent D 75 D11
Wiesenthau D 75 C9
Wiesentheid D 75 C7
Wiesloch D 21 F11
Wiesmath A 148 A6
Wiesmoor D 17 B9
Wieszowa PL 142 F6
Wietmarschen D 17 C8
Wietze D 78 A6
Wietzen D 17 C12
Wietzendorf D 83 E7
Wiewiórczyn PL 143 C7
Wigan GB 10 D6
Wiggensbach D 71 B10
Wigierska Górka PL 147 B8
Wigliniec PL 81 D8
Wigmore GB 13 A9
Wigorzewo PL 136 E4
Wigorzyno PL 85 C9
Wigrów PL 139 F13
Wigrzynice PL 81 B8
Wigrzynowo PL 139 F9
Wigston GB 11 F9
Wigton GB 5 F10
Wigtown GB 5 F8
Wijchen NL 16 E5
Wijewo PL 81 C10
Wijhe NL 183 A8
Wijk aan Zee NL 16 D3
Wijk bij Duurstede NL 16 E4
Wijk en Aalburg NL 183 B6
Wil CH 27 F11
Wilamowice PL 147 B8
Wilczjta PL 139 B8
Wilczogóra PL 138 F5
Wilczyn PL 138 F5
Wildalpen A 73 A10
Wildau D 80 B5
Wildberg D 27 C10
Wildberg D 83 E13
Wildberg D 84 C4
Wildeck-Richelsdorf D 79 E7
Wildendürnbach A 77 E10
Wildenfels D 79 E12
Wildeshausen D 17 C10
Wildflecken D 74 B6
Wildon A 148 C5
Wildpoldsried D 71 B10
Wildshut A 76 F3
Wilga PL 141 G4
Wilhelminadorp NL 183 C6
Wilhelmsburg A 77 F9
Wilhelmsburg D 84 C5
Wilhelmsdorf D 27 E11
Wilhelmshaven D 17 A10
Wilkau-Haßlau D 79 E12
Wilkinstown IRL 7 E9
Wilkołaz Pierwszy PL 144 A5
Wilków PL 141 H5
Wilków PL 142 D4
Wilkowice PL 147 B8
Wilkowo PL 81 B8
Willand GB 13 D8
Willebadessen D 17 E12
Willebroek B 19 B9
Willemstad NL 16 E2
Willich D 17 F7
Willingdon GB 15 F9
Willingen (Upland) D 17 F11
Willingshausen D 21 C12
Willisau CH 27 F9
Williton GB 13 C8
Willstätt D 27 C8
Wilmersdorf D 84 D5
Wilmslow GB 11 E7
Wilnis NL 182 A5
Wilnsdorf D 21 C10
Wilp NL 183 A8
Wilsdruff D 80 D5
Wilsickow D 84 D5
Wilster D 82 C6
Wilsum D 17 C7
Wiltersdorf A 77 E11
Wiltingen D 21 E7
Wilton GB 13 C11
Wiltz L 20 E5
Wimblington GB 11 F12
Wimborne Minster GB 13 D11
Wimereux F 15 F12
Wimmelburg D 79 C10
Wimmis CH 70 D5
Wimpassing A 148 A6
Wincanton GB 13 C10
Winchburgh GB 5 D10
Winchelsea GB 15 F10
Wincheringen D 186 B1
Winchester GB 13 C12
Wincrange L 20 D5
Winda PL 136 E3
Windach D 71 A12
Windeby D 83 B7
Windermere GB 10 C6
Windesheim D 21 E9
Windhagen D 21 C8
Windigsteig A 77 E8
Windischeschenbach D 75 C11
Windischgarsten A 73 A9
Windorf D 76 E4
Windsbach D 75 D8
Windsor GB 15 E7
Wingate GB 5 F14
Wingene B 19 B7
Wingen-sur-Moder F 27 C7
Winklarn D 75 D11
Winkleigh GB 13 D7
Winklern A 73 C6
Winklern bei Oberwölz A 73 B9
Winnenden D 27 C11
Winnert D 82 B6
Winnica PL 139 E10
Winningen D 79 C9
Winningen D 185 D8
Winnweiler D 186 B4
Winschoten NL 17 B8
Winsen (Aller) D 83 E7
Winsen (Luhe) D 83 D8
Winsford GB 10 E6
Wińsko PL 81 D11
Winslow GB 15 D7
Winssen NL 183 B7
Winston GB 11 B8
Winsum NL 16 B5
Winterberg D 21 B11
Winterbourne Abbas GB 13 D9
Winterfeld D 83 E10
Winterswijk NL 17 E7
Winterthur CH 27 E10
Winterton GB 11 D10
Winton GB 11 C7
Wintrich D 185 E6
Wintzenheim F 27 D7
Winwick GB 15 C8
Winzenburg D 78 C6
Winzer D 76 E4
Wipperdorf D 79 D8
Wipperfürth D 21 B8
Wippra Kurort D 79 C9
Wirdumer (Wirdum) D 17 B8
Wirges D 185 D8
Wirksworth GB 11 E8
Wirsberg D 75 B10
Wisbech GB 11 F12
Wischhafen D 17 A12
Wishaw GB 5 D9
Wiskitki PL 141 F2
Wisła PL 147 B7
Wiślica PL 143 F10
Wismar D 83 C10
Wiśniew PL 141 F6
Wiśniewo PL 139 D9
Wiśniowa PL 144 D1
Wiśniowa PL 144 D4
Wissant F 15 F12
Wissembourg F 27 B8
Wissen D 21 C9
Wissenkerke NL 16 E1
Wistedt D 82 D7
Wisznia Mała PL 81 D12
Wisznice PL 141 G8
Witaszyce PL 142 C4
Witham GB 15 D10
Witheridge GB 13 D7
Withernsea GB 11 D12
Witkowo PL 85 D8
Witkowo PL 138 F4
Witley GB 15 E7
Witmarsum NL 16 B4
Witney GB 13 B12
Witnica PL 84 E6
Witnica PL 85 E7
Witonia PL 143 B7
Witosław PL 85 D12
Witry-lès-Reims F 19 F9
Wittdün D 82 A4
Witten D 17 F8
Wittenbach CH 27 F11
Wittenberge D 83 E11
Wittenburg D 83 C10
Wittenförden D 83 C10
Wittenhagen D 84 B4
Wittenheim F 27 E7
Wittibreut D 76 F3
Wittichenau D 80 D6
Wittighausen D 74 C6
Wittingen D 83 E9
Wittlich D 21 E7
Wittmar D 79 B8
Wittmund D 17 A9
Wittstock D 83 D12
Witzenhausen D 78 D6
Witzin D 83 C11
Witzwort D 82 B5
Wiveliscombe GB 13 C8
Wivenhoe GB 15 D10
Wiżajny PL 136 E6
Wizernes F 18 C5
Wizna PL 140 D6
Władysławów PL 142 B5
Władysławowo PL 138 A5
Wleń PL 81 D9
Włocławek PL 138 F7
Włodawa PL 141 G9
Włodzienin PL 142 F4
Włodzimierzów PL 143 D8
Włostów PL 143 E11
Włoszakowice PL 81 C10
Włoszczowa PL 143 E8
Wöbbelin D 83 D11
Woburn GB 15 D7
Wodynie PL 141 F5
Wodzierady PL 143 C7
Wodzisław PL 143 E9
Wodzisław Śląski PL 142 F5
Woensdrecht NL 182 C4
Woerden NL 16 D3
Wœrth F 27 C8
Wohlen CH 27 F9
Wohlen CH 31 B11
Wohlmirstedt D 79 D9
Wohltorf D 83 C8
Wöhrden D 82 B6
Wohyń PL 141 G7
Woippy F 26 B5
Wojaszówka PL 144 D4
Wojcieszków PL 141 G6
Wojcieszów PL 81 E9
Wójcin PL 138 E5
Wojkowice PL 143 F7
Wojnicz PL 143 G10
Wojnowo PL 138 D4
Wojsławice PL 144 B8
Woking GB 15 E7
Wokingham GB 15 E7
Wola PL 138 E7
Wola Mołodycka PL 144 C6
Wola Mysłowska PL 141 G5
Wolanów PL 141 H3
Wola-Rjbkowska PL 141 G5
Wola Uhruska PL 141 H9
Wola Wierzbowska PL 139 E10
Wołbórz PL 141 H1
Wolbrom PL 143 F8
Wołczyn PL 142 D5
Woldegk D 84 D5
Woldendorp NL 17 B8
Wolfach D 27 D9
Wolfegg D 71 B9
Wolfen D 79 C11
Wolfenbüttel D 79 B8
Wolfenschiessen CH 71 D6
Wölfersheim D 21 D11
Wolfhagen D 17 F12
Wölfis D 79 E8
Wolfpassing A 77 F8
Wolfratshausen D 72 A3
Wolfsberg A 73 C10
Wolfsburg D 79 B8
Wolfstein D 21 E9
Wolfurt A 71 C9
Wolgast D 84 B5
Wolhusen CH 70 C6
Wolin PL 84 C7
Wólka PL 139 E7
Wólka PL 141 H7
Wólka Dobryńska PL 141 F8
Wolkersdorf A 77 F11
Wollbach D 75 B7
Wollerau CH 27 F10
Wolmirstedt D 79 B10
Wolnzach D 75 E10
Wołomin PL 139 F11
Woloskowola PL 141 H8
Wołów PL 81 D11
Wolpertshausen D 74 D6
Wolpertswende D 71 B9
Wolphaartsdijk NL 182 B3
Wölpinghausen D 17 D12
Wolsingham GB 5 F13
Wolsztyn PL 81 B10
Woltersdorf D 80 B4
Woltersdorf D 83 E10
Wolvega NL 16 C6
Wolverhampton GB 11 F7
Wombwell GB 11 D9
Wommelgem B 19 B10
Wommels NL 16 B5
Wonfurt D 75 B7
Wonsees D 75 C9
Woodbridge GB 15 C11
Woodcote GB 13 B12
Woodford IRL 6 F6
Woodhall Spa GB 11 E11
Woodland GB 5 F13
Woodley GB 15 E7
Woodstock GB 13 B12
Woodton GB 15 C11
Woodtown IRL 7 E9
Wool GB 13 D10
Wooler GB 5 D12
Wootton Bassett GB 13 B11
Worb CH 31 B12
Worbis D 79 D7
Worcester GB 13 A10
Wördern A 77 F10
Worfield GB 11 F7
Wörgl A 72 B5
Workington GB 5 F9
Worksop GB 11 E9
Workum NL 16 C4
Wörlitz D 79 C11
Wormeldange L 20 E6
Wormerveer NL 16 D3
Wormhout F 18 C5
Worms D 21 E10
Worpswede D 17 B11
Wörrstadt D 21 E10
Wörschach A 73 A9
Wortel B 182 C5
Wörth A 73 B6
Worth GB 15 E8
Wörth am Main D 187 B7
Wörth am Rhein D 27 B9
Worthing GB 15 F8
Woudenberg NL 183 A6
Woudrichem NL 16 E3
Woudsend NL 16 C5
Woustviller F 27 B7
Wouw NL 16 E2
Woźniki PL 143 E7
Wragby GB 11 E11
Wrangle GB 11 E12
Wrecsam GB 10 E6
Wręczyca Wielka PL 143 E6
Wredenhagen D 83 D13
Wrelton GB 11 C10
Wremen D 17 A11
Wrestedt D 83 E9
Wrexham GB 10 E6
Wriedel D 83 D8
Wriezen D 84 E6
Wrist D 82 C7
Wróblew PL 142 C6
Wrocław PL 81 D12
Wrohm D 82 B6
Wronki PL 85 E10
Wronki PL 136 E5
Wrotnów PL 139 E13
Wrząsielka PL 142 B6
Wrzelowiec PL 144 A4
Wrzeście PL 85 A12
Września PL 85 F13
Wrzosowo PL 85 B9
Wschowa PL 81 C10
Wulfen D 79 C10
Wulfersdorf D 83 D12
Wülfershausen an der Saale D 75 B7
Wulfsen D 83 D8
Wulften D 79 C7
Wulkau D 83 E12
Wullersdorf A 77 E10
Wundschuh A 148 C4
Wünnenberg D 17 E11
Wünsdorf D 80 B4
Wunsiedel D 75 B11
Wunstorf D 78 B5
Wuppertal D 17 F8
Wurmlingen D 27 D10
Würselen D 20 C6
Wurzbach D 75 B10
Würzburg D 74 C6
Wurzen D 79 D12
Wüstenrot D 27 B11
Wusterhausen D 83 E12
Wusterhusen D 84 B5
Wustermark D 79 A12
Wusterwitz D 79 B11
Wustrau-Altfriesack D 84 E3
Wustrow D 83 E10
Wustrow D 84 D3
Wustrow D 83 B12
Wutha D 79 E7
Wutöschingen D 27 E9
Wuustwezel B 16 F3
Wyczechy PL 85 C12
Wydminy PL 136 F5
Wye GB 15 E10
Wygoda PL 143 E7
Wygon PL 85 D9
Wyhl D 27 D8
Wyk auf Föhr D 82 A5
Wylatowo PL 138 E4
Wylye GB 13 C11
Wymondham GB 15 B11
Wyre Piddle GB 13 A10
Wyrozjby-Konaty PL 141 F6
Wyry PL 143 F6
Wyryki-Połód PL 141 G8
Wyrzysk PL 85 D12
Wyśmierzyce PL 141 G3
Wysoka PL 85 D12
Wysoka PL 85 E8
Wysoka Kamieńska PL 85 C7
Wysokie PL 136 F6
Wysokie PL 144 B6
Wysokie Mazowieckie PL 141 E7
Wysowa PL 145 E3
Wyszanów PL 142 D5
Wyszki PL 141 E7
Wyszków PL 139 E11
Wyszogród PL 139 F9
Wyszyny PL 85 E11
Wythall GB 13 A11
Wytyczno PL 141 H8

X

Xanceda E 38 B3
Xanten D 17 E6
Xanthi GR 171 B7
Xarrë AL 168 E3
Xátiva E 56 D3
Xeraco E 56 C4
Xeresa E 56 C4
Xermade E 38 B4
Xerta E 42 F5
Xertigny F 26 D5
Xifiani GR 169 C7
Xino Nero GR 169 C6
Xinzo de Limia E 38 D4
Xirivella E 48 F4
Xirochori GR 174 D4
Xirokampi GR 174 F5
Xirokampo GR 177 E8
Xiropotamos GR 170 B6
Xonrupt-Longemer F 27 D6
Xove E 38 A4
Xunqueira de Ambía E 38 D4
Xylagani GR 171 C8
Xylokastro GR 175 C6
Xyloupoli GR 169 C9

Y

Yablanitsa BG 165 C9
Yablanovo BG 167 D7
Yabluniv UA 152 A5
Yabŭlchevo BG 167 D8
Yabŭlkovo BG 166 E4
Yağcı TR 173 C7
Yağcılar TR 173 F9
Yağcili TR 173 F8
Yagoda BG 166 D5
Yakimovo BG 160 F2
Yakoruda BG 165 F8
Yakovo BG 169 A9
Yaliçiftlik TR 173 D10
Yalikavak TR 177 E9
Yaliköy TR 173 B9
Yalova TR 171 D10
Yambol BG 167 E7
Yamkino RUS 132 F5
Yamm RUS 132 E3
Yampil' UA 154 A2
Yangi TR 181 C9
Yanguas E 41 D7
Yanikağil TR 173 B8
Yaniskoski RUS 114 F5
Yankavichy BY 133 E5
Yankovo BG 167 C8
Yantarnyy RUS 139 A8
Yapildak TR 172 D6
Yaraş TR 181 B8
Yareva BY 135 F13
Yarlovo BG 165 E7
Yarm GB 11 B9
Yarmouth GB 13 D12
Yarnton GB 13 B12
Yarove UA 154 E4
Yarrow GB 5 D10
Yasen BG 165 C10
Yasen' UA 145 F9
Yasenkovo BG 167 B7
Yasenovets BG 161 F9
Yasinya UA 152 A4
Yas'ky UA 154 D6
Yasna Polyana BG 167 E9
Yasnoye RUS 134 F3
Yassiören TR 173 B10
Yasski RUS 132 F7
Yatağan TR 181 B8
Yate GB 13 B10
Yatova E 48 F3
Yatton GB 13 C9
Yavora UA 145 E7
Yavoriv UA 144 D7
Yavoriv UA 152 A5
Yaxley GB 11 F11
Yaylagöne TR 172 C6
Yazıbaşı TR 177 C9
Yazıköy TR 181 C6
Yazna BY 133 F4
Yazvina BY 133 F7
Ybbs an der Donau A 77 F8
Ybbsitz A 77 G7
Ychoux F 32 B4
Ydby DK 86 B2
Ydes F 29 E10
Ydra GR 175 E7
Ydrefors S 92 D7
Y Drenewydd GB 10 F5
Yeadon GB 11 D8
Yealmpton GB 12 E7
Yebra E 47 D7
Yebra de Basa E 32 F5
Yecla E 56 D2
Yecla de Yeltes E 45 C8
Yedy BY 133 F2
Yémeda E 47 E9
Yemişendere TR 181 B9
Yenice TR 171 C10
Yenice TR 173 D7
Yenice TR 173 D9
Yenice TR 181 B8
Yeniçiftlik TR 173 B8
Yeniçiftlik TR 173 D7
Yeniçiftlik TR 177 C9
Yenifoça TR 177 B8
Yenihisar TR 177 E9
Yeniköy TR 172 D6
Yeniköy TR 173 B6
Yeniköy TR 173 E8
Yeniköy TR 177 B9
Yeniköy TR 177 B10
Yeniköy TR 177 C9
Yeniköy TR 177 D10
Yeniköy TR 177 E9
Yeniköy TR 181 B8
Yenimuhacirköy TR 172 C6
Yenişakran TR 177 B9
Yenne F 31 D8
Yeovil GB 13 D9
Yepes E 46 E5
Yerkesik TR 181 B8
Yerseke NL 16 F2
Yershovo RUS 132 F3
Yerville F 18 E2
Yesa E 32 E3
Yeşilsırt TR 173 B7
Yeşilyurt TR 181 B8
Yeste E 55 C8
Yevtodiya UA 154 B4
Yezyaryshcha BY 133 E7
Y Fenni GB 13 B8
Ygos-St-Saturnin F 32 C4
Ygrande F 30 B2
Ykspihlaja FIN 123 C10
Ylakiai LT 134 D3
Yläkönkäs FIN 113 D17
Ylä-Luosta FIN 125 D11
Ylämaa FIN 129 D9
Ylämylly FIN 125 E13
Yläne FIN 126 D7
Ylä-Valtimo FIN 125 C11
Ylihärmä FIN 122 D9
Yli-li FIN 119 D15
Ylijärvi FIN 128 D8
Yli-Kärppä FIN 119 C15
Ylikiiminki FIN 119 D16
Yli-Körkkö FIN 119 B16
Ylikulma FIN 127 E9
Yli-Kurki FIN 121 D10
Ylikylä FIN 115 E2
Ylikylä FIN 117 E15
Ylikylä FIN 123 D12
Ylikylä FIN 123 E10
Ylikylä FIN 125 C12
Yli-Kyrö FIN 117 B12
Yli-Lesti FIN 123 D13
Yli-Liakka FIN 119 C12
Yli-Livo FIN 120 C9
Yli-Muonio FIN 117 B10
Yli-Nampa FIN 117 E16
Ylinenjärvi S 117 E10
Yli-Olhava FIN 119 C15
Ylipää FIN 119 E12
Ylipää FIN 119 E13
Ylipää FIN 119 E13
Ylipää FIN 119 E14
Ylipää FIN 119 E16
Ylipää FIN 119 F13
Ylipää FIN 123 C14
Ylipää FIN 123 D11
Yli-Paakkola FIN 119 B13
Yli-Siurua FIN 119 C17
Ylistaro FIN 122 E9
Yli-Tannila FIN 119 D16
Ylitornio FIN 119 B11
Yli-Utos FIN 120 E8
Yli-Valli FIN 123 F9
Ylivieska FIN 123 B13
Yli-Vuotto FIN 119 E17
Yllásjärvi FIN 117 C12
Ylöjärvi FIN 127 B10
Ylönkyla FIN 127 E9
Ylvingen N 108 E3
Ymonville F 24 D6
Yngsjö S 88 D6
Yoğuntaş TR 167 F8
Yolageldi TR 173 A6
Yonkovo BG 161 F9
York GB 11 D9
Youghal IRL 9 E7
Yovkovo BG 155 F2
Yoxford GB 15 C12
Ypäjä FIN 127 D9
Ypäjänkylä FIN 127 D9
Ypati GR 174 B5
Yport F 18 E1
Yppäri FIN 119 F12
Ypsos GR 168 E2
Ypyä FIN 123 C13
Yrittäperä FIN 121 D10
Yrttivaara S 116 E7
Ysane S 88 C7
Ysbyty Ystwyth GB 13 A7
Yset N 101 A12
Ysselsteyn NL 183 C7
Yssingeaux F 30 E5
Ystad S 87 E13
Ystalyfera GB 13 B7
Ytre Arna N 94 B2
Ytre Årnes N 111 B15
Ytre Billefjord N 113 C15
Ytre Kjæs N 113 B16
Ytre Sandvik N 113 C15
Ytterån S 105 E16
Yttergård S 105 D14
Ytterberg S 102 B7
Ytter-Busjö S 107 B15
Ytteresse FIN 123 C9
Ytterhogdal S 102 B8
Ytterjeppo FIN 122 D9
Yttermalung S 102 E6
Yttersta S 118 D6
Ytterträsk S 118 F4
Ytterturingen S 103 B9
Yttervik S 109 E10
Yttre Lansjärv S 116 E8
Yukaribey TR 177 A9
Yukarikizilca TR 177 C9
Yukhavichy BY 133 D5
Yuncler E 46 D5
Yuncos E 46 D5
Yundola BG 165 E8
Yunquera E 53 C7
Yunquera de Henares E 47 C6
Yuper BG 161 F8
Yuratsishki BY 137 E12
Yuravichy BY 133 E5
Yürücekler TR 173 E10
Yürük TR 173 C7
Yutz F 20 F6
Yuzhnyy RUS 136 D2
Yverdon CH 31 B10
Yvetot F 18 E2
Yvignac F 23 D7
Yvoir B 19 D10
Yvoire F 31 C9
Yvonand CH 31 B10
Yxnerum S 93 C8
Yxsjö S 107 C13
Yxsjöberg S 97 B12
Yxskaftkälen S 106 D8
Yzeure F 30 B3
Yzeures-sur-Creuse F 29 B7

Z

Zaamslag NL 182 C3
Zaandam NL 16 D3
Zaazyer"ye BY 133 F5
Zăbala RO 153 F8
Žabalj SRB 158 C5
Žabari SRB 159 E7
Zabeltitz-Treugeböhla D 80 D5
Żabia Wola PL 141 F3
Zabica BIH 162 D5
Zabiče SLO 67 A9
Zabiele PL 139 D12
Zabierzów PL 143 F8
Ząbki PL 141 F4
Ząbkowice Śląskie PL 81 E11
Zablaće SRB 158 D4
Zablaće SRB 158 F5
Zableće BIH 157 D6
Žabljak MNE 163 C7
Zabłudów PL 140 D8
Žabno HR 149 E7
Żabno PL 143 F10
Żabno PL 144 B6
Zabok HR 148 D5
Žabokreky SK 147 C7
Žabokreky nad Nitrou SK 146 D6
Zabolova LV 133 A2
Zabór PL 81 C9
Zabor"ye BY 133 E6
Żabów PL 85 D7
Żabowo PL 85 C8
Zăbrani RO 151 E8
Zabrđe BIH 157 C10
Zábřeh CZ 77 C11
Zăbriceni MD 153 A10
Zabrze PL 142 F6
Zabŭrdo BG 165 F10
Zabuzhzhya UA 141 H9
Zacharo GR 174 E4
Zaclău RO 155 C2
Žacléř CZ 81 E9
Zaczopki PL 141 F8
Zadar HR 156 D3
Zadunayivka UA 154 F4
Zádveřice CZ 146 C5
Zadzim PL 142 C6
Zadzyezhzha BY 133 E4
Zafarraya E 53 C8
Zafferana Etnea I 59 D7
Zafirovo BG 161 F9
Zafra E 51 C7
Zafra de Záncara E 47 E7
Zafrilla E 47 D9
Žaga SLO 73 D7
Żagań PL 81 C8
Zagăr RO 152 E5
Žagarė LT 134 D6
Zagarise I 59 A10
Zagkliveri GR 169 C9
Žaglav HR 67 E11
Zagnańsk PL 143 E10
Zagon RO 153 F8
Zagora GR 169 F9
Zagorë AL 163 E8
Zagorje SLO 73 E9
Zagorje ob Savi SLO 73 D10
Zagórów PL 142 B4
Zagortsi BG 167 E8
Zagórz PL 145 D5
Zagra E 53 B8
Zagra RO 152 C4
Zagrazhden BG 160 F5
Zagrazhden BG 166 F3
Zagreb HR 148 E5
Zagrodno PL 81 D9
Žagrović HR 156 D5
Žagubica SRB 159 E8
Zagvodz HR 157 F7
Zagyvarékas H 150 C5
Zahara E 51 F9
Zahara de los Atunes E 52 D5
Zahinos E 51 C6
Zahna D 79 C12
Zahnitkiv UA 154 A3
Záhony H 145 G5
Záhorská Ves SK 77 F11
Zahor"ye BY 133 F5
Zăicani MD 153 B10
Zaiceva LV 133 B2
Zaidín E 42 D4
Žaiginys LT 134 F6
Zaim MD 154 D4
Zajas MK 168 A4
Zaječar SRB 159 F9
Zaječí CZ 77 E11
Zaječov CZ 76 C5
Zajezierze PL 85 C9
Zákamenné SK 147 C8
Zákány H 149 D7
Zákányszek H 150 E4
Zakharnichy BY 133 E5
Zakliczyn PL 144 D2
Zaklików PL 144 B5
Zaklopača BIH 157 D11
Zakoma BIH 157 E10
Zakopane PL 147 C9
Zakros GR 179 E11
Zakrzew PL 141 H4
Zakrzewo PL 85 D12
Zakrzewo PL 138 E6
Zakrzówek-Wieś PL 144 B5
Zákupy CZ 81 E7
Zakynthos GR 174 D2
Zalaapáti H 149 C8
Zalaegerszeg H 149 C7
Zalakaros H 149 C8
Zalakomár H 149 C8
Zalalövő H 149 C7
Zalamea de la Serena E 51 B8
Zalamea la Real E 51 D6
Zalaszántó H 149 C8
Zalaszentbalázs H 149 C7
Zalaszentgrót H 149 C8
Zalaszentiván H 149 C7
Zalău RO 151 C11
Zalavár H 149 C8
Zalavas LT 137 D13
Załazy PL 141 H5
Zaldibar E 41 B6
Žalec SLO 73 D11
Zalenieki LV 134 C7
Zalesie PL 85 E13
Zalesie PL 141 F8
Zalesie Śląskie PL 142 F5
Zalesje LV 133 D4
Zales'ye RUS 136 D4
Zaleszany PL 144 B4
Zalewo PL 139 C8
Zalha RO 152 C3
Zālīte LV 135 C8
Zalivnoye RUS 136 D2
Zall-Dardhë AL 163 F9
Żalno PL 138 C4
Zalogovac SRB 159 F7
Zaltbommel NL 16 E4
Załuski PL 139 E10
Zalužje BIH 158 E3
Zalužnica HR 156 C3
Zalve LV 135 D10
Zalyessye BY 133 F3
Zalyessye BY 137 E13
Zam RO 151 E9
Zamárdi H 149 C9
Zamarte PL 85 C12
Žamberk CZ 77 B10
Zambrana E 40 C6
Zămbreasca RO 160 E6
Zambrów PL 140 E6
Zambujal de Cima P 50 C1
Zambujeira do Mar P 50 D2
Zamјcin PL 85 D8
Zamfirovo BG 165 C7
Zamogil'ye RUS 132 D2
Zámoly H 149 B10
Zamora E 39 E8
Zamość PL 139 D12
Zamość PL 144 B7
Zamoshsha BY 133 F2
Zamostea RO 153 B8
Zams A 71 C11
Zámutov SK 145 F4
Zandhoven B 19 B10
Žandov CZ 80 E6
Zandvliet B 16 F2
Zandvoort NL 16 D3
Zănești RO 153 D9
Zaniemyśl PL 81 B12
Zante LV 134 C5
Zaorejas E 47 C8
Zaovine SRB 158 F3
Zapałów PL 144 C6
Zaplanik BIH 162 D5
Zaplyus'ye RUS 132 E6
Zăpodeni RO 153 D11
Zapolice PL 142 C6
Zapolyarnyy RUS 114 E9
Zapol'ye RUS 132 E6
Zaporozhskoye RUS 129 D14
Zappeio GR 169 F7
Zapponeta I 60 A5
Zaprešić HR 148 E5
Zapruddzye BY 133 F3
Zapytiv UA 144 D9
Zaragoza E 41 E10
Zărand RO 151 E8
Zarańsko PL 85 C9
Zarasai LT 135 E12
Zaratamo E 40 B6
Zaratán E 39 E10
Zarautz E 32 D1
Zarcilla de Ramos E 55 D9
Zarjby PL 139 D11
Zarjby-Kościelne PL 139 E13
Zarechcha BY 133 E7
Žarėnai LT 134 E4
Zaricheve UA 145 F6
Żarki PL 143 E7
Żarki Wielkie PL 81 C7
Zărnești RO 160 B6
Zărnești RO 161 C9
Žarnovica SK 147 D7
Żarnów PL 141 H2
Żarnowiec PL 143 F8
Zaronava BY 133 F7
Zaros GR 178 E8
Žarošice CZ 77 D11
Żarów PL 81 E10
Zarpen D 83 C9
Zarra E 47 F10
Zarren B 182 C1
Zarrentin D 83 C9
Zarszyn PL 145 D5
Żary PL 81 C8
Zarza Capilla E 51 B9
Zarza de Alange E 51 B7
Zarza de Granadilla E 45 D8
Zarza de Tajo E 47 D6
Zarzadilla de Totana E 55 D9
Zarza la Mayor E 45 E7
Zarzecze PL 144 D6
Zarzuela del Monte E 46 C4
Zarzuela del Pinar E 40 F3
Zas E 38 B2
Zasa LV 135 D11
Zaskarki BY 133 F5
Žaškov SK 147 C8
Zasliai LT 137 D10
Zásmuky CZ 77 C8
Zasów PL 143 F11
Zastražišće HR 157 F6
Žatec CZ 76 B5
Zaton HR 156 E4
Zaton HR 162 D5
Zátor CZ 142 F4
Zator PL 143 G7
Zatory PL 139 E11
Zătreni RO 160 D3
Zatyshshya UA 154 C5
Zaube LV 135 C10
Zau de Câmpie RO 152 D4
Zavadka UA 145 E7
Závadka nad Hronom SK 147 D9
Zavala BIH 162 D4
Zavala HR 157 F6
Zavalje BIH 156 C4
Zavallya UA 153 A7
Zavallya UA 154 A6
Zavattarello I 37 B10

Závažná Poruba SK 147 C9
Zaventem B 19 C9
Zavet BG 161 F9
Zavidoviči BIH 157 D9
Zavlaka SRB 158 E3
Zăvoaia RO 161 D10
Závod SK 77 E12
Zăvoi RO 159 B9
Zavoj SRB 165 C6
Zavutstsye BY 133 F4
Zavyachellye BY 133 F5
Zavydovychi UA 144 D8
Zawada PL 81 C9
Zawada PL 141 G1
Zawada PL 142 E4
Zawada PL 143 E7
Zawada PL 144 B7
Zawady PL 140 D7
Zawadzkie PL 142 E5
Zawichost PL 144 B4
Zawidów PL 81 D8
Zawidz Kościelny PL 139 E8
Zawiercie PL 143 F7
Zawoja PL 147 B9
Zawonia PL 81 D12
Zaytsevo RUS 132 F4
Žažina HR 148 E6
Zázrivá SK 147 C8
Žažvic HR 156 E4
Zbąszyn PL 81 B9
Zbąszynek PL 81 B9
Zbehy SK 146 E6
Zberoaia MD 153 D12
Zbiczno PL 139 D7
Zbiersk PL 142 C5
Zbiroh CZ 76 C5
Zblewo PL 138 C5
Zbludowice PL 143 F10
Zbójna PL 139 D12
Zbójno PL 139 D7
Zborov SK 145 E3
Zborovice CZ 146 C4
Zborov nad Bystricou SK 147 C7
Zbraslav CZ 77 D10
Zbraslavice CZ 77 C8
Zbrzeźnica PL 140 D6
Zbuczyn Poduchowny PL 141 F6
Ždala HR 149 D8
Ždánice CZ 77 D12
Žďár CZ 77 A8
Žďár nad Sázavou CZ 77 C9
Zdenci HR 149 E9
Ždiar SK 145 E1
Zdice CZ 76 C5
Zdihovo HR 67 B11
Zdíkov CZ 76 D5
Ždírec nad Doubravou CZ 77 C9
Zdounky CZ 146 C4
Zdralovac BIH 157 E6
Zdravets BG 167 C9
Zdravinje SRB 164 C3
Ždrelac HR 156 D3
Ždrelo SRB 159 E8
Zdunje MK 164 F3
Zduńska Wola PL 143 C6
Zduny PL 81 C12
Zduny PL 141 F1
Zdynia PL 145 E3
Zdziarzec PL 143 F11
Zdziechowa PL 85 E13
Zdzieszowice PL 142 F5
Zdziłowice PL 144 B6
Zjbowice PL 142 E5
Žebrák CZ 76 C5
Zebreira P 45 E6
Zebrene LV 134 C5
Zebrzydowa PL 81 D8
Zechlinerhütte D 84 D3
Zeddam NL 183 B8
Zeddiani I 64 D2
Zedelgem B 19 B7
Zederhaus A 73 B8
Žednik SRB 150 F4
Zjdowice PL 142 E6
Zeebrugge B 19 B7
Zeeland NL 16 E5
Zeewolde NL 183 A7
Zegama E 32 E1
Żegiestów PL 145 E2
Žegljane MK 164 E4
Żegocina PL 144 D1
Zehdenick D 84 E4
Zehna D 83 C12
Žehra SK 145 F2
Zehren D 80 D4
Zeilarn D 76 F3
Žeimelis LT 135 D8
Žeimiai LT 135 F8
Zeiselmauer A 77 F10
Zeiskam D 187 C5
Zeist NL 16 D4
Zeithain D 80 D4
Zeitlofs D 74 B6
Zeitz D 79 D11
Zejmen AL 163 F8
Żelazków PL 142 C5
Zele B 19 B9
Želechlinek PL 141 G2
Żelechów PL 141 G5
Zelena UA 152 A5
Zelena UA 152 B5
Zelena UA 153 A9
Zeleneč SK 146 E5
Zeleni Jadar BIH 158 E3
Zelenikovo BG 166 E4
Zelenikovo MK 164 F4
Zelenogorsk RUS 129 E12
Zelenogradsk RUS 136 D1
Zelenohirs'ke UA 154 B6
Želetava CZ 77 D9
Železná Ruda CZ 76 D4
Železné SK 147 D8
Železnice CZ 77 B8
Železniki SLO 73 D9
Železný Brod CZ 81 E8
Zelhem NL 16 D6
Želiezovce SK 147 E7
Zelina HR 148 E6
Želinja BIH 157 C9
Želino MK 164 F3
Želiv CZ 77 C8
Željuša BIH 157 F8
Żelków-Kolonia PL 141 F6
Zell D 75 B10
Zell (Mosel) D 21 D8
Zella-Mehlis D 79 E8
Zell am Harmersbach D 27 D9
Zell am Main D 187 B8
Zell am See A 73 B6
Zell am Ziller A 72 B4
Zell im Wiesental D 27 E8
Zellingen D 74 C6
Zell-Pfarre A 73 D9
Zelmeņi LV 134 D6
Želovce SK 147 E8
Zelów PL 143 D7
Zeltingen-Rachtig D 21 E8
Zeltiņi LV 135 B13
Zeltweg A 73 B10
Želva LT 135 F10
Zelzate B 19 B8
Žemaičių Naumiestis LT 134 F3
Žemberovce SK 147 E7
Zemblak AL 168 C4
Zembrów PL 141 E6
Zembrzyce PL 147 B9
Zemen BG 165 E6
Zemeno GR 175 C6
Zemeş RO 153 D8
Zemianska Oľča SK 146 F5
Zemīte LV 134 C5
Zemitz D 84 C5
Zemmer D 21 E7
Zemné SK 146 F6
Zemplénagárd H 145 G5
Zemplínske Hámre SK 145 F5
Zemst B 19 C9
Zemun SRB 158 D5
Zenica BIH 157 D8
Zennor GB 12 E3
Zentene LV 134 B5
Žepa BIH 157 E11
Žepče BIH 157 D9
Žeravice CZ 146 C4
Zerbst D 79 C11
Zerf D 21 E7
Zerind RO 151 D8
Żerków PL 142 B4
Zernez CH 71 D10
Zernien D 83 D9
Zernitz D 83 E12
Zero Branco I 72 E5
Zerpenschleuse D 84 E5
Zerrenthin D 84 D6
Zestoa E 32 D1
Žetale SLO 148 D5
Zetea RO 152 E6
Zetel D 17 B9
Zet'ovo BG 166 E4
Zeulenroda D 79 E10
Zeven D 17 B12
Zevenaar NL 16 E6
Zevenbergen NL 16 E3
Zevgolatio GR 175 D6
Zevio I 66 B3
Zeytinalani TR 181 C9
Zeytinbağı TR 173 D10
Zeytindağ TR 177 B9
Zeytineli TR 177 C8
Zeytinli TR 173 E6
Zeytinliova TR 177 B10
Zgierz PL 143 C7
Zgłobice PL 143 G10
Zgornje Bitnje SLO 73 D9
Zgornje Jezersko SLO 73 D9
Zgornji Duplek SLO 148 C5
Zgorzelec PL 81 D8
Zgropolci MK 169 A6
Zgurița MD 153 A11
Zhabinka BY 141 F10
Zhabokrychka UA 154 A3
Zhdeniyevo UA 145 F7
Zhegër RKS 164 E3
Zheleznodorozhnyy RUS 136 E3
Zhelyazkovo BG 167 E8
Zhelyu Voyvoda BG 167 D6
Zheravna BG 167 D6
Zhilino RUS 136 D4
Zhitkovo RUS 129 D11
Zhitnitsa BG 167 C9
Zhitom AL 168 C2
Zhodzishki BY 137 D13
Zhorany UA 141 H9
Zhovkva UA 144 C8
Zhovtantsi UA 144 D9
Zhovtneve UA 144 B9
Zhovtneve UA 155 B3
Zhovtyy Yar UA 154 F5
Zhuprany BY 137 E13
Zhur RKS 164 E2
Zhvyrka UA 144 C9
Zhydachiv UA 145 E9
Zhyrmuny BY 137 E11
Žiar nad Hronom SK 147 D7
Zibalai LT 137 C10
Zibello I 66 B1
Zibreira P 44 F3
Zicavo F 37 H10
Žichovice CZ 76 D5
Zickhusen D 83 C10
Zidani Most SLO 73 D11
Zidarovo BG 167 E8
Zīdikai LT 134 D4
Židlochovice CZ 77 D11
Ziduri RO 161 C10
Zijbice PL 81 E12
Ziedkalne LV 134 D6
Ziegelroda D 79 D9
Ziegendorf D 83 D11
Ziegenrück D 79 E10
Ziegra D 80 D4
Zieleniewo PL 85 B9
Zieleniewo PL 85 D9
Zielitz D 79 B10
Zielkowice PL 141 F2
Zielona PL 139 D8
Zielona Chocina PL 85 C12
Zielona Góra PL 81 C9
Zielona Góra PL 85 E11
Zielonka PL 139 F11
Zielonki PL 143 F8
Zieluń PL 139 D8
Ziemeri LV 131 F14
Ziemnice Wielkie PL 142 E4
Ziemupe LV 134 C2
Zierenberg D 17 F12
Zierikzee NL 16 E1
Ziersdorf A 77 E9
Zierzow D 83 D11
Ziesar D 79 B11
Žiežmariai LT 137 D9
Žigljen HR 67 C10
Žīguri LV 133 B3
Žihárec SK 146 E5
Žihle CZ 76 B4
Zilaiskalns LV 131 F10
Žilina SK 147 C7
Žilinai LT 137 E10
Zillis CH 71 D8
Ziltendorf D 81 B7
Zilupe LV 133 D4
Zimandu Nou RO 151 E7
Zimbor RO 151 C11
Zimmersrode (Neuental) D 21 B12
Zimnicea RO 160 F6
Zimnitsa BG 167 D7
Žindaičiai LT 134 F5
Zingst D 83 B13
Zinkgruvan S 92 B6
Zinnowitz D 84 B5
Ziras LV 134 B3
Zirc H 149 B9
Zirchow D 84 C6
Žiri SLO 73 D9
Zirndorf D 75 D8
Zîrnești MD 154 E2
Zirņi LV 134 C4
Ziros GR 179 E11
Žirovnice CZ 77 D8
Zistersdorf A 77 E11
Žitište SRB 158 C6
Žitkovac SRB 164 B4
Žitni Potok SRB 164 C4
Žitomislići BIH 157 F8
Žitorsda SRB 164 C4
Žitoše MK 168 B5
Zitsa GR 168 E4
Zittau D 81 E7
Zitz D 79 B11
Živaja HR 157 B6
Živinice BIH 157 D10
Živogošće HR 157 F7
Žiželice CZ 77 B8
Zizers CH 71 D9
Zizurkil E 32 D1
Zlarin HR 156 E4
Zlata SRB 164 C4
Zlatar BG 167 C7
Zlatar HR 148 D6
Zlatar-Bistrica HR 148 D6
Zlataritsa BG 166 C5
Zlaté Hory CZ 142 F3
Zlaté Klasy SK 146 E4
Zlaté Moravce SK 146 E6
Zlaten Rog BG 159 E10
Zlatitsa BG 165 D9
Zlatna RO 151 E11
Zlatna Panega BG 165 C9
Zlatograd BG 171 B8
Zlatokop SRB 164 D4
Zławieś Wielka PL 138 D5
Žlebič SLO 73 E10
Žleby CZ 77 C8
Zlēkas LV 134 B3
Zletovo MK 164 F5
Žlibinai LT 134 E4
Zlín CZ 146 C5
Zliv CZ 76 D6
Žljebovi BIH 157 D10
Zllakuqan RKS 164 D2
Złocieniec PL 85 C10
Złoczew PL 142 D6
Zlokuchene BG 165 E8
Zlonice CZ 76 B6
Złota PL 141 G2
Złota PL 143 F10
Złotniki Kujawskie PL 138 E5
Złotoryja PL 81 D9
Złotów PL 85 D12
Złoty Stak PL 77 B11
Zlozela BIH 157 D7
Žlutice CZ 76 B4
Zmajevac BIH 156 C5
Zmajevac HR 149 E11
Zmajevo SRB 158 C4
Zmeyovo BG 166 E5
Żmigród PL 81 D11
Zmijavci HR 157 F7
Žminj HR 67 B8
Żmudź PL 144 A8
Znamensk RUS 136 D3
Żnin PL 138 E4
Znojmo CZ 77 E10
Zoagli I 37 C10
Zöblitz D 80 E4
Zoelen NL 183 B6
Zoersel B 16 F3
Zoetermeer NL 16 D2
Zofingen CH 27 F8
Zogno I 69 B8
Zografou GR 175 D8
Zola Predosa I 66 C3
Zolder B 19 B11
Zoldo Alto I 72 D5
Żółkiewka-Osada PL 144 B6
Zölkow D 83 C11
Zollikofen CH 31 A11
Zollikon CH 27 F10
Zolotkovychi UA 144 D6
Zółtnica PL 85 C11
Żołynia PL 144 C5
Zomba H 149 D11
Zomergem B 19 B8
Zonhoven B 19 C11
Zoni GR 171 A10
Zoniana GR 178 E8
Zonnebeke B 18 C6
Zonza F 37 H10
Zórawina PL 81 E12
Zörbig D 79 C11
Zorita E 45 F9
Zorita del Maestrazgo E 42 F3
Zorleni RO 153 E11
Zorlențu Mare RO 159 C8
Zorneding D 75 F10
Zornheim D 21 E10
Zörnigal D 79 C12
Zornitsa BG 167 C9
Zornitsa BG 167 E7
Żory PL 142 F6
Zossen D 80 B4
Zottegem B 19 C8
Zoutkamp NL 16 B6
Zoutleeuw B 183 D6
Zovi Do BIH 157 F9
Zovka RUS 132 E4
Zreče SLO 148 D4
Zrenjanin SRB 158 C5
Zrin HR 156 B5
Zrinski Topolovac HR 149 D7
Zrmanja Vrelo HR 156 D5
Zrnovci MK 164 F5
Zruč CZ 76 C4
Zruč nad Sázavou CZ 77 C8
Zsadány H 151 D7
Zsáka H 151 C7
Zsámbék H 149 A11
Zsámbok H 150 B4
Zsana H 150 E4
Zschaitz D 80 D4
Zscherben D 79 D10
Zschopau D 80 E4
Zschortau D 79 D11
Zsombó H 150 E4
Zuberec SK 147 C9
Zubia E 53 B9
Zubiaur E 40 B6
Zubići BIH 157 D8
Zubiena I 68 C5
Zubieta E 32 D1
Zubieta E 32 D2
Zubin Potok RKS 164 D2
Zubiri E 32 E2
Zubřf CZ 146 C6
Zubrohlava SK 147 C9
Żubrów PL 81 B8
Žuč SRB 164 C3
Zucaina E 48 D4
Zuchwil CH 27 F8
Zudaire E 32 E1
Zudar D 84 B4
Zuera E 41 E10
Zufre E 51 D7
Zug CH 27 F10
Zuhatzu-Kuartango E 40 C6
Zuheros E 53 A8
Zuid-Beijerland NL 182 B4
Zuidhorn NL 16 B6
Zuidland NL 182 B4
Zuidlaren NL 17 B7
Zuidwolde NL 17 C6
Zuienkerke B 182 C2
Zújar E 55 D7
Żuków PL 141 F2
Żuków PL 141 G8
Żukowice PL 81 C9
Żukowo PL 138 B5
Žuljana HR 162 D3
Žulová CZ 77 B12
Zülpich D 21 C7
Zulte B 19 C7
Zumaia E 32 D1
Zumarraga E 32 D1
Zundert NL 16 F3
Zungri I 59 B8
Zunzarren E 32 E3
Zuoz CH 71 D9
Županja HR 157 B10
Zūras LV 134 B3
Zúrgena E 55 E8
Zürich CH 27 F10
Zurndorf A 77 G12
Zŭrnevo BG 161 F10
Żuromin PL 139 D8
Zurow D 83 C11
Zusmarshausen D 75 F8
Züsow D 83 C11
Züssow D 84 C5
Žuta Lokva HR 67 C11
Žutautai LT 134 E4
Zutendaal B 19 C12
Zutphen NL 16 D6
Žužemberk SLO 73 E10
Zveçan RKS 164 D2
Zvejniekciems LV 135 B8
Zverino BG 165 C8
Zvezdë AL 168 C4
Zvezdel BG 171 B8
Zvezdets BG 167 E8
Zvolen SK 147 D8
Zvolenská Slatina SK 147 D8
Zvonce SRB 164 D6
Zvoriștea RO 153 B8
Zvornik BIH 157 D11
Zwartemeer NL 17 C8
Zwartsluis NL 16 C6
Zweeloo NL 17 C7
Zweibrücken D 21 F8
Zweisimmen CH 31 B11
Zwenkau D 79 D11
Zwethau D 80 C4
Zwettl A 77 E8
Zwevegem B 19 C7
Zwevezele B 182 C2
Zwickau D 79 E12
Zwiefalten D 27 D11
Zwierzyn PL 85 E9
Zwierzyniec PL 144 B6
Zwiesel D 76 D4
Zwijndrecht B 19 B9
Zwijndrecht NL 16 E3
Zwinge D 79 C7
Zwingen CH 27 F8
Zwingenberg D 21 E11
Zwochau D 79 D11
Zwoleń PL 141 H5
Zwolle NL 16 C6
Zwönitz D 79 E12
Zwota D 75 B11
Zyabki BY 133 F4
Zyal'ki BY 133 E4
Zyalyonka BY 133 E3
Żychlin PL 143 B8
Żydowo PL 85 B11
Żydowo PL 85 F13
Žygaičiai LT 134 F4
Zygos GR 171 B6
Zygry PL 143 C6
Žyniai LT 134 F2
Żyraków PL 143 F11
Żyrardów PL 141 F2
Żyrzyn PL 141 H6
Żytkiejmy PL 136 E6
Żytniów PL 142 D6
Żytno PL 143 E8
Żywiec PL 147 B8
Żywocice PL 142 F4

Æ

Ærøskøbing DK 86 F6

Ø

Ødis DK 86 E4
Ødsted DK 86 D4
Øie N 105 B12
Økdal N 101 A12
Øksfjord N 112 C9
Øksnes N 110 C8
Øksneshamn N 110 D9
Ølen N 94 C3
Ølgod DK 86 D3
Ølholm DK 86 D5
Ølsted DK 86 D5
Ølsted DK 87 D10
Ølstykke DK 87 D10
Ønslev DK 83 A11
Øra N 112 C8
Ørbæk DK 86 E7
Ørgenvika N 95 B11
Ørjavik N 104 F2
Ørje N 96 D6
Ørnes N 108 C6
Ørnhøj DK 86 C3
Ørslev DK 87 E9
Ørsnes N 100 A5
Ørsta N 100 B4
Ørsted DK 86 C6
Ørting DK 86 D6
Ørum DK 86 C5
Ørum DK 86 C7
Øsby DK 86 E5
Østbirk DK 86 D5
Østby N 91 A9
Østby N 102 D4
Østengård DK 86 D4
Øster Assels DK 86 B3
Øster Bjerregrav DK 86 C5
Øster Brønderslev DK 86 A5
Østerby DK 86 A5
Øster Hornum DK 86 B5
Øster Hurup DK 86 B6
Øster Højst DK 86 E4
Østerild DK 86 A3
Øster Jølby DK 86 B3
Østerlars DK 89 E7
Øster Lindet DK 86 E4
Østermarie DK 89 E8
Øster Tørslev DK 86 B6
Øster Ulslev DK 83 A11
Øster Vedsted DK 86 E3
Østervrå DK 90 E7
Øster Vrøgum DK 86 D2
Østese N 94 B4
Østrup DK 86 B4
Øverbygd N 111 C17
Øvergard N 111 B18
Øvre Alta N 113 D11
Øvre Kildal N 112 D7
Øvrella N 95 C10
Øvre Rendal N 101 C14
Øvre Årdal N 100 D7
Øvre Åstbru N 101 D13
Øyangen N 104 E7
Øydegarden N 104 E4
Øyenkilen N 91 A8
Øyer N 101 D12
Øyeren N 96 B7
Øyjord N 108 B9
Øynes N 108 B9
Øynes N 111 C11
Øyslebø N 90 C2
Øyvatnet N 111 C12

Å

Å N 104 F7
Å N 110 E4
Å N 111 B12
Å N 111 C13
Åberget S 109 E18
Åbo S 103 C10
Åbodarna S 107 E14
Åbogen N 96 B7
Åbosjö S 107 D13
Åby S 89 A7
Åby S 93 B8
Åbyen DK 90 D7
Åbyggeby S 103 E13
Åbyn S 118 D6
Åbytorp S 92 A6
Ådalsliden S 107 E11
Ådum DK 86 D3
Åfarnes N 100 A7
Åfjord N 104 D8
Åfoss N 90 A6
Ågerup DK 87 D10
Ågotnes N 94 B2
Ågskaret N 108 C5
Åheim N 100 B3
Åhus S 88 D6
Åkarp S 87 D12
Åkerbränna S 107 D11
Åkerby S 99 B9
Åkerholmen S 118 C6
Åkersberga S 99 D10
Åkers styckebruk S 98 D8
Åkerstrømmen N 101 C14
Åknes N 110 C9
Åkran N 105 D12
Åkrehamn N 94 D2
Åkullsjön S 118 F5
Åkvisslan S 107 E13
Ål N 101 E9
Ålberga S 93 B9
Ålbo S 98 B7
Ålbæk DK 90 D7
Åle DK 86 D5
Åled S 87 B11
Ålem S 89 B10
Ålen N 101 A14
Ålesund N 100 B4
Ålgnäs S 103 D12
Ålgård N 94 E3
Ålhult S 92 D7
Ålloluokta S 109 B17
Ålmo N 104 E4
Ålsrode DK 87 C7
Ålstad N 110 E9
Ålund S 118 D6
Ålvik N 94 B4
Ålvund N 101 A9
Ålvundeid N 101 A9
Ålåsen S 106 D7
Åmdals Verk N 95 D8
Åminne FIN 122 E7
Åminne S 87 A14
Åmland N 94 F5
Åmli N 90 A3
Åmli N 90 B3
Åmmeberg S 92 B6
Åmot N 94 C7
Åmot N 95 B11
Åmot N 95 C8
Åmot N 95 C11
Åmot S 103 E11
Åmotfors S 96 C7
Åmsele S 107 B16
Åmsosen N 94 D3
Åmynnet S 107 E15
Åmål S 91 A12
Åmål S 91 B12
Åmøyhamn N 108 C5
Åna-Sira N 94 F4
Åndalsnes N 100 A7
Åneby N 95 B13
Ånes N 104 E4
Ånge S 103 A10
Ånge S 109 E14
Ångelsberg S 97 C15
Ångersjö S 102 C8
Ånn S 105 E13
Ånstad N 110 C8
Ånsvik N 109 B9
Ånäset S 118 F6
Årbostad N 111 C13
Årby DK 87 D8
Årbyn S 118 C8
Årdal N 100 C4
Årdalstangen N 100 D7
Åre S 105 E14
Årfor N 105 B11
Årgård N 105 C10
Århult S 89 A10
Årjäng S 96 D7
Årnes N 95 B14
Årnes N 104 F5
Årnes N 111 B15
Årnäs S 91 B14
Åros N 95 C12
Årosjåkk S 111 E17
Årre DK 86 D3
Årrenjarka S 109 C15
Årsandøy N 105 A12
Årsdale DK 89 E8
Årset N 105 A11
Årslev DK 86 E6
Årstein N 111 C14
Årsunda S 98 A7
Årvik N 100 B3
Årviksand N 112 C6
Årvågen N 104 E5
Åryd S 89 B7
Åryd S 89 C8
Årøybukta N 111 A19
Årøysund N 90 A7
Ås N 95 C13
Ås N 105 E11
Ås S 96 C7
Ås S 97 C12
Ås S 106 E7
Ås S 107 E11
Åsa N 95 B12
Åsa S 91 E11
Åsan N 105 B12
Åsarna S 102 A7
Åsby S 87 A10
Åse N 111 B10
Åsebyn S 96 D7
Åseda S 89 A8
Åsegg N 105 C9
Åsele S 107 C12
Åselet S 118 D4
Åsen N 105 D10
Åsen S 102 C7
Åsen S 102 D6
Åsen S 106 E7
Åsen S 109 E16
Åsenbruk S 91 B11
Åseral N 90 B1
Åshammar S 103 E12
Åskilje S 107 B13
Åskogen S 118 C7
Åsli N 101 E11
Åsljunga S 87 C12
Åsmansbo S 97 B13
Åsmarka N 101 D13
Åsskard N 104 E5
Åsta N 101 D14
Åstan N 104 E7
Åsteby S 97 B9
Åstorp S 87 C11
Åstrand S 97 B9
Återvänningen S 103 A13
Åtorp S 92 A4
Åträsk S 118 B7
Åträsk S 118 D5
Åttonträsk S 107 C14
Åtvidaberg S 92 C7
Åva FIN 126 E5
Åvestbo S 97 C14
Åvist FIN 122 D9

Ä

Äetsä FIN 126 C8
Ähtäri FIN 123 E12
Ähtärinranta FIN 123 E12
Äijäjoki FIN 116 B10
Äijälä FIN 123 E16
Äkäsjokisuu FIN 117 D11
Äkäslompolo FIN 117 C12
Älandsbro S 103 A14
Älgarås S 92 B4
Älgered S 103 B12
Älghult S 89 A9
Älmestad S 91 D13
Älmhult S 88 B6
Älmsta S 99 C11
Älta S 99 D10
Älvdalen S 102 D7
Älvho S 102 D8
Älvkarleby S 103 E13
Älvkarleö S 99 A8
Älvros S 102 B8
Älvsbyn S 118 C6
Älvsered S 87 A11
Älvängen S 91 D11
Ämmälänkylä FIN 123 E9
Ämmänsaari FIN 121 E12
Åmådalen S 102 D8
Äng S 92 D5
Änge S 105 E16
Ängebo S 103 C11
Ängelholm S 87 C11
Ängersjö S 122 C3
Ängeslevä FIN 119 E15
Ängesträsk S 118 B8
Ängesån S 116 E8
Ängom S 103 B13
Äppelbo S 97 B11
Ärla S 98 D7
Ärnäs S 102 D5
Ärnäs S 102 E5
Ärtled S 103 E9
Ärtrik S 107 E11
Äsarp S 91 C14
Äsbacka S 103 D11
Äsköping S 92 A8
Ässjö S 103 B12
Ätran S 87 A11
Äyskoski FIN 123 D17
Äystö FIN 122 F7
Äänekoski FIN 123 E15

Ö

Öckerö S 91 D10
Ödeborg S 91 B10
Ödeshog S 92 C5
Ödkarby FIN 99 B13
Ödsmål S 91 C10
Ödåkra S 87 C11
Öja FIN 123 C9
Öja S 93 E12
Öjarn S 106 D8
Öje S 102 E6
Öjebyn S 118 D6
Öjeforsen S 103 B9
Öjingsvallen S 103 C8
Öjung S 103 C10
Öksajärvi S 116 C8
Öllölä FIN 125 F15
Ölmbrotorp S 97 D13
Ölme S 97 D11
Ölsboda S 92 A4
Ömossa FIN 122 F7
Önnestad S 88 C6
Önningby FIN 99 B14
Öratjärn S 103 C10
Öravan S 107 B14
Öravattnet S 106 E9
Örbyhus S 99 B9
Örbäck S 97 C15
Örebro S 97 D13
Örebäcken S 102 C4
Öregrund S 99 B10
Öreström S 107 C16
Öretjändalen S 103 A10
Örkelljunga S 87 C12
Örnsköldsvik S 107 E15
Örnäsudden S 109 E13
Örsbäck S 107 D17
Örserum S 92 C5
Örsjö S 89 B9
Örsundsbro S 99 C8
Örträsk S 107 C15
Örviken S 118 E6
Ösmo S 93 B11
Östa S 98 B7
Östanfjärden S 119 C10
Östansjö S 92 A5
Östansjö S 109 E16
Östanskär S 103 A13
Östanvik S 103 D9
Östanå S 88 C6
Östavall S 103 B9
Östbjörka S 103 E9
Östby S 107 D13
Österbybruk S 99 B9
Österbymo S 92 D6
Österede S 107 E11
Österforse S 107 E12
Österfärnebo S 98 B7
Östergarn S 93 E13
Östergraninge S 107 F12
Österhankmo FIN 122 D7
Österjörn S 118 D4
Österlisa S 99 C11
Östermark FIN 126 E8
Österoret S 107 C12
Östero FIN 122 D8
Österskucku S 102 A8
Östersund S 106 E7
Östersundom FIN 127 E13
Östervåla S 98 B8
Östervåla S 98 B8
Österås S 107 E12
Östhammar S 99 B10
Östloning S 103 A13
Östmark S 97 B8
Östmarkum S 107 E14
Östnor S 102 D7
Östra Ed S 93 C9
Östra Frölunda S 91 E13
Östra Granberg S 118 C4
Östra Grevie S 87 E12
Östra Husby S 93 B9
Östra Ljungby S 87 C12
Östra Lovsjön S 106 D7
Östra Löa S 97 C13
Östra Ormsjö S 107 C10
Östra Ryd S 93 C8
Östra Skråmträsk S 118 E5
Östra Stugusjö S 103 A9
Östra Sönnarslöv S 88 D6
Östra Vemmerlöv S 88 D6
Östra Yttermark FIN 122 E6
Östra Åliden S 118 D4
Överammer S 107 E9
Överberg S 102 B7
Överbyn S 103 C12
Överhogdal S 102 B8
Överhörnäs S 107 E15
Överissjö S 107 C13
Överkalix S 119 B9
Överlida S 91 E12
Överlännäs S 107 E13
Övermalax FIN 122 E7
Övermark FIN 122 E6
Övermorjärv S 118 B9
Övernäs S 109 D14
Överstbyn S 118 B7
Övertorneå S 119 B11
Överturingen S 102 B8
Övertänger S 103 E10
Överum S 93 D8
Överäng S 105 D14
Överö FIN 99 B15
Öv Långträsk S 109 E16
Övra S 107 D11
Övre Bredåker S 118 C6
Övre Flåsjön S 118 B7
Övre-Konäs S 105 D14
Övre Soppero S 116 B7
Övre Tväråsel S 118 C5
Övsjöbyn S 107 E9
Öxabäck S 91 E12

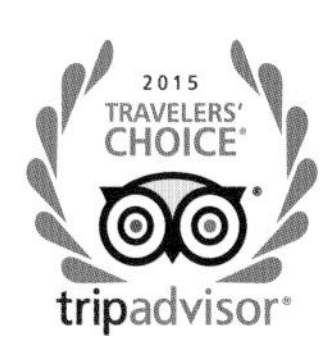

TRAVELLER'S CHOICE
TOP 25 DESTINATIONS IN EUROPE

1

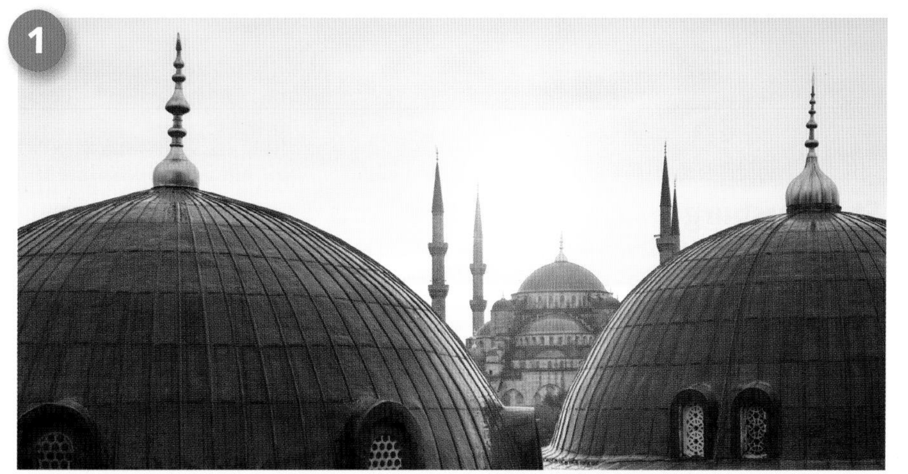

Istanbul

Europe and Asia meet in Istanbul, this year's #3 Travellers' Choice Destination in the World, where breathtaking ancient architecture coexists with modern restaurants and nightlife. The city's mosques, bazaars and hammams (Turkish baths) could keep you happily occupied. Start with the awe-inspiring Sultan Ahmet Camii (Blue Mosque), Stroll the Galata Bridge and stop by the Miniaturk Park to see its tiny artifacts.

2

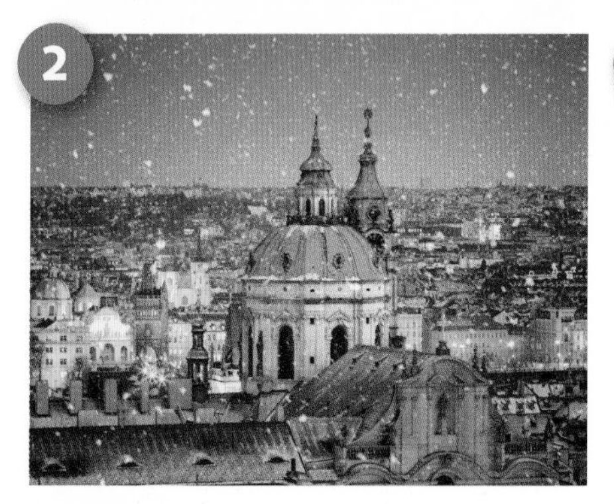

Prague

The bohemian allure and fairytale features of Prague, #5 in the World in this year's Travellers' Choice Destination Awards, make it a perfect destination for culture lovers. Explore Prazsky hrad (Prague Castle) refuel over a hearty dinner at a classic Czech tavern and enjoy a night of for a night of traditional tippling in the cellars of Prague's historic pubs.

3

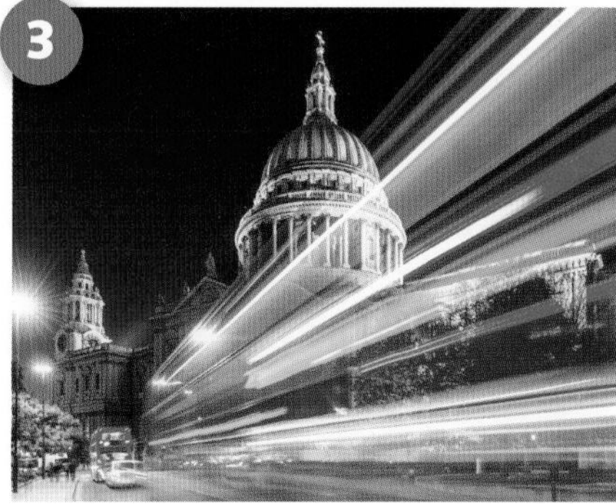

London

The crown jewels, Buckingham Palace, Camden Market…in London, history collides with art, fashion, food and good British ale. There's something for everyone: culture aficionados shouldn't miss the Tate Modern, foodies should indulge in a cream tea at Harrod's or crispy fish from a proper chippy. Music and book buffs will love seeing Abbey Road and the Sherlock Holmes Museum.

4

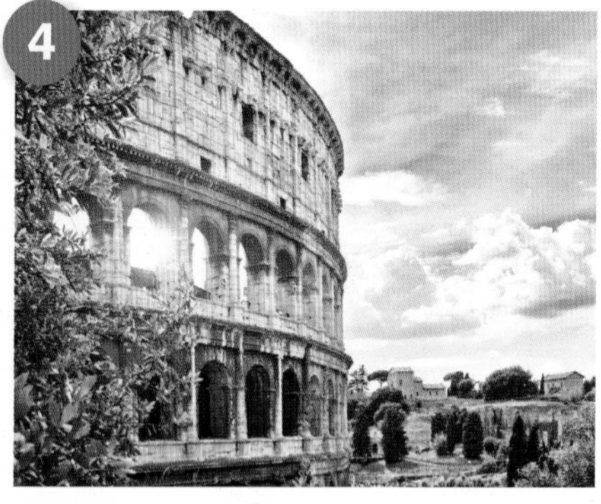

Rome

The Travellers' Choice #7 Destination in the World for 2015, the city is a real-life collage of piazzas, open-air markets, and astonishing historic sites. Toss a coin into the Trevi Fountain, contemplate the Colosseum and the Pantheon, and sample a perfect espresso or gelato before spending an afternoon shopping at the Campo de'Fiori or Via Veneto.

5

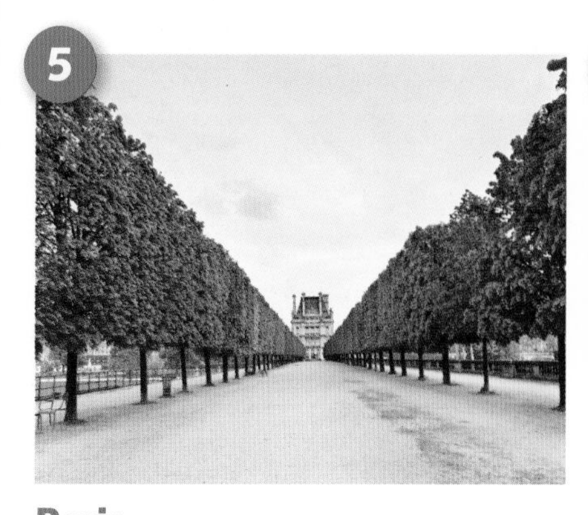

Paris

Lingering over pain au chocolat in a sidewalk café, relaxing after a day of strolling along the Seine and marvelling at icons like the Eiffel Tower and the Arc de Triomphe… the perfect Paris experience combines leisure and liveliness with enough time to savour both an exquisite meal and exhibits at the Louvre..

6

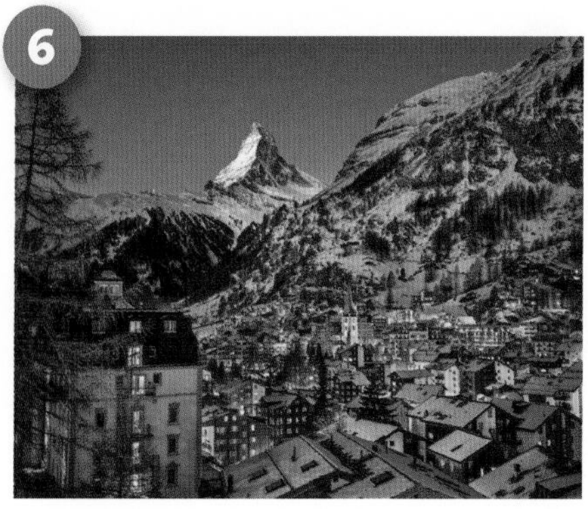

Zermatt

When most people think of Zermatt, they think of The Matterhorn. This ultimate Swiss icon looms over Zermatt, first drawing visitors here in the 1860s. The village of Zermatt, a Travellers' Choice Destination, with old-fashioned brown chalets and winding alleys. Skiing in the region often lasts through early summer, but when the weather's warmer, it's a great time to hike.

7

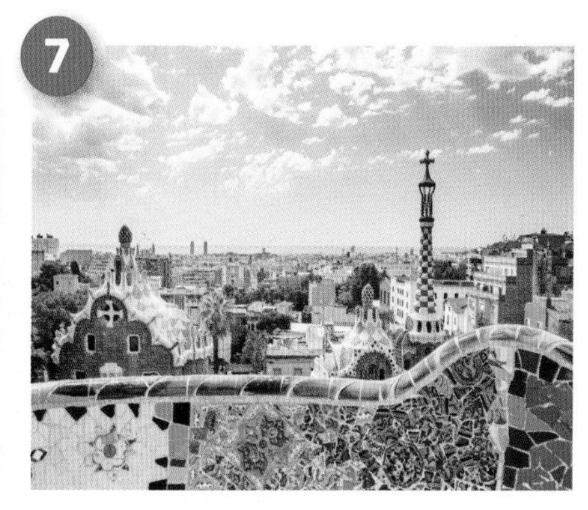

Barcelona

Barcelona feels a bit surreal – appropriate, since Salvador Dali spent time here and Spanish Catalan architect Antoni Gaudí designed several of the city's buildings. Sip sangria at a sidewalk café in Las Ramblas while watching flamboyant street performers, then create your own moveable feast in this Travellers' Choice Destination by floating from tapas bar to tapas bar.

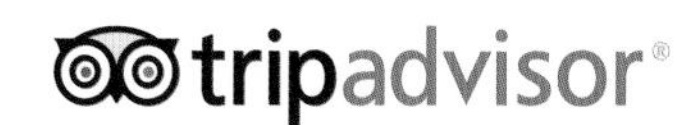

8

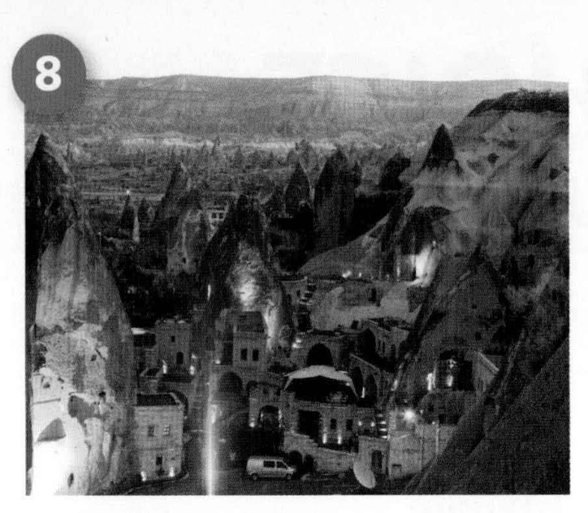

Goreme

A town literally carved into the volcanic rock, Goreme is the gateway to the Goreme National Park, a vast UNESCO World Heritage Site that houses spectacular 10th- and 11th-century cave churches. The park itself is known for its chimney rock formations and is popular with backpackers. This Travellers' Choice Destination is a great area to sample Turkish cuisine and wine.

9

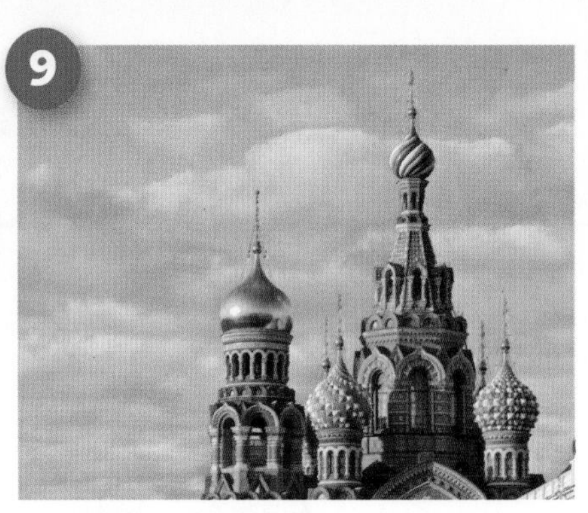

St Petersburg

The second largest city in Russia, St. Petersburg is the country's cultural heart. View architectural gems like the Winter Palace and the Kazan Cathedral, and give yourself plenty of time to browse the world-renowned art collection of the Hermitage. Sprawling across the Neva River delta, St. Petersburg offers enough art, nightlife, fine dining and cultural destinations for many repeat visits.

10

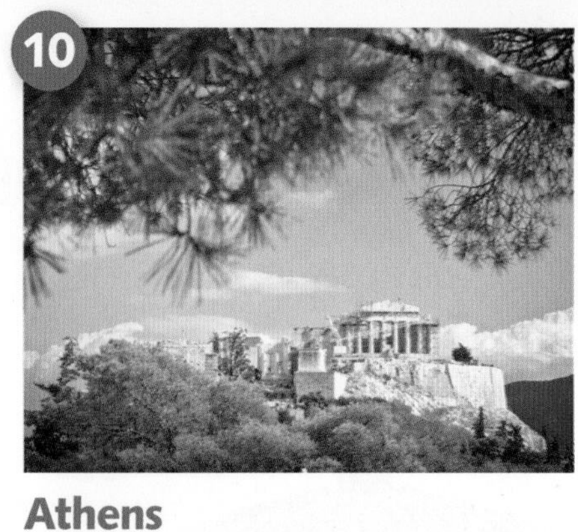

Athens

Athens boasts spotless parks and streets, an ultra-modern subway and merits more than a stopover en route to the islands, sophisticated sites in this Travellers' Choice Destination include many pillars of Western history, from the Acropolis to the Temple of Olympian Zeus, as well as treasures in the National Archaeological Museum.

11

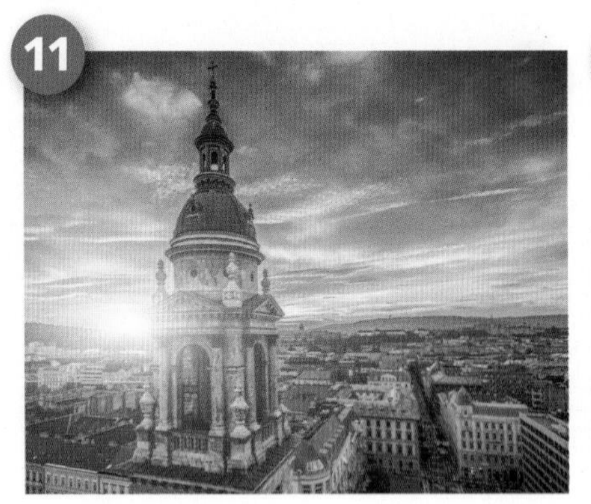

Budapest

The city of spas offers an astounding array of baths, from the sparkling Gellert Baths to the vast 1913 neo-baroque Szechenyi Spa to Rudas Spa, a dramatic 16th-century Turkish pool with original Ottoman architecture. This Travellers' Choice Destination, called the "Queen of the Danube," is also steeped in history, culture and natural beauty.

12

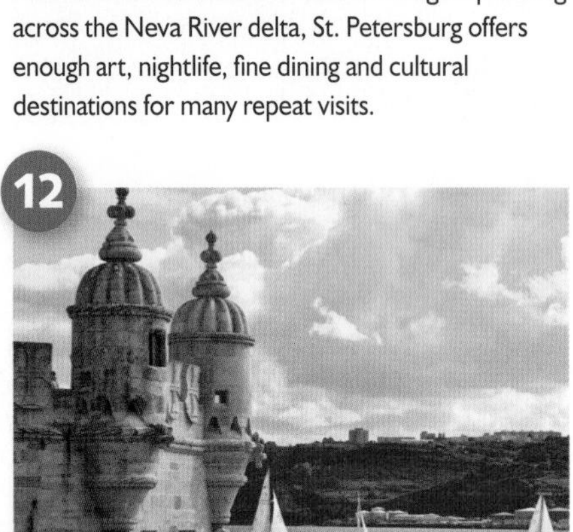

Lisbon

Lisbon, the capital city of Portugal, has become an increasingly popular place to visit in recent years, with a warm Mediterranean climate in spite of its place facing the Atlantic Ocean. Full of bleached white limestone buildings and intimate alleyways, Lisbon's mix of traditional architecture and contemporary culture makes it the perfect place for a family holiday.

13

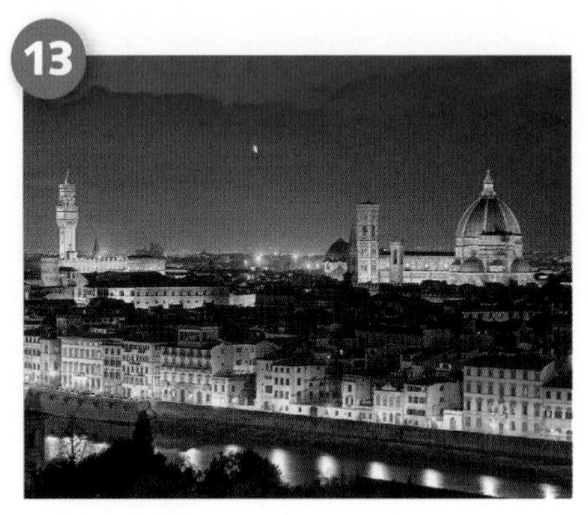

Florence

Everyone's heard the Doors of Paradise, the Duomo, and Michelangelo's David, but in Florence, unexpected beauty can sneak up on a traveller. You'll duck into a church to escape the heat only to spend two hours staring at an impossibly pure blue in a fresco. Don't miss the sunset over the Arno and the famous wines of the Chianti region.

14

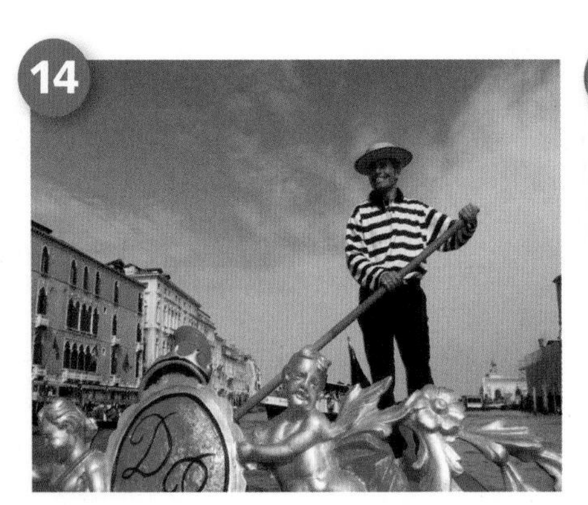

Venice

Stunning architecture. Mysterious passageways. And of course, the canals. Venice is one of the most alluring cities in the world—the type of place where, as a visitor, you'll welcome getting lost (as you inevitably will). Relax in Piazza San Marco, take a moonlit gondola ride or taste the original Bellini at Harry's Bar.

15

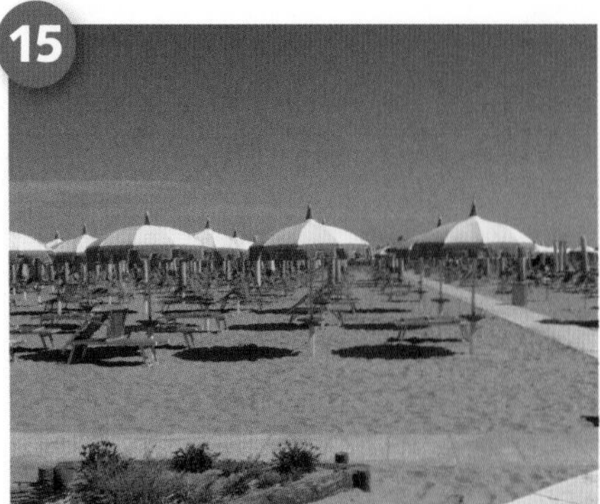

Rimini

The biggest beach resort on the Adriatic Sea, Rimini is a favoured Italian seaside holiday destination for Italians themselves. The old town, about a 15-minute walk inland, has many interesting sights, including the Arch of Augustus from 27 BC, and Tiberius Bridge from the early 1st century. Rimini also boasts many great restaurants and an energetic nightlife.

16

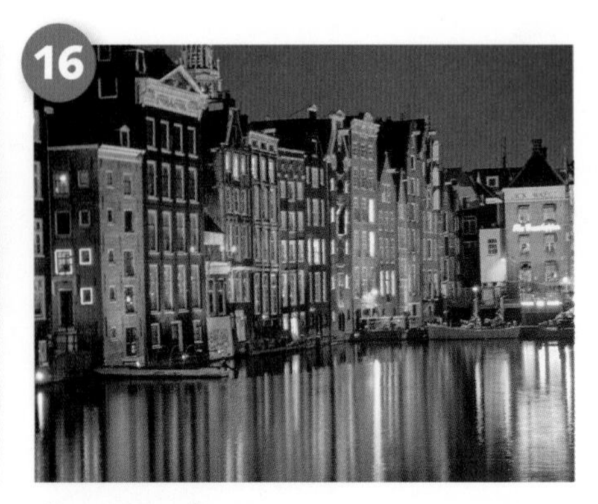

Amsterdam

Amsterdam is truly a biker's city, although pedalling along the labyrinthine streets can get a little chaotic. Stick to walking and you won't be disappointed. The gentle canals make a perfect backdrop for exploring the Jordaan and Rembrandtplein square. The Anne Frank House is one of the most moving experiences a traveller can have, and the Van Gogh Museum boasts a sensational collection of works.

17

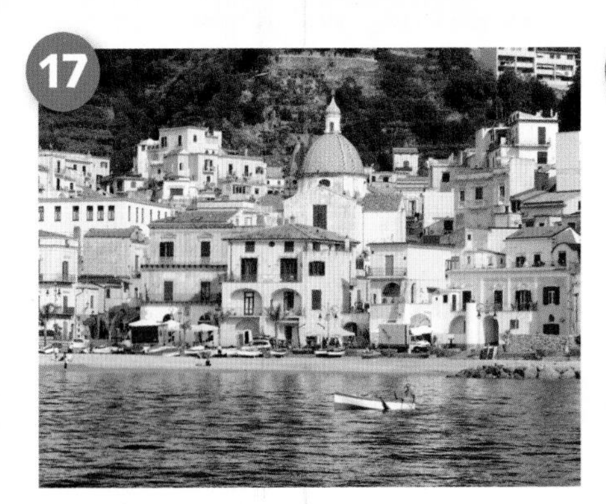

Sorrento

This small city in Campania is famed for its sea cliffs, the town's steep slopes look out over azure waters to Ischia, Capri and the Bay of Naples. The birthplace of Limoncello liqueur also offers some great diving, fishing, appetizing restaurants and excellent hiking trails cross the peninsula.

18

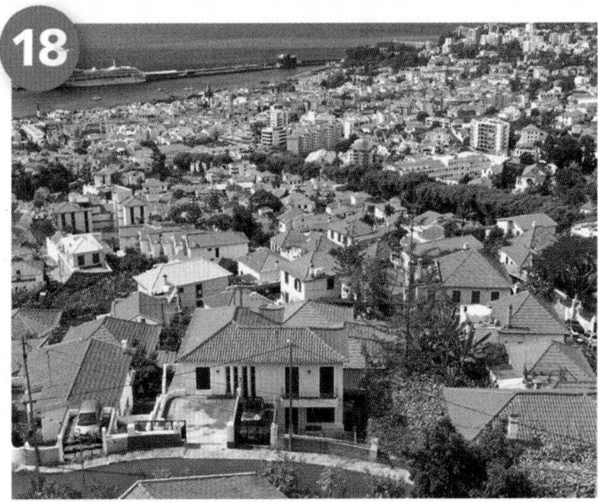

Funchal

Funchal, the capital of the Madeira archipelago, owes much of its historical prominence to the white gold; the Madeiran sugar and today boasts appealing temperatures, great wine and crafts. Top spots to visit include the open Worker's Market, Blandy's Wine Lodge and the Sacred Art Museum. Friendly locals, walkable streets and cheap taxis make the city easy to get around.

19

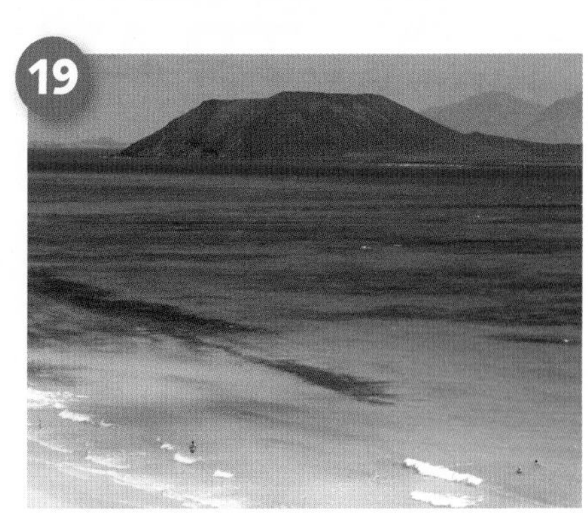

La Oliva

Nestled in the northern part of the Canary Islands' Fuerteventura, charming La Oliva features beautiful Spanish architecture, dramatic views, and eclectic nightlife. Picnic on a pearly stretch of sand, take a dip or snorkel in the serene waters or brave the waves with the locals' most popular pastime; surfing.

20

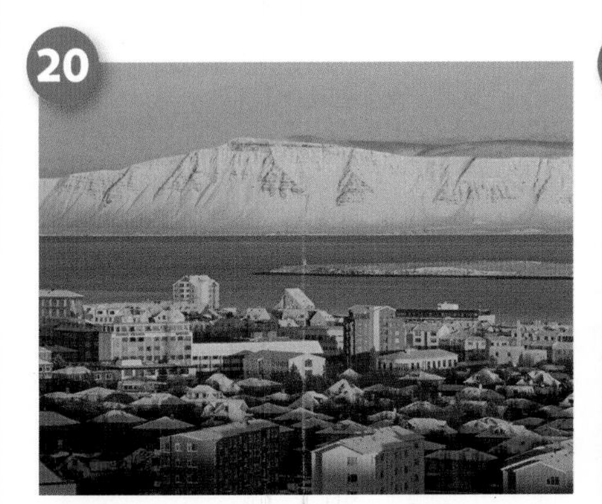

Reykjavik

Reykjavik bears the distinction of being the world's northernmost capital, and for many visitors it also serves as a gateway to the rugged adventure options beyond. Recharge after outdoor pursuits in one of the many geothermal springs or luxurious indoor spas. Reykjavik's open-minded and energetic culture includes a hip and internationally recognised music and arts scene, great food and nightlife.

21

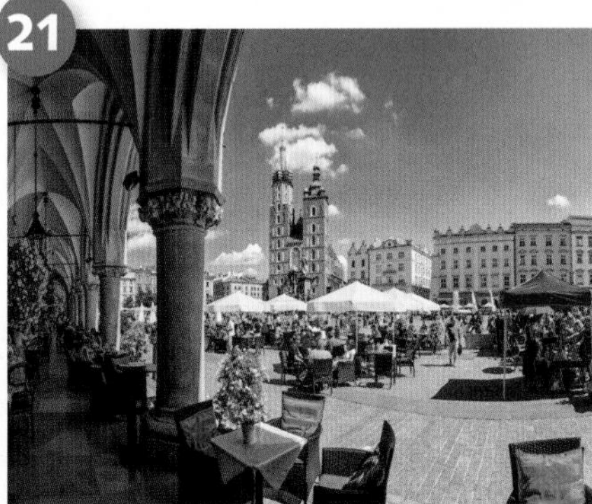

Krakow

Retaining its old-world ambiance and charm, Krakow is the prettiest of Poland's main cities. The former Polish capital's atmospheric Old Town and Kazimierz's streets in the Jewish district are crammed with exciting galleries, cafes, pubs and restaurants. Multi-day Krakow Tourist Cards offer museum entry and free bus and tram travel between sights.

22

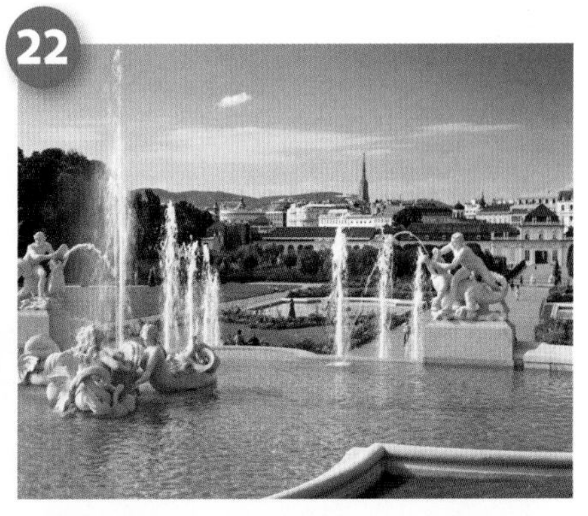

Vienna

If you think your neighbourhood coffee shop is nice, you might want to stay out of Vienna's coffeehouses. Palatial, yet welcoming cafes with delicious coffee and Sacher torte lure in tourists and locals alike. Explore Vienna's Schonbrunn Palace and Imperial Palace. And if you have a chance, catch a performance at the State Opera House—it's not to be missed.

23

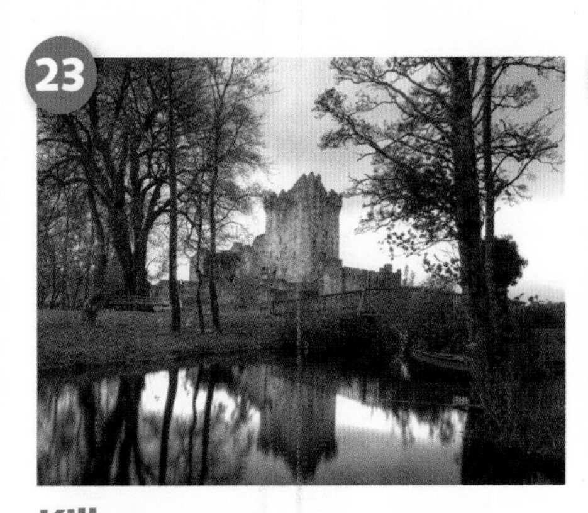

Killarney

Journey on foot through Ireland's first national park, 26,000 acres of woodlands, sandstone mountains and low-lying lakes. When your feet wear out, take in Killarney National Park via boat from Ross Castle. With more hotel beds in Killarney than in any other Irish town or city (besides Dublin) ensuring you'll always have a place to rest your head (and feet).

24

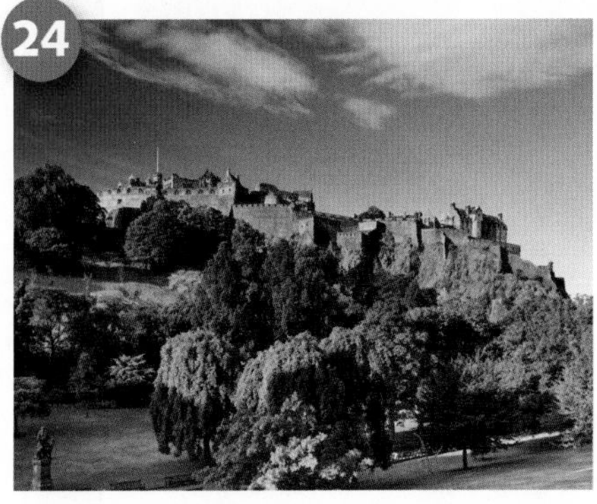

Edinburgh

While dramatic windswept hills make Edinburgh a sight to behold, its rich history makes it a city to remember. From the world-famous Edinburgh Castle, to St. Giles Cathedral, to Real Mary King's Close and the Museum of Scotland, the sights are plentiful. And yes, you must try the traditional fruitcake.

25

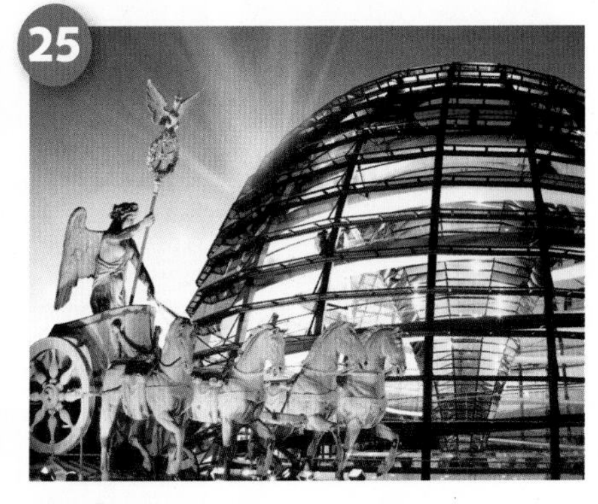

Berlin

In progressive Berlin, the old buildings of Mitte gracefully coexist with the modern Reichstag. Don't miss top historical sights like the Berlin Wall, Checkpoint Charlie, the Brandenburg Gate and Potsdamer Platz.

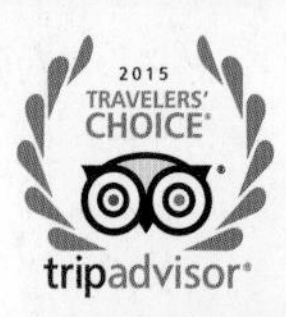

TRAVELLER'S CHOICE 2015
TOP 25 HOTELS IN EUROPE

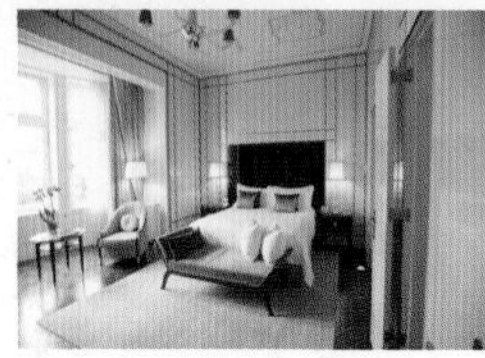

Four Seasons Hotel Gresham Palace
Szechenyi Istvan ter 5-6.,
Budapest 1051 • HUNGARY
36 (1) 268 6000
fourseasons.com/budapest
TripAdvisor Traveller Rating
⊙⊙ ⬤⬤⬤⬤⬤ based on 1340 reviews

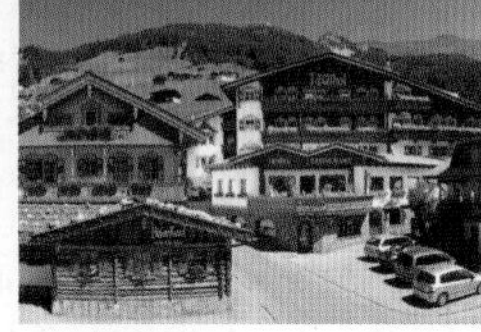

Hotel Alpin Spa Tuxerhof
Vorderlanersbach 80, Tux 6293
• AUSTRIA
43 (5287) 8511
www.tuxerhof.at
TripAdvisor Traveller Rating
⊙⊙ ⬤⬤⬤⬤⬤ based on 272 reviews

Hotel Belvedere
Viale Gramsci 95, 47838 Riccione
• ITALY
39 051 042 0906
belvedererictione.com/en/beach-hotel-italy
TripAdvisor Traveller Rating
⊙⊙ ⬤⬤⬤⬤⬤ based on 1,210 reviews

Four Seasons Country Club
Av. Andre Jordan, Quinta do Lago
8135-024
• PORTUGAL
351 289 357 145
fourseasonscountryclub.com
TripAdvisor Traveller Rating
⊙⊙ ⬤⬤⬤⬤⬤ based on 426 reviews

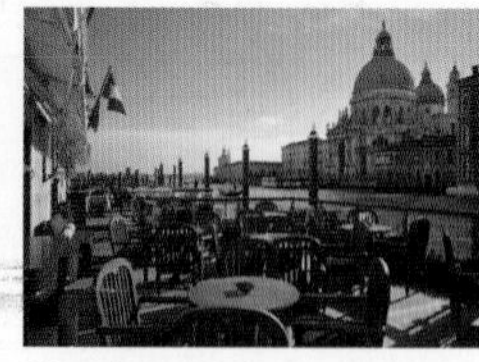

The Gritti Palace
Campo Santa Maria del Giglio
2467, 30124 Venice • ITALY
39 041 794611
thegrittipalace.com
TripAdvisor Traveller Rating
⊙⊙ ⬤⬤⬤⬤⬤ based on 510 reviews

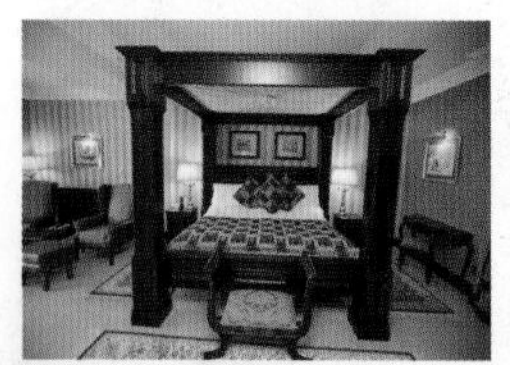

Harvey's Point
Lough Eske, Donegal Town
• IRELAND
353 74 972 2208
harveyspoint.com
TripAdvisor Traveller Rating
⊙⊙ ⬤⬤⬤⬤⬤ based on 2655 reviews

Haymarket Hotel
1 Suffolk Place, London SW1Y
4BP • ENGLAND
44 (0)20 7470 4000
firmdalehotels.com/hotels/
london/haymarket-hotel
TripAdvisor Traveller Rating
⊙⊙ ⬤⬤⬤⬤⬤ based on 520 reviews

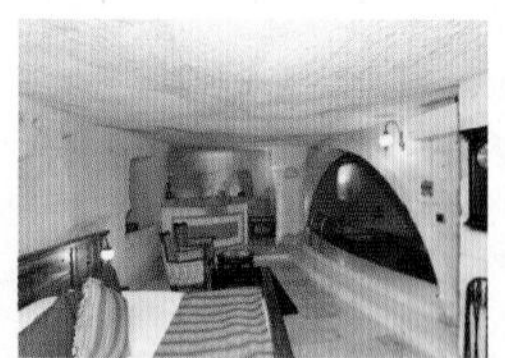

Kayakapi Premium Caves - Cappadocia
Kayakapi Mahallesi | Kuscular
Sokak No:43, Urgup 50400
• TURKEY
90 384 341 8877
kayakapi.com
TripAdvisor Traveller Rating
⊙⊙ ⬤⬤⬤⬤⬤ based on 629 reviews

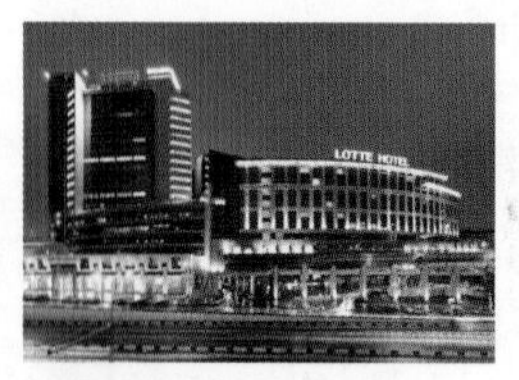

Lotte Hotel Moscow
Novinskiy Blvd, 8/2, Moscow
121099 • RUSSIA
7 495 287-05-00
lottehotel.com/moscow
TripAdvisor Traveller Rating
⊙⊙ ⬤⬤⬤⬤⬤ based on 576 reviews

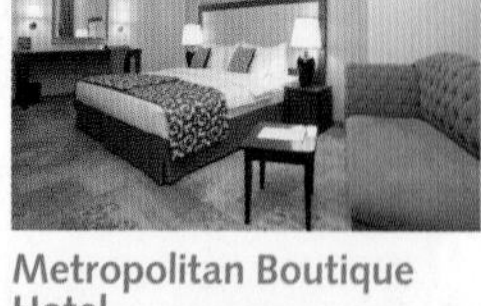

Metropolitan Boutique Hotel
ul. Berka Joselewicza 19, Krakow
31-031 • POLAND
48 12 881 10 40
hotelmetropolitan.pl
TripAdvisor Traveller Rating
⊙⊙ ⬤⬤⬤⬤⬤ based on 845 reviews

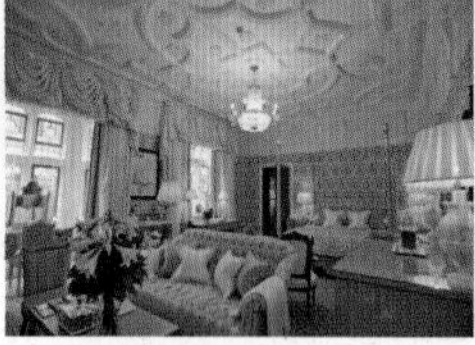

The Milestone Hotel
1 Kensington Court | Kensington,
London W8 5DL • ENGLAND
028 2003 2235
milestonehotel.com
TripAdvisor Traveller Rating
⊙⊙ ⬤⬤⬤⬤⬤ based on 1206 reviews

Aria Hotel
Trziste 368/9, Prague 118 00
• CZECH REPUBLIC
420 225 334 111
ariahotel.net
TripAdvisor Traveller Rating
⊙⊙ ⬤⬤⬤⬤⬤ based on 1209 reviews

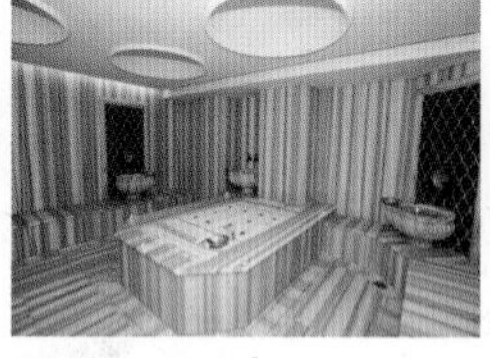

Neorion Hotel
Orhaniye Street No 14 | Sirkeci,
Istanbul 34120 • TURKEY
90 212 527 9090
neorionhotel.com
TripAdvisor Traveller Rating
⊙⊙ ⬤⬤⬤⬤⬤ based on 2372 reviews

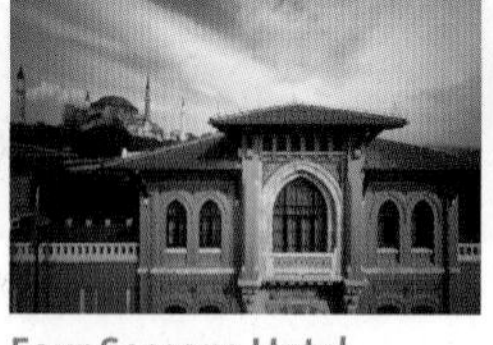

Four Seasons Hotel Istanbul at Sultanahmet
Teyfikhane Sok No 1 Sultanahmet,
Istanbul 34110 • TURKEY
90 212 402 3000
fourseasons.com/istanbul
TripAdvisor Traveller Rating
⊙⊙ ⬤⬤⬤⬤⬤ based on 1023 reviews

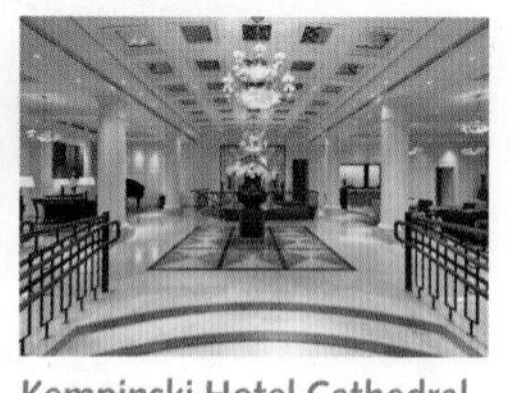

Kempinski Hotel Cathedral Square
Universiteto Street 14, Vilnius
01122 • LITHUANIA
370 5 220 1100
kempinski.com/en/vilnius/hotel-cathedral-square
TripAdvisor Traveller Rating
⊙⊙ ⬤⬤⬤⬤⬤ based on 313 reviews

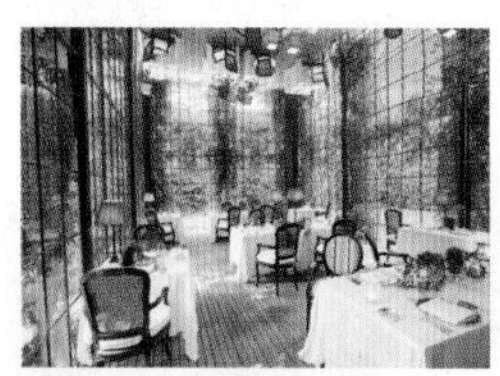

Meister's Hotel Irma
Via Belvedere 17, 39012 Merano
• ITALY
39 0473 980014
hotel-irma.com
TripAdvisor Traveller Rating
⊙⊙ ⬤⬤⬤⬤⬤ based on 449 reviews

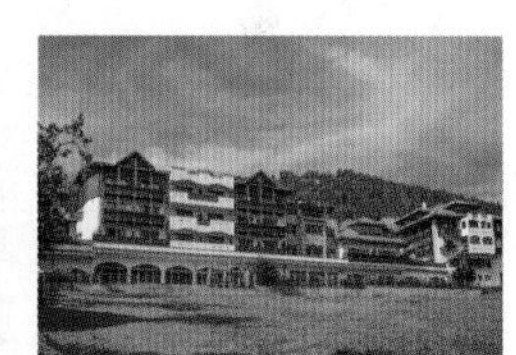

Hotel Excelsior
Valiares Street 44, 39030 San
Vigilio, Marebbe • ITALY
39 0474 501036
myexcelsior.com
TripAdvisor Traveller Rating
⊙⊙ ⬤⬤⬤⬤⬤ based on 477 reviews

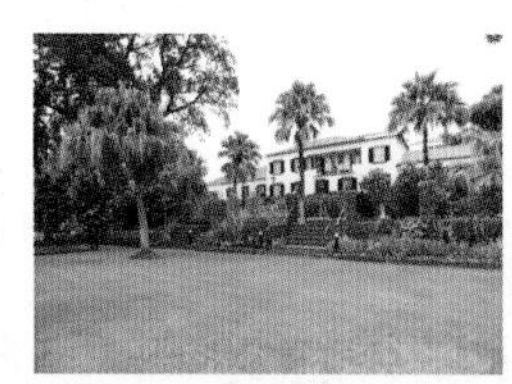

Quinta Jardins do Lago
Rua Dr. Joao Lemos Gomes 29
| São Pedro, Funchal, Madeira
9000-158 • PORTUGAL
351 308 805 653
jardins-lago.pt
TripAdvisor Traveller Rating
⊙⊙ ⬤⬤⬤⬤⬤ based on 736 reviews

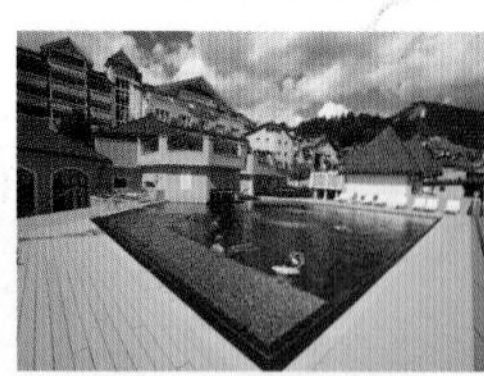

Cavallino Bianco Family Spa Grand Hotel
Via Rezia, 22, 39046 Ortisei
• ITALY
39 0471 783333
cavallino-bianco.com
TripAdvisor Traveller Rating
⊙⊙ ⬤⬤⬤⬤⬤ based on 1433 reviews

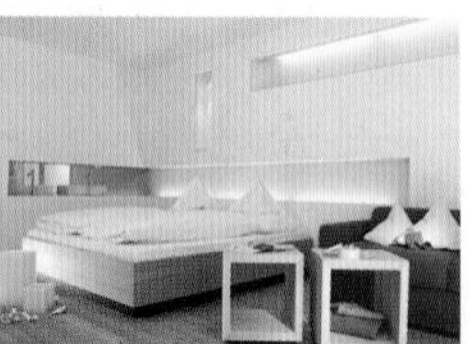

Hotel Monika
Parkweg 2, 39030 Sesto
• ITALY
39 0474 710384
monika.it
TripAdvisor Traveller Rating
⊙⊙ ⬤⬤⬤⬤⬤ based on 591 reviews

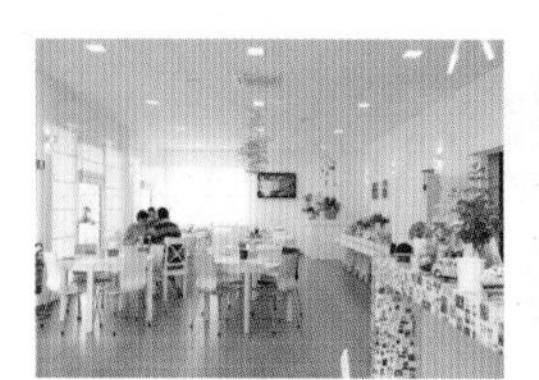

Maree Hotel
Nicoloso da Recco | via N. da
Recco 12, 47042 Cesenatico
• ITALY
39 055 062 0437
mareehotel.com
TripAdvisor Traveller Rating
⊙⊙ ⬤⬤⬤⬤⬤ based on 366 reviews

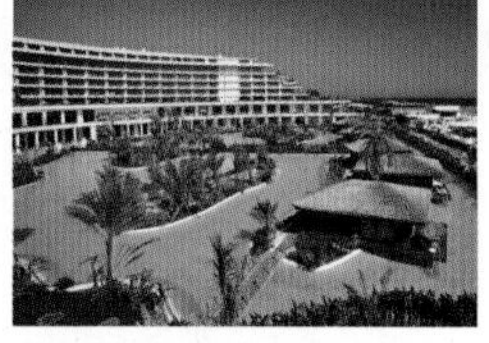

Maxx Royal Belek Golf & Spa
Iskele Mevkii, Belek • TURKEY
90 242 444 6299
maxxroyal.com
TripAdvisor Traveller Rating
⊙⊙ ⬤⬤⬤⬤⬤ based on 1266 reviews

The Residence Porto Mare (Porto Bay)
Rua Leichlingen 7, Funchal,
Madeira 9004-532
• PORTUGAL
351 291 708 750
portobay.com
TripAdvisor Travel Rating
⊙⊙ ⬤⬤⬤⬤⬤ based on 545 reviews

Lindos Blu
46, 5 Km Rhodes - Lindos
Avenue, Lindos 85107 • GREECE
30 261 118 0400
lindosblu.gr
TripAdvisor Traveller Rating
⊙⊙ ⬤⬤⬤⬤⬤ based on 758 reviews

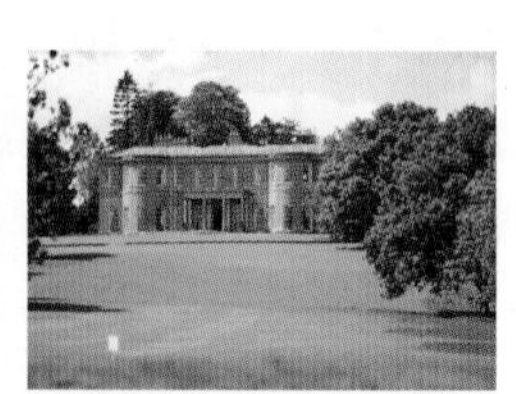

Rudding Park Hotel
Rudding Park, Follifoot, Harrogate
HG3 1JH • ENGLAND
01423 740430
ruddingpark.co.uk
TripAdvisor Traveller Rating
⊙⊙ ⬤⬤⬤⬤⬤ based on 3235 reviews

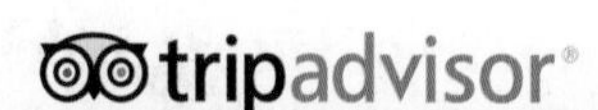